Ginkgolides - Chemistry, Biology, Pharmacology and Clinical Perspectives

Volume 1

Edited by P. Braquet, Ph.D., D.Sc.

Director of Research, General Manager. Institut Henri Beaufour. 17, Avenue Descartes. F-92350 Le Plessis Robinson (France)

J.R. Prous Science Publishers

Published by
J.R. Prous Science Publishers
Provenza 385-387
08025 Barcelona
Spain

ISBN: 84-404-1648-2
Depósito Legal: B. 16.300-1988
Printed in Spain by ROMARGRAF, S.A. - Juventud, 55 - Hospitalet de Ll.

List of authors

Adnot, S., Paris, France
Afek, A., Rehovot, Israel
Agrawal, D.K., Omaha, Nebraska, USA
Akkerman, J.-W.N., Utrecht, The Netherlands
Allix, M., Paris, France
Andries, R., Brussels, Belgium
Arese, P., Torino, Italy
Arnoux, B., Clamart, France
Arriba, G., Madrid, Spain
Ashkenazy, Y., Holon, Israel

Barnes, P.J., London, England
Baroggi, N., Paris, France
Barrio, V., Madrid, Spain
Bazan, H.E.P., New Orleans, Louisiana, USA
Bazan, N., New Orleans, Louisiana, USA
Beladi, I., Szeged, Hungary
Bentwich, Z., Rehovot, Israel
Benveniste, J., Clamart, France
Berti, F., Milan, Italy
Betin, C., Paris, France
Blavet, N., Paris, France
Bonhomme, B., Clermont-Ferrand, France
Boralle, N., Sao Paulo, Brasil
Borgeat, P., Québec, Canada
Boulu, R.G., Paris, France
Bourgain, C., Brussels, Belgium
Bourgain, R.H., Brussels, Belgium
Bradley, L., Bethesda, Maryland, USA
Brambilla, C., London, England
Braquet, P., Paris, France
Broquet, C., Paris, France
Brown, L., Greenville, N. Carolina, USA
Bureau, M., Paris, France
Bussolino, F., Torino, Italy
Butterworth, A.E., Cambridge, England

Camussi, G., Buffalo, New York, USA

Capron, A., Lille, France
Capron, M., Lille, France
Caramelo, C., Madrid, Spain
Carré, C., Paris, France
Caspi, A., Rehovot, Israel
Chabrier, P.E., Paris, France
Chap, H., Toulouse, France
Chinis, A., Holon, Israel
Chung, K.F., London, England
Clostre, F., Paris, France
Coëffier, E., Paris, France
Colliez, Ph., Paris, France
Cordeiro, R.S.B., Rio de Janeiro, Brasil
Coyle, T., London, England
Csató, M., Szeged, Hungary
Czarnetzki, B.M., Münster, W. Germany

Damas, J., Liège, Belgium
Delgado, C., Madrid, Spain
Delpón, E., Madrid, Spain
Desquand, S., Paris, France
Díez, J., Madrid, Spain
DiSimone, A.G., Nashville, Tennessee, USA
Dobozy, A., Szeged, Hungary
Doly, M., Clermont-Ferrand, France
Domingo, M.T., Paris, France
Dosne, A.-M., Paris, France
Douste-Blazy, L., Toulouse, France
Dray, F., Paris, France
Drouet, Y., Paris, France
Droy-Lefaix, M.T., Paris, France
Duchier, J., London, England
Dupont, L., Liège, Belgium

Earnest, M., Nashville, Tennessee, USA
Egido, J., Madrid, Spain
Etiemble, E., Paris, France
Etienne, A., Paris, France

Farkas, G., Szeged, Hungary
Feigel, D., Holon, Israel
Fernández-Gallardo, S., Madrid, Spain
Feuerstein, G., Bethesda, Maryland, USA
Fierro, C., Madrid, Spain
Filep, J., Hannover, W. Germany
Fink, A., Rehovot, Israel
Fletcher, J.R., Nashville, Tennessee, USA
Foegh, M.L., Washington, D.C., USA
Földes-Filep, E., Hannover, W. Germany
Fuchs, A., Münster, W. Germany

Galli, G., Milan, Italy
Garay, R., Paris, France
Gebhardt, B.M., New Orleans, Louisiana, USA
Geraud; G., Paris, France
Gillis, C.N., New Haven, Connecticut, USA
Goldstein, R.E., Bethesda, Maryland, USA
González, E., Madrid, Spain
Gottlieb, O.R., Sao Paulo, Brasil
Grzych, J.-M., Lille, France
Guillon, J.M., Paris, France
Guilmard, C., Paris, France
Guilmard, G., Paris, France
Guinot, Ph., London, England

Haeringen, N.J., Amsterdam, The Netherlands
Hebert, R.L., Québec, Canada
Hecquet, F., Paris, France
Hénane, S., Paris, France
Henriques, M.G.M.O., Rio de Janeiro, Brasil
Hernando, P., Madrid, Spain
Hosford, D., Paris, France
Hunyadi, J., Szeged, Hungary

Jacob, H.S., Minneapolis, Minnesota, USA
Jancar, S., Sao Paulo, Brasil

Kauli, N., Rehovot, Israel
Koltai, M., Szeged, Hungary
Korth, R., Clamart, France

Lachachi, H., Toulouse, France
Lagente, V., Sao Paulo, Brasil
Lamant, V., Toulouse, France
Lamas, S., Madrid, Spain
Lefort, J., Paris, France
Lellouch-Tubiana, A., Paris, France
Leprán, I., Szeged, Hungary
Lima, M.C.R., Rio de Janeiro, Brasil
Lindahl, M., Linköping, Sweden
López-Novoa, J.M., Madrid, Spain
Lutcher, F., Paris, France

Magni, G., Milan, Italy
Mampaso, F., Madrid, Spain
Mandi, Y., Szeged, Hungary
Marcheselli, V.L., New Orleans, Louisiana, USA
Martins, M.A., Rio de Janeiro, Brasil
Massad, L., Paris, France
Mauco, G., Toulouse, France
Mencia-Huerta, J.M., Paris, France

Metzger, W.J., Greenville, N. Carolina, USA
Meyniel, G., Paris, France
Michel, P.F., Paris, France
Millerin, M., Paris, France
Moshonov, S., Rehovot, Israel

Nadeau, M., Québec, Canada
Nakanishi, K., New York, New York, USA
Neto, H.C.C.F., Rio de Janeiro, Brasil
Neuwirth, R., Bronx, New York, USA
Nieto, M.L., Madrid, Spain
Nuñez, D., Clamart, France

Olivera, A., Madrid, Spain
Ortiz, A., Madrid, Spain
Otamiri, T., Linköping, Sweden

Page, C.P., London, England
Panetta, T., New Orleans, Lousisiana, USA
Perly, B., Gif/Yvette, France
Pfister, A., Paris, France
Pignol, B., Paris, France
Pirotzky, E., Paris, France
Plantavid, M., Toulouse, France
Plante, G.E., Québec, Canada
Plotkine, M., Lille, France
Poubelle, P., Québec, Canada
Puglisi, L., Milan, Italy

Ramírez, F., Madrid, Spain
Ramwell, P.W., Washington, D.C., USA
Robertson, D.N., London, England
Robles, A., Madrid, Spain
Rodrigues-Silva, P.M., Rio de Janeiro, Brasil
Rodríguez, M.J., Madrid, Spain
Rodríguez-Puyol, D., Madrid, Spain
Rola-Pleszczynski, M., Québec, Canada
Rosenfeld, Y., Petach Tikva, Israel
Rossoni, G., Milan, Italy
Rouleau, G., Québec, Canada
Roumestand, C., Gif/Yvette, France

Sánchez-Crespo, M., Madrid, Spain
Sanz, E., Madrid, Spain
Schaeverbeke, J., Paris, France
Schlondorff, D., Bronx, New York, USA
Shalev, Y., Rehovot, Israel
Shmuely, H., Petah Tikva, Israel
Simon, M.F., Toulouse, France
Simon, M.-T., Paris, France

Sirén, A.-L., Bethesda, Maryland, USA
Sirois, P., Québec, Canada
Sjoerdsma, K., Greenville, N. Carolina, USA
Soulard, C., Paris, France
Spinnewyn, B., Paris, France
Summerhayes, C., London, England
Szekeres, L., Szeged, Hungary

Tagesson, C., Linköping, Sweden
Tamargo, J., Madrid, Spain
Tamura, N., Omaha, Nebraska, USA
Taytard, A., London, England
Teng, B.P., Paris, France
Thiévant, P., Paris, France
Thonier, F., Paris, France
Tiberghein, C., Paris, France
Touvay, C., Paris, France
Townley, R.G., Omaha, Nebraska, USA
Turrini, F., Torino, Italy

Vannier, E., Paris, France
Vargaftig, B., Paris, France
Verbeij, N.L.J., Amsterdam, The Netherlands
Vercellotti, G.M., Minneapolis, Minnesota, USA
Vilain, B., Paris, France
Villa, L., Milan, Italy
Villamediana, L.M., Madrid, Spain
Viossat, I., Paris, France

Wallace, J.L., Ontario, Canada
Weg, V.B., Rio de Janeiro, Brasil
Wisner, A., Paris, France

Zor, U., Rehovot, Israel

Contents

Cardiovascular System

Endotoxemia and Other Models of Shock

*Ginkgolides - Chemistry, Biology, Pharmacology
and Clinical Perspectives.* P. Braquet (Ed.) ·
Copyright © 1988, J.R. Prous Science Publishers, S.A.

THE GINKGOLIDES. FROM CHINESE PHARMACOPEIA TO A NEW CLASS OF PHARMACOLOGICAL AGENTS: THE ANTAGONISTS OF PLATELET-ACTIVATING FACTOR

Pierre Braquet

Institut Henri Beaufour, 17 avenue Descartes, F-92350 Le Plessis-Robinson, France

INTRODUCTION

In spite of the substantial advances that have been made in synthetic organic chemistry, plant products still remain an integral part of modern therapeutics. At the present time, substances derived from higher plants constitute approximately 25% of prescribed medicines (36). With the advent of biotechnology, it seems likely that this figure will increase. Recent progress in genetic manipulation and vegetal cell culture scale-up techniques offer great potential for the biosynthetic production of many natural drugs. In this context, it is interesting to note that only 5-10% of the 250,000-500,000 species of higher plants have been investigated pharmacologically (18), and thus represent a vast untapped source of potential clinical agents. In Western countries, plant substances have also recently found favour via a resurgence of public interest in homeopathy and herbal remedies. This is paradoxical, considering the sophisticated medical technology available in such countries today. Unfortunately, most of the inhabitants of developing nations do not have the luxury of this choice. Modern life-saving drugs are beyond the reach of nearly 75% of the Third World's population, despite the fact that many of these countries spend up to 50% of their total health budget on such products (1).

Thus, in many areas of the world, indigenous natural drugs are still widely used. The Chinese in particular, place great importance on herbal medicines and a considerable number of plants are utilized for their analgesic, sedative, diuretic, antitumor, antibacterial, antirheumatic, antihelminthic and antihypertensive effects. One of the oldest natural therapeutic agents still used is a leaf-extract of the "fossil tree", *Ginkgo biloba*. This tree has long been part of the traditional Chinese pharmacopeia, being first cited as a medicinal agent some 5000 years ago. In the modern Chinese pharmacopeia, *Ginkgo* is still highly regarded and inhalation of a decoction of the leaves is widely used to alleviate asthma and bronchitis.

Although the traditional medicinal properties of *Ginkgo biloba* have been known for many centuries, it is only recently that they have been explained in terms of modern pharmacology. In 1983, we demonstrated that the therapeutic effects of *Ginkgo biloba* could be largely accounted for by the remarkable biological activity of a discrete chemical component of the leaves and roots (5, reviewed in 6 and 7). Pharmacological investigations on a standardized extract of dried *Ginkgo biloba* leaves (GBE 761) showed that it possessed potent antagonistic properties against platelet-activating factor (PAF; Fig. 1), an inflammatory autacoid structurally characterized as 1-O-alkyl-2-acetyl-*sn*-glycero-3-phosphocholine (reviewed in 10, 12 and 32). For example, the extract very selectively antagonizes PAF-induced platelet aggregation. In rabbit platelet rich plasma (PRP), 1.0 and 2.5 mg/ml GBE 761 causes total inhibition of the maximal aggregation induced by 0.25 μM of the autacoid. The IC_{50} determined with a lower dose of PAF (2.5 nM) is equal to 4.25 μg/ml (11). In the same test, the IC_{50} of kadsurenone, a lignan isolated from *Piper futokadsurae* with specific PAF antagonistic activity (31) is only 6-fold lower (0.70 μg/ml) than GBE 761, which indicates that as the leaf extract is a mixture of many products, it contains antagonists that are more powerful than the reference product itself. An analysis of the inhibition curves of increasing doses of PAF indicated the existence of several inhibitors in the total extract (11). In addition, this antagonism was highly specific, as under the same conditions, GBE 761 did not inhibit platelet aggregation induced by the other agonists such as ADP, arachidonic acid, A 23187, collagen or thrombin (11).

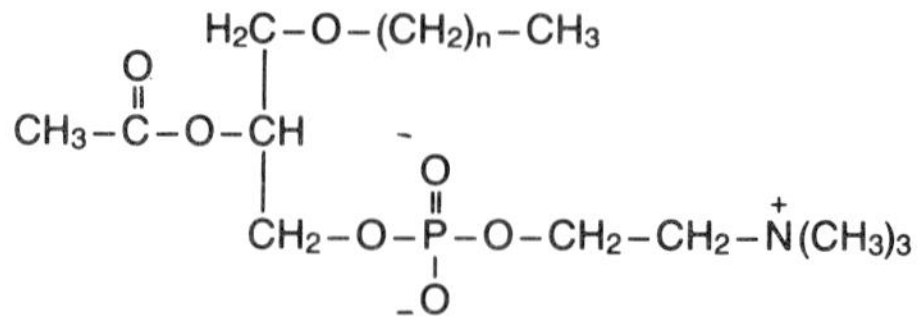

$$
\begin{array}{c}
H_2C-O-(CH_2)_n-CH_3 \\
\underset{\underset{CH_3-C-O-CH}{\overset{O}{\parallel}}}{\qquad} \; | \\
\qquad\qquad |\qquad \overset{O}{\underset{\parallel}{}} \\
\qquad CH_2-O-P-O-CH_2-CH_2-\overset{+}{N}(CH_3)_3 \\
\qquad\qquad\quad |_{-O}
\end{array}
$$

Figure 1   Platelet-activating factor (1-O-alkyl-2-acetyl-*sn*-glyceryl-3-phosphocholine); n is usually 15 or 17.

Examination of different sub-fractions of GBE 761 in platelet aggregation assays demonstrated that the PAF antagonistic activity was present
only in the non-flavonoidic, terpenoidic fraction of the extract (5, 11). Further chemical analysis by thin-layer chromatography, high-performance liquid chromatography and gas chromatography-mass spectrometry revealed that the activity was confined to four closely related products. These
compounds were identified as "Ginkgolides", a unique family of molecules
which only occur naturally in the leaves and roots of *Ginkgo biloba* (5,
11, reviewed in 7).

STRUCTURAL ELUCIDATION, PHYSICO-CHEMICAL PROPERTIES AND SYNTHESIS OF THE GINKGOLIDES

Ginkgolides were first isolated by Furukawa in 1932 (20) from the bitter
principles of *Ginkgo biloba* but their structure was only resolved in 1967
by the pioneering works of Nakanishi and colleagues (see Section 1, pages
27-36). In a series of studies, Maruyama *et al.* (24-27) characterized the
ginkgolides as twenty carbon cage molecules, incorporating a *t*-butyl group
and six 5-membered rings A to F including a spiro [4.4] nonane, a
tetrahydrofuran cycle and three lactone rings. Four structures were identified, differing only by the number and position of hydroxyl groups on
the C_1, C_3 or C_7 of the spirononane framework. These compounds were
named ginkgolides A, B, C and M (Fig. 2). Termed BN 52020, BN 52021,

Ginkgolide	IHB nomenclature	R_1	R_2	R_3
A	BN 52020	OH	H	H
B	BN 52021	OH	OH	H
C	BN 52022	OH	OH	OH
J	BN 52024	OH	H	OH
M	BN 52023	H	OH	OH
synthetic	BN 50580	OH	OMe	H
synthetic	BN 50585	OH	OEt	H

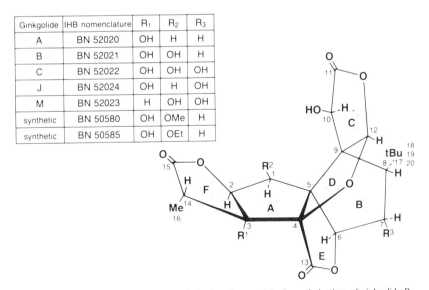

Figure 2   Ginkgolides A, B, C, J, M and the 1-methoxy and 1-ethoxy derivatives of ginkgolide B.

BN 52022 and BN 52023, respectively, in IHB internal nomenclature, these represent the four PAF antagonists initially characterized in GBE 761. Recently, a new ginkgolide, "J" (BN 52024), which is also present in GBE 761, has been identified in leaves of *Ginkgo biloba* (35). In addition, ginkgolides with various substitutions have been prepared from the natural products for pharmacological investigation, for example, the 2,3-dehydro, 1-methoxy, and 1-ethoxy derivatives of BN 52021, as illustrated in Figure 2.

Ginkgolides derive from one of the most complex natural molecular frameworks. The *cis*-fused cyclopentanoid rings F, A, D and C are folded in such a way that a semi-spherical cavity of significant size is formed (*i.e.*, 4 Å wide x 5 Å deep). In relative molecular terms the cavity is sufficiently large to receive most atoms (*e.g.*, Fe^{2+}, Ca^{2+}) or organic moieties (*e.g.*, the trimethylammonium group). The two parallel sides of the cavity are defined by the C_{11} and C_{15} lactone carbonyls included in the F and C rings, respectively. The head or the cap of the cavity is defined by rings A and D. The tetrahydrofuran ring (D) occupies a central position in the cage; its etheral oxygen, along with F and C ring ester oxygens and the C_{10} hydroxyl oxygen constitute a polydentate system similar to that observed in the "crown" ether series. This electron-rich cavity is ideally suited to the charged binding of cationic or positively polarized molecules. Another important feature is the *t*-butyl group which is prominent outside the main framework. Due to the shape of the cavity, if binding does occur, it may well be stereospecific.

Chemical characterization of the ginkgolides has been mainly accomplished by gas chromatography - mass spectrometry of the trimethyl-silyl derivates (Fig. 3a and b), 60 MHz ^{1}H NMR, ^{13}C and ^{1}H 500 MHz NMR (29; see Section 1, pages 49-68) and X-ray crystallographic analysis (17; see Section 1, pages 69-78). 500 MHz ^{1}HNMR analysis of the vicinal coupling constants yielded useful information concerning the conformations of the A and B rings and their torsional angles. For instance, these studies revealed that while ginkgolides B, C and J have identical conformations at this point, a small ring distorsion is observed for ginkgolide A (29). A detailed account of the structural elucidation and physico-chemistry of the ginkgolides is presented in the first section of this book.

Nakanishi and Habaguchi (28) have investigated the biosynthetic pathways of ginkgolide B (Fig. 4). Mevalonate and methionine are incorporated in the framework; the direct precursor of ginkgolide B could be an entpimaradienone cation resulting from the cyclization of geranylgeranyl pyrophosphate *via* the formation of labdadienyl pyrophosphate. This precursor apparently undergoes three major modifications: (a) migration of the methyl group from C_3 to C_{14}; (b) formation of the characteristic spiro [4.4] nonane moiety with the correct stereochemistry at C_9; and (c) formation of the *t*-butyl group initiated by cleavage of the bond adjacent to the

A

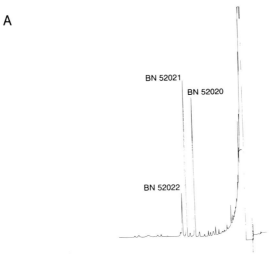

t = 240° → 265°C (Δ = 2°/min) Cap column type OV 1

B

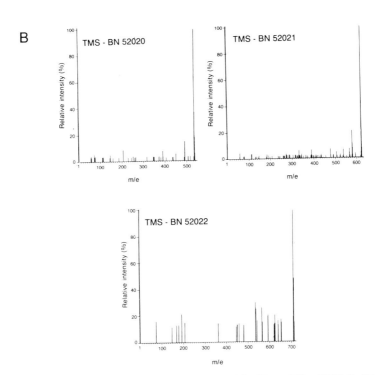

Figure 3   A) Gas chromatography of trimethylsilyl derivatives of ginkgolides. t = 240° → 265°C (Δ = 2°/min) Cap column type OV1. B) Mass spectra of trimethylsilyl derivatives of ginkgolides.

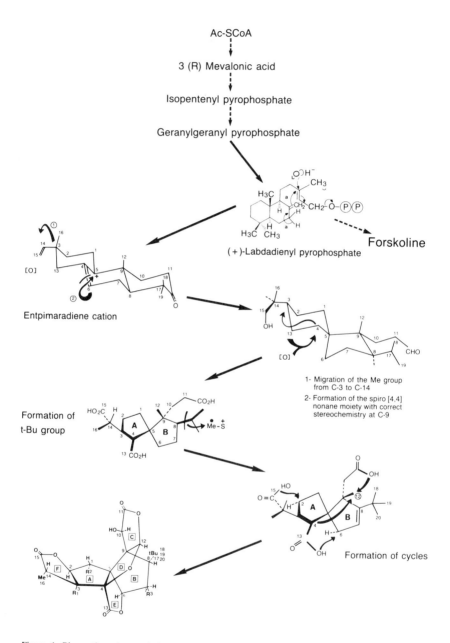

Figure 4 Biogenetic pathway of ginkgolides (28). As all terpenoids, ginkgolides are formed from an isopentenyl pyrophosphate framework.

gem-dimethyl group (?8).

It is of interest to note that labdadienyl pyrophosphate is also the precursor of forskolin, a compound which is a non-specific inhibitor of PAF-induced bioactions. While *Ginkgo biloba* achieves total biosynthesis of ginkgolides with great ease, the synthesis of these compounds in the laboratory has provided one of the most formidable challenges to modern organic chemistry.

As shown in Figure 5a, Weinges and colleagues reported the synthesis of hexahydro-5H- dicyclopenta [b,c] furan-5a (6H)-ol [3], which represents the main framework of ginkgolides (rings A, B, D) (34): Grignard reaction of 1-oxo-spiro [4.4] nonan-6(R)-ol [1], with chloromethyl benzyl ether and subsequent hydrogenolysis provides 1-hydroxymethyl-spiro [4.4] nonane-1,6-diol [2a] and [2b], in a racemic form. Only the 2(R) 6(R) isomer [2a] can be cyclized to [3] in absolute dimethylsulfoxide.

Corey *et al.* (13) initially reported the general synthesis of polycyclic γ-lactones by double annulation (see Fig. 5b). The synthesis uses manganese (III) acetate [Mn$_3$O (OAc)$_7$] for converting 4-(2-cyclo-hexenyl)-3-oxobutanoic acid [4] to the ketolactone [5]. Similarly, the half malonate ester of 2-cyclohexen-1-ol [6] the keto acids [8], [10] and [12] are converted, respectively, into the γ-lactones [7], [9], [11] and [13]. Reaction of [13] with sodium anhydride and methylbromoacetate in THF affords the keto ester [14], which is converted into the hydroxy ester [15], upon treatment with aluminium amalgam in THF-water; conversion of [15] into the tetracyclic dilactone is accomplished by (i) subsequent mesylation, (ii) methyl ester hydrolysis and acidification (13).

Vilhauer and Anderson (33) published the first attempt to synthesize the CDE ring system of ginkgolides using the epoxide [17] as the starting material (see Fig. 5c). Addition of dimethylmalonate to [17] yields the lactone [18]. Krapcho decarbomethoxylation of [18] produces the lactone [19], which is then alkylated with benzyl bromide to [20]. The C-ring skeleton is appended by further alkylation of [20] with *tert*-butyl bromoacetate to give the diastereoisomer [21]. The bicycle [23] is then prepared by de-esterification, selective lactone reduction and cylization of [21]. The remaining E-ring is obtained by subsequent hydrogenolysis of the benzyl ether [23], followed by partial hydrolysis of [24] with *p*-toluenesulfonic acid, yielding a mixture of anomers of [25]. The major anomer of [25] is then converted to the hemiacetal [26], which gives the ginkgolide CDE fragment [27] under oxidation with pyridinium chlorochoromate.

However, following their successful synthesis of other ginkgolide intermediates (16) and bilobalide (15), and appropriately as this volume was going to press, Corey *et al.* (14) finally accomplished the first total synthesis of ginkgolide B, by means of the sophisticated and elegant pathway

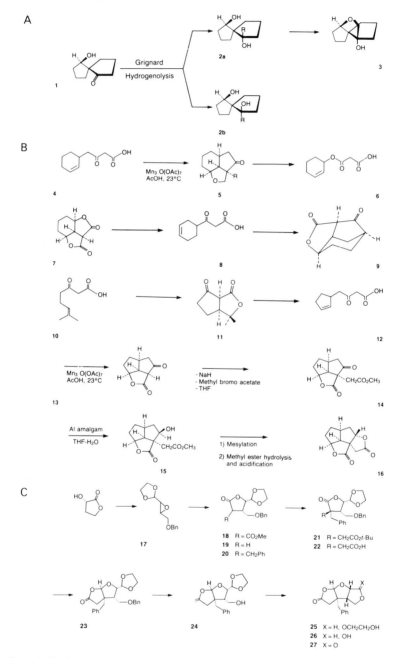

Figure 5 Synthesis of various ginkgolide intermediates by: A) Grignard hydrogenolysis; B) Double annulation; C) Krapcho decarbomethoxylation and alkylation.

described below and presented in Figure 6. For specific details and references concerning certain stages of the synthesis the interested reader is referred to the original publication (14).

The synthesis was achieved as follows. Reaction of 1-morpholino-cyclopentene with dimethoxyacetaldehyde in benzene at 23°C for 18 h, stirring of the resulting solution with 6 N hydrochloric acid at 0°C for 30 min, extractive isolation and distillation (145-146°C at 15 Torr) provided enone [28] in 70% yield. Enone [28] was converted into the enol silyl ether [29] (93% yield) by reaction in ether with the cuprate reagent t-Bu$_2$CuCNLi$_2$ (1.5 equiv relative to [28] at —45°C for 30 min, —78°C for 10 min and then at —45°C for 30 min) followed by silylation of the resulting enolate with 5 equiv each of trimethylchlorosilane and triethylamine (—45°C for 45 min, then —10°C for 5 min) and extractive isolation. Addition of [29] in methylene chloride to a solution of 1,3,5-trioxane (1.2 mol equiv) and titanium tetrachloride (3.6 equiv) in methylene chloride at —78°C (over 20 min), further reaction (—78°C for 2 h and —45°C for 1 h), and finally treatment with one-half volume of methanol (0°C initially then 23°C for 12 h) produced stereoselectively cyclopentanone [30], mp 25-27°C, as a 2:1 mixture of two C$_{11}$ anomeric methyl acetals (ginkgolide numbering) in 65% yield. Deprotonation of [30] with 1.25 equiv of lithium diisopropylamine (LDA) in demithoxyethane (—78°C for 1 h, 0°C for 20 min) and subsequent reaction with N-phenyltriflimide (0°C for 1.5 h, 23°C for 1 h) afforded after isolation and silica gel chromatography (SGC) and 80% yield of enol triflate [31]. A solution of [31] and Pd(PPh$_3$)$_4$ (5.7 mol %) in benzene, stirred at 16°C for 15 min and then treated successively with a benzene solution of acetylenic OBO ester [32] (1 equiv), n-propylamine (2.3 equiv), and 0.5 equiv of cuprous iodide, all at 16°C, gave after 4 h at 16°C, extractive isolation and SGC, 76-84% of the coupling product [33] (2:1 mixture of anomers), mp 44-47°C. The triple bond of [33] was reduced by reaction with 1.5 equiv of dicyclohexylborane in tetrahydrofuran (THF) (0°C for 2 h, 23°C for 0.5 h), followed by protonolysis (acetic acid 23°C for 16 h), and decomposition of residual boranes (H$_2$O$_2$, 23°C, pH 10). The resulting solution was acidified to pH 3 with 1 N hydrochloric acid, brought to pH 11 (vigorous stirring, 4 h) and reacidified to pH 3 to cleave the OBO ester unit, and the (Z)-olefinic acid [34] was isolated by extraction and removal of solvent (70% yield, colourless oil). Conversion of [34] to the corresponding acid chloride (5 equiv of oxalyl chloride in benzene at 23°C for 2 h) and addition of the acid chloride in toluene solution (0.2 M) over 2 h to a stirred solution of tri-n-butylamine (10 equiv) in toluene at reflux, followed by further reaction at reflux for 1 h, produced stereospecifically (71-87% yield) the tetracyclic ketone [35], mp 59°C. Structure [35], which results from internal ketene-olefin cycloaddition and elimination of the

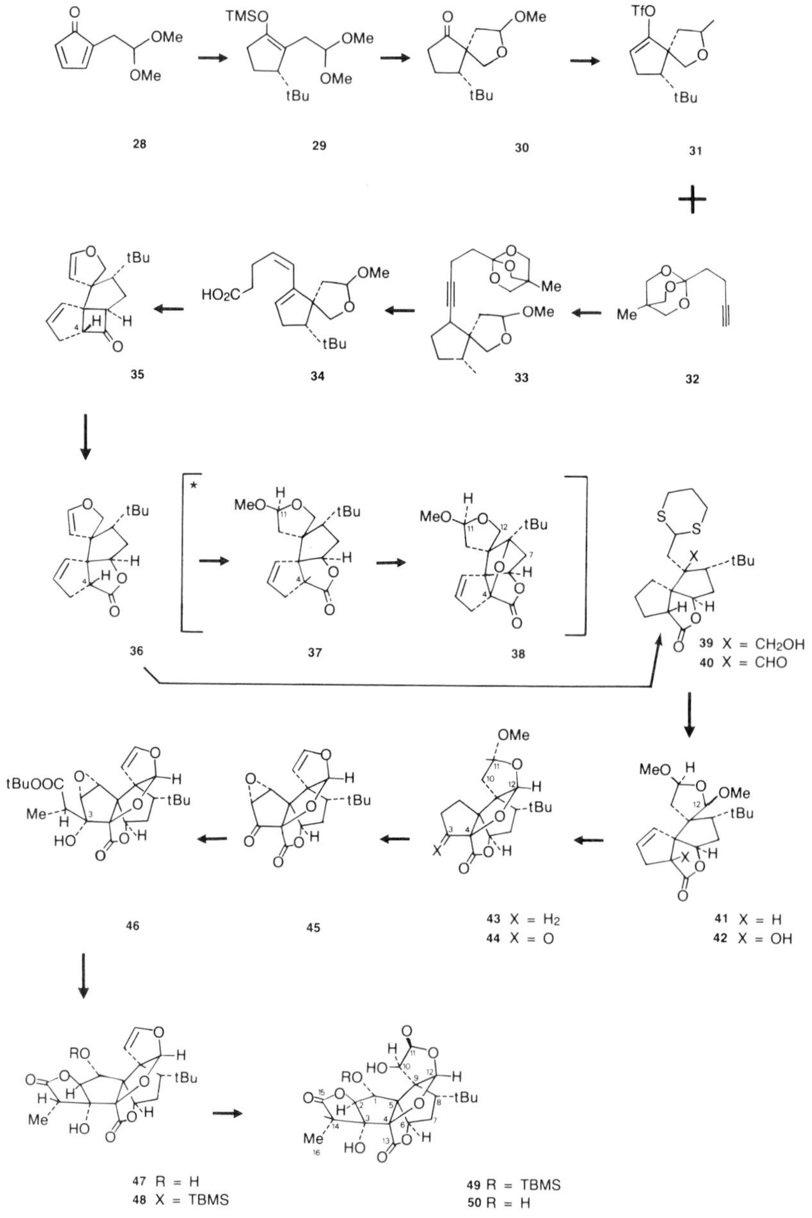

Figure 6 The synthetic pathway of (±)-ginkgolide B. From Corey *et al.* (14). *Although the stage of the reaction in parenthesis was not a useful synthetic step, it did provide conformation of the stereochemistry of intermediates [35], [36] and [37].

anomeric methoxy group (under tri-*n*-butylammonium chloride catalysis), was confirmed by spectroscopic data and the transformation [37 → 38] described below.

Addition of [35] in acetone (at —30°C) to a stirred solution of triphenylmethyl hydroperoxide in 8:1 acetone-1 N aqueous sodium hydroxide at —30°C over 10 min and a further reaction time of 2 h at —30°C produced a single Baeyer-Villiger product [36], mp 163°C, in 86% yield. Lactone [36] was transformed into 4-hydroxylactone [37] (ginkgolide numbering as in [50] by a two-step sequence: (i) deprotonation (1.5 equiv of sodium bis(tri-methylsilyl)amide in THF at —50°C (for 20 min) followed by reaction of the resulting anion with 2 equiv of (*E*)-2-(phenylsulfonyl)-3-phenyloxaziridine (at —50°C for 5 min and then at —50°C for 5 min and then at —50°C to 0°C over 10 min) to afford the corresponding α-hydroxylactone (73% after SGC), and (ii) exposure to a 1% solution of camphorsulfonic acid (CSA) in methanol at 23°C for 48 h to give [37], mp 155°C (75%). Reaction of [37] with lead tetra-acetate (4.5 equiv) and iodine (3 equiv) in pyridine-1,2-dichloroethane at 5°C under sunlamp irradiation for 10 min resulted in complete conversion to a single product. Following analysis by 500-MHz ^{1}H NMR, Corey *et al.* (14) determined this compound to be the cyclic ether [38], rather than the hoped for product of functionalization at C_{12}. Although this result was not useful as a synthetic step, it did provide conformation of the stereochemistry of intermediates [35], [36] and [37].

The required oxygen bridge between C_4 and C_{12} was established by an alternative route starting from [36]. Reaction of [36] with 1.2 equiv of propane-1,3-dithiol and excess titanium tetrachloride in methylene chloride at 0°C for 10 min and then at 23°C for 40 min produced the thioacetal-primary alcohol [39], mp 230°C (98%), which was transformed into the aldehyde [40], mp 165-166°C (75% yield), by treatment with pyridinium dichromate (PDC, 1 mol equiv), powdered 3-Å molecular sieves and acetic acid in methylene chloride at 0°C for 1 h. The aldehyde [40] was converted into the bis-acetal [41] (80% overall yield as a 2:1 mixture of C_{12} anomers) (major anomer from SGC, mp 107°) by the following process: (i) oxidative dithiane cleavage by reaction of [40] with 0.5 mol equiv of periodic acid in 1:1 methanol-methylene chloride containing *ca.* 1% at —30°C initially, then at 0°C for 20 min and 23°C for 40 min; and (ii) stirring of the resulting product with methanolic CSA at 23°C. The C_4-C_{12} oxygen bridge was generated by the following sequence: (i) deprotonation of bis-acetal [41] with use of 1.9 equiv of lithium diethylamide initially at —25°C and then at 0°C for 15 min and subsequent oxygenation with (E)-2-(phenylsulfonyl)-3-phenyloxaziridine (2 equiv, 0°C for 30 min) to form the α-hydroxylacetone [42], mp 115-116°C; and (ii) reaction with a solution of CSA in methylene chloride (20 mg/100 ml) at 23°C for 24 h to afford [43], mp 151-153°C (75%). The introduction of an oxo function at C_3 was accomplished in 50% overall yield by the following transformations: (i) allylic bromination with 1.3 equiv of N-bromosuccinimide in carbon tetrachloride (0.02 M) under external tungsten lamp irradiation at 10°C for 2-3 h (monitored by SG TLC) to give a mixture of 60% of the C_3 brominated product (Br^3), 30% of the C_1 brominated product (Br^1), and 10% of the 3,3-dibrominated product ($Br^{3.3}$); (ii) reaction of the mixture with 10 M silver nitrate in acetonitrile at 23°C for 15 min which generates a mixture of the enone [44], mp 267-268°C (from $Br^{3.3}$), the 1-nitrate ester (from Br^3), and the 3-nitrate ester (from Br^1), easily separated by SGC; (iii) conversion of the 3-nitrate ester to [44] by nitrate cleavage with zincacetic acid followed by oxidation of the resulting C_3 alcohol with PDC in methylene chloride at 23°C for 5 h; and (iv) conversion of the 1-nitrate ester to [44] by exposure to 20 equiv of 1,8-diazabicyclo [5.4.0] undec-7-ene and 20 equiv of water in 10:1 benzene-methanol at 23°C for 30 h followed by oxidation of the resulting C_3 alcohol (from overall S_N2' reaction) by PDC.

The final γ-lactone ring was affixed starting with epoxy ketone [45], which was obtained from [44] by the following two steps: (i) elimination of methanol from C_{10} - C_{11} by heating [44] under argon with 5 equiv of pyridinium tosylate and 2.5 equiv of dry pyridine in chlorobenzene at 135°C for 16 h (80% yield); and (ii) enone epoxidation with triphenylmethyl hydroperoxide (5 equiv) and benzyltrimethylammonium isopropoxide (0.5 equiv) in THF at −10°C for 3 h to give after reduction of excess hydroperoxide by trimethyl phosphite (10 equiv) and SGC, 72% of [45]. Reaction of [45] with 7 equiv of the lithium enolate of tert-butyl propionate (from LDA) in 4:1 THF-hexamethylphosphorictriamide, at −78°C to −30°C for 2 h and then at −30°C for 10 h, furnished the desired aldol adduct [46] in 60% yield after SGC. Exposure of [46] to 4 equiv of CSA in methylene chloride (23°C for 15 h) afforded bis-lactone [47] (82%), which was converted to the tert-butyldimethylsilyl (TBMS) ether [48] upon treatment with 2.5 equiv of TBMS triflate and 5 equiv of 2,6-lutidine in acetonitrile at 23°C for 1 h (89%). Hydroxylation of [48] using osmium tetroxide in pyridine followed by oxidation of the resulting product with excess iodine in methanol in the presence of $CaCO_3$ (23°C for 12 h) produced trilactone [49] (ca. 40% from [48]) along with a small amount of the C_{10} epimer. Desilylation of [49] (5 equiv of BF_3Et_2O in methylene chloride at 23°C for 14 h) gave 89% yield of (±)-ginkgolide B [50]. This was identical with an authentic sample by 500-MHz ^1H NMR, FT-IR, SG-TLC analysis in several solvent systems, and mass spectral comparison.

SPECIFICITY OF GINKGOLIDE BINDING WITH PAF RECEPTOR SITES, STRUCTURE-ACTIVITY RELATION- SHIPS AND CONFORMATIONAL STUDIES

Ginkgolides inhibit the binding of [^{3}H]-PAF to its membrane platelet recep- tor (5, 11, reviewed in 6 and 7; see Section 2, pages 79-104). This inhibition is competitive, ginkgolides displacing [^{3}H]-PAF as an excess of the cold autacoid. The IC_{50} values obtained are 2.5 x 10^{-7} M, 7.4 x 10^{-7} M, 7.1 x 10^{-6} M and 5.4 x 10^{-5} for BN 52021, BN 52020, BN 52022 and BN 52024, respectively (5, 11). Characterized by the presence of two hydroxyl groups on C_1 and C_3, ginkgolide B is the most powerful antagonist. Conversely, BN 52022 and BN 52024 which have a hydroxyl group on C_7, in α position of the lipophilic t-butyl moiety, are less active. With regard to BN 52024, the loss of the hydroxyl group on C_1 further decreases the activity in com- parison with BN 52022.

These data corroborate two important physico-chemical findings obtained using various analytical techniques. Firstly, as the ginkgolide becomes less polar, its PAF antagonistic activity increases (Fig. 7). Although ginkgolide B has one hydroxyl more than ginkgolide A, it is less polar. This result may be explained by the presence of intramolecular hydrogen bond in BN 52021 evidenced by IR spectroscopy [OH (BN 52021) = 3455 cm^{-1}; OH (BN 52020) = 3450 cm^{-1}, 3545 cm^{-1}; OH (BN 52022) = 3390 cm^{-1}, 3500 cm^{-1}; OH (BN 52024) = 3440 cm^{-1} 3550 cm^{-1}, 3600 cm^{-1}; see Section 1, pages 43-48]. The hydrogen bond involving OH on C_1 significantly increases the lipophilic character. Secondly, introduction of a polar group in the vicini- ty of the lipophilic t-butyl group dramatically impairs the chemical shift of the proton $H_{7\alpha}$, demonstrating a significant change in the molecular organization of ring B (Fig. 7; see Section 1, pages 49-68).

As mentioned previously, we are currently examining the structure-activity relationships of various ginkgolide derivatives; among numerous structures, the 1-methoxy (BN 50580) and 1-ethoxy (BN 50585) derivatives of BN 52021 (Fig. 2) display activity similar to that of the natural product. A substan- tial loss of antagonism is apparent after opening of the ginkgolide lactone rings or after the loss of the OH group in position 3 (2,3- dehydroderivative), although in this latter case the reduction of activity is less marked.

Ginkgolide inhibition of the binding of PAF to its cellular receptors is highly specific since these antagonists do not interact with any other known receptor [α_1, α_2, β_1 and β_2-adrenergic, dopamine D1 and D2, serotonin S1 and S2, μ, δ and $\varkappa$ opiate, histamine H1 and H2; central and peripheral benzodiazepine, TRH muscarine, imipramine, desimipramine, adenosine, thromboxane or leukotriene C_4] (5, 11). This specific action is reinforced

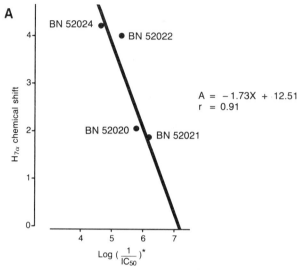

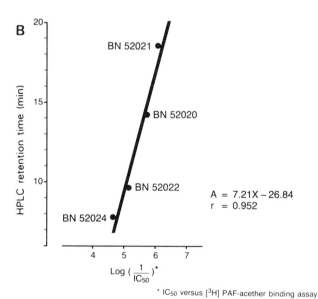

Figure 7   Correlation between the PAF antagonist activity of ginkgolides and: 1) the chemical shift of proton 7α [500 MHz NMR (A)]; 2) the lipophilicity deduced from HPLC retention time (B).

by the non-inhibition of the various metabolic pathways of arachidonic acid: cyclooxygenase (bull seminal vesicles); 5-, 12- and 15- lipoxygenases (human leukocyte; soya) (5, 11).

The binding of [^{3}H]-PAF to its receptor sites is affected by the presence of Mg^{2+} and/or Na^+ ions (22; see Section 2, pages 79-84). Consequently, the IC_{50} of ginkgolide B is shifted from $3.0 \times 10^{-7}M$ in 150 mM NaCl to $7.6 \times 10^{-7}M$ in 10 mM $MgCl_2$. This phenomenon is also observed with other PAF antagonists (22). BN 52021 also displaces the [^{3}H]-dihydro-kadsurenone- specific binding and shows no effects on the non-specific binding of the lignan (21). In addition, BN 52021 is also a very potent inhibitor of the binding of [^{3}H]-PAF to human endothelial cell (23), neutrophil (19; see Section 3, pages 151-160), gerbil and rat brain membranes, lung (2-4; see Section 5, pages 355-360) ciliary bodies and retina (M. Doly and P. Braquet, in preparation) receptors. In the lung, Agrawal and Townley (2-4) found an IC_{50} of $10^{-9}M$ (Ki = 8.2 ± 4.3 nM), which may explain the high capacity of BN 52021 to inhibit human and animal airway hyperreactivity in comparison with other antagonists which displayed lower affinity for this PAF receptor.

Q.S.A.R. studies with various agonists including variations on C_1, C_2 and C_3 of the PAF glyceryl framework, have suggested a putative conformation of high affinity membrane binding sites for the autacoid (8, 9). Three

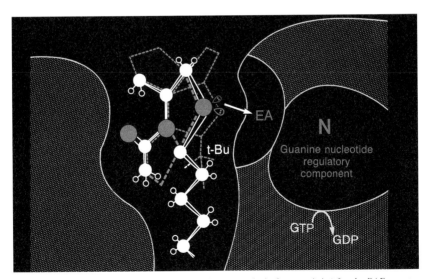

Figure 8 Competition between PAF and ginkgolide B (tetrahydrofuran moieties) for the PAF receptor (initial hypothesis). Competition between the tetrahydrofuran ring of BN 52021 (--) and that part of PAF backbone, including the etheroxide function (—), is assumed in the model. The present conformation of BN 52021 in the PAF binding site shows that the ±-butyl group fits into the membrane instead of the lipophilic moiety of PAF. It is, thus, not surprising that the introduction of a polar group in the vicinity of the lipophilic moiety reduces the antagonist activity.

interactions may be of particular importance in the binding process: (a) The long fatty chain of PAF deeply enters the membrane in a hydrophobic area exchanging hydrophobic bonds with the vicinity; (b) Membrane activation may possibly derive from an electronic transfer from oxygen doublets of the etheroxide function to an unknown membrane target (G protein subunit?). The presence of *non delocalized* doublets could be made necessary by a possible protonation from the active site; (c) The short chain on C_2 may take part in the anchorage of PAF to its receptor, using a small hydrophobic area of <6.5 Å in length.

Such a receptor model allowed the construction of an *initial* hypothesis to account for the interaction between BN 52021 and the PAF receptor site: (i) BN 52021 incorporates a tetrahydrofuran ring, the oxygen of which is more basic than the etheroxide oxygen in PAF and thus more likely to undergo protonation. Furthermore, competition between the tetrahydrofuran ring of BN 52021 and the part of PAF framework incorporating the etheroxide moiety is sterically possible as determined by molecular modelling (8, 9; Fig. 9). Once the antagonist has become well positioned in the receptor site, the two doublets of tetrahydrofuran ring may interact with the unknown target, but, due to the rigidity of the cycle, the subsequent membrane signalling cannot occur (ii). However, with regard to the importance of the tetrahydrofuran oxygen, this initial hypothesis is no longer certain. A very recent report by Chiang and colleagues of Merck & Co (European Patent 257921 A2 880302) has shown that cyclopentane derived isosters of tetrahydrofuran compounds are also specific antagonists of the mediator, demonstrating that the tetrahydrofuran oxygen is not essential for PAF inhibition. However, the presence of a group with a small steric hindrance and a heteroatom (N or O) substituting H on the carbon 1 position increases the PAF receptor binding inhibition. The assumed conformation of the inhibitor suggests that the lipophilic *t*-butyl group lodges in the hydrophobic area of the membrane in place of the lipophilic moiety of the PAF molecule. Thus, it is not surprising that the introduction of a polar group close to the lipophilic moiety diminishes the antagonistic activity as is demonstrated by the reduced potency of BN 52022 and BN 52024 (8, 9) and semi-synthetic ginkgolide analogues (P. Braquet, unpublished data).

Further studies based on molecular electrostatic potential computation demonstrated the existence of two (ginkgolide A) or three (ginkgolides B and C) areas of negative potential (-10 Kcal) resulting from the high electronic density possessed by the three lactonic groups (Fig. 9). In ginkgolide A, as the cage is relatively closed, the fusion of the two areas of negative potential born by lactonic rings C and F leads to an unique and very large area of negative potential. The distance between the two geometric centers

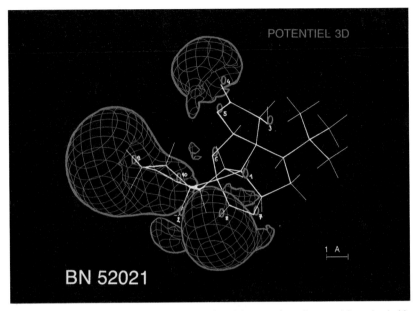

Figure 9 Diagram showing 3-dimensional representation of the areas of negative potential associated with the lactonic rings of ginkgolide B. Model based on molecular electrostatic potential computation (Chrétien, Busine and Braquet, unpublished data).

of negative potential (cycles C/F ⟷ cycle E) is 7-9 Å depending on the various ginkgolides (Dives, Godfroid and Braquet, in preparation).

The formation of these areas of high electronic density may result from electronic delocalization. Indeed, according to Schreiber (30), the most striking feature of ginkgolide B, as well as kadsurenone and 48740 RP, two other specific PAF antagonists, is the presence of a geometrically fixed (rigid) five-atom network which is terminated with heteroatoms that are engaged in "push-pull" electron delocalization. In addition, the polarization of these subunits is identical; in each case the heteroatom "donor" is part of a five-membered ring heterocycle and the heteroatom acceptor is a basic carbonyl oxygen. Other similarities include the presence of hydrophobic groups that occupy similar regions of space.

These areas of negative potential could be involved in the binding of the ginkgolide inside the PAF receptor site. In this model we also confirmed that the *t*-butyl lipophilic moiety could lodge in the hydrophobic area of the membrane, instead of the lipophilic moiety of the PAF molecule, as postulated in our initial hypothesis.

THE PATHOPHYSIOLOGICAL IMPORTANCE OF PAF, THERAPEUTIC POTENTIAL OF THE GINKGOLIDES AND THE SCOPE OF THE PRESENT VOLUME

The growing importance of PAF as a mediator of diverse pathologies is demonstrated by the wide range of subjects covered in this book. Since we commenced our research programme in 1983 to explore the pharmacology and therapeutic potential of the ginkgolides, the autacoid which they antagonize has become implicated in an ever increasing number of physiological responses and disorders. The ginkgolides and other PAF antagonists have played a crucial role in elucidating the involvement of PAF in many of these conditions, as demonstrated by the studies presented in this volume.

PAF was originally named because of its capacity to aggregate and degranulate platelets *in vitro*. Indeed, this still remains one of its most impressive properties and the inhibitory effect of ginkgolides on this aspect of its pharmacology is considered in Section 2. In addition to platelets, PAF is now recognized as a potent activator of a variety of cell types, such as neutrophils, eosinophils and macrophages. Endothelial cells are also an important target for the mediator. The relationship between these cell types, PAF and the ginkgolides in various experimental models is discussed in Section 3. In this section, particular attention is focused on the role of PAF as an amplifier of biological processes *via* its ability to "prime" cell responses.

The remainder of the book is devoted to consideration of the involvement of PAF, and therapeutic effects of the ginkgolides, in different pathophysiologial processes and models of disease. There are extensive discussions concerning inflammation (Section 4), airway hyperreactivity (Section 5), the cardiovascular system (Section 6), endotoxemia and other models of shock (Section 7), gastrointestinal ulceration (Section 8), the renal system (Section 9), CNS functions (Section 10), immune processes (Section 11), ocular diseases (Section 12) and skin diseases (Section 13).

In recent years our understanding of PAF as a mediator of different pathological conditions has greatly increased, although many questions concerning the role of the autacoid still remain unanswered. Ginkgolides and other PAF antagonists may constitute a means of both elucidating its role biologically and modulating its effects therapeutically. We hope that the studies presented in this volume, which contribute to both these areas, will provide the reader with a stimulating insight into this exciting field of research.

References

1. Agrawal, A. *Pharmaceuticals and the Third World.* New Scientist 1978; 80: 442-443.
2. Agrawal, D.K., Townley, R.G. *Effect of platelet-activating factor on β-adrenoceptors in human lung.* Biochem Res Commun 1987; 143: 1-6.
3. Agrawal, D.K., Townley, R.G. *Effect of platelet-activating factor on human pulmonary β-adrenoceptors.* Fed Proc 1987; 46: 739.
4. Agrawal, D.K., Townley, R.G. *BN 52021, a platelet-activating factor PAF antagonist protects the PAF-induced down-regulation of beta-adrenoceptors in human lung.* Am Rev Respir Dis 1987; 135: A162.
5. Braquet, P. *Treatment or prevention of PAF-acether disorders provoked by a new series of highly specific inhibitors.* GB Patent 84/18 424 (July 19, 1984). BE 901, 915. USA, Japan, Germany, etc... patent pending (see CA 103: 189808d).
6. Braquet, P. *Involvement of PAF-acether in various immune disorders using BN 52021 (Ginkgolide B): A powerful PAF-acether antagonist isolated from Ginkgo biloba.* In: Advances in Prostaglandin, Thromboxane and Leukotriene Research. Raven Press: New York 1986; 16: 179-198.
7. Braquet, P. *The Ginkgolides: Potent platelet-activating factor antagonists isolated from Ginkgo Biloba.* Drugs of the Future 1987; 12: 643-699.
8. Braquet, P., Godfroid, J.J. *PAF-acether specific binding sites: 2. Design of specific antagonists.* Trends Pharmacol Sci 1986; 7: 397-403.
9. Braquet, P., Godfroid, J.J. *Conformational properties of the PAF-acether receptor in platelets based on structure-activity studies.* In: Platelet Activating Factor. F. Snyder (Ed.). Plenum Press: New York 1987; 191-235.
10. Braquet, P., Rola-Pelszczynski, M. *Platelet-activating factor and cellular immune responses.* Immunology Today 1987; 8: 345-352.
11. Braquet, P., Spinnewyn, B., Braquet, M., Bourgain, R.H., Taylor, J.E., Etiene, A., Drieu, K. *BN 52021 and related compounds: A new series of highly specific PAF-acether receptor antagonists isolated from Ginkgo biloba.* Blood and Vessel 1985; 16: 559-572.
12. Braquet, P., Touqui, L., Shen, T.S., Vargaftig, B.B. *Perspectives in platelet-activating factor research.* Pharmacol Reviews 1987; 39: 97-145.

13. Corey, E.J., Kang, M.C. *New and general synthesis of polycyclic γ-lactones by double annulation.* J Am Chem Soc 1984; 106: 5384-5385.
14. Corey, E.J., Kang, M.C., Desai, M.C., Ghosh, A.K., Houpis, I.N. *Total synthesis of (±)-ginkgolide B.* J Am Chem Soc 1988; 110: 649-651.
15. Corey, E.J., Su, W.G. *Total synthesis of a C_{15} Ginkgolide, (±) Bilobalide.* J Am Chem Soc 1987; 109: 7534.
16. Corey, E.J., Su, W.G., Houpis, L.N. *Useful new annulation reactions of vicinal dicarboxylic esters.* Tetrahedron Letters 1986; 27: 5951-5954.
17. Dupont, L., Germain, G., Dideberg, O. *Crystal and molecular structure of BN 52021, a PAF-acether antagonist. Comparison with the conformation of kadsurenone and related compounds.* Pharmacol Res Commun 1986; 18: 25-32.
18. Farnsworth, N.R., Bingel, A.S. *Problems and prospects of discovering new drugs from higher plants by pharmacological screening.* In: New Natural Products and Plant Drugs with Pharmacological, Biological or Therapeutical Activity. H. Wagner, P. Wolff (Eds.). Springer-Verlag: Berlin/Heidelberg/New York 1977; 1-22.
19. Földes-Filep, E., Küster, L.J., Braquet, P., Filep. J. (1987) *Inhibition by BN 52021 (ginkgolide B) of the binding of ³H-platelet-activating factor to human neutrophil granulocytes.* Biochem Biophys Res Commun 1987; 3: 1412-1417.
20. Furukawa, S. *Constituents of Ginkgo biloba L. leaves.* Sci Papers Inst Phys Chem Res Tokyo 1932; 19: 27-38.
21. Hwang, S.B., Lam, M.H., Chang, M.N. *Specific binding of [³H] dihydrokadsurenone to rabbit platelet membranes and its inhibition by the receptor agonists and antagonists of platelet-activating factor.* J Biol Chem 1986; 261: 13720-13726.
22. Hwang, S.B., Lam, M.-H., Pong, S.-S. *Ionic and GTP regulation of binding of platelet-activating factor to receptors and platelet-activating factor-induced activation of GTPase in rabbit platelet membranes.* J Biol Chem 1986; 261: 532-537.
23. Korth, R., Hirafuji, M., Benveniste, J. *Comparison of human endothelial cells in culture and platelets for [³H]-PAF-acether binding.* Fed Proc 1987; 46: 444.

24. Maruyama, M., Terahara, A., Itagaki, Y., Nakanishi, K. *The ginkgolides I. Isolation and characterization of the various groups.* Tetrahedron Lett 1967; 4: 299-302.

25. Maruyama, M., Terahara, A., Itagaki, Y., Nakanishi, K. *The ginkgolides. II. Derivation of partial structures.* Tetrahedron Lett 1967; 4: 303-308.

26. Maruyama, M., Terahara, A., Nakadaira, Y., Woods, M.C., Nakanishi, K. *The ginkgolides. III. Structure of the ginkgolides.* Tetrahedron Lett 1967; 4: 309-313.

27. Maruyama, M., Terahara, A., Nakadaira, Y., Woods, M.C., Takagi, Y., Nakanishi, K. *The ginkgolides. IV. Stereochemitry of the ginkgolides.* Tetrahedron Lett 1967; 4: 314-319.

28. Nakanishi, K., Habaguchi, K. *Biosynthesis of ginkgolide B, its diterpenoid nature, and origin of the tert-butyl group.* J Am Chem Soc 1971; 93: 3546-3547.

29. Roumestand, C., Perly, B., Braquet, P. *Carbon 13 and proton 500 MHz NMR of ginkgolides.* Tetrahedron Lett 1988; In press.

30. Schreiber, S.L. 30th National Organic Chemistry Symposium (A.C.S.), Vancouver, June 21-25, 1987; Abbst.

31. Shen, T.Y., Hwang, S.B., Chang, M.N., Doebber, T.W., Lam, M.H., Wu, M.S., Wang, X., Han, G.Q., Li, R.Z. *Characterization of a plateleet-activating factor receptor antagonist isolated from haifenteng (Piper futokadsura): Specific inhibition of in vitro and in vivo platelet-activating factor-induced effects.* Proc Natl Acad Sci USA 1985; 82: 672-676.

32. Vargaftig, B.B., Braquet, P. *PAF-acether today - Relevance for acute experimental anaphylaxis.* Brit Med Bull 1987; 43: 312-335.

33. Villhauer, E.B., Anderson, R.C. *Synthesis of the CDE ring system of the ginkgolides.* J Org Chem 1987; 52: 11867-11869.

34. Weinges, K., Bähr, W., Rao, M.P. *Synthese des Hexahydro-5H-dicyclopenta [b,c]furan-5a(6H)-ols.* Liebigs Ann Chem 1971; 753: 100-105.

35. Weinges, K., Hepp, M., Jaggy, H. *Isolierung und strukturaufklärung eines neuen Ginkgolides.* Liebigs Ann Chem 1987; 6: 521-526.

36. Zenk, M.H. Proc 4th Int Congress Plant Tissue and Cell Culture: Frontiers of Plant Tissue Culture. T.A. Thorpe (Ed.). University of Calgary Offset Printing Service: Calgary 1978; 1-13.

Ginkgolides - Chemistry, Biology, Pharmacology and Clinical Perspectives. P. Braquet (Ed.)
Copyright © 1988, J.R. Prous Science Publishers, S.A.

GINKGO BILOBA: FROM "LIVING FOSSIL" TO MODERN THERAPEUTIC AGENT

*Pierre François Michel and David Hosford**

IPSEN, 30 rue Cambronne, Paris and *Institut Henri Beaufour, 17 avenue Descartes, F-92350 Le Plessis-Robinson, France

At the end of the Paleozoic era the landscape of earth was very different from that of today. Although algae, bryophytes (mosses and liverworts) and pteridophytes (horsetails and ferns) had evolved there were no grasses or trees. The vegetation was dominated by giant horsetails, ferns and other plants which are now extinct. The first real trees, characterized by a dense wooden trunk, branches and leaves appeared 250-200 million years ago. These new classes of plants consisted mainly of the Cordaites, the Cycadales and the Ginkgoales. Their evolution was rapid and they quickly replaced the primary vegetation that had covered the ground for a hundred million years. In turn, these plants were soon overtaken by the Coniferae and Angiospermae, from which most of the vegetation present today has evolved. This succession of changes in the worlds' dominant flora directly resulted from evolutionary modifications in the method of reproduction.

The most important vector in the evolution of life is the insurance of the siblings. The further we progress along the evolutionary line of animals and plants, the less is left to chance to secure the future of the reproductive cells and thus, perpetuation of the genes. Ferns, for example, like algae and fungi, reproduce by means of "spores", a complex and hazardous process taking place outside the plant. Water is an absolute requirement for this mechanism as the reproductive cells have to "swim" to each other in order to fuse. The revolutionary change accomplished by the Cordaites, Cycadales and Ginkgoales was the development of the "ovule". In *Ginkgo*

Address all correspondence to: Dr. David Hosford, Institut Henri Beaufour, 17 avenue Descartes, F-92350 Le Plessis-Robinson, France.

1

biloba for instance, the sexes are separated on different trees. The female reproductive structures appear during the first days of spring and consist of a stalk or peduncle bearing at its tip two (occasionally three or more) erect ovules. At the apex of the ovule a tiny hole extrudes a drop of liquid ready to trap a passing grain of pollen. The male gametophyte which is strictly endosporic, begins its development within the microsporangium, and when shed consists of two prothallial cells (one of which is abortive), a generative cell and a tube cell. Pollination is achieved by the wind and after the grain reaches the pollen chamber of the nucellus a haustorial pollen tube is produced. During the growth of the pollen tube the generative cell divides, forming the stalk and body cell. The latter, by single division, produces two large mutiflagellate sperms. The development of the female gametophyte begins at the time of pollination of the ovule and subsequently, the flagellated sperms escape into the archegonial chamber. Although two sperms may enter the archegonium, only one functions; the male nucleus slips out of its cytoplasmic sheath and fuses with the egg nucleus. In *Ginkgo*, the process of fertilization and embryogeny may occur either on the tree or after the ovule has fallen to the ground (Fig. 1). After fertilization the embryo must at once meet the right conditions required for germination and survival: adequate water, temperature and soil type. There is no period of dehydration and dormancy, as is the case with the conventional seed.

Thus, for a brief period the ovule plants exploited their advantage over their sporophytic counterparts. Many *Ginkgos* and related genera occupied

Figure 1 Mature ovules of the *Ginkgo* containing the embryo.

Figure 2   Fossil remains of *Ginkgo* leaves from Argentina.

most of the worlds' ground-surface in the Jurassic and Cretaceous eras, some 200 to 100 million years ago. Fossil *Ginkgos* have been discovered in Asia, Europe, America, Argentina and Australia (Fig. 2). However, the "ovule" method of reproduction was only a transient step on the way to the "seed". This step was quickly crossed and modern seed plants, with their ability to remain dormant until favorable germination conditions and improved mechanisms of dispersal, spread rapidly over the earth replacing their competitors. Overcome by evolutionary pressure, the great upheavals of the earth during the Tertiary and Quaternary periods and the subsequent Ice Age, most ovule plants disappeared from the world. The Cordaites became extinct, while the Cycadales succeeded in adapting themselves into new entities capable of surviving until present times. All the Ginkgoales vanished except one species, whose existence we can trace back to about 150 million years ago, due to certain special features such as the double nervation of the petiole. Contrary to the Cycadales and the most archaic of the Coniferae, whose species have evolved since these ancient times, the *Ginkgo biloba* of today appears to be unchanged from its ancestors pre-

Figure 3   A *Ginkgo* in the gardens of a Chinese Buddhist temple.

sent in Cretaceous times. Thus, this "living fossil" has probably existed on earth longer than any other tree.

Whether *Ginkgo* still survives in the wild state in the more remote and poorly explored forests of China is still a matter of controversy. It has been found growing spontaneously over some ten square miles near Changhua Hsien in the Chekiang province in China, but whether these are the remains of an ancient forest or the off-spring of specimens introduced by man is not known. In China and Korea it is commonly planted and appears to have been cultivated for many centuries. It has been especially used for the embellishment of grounds surrounding Buddhist temples, where magnificient examples can be found (Fig. 3). It has also been planted extensively in the vicinity of Chinese palaces. In some of the grounds attached to temples there are *Ginkgos* reputed to be over a 1000 years old; thus, its preservation may be attributed, in part, to the interest taken in it by Buddhist priests, who also probably introduced it into Japan.

Ginkgo biloba was first made known to European botanists by Kaempfer, a surgeon in the employ of the Dutch East India Company, who observed it in 1690 and published a description in 1712. He proposed the name *"Ginkgo"*, and Linnaeus adopted this generic appelation in 1771, adding the descriptive species name *"biloba"* in reference to the frequently notched character of the fan-shaped leaves (Fig. 4). The tree was introduced into Europe about 1930, being first planted in the Botanic Garden at Utrecht. It was introduced into England in 1754 and into America about 1784.

The *Ginkgo* develops into an imposing and handsome tree of distinctive appearance, the leaves turning bright yellow in autumn before they fall

Figure 4 The juvenile (left) and adult (right) forms of the *Ginkgo* leaf.

(Fig. 5). The tree succeeds well under urban conditions and thus, has been widely planted as an ornamental, although the unpleasant odor of the female fruits combined with the fact that their juice can cause skin irritations, has limited its value for street planting. This phenomenon, while being inconvenient to the modern urban planner, points to perhaps the most interesting aspect of this remarkable tree, its phytochemical constituents. The importance of these components cannot be over-stressed; they have probably been largely responsible for the survival of the *Ginkgo* over 200 million years, in which time innumerable other plant species have died out. They have also made *Ginkgo biloba* one of the oldest phytotherapeutic agents known to man.

The reason for the longevity of the *Ginkgo* still remains a mystery, but it is apparent that it possesses an extraordinary ability to adjust to a wide variety of environments. The *Ginkgo* appears to be as susceptible as other gymnosperms to the chromosomal mutagenic effects of radiation; however, it should be noted that *Ginkgo* trees do not reproduce until they are more than 20 years old and then can continue to do so for more than a 1000 years. As a result, they have much less chance of changing their characteristics than other plants, which have a shorter reproductive period. The *Ginkgo* tree shows a high tolerance to urban and industrial pollution and is extremely resistant to all serious pests and diseases. The only leaf disease reported on this host is anthracnose caused by the fungus *Glomerella*

Figure 5 A mature *Ginkgo* in the grounds of Versailles prior to leaf-fall.

cingulata, and the damage produced by this is negligible. While the mechanisms of *Ginkgo* resistance to insects, bacteria, viruses and fungi remain to be elucidated, there is some evidence that secondary metabolites present in various tissues of the tree may represent a means of defense.

Alcoholic extracts of the leaves and roots, respectively, inhibit the growth of larvae of the cabbage butterfly (*Pieris rapae crucivora*) and the European corn borer (*Pyrausta mubilalis*). Leaf extracts abolish the development of various bacteria such as *Erwinia amylovora*, *Escherichia coli*, *Pseudomonas phaseolicola*, *Xanthomonas phaseoli* and *Bacillus pumilus* and also possess some antifungal activity. Similarly, components of the root alleviate symptoms in plants infected with southern bean and tobacco mosaic virus. The anti-feedant activity of the leaves has been attributed to the acidity of this tissue, the presence of 2-hexenal and various bitter terpenoids and flavone glycosides.

Indeed, various tissues of *Ginkgo biloba* produce a wide range of secondary metabolites. The fruit produces the phenolic compounds ginkgol, bilobol and ginkgolic acid. The seeds contain various cyanogenetic glycosides and amino acids, while D-sesamin and the sesquiterpenoid bilobalide occur in the heartwood. However, as we shall see, the most interesting pharmacological agents are present in the leaves. These contain the aliphatic compounds ginnol, ginnon and *n*-hexenal as well as shikimic acid, bilobalide kaempferol, quercetin and the glycosides of these latter two compounds.

Finally, various ginkgolides are also found in this tissue. These are unique C_{20} cage molecules incorporating a *tert*-butyl group and six 5-membered rings including a spiro [4.4] nonane system, a tetrahydrofuran cycle and three lactonic groups.

With respect to its pharmacological properties, extracts of *Ginkgo* have been used as therapeutic agents by man for many centuries. The tree has apparently always been part of the traditional Chinese pharmacopeia as it is referred to in the medicinal book "Chen Noung Pen T'sao", published in 2800 BC. In the modern Chinese pharmacopeia, *Ginkgo* is still recommended as "beneficial for the heart and lungs" and inhalation of a decoction of the leaves is used to alleviate asthma. The boiled leaves are still used against chillblains, which may be explained by the vasoactive properties demonstrated by modern pharmacology. Today, a standarized extract of *Ginkgo* leaves, Tanakan (GBE 761), is produced and marketed by IPSEN. This is active against a broad spectrum of physiological disorders. The pharmacological effects of *Ginkgo biloba* extract concern vascular, rheological metabolic and immunological mechanisms. The beneficial actions of Tanakan appear to occur *via* its anti-free radical properties and its modulation of various enzyme systems and ion pumps. These processes appear to be largely effected by an interaction of certain components of Tanakan with various biologically active chemical mediators. Indeed, a major component of Tanakan are the ginkgolides A, B, C, M and J (BN 52020, BN 52021, BN 52022, BN 52023 and BN 52024; respectively), which show varying degrees of potency as specific antagonists of the inflammatory autacoid, platelet-activating factor. This compound is rapidly emerging as a crucial mediator of a wide range of physiological processes and pathological conditions. Thus, the ginkgolides may possess considerable potential as therapeutic agents and it is to pharmacology of these compounds that this book is devoted.

It is not known when man first encountered *Ginkgo biloba*, but it is clear that since that time a special relationship has existed between the two. Whilst man must shoulder the burden of responsibility for the destruction of much of the worlds' flora and fauna, *Ginkgo* is one of the few species to have benefited from his intervention and protection. It is ironic that this living fossil should be one of the few organisms to survive one of mans' most destructive acts, the nuclear obliteration of Hiroshima. Today a *Ginkgo* tree fluorishes in what was virtually the epicenter of the nuclear explosion (Fig. 6).

This introduction can be most suitably brought to a close by the words of the eminent Cambridge paleobotanist, Professor A.C. Seward. In 1936, he wrote to The Times, commenting on the history and occurrence of the *Ginkgo* tree. His letter concluded: "To *Ginkgo biloba* must be assigned

Figure 6 The *Ginkgo* tree growing at Hiroshima.

the first place as a link with the past; a sacred tree in the Far East, it should
be so regarded by all who desire to safeguard natural monuments; it is the
last of a race that, ages before the evolution of man, occupied a position
in the floras of the world.''

Ginkgolides - Chemistry, Biology, Pharmacology and Clinical Perspectives. P. Braquet (Ed.)
Copyright © 1988, J.R. Prous Science Publishers, S.A.

GINKGO BILOBA: A REVIEW OF ITS CHEMICAL COMPOSITION

Nivaldo Boralle[1], Pierre Braquet[2] and Otto R. Gottlieb[1]

[1]Instituto de Química, Universidade de Sao Paulo, Sao Paulo, SP, Brasil;
[2]Institut Henri Beaufour, F-92350 Le Plessis-Robinson, France

INTRODUCTION

Ginkgo biloba has already been subject to numerous general analyses (Table 1) and more detailed chemical investigations, the latter summarized in Tables 2-11. Most products or constituents isolated so far from the tree are considered to be normal for higher plants, and especially for a gymnosperm, and need little comment. The sole exception to this fact is provided by a group of bitter principles not yet located in any other living species. A review of their chemistry follows.

CHEMICAL COMPOSITION OF GINKGO EXTRACTS

One of the bitter principles was first isolated from *Ginkgo* root by Furukawa in 1932 (18), but the structure of the ginkgolides continued to be an unsolved problem (51, 62) up to 1967, when Nakanishi's group in Japan reported their structures [1] and called them ginkgolides A, B, C and M (46-49, 52). A new ginkgolide, termed J, has been recently identified (83). All these compounds differ only by the number and the position of hydroxyl groups which may be present on C-1, C-3 and/or C-7 of the spirononane framework (Table 2). Their chemical characterization was mainly obtained by gas chromatography-mass spectrometry of the trimethylsilyl derivatives (60, 77), ^{13}C and ^{1}H 500 MHz NMR (61) and X-ray crystallographic analysis (14, 15, 63). 500 MHz ^{1}H NMR analysis of the vicinal coupling constants yielded useful information concerning the conformations of the A and B rings and their torsional angles. This system

---

Address all correspondence to: Prof. Otto R. Gottlieb, Instituto de Química, Universidad de Sao Paulo, 05508 Sao Paulo, SP, Brazil.

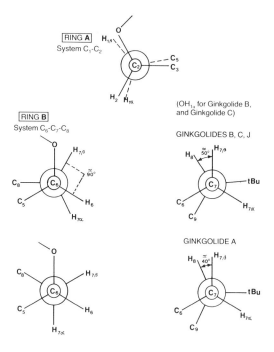

Figure 1   Ring distorsions in ginkgolides deduced from a 500 MHz ^{1}H NMR study.

appears in two slightly different conformations, one prevalent in ginkgolide A and the other prevalent in ginkgolides B, C and J (61) (Fig. 1). The ginkgolide structure [1] bears a striking resemblance to that of bilobalide [2], another constituent of *Ginkgo biloba*. This incorporates a *tert*-butyl group and five fused cyclopentanoid rings, among which are again three γ-lactone (but no tetrahydrofuran) and only one cyclopentane (and hence no spiro [4,4] nonane) units (54, 76).

The ginkgolides are unique cage molecules, incorporating a *tert*-butyl group and six fused five-membered rings A-F, including three γ-lactone, a tetrahydrofuran and a spiro[4,4] nonane units [1]. The *cis*-fused rings F, A, D and C are folded in such a way that a semi-spherical cavity of significant size is formed (*ca* 4 Å wide x 5 Å deep). In relative molecular terms the cavity is sufficiently large to host inorganic (*e.g.*, Fe^{2+}, Ca^{2+}) or organic (*e.g.*, trimethylammonium) ions. Two sides of the cavity are defined by the C-11 and C-15 lactone carbonyls included in the C and F rings, respectively. The head of the cap of the cavity is defined by rings A and D. The tetrahydrofuran ring (D) occupies a central position in the cage;

its ether (or better ketal) oxygen, along with the C and F ring ester oxygens and the C-10 hydroxyl oxygen, define a polydentate system much like that observed in the "crown" ether series. This electron-rich cavity is ideally suited for the binding of cationic or positively polarized species. It is important to observe that the *tert*-butyl group is very prominent outside the main framework. Due to the shape of the cavity, if binding does occur, it would not be surprising to find it to be stereospecific.

The various lactone functions of ginkgolides may be opened by alkali. The equilibrium constants of the reactions were determined and seven derivatives, including mono- and dicarboxylic acids as well as a tricarboxylic acid were prepared. Reacidifications of the medium always supplied quantitatively the parent ginkgolide, without any alteration of the structure (5).

Biosynthetic pathways to ginkgolide B have been elucidated by Nakanishi and Habaguchi (53) (Fig. 2). Mevalonate and methionine are incorporated in the framework, most probably via geranylgeranyl pyrophosphate, (+)-labdadienyl pyrophosphate and an *ent*-primaraenone cation. In the representation of this precursor (2.*1*) the bonds destined to form the spiro[4,4] nonane system of the ginkgolides are thickened and the carbon atoms are numbered according to their positions in the final product. Precursor 2.*1* is postulated to pass into precursor 2.*2* by rearrangements of C-6 from C-4 to C-5 and of C-16 from C-3 to C-14. Besides, cleavage of the bond adjacent to the gem-dimethyl group initiates the formation of the *tert*-butyl group, a reaction which, jointly with the rearrangement of C-3 from C-13 to C-4, completes the formation of the spiro[4,4] nonane unit in precursor 2.*3*. Subsequent oxidation at various positions, including loss of CO_2 by α-oxidation at C-11 should give one more putative precursor (2.*4*). Designating in 2.*4* vicinal carbons and oxygens as C-n and O-n', mostly oxidative cyclizations involving positions 2-15', 4-12', 6-13' and 12-11', lead to the ginkgolide skeleton.

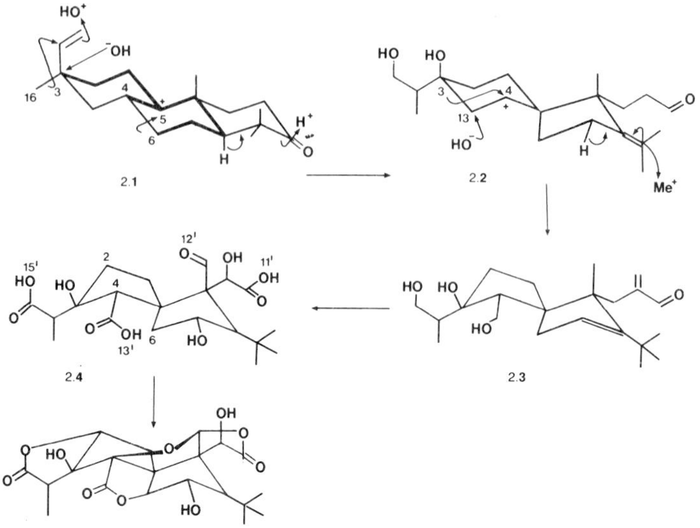

Figure 2 Biogenetic pathway to ginkgolide J. The incorporation of the universal terpenoid precursor, mevalonate, into ginkgolide B and of methionine into its *tert*-butyl group are experimental facts (53); the structures of the precursors are hypothetical.

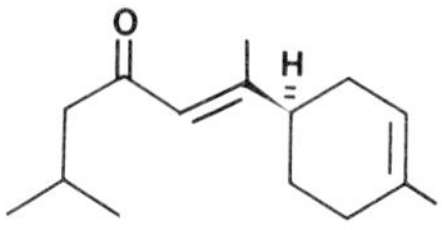

3

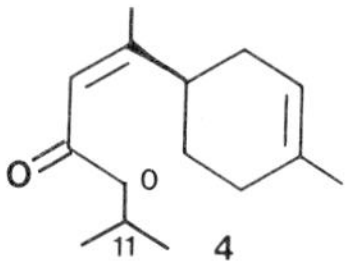

4

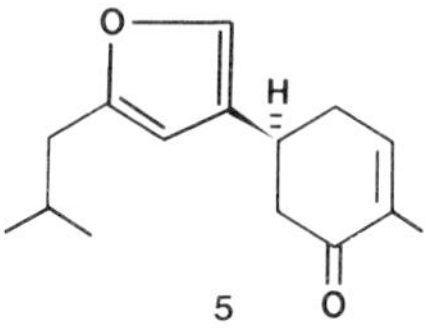

5

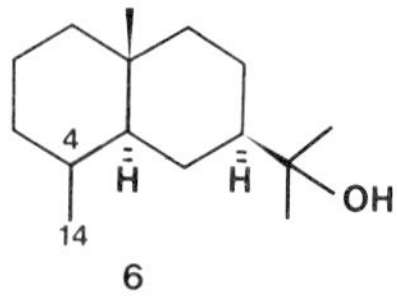

6

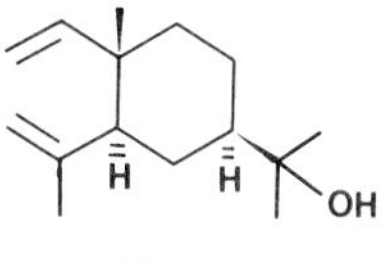

7

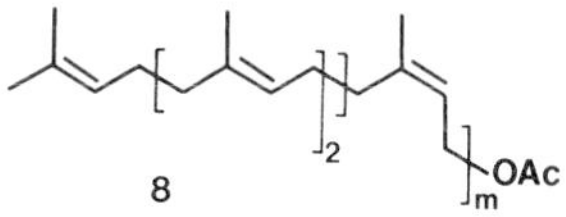

8

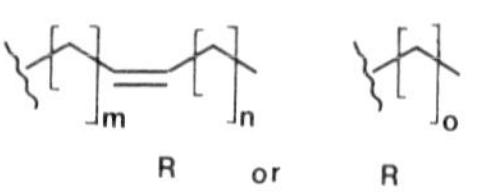

R or R

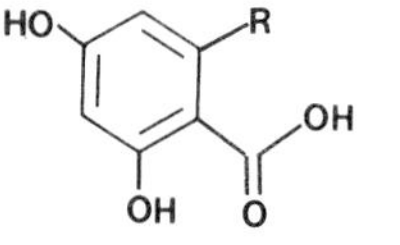

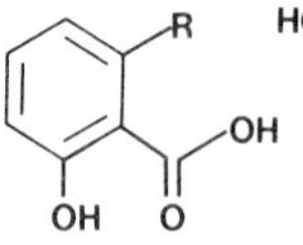

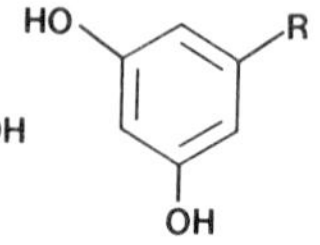

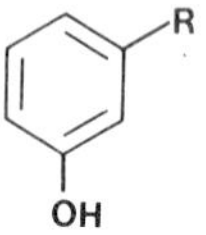

9 10 11 12

Clearly bilobalide [2] should be a monomethyl-mononor sesquiterpene. Numbering of *2* is here molded on numbering of *1*. This simplifies racionalization of bilobalide's biosynthesis by loss of carbons 3, 13, 14, 15 and 16 from a ginkgolide. Alternatively, analogous pathways as shown for the cyclizations of geranylgeranyl pyrophosphate into the ginkgolides may lead from farnesyl pyrophosphate to bilobalide (53).

Since ginkgolides are among the most complex organic natural products, the synthetic pathways are limited and depend on the availability of methods for the concurrent generation of *cis*-fused cyclopentanoid rings with highly specific stereochemistry. Few groups have attempted exploratory efforts aimed at the total synthesis of ginkgolides and bilobalide.

Weinges' group (80) (Fig. 3) reported the synthesis of hexahydro-5*H*-dicyclopenta[b,c]furan-5a(6*H*)-ol (*3.3*), which represents the main framework (rings A, B, D) of the ginkgolides: Grignard reaction of 1-oxospiro[4,4]nonan-6(R)-ol (*3.1*) with chloromethyl benzyl ether and subsequent hydrogenolysis provided the 1-hydroxymethylspiro[4,4] nonane-1,6-diol *3.2a* and *3.2b*. Only the 2R, 6R-epimer *3.2a* could be cyclized into *3.3* in absolute dimethylsulfoxide. The same group also achieved a partial synthesis of bilobalide from ginkgolide A and B (82).

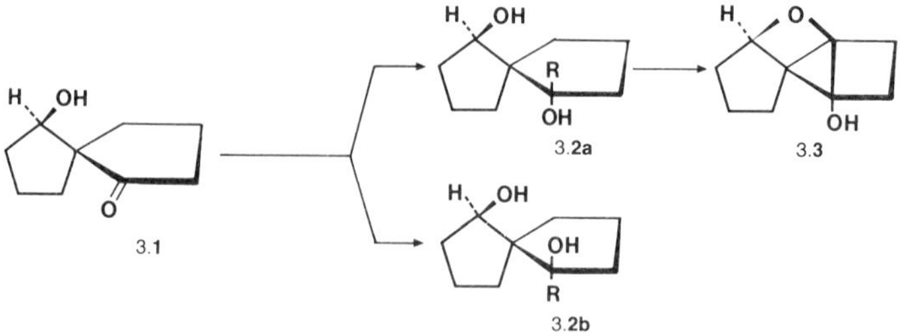

Figure 3   Synthesis of the ginkgolide A, B, D-ring system (80).

Recently, Villhauer and Anderson (74) reported the first attempt to synthesize the C, D, E ring system of the ginkgolides using the epoxide 4.*1* as starting material. Addition of dimethylmalonate yielded the lactone 4.*2a*. Krapcho decarbomethoxylation of this compound produced the lactone 4.*2b* which was then alkylated with benzyl bromide to 4.*2c*. This concluded the construction of the C-ring, further appended by alkylation of 4.*2c* with *tert*-butyl bromoacetate to the diastereoisomer 4.*3*. Subsequent deesterification, selective lactone reduction and cyclization gave 4.*4a*. The remaining E-ring was obtained by hydrogenolysis of this benzyl ether, followed by partial hydrolysis of 4.*4b* with *p*-toluenesulfonic acid to a mixture of anomers. The major constituent 4.*5a* was then converted to the hemiacetal 4.*5b*, which gave the ginkgolide C, D, E fragment 4.*5c* by oxidation with pyridinium chlorochromate.

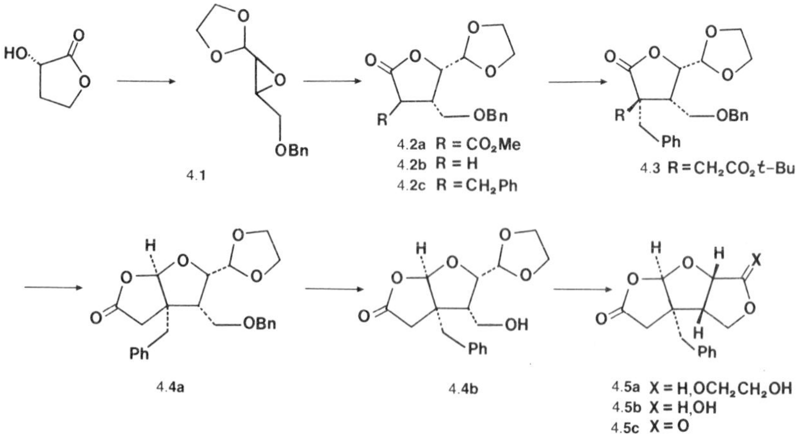

Figure 4   Synthesis of the ginkgolide C, D, E-ring system (74).

Corey's group reported a general process for the synthesis of polycyclic γ-lactones by double annulation (12). In its application to the present purpose manganese (III) acetate [$Mn_3O(OAc)_7$] was used for the conversion of 4-(2-cyclopentenyl)-3-oxobutanoic acid (*5.1*) into *5.2*. Reaction of this ketolactone with sodium hydride and methylbromoacetate in THF afforded the keto ester *5.3*, which was converted into *5.4* upon treatment with aluminium amalgam in aqueous THF. Conversion of this hydroxy ester into the tetracyclic dilactone *5.5* was then accomplished by subsequent mesylation, methyl ester hydrolysis and acidification. The synthesis of the bicyclic keto ester *5.6*, a potential intermediate for the synthesis of *Ginkgo* terpenoids, has also been recently described by Corey *et al.* (13).

Using these various sophisticated synthetic pathways, the total synthesis of ginkgolides has been recently realized in more than 20 steps (E.J. Corey, personal communication).

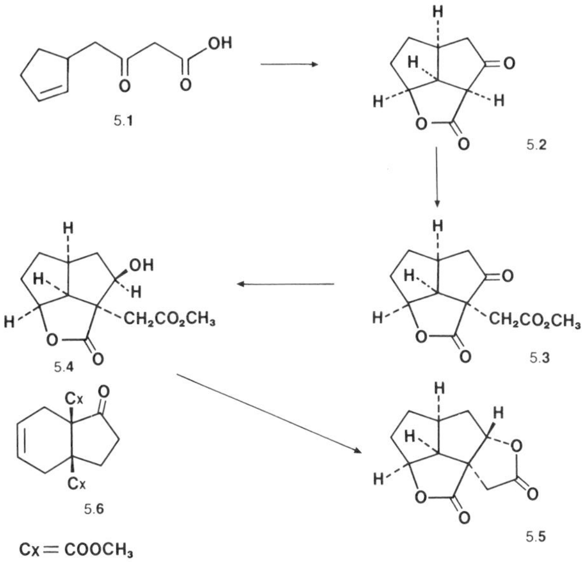

Figure 5 Synthesis of a tetracyclic dilactone (12).

Ginkgo biloba has survived for more than 200 million years of changing climatic and geologic conditions, including ice ages and at least two catastrophic extinctions of a major percentage of then thriving species. Not even the atomic bomb on Hiroshima was destructive enough to avoid its spontaneous revival from the roots. In the forefront of the biologist's marvels concerning the longevity of the species is its concommitant resistance against a permanently diversifying host of predators, from virus and bacteria to algae, fungi, lichens and mosses as well as to insects and other herbivorous fauna, and not least to competitive trends of other higher plants. Clearly, a chemist would like to explain such stability in an ecologically variable habitat by existence of an array of biologically potent, *i.e.*, generally toxic, allelochemicals. In this respect one might also consider lacticiferous conduits, tanniferous vesicles, calcium oxalate crystals and the like (Table 1). However, such features are hardly restricted to *Ginkgo* and although

Table 1   General analyses of *Ginkgo* parts (27, 28)

Leaves
  Calcium oxalate raphids
  Condensed tannins in tracheids
  Oil, balsam, benzoic acid in cavities
  Starch in sieve tube plastids
  Wax (0.7-1% of dry leaves):

alkanes and alcohols	75%
esters	15%
free acids	10%
estolides absent	

Wood
  Syringyllignins absent

Raffinose	1-2%

  Glucomannan (galactose-glucose-mannose 1:5:18)
  Arabino-4-O-methylglucuronoxylan (50)
  Suberin (66)
  Extract free wood, hydrolysis products:

glucose	41%
mannose	10%
xylose	5%
galactose	3%
arabinose	2%

Nuts (59% of dry seeds)

Starch	67.9%
Protein	13.1%
globulins	
glutelin	
albumins	
Lipid	2.9%
Pentosans	1.6%
Fiber	1.0%
Ash	3.4%

  Cyanogenetic glucosides absent

Table 2   Terpenoids

Monomethyl-mononor-diterpenes [1] and sesquiterpene [2]			
Ginkgolide A (= BN 52020)	[*1*] 3-αOH, 10-βOH	leaves root-bark	(3, 4, 41, 46, 51, 52, 55, 56, 82)
Ginkgolide B (= BN 52021)	[*1*] 1,3-αOH, 10-βOH	leaves root-bark	(3, 14, 15, 41, 46, 51, 52, 53, 56, 74)
Ginkgolide C (= BN 52022)	[*1*] 1,3-αOH, 7,10-βOH	leaves root bark	(3, 4, 14, 41, 46, 52, 56, 63)
Ginkgolide M (= BN 52023)	[*1*] 1-αOH, 7, 10-βOH	root bark	(46, 52)
Ginkgolide J (= BN 52024)	[*1*] 3-αOH, 7,10-βOH	leaves	(3, 83)
Bilobalide	[2] 10-αOH, 8-βOH	leaves	(53, 54, 74, 82)
Sesquiterpenes from wood			
E-10, 11-dihydroatlantone	[*3*]		(30)
E-10, 11-dihydroatlantone 6-oxo	[*3*]	6-(= 0)	(30)
Z-10, 11-dihydroatlantone	[*4*]		(30)
Bilobanone	[*5*]		(30, 31, 39)
Eudesmol, β—	[*6*]	Δ-4 (14)	(28)
Eudesmol γ—	[*6*]	Δ-4	(28)
Elemol	[*7*]		(28)

Monoterpenes and other components of essential oil from wood (29)
2,5,8-Trimethyldihydronaphthalene
Acenaphthene
1,4-Dimethyl-2,5-diisopropylbenzene
Ionone, α—
Ionone, β—
Thymol
p-Tolylpropylene
p-Cymene
2-Isopropylphenol
trans-Linalool oxide

Polyprenyl acetates (35, 69, 70)
Betulaprenols 14-22 (mainly 17-19) [*8*] n = 11-19 (mainly 14-16)

Steroids from leaves (27)
Sitosterol
Sitosterol, glucoside (= ipuranol)

Table 3   Anacardic acid analogues from seed sarcotesta*

4-Hydroxyanacardic acids [9]		(21, 23)
4-Hydroxyginkgolic acid	m = 7, n = 5	(22)
	o = 12	(22)
Anacardic acids [10]		
Ginkgolide acid**	m = 7, n = 5	(25, 32, 36, 67)
**	m = 11, n = 3	(25)
Hydroginkgolic acid	o = 14	(17, 25)
Cardols [11]		
Bilobol	m = 7, n = 5	(32, 52, 67)
	o = 14	(59)
Cardanols [12]		
Ginkgol**	m = 7, n = 5	(11, 52, 67)

*Often erroneously designated "fruit" or "fruit pulp" in the literature.
**Also isolated from leaves.

Table 4   Flavonoids from leaves

Flavones [13]		
Luteolin		(78)
Tricetin (= dalphidenon)	5'-OH	(78)
Biflavones [14]		
Amentoflavone	7,4', 4'''-OH	(6)
Bilobetin	7,4'''-OH; 4'-OMe	(6, 7)
Ginkgetin	4'''-OH; 7,4'-OMe	(2, 6, 7)
Isoginkgetin	7-OH; 4',4'''-OMe	(2, 6, 7)
Sciadopitysin	7,4', 4'''-OMe	(2, 6, 7)
5'-Methoxybilobetin	7,4'''-OH; 3', 4'-OMe	(45)
Flavonols [15]		
Kaempferol	3-OH	(16, 57)
Kaempferol, 3-rutinoside	3-ORu	(20)
Kaempferol, 3-O-α(6'''-p-coumaroyl-	3-O(X)	(9)
glucosyl-β-1,4-rhamnoside)		
Quercetin	3,3'-OH	(16, 57, 68)
Quercetin, 3-rutinoside (= rutin)	3-ORu; 3'-OH	(20)
Quercetin, 3-glucoside (= isoquercitrin)	3-OGl; 3'-OH	(78)
Quercetin, 3-O-α(6'''-p-coumaroyl-		
glucosyl-β-1,4-rhamnoside)		(84)
Isorharmnetin	3-OH; 3'-OMe	(57)
3'-O-Methylmyricetin-3-rutinoside	3-ORu; 3'-OMe; 5'-OH	(19)
Catechins [16]		
(+)-Catechin	3S	(81)
(—)-Epicatechin	3R	(81)
(+)-Gallocatechin	3S; 5'-OH	(81)
(—)-Epigallochatechin	3R; 5'-OH	(81)
Proanthocyanidins		
Gallochatechin, 4,8''-catechin (= procyanidin)		(79)
Gallochatechin, 4,8''-gallocatechin (= prodelphinidin)		(79)
Condensed tannins		

Table 5 Lignoids

Z,Z-4,4'-(1,4-Pentadien-1,5-diyl)diphenol	[17]	leaves	(58)
(+)-Sesamin		wood	(39, 40)

Table 6 Lipids from seeds (38, 73)

Glycerides, tri-		
Glycerides, di-		linoleic
Glycerides, mono-		oleic
Phosphatidyl-choline	main acids:	palmitic
Phosphatidyl-serine		stearic
Phosphatidyl-inositol		linolenic
Phosphatidyl-ethanolamine		
Galactosyldiglyceride, di-	main acids:	oleic
Galactosyldiglyceride, mono-		linoleic
Cerebroside	main acid:	α-hydroxypalmitic
Sitosterol		
Sterol esters		
Free acids		

very many of the secondary metabolites mentioned in the present chapter show remarkable biodynamic activity (Tables 2, 3 and 4), none of the known effects seem aggressive enough to permanently justify such a strong defensive action.

Somewhat more interesting is the fact that it took more than 50 years of intense analytical effort to isolate the first nitrogen-containing secondary metabolites from *Ginkgo biloba* seed (75) and leaf (64) (Table 11). Indeed all the available nitrogen seems to be channelled into aminoacids and proteins, a remarkable economy which may contribute to the tree's vitality.

During the present survey we did, nevertheless, note an even more striking feature: the extraordinarily high oxidation level of many *Ginkgo* metabolites. Indeed, ginkgolide A ($C_{20}H_{24}O_9$), B ($C_{20}H_{24}O_{10}$), C ($C_{20}H_{24}O_{11}$) and bilobalide ($C_{15}H_{18}O_8$) have previously been considered to be sugar derivatives (53); the components of the essential oil are highly aromatized (Table 2) and even stearic acid appears in an octadehydro-form (Table 7). Based on this postulate, one is entitled to wonder if the secondary metabolites of *Ginkgo biloba* are not simply clues to the answer, suggesting the existence of enzyme systems with a high oxidative power. Transference

Table 7 Fatty acids

Saturated and unsaturated acids from leaves and seed (10, 24, 72)

	N° of C
Formic	1
Acetic	2
Propionic	3
Butyric	4
Valeric	5
Caproic	6
Caprylic	8
Myristic	14
Palmitic	16
	16: Δ-7
	16: Δ-9
	16: Δ-11
	16: Δ-7, 10
	16: Δ-9, 12
	16: Δ-7, 10, 13
	16: Δ-9, 12, 15
Stearic	18
	18: Δ-9
	18: Δ-11
	18: Δ-5, 11
	18: Δ-9, 12
	18: Δ-5, 11, 14
	18: Δ-9, 12, 15
	18: Δ-5, 9, 12, 15
	20: Δ-5, 11
	20: Δ-11, 14
	20: Δ-14, 17
	20: Δ-5, 11, 14
	20: Δ-5, 11, 14, 17
	20: Δ-9, 12, 15, 18

Hydroxyacids from cutin of leaves [34]

	15: 7-OH, 15-OH
	15: 6-OH, 15-O_2H
Pamitic	16
	16: 16-OH, Δ-?
	16: 16-OH
	16: 7-OH, 16-O_2H
	16: 8-OH, 16-O_2H
	16: 9, 16-OH
	16: 10, 16-OH

Table 8 Aliphatics from leaf wax

	N° of C		
Alkanes, minor	19→		(1, 8)
Alkanes, major	25, 27, 29		
Alcohols	26	1-OH	(79)
	28	1-OH	(1, 79)
Ginnol	29	10-OH	(1, 8, 52, 67)
Aldehydes	6	1-(=O), Δ-2	(43, 44, 52)
Ketones	27	10-(=O)	(8)
Ginnon	29	10-(=O)	(1, 8)
	29	13-(=O)	(8)
Esters	38-42		(8)

Table 9. Miscellaneous acids

Aminoacids from seeds

γ-Aminobutyric		(26, 33)
Homoserine		(33)
Threonine		(33)
Cysteine		(33)
Valine		(26)

Other acids

Citric	seeds	(33)
Quinic	seeds	(33)
Shikimic	leaves	(71, 79)
Ascorbic		(79)
Succinic	leaves	(56)

Table 10 Sugars and sugar alcohols

Sucrose	seeds	(33)
Glucose	seeds	(33)
Fructose	seeds	(33)
Pinitol (18)	leaves	(79)
Sequoyitol (19)	leaves	(79)
O-Methylmucoinositol absent	leaves	(28)
D-Glucaric acid	leaves	(28)

Table 11. Miscellaneous N-containing compounds

4'-Methoxypyridoxine [20]	seeds	(75)
6-Hydroxykynurenic acid [21]	leaves	(64)

of oxygen from air to the mevalonate and polyketide precursors (antioxidants) of the compounds would result in internal protection, while transference to invading organisms would lead to their molecules' destruction.

References

1. Ageta, H. *XXVI. Plant waxes. 13. Waxes from leaves of Ginkgo biloba and from Ephedra gerardiana.* Yakugaku Zasshi 1959; 79: 58-60.

2. Baker, W., Finch, A.C.M., Ollis, W.D., Robinson, K.W. *Biflavonyls, a new class of natural products. The structures of ginkgetin, isoginkgetin and sciadopitysin.* Proc Chem Soc 1959; 91-92.

3. Braquet, P. *The ginkgolides: Potent platelet-activating factor antagonists isolated from Ginkgo biloba L.: Chemistry, pharmacology and clinical applications.* Drugs of the Future 1987; 12: 643-699.

4. Braquet, P., Drieu, K., Etienne, A. *Le ginkgolide B (BN 52021): Un puissant inhibiteur du PAF-acether isolé du Ginko biloba L.* Actual Chim Thér 1986; 13: 237-254.

5. Braquet, P., Spinnewyn, B., Braquet, M., Bourgain, R.H., Taylor, J.E., Etienne, A., Drieu, K. *BN 52021 and related compounds: A new series of highly specific PAF-acether receptor antagonists isolated from Ginkgo biloba.* Ketsueki Myakkan 1985; 16: 558-572.

6. Briancon-Scheid, F., Lobstein-Guth, A., Anton, R. *High-performance liquid chromatography of biflavones from Ginkgo biloba L.* J Chromatogr 1982; 245: 261-267.

7. Briancon-Scheid, F., Lobstein-Guth, A., Anton, R. *HPLC separation and quantitative determination of biflavones in leaves from Ginkgo biloba.* Planta Med 1983; 49: 204-207.

8. Casal, H.L., Moyna, P. *Components of Ginkgo biloba leaf wax.* Phytochemistry 1979; 18: 1738-1739.

9. Nasr, C., Haag-Berrurier, M., Lobstein-Guth, A., Anton, R. *Kaempferol coumaroyl glucorhamnoside from Ginkgo biloba.* Phytochemistry 1986; 25: 770-771.

10. Chung, A.-S., Shin, H.-S. *Studies on the lipid components of ginkgo nut.* Hanguk Sikp'um Hwahakhoe Chi 1978; 10: 119-123.

11. Chung, B.-Y., Won, L.S., Lee, B.R., Lee, C.H. *A new chemical constituent of green leaves of Ginkgo biloba L.* Taehan Hwahakhoe Chi 1982; 26: 95-98.

12. Corey, E.J., Kang, M.-C. *New and general synthesis of polycyclic-γ-lactones by double annulation.* J Am Chem Soc 1984; 106: 5384-5385.

13. Corey, E.J., Su, W.-G., Houpis, L.N. *Useful new annulation reactions of vicinal dicarboxylic esters.* Tetrahedron Lett 1986; 27: 5951-5954.

14. Dupont, L., Dideberg, O., Germain, G., Braquet, P. *Structure of ginkgolide B (BN 52021) monohydrate, a highly specific PAF-acether receptor antagonist isolated from Ginkgo biloba L.* Acta Cryst 1986; C42: 1759-1762.

15. Dupont, L., Germain, G., Dideberg, O. *Crystal and molecular structure of BN 52021, a PAF-acether antagonist. Comparison with the conformation of kadsurenone and related compounds.* Pharmacol Res Commun 1986; 18: 25-32.

16. Fisel, J. *Preparation of kaempferol, quercetin and isorhamnetin from the green leaves of Ginkgo biloba.* Naturwissenschaften 1965; 52: 592.

17. Fu, F.-Y., Yu, T.-C., Sung, W.-L., Jai, Y.-F., Sun, N.-C. *Chemical study of hydroginkolinic acid - new constituent of Ginkgo biloba.* Hua Hsueh Hsueh Pao 1962; 28: 52-56.

18. Furukawa, S. *Constituents of Ginkgo biloba L. leaves.* Sci Papers Inst Phys Res Tokyo 1932; 19: 27-38.

19. Geiger, H. *3'-0-Methylmyricetin-3-rhamnoglucoside, a new flavonoid from the autumnal leaf of Ginkgo biloba L.* Z Naturforsch 1979; 34C: 878-879.

20. Geiger, H., Beckmann, S. *Occurrence of rutin and kaempferol 3-rhamnoglucoside in Ginkgo biloba.* Z Naturforsch 1965; 20B: 1139-1140.

21. Gellerman, J.L., Anderson, W.H., Schlenk, H. *Byosynthesis of anacardic acids from acetate in Ginkgo biloba.* Lipids 1974; 9: 722-725.

22. Gellerman, J.L., Anderson, W.H., Schlenk, H. *6-(Pentadec-8-enyl)-2,4-dihydroxybenzoic acid from seed of Ginkgo biloba.* Phytochemistry 1976; 15: 1959-1961.

23. Gellerman, J.L., Anderson, W.H., Schlenk, H. *Synthesis of anacardic acids in seeds of*

Ginkgo biloba. Biochim Biophys Acta 1976; 431: 16-21.

24. Gellerman, J.L., Schlenk, H. *A group of fatty acids with "tetramethylene interruption" in the double bond system.* Experientia 1963; 19: 522-523.

25. Gellerman, J.L., Schlenk, H. *Methods for isolation and determination of anacardic acids.* Anal Chem 1968; 40: 739-743.

26. Hatano, K. *Paper chromatography of aminoacids.* Nippon Ringaku Kaishi 1956; 38: 425-427.

27. Hegnauer, R. Chemotaxonomie der Pflanzen, Vol. 1. Birkhäuser: Basel Stuttgart 1962; 327-330.

28. Hegnauer, R. Chemotaxonomie der Pflanzen, Vol. 7. Birkhäuser: Basel Stuttgart 1986; 462-478.

29. Hirao, N., Shogaki, T. *The essential oil of Ginkgo biloba L. (Icho).* Kinki Daigaku Rikogakubu Ken Kyu Hokoku 1981; 47-50.

30. Hiroshi, I., Kosei, O., Yukie, I., Shojiro, U. *Isolation and characterization of 10,11-dihydroatlantone and related compounds from Ginkgo biloba L.* Chem Pharm Bull 1975; 23: 1892-1894.

31. Hiroshi, K., Hiroshi, I., Kanichi, U., Shojiro, U. *Constituents of the heartwood of Ginkgo biloba. L.V. Structure and absolute configuration of bilobanone.* Yakugaku Zasshi 1968; 88: 562-572.

32. Hiroshi, M., Yutaka, K., Hirosada, S.H. *Steric structure of the toxic substances from the fruit pulp of Ginkgo biloba.* Chem Pharm Bull 1968; 16: 2282-2286.

33. Huang, W.-H. *Liberation of organic materials in root exudates.* Kuo Li T'ai-wan Ta Hsueh Chih Wu Ping Ch'ung Hai Huseh K'an 1972; 178-187.

34. Hunneman, D.H., Eglinton, G. *The constituent acids of gymnosperm cutins.* Phytochemistry 1972; 11: 1989-2001.

35. Ibata, K., Mizuno, M., Takigawa, T., Tanaka, Y. *Long-chain betulaprenol-type polyprenols from the leaves of Ginkgo biloba.* Biochem J 1983; 213: 305-311.

36. Inoue, Y., Noda, M. *Paper partition chromatography of aliphatic carboxylic acids by means of hydroxamic acid method.* J Agr Chem Soc Japan 1950; 23: 368.

37. Kameyama, H., Matsuoka, K., Izumi, T. *Studies on glyceroglycolipids of Ginkgo nuts. (Ginkgo biloba).* Kumamoto Joshi Daigaku Gakujutsu Kiyo 1981; 68-73.

38. Kameyama, H., Urakami, C. *Glycolipids isolated from Ginkgo nuts (Ginkgo biloba) and their fatty acid compositions.* J Am Oil Chem Soc 1979; 56: 549-551.

39. Kariyne, T., Kimura, H., Nakamura, I. *Components of Ginkgo biloba. I. Isolation of bilobanone.* Yakugaku Zasshi 1958; 78: 1152-1155.

40. Kimura, H. *Extraction of sesamin from Ginkgo biloba wood.* Japan 1959; 8129, Sept 11.

41. Lobstein-Guth, A., Briancon-Scheid, F., Anton, R. *Analysis of terpenes from Ginkgo biloba L. by high-performance liquid chromatography.* J Chromatogr 1983; 267: 431-438.

42. Major, R.T. *The ginkgo, the most ancient living tree.* Science 1967; 157: 1270-1273.

43. Major, R.T., Marchini, P., Boulton, A.J. *The production of 2-hexenal by leaves of certain plants.* J Biol Chem 1963; 238: 1813-1816.

44. Major, R.T., Thomas, M. *Formation of 2-hexenal from linoleic acid by macerated Ginkgo leaves.* Phytochemistry 1972; 11: 611-617.

45. Joly, M., Laag-Berrurier, M., Anton, R. *5'-Methoxybilobetin, a biflavone extracted from Ginkgo biloba.* Phytochemistry 1980; 19: 1999-2002.

46. Maruyama, M., Terahara, A., Itagaki, Y., Nakanishi, K. *The ginkgolides. I. Isolation and characterization of the various groups.* Tetrahedron Lett 1967; 299-302.

47. Maruyama, M., Terahara, A., Itagaki, Y., Nakanishi, K. *The ginkgolides. II. Derivation of partial structures.* Tetrahedron Lett 1967; 303-308.

48. Maruyama, M., Terahara, A., Itagaki, Y., Nakanishi, K. *The ginkgolides. III. Structure of the ginkgolides.* Tetrahedron Lett 1967; 309-313.

49. Maruyama, M., Terahara, A., Itagaki, Y., Nakanishi, K. *The ginkgolides. IV. Stereochemistry of the ginkgolides.* Tetrahedron Lett 1967; 314-319.

50. Meau, A.J., Timell, T.E. *Ginkgo biloba. II. The constitution of an arabino-4-0-methylglucuronoxylan from the wood.* Svensk Papperstidn 1960; 63: 769-774.

51. Nakanishi, K. *Structural determination of natural products. IX. Chemistry of ginkgolide.* Kagaku To Seibutsu 1968; 6: 628-636.

52. Nakanishi, K. *The ginkgolides.* Pure Appl Chem 1967; 89-113.

53. Nakanishi, K., Habaguchi, K. *Biosynthesis of ginkgolide B, its diterpenoid nature, and origin*

of the tert-butyl group. J Am Chem Soc 1971; 93: 3546-3547.

54. Nakanishi, K., Habaguchi, K., Nakadaira, Y., Woods, M.C., Maruyama, M., Major, R.T., Alauddin, M., Patel, A.R., Weinges, K., Baehr, W. *Structure of bilobalide, a rare tert-butyl containing sesquiterpenoid related to the C-20 ginkgolides.* J Am Chem Soc 1971; 93: 3544-3546.

55. Noriyoshi, S., Takada, S., Okabe, K. *The structure of ginkgolide A, a novel diterpenoid trilactone.* J Chem Soc Chem Comm 1967; 259-261.

56. Okabe, K., Yamada, K., Yamamura, S., Takada, S. *Ginkgolides.* J Chem Soc C 1967; 2201-2206.

57. Peter, H., Fisel, J., Weisser, W. *Pharmacological study of the active substances of Ginkgo biloba.* Arzneim-Forsch 1966; 16: 719-725.

58. Plieninger, H., Schwarz, B., Jaggy, H., Huber-Patz, U., Rodewald, H., Irngartinger, H., Weinges, K. *Natural products from medicinal plants. XXIV. Isolation, structure determination, and synthesis of (Z,Z)-4,4'-(1,4-pentadien-1,5-diyl)diphenol. An unusual natural product from the leaves of the Ginkgo tree (Ginkgo biloba L.)* Liebigs Ann Chem 1986; 1772-1778.

59. Prakash, A., Mahmoud, A., El, S. *Isolation, purification and antimicrobial activity of anacardic acids from Ginkgo biloba fruits.* Fitoterapia 1981; 52: 129-135.

60. Rigaud, J.

61. Roumestand, C., Perly, B., Braquet, P. *Carbon 13 and proton 500 MHz NMR of ginkgolides.* Tetrahedron Lett; in press.

62. Sakane, N., Takada, S., Okabe, K. *The structure of ginkgolide a, a novel diterpenoid trilactone.* Chem Comm 1967; 259-261.

63. Sbit, M., Dupont, L., Dideberg, O., Braquet, P. *Structure of ginkgolide C (BN 52022), ethanol. 1.5 hydrate, isolated from Ginkgo biloba L.* Acta Crystallogr; submitted.

64. Schennen, A., Hoelz, J. *6-Hydroxykynurenic acid, the first nitrogen-containing compound from the Ginkgo biloba leaf.* Planta Med 1986; 235-236.

65. Seoane, E., Arino, P., Ahsan, A.M. *Identity of celidoniol and ginnol.* An Quim 1969; 65: 303-304.

66. Sogo, M., Fukuhara, T., Hochi, M. *Suberin in the outer bark of some Japanese tree species.* Kagawa Daigaku Nogakubu Gakujutsu Hokoku 1969; 20: 112-119.

67. Sosa, A. *Sur quelques constituants du Ginkgo biloba L.* Bull Soc Chim Biol 1947; 29: 833-836.

68. Suzu, M. *Glycosides containing hydrocyanic acids in plums and ginkgo nuts.* Fukuoka Igaku Zasshi 1959; 50: 5394-5398.

69. Takak, F., Urabe, A., Shimamura, M., Mizuno, M. *Pharmaceutical composition containing dolichol and its esters.* Eur Pat Appl EP 166, 436 (Cl. C07C33/02), 02 June 1986, JP Appl. 841/132, 945. 29 June 1984, 34pp.

70. Takashi, O., Suzuki, S., Takigawa, T., Fujita, Y., Mizuno, M., Nishida, T., Mori, F. *Polyprenyl compounds.* Eur Pat Appl EA 87, 638 (Cl. C07C147/10), 07 Sept. 1983, JP Appl. 82/20, 855, 11 Feb. 1982; 58pp.

71. Takeoka, T.N. *The synthetic pathway of shikimic acid in Ginkgo biloba.* Botan Mag 1963; 76: 391-394.

72. Toru, T., Yutaka, I. *cis-5-Olefinic unusual fatty acids in seed lipids of Gymnospermae and their distribution in triacylglycerols.* Lipids 1982; 17: 716-723.

73. Tsuyuki, H., Itoh, S., Nakatsukasa, Y. *Lipids in ginkgo seeds.* Nihon Daigaku Nojuigakubu Gakujutsu Kenkyu Hokoku 1979; 156-162.

74. Villhauer, E.B., Anderson, R.C. *Synthesis of the CDE ring system of the ginkgolides.* J Org Chem 1987; 52: 1186-1189.

75. Wada, K., Ishigaki, S.K., Ueda, K., Sakata, M., Haga, M. *An antivitamin B6, 4'-methoxypyridoxine, from the seed of Ginkgo biloba L.* Chem Pharm Bull 1985; 33: 3555-3557.

76. Weinges, K., Baehr, W. *Bilobalid A, ein neues Sesquiterpen mit tert-Butyl - Gruppe aus den Blaettern von Ginkgo biloba L.* Liebigs Ann Chem 1969; 724: 214-216.

77. Weinges, K., Baehr, W. *NMR-und massenspektrometrischer Vergleich des Bilobalids $C_{15}H_{18}O_8$ mit den Ginkgoliden $C_{20}H_{24}O_{9-11}$.* Liebigs Ann Chem 1972; 759: 158-172.

78. Weinges, K., Baehr, W., Kloss, P. *Natural phenolic compounds. X. Phenolic components of Ginkgo biloba leaves.* Arzneim-Forsch 1968; 18: 539-543.

79. Weinges, K., Baehr, W., Kloss, P. *Natural phenolic compounds. XI. Review of the components of Ginkgo biloba leaves.* Arzneim-Forsch 1968; 18: 537-539.

80. Weinges, K., Baehr, W., Rao, M. *Synthese des hexahydro-5H-dicyclopenta [b, cl]furan-5a (6H)-ols.* Liebigs Ann Chem 1971; 753: 100-105.

81. Weinges, K., Baehr, W., Theobald, H., Wiesenhuetter, A., Wild, R., Kloss,. P. *Proanthocyanidins. XII. Occurrence of proanthocyanidins in plant extracts.* Arzneim-Forsch 1969; 19: 328-330.

82. Weinges, K., Hepp, M., Huber-Patz, U., Rodewald, H., Irngartiner, H. *Chemie der Ginkgolide. I. 10-Acetyl-methoxycarbonyl-2,3,14,15,16-pentanorginkgolid A, ein Zwischenprodukt zur Herstellung von Bilobalid.* Liebigs Ann Chem 1986; 105: 1057-1066.

83. Weinges, K., Hepp, M., Jaggu, H. *Chemie der Ginkgolide, II. Isolierung und Strukturauflaerung eines neuen Ginkgolids.* Leibigs Ann Chem 1987; 521-526.

84. Nasr, C., Lobstein-Guth, A, Haag-Berrurier, M., Anton, R. *Quercetin coumaroyl glucorhamnoside from Ginkgo biloba.* Phytochemistry 1987; 26: 2869-2870.

Ginkgolides - Chemistry, Biology, Pharmacology and Clinical Perspectives. P. Braquet (Ed.)

GINKGOLIDES — ISOLATION AND STRUCTURAL STUDIES CARRIED OUT IN THE MID 1960'S

Koji Nakanishi

Department of Chemistry, Columbia University, New York, NY 10027, USA

INTRODUCTION

It is an unexpected and pleasant surprise to learn that the ginkgolides are attracting world-wide interest as antagonists of platelet-activating factor (PAF) twenty years after their structures were determined. Although the ginkgolides were screened for various activities during and after our structural studies it was not possible to detect any worthwile activity. On the other hand, since they can be obtained in several large polymorphic crystalline forms (Fig. 1), and because of their extreme stability, we finally thought they might be nice as pendants.

The ginkgo (*Ginkgo biloba* L.) is the last surviving member of a family of trees which first appeared more than 200 million years ago (Paleozoic) and which reached their climax during the Jurassic period. During the last few million years all species except *Ginkgo biloba* have become extinct, the other species being found only as fossils in petrified woods. The best known is the Ginkgo Petrified Forest which lies on the west bank of the Columbia River near Vantage, Washington, USA; it was discovered in 1931 by the late Professor G.F. Beck of Central Washington State College, Ellensburg, Washington, USA. I had the good fortune of being shown around the Ginkgo Forest by Professor Beck in the late 60's and giving a talk on ginkgolides at the Ellensburg Lion Club.

Ginkgo biloba itself is believed to have remained unchanged for the last million years, and therefore it is called the "living fossil" or "fossil tree".

Figure 1 Polymorphic crystals of ginkgolide C. The ruler is in cm.

It escaped extinction because of its cultivation in Chinese Buddhist temples. It is believed that it first came to Japan from Korea together with Buddhism 1500 years ago, and then was introduced to Europe from Japan in 1692. It is now a fairly common ornamental tree in other continents as well. The sparingly branched tree, with its dichotomously veined, fan-shaped leaves, grows to a height of 40 m. Production of motile sperms and terminally borne seeds is another characteristic feature of the dioecious *Ginkgo biloba.*

Our structural and biosynthetic studies on the ginkgolides (3-13, 16) started in 1963 when I moved from Tokyo Kyoiku University (now called Tsukuba University) to Tohoku University, Sendai, in 1963. In 1932 Furukawa (2) reported the isolation of bitter compounds from Ginkgo leaves, the studies of which were extended by Sawada (15). Studies at Sendai were commenced in 1960 by the late Professor S. Fujise, whom I had succeeded, but were seriously hampered by the remarkable tendency of the compounds to exhibit polymorphism and form mixed crystals. It was only after several years of further studies that led to the isolation of four distinct compounds, ginkgolides A, B, C and M (for "minor"), and establishment of their molecular formula as C_{20} diterpenoids rather than C_{11} compounds. The late Dr. Randolph Major (Director of Research at Merck) and Professor K. Weinges, University of Heidelberg, had also isolated and structurally investigated meroginkgolide, a sesquiterpenoid congener of the ginkgolides (12).

The uniqueness of the ginkgolide structures which carry a t-Bu group (they still could be the only example for natural products) on an esthetically beautiful cage skeleton consisting of six 5-membered rings, *i.e.*, a spiro [4.4]nonane carbocyclic ring/three γ-lactones/ether, and their extraordinary inertness towards chemical reagents necessarily led to great difficulties in structural work; crystals can be recovered after boiling off a nitric acid solution. On the other hand, the extensive investigations conducted by a team headed by Masao Maruyama which involved preparation of over 50 derivatives (7) led to discoveries of the now familiar nuclear Overhauser effect (NOE) (16) as well as a number of fascinating reactions.

In the early 1960's the highest field for nuclear magnetic resonance (NMR) was 100 megacycles (Mc, now MHz), high resolution mass spectrometry was in its early stages and high performance liquid chromatography was unknown. Structural studies of organic molecules have now become routine largely due to the advancement in spectroscopic methods and one does not derive much excitement upon clarification of a structure. However, during the chemical and spectroscopic studies of the ginkgolides we were constantly thinking about what the ultimate structures of these bitter principles might be. The following describes some of the unique chemistry of the ginkgolides and recollections of the events which occurred during our studies.

ISOLATION

The best source of the ginkgolides is the root bark but this cannot be collected without destroying the trees. Fortunately for us, however, Sendai was hit by a typhoon that damaged many ginkgo trees and this resulted in the City Office granting us permission to cut five trees of ca. 30 cm in diameter (Fig. 2). The bark was then peeled off from the chopped roots with the help of a part-time working force as well as ourselves (Fig. 3). The root bark from five trees, 100 kg, gave after extraction, chromatography, and a 10-15 step fractional recrystallization, 10 g of ginkgolide A (GA), 10 g of GB, 20 g of GC and 200 mg of GM.

THE FINAL STRUCTURE (Fig. 4)

Attempts were made to prepare samples for X-ray crystallography including derivatives with heavy atoms. Several crystalline derivatives were prepared and were sent to Professors M. Kakudo and Y. Sasada at Osaka University and Professor W.N. Lipscomb and Dr. J.W. Moncreif at Harvard

Figure 2   Collecting ginkgo roots after a storm.

University, but they were either inherently unsuited or deteriorated during shipment.

Since I had been invited to give a talk at the 4th IUPAC Natural Products Symposium, Stockholm, July 1966 (10), all members literally worked day and night. An outcome of this was the discovery of NOE, the modified lactone titration (see below) and clarification of many unusual reactions; however, the nature of one crucial reaction, the spontaneous con-

Figure 3   Collecting root barks by the chemistry building of Tohoku University.

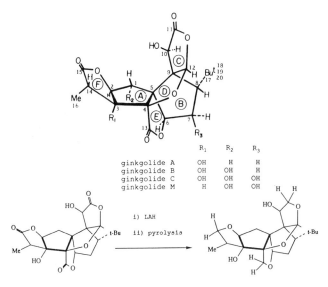

	R_1	R_2	R_3
ginkgolide A	OH	H	H
ginkgolide B	OH	OH	H
ginkgolide C	OH	OH	OH
ginkgolide M	H	OH	OH

Figure 4   Ginkgolide structure and ginkgolide A triether.

version of dehydro-GA into photodehydro-GA in light (Fig. 5) was not detected before the Stockholm meeting. This led to a structure that contained a hemiacetal ring (structure I) which was proposed in my talk together with the NOE results. The lecture apparently left quite a positive impression on the audience judging from the comments received. However, dur-

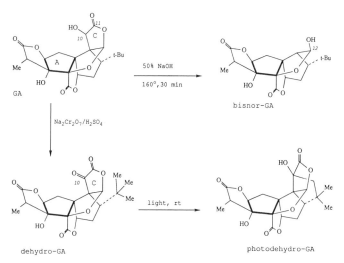

Figure 5   Bisnor-GA, dehydro-GA and photodehydro-GA.

	R_1	R_2	R_3
Ginkgolide A	OH	H	H
Ginkgolide B	OH	OH	H
Ginkgolide C	OH	OH	OH
Ginkgolide M	H	OH	OH

[I]

ing my summer absence, Maruyama and others in my home lab were able to notice occurrence of the photoconversion, and consequently the hemiacetal structure had to be modified to that which contained an ether ring and hydroxyl group. It did not take us long to modify structure I to the final correct one.

One day before we had the final structure, we heard that Sakabe *et al.* (14) who had been working on the ginkgolide by X-ray had arrived at a structure. After the exhausting efforts I could not let our structure slip and so we gambled and decided to disclose our results also; if we were wrong, we would have to admit it and reanalyze all chemical reactions and spectral data accordingly. Professor H. Kakisawa, then at Tokyo Kyoiku University (currently at Tsukuba University) acted as mediator and received both structures over the phone which took one hour each from both parties. He then made molecular models from the two scribbled structures communicated over the phone, found them to be identical and told both groups that the ginkgolide structure including the absolute configuration was solved! We presented the ginkgolide structures at the 10th Symposium on the Chemistry of Natural Products, late October, Tokyo, 1966, and the five communications (3-6, 16), were submitted in mid-October.

PRELIMINARY INFORMATION, NUMBER OF LACTONE RINGS

Establishment of the molecular formula was not straightforward because the ginkgolides readily undergo fragmentation under electron impact, presumably due to the presence of many oxygen atoms and quaternary carbons. The technique of chemical ionization MS was unknown. The formula was finally established with the preparation of GA monomethyl ether which gave a clean M^+ peak at 436.168 for $C_{22}H_{28}O_9$ (calcd. 436.173). The t-Bu group (probably still the only known case in nature) appearing as a 9H NMR singlet was verified by production of pivalic acid upon Kuhn-

Roth oxidation. The nature of all hydroxyl functions was also clarified by NMR taken in DMSO-d_6 before and after addition of D_2O.

The infrared spectrum (IR) showed a broad band around 1790 cm^{-1}, which is due only to lactone rings since it was replaced by carboxylate bands when an aqueous NaOH solution of GB was evaporated to dryness at room temperature, and the residual mixture of GB sodium salt and NaOH was pressed into a KBr disk. Dissolution of the disk and acidification gave unchanged GB, an indication of the stability and lack of strain of the ginkgolide skeleton.

The ginkgolides possess three lactone rings. However, acid titration of aqueous solutions of ginkgolides in 0.1 N NaOH showed the presence of two lactone rings while other results, *e.g.*, introduction of six additional hydrogens in GA triether (Fig. 1), suggested that the number should be three.

The correct number was finally achieved by evaporating the alkali solutions to dryness, then adding water and carrying out the titration. Apparently, the high base concentration achieved during the evaporation process opens all three lactone rings.

GA TRIETHER AND DISCOVERY OF NOE (Fig. 4)

The NMR of ginkgolides were uninformative since the protons appear as singlets (t-Bu, 12-H) or are separated into isolated groups by quaternary carbons, oxygens and lactones. Out of desperation to secure structural information, GA was reduced with lithium aluminum hydride (LAH) but as expected this only gave a thick oil, the product being an octaol. An undergraduate (M. Miyashita) left the oil, probably contaminated with acid due to unsufficient rinsing, in a drying oven, and so was horrified to return from group baseball game and find that the syrup had become scorched tar. However, chromatography of the tar yielded crystals of GA triether, the most important of all derivatives! The octaol had recycled back to the original cage structure, but now the three lactones were replaced by three tetrahydrofurans. Because of the extra six protons, the NMR of this GA triether was far more complex and consequently contained more information. It was during scrutinizing NMR measurements carried out by the late Vyn Woods (postdoctor from Perth) and Iwao Miura that they found irradiation of the t-Bu peak led to 10-33% enhancements in the area of certain proton signals. Instead of dismissing this as an integrator error, they repeated the measurements numerous times until they were convinced of the increments. Woods was an uncompromising person and this attitude had led to the discovery of NOE (16) which was unknown at that time; soon after we had interpreted the results correctly, we found that the first NOE paper dealing with β,β-dimethylacrylic acid and another cage molecule had just appeared (1). The crucial finding of NOE enabled us to put together all available structural information into a logical (but incorrect) structure I within a short period. If the octaol had been properly rinsed, probably we would neither have discovered NOE nor clarified the ginkgolide structure.

This triether was subsequently prepared as follows: A suspension of 1.0 g of GA and 1.5 g of LAH in 100 ml of anhydrous dioxane was stirred at 90° for 30 hours. The excess LAH was decomposed with water, and the solvent was evaporated *in vacuo*. The residue was treated with 50 ml of 20% sulfuric acid and the resulting precipitate was filtered, washed with water and dried to afford 585 mg of the triether.

PHOTODEHYDRO-GA AND BISNOR-GA (Fig. 5)

Formation of both compounds is quite remarkable, the former leading to the confusion which resulted in the proposal of the short-lived but wrong structure I. Dehydro-GA was obtained as follows: To an ice-cooled solution of 2.0 g of GA in 50 ml of concentrated sulfuric acid, a solution of 0.8 g of sodium dichromate in 20 ml of 50% sulfuric acid was added in one portion. The green solution was poured into ice-water and the crystals were cooled, washed with water and dried, 1.7 g. The crystals were recrystallized from dilute acetone to give fine needles, 670 mg, sublimed at 180°/10 mmHg.

The confusion arose because we did not detect the newly formed keto lactone C for some time. Namely, the NMR of dehydro-GA was measured immediately and therefore showed the familiar 9-proton singlet which was present in all gingkolide spectra. However, if this were an α-keto lactone it should demonstrate weak but distinct UV bands and accompanying Cotton effects around 400 nm, which was not the case. It was, therefore, concluded that the oxidation product must be a tetralactone (structure I). What happened was that the optical rotatory dispersion of the product was measured on a sample which had been left for some time. During this period photocyclization to photodehydro-GA had taken place with concomitant loss of the keto lactone function. Only when the NMR of an old sample of dehydro-GA was remeasured by chance did it become clear that the t-Bu group had disappeared and had been replaced by a gem-dimethyl group! The unusual spectroscopic (8) and photochemical (9) properties od dehydro-GA were subsequently clarified.

Photodehydro-GA is made by dissolving 300 mg of dehydro-GA in 50 ml of methanol and irradiating with a fluorescent desk lamp until the solution shows only a single spot on TLC. Evaporation of the solution *in vacuo* and recrystallization from dilute acetone gives 120 mg of the cyclized photo-product as fine needles. Note that photodehydro-GA now contains seven 5-membered rings in a compact cage structure.

Alkali fusion of GA resulted in the loss of only two carbons to yield bisnor-GA; the lost carbons were also identified as oxalic acid. Namely, 3 g of NaOH was added to a suspension of 300 mg of GA in 3 ml of water under cooling, the mixture was heated at 160° for 30 minutes, cooled, diluted with 10 ml of water, acidified with dilute HCl, extracted with ether, and the ether extract was chromatographed to give 130 mg of bisnor-GA. This derivative also played an important role in defining the structure of rings C and B.

BIOSYNTHETIC STUDIES (11, 13)

We succeeded in growing undifferentiated cells of *Ginkgo biloba* by adding 2,4-dicholorophenoxyacetic acid to an agar culture of its embryo containing glucose, glutamine and inorganic salts. A differentiated culture is shown in Figure 6. Preliminary biosynthetic studies (11, 13) with labeled precursors clarified the gross biosynthetic pathway as well as the surprising fact that the t-Bu group is formed by cleavage of a diterpenoid ring A containing the 4-gem-dimethyl group, loss of one C, and reintroduction of one C from methionine.

In the structural studies of the ginkgolides, practically all derivatives were submitted to elemental analysis, the last such operation that we have done. Further studies were discontinued because of my transfer to Columbia University in the summer of 1969. We indeed derived great enjoyment besides learning many fascinating aspects regarding the chemical behavior of natural products; however, they were the last of the "romantic" and classical structure determinations we carried out.

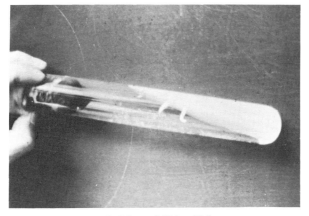

Figure 6 Culture of *Ginkgo biloba*.

ACKNOWLEDGEMENTS

I am grateful to the insight of the late Professor S. Fujise who initiated investigation on this intriguing and now important group of compounds. I am deeply indebted to the ginkgo group: M. Maruyama, A. Terahara, Y. Nakadaira, M.C. Woods, Y. Itagaki, I. Miura, Y. Takagi, K. Habaguchi (assistant, post-doctoral fellow, technician, and graduate students at the time) and Y. Hirota, Y. Sugawara, T. Dei, and M. Miyashita (undergraduates).

References

1. Anet, F.A.L., Bourn, A.J.R. J Am Chem Soc 1965; 87: 5250.
2. Furukawa, S. Sci Papers Inst Phys Chem Res (Japan) 1932; 19: 27.
3. Maruyama, M., Terahara, A., Itagaki, Y., Nakanishi, K. Tetr Lett 1967; 299.
4. Maruyama, M., Terahara, A., Itagaki, Y., Nakanishi, K. Tetr Lett 1967; 303.
5. Maruyama, M., Terahara, A., Nakadaira, Y., Woods, M.C., Nakanishi, K. Tetr Lett 1967; 309.
6. Maruyama, M., Terahara, A., Nakadaira, Y., Woods, M.C., Takagi, Y., Nakanishi, K. Tetr Lett 1967; 315.
7. Maruyama, M., Terahara, A. Sci Reports Tohoku Univ Series I, 1967; Vol L, N° 2: 92.
8. Nakadaira, Y., Hirota, Y., Nakanishi, K. Chem Commun 1969; 1467.
9. Nakadaira, Y., Hirota, Y., Nakanishi, K. Chem Commun 1969; 1469.
10. Nakanishi, K. Pure Appl Chem 1967; 14: 89.
11. Nakanishi, K., Goto, T., Ito, S., Natori, S., Nozoe, S. ed., Natural Products Chemistry, Vol. 1. Kodansha (Tokyo)/Academic Press (New York) 1974; 295-300.
12. Nakanishi, K., Habaguchi, H., Nakadaira, Y., Woods, M.C., Maruyama, M., Major, T., Alauddin, M., Patel, A.R., Weinges, K., Bahr, W. J Am Chem Soc 1971; 93: 3544.
13. Nakanishi, K., Habaguchi, K. J Am Chem Soc 1971; 93: 3546.
14. Sakabe, N., Takada, S., Okabe, K. Chem Commun 1967; 259; Okabe, K., Yamada, K., Yamamura, S., Takada, S. J Chem Soc 1967; 220.
15. Sawada, T. 14th Ann Meeting Pharm Soc Japan 1961.
16. Woods, M.C., Miura, I., Nakadaira, Y., Terahara, A., Maruyama, M., Nakanishi, K. Tetr Lett 1967; 321.

Ginkgolides - Chemistry, Biology, Pharmacology and Clinical Perspectives. P. Braquet (Ed.)
Copyright © 1988, J.R. Prous Science Publishers, S.A.

CHEMISTRY OF GINKGOLIDES

Ben Poon Teng

Dept. of Chemistry (Natural Products), Institut Henri Beaufour, 72, avenue des Tropiques, F-91952 Les Ulis Cédex, France

INTRODUCTION

Due to its unique position in the plant kingdom, the *Ginkgo biloba* tree is able to biosynthesize some extraordinary chemical structures, among which is a group of bitter principles called the ginkgolides.

The first isolation of ginkgolides was described by Furukawa in 1932. It was not until 1967, after a lapse of 35 years, that their structures were elucidated by Nakanishi (2) and Okabe *et al.* (4) using chemical and spectroscopic methods. The structure was later confirmed by X-ray crystallography and more recently by 500 MHz NMR.

STRUCTURE OF GINKGOLIDES

Five ginkgolides are known and have been named alphabetically A, B, C, J and M, albeit in a non-sequential order. They differ from each other only by the number and positions of their hydroxyl groups (Fig. 1).

Theoretically, there are seven possible isomers, if one imagines that there are 3 possible ways of placing 1 hydroxyl, 3 ways of taking out one hydroxyl from ginkgolide C (and ginkgolide C) itself, in which all the three positions are occupied. These isomers are shown diagramatically in Figure 1.

The principal features of the parent C 20 diterpene molecule are as follows.

There are 6 five-membered rings joined together to form a constrained structure. Of the 6 rings, 3 are lactonic groups, 2 are pentane rings joined at a single carbon to form a spiro -[4,4] nonane system and 1 tetrahydrofuran cycle.

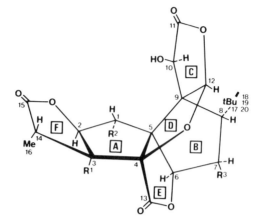

Figure 1 Structure. *These are theoretical isomers that have not been isolated nor described. (Probably either too little or biosynthetically unpreferred).

	R_1	R_2	R_3
ginkgolide A	OH	H	H
ginkgolide B	OH	OH	H
ginkgolide C	OH	OH	OH
ginkgolide M	H	OH	OH
ginkgolide J	OH	H	OH
*1° isomer of A	H	OH	H
*2° isomer of A	H	H	OH

The most distinguishing feature of the ginkgolides is the presence of a tertiary butyl side-chain, which, hitherto, has never before been encountered in natural product chemistry.

EXTRACTION

Ginkgolides have been extracted from various organs of the ginkgo tree. They are found in the leaves, roots and rootbark.

Recently, ginkgolides have also been extracted from roots and shoots of 6 week-old seedlings that have been germinated in the dark. This shows that the biosynthesis of ginkgolides occurs at a very early stage in the development of the tree.

Table 1 gives a summary of the different methods of extraction and purification of ginkgolides described in the chemical literature since 1967. These are laboratory methods for the isolation of pure substances for structural analysis and are not, *per se*, suitable for industrial application.

Table 1 A summary of extraction methods previously described in the chemical literature since 1967

Year	Authors	Literature source	Starting material	Principal extraction steps	Yield claimed per kg of dry material	
1967	Okabe	J. Chem. Soc. pp. 2201-2206	Green mid November leaves Nagoya Japan	Extraction with boiling water Absorption with activating carbon Desorption with acetone Crystallization in ethanol Separation on silica column	GA GB GC Bb	0.013% 0.17 % 0.025% N.A.
1967	Nakanishi	Pure & Applied Chemistry Vol. 14 pp. 89-113	Freshly chopped root bark	Extraction with ethanol Defatting with benzene Separation on silica column	GA GB GC GM	0.25 % 0.25 % 0.50 % 0.005%
1971	Weinges & Bahr	Liebigs Ann. Chem.	Leaves	Extraction with ethanol and boiling water Defatting with chloroform Extraction with ethyl acetate	GA GB GC Bb	0.1 %
1972	Weinges & Bahr	Liebigs Ann. Chem.	Roots	Extraction with methanol Defatting with benzene Extraction with choroform	GA GB GC Bb	1.55 %

Choice of Starting Material

Because leaves are a renewable resource which can be harvested from year to year, it is, of course, the organ of choice for the large scale extraction of ginkgolides.

As is commonly the case with plant material, there are seasonal variations in the ginkgolide content of the leaves. Indeed, it reaches a maximum in late summer and falls to a minimum at the end of autumn. This is in opposition to some other chemical constituents such as biflavonoids.

Also, there are variations in the ratios of the individual ginkgolides with each other in leaves originating from different geographical locations. This may be attributed to variation in climate and conditions of culture or varieties of the same specie.

Choice of Solvent and Cleanup

Although the use of methanol, ethanol and water have been described in the literature, the best solvent in our experience seems to be a mixture of acetone and water. Also, the extraction is more efficient with warm, rather than with cold solvent.

The major impurities that are co-extracted consist of plant lipids, bilobalide, flavone glycosides, biflavones and tannins (1,3,5). Plant lipids can be removed by defatting with alkanes and chlorinated hydrocarbons. Tannins and plant polyphenols can be removed by absorption on silica gel.

Crystallization

Ginkgolides crystallize out without difficulty from alcohol-water solutions of the cleaned-up extract. Mixtures of ginkgolides are obtained, which have to be separated from each other by column chromatography in order to obtain pure, individual ginkgolides.

Column Chromatography

Isolation of pure ginkgolides can be achieved by column chromatography on silica gel using chloroform containing traces of methanol or acetone. The order of elution is ginkgolides A, B, J and C. Ginkgolides A and B, as well as J and C, move very closely to each other and are thus difficult to resolve.

We have recently developed a chromatography system using sephadex LH-20 using mixtures of chlorinated hydrocarbons with acetone. In this system, the separation is better than that of silica gel systems. The order of elution of ginkgolides is a function of the number and position of hydroxyl groups on the molecule, *i.e.*, A→B→J→C. This is due to the hydrogen bonding interactions between the glucose hydroxyls of the dextran and the hydroxyls of the ginkgolides.

ANALYSES

Thin-Layer Chromatography

The ginkgolides are well separated on silica gel plates using toluene: acetone (7.3) as solvent. Rf values for ginkgolides A, B, and C, are respectively, 0.22, 0.19, 0.10.

Ginkgolides are revealed by heating the plate to 170°C for 30 minutes. They appear as pale blue fluorescent spots under UV at 254 nm.

Spraying the plate with a fine mist of water before drying is sometimes necessary in order to achieve good revelation of the spots.

High Pressure Liquid Chromatography

High pressure liquid chromatography on reverse-phase columns (RP-HPLC) is the method of choice for the quantification of ginkgolides in crude extracts (1).

The ginkgolides are well separated on RP C 18 columns using water:

methanol: tetrahydrofuran in the proportion of [7:2:1] as solvent.

The order of elution is ginkgolide J, C, bilobalide, ginkgolide A and B with K' values of 1.85, 2.62, 3.30, 4.29 and 6.05, respectively. Bilobalide is a sesquiterpene lactone that is extracted along with the ginkgolide.

Ginkgolides can be detected using a UV detector at 220 nm. This wavelength is non-specific and when analysing extracts, the background interference from impurities is so large that the ginkgolide peaks are hidden.

The refractive index detector overcomes this problem of background interference and ginkgolide peaks can be easily quantified.

A typical HPLC chromatogram of a cleaned-up leaf extract is shown in Figure 2.

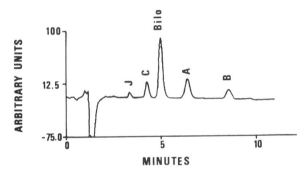

Figure 2   Resolution of *Ginkgo biloba* extract by reverse phase high pressure liquid chromatography. Column: RP C18e Merck 125 x 4 mm T = 30*C. Solvent water: methanol: THF (7:2:1). Flowrate, 1.0 ml/mn. Detection: Refractometer RI 410 (Waters) sensitivity = 16, Scale Factor = 40. Peak ginkgolide J; Rt 3.31 min, ginkgolide C; Rt 4.23 min, bilobalide; 4.95 min, ginkgolide A; Rt 6.37 min, ginkgolide B; Rt 8.53 min.

CONCLUSIONS

Ginkgolides as a group form another example of natural products with interesting pharmacological properties (this volume). As often the case, these substances exist only in small amounts in plant tissues. The exploitation of these molecules as pharmaceutical products poses a challenge to industry to obtain these substances in high yield and in commercial quantities.

One promising way to resolve the problem of supply is the mass culture of *Ginkgo biloba* cells in large bioreactors of selected cell lines with very high yields. Therefore, biotechnology holds the promise of obtaining ginkgolides in commercially viable quantities.

References

1. Lobstein-Guth, A., Briacon-Scheid, F., Anton, R. *Analyses of terpenes from Ginkgo biloba L.* J Chromatogr 1983; 267 (2): 431-438.

2. Nakanishi, K. *The ginkgolides.* Pure Appl Chem 1967; 14: 1: 89-113.

3. Nakanishi, K., Habaguchi, K., Nakadaira, Y., Woods, M.C., Marhyama, M., Major, R.T., Alanddin, M., Patel, A.R., Weinges, K., Baehr, N. *Structure of bilobalide, a rare tert-butyl containing sesquiterpenoid related to the C$_{20}$-ginkgolides.* J Amer Chem Soc 1971; 93(14): 3544-3546.

4. Okabe, K., Yamada, K., Yamamura, S., Takada, S. *Ginkgolides.* J Chem Soc C 1967; 21: 2201-2206.

5. Weinges, K., Baehr, N. *Condensed ring systems II. Bilobalide A, a new sesquiterpene obtained from the leaves of Ginkgo biloba and containing a tert-butyl group Justuo Liebugs.* Ann Chem 1969; 724: 214-216.

INFRA-RED STUDIES OF THE GINKGOLIDES BN 52020, BN 52021 AND BN 52022

Colette Broquet and Pierre Braquet

Institut Henri Beaufour, 72, avenue des Tropiques, F-91952 Les Ulis Cédex, France

INTRODUCTION

The standardized extract of *Ginkgo biloba* (GBE 761) has been shown to antagonize very selectively platelet aggregation induced by platelet-activating factor (PAF) with an EC_{50} of 4.25 $\mu g/ml$ (1-3). Analysis of the inhibition curves with increasing doses of PAF and GBE 761 demonstrated the presence of several inhibitors in the total extract (1-3). In addition, this inhibition was highly specific since, under the same conditions, GBE 761 does not inhibit the aggregation induced by ADP, arachidonic acid, ionophore A 23187, collagen or thrombin.

Different subfractions of GBE 761 were prepared and aggregation studies showed that the antagonistic activity was present only in the non-flavonoidic, terpenoidic fraction (1-3). After analyses by thin-layer chromatography and high-performance liquid chromatography the products responsible for the inhibition were isolated (4). The four products responsible for the antagonism are unique cage molecules, incorporating a *t*-butyl group and six 5-membered rings A-F including a spirol 4-4 nonane, a tetrahydrofuran cycle and three lactone rings (Fig. 1).

These compounds were first isolated by Furukawa (5) in 1939 from the bitter principles of *Ginkgo biloba,* but their structures have' long been an unsolved problem (6,7). In 1967, Nakanishi's group in Japan reported their structures and called them "ginkgolides A, B, C and M" (8,11). Subsequently, we adopted an internal nomenclature: BN 52020, BN 52021, BN

Address all correspondence to: C. Broquet, Dept. of Synthetic Chemistry-2, Institut Henri Beaufour, 72, avenue des Tropiques, F-91952 Les Ulis Cédex, France.

52022 and BN 52023, respectively. A new ginkgolide, termed "J" (BN 52024) has been recently identified (12). All these compounds differ only by the number and position of hydroxyl groups which may be present on C1, C3 or C7 of the spirononane framework. Their chemical characterization was mainly obtained by gas chromatography-mass spectrometry of the trimethylsilyl derivatives (13 and M. Riguad, in preparation), 60 MHz [1]NMR ^{13}C and ^{1}H MHz NMR and x-ray crystallographic analysis (Reviewed in). 500 MHz ^{1}H NMR analysis of the vicinal coupling constants yielded useful information concerning the conformations of the A and B rings and their torsional angles.

MATERIALS AND METHODS

Reagents

BN 52021, BN 52020 and BN 52022 were obtained from I.H.B., Le Plessis-Robinson (France) (Fig. 1).

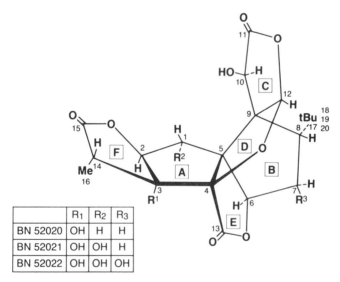

	R₁	R₂	R₃
BN 52020	OH	H	H
BN 52021	OH	OH	H
BN 52022	OH	OH	OH

Figure 1 Structure of the ginkgolides.

IR Spectrophotometry

The various compounds were dispersed in nujol and IR spectra were performed in a Perkin Elmer spectrophotometer (model 1420). IR spectra were also performed (KBr disk) using a Perkin Elmer spectrophotometer (model 983) with Fourier transform.

RESULTS AND DISCUSSION

The spectra of all compounds are very complex and only the most characteristic bands will be described. To localize the stretch vibrations of the hydroxyl groups and avoid confusion with the harmonics of the carbonyl bonds, some experiments were performed with deuterated compounds. In this case, the various compounds were heated in CD_3OD followed by elimination of the solvent under reduced pressure. This procedure induces the disappearance of OH bonds in the spectrum.

IR Spectrum of BN 52021 (Fig. 2)

C-O-H GROUPS

The stretching vibrations of the oxygen-hydrogen bonds cause strong absorption with v_{OH} at 3446 cm⁻¹ (wide) with a shoulder at 3480 cm⁻¹. The carbon-oxygen stretching vibration bands are observed at 1070 and 1043 cm⁻¹.

C-O-C GROUPS
$$\underset{O}{\overset{\|}{}}$$

The stretch absorption bands of the three lactones lie very close to each other. Two carbonyl vibrations are observed $v_{C=O}$ 1789 and 1774 cm⁻¹ (broad bands). The presence of the stretch bands of the carbone-oxygen single bonds are also observed at v_{C-O-C} 1175, 1160 and 1131 (broad) cm⁻¹.

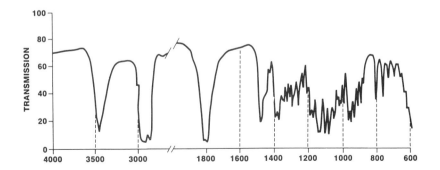

Figure 2 IR spectrum of BN 52021.

IR Spectrum of BN 52020 (Fig. 3)

C-OH

v_{O-H}: 3546 and 3450 cm^{-1} two distinct bands corresponding to the two OH present in the molecule (OH at C_1 and C_{10}). v_{C-OH}: 1065, 1044 cm^{-1}.

C-O-C
||
O

$v_{C = O}$: 1798, 1759 with a shoulder at 1761 cm^{-1}. v_{C-O-C}: 1184, 1150 and 1134 cm^{-1}.

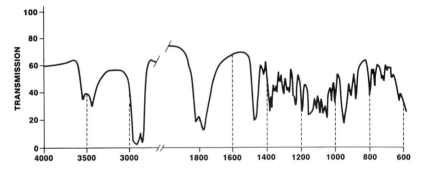

Figure 3   IR spectrum of BN 52020.

IR Spectrum of BN 52022 (Fig. 4)

C-OH

v_{OH}: 3560 (sharp), 3500 and 3400 (broad) cm^{-1}. v_{C-OH}: 1080 (broad) and 1049 cm^{-1}.

C-O-C
||
O

$v_{C = O}$: 1835, 1789 with a shoulder at 1768 cm^{-1}. v_{C-O-C}: 1165, 1140 cm^{-1}.

For all compounds, the stretching bands are very difficult to determine in the region between 1200 and 1050 cm^{-1} where all C-O absorption bands are located. One of these absorption bands could correspond to the C-O-C moiety of the tetrahydrofuran ring (ring D) which undergo conformation changes according to the degree of substitution. The analysis of the absorption bands corresponding to the hydroxyl and carbonyl groups does

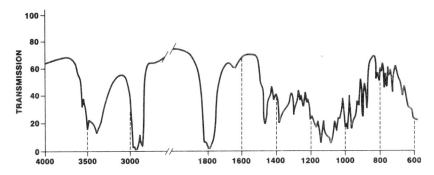

Figure 4   IR spectrum of BN 52022.

not allow determinaton of the precise stereochemistry of the hydroxyl group at the carbon 1. Indeed, the presence of intra-molecular hydrogen bonds, possibly with molecules of water during crystallization, seems probable. These intra-molecular hydrogen bonds induce a broadening and a shift to higher wavelengths. For BN 52022, the presence of a narrow band at 3560 cm^{-1} corresponding to the hydroxyl group on C_7 of ring B is observed.

In the region of carbonyl bands, the spectrum of BN 52020 allows distinguishing among the three different lactones. This is due to the fact that only two hydroxyl groups are present in the molecule.

For the three compounds, it is almost impossible to attribute one specific absorption band to a particular chemical group. Indeed, the position of these peaks of absorption varied from one spectrum to the other, due not only to the environment but also probably to a deformation of the molecule. This is unusual since on the basis of its structure, the ginkgolide seems to be particularly rigid.

Only a study performed in an inert solvent such as carbon tetrachloride would allow obtaining the spectrum of the complete molecule and thus to link the frequences v_{OH} and v_{CO} to specific locations. Unfortunately, the ginkgolide compounds are not soluble in this kind of solvent.

References
1. Braquet, P. BE 90,915; GB 84/18 424.
2. Braquet, P., Spinnewyn, B., Braquet, M., Bourgain, R.H., Taylor, J.E., Etienne, A., Drieu, K. *BN 52021 and related compounds: A new series of highly specific PAF-acether receptor antagonists isolated from Ginkgo biloba.* Blood Vessels 1985; 16: 559-572.
3. Braquet, P. *Involvement of PAF-acether in various immune disorders using BN 52021 (ginkgolide B): A powerful PAF-acether antagonist isolated from Ginkgo biloba L.* In: Advances in Prostaglandin, Thromboxane and Leukotriene Research. Raven Press: New York 1986; 16: 179-198.
4. Lobstein-Guth, A., Briançon-Scheid, F., Anton, R. *Analysis of terpenes from Ginkgo*

biloba L. by high-performance liquid chromatography. J Chromatogr 1983; 267: 431-438.

5. Furukawa, S. *Constituents of Ginkgo biloba L. leaves.* Sci Papers Inst Phys Chem Res Tokyo 1932; 19: 27-38.

6. Òkabe, K., Yamada, K., Yamamura, S., Takada, S. *Ginkgolides.* J Chem Soc 1967; 21: 2201-2206.

7. Sakane, N., Takada, S., Okabe, K. *The structure of ginkgolide A, a novel diterpenoid trilactone.* Chem Commun 1967; 6: 259-261.

8. Maruyama, M., Terahara, A., Itagaki, Y., Nakanishi, K. *The ginkgolides. I. Isolation and characterization of the various groups.* Tetrahedron Lett 1967; 4: 299-302.

9. Maruyama, M., Terahara, A., Itagaki, Y., Nakanishi, K. *The ginkgolides. II. Derivation of partial structures.* Tetrahedron Lett 1967; 4: 303-308.

10. Maruyama, M., Terahara, A., Nakadaira, Y., Wood, M.C., Nakanishi, K. *The ginkgolides. III. Structure of the ginkgolides.* Tetrahedron Lett 1967; 4: 309-313.

11. Maruyama, M., Terahara, A., Nakadaira, Y., Woods, M.C., Takagi, Y., Nakanishi, K. *The ginkgolides. IV. Stereochemistry of the ginkgolides.* Tetrahedron Lett 1967; 4: 314-319.

12. Weinges, K., Hepp, M., Jaggi, H. *Isolierung und strukturaufklärung eines neuen Ginkgolides.* Liebig Ann 1987; 521-526.

13. Weinges, K., Bahr, W. *NMR- und massenspektrometrischer vergleich des bilobalis $C_{15}H_{18}O_6$ mit den Ginkgoliden $C_{20}H_{24}O_{9-11}$.* Liebigs Ann Chem 1972; 759: 158-172.

14. Braquet, P. *The ginkgolides: Potent platelet-activating factor antagonists isolated from Ginkgo biloba L.: Chemistry, pharmacology and clinical applications.* Drugs of the Future 1987; 123: 643-699.

Ginkgolides - Chemistry, Biology, Pharmacology and Clinical Perspectives. P. Braquet (Ed.)*
Copyright © 1988, J.R. Prous Science Publishers, S.A.

PROTON AND CARBON-13 NMR OF GINKGOLIDES

Christian Roumestand[1], Bruno Perly[1] and Pierre Braquet[2]

[1]DESICP/DPC, CEN de Saclay, F-91191 Gif/Yvette Cédex, France;
[2]Institut Henri Beaufour, F-92350 Le Plesss Robinson, France

INTRODUCTION

The ginkgolides represent a challenge for the organic chemist owing to their unique cage structure and their high potential biological activities. The strong variability of these activities in the complete ginkgolide series constitutes a unique system for establishment of structure-activity relationships since the basic molecular backbone is identical in all ginkgolides and the observed activity variations should only be due to subtle structural or conformational changes. A deeper insight into the molecular origin of these remarkable biological activities would also open the field for the conception of even more potent or more specific derivatives. In many cases, NMR has been found to be a very useful and powerful tool for structural and conformational analysis of bioactive molecules (12). Our purpose is, thus, to perform an extensive and complete NMR analysis in these series in order to better understand the basic molecular origins of their activities. The ginkgolide series also represents a very convenient database since it is expected that the basic assignment rules normally derived for unstrained organic molecules will fail in such structures. Owing to the large number of unprotonated carbon atoms in ginkgolides, proton NMR alone will not be sufficient to fully characterize these compounds and for·this reason we also extensively used carbon-13 NMR. The complete assignment of all protons and carbons will require the use of sophisticated approaches.

Address all correspondence to: Dr. C. Roumestand, DESICP/DCP, B.P. 121, CEN de Saclay, F-91191 Gif/Yvette Cédex, France.

MATERIALS AND METHODS

The four ginkgolides under study are presented on Figure 1 and will later be referred to as ginkgolides A, B, C and J. They were obtained from the Institut Henri Beaufour and used without further purification. All NMR experiments were performed on solutions in DMSO-d6 (CEA, France), the final concentrations being 20 mM and 250 mM for proton and carbon-13 NMR, respectively. In all cases the sample temperature was regulated to 300 K and chemical shifts are given relative to internal tetramethylsilane (TMS).

Compound n°	Ginkgolide	IHB nomenclature	R_1	R_2	R_3
2	A	BN 52020	OH	H	H
3	B	BN 52021	OH	OH	H
4	C	BN 52022	OH	OH	OH
5	J	BN 52024	OH	H	OH
6	M	BN 52023	H	OH	OH
7	synthetic	BN 50580	OH	OMe	H
8	synthetic	BN 50585	OH	OEt	H

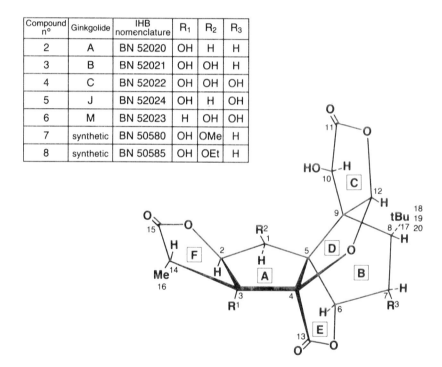

Figure 1 Structure and atoms numbering of the ginkgolides.

Proton NMR experiments were performed at 500.13 MHz using a Bruker WM500 spectrometer. Carbon-13 measurements were done on a Bruker MSL300 spectrometer operating at 75.47 MHz for C-13. Both systems are equipped with an Aspect 3000 computer and a process controller. Unless otherwise specified, all experiments were performed using standard parameters.

RESULTS

Proton NMR Experiments

Since these molecules contain a limited number of protons, they yield very simple spectra especially when performed at high magnetic fields. In some cases, however, the complete assignment is not unequivocal and specific techniques are required. This limitation has precluded a complete analysis in previous works performed at much lower fields (9, 10). Since the various ginkgolides differ only in the number and position of substituents, it is expected that proton NMR could yield a very specific fingerprint for these compounds. The complete proton NMR spectra of the four ginkgolides are shown in Figure 2. The spectral assignment can be easily started from

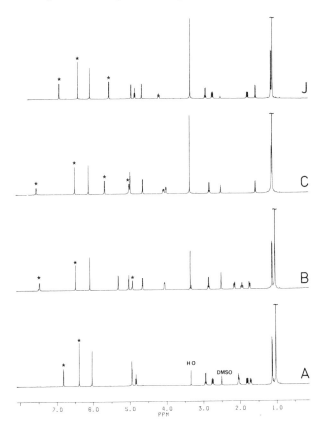

Figure 2   500 MHz proton NMR spectra of the ginkgolides in DMSO-d6 at 300°K. Peaks labelled by stars indicate labile protons from the hydroxyl groups which disappear upon addition of D20.

the identification of labile hydroxyl protons which can be exchanged to deuterons by addition of a very small amount of D20 and are indicated by stars on the spectra. This exchange also simplifies some of the multiplets in the spectrum due to the suppression of scalar couplings.

Since most of the signals appear as multiplets with the exception of H-12, OH-3 and the t-Bu group, a complete neighbor analysis can be performed by successive homonuclear decoupling or preferably by using the most efficient two-dimensional analysis of proton vicinity namely the COSY (COrrelation SpectroscopY) experiment. The reader is referred to specialized bibliography for the complete description of the two-dimensional NMR approaches (7) which will be extensively used in this work. Some definitions will be given, however, to explain the basics of these techniques.

In the COSY experiment, a second frequency domain is created and the "normal spectrum" lies along a diagonal (1). This is clearly observed in Figure 3a and it is also clear that non-diagonal peaks are present. An easier representation is shown in Figure 3b and represents a "contour plot" of Figure 3a. In this representation, contours have been drawn at different altitudes above the plane and allow a much easier visualization of non-diagonal peaks. The "cross-peaks" appear at the frequency coordinates of protons which share energy levels, *i.e.*, which are coupled. This coupling is possible only (in general) if the corresponding protons are separated by a limited number of bonds (1 to 3, generally). The presence of a cross-peak is, thus, an indication of the through-bonds proximity of two protons in the molecular structure. This is exemplified in Figure 3b by the direct assignment of proton H-14 coupled to the methyl group 16.

Using this procedure most protons can be assigned but an uncertainty still remains concerning the H6-H7-H7-H8 systems since the coupling constant between H-6 and one of the H-7 protons is very close to zero. Using the multiplet analysis only, several assignments are possible and all yield different sets of chemical shifts and coupling constants. This can be further used to derive the conformation of the ring containing these protons and it is obviously very important to make sure that the correct set of data is used. This information can, however, be easily disclosed on the COSY contour plot. In the present case, we have used a pulse sequence version (COSY-45) (2), which is potentially capable of indicating the relative signs of the coupling constants connecting different protons. This information is visualized on the contour plot by a significant inclination of the cross peaks. The latter is shown in Figure 3c and indicated by arrows. Since it is well known that the vicinal coupling constants (connecting two protons on two neighboring carbons) are positive and that geminal coupling constants (connecting two protons on the same carbon atom) are negative, the assignment of the protons 7α, 7β and 8 is unequivocal. We will show later

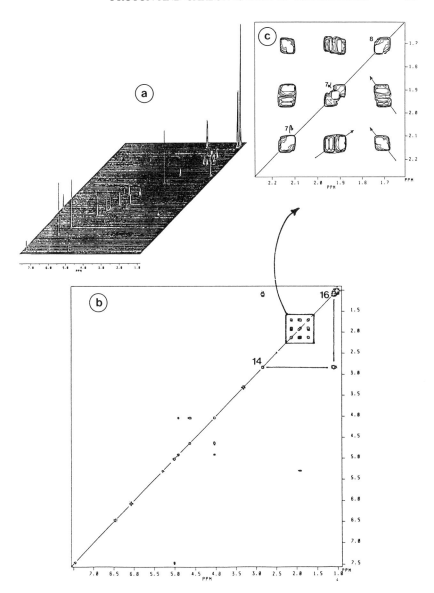

Figure 3 Homonuclear proton shift correlation experiment (COSY) for ginkgolide B. a) Tridimensional plot showing the normal diagonal spectrum (identical to Fig. 2) and cross peaks. b) Contour plot of Figure 3a. The cross peak, the connectivity of H-14 and the methyl-16 is indicated as illustrated. c) Extension of the insert of Figure 3b showing how the relative signs of the couplings can affect the cross-peaks. This effect is presently used to assign the 6-7 -7-8 spins.

on that heteronuclear correlation experiments will confirm these assignments.

Using this technique of two-dimensional correlation all protons can be safely assigned for all four ginkgolides. The relevant coupling constants can be derived from multiplet analysis as shown in Figure 4a for the 6-7α-7β-8 system of ginkgolide B.

The complete data for proton NMR is collected in Table 1.

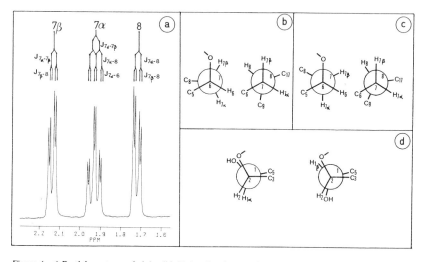

Figure 4 a) Partial spectrum of ginkgolide B showing the complete multiplet analysis. b) Ring B conformation in ginkgolide B, C and J. c) Ring B conformation for ginkgolide A. d) Two possible conformations for the C2-C1 bond in ginkgolides B and C corresponding to OH-1 in or position. In both cases, the torsion angles (0° or 120°) will yield identical J1-2.

CONFORMATION OF THE GINKGOLIDES   The coupling constants derived from proton NMR analysis can be used to determine the ring conformations and eventually to derive the orientation of the OH groups relative to these rings.

CONFORMATION OF RING B   A complete set of coupling constants is available for bonds C6-C7 and C7-C8 for all ginkgolides and allows a full determination of the torsion angles at these sites. As shown in Figure 4b and 4c, the same conformation was found for ring B in ginkgolides B, C and J, and a slightly distorted form was encountered for ginkgolide A. The beta orientation of the OH group at C7 in ginkgolides C and J is unequivocally determined by this analysis.

Table 1 Chemical shifts and coupling constants of protons

Ginkgolide	A	B	C	J
H-1 alpha	1.80	——	——	1.77
H-1 beta	2.75	4.04	3.98	2.72
H-2	4.83	4.61	4.62	4.83
H-6	4.92	5.30	4.96	4.64
H-7 alpha	2.05	1.93	4.04	4.16
H-7 beta	2.05	2.14	——	——
H-8	1.72	1.72	1.54	1.54
H-10 alpha	4.92	5.02	4.99	4.94
H-12	6.02	6.07	6.10	6.03
H-14	2.93	2.84	2.81	2.85
t-Bu	1.02	1.03	1.09	1.09
H-16	1.18	1.11	1.10	1.05
OH-3	6.38	6.47	6.48	6.40
OH-10	6.81	7.47	7.54	6.90
OH-1	——	4.92	4.97	——
OH-7	——	——	5.66	5.53
Coupling constants (Hz)				
J 1-1	−15.2	——	——	−15.2
J 2-1	8.3	——	——	7.8
J 2-1	7.2	7.4	7.3	8.2
J 6-7	2.5	4.1	4.2	4.1
J 6-7	2.5	0	——	——
J 7-7	−13.0	−14.0	——	——
J 7-8	11.0	14.6	12.4	12.3
J 7-8	8.0	4.7	——	——
J 14-16	7.2	7.0	7.1	7.1

CONFORMATION OF RING A AND ORIENTATION OF THE OH1 GROUP   A more complex situation is encountered concerning the orientation of the OH-1 group of ring A in ginkgolides B and C and this is still a matter of controversy. The spin coupling analysis around the C2-C1 bond should be expected to solve this problem. However, as shown in Figure 4d, the two possible solutions yield 0° or 120° torsion angles between H2 and H1 and both situations correspond roughly to the same coupling constant if a classical Karplus law is considered. It is, thus, not possible at this stage to determine whether the OH-1 group is located up or down relative to ring A. We will show later on that specially designed experiments made it possible to decide between the two possibilities.

Carbon-13 NMR experiments

The ginkgolides molecules contain a very large number of non-protonated carbons and their cage structure is expected to induce very important strains which may severely affect the NMR parameters. We will attempt to show that the complete use of the carbon-13 NMR information content can yield unequivocal non-destructive structure determination if modern techniques are used for assignments. The latter depend upon spectroscopic properties and will not require *a priori* knowledge of the structure. Moreover, since sinificant variations may be present in the series, no information from one given ginkgolide will ever be used to assign the signals of other derivatives. At this stage, all four ginkgolides will be considered as unrelated molecules.

NUMBER OF CARBON ATOMS AND MULTIPLICITY   The very first useful information which can be derived from the C-13 NMR spectrum concerns the determination of the number of carbon atoms and their multiplicity, *i.e.,* the number of directly bound protons.

The number of carbon atoms is easily determined by integration of the proton-decoupled C-13 spectrum. This analysis requires, however, some additional care and the following conditions have to be used: 1) Large recycle delays have to be used (in the 15-20 sec range here) to ensure efficient relaxation of the non-protonated carbons; 2) The heteronuclear H-C nuclear Overhauser effect (nOe) must be suppressed to cancel differences between carbons. This is performed by switching the proton broad-band decoupler off during the recycle delays.

The proton-decoupled C-13 spectra of the four ginkgolides in DMSO are shown in Figure 5 and in all cases each line corresponds to a single carbon atom with the general exception of the peak at 28.9 ppm containing the signals from three equivalent carbons.

The multiplicity information can be derived from a number of techniques, the most commonly used being the analysis of the proton coupled spectrum. It is, however, not sensitive and almost useless in the case of complicated spectra.

This first approach is briefly described in Figure 6 and uses a spin-echo sequence to transfer the heteronuclear coupling constants in a new frequency dimension (5). This experiment is very easily implemented and yields precisely both the multiplicities and the one-bond-heteronuclear coupling constants. Quaternary, CH, CH-2 and CH-3 groups yield singlet, doublet, triplet and quadruplet systems in the F1 dimension, respectively.

There are however faster approaches based upon polarization transfers between the eventually bound protons and the carbon. Among all possible techniques the DEPT approach (Distorsionless Enhancement by Polariza-

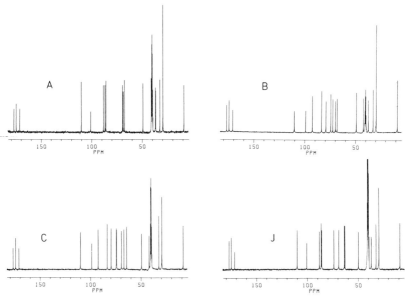

Figure 5 Complete proton decoupled C-13 spectra of the four ginkgolides in DMSO-d6 at 75.47 MHz. The septuplet signal at 39.6 ppm arises from DMSO-d6.

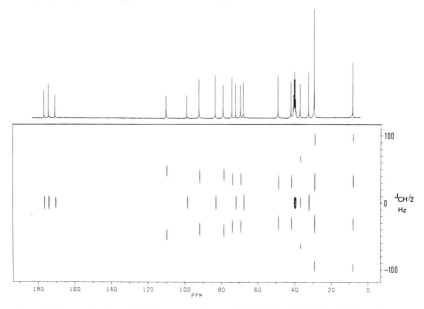

Figure 6 Heteronuclear J-resolved CH contour plot for ginkgolide B in DMSO. The F2 dimension contains the normal proton decoupled C-13 spectrum as shown by the projection plotted above the contour and the F1 dimension contains only the proton multiplicity and the C-H couplings (see information in the text).

tion Transfer) (4) is very commonly used owing to its short pulse sequence and its relative insensitivity to variations in coupling constants. The results obtained in Figure 7 for ginkgolide B illustrate the qualities of this approach. Three spectra can be obtained by variation of the selection pulse in Figure 7. In all cases the unprotonated carbons (quaternary carbons) will not appear in DEPT spectra since magnetization is transferred from the bound protons. DEPT 45 (Fig. 7b) gives all protonated carbons whatever the multiplicities as positive signals. At this stage, simple comparison with the normal spectrum allows a direct determination of the quaternary carbons. The DEPT 90 subspectrum yields signals from carbons bearing one single proton (CH) and finally DEPT 135 yields all protonated carbons but with specifiç phase inversion of the CH-2 groups only. This complete set of edited subspectra allows then a complete determination of the carbon populations. It can be concluded that ginkgolide B contains 8 quaternary carbons, 7 CH groups, 1 single CH-2 group and 4 methyls, three of which are equivalent indicating the presence of a t-butyl fragment.

CONNECTION OF THE PROTONATED CARBONS TO THEIR RESPECTIVE PROTONS   Up to now, only the presence of protons bound to a given carbon atom has been detected. It is now important to determine where the respective protons will appear in the H-1 spectrum. If we can obtain this information, it will be possible to start connecting the carbon atoms together, at least partially since we know from the COSY experiment the neighbors of all protons. This important step in the determination of the structure can be achieved by a heteronuclear correlation experiment. Illustration is given in Figure 8 for ginkgolide B. The experiment relies on specific magnetization transfer between a proton and the bond carbon via the coupling constant (6). A new frequency domain is created to determine what is the resonance frequency of this proton. The final result is a correlation map between the carbon and proton spectra. It is very important to stress that in this experiment as well as in the previously descibed DEPT subspectra, the quaternary carbons as well as the signals from the deuterated solvent will never show up owing to the lack of protons as magnetization sources.

Figure 8 shows a typical heteronuclear correlation experiment and allows a very safe determination of proton-carbon pairs. The present version of the pulse sequence (3) is designed to cancel vicinal proton-proton couplings and the H-1 projection spectrum contains only chemical shifts for simplification and sensitivity enhancement. This is, however, not true for geminal coupling and this explains why the protons bound to the single CH-2 (C7) appear as a quadruplet due to inequivalence and to the non-suppression of their mutual coupling.

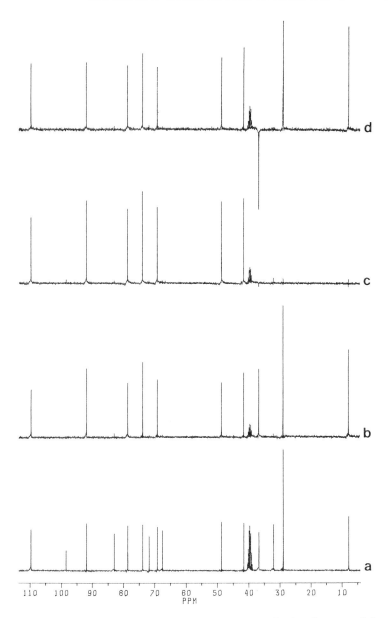

Figure 7 DEPT assignment of the number of directly bound protons using the pulse sequence indicated in the insert. a) Normal spectrum with all carbons. b) DEPT 45 (= 45° in the pulse sequence) showing all protonated carbons. c) DEPT 90 (= 90°) subspectrum of carbons bearing one single proton (CH's). d) DEPT 135 (= 135°) showing CH and CH-3 signals as positive and CH-2 negative.

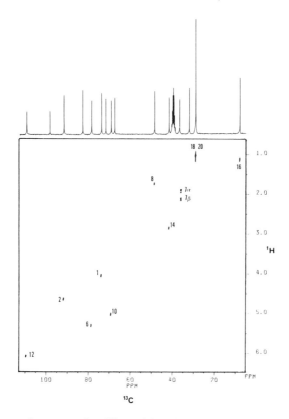

Figure 8 Heteronuclear proton-carbon shift correlation using direct H-C couplings. The horizontal (F2) dimension contains the C-13 chemical shifts only (quaternary carbons suppressed) and the vertical dimension (F1) the chemical shifts of connected protons. The pulse sequence is indicated in the insert).

Although a number of useful assignments have been obtained at this stage, the positions of the quaternary carbons are still undetermined and this precludes any complete identification of the complete structure.

NEIGHBOR DETERMINATION FOR QUATERNARY CARBONS   Although quaternary carbons do not experience large scalar interactions with directly bound protons, smaller coupling constants via 2, 3, 4... bonds can exist with remote protons. This can be observed in Figure 9 showing an extension of the undecoupled carbon spectrum corresponding to the three carbonyl carbons. Since these so called long-range couplings with protons are present they can be used to transfer information between the assigned protons and the unassigned quaternary carbons. The relevant experiment named COLOC

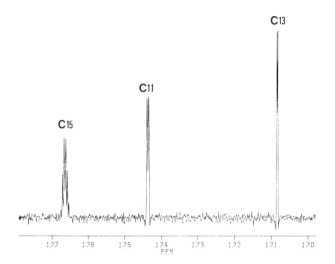

Figure 9 Proton coupled C-13 spectrum of ginkgolide B (partial) showing that several long-range couplings are present between the quaternary carbons and remote protons.

(COrrelation via LOng range Couplings) (8) also rests upon polarization transfer through the small long-range couplings. It is illustrated in Figure 10 by a contour plot for ginkgolide B and the several relevant slices taken through this plot to show how each carbon atom is coupled with remote protons and can be assigned. The assignment of the three carbonyl carbons is very representative. For all other carbons, the assignments are not always completely unequivocal since different carbons can experience long-range couplings with the same protons. Although in the present case the situation is almost clear we have decided to use the ultimate tool to assign all carbons in one step and to confirm our previous assignments. This approach is limited by a very weak sensitivity and should be reserved for very difficult cases when all other approaches have failed.

CARBON-CARBON SHIFT CORRELATION EXPERIMENTS (INADEQUATE)   It has been shown before that protons can be correlated by a simple two-dimensional experiment using the scalar coupling constant to transfer the information. It can be expected that neighboring carbons could be easily correlated using a C13-C13 coupling constant between directly bound carbons. The feasibility of this experiment is in fact precluded by the intrinsic low abundance of Carbon-13 (1.1%). This means that the probability of a C13-C13 pair is in the 0.01% range. Both carbons of the pair will appear as doublets due to the coupling constant. Although the correlation of these

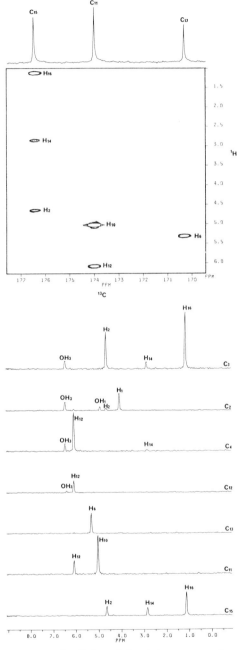

Figure 10   Heteronuclear H-C correlation via long-range couplings (COLOC).

Table 2   C13 chemical shifts

Ginkgolide	A	B	C	J
C-1	36.01	73.87	73.65	36.56
C-2	85.20	91.68	91.93	87.72
C-3	68.14	83.01	82.92	86.05
C-4	100.33	98.55	98.25	100.06
C-5	86.14	71.79	66.42	63.16
C-6	87.77	78.68	79.05	85.87
C-7	36.39	36.71	74.00	73.42
C-8	48.65	48.65	48.99	49.29
C-9	66.90	67.52	63.76	62.55
C-10	68.91	69.16	68.98	68.63
C-11	174.37	174.01	173.90	174.31
C-12	109.57	109.72	109.52	109.47
C-13	170.84	170.35	170.57	171.06
C-14	40.50	41.62	41.56	40.51
C-15	176.64	176.47	176.40	176.62
C-16	8.24	7.93	7.93	8.26
C-17				
C-18, 19, 20	28.95	28.96	28.95	28.99

pairs is theoretically possible other experimental problems strongly limit its feasibility since the normal signals corresponding to C13-C12 pairs are about 200 times larger than the useful doublets and will very easily saturate the computer memory unless high dynamic range analog-digital converters are used. A way to prevent this is to selectively eliminate the large singlets. This can be performed by using the double-quantum excitation scheme (11). Since C13-C12 pairs cannot give rise to this type of coherence, they can be strongly eliminated from the spectrum. This approach named INADE-QUATE represents a very powerful assignment technique for carbon NMR. It is obviously limited by a very low intrinsic sensitivity since only one in every 10,000 carbons is indeed active. Large sample concentrations are required (in the 0.2-0.4M range) and long experiment times (24-48 hours). A complete INADEQUATE contour plot for ginkgolide B is shown in Figure 11 as illustration of the usefulness of this experiment. The interpretation is very simple since if one single carbon has been assigned, the complete carbon skeleton can be determined. This experiment completely confirms our previous assignments for this molecule. It is extremely powerful but is of limited use due to the very large concentrations required by the low intrinsic sensitivity. In most cases, all other techniques based upon short- or long-range polarization transfer between protons and carbons should yield a safe assignment of the spectra without any *a priori* knowledge of

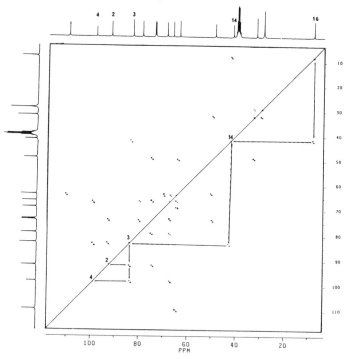

Figure 11   Carbon carbon correlation via double quantum coherences (INADEQUATE) showing a complete analysis of the carbon skeleton starting from t-butyl group.

the structure and without requiring the somewhat risky use of data bases from related compounds.

Stereochemistry and Conformation

The final problem encountered in the structure analysis of ginkgolides is the determination of the absolute configuration of the assymetric carbons. The main problem concerns the determination of the orientation of the hydroxyl groups relative to the ring planes. This has been unequivocally determined for OH-3, OH-10 and OH-7 using chemical considerations and/or coupling constants analysis (9, 10). In the present case Figure 4 shows the complete analysis for the OH-7 of ginkgolides C or J where the location of the hydroxyl-group is obvious. The situation is, however, not clear for the OH-1 group of ginkgolides B and C. The determination of the exact orientation of this group is nevertheless essential for the complete understanding of biological activities since it seems to be necessary that the compound be active. A controversy still exists at this stage since both solutions were considered (α or β orientations) by previous studies (9, 10). However, in both cases, no definitive decision could be made and no experimental evidence could be given.

For this reason we decided to design specific NMR experiments to select between the two possible solutions. Figure 4 shows that coupling constants cannot yield any direct answer since the torsion angles in both cases correspond to similar values of the coupling constant J-12. The following experiments will consider the specific properties of the labile OH protons to give a tentative solution to this problem. Since these protons are "acidic" they will be sensitive to variations of the properties of the medium and will in some cases tend to exchange between all the possible sites.

TEMPERATURE DEPENDENCE OF LABILE PROTONS   The variation of the chemical shifts of labile protons with temperature can give information about the degree of solvent exposure since they are due to modifications of the interactions with the solvent. This is especially true for DMSO since it can give hydrogen bonds with the OH or NH groups. This has been used extensively for peptides to determine exposed or buried amide protons.

In the present case, the, variations of chemical shifts of hydroxy protons are shown in Figure 12. It is very clearly observed that for OH-3, OH-10 and OH-7 very large variations are found indicating-strong interactions with the solvent. On the other hand, the OH-1 protons from ginkgolides B and C experience very weak variations indicating shielding from the solvent. This observation strongly supports the orientation of the hydroxyl groups

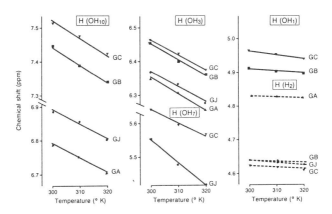

Figure 12   Temperature dependence of the chemical shifts of hydroxyl protons for dilute solutions of the ginkgolides in DMSO.

since it is expected that it will be more buried in the interior of the molecule in this situation. This will be supported by the next experiments. The OH-1 group can then have specific interaction with the oxygen from the OH-10 group and this is well supported by the chemical shift variability of OH-10 in the presence and in the absence of OH-1, as will be described in the next section.

SATURATION TRANSFER EXPERIMENTS   The relations between the exchangeable protons can be rationalized by saturation transfer experiments. If a given labile proton is saturated by irradiation it will disappear from the spectrum. Moreover, if this proton further exchanges with other labile protons and if the spin-lattice relaxation is longer than the exchange rate, saturated spins can be transferred from one site to the other. This will be visualized by a decrease of the intensity of the other sites as one of them is saturated. It should be stressed that this phenomenon can be superimposed to the nOe effect due to through-space dipolar transfer of magnetization. In the present case this by-effect is negligible since it has been observed that for this type of molecule at room temperature and 500 MHz, the nOe effects are very close to zero.

For ginkgolides A and J, no saturation transfer could be observed between hydroxyl protons whatever the location or duration of the saturation pulse. Conversely, for ginkgolides B and C, strong transfer can be observed between OH-10 and OH-1 as shown in Figure 13. This strongly supports the location of OH-1 creating a very specific interaction between these two groups. This is further supported by the following observations:

a) Although the ginkgolides all contain identical ring C the hydroxyl OH-10 proton is found at ca. 7.5 ppm for ginkgolides B and C and at ca. 6.8 ppm for ginkgolides A and J. This indicates a strong variation upon introduction of the hydroxyl group OH-1 which can only be rationalized by the orientation of this group.

b) Substitution of the OH-1 by a methoxy group in ginkgolide B leads to a stong upfield shift of OH-10 which is found at 6.8 ppm as in ginkgolides A and J due to the suppression of the specific interaction between OH-1 and OH-10.

c) The chromatographic behavior of all ginkgolides cannot be rationalized by their expected polarity which can be derived from the number of hydroxyl groups. Ginkgolide B appears as the least-polar compound and this strange behavior can be explained if OH-1 is buried in the cage of the molecule.

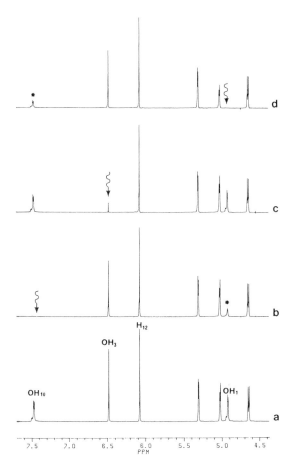

Figure 13 Saturation transfer experiments for ginkgolide B in DMSO. a) Reference spectrum with assignments. b) Saturation of OH-10 and transfer to OH-1. c) Saturation of OH-3 showing no transfer. d) Saturation of OH-1 and transfer to OH-10. All saturation experiments were performed by 0.5 sec low power saturation at the frequency indicated by an arrow. The * symbol indicates signal saturated by transfer.

CONCLUSIONS

It has been shown that NMR can provide a large amount of useful information for complex molecules. Although in the present case the structures were almost completely known from previous work, we have tried to prove that a carefully designed strategy can afford the structure of unknown molecules. Moreover, NMR can yield conformational information of molecules in solution without requiring monocrystal and degradation. Finally the specific analysis of the dynamical behavior of labile protons can give further information about the solute-solvent interactions. In the present case for ginkgolides, the collected data can serve as starting elements to define a model for the structure-activity relationships in these series and already explains some of the apparent discrepancies between the known overall structures and the observed activities.

References

1. Aue, W.P., Bartholdi, E., Ernst, R.R. J Chem Phys 1976; 64: 2229.
2. Bax, A., Freeman, R. J Magn Res 1981; 44: 542-561.
3. Bax, A. J Magn Res 1983; 53: 517.
4. Bendall, M.R., Pegg, D.T. J Magn Res 1983; 53: 272.
5. Bodenhausen, G., Freeman, R., Niedermeyer, R., Turner, D.L. J Magn Res 1976; 24: 291.
6. Bodenhausen, R., Freeman, R. J Magn Res 1977; 28: 471.
7. Ernst, R.R., Bodenhausen, G., Wokaun, A. Principles of Nuclear Magnetic Resonance in One or Two Dimensions. Clarendon Press: Oxford 1987.
8. Kessler, H., Griesinger, C., Zarbock, J., Loosli, H. J Magn Res 1984; 57: 331.
9. Maruyama, M., Terahara, A., Itagaki, Y., Nakanishi, I. Tetrahedron Lett 1967; 4: 299-326.
10. Okabe, K., Yamada, K., Yamamura, S., Takada, S. J Chem Soc (C) 1967; 2201.
11. Turner, D.L. J Magn Res 1982; 49: 158.
12. Wütrich, K. NMR of Proteins and Nucleic Acids. Wiley Interscience: New York 1986.

X-RAY CRYSTALLOGRAPHY OF GINKGOLIDES

Léon Dupont

Cristallographie, Institut de Physique B5, Université de Liège au Sart Tilman, B-4000 Liège, Belgium

INTRODUCTION

Crystal structure analysis of ginkgolides has been undertaken because it provides a rigid model of a molecular structure which can serve as a reference for comparison of PAF-acether and its specific antagonist conformations.

MATERIALS AND METHODS

Ginkgolide A (BN 52020). $C_{20}H_{24}O_9$

The X-ray analysis of a mono-p-bromobenzoate of ginkgolide A has been published by Sakabe, Takada and Okabe (18). This communication includes the absolute configuration as determined by the method of Bijvoet, Peerdeman and van Bommel (16). The crystal data are: $C_{27}H_{27}O_{10}Br.2$ C_2H_5OH; $M = 591.44 + 92.14$; monoclinic, $a = 12.54(3)$, $b = 12.69(3)$, $c = 11.52(3)$ Å, $\beta = 57.82°$; $Z = 2$, $D_m = 1.46$, $D_c = 1.463$ g.cm^{-3}; space group $P2_1$; absorption coefficient $\mu(CuK\alpha$: $\lambda = 1.5418$ Å$) = 26.5$ cm^{-1}. No corrections for absorption were applied. Intensity data were collected with CuKα radiation from equi-inclination Weissenberg photographs. The structure was solved by the Patterson method and Fourier-synthesis. The refinement of atomic parameters was realized until a final value of the reliability factor R equaled 0.19. This high value presumibly resulted from the fact that the ethanol molecules were gradually lost. This was confirmed by the large

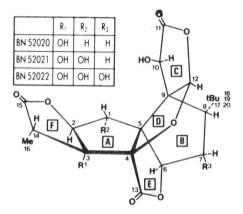

	R₁	R₂	R₃
BN 52020	OH	H	H
BN 52021	OH	OH	H
BN 52022	OH	OH	OH

Figure 1   Stereo-chemistry of PAF-acether inhibitors isolated from *ginkgo biloba*.

temperature factors of the ethanol atoms. Neither atomic coordinates nor distances or angles were published. The configuration shown in Figure 1 corresponds to the absolute configuration described by Sakabe *et al.*

At the moment, a re-determination of the crystal structure of BN 52020 is being undertaken at Liège, using diffractometer data to obtain accurate values of atomic coordinates and to confirm the absolute configuration. Crystal data: $C_{20}H_{24}O_9.H_2O$; $M = 408.40 + 18.01$; orthorhombic, $a = 8.9906(3)$, $b = 12.4256(10)$, $C = 17.8140(11)$; $Z = 4$, $D_c = 1.423$ g.cm⁻³; space group $P2_12_12_1$; absorption coefficient $\mu(CuK\alpha) = 8.2$ cm⁻¹. Final R: 0.042 (9).

Ginkgolide B (BN 52021).$C_{20}H_{24}O_{10}$

The crystal structure of ginkgolide B monohydrate has been published by Dupont, Dideberg, Germain and Braquet (7). The crystal data are: $C_{20}H_{24}O_{10}.H_2O$; $M = 424.40 + 18.01$; triclinic, $a = 7.627(4)$, $b = 11.514(9)$, $c = 12.941(8)$ Å, $\alpha = 97.05(5)$, $\beta = 90.27(5)$ and $\gamma = 108.71(5)$Å; $Z = 2$, $D_c = 1.377$ g.cm⁻³, space group P1; $\mu(MoK_a, \lambda = 0.7107$ Å$) = 1.215$ cm⁻¹. Absorption corrections were made by the empiric method of North, Phillips and Matthews (15). The structure was solved by the Patterson method with SHELXS, PATSEE (10) and DIRDIF (3) computer programs. The starting model was built with EUCLID (11) using distances and angles measured on a dreiding stereomodel. Because of the large number of parameters, the refinement was made on F, with blocked diagonal approximation (one block 9x9 per atom) using an NRC-10 program (1). The final R value was 0.089 for 3834 observed reflexions. This relatively high value is the result of the

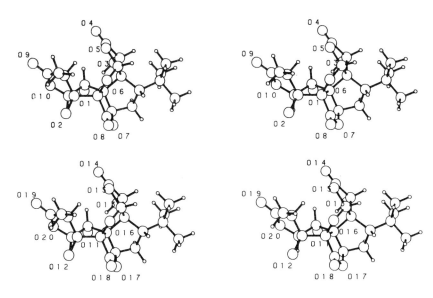

Figure 2 Stereoscopic view of BN 52021. a) Molecule A; b) Molecule B.

poor quality of the crystals obtained. A first description of the structure (mainly torsional angles) at an intermediate level of refinement was given by Dupont, Germain and Dideberg (8). Figure 2 shows a stereoscopic view of molecules A and B of ginkgolide B. H(01) and H(02) could not be placed unambiguously and are not represented in Figure 2.

Ginkgolide C (BN 52022). $C_{20}H_{24}O_{11}$

The crystal structure of ginkgolide C ($C_2H_5OH.1.5\ H_2O$) was recently determined by Dupont, Dideberg and Sbit (9). The crystal data are: $C_{20}H_{24}O_{11}$. C_2H_6O. 1.5 H_2O; M = 880.80 + 92.14 + 54.04; monoclinic, a = 12.9668(5), b = 13.1218(6), c = 15.3083(5) Å, β = 112.95(3) Å; Z = 4, D_c = 1.422 g.cm^{-3}; space group $P2_1$; μ(CuK$_\alpha$) = 9.14 cm^{-1}. Absorption corrections were applied (15). The same method as for BN 52021 was used for solving the structure, which was then refined with a SHELX 76 (19) program. There are two independent molecules in the asymmetrical part of the unit cell resulting in a large number of parameters to refine (maximum 668). So the blocked full matrix approximation was used and only the 22 oxygen atoms of ginkgolide C were refined anisotropically to limit the ratio:number of parameters/number of reflexions to a reasonable value. Accordingly, the absolute configuration could not be stated. The final R value was 0.074 for 2964 observed reflexions. Figure 3 is a stereoscopic view of molecules

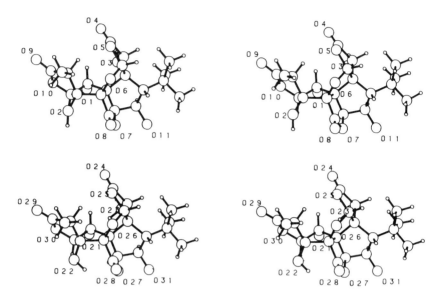

Figure 3 Stereoscopic view of BN 52022. a) Molecule A; b) Molecule B.

A and B of ginkgolide C. H(O1) and H(O11) could not be positioned con-
fidently from the Fourier-difference synthesis or the very complex hydrogen
bonds system.

DISCUSSION

Best molecules fits of the independent molecules A and B of ginkgolides
B and C were calculated with a BMFIT program (14). Table 1 gives the
values $\triangle = (\Sigma\, d_i^2/n)^{1/2}$, where d_i is the distance between corresponding atoms
i of the two molecules when their C and O atoms (n = 30) are fitted. All

Table 1 Results of best molecular fits

Molecules being fitted	$\triangle = \sqrt{\dfrac{\sum\limits_{i} d_i^2}{n}}$ (Å)	$\triangle'$(after MM2 run)
BN 52021 A←BN 52021 B	0.038	0.005
BN 52022 A←BN 52022 B	0.151	0.053
BN 52021 A←BN 52022 A	0.063	0.045
BN 52021 A←BN 52022 B	0.154	0.047
BN 52021 B←BN 52022 A	0.072	0.043
BN 52021 B←BN 52022 B	0.169	0.050

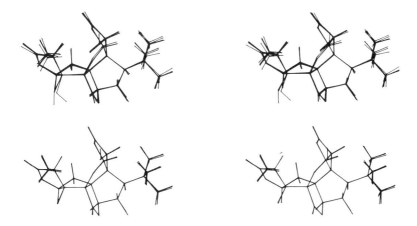

Figure 4   Stereoscopic view of the four fitted molecules. a) Crystallographic conformations; b) After energy minimization.

deviations between atoms of BN 52021 A and B are lower than 0.10 Å. The largest distance between equivalent atoms of BN 52021A and BN 52022A is 0.17 Å. The fit BN 52022 A-B gives a maximum distance of 0.33 Å, and BN 52021 A-BN 52022 B of 0.32 Å. So, in crystal, structure of BN 52022 B deviates significantly from the other three: the values of $\triangle$ connected with this molecule are systematically higher. Figure 4 shows the four molecules when they are fitted, before and after energy minimization with a molecular mechanics program MM2 (2). Different orientations of the OH groups partially visible in Figure 4 and due to hydrogen binding may result in the divergence of BN 52022 B from the other three molecules, which is also obvious in Table 2, where some O-O intra-molecular distances are listed. Several values in BN 52022 B are significantly different from the averages d(O-O) taken from BN 52021 A, B and BN 52022 A values. In Table 3 torsional angles around C1-C2, C6-C7 and C7-C8 bonds are given. O1 bonded to C1 is in α position and O11 bonded to C7 is in β position. As no crystallographic data on BN 52020 conformation are available it is not possible to entirely check the conclusions of the NMR study of Perly and Foldu (17): the conformations around C1-C2 in the ginkgolides A, B, C would be identical, whereas the conformations of the B rings (the most flexible one) seem to be similar for BN 52021 and BN 52022 and slightly different for BN 52020. The shapes of the six non-planar five-membered rings may be defined by the Cremer and Pople (6) puckering parameters. Their numerical values, calculated with a PUCK2 program (13), are presented in Table 4. One can see that rings A and B have a nearly twist

Table 2 Some d(O-O) intramolecular distances (Å)

	BN 52021		BN 52022		d
	A	B	A	B	
O1-O2	4.671	4.608	4.724	4.652	4.668
O1-O3	2.822	2.808	2.785	2.801	2.805
O1-O4	4.336	4.354	4.394	4.330	4.361
O1-O8	5.666	5.659	5.666	5.728	5.564
O1-O9	5.100	5.127	5.118	5.204	5.115
O1-O11	—	—	4.861	4.841	—
O2-O3	6.326	6.293	6.323	6.308	6.314
O2-O4	6.339	6.300	6.361	6.547	6.333
O2-O8	3.002	2.997	2.990	2.918	2.996
O2-O9	4.073	4.095	4.083	4.115	4.084
O2-O11	—	—	6.320	6.066	—
O3-O8	6.421	6.432	6.403	6.373	6.419
O3-O9	6.443	6.405	6.435	6.758	6.428
O3-O11	—	—	4.717	4.576	—
O4-O8	7.037	6.994	7.064	7.104	7.032
O4-O9	5.067	4.960	5.089	5.556	5.039
O4-O11	—	—	7.076	6.983	—
O8-O9	6.675	6.637	6.696	6.639	6.669
O8-O11	—	—	4.616	4.586	—

Average standard deviations: 0.007 Å. d is the average of distances taken from BN 52021 A, B and BN 52022 A.

(or half-chair) conformation; rings C are intermediate between twist and envelope with a nearly twist conformation in BN 52022 B; rings D are envelope; rings E are envelope in BN 52021 B, twist in BN 52022 B and intermediate for the others; rings F are envelope except in BN 52022 B, where it is intermediate between twist and envelope. The largest values of the Cremer and Pople total puckering amplitude Q which characterize the deviation from the plane are found in ring B and then in ring A.

CONCLUSIONS

This study provides a rigid model of a PAF-acether specific antagonist which should be very useful in guiding further investigations including comparison between energetically accessible conformations of PAF and of its antagonists. Some attempts have already been made to design the PAF-acether specific binding sites and potent antagonists (4, 12). Moreover, Dupont *et al.* (8) have shown that the distance between the functional groups O(2)-O(5) (= 6.69 Å) in the model of Kadsurenone (Fig. 5) is very dependent of the conformation: its value is, for instance, 8.55 Å in piperenone, a related compound characterized by a poor PAF antagonist activity. Similar values (6.4 to 6.7 Å) are also found in ginkgolides between O(8) and O(9).

Table 3   Some torsional angles of rings A and B. NMR results are deduced from Perly and Foldu study (17)

	BN 52020(NMR)	BN 52021(RX) A	B	BN 52022(RX) A	B	BN 52021(NMR) BN 52022
C5-C1-C2-C3		36.5	35.4	35.0	35.8	
C5-C1-C2-H2		−85.2	−88.3	−89.8	−88.1	
O1-C1-C2-C3		157.9	158.1	161.0	159.7	
O1-C1-C2-H2		36.3	34.4	36.2	35.8	
H1$_\alpha$-C1-C2-H2	0	—	—	—	—	0
H1$_\beta$-C1-C2-C3		−84.6	−84.5	−83.9	−83.4	
H1$_\beta$-C1-C2-H2	120	153.8	151.8	151.3	152.7	120
C5-C6-C7-C8		35.7	33.7	33.4	34.7	
C5-C6-C7-H7$_\alpha$		−83.0	−85.2	−84.7	−84.1	
C5-C6-C7-H7$_\beta$		154.2	153.1	—	—	
C5-C6-C7-O11		—	—	162.5	165.7	
H6-C6-C7-C8		160.7	157.3	156.6	157.6	
H6-C6-C7-H7$_\alpha$	60	42.0	38.4	38.5	38.7	30
H6-C6-C7-H7$_\beta$	−60	−80.8	−83.3	—	—	−90
H6-C6-C7-O11		—	—	−74.2	−71.4	
C6-C7-C8-C9		−43.7	−40.7	−41.7	−43.0	
C6-C7-C8-C17		−175.4	−175.0	−173.6	−176.8	
C6-C7-C8-H8		72.5	77.9	77.4	77.2	
H7$_\alpha$-C7-C8-C9		76.1	78.3	80.9	78.1	
H7$_\alpha$-C7-C8-C17		−55.6	−56.0	−51.0	−55.7	
H7$_\alpha$-C7-C8-H8	−160	−167.7	−163.0	−159.9	−161.7	−170
H7$_\beta$-C7-C8-C9		−163.9	−160.3	—	—	
O11-C7-C8-C9		—	—	−167.0	−172.4	
H7$_\beta$-C7-C8-C17		64.3	65.4	—	—	
O11-C7-C8-C17		—	—	61.1	53.8	
H7$_\beta$-C7-C8-H8	−40	−47.7	−41.6	—	—	−50
O11-C7-C8-H8		—	—	−47.7	−52.2	

Table 4   Cremer-Pople (6) puckering parameters*

Ring		BN 52021 A	B	BN 52022 A	B
A	Q =	0.346(7) Å	0.339(7)	0.333(7)	0.335(7)
	σ =	198(1)°	199(1)	202(1)	192(1)
B	Q =	0.426(8)	0.393(8)	0.401(7)	0.428(7)
	Q =	90(1)	91(1)	92(1)	94(1)
C	Q =	0.306(7)	0.309(7)	0.289(7)	0.323(7)
	σ =	10(2)	13(1)	9(1)	4(2)
D	Q =	0.259(7)	0.239(6)	0.262(7)	0.269(7)
	σ =	252(2)	253(2)	247(1)	247(2)
E	Q =	0.109(7)	0.112(7)	0.101(7)	0.148(7)
	σ =	186(4)	182(4)	172(4)	161(3)
F	Q =	0.308(8)	0.297(8)	0.295(7)	0.305(8)
	σ =	36(2)	36(2)	35(2)	44(2)

*Twist conformation (C$_2$ symmetry): σ = 18, 54, 90, 126, 162, 198, 234, 270, 306, 342°.
Envelope conformation (C, symmetry): σ = 0, 36, 72, 108, 144, 180, 216, 252, 288, 234°.
Typical Q value: 0.35 Å in furanoid ring of sucrose (5).

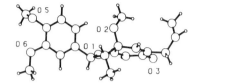

Figure 5   Model of kadsurenone (stereoscopic view).

In this connection it must be emphasized that in any evaluation of the steric effect on activity, the proper enantiomer of the model has to be used. The absolute configurations should be carefully stated either by crystallography or in some cases by biosynthesis or chemical argumentation.

ACKNOWLEDGEMENTS

Thanks are due to O. Dideberg for helpul discussion, to M. Sbit for MM2 calculations, and to M. Vermeire for diffractometric measurements.

References

1. Ahmed, F.R. NRC Crystallographic Programs. Division of Pure Physics: National Research Council of Canada, Ottawa 1970.
2. Allinger, N., Yuh, Y.H. *MM2: Molecular mechanics II.* QCPE 1980; 395.
3. Beurskens, P.T., Bosman, W.P., Doesburg, H.M., Gould, R.O., van den Hark, Th.E.M., Prick, P.A.J. DIRDIF. Direct Method for Difference Structures. Univ. of Nijmegen: The Netherlands 1980.
4. Braquet, P., Godfroid, J.J. *PAF-acether specific binding sites: 2. Design of specific antagonists.* TIPS 1986; 7: 397-403.
5. Brown, G.M., Levy, H.A. *Further refinement of the structure of sucrose based on neutron-diffraction data.* Acta Cryst 1973; B29: 790-797.
6. Cremer, D., Pople, J.A. *A general definition of ring puckering coordinates.* J Amer Chem Soc 1975; 97: 1354-1358.
7. Dupont, L., Dideberg, O., Germain, G., Braquet, P. *Structure of ginkgolide B (BN 52021) monohydrate, a highly specific PAF-acether receptor antagonist isolated from Ginkgo biloba L.* Acta Cryst 1986; C42: 1759-1762.
8. Dupont, L., Germain, G., Dideberg, O. *Crystal and molecular structure of BN 52021, a PAF-acether antagonist. Comparison with*

the conformation of kadsurenone and related compounds. Pharmacol Res Commun 1986; 18(Suppl.): 25-31.
9. Dupont, L., Dideberg, O., Sbit, M., Braquet, P. *Structure of ginkgolides A and C.* Acta Cryst 1987; C43: to be published.
10. Egert, E., Sheldrick, G.M. *Search for a fragment of known geometry by integrated Patterson and direct methods.* Acta Cryst 1985; A41: 262-268.
11. Essen, J. *EUCLID. An interactive, user-oriented program capable of most calculations arising in analytical Euclidean geometry especially in specifications of molecular geometrics.* QCPE Bull 1983; 3: 452.
12. Godfroid, J.J., Braquet, P. *PAF-acether specific binding sites: 1. Quantitative SAR study of PAF-acether isosteres.* TIPS 1986; 7: 368-372.
13. Luger, P., Bülow, R. *PUCK2, an improved version of the Cremer-Pople puckering program.* J Appl Cryst 1983; 16: 431-432.
14. Nijburg, S.C. *Some use of a best molecular fit routine.* Acta Cryst 1974; B30: 251-253.
15. North, A.C.T., Phillips, D.C., Mathews, F.S. *A semi-empirical method of absorption correction.* Acta Cryst 1968; A24: 351-359.
16. Peerdeman, A.F., van Bommel, A.J., Bijvoet,

J.M. *Determination of the absolute configuration of optically active compounds in the solid state*. Proc Koninkl Ned Akad Wetenschap 1951; B54: 16-19.

17. Roumestand, C., Perly, B., Braquet, P. *Proton and carbon-13 NMR of ginkgolides*. In: Ginkgolides - Chemistry, Biology, Pharmacology and Clinical Perspectives. P. Braquet (Ed.). J.R. Prous Publishers: Barcelona 1988; 49-68.

18. Sakabe, N., Takada, S., Okabe, K. *The structure of ginkgolide A, a novel diterpenoid trilactone*. Chem Commun 1967; 259-261.

19. Sheldrick, G.M. SHELX 76, a Program for the Determination of the Crystal Structure. Univ. of Cambridge: England 1976.

*Ginkgolides - Chemistry, Biology, Pharmacology
and Clinical Perspectives.* P. Braquet (Ed.)
Copyright © 1988, J.R. Prous Science Publishers, S.A.

INHIBITION BY GINKGOLIDES OF THE BINDING OF [³H]-PAF PLATELET-ACTIVATING FACTOR (PAF) TO PLATELET MEMBRANES

Marie-Thérése Domingo, Pierre-Etienne Chabrier, Christophe Thiberghien*, Anna Wisner*, Fernand Dray* and Pierre Braquet

Institut Henri Beaufour, 72, avenue des Tropiques, F-91952 Les Ulis Cédéx; *INSERM U 207 URIA, Institut Pasteur, 28, rue du Dr. Roux, F-75015 Paris, France

INTRODUCTION

Platelet-activating factor (PAF; 1-0-alkyl-2-0-acetyl-*sn*-glyce-ro-3-phosphorylcholine) is a potent phospholipid mediator involved in various inflammatory, cardiovascular and respiratory disorders (1-3).

Specific binding sites of PAF have been demonstrated in lysed or whole platelets of rabbit and human platelets (4-6), suggesting that platelet aggregation triggered by PAF may be induced via a receptor-mediated mechanism.

Moreover, the binding of PAF is not only displaceable by PAF itself but also by compounds with diverse chemical structures which inhibit PAF-induced aggregation, bronchoconstriction and hypotension. These compounds are generally termed PAF antagonists and their chemical structures and biological activities both *in vitro* and *in vivo* have been recently reviewed (7).

Interestingly, the binding of PAF to platelet plasma membranes is regulated by monovalent and divalent cations and by guanosine triphosphate (GTP) and appears to be coupled to the adenylate cyclase system via an inhibitory nucleotide regulatory protein (8).

Address all correspondence to: P.E. Chabrier, Institut Henri Beaufour, 72, avenue des Tropiques, F-91952 Les Ulis Cédéx, France.

In the present study we have evaluated the direct effect of the natural products and potent PAF-antagonists, the ginkgolides, on [³H] PAF binding on rabbit platelet membrane preparations using ginkgolide B (BN 52021) and related compounds, ginkgolide A (BN 52020), ginkgolide C (BN 52022) and a mixture of the three ginkgolides (B/A/C 2 : 2 : 1, BN 52063).

MATERIALS AND METHODS

Synthetic tritiated [³H] PAF in ethanol solution was purchased from New England Nuclear with a specific activity of 59.5 ci/mmols. Unlabelled PAF and lyso-PAF (Calbiochem, Switzerland) were solubilized in ethanol solution and stored at-80°C. BN 52021, BN 52020, BN 52022 and BN 52063 were solubilized in DMSO.

Platelet Membrane Preparations

Rabbit whole blood (6 volumes) was drawn from the central ear artery into 1 volume of ACD solution (citric acide 1.4 g, sodium citrate 2.5 g, dextrose 2 g per 100 ml of H_2O) and centrifuged at 150 g for 15 minutes. The platelet-rich plasma (PRP) was carefully removed and centrifuged for 15 minutes at 1000 g. The platelet pellet was then washed 3 times: twice in Tris-HCl buffer 10 mM pH 7.4 containing NaCl 150 mM, $MgCl_2$ 5 mM, EDTA 2 mM and the last time in the same but sodium-free buffer.

The platelet pellet was resuspended in this latter buffer, quickly frozen in liquid nitrogen and slowly thawed at room temperature for at least 3 times as described by Shen et al. (9). The lysed platelets were centrifuged at 100,000 g for 30 minutes in a Beckman model L8.55 ultra centrifuge (rotor 50.2 Ti). Platelet membrane homogenate was stored at-80°C and used within two weeks without noticeable changes in PAF-acether binding characteristics.

Proteins content was determined by the Lowry method using bovine serum albumin as standard.

Binding Assay

60 to 100 μg of membrane proteins were added to a final volume of 1 ml in plastic tubes containing 1 nM [³H] PAF in Tris-HCl 10 mM pH 7 buffer containing 0.025% bovine serum albumin and incubated with or without unlabelled PAF or PAF antagonists. The incubation was carried out for 1½ h at 0°C. The bound [³H] PAF was separated from free [³H] PAF by immediate filtration through Whatman GF/C glass fiber filters under vacuum (Brandel system). The reaction and the filters were washed 3 times with 5 ml of ice-cold buffer. The filters were then placed into polyethylene

vials filled up with 10 ml of liquid scintillation fluid (Instagel, Packard) and the radioactivity was measured by an LKB β counter with 45% efficiency.

The non-specific binding was determined in the presence of 10^{-6} M of unlabelled PAF. The specific binding was calculated by substracting non-specific binding from the total binding. The inhibition by ginkgolides on the specific [³H] PAF binding was normalized as the percent inhibition by the equation:

$$\%\text{Inhibition} = \frac{\text{[³H] PAF total bound-[³H] PAF bound in presence of ginkgolides}}{\text{[³H] PAF specifically bound}} \times 100$$

RESULTS

Specific [³H] PAF Binding in Rabbit Platelet Preparation

The binding of [³H] PAF to rabbit platelet membrane preparations was found specific, saturable, time-dependent reversible and of high affinity. The specific binding was a linear function of membrane protein concentration from 60 μg to 120 μg of protein. Experiments using increasing concentrations of [³H] PAF ranged from 1 to 8 nM showed a specific and saturable binding. The specific [³H] PAF binding accounted for about 45% of total binding. Scatchard analysis of the binding data revealed a single class of binding sites with a dissociation constant (K_D) of 3 nM and a number of sites (B_{max}) of 2.25 ± 0.2 pmol/mg protein (Fig. 1). Similar results were reported by other groups (4-6).

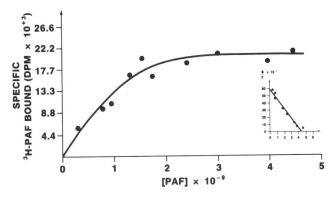

Figure 1   Specific binding of [³H] PAF binding to rabbit platelet membrane and Scatchard plot of binding data. Each data point is the average of triplicate.

Inhibition of [³H] PAF Binding by Ginkgolides

Displacement of [³H] PAF (1 nM) binding in rabbit platelet membranes by BN 52020, BN 52021, BN 52022 and BN 52063 are shown in Figure 2. All these compounds inhibited [³H] PAF binding dose-dependently. The most important inhibition of [³H] PAF binding was observed with BN 52021 with an IC_{50} value of $2.5 \ 10^{-7}$ M. BN 52063, BN 52020 and BN 52022 showed IC_{50} values of $7 \ 10^{-7}$ M, $8.3 \ 10^{-7}$ M, $6 \ 10^{-6}$ M, respectively.

In comparison, the concentration required to inhibit the specific binding by 50% was $2 \ 10^{-9}$ M for unlabelled PAF, whereas lyso-PAF, the biologically inactive PAF metabolite, was unable to displace [³H] PAF binding up to 10^{-5} M.

The specificity of BN compounds to PAF-specific binding sites was also assessed in experiments using other radioligands receptor binding. The BN compounds (10^{-8} to 10^{-5} M) were found to be totally inactive in inhibiting the binding of the appropriate [³H]-ligands to α_1, α_2, β_1 and β_2 adrenergic receptors, H_1, H_2 histamine receptors 5-HT$_1$, 5-HT$_2$ serotoninergic receptors, μ, δ and K opiate receptors, benzodiazepine, muscarinic and imipraminic receptors (10).

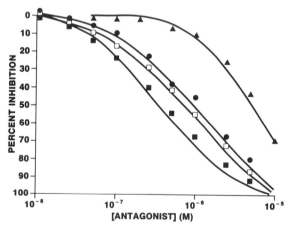

Figure 2 Inhibition of [³H] PAF (1 nM) specific binding to rabbit platelet membrane by BN 52020 (●), BN 52021 (■), BN 52022 (▲) and BN 52063 (□).

Effect of Monovalent and Divalent Ions on the Binding

As reported previously (8), the binding of [³H] PAF was modulated by monovalent and divalent cations. A decrease of the binding was observed with the monovalent cations Li⁺ and Na⁺, whereas K⁺ and divalent cations

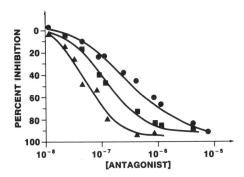

Figure 3 Displacement curves of bound [³H] PAF (1 nM) to rabbit platelet membrane by BN 52021 under various ionic conditions. (■) with 0.3 mM $MgCl_2$, (▲) with 150 mM NaCl and 0.3 mM $MgCl_2$, (●) with 5 mM $MgCl_2$.

such as Mg^{2+} and Ca^{2+} potentiated the specific [³H] PAF binding (data not shown). In this respect, the inhibition of [³H] PAF binding by BN 52021, the most effective BN compound, was investigated in presence of high concentrations of NaCl or $MgCl_2$. Figure 3 shows the displacement curves of [³H] PAF (1 nM) binding by BN 52021 with 150 mM NaCl or 5 mM $MgCl_2$.

In presence of 150 mM NaCl the IC_{50} of the displacement curve was shifted to 4.8 10^{-8} M. In presence of 5 mM $MgCl_2$ the displacement curve shifted to the right with an increase in the IC_{50} value to 5 10^{-7} M (1).

DISCUSSION

Ginkgolides have been shown to counteract *in vitro* and *ex vivo* the effects of PAF in human and rabbit platelets (10).

The present results demonstrate that the ginkgolides (BN 52020, BN 52021, BN 52022 and BN 52063) antagonize specifically and dose-dependently the specific binding of [³H] PAF on rabbit platelet membrane. Ginkgolide B, or BN 52021, is the most potent compound to displace [³H]PAF binding. Conversely, BN 52020 and BN 52022 are less active. This inhibition of PAF recognition sites is highly specific, since BN compounds do not interact with any other known receptors. These results corroborate well with those obtained in the inhibition of PAF-induced platelet aggregation, where BN 52021 is the most effective antagonist followed by BN 52063, BN 52021 and BN 52022 (11). Moreover, the affinity of BN 52021 for PAF receptor sites is altered by Na^+ and Mg^+. Based on a previous report (8), the PAF receptor appears to be in a low affinity state in the presence of Na^+ and in high affinity state in the presence of Mg^{2+}. Accordingly, the ability of BN 52021 to displace specific [³H] PAF was dependent of the ionic conditions. This phenomenon was also observed with other PAF antagonists, including CV-3988, ONO 6240 and L-651731 (8, 11) but not with kadsurenone, which equally binds to the PAF receptor at both the high affinity and the low affinity states (8). Therefore, the mode of interaction of BN 52021 with PAF receptor is comparable to L-651731 or CV-3988 but may be somewhat different from that of kadsurenone. The binding sites for PAF receptor antagonists sensitive to the ionic changes may be quite different from those for PAF receptor antagonists, which are not affected by the ionic regulation and suggest different subpopulations of PAF receptors.

References

1. Braquet, P. et al. *Perspectives in platelet-activating factor research.* Pharmacol Rev 1987; 39: 97-145.

2. Pinckard, R.N. et al. *Immunopharmacology of acetyl glyceryl ether phosphorylcholine (AGEPC).* In: Immunopharmacology of the Lung. Newball (Ed.). Marcell-Dekker: New York 1983; 73-107.

3. Braquet, P. et al. *The promise of platelet-activating factor.* ISI Atlas of Science: Pharmacol 1987; 187-198.

4. Klopproge, E. et al. *Binding kinetic of PAF-acether (1-0-alkyl-sn-glycero-3-phosphocholine) to intact human platelets.* Biochem J 1984; 223: 901-909.

5. Hwang, S.B. et al. *Specific receptor sites for 1-0-Alkyl-2-0-acetyl-sn-glycero-3-phosphocholine (platelet-activating factor) on rabbit platelet and guinea-pig smooth muscle membranes.* Biochem J 1983; 22: 4756-4763.

6. Valone, F.H. et al. *Inhibition of binding of the platelet-activating factor AGEPC to platelets by the AGEPC analog rac-3-(N-octadecyl- carbamoyloxy)-2-methoxypropyl -2-triazolioethylphosphate (CV-3988).* Biochem Biophys Res Commun 1985; 126: 502-508.

7. Braquet, P. et al. *The promise of PAF-acether antagonists.* Adv Inflamm Res 1988; 12: 135-157.

8. Hwang, S.B. et al. *Ionic and GTP regulation of binding of platelet-activating factor to receptors and platelet-activating factor-induced activation of GTPase in rabbit platelet membranes.* J Biol Chem 1986; 261: 532-537.

9. Shen, T.Y. et al. *Characterization of a platelet-activating factor (PAF) receptor antagonist isolated from hainfenteng (piper futokadsura). Specific inhibition of* in vitro *and* in vivo *PAF-induced effects.* Proc Nat Acad Sci USA 1985; 82: 672-676.

10. Braquet, P. et al. *BN 52021 and related compounds: A new series of highly specific PAF-acether receptor antagonists isolated from Ginkgo biloba.* Blood Vessels 1985; 16: 559-572.

11. Nuñez, D. et al. *Structure activity relationship of a new series of PAF-acether antagonists (BN 52020, BN 52021, BN 52022).* 6th Int Conf Prostaglandins Related Compounds 1986; 319.

12. Hwang, S.B. et al. *L-652,469 a dual receptor antagonist of platelet-activating factor and dihydropynidine from Tussilago farfara L.* Eur J Pharmacol 1987; 141: 269-281.

Ginkgolides - Chemistry, Biology, Pharmacology and Clinical Perspectives. P. Braquet (Ed.)
Copyright © 1988, J.R. Prous Science Publishers, S.A.

INHIBITION BY GINKGOLIDES OF SPECIFIC PAF-ACETHER BINDING TO INTACT HUMAN PLATELETS

Ruth Korth, Daniel Nuñez and Jacques Benveniste

INSERM U 200, Université Paris-Sud, F-92140 Clamart, France

INTRODUCTION

Paf-acether (platelet-activating factor) (1, 22) was identified as 1-O-alkyl-2-acetyl-*sn*-glycero-3-phosphocholine) (2, 7). Different cells from various species release the mediator which activates platelets, neutrophils and macrophages most probably via a receptor-dependent pathway (3, 20, 21). Recently, a second very high affinity paf-acether receptor was reported in human endothelial cells (HEC) (12).

Different antagonists of paf-acether-induced biological effects, such as CV 3988, kadsurenone and BN 52021 (this Telesymposium) have recently been described (4, 18, 19). Calcium channel blockers and triazolobenzodiazepines also antagonized paf-acether-induced effects (6, 23). Paf-acether activation of platelets could be inhibited specifically by BN 52021 in the absence of serum albumin (16). BN 52021 and related compounds (BN 52020 and 52022) showed inhibitory effects on platelet aggregation and ^{3}-paf-acether binding to rabbit platelet membranes (3) and the ginkgolide mixture BN 52063 inhibited cutaneous response to paf-acether (10). Most of the paf-acether receptor antagonists inhibited the very high affinity ^{3}H-paf-acether binding to HEC in a concentration-dependent manner (12). Paf-acether induced at rather high concentrations the synthesis of prostacyclin by HEC which could be inhibited by BN 52021 (8). Finally, CV 3988 antagonized paf-acether-induced Ca^{2+}-fluxes in HEC (5).

Address all correspondence to: R. Korth, INSERM U200, Université Paris-Sud, 32, rue des Carnets, F-92140 Clamart, France.

The purpose of this study was to investigate the effects of different ginkgolides on the binding of ^{3}H-paf-acether to intact human platelets in the presence of serum albumin, the latter acting as a necessary phospholipid carrier for paf-acether binding.

MATERIALS AND METHODS

Buffers and Reagents

Tyrode's buffer was composed of (in mM) NaCl,137; KCl, 2.68; NaHCO$_3$, 11.9; MgCl$_2$, 1.0; NaH$_2$PO$_4$, 0.41; dextrose 0.5; HEPES, 5.0.

The following reagents were used: ACD composed of citric acid (0.8%), trisodic citrate (2.2%) and glucose (2.45%): citric acid (0.15 M) (all from Merck, Darmstadt, GFR). Aspirin as lysin salt (Aspegic, Egic Laboratoires, Amilly, France). Fatty acid-free bovine serum albumin (BSA, Sigma Chemicals, St. Louis, MO, USA). Radiolabelled paf-acether (1-O-^{3}H-octadecyl-2-acetyl-sn-glycero-3-phosphocholine, 80 Ci/mmol, Amersham, Amersham, UK) was dissolved in pure ethanol. Paf-acether, 1-octadecyl-2-acetyl-sn-glycero-3-phosphocholine (Bachem, Bubendorf, Switzerland) was solubilized in isotonic NaCl in the presence of 0.25% BSA. BN 52021, 52020, 52022 and their mixture in 52063 (Ipsen, Plessis-Robinson, France) were solubilized in dimethylsulfoxide (DMSO). Whatman GF/C filters (Ferrière, France), Millipore vacuum system (Molsheim, GFR), and PCS (Amersham) were used. Human fibrinogen treated with diisopropylfluorophosphate (Kabi, Stockholm, Sweden) was a gift from B.B. Vargaftig (Institut Pasteur, Paris, France).

Preparation of Platelets and Platelet Activation

Venous blood from healthy volunteers was taken in ACD 9:1 and centrifuged (100 x g: 15 min) to obtain platelet-rich plasma. Platelets were then washed and aggregated with paf-acether, as previously described (15). The paf-acether concentration inducing 80% aggregation (2.5 nM) was used for the inhibitory experiments. Different ginkgolide concentrations were then incubated for 1 minute with the platelet suspension before aggregation was performed under stirring at 37°C. For paf-acether binding studies, aspirinated platelets (1 x 10^9/ml) were kept after the last centrifugation in Tyrode's buffer without ACD (pH 6.4) in the presence of 0.25% BSA as described previously (13, 14, 16).

^{3}H-Paf-Acether Binding Studies

All binding assays were performed at 20°C in the presence of 0.25% BSA and 1.3 mM Ca^{2+} at 20°C using either filtration or centrifugation as described (13, 16). In short: platelets were separated from medium by vacuum filtration with Whatman GF/C filters in a Millipore vaccum system. Filters were washed with cold buffer and values without platelets were substracted from filter-bound radioactivity in the presence of platelets. All concentrations given are final and all values were calculated as means ±1 SD of 3-4 experiments. Platelets were incubated with increasing ^{3}H-paf-acether concentrations (0.325-6.5 nM) for 30 minutes in the presence or absence of BN 52021 (60 μM) or of unlabelled paf-acether (50 nM). Platelet-bound ^{3}H-paf-acether was calculated in fmol bound to 5 x 10^7 platelets.

Platelets were incubated for 30 minutes with ginkgolides at different concentrations (0.7-70 μM) together with ^{3}H-paf-acether (0.065 nM). Platelets were separated using vacuum filtration and platelet-bound ^{3}H-paf-acether in the presence of ginkgolides was calculated in percent of total platelet-bound ^{3}H-paf-acether. For Scatchard plot analysis, unlabelled paf-acether (0.1-50 nM) was added to 500 μl platelet suspension together with ^{3}H-paf-acether (0.65 nM). Following incubation for 15 minutes under binding conditions, platelets were separated by dilution (1:1) with the same buffer and centrifugation (11,000 x g: 1 min) from the suspension. Free (F) and platelet-bound (B) radioactivity, as well as total platelet-bound labelled and unlabelled paf-acether (nM B) were calculated.

^{3}H-Paf-Acether Displacement

After 15 minutes preincubation of platelets with ^{3}H-paf-acether in Tyrode's buffer containing different BSA concentrations (0, 0.1, 0.25%), unlabelled paf-acether (50 nM) or BN 52021 or vehicle was added at different time intervals. Platelets were then separated by vacuum filtration as described above.

^{3}H-Paf-Acether Degradation

Platelets were incubated with ^{3}H-paf-acether under binding conditions in the presence of BN 52021 (60 μM) and platelet suspension was then extracted as described (2).

RESULTS

Correlation of Platelet-Activation with ^{3}H-Paf-Acether Binding

The different ginkgolides BN 52021, 52020, 52022 and their mixture in 52063 inhibited paf-acether-induced (2.5 nM) platelet activation as well as ^{3}H-paf-acether binding in a concentration-dependent manner. Fifty percent inhibitory concentrations (IC$_{50}$) were 0.8 ± 0.4 μM, 10.8 ± 2.8 μM, 50 ± 20 μM and 2.5 ± 0.6 μM for BN 52021, 52020, 52022 and 52063, respectively. Essentially the same IC$_{50}$ values could be obtained with ^{3}H-paf-acether binding (data not shown). Therefore, a correlation of r^2 = 0.97 could be calculated by a computer system.

^{3}H-Paf-Acether Binding

^{3}H-paf-acether binding in the absence or presence of BN 52021 (60 μM) increased in a concentration-dependent manner (Fig. 1). Essentially the same increase was observed in the presence of unlabelled paf-acether (data not shown). Specific binding defined as total ^{3}H-paf-acether binding minus unspecific binding in the presence of unlabelled ligands reached a plateau at 0.65 nM ^{3}H-paf-acether. The calculated specific paf-acether binding to 5 x 10^7 platelets was 17.5 ± 7.0 fmol in the presence of BN 52021 as compared with essentially the same specific binding in the presence of unlabelled paf-acether. Scatchard plot analysis of saturated specific binding in the presence of unlabelled paf-acether demonstrated a Kd-value of 0.54 ± 0.017 nM with 602 binding sites per platelet. A Kd value of 0.13 nM could be obtained with a Scatchard plot analysis using the centrifugation method after incubation of ^{3}H-paf-acether (0.65 nM) with increasing concentrations of unlabelled paf-acether (Fig. 2).

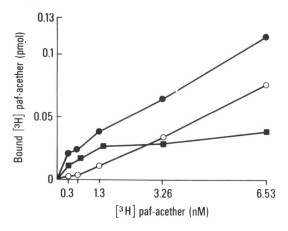

Figure 1 ^{3}H-Paf-acether binding to intact human platelets. After a 30 minute incubation with increasing concentrations of ^{3}H-paf-acether (0.065-6.5 nM) in the absence (●) or presence of BN 52021 (60 μM) (○), platelets were separated by vacuum filtration. The differences of both defined as specific binding (■) was calculated in pmol ^{3}H-paf-acether bound to 5 x 10^7 platelets. Values are means of three experiments.

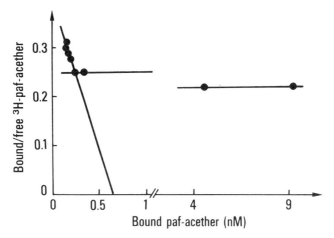

Figure 2 Scatchard representation of ^{3}H-paf-acether binding to intact human platelets. After 15 minutes incubation with increasing concentrations of unlabelled paf-acether (0-50 nM) in the presence of ^{3}H-paf-acether (0.65 nM), platelets were separated by centrifugation. The ratio of platelet-bound (B) to free radioactivity (F) and the total platelet-bound labelled and unlabelled paf-acether (nM B) was calculated. One experiment is representative of three.

[3]H-Paf-Acether Displacement

Platelet-bound ^{3}H-paf-acether could be partially displaced by unlabelled paf-acether in the presence of 0.25% BSA in a time-dependent manner reaching a plateau at 15 minutes incubation. Essentially the same results could be obtained with BN 52021 since unlabelled paf-acether (50 nM), BN 52021 (60 μM) and both substances together displaced $32.2 \pm 8.6\%$, $42.3 \pm 0.43\%$ and $40.4 \pm 3.3\%$, respectively, of platelet-bound ^{3}H-paf-acether. Platelet-bound ^{3}H-paf-acether displacement decreased with decreasing BSA concentrations and no displacement could be obtained without BSA (Fig. 3). The enantiomer of paf-acether failed to displace platelet-bound ^{3}H-paf-acether since $104 \pm 17.5\%$ could be obtained platelet-bound after a 30 minute incubation period demonstrating the stereospecificity of paf-acether receptors.

[3]H-Paf-Acether Degradation

After 60 minutes of incubation of platelets with ^{3}H-paf-acether (0.65 nM) in the presence of BN 52021 for 60 minutes under binding conditions, only intact ^{3}H-paf-acether (97.2%) was recovered after extraction and high pressure liquid chromatography of platelet phospholipids.

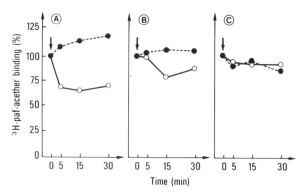

Figure 3   Platelet-bound ³H-paf-acether (0.65 nM) displacement by enlabelled paf-acether (50 nM) (○) after 15 minutes preincubation of platelets with ³H-paf-acether alone (T₀) controlled by vehicle alone (●). Displacement was performed in the presence of different BSA concentrations (A: 0.25%; B: 0.1% and C: 0%). Platelets were separated after the given time intervals by vacuum filtration. Platelet-bound radioactivity in the presence of unlabelled paf-acether was calculated as percent of radioactivity without the agonist (T₀). One experiment is representative of three.

DISCUSSION

The present results support, as already described (4, 14, 16), the competition of ginkgolides with paf-acether binding sites in intact human platelets since ginkgolides inhibited with a close correlation paf-acether-induced platelet activation and ³H-paf-acether binding. A direct competition of BN 52021 with paf-acether binding sites in platelets can be proposed since BN 52021 displaced platelet-bound ³H-paf-acether in a concentration-dependent manner as compared with unlabelled paf-acether. No additive displacement was observed when BN 52021 and unlabelled paf-acether were added together. BN 52021 showed the strongest inhibitory activity of the investigated ginkgolides followed by the ginkgolide mixture 52063 and then 52020 and 52022. A competition of BN 52021 with paf-acether was recently demonstrated with a rightward shift of the paf-acether concentration-dependent response curve in the presence of increasing antagonist concentrations (16). The present results correspond well with those described in the literature with ginkgolide inhibition of rabbit platelet aggregation and ³H-paf-acether binding to rabbit platelet membranes (4, and this Telesymposium).

³H-paf-acether metabolism in the presence of BN 52021 or platelets was excluded under binding conditions. It might thus be hypothesized that intracellular metabolism (17) is not a prerequisite for platelet activation. The latter occurs within seconds and it is unlikely that complex metabolic events occur in such a short time especially when paf-acether is bound to BSA.

It seems more likely that up-regulation of fibrinogen receptors resulting from the interaction of paf-acether with its receptor is the decisive step of paf-acether-induced platelet activation as previously described (11).

Platelet-bound ^{3}H-paf-acether displacement by ginkgolides or unlabelled paf-acether could only be obtained in the presence of BSA (14). However, inhibition of paf-acether-induced platelet activation was performed without BSA and correlated well with binding inhibition. Therefore, it is not likely that BSA is directly involved in the binding process but is essential as phospholipid carrier for expression of the specific paf-acether binding in human platelets. Up to now albumin receptors in platelets have been discussed (9) but could neither be demonstrated nor excluded.

The present results demonstrate the competition of ginkgolides with paf-acether binding sites in intact human platelets. The very good correlation that we found between inhibition of aggregation and binding IC_{50} is very much in favor of the existence of functionally relevant receptors for paf-acether in human platelet plasma membranes.

References

1. Benveniste, J., Henson, P.M., Cochrane, C.G. *Leukocyte-dependent histamine release from rabbit platelets. The role of IgE, basophils and a platelet-activating factor.* J Exp Med 1972; 136: 1356-1377.

2. Benveniste, J., Tencé, M., Varenne, P., Bidault, J., Boullet, C., Polonsky, J. *Semisynthèse et structure proposée du facteur activant les plaquettes (paf): paf-acéther, un alkyl ether analogue de la lysophosphatidylcholine.* CR Acad Sci (Paris) 1979; 289: 1037-1040.

3. Braquet, P., Spinnewyn, B., Braquet, M., Bourgain, R.H., Taylor, J.E., Etienne, A., Driew, K. *BN 52021 and related compounds: A new series of highly specific paf-acether receptor antagonists isolated from Ginkgo biloba.* Blood and Vessels 1985; 16: 558-572.

4. Braquet, P., Godfroid, J.J. *Paf-acether specific binding sites: 2. Design of specific antagonists.* TIPS 1986; 7(10): 397-403.

5. Bussolino, F., Aglietta, M., Sanavio, F., Stacchini, A., Lauri, D., Camussi, G. *Alkyl-ether phosphoglycerides influence calcium fluxes into human endothelial cells.* J Immunol 1985; 135: 2748-2753.

6. Casals-Stenzel, J., Weber, K.H. *Triazolodiazepines: Dissociation of their paf (platelet-activating factor) antagonistic and CNS activity.* Br J Pharmac 1987; 90: 139-146.

7. Demopoulos, C.A., Pinckard, R.N., Hanahan, D.J. *Platelet-activating factor: Evidence for 1-O-alkyl-2-acetyl-2-acetyl-sn-glycero-3-phosphocholine as the active component (a new class of lipid mediators).* J Biol Chem 1979; 254: 9355-9358.

8. D'Humières, S., Russo-Marie, F., Vargaftig, B.B. *Paf-acether-induced synthesis of prostacyclin by human endothelial cells.* Eur J Pharmacol 1987; 131: 13-19.

9. Ghitescu, L., Fixman, A., Simionescu, M., Simionescu, N. *Specific binding sites for albumin restricted to plasmalemmal vesicles of continous capillary endothelium: receptor-mediated transcytosis.* J Cell Biol 1986; 102: 1304-1311.

10. Guinot, P., Braquet, P., Duchier, J., Cournot, A. *Inhibition of paf-acether-induced weal and flare reaction in man by a specific PAF-antagonist.* Prostaglandins 1986; 32: 160-165.

11. Kloprogge, E., Mommersteeg, M., Akkerman, J.W.N. *Kinetics of platelet-activating factor 1-O-alkyl-2-acetyl-sn-glycero-3-phosphocholine-induced fibrinogen binding to human platelets.* J Biol Chem 1986; 262: 11071-11076.

12. Korth, R., Hirafuji, M., Benveniste, J. *Comparison of human endothelial cells in culture and platelets for ^{3}H-paf-acether binding.* Fed Proc 1987; 46: Abst 444.

13. Korth, R., Riess, H., Brehm, G., Hiller, E. *Unsaturated platelet-activating factor: Influence of aggregation, serotonin release and thromboxane synthesis of human thrombocytes.* Thromb Res 1986a; 41: 699-705.

14. Korth, R., Le Couedic, J.P., Benveniste, J. *[³H]paf-acether displacement and inhibition of binding in intact human platelets by BN 52021.* Fed Proc 1986b, 45: Abst 856.

15. Lalau Keraly, C., Delautier, D., Delabassée, D., Chignard, M., Benveniste, J. *Inhibition by ticlopidine of paf-acether-induced in vitro aggregation of rabbit and human platelets.* Thromb Res 1984; 34: 463-471.

16. Nuñez, D., Chignard, M., Korth, R., Le Couedic, J.P., Norel, X., Spinnewyn, B., Braquet, P., Benveniste, J. *Specific inhibition of paf-acether-induced platelet activation by BN 52021 and comparison with the paf-acether inhibitors kadsurenone and CV 3988.* Eur J Pharmacol 1986; 123: 197-205.

17. O'Flaherty, J.T., Surles, J.R., Redman, J., Jacobson, D., Piantadosi, C., Wykle, R.M. *Binding and metabolism of platelet-activating factor by human neutrophils.* J Clin Invest 1986; 78: 381-388.

18. Shen, T.Y., Hwang, S.B., Chang, M.N., Doebber, T.W., Lam, M.H.T., Wu, M.S., Wang, X., Han, G.Q., Li, R.Z. *Characterization of a platelet-activating factor receptor antagonist isolated from haifenteng (Piper futokadsura): Specific inhibition of in vitro and in vivo platelet-activating factor-induced effects.* Proc Natl Acad Sci (USA) 1984; 82: 672-676.

19. Terashita, Z.I., Tsushima, S., Yoshioka, Y., Nomura, H., Inada, Y., Nishikawa, K. *CV 3988, a specific antagonist of platelet-activating factor (paf).* Life Sci 1983; 32: 1975-1982.

20. Valone, F.H., Coles, E., Reinhold, V.R., Goetzl, E.J. *Specific binding of phospholipid platelet-activating factor by human platelets.* J Immunol 1982; 129: 1637-1641.

21. Valone, F.H., Goetzl, E.J. *Specific binding by human polymorphonuclear leucocytes of the immunological mediator 1-O-hexadecyl-2-acetyl-sn-glycero-3-phosphocholine.* Immunology 1983; 48: 141-149.

22. Vargaftig, B.B., Chignard, M., Benveniste, J., Lefort, J., Wal, F. *Background and present status of research on platelet-activating factor (paf-acether).* Ann NY Acad Sci 1981; 370: 119-137.

23. Wade, P.J., Lunt, D.O., Lad, N., Tuffin, D.P., McCullagh, K.G. *Effect of calcium and calcium antagonists on [³H]paf-acether binding to washed human platelets.* Thromb Res 1986; 41: 251-262.

Ginkgolides - Chemistry, Biology, Pharmacology and Clinical Perspectives. P. Braquet (Ed.)
Copyright © 1988, J.R. Prous Science Publishers, S.A.

INTERACTION BETWEEN THE PAF RECEPTOR AND FIBRINOGEN BINDING SITES ON HUMAN PLATELETS

Jan-Willem N. Akkerman

Department of Haematology, University Hospital Utrecht, P.O. Box 16250, NL-3500 CG Utrecht, The Netherlands

INTRODUCTION

One of the most striking properties of platelet activating factor (PAF) is its capacity to induce aggregation of blood platelets in extremely low concentrations. Human platelets respond to stimulation with 1-5 nM PAF with shape change and a reversible aggregation response. At slightly more PAF, aggregation becomes irreversible and is accompanied by secretion of dense α- and lysosomal-granule contents reaching maximal levels in the range between 50 and 100 nM PAF (2). Aggregation is mediated by the binding of fibrinogen to specific sites on the glycoprotein IIb/IIIa complex in the plasma membrane. Fibrinogen forms bridges between the platelets, which are further strengthened by thrombospondin, an endogenous lectin, that is secreted from the α-granules. The platelet glycoprotein IIb/IIIa complex is a member of a family of glycoproteins that recognizes the Arg-Gly-Asp sequence in such molecules as fibrinogen, von Willebrand Factor, fibronectin and vitronectin, which all play a role in cell attachment phenomena (10). Similar, but not identical complexes have been identified on endothelial cells, monocytes and various cellines.

Normally, platelets do not bind fibrinogen. Once the cells are activated by specific platelet stimulating agents, the glycoprotein IIb/IIIa complex undergoes an alteration that exposes the binding sites for fibrinogen. Thus, binding of ^{125}I-labelled fibrinogen has been demonstrated following stimulation with ADP, adrenalin, collagen, prostaglandin endoperoxides and PAF (4, 9). These stimuli activate the platelets via binding to specific receptors on the plasma membrane. Formation of an agonist-receptor complex initiates a sequence known as stimulus-response coupling, in which the stimulating signal of the activating agent (first messenger) is transduced to intracellular metabolites (second messengers) that activate the processes that execute shape change of the platelets, exposure of fibrinogen binding sites, secretion of granule contents and the generation of procoagulant activity on the plasma membrane, thereby facilitating coagulation. The present chapter describes a few aspects of the coupling between the PAF receptor and the exposure of fibrinogen binding sites with special emphasis on the signal generating properties of the PAF receptor.

MATERIALS AND METHODS

Platelet Isolation, Aggregation Studies and Measurement of Cytosolic Free Calcium

Freshly drawn venous blood was collected from healthy volunteers (with informed consent) into citrate (0.1 volume of 130 mM trisodiumcitrate). The donors claimed not to have taken any medicine during the 10 days prior to blood collection and were asked to fast for at least 10 hours before vena puncture. The blood was centrifuged (200 x g, 10 min, 22°C) and the platelet-rich plasma was collected. Platelets were isolated by gel filtration on Sepharose 2B at room temperature in Ca^{2+}-free Tyrode solution (pH 7.25), containing 0.2% bovine serum albumin and 1.7 mM $MgCl_2$. For measurement of cytosolic calcium, albumin was replaced by gelatin and $MgCl_2$ by 1 mM $CaCl_2$. The final cell suspension was adjusted to 2.0 x 10^8 platelets/ml.

Aggregation was measured as the disappearance of single platelets by collecting samples of cell suspension into 9 volumes of a mixture of cold 0.5% glutaraldehyde. The platelets were counted electronically in a Baker 810 platelet analyzer with apertures set at 3.2 and 16 μm^3. This method provides a sensitive means to evaluate the early formation of small aggregates, which are poorly recognized in optical aggregometers (14).

Platelet- free cytosolic Ca^{2+} content was measured by incubating platelet-rich plasma with Quin 2-acetoxy-methyl-ester (Sigma), followed by gel filtration in Ca^{2+}-containing buffer. Quin 2 fluorescence was detected in a Perkin-Elmer MPF-3 fluorescence spectrophotometer at an exitation wavelength of 339 nm and an emission wavelength of 485 nm, essentially as described by Tsien et al. (13).

Binding Studies with ³H-Platelet Activating Factor

Platelets were incubated with different concentrations of ³H-labelled PAF (1-O-hexadecyl-octadecyl-2-actyl-sn-glycero-3-phosphocholine, Amersham International) without stirring at 22°C. After the cells had been incubated for several periods, the platelets were isolated by centrifugation in an Eppendorf Microfuge (10000 x g, 2 min) followed by two times washing in cold Tyrode solution. The cells were lyzed with 1% Triton and the radioactivity was measured according to standard procedures. Non-specific binding was measured by adding ³H-PAF in the presence of a 200-fold molar excess of non-radiolabelled PAF (Galbiochem-Behring Corp.). Details of these procedures have been published (3). In some experiments PAF-receptor interaction was disturbed by addition of BN 52021, kindly provided by Dr. P. Braquet, Institut Henri Beaufour, La Plessis, France.

Binding Studies with ¹²⁵I-Fibrinogen

PAF-induced fibrinogen binding was measured using ¹²⁵I-labelled fibrinogen obtained with the iodogen-labelling procedure. Fibrinogen (KABI) was purified and treated with radiolabelled iodine from Amersham International. Details have been described (5-7). Platelets were incubated with different concentrations of PAF and 1 μM ¹²⁵I-fibrinogen for various periods of time at 22°C without stirring. After the cells had been incubated for several periods, samples (in six-fold; 200 μl each) were collected and placed on 100 μl 20% (w/v) sucrose in Tyrode. After centrifugation (2 min, 12000 x g, 22°C), the tips of the centrifugation tubes (Sarstedt) were cut off above the pellets. The radioactivity in supernatant and pellet was measured by standard procedures. Non-specific binding was measured in parallel incubations in the absence of PAF.

RESULTS

Properties of PAF Receptors on Platelets

Figure 1 illustrates a typical binding experiment in which platelets have been incubated with 0.1 nM ³H-PAF. Depending on the concentration of PAF, maximal binding is reached after about 60 minutes (0.01-0.1 nM PAF) or about 20 minutes (0.1-1.0 nM PAF). Within the range between 0.01 and 1.0 nM, the binding of ³H-PAF shows the characteristics of binding to a receptor: (i) the binding is specific and saturable, (ii) the ligand remains intact during interaction with the receptor and, (ii) binding results in signal processing as illustrated by alterations in the metabolism of polyphosphoinositides, mobilization of calcium ions and phosphorylation

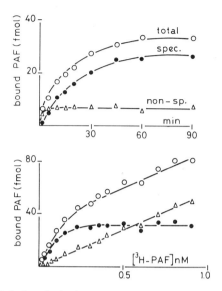

Figure 1 Binding of ³H-platelet-activating factor to human platelets. The symbols represent total binding (0-0), non-specific binding (△-△) and specific binding (●-●) of PAF.

of specific proteins, *e.g.*, a 47000 D protein, one of the substrates for pro-teinkinase C, and the 20000 D protein, the substrate for myosin-light chain kinase (3). Analysis of binding data after 90 minutes incubation (pseudo-equilibrium) as well as during initial PAF-platelet interaction (0.5-15 minutes) shows that platelets possess about 240 PAF receptors per platelet, which bind PAF with an association constant Ka of about 18 x 10⁹ M⁻¹ (3). When the cells are incubated with PAF concentrations above about 1 nM, the total binding rapidly increases with increasing doses of PAF. This is mainly due to aspecific binding, which exceeds the specific binding several-fold. Under these conditions, ³H-labelled PAF is converted to ³H-alkyl-acyl-phosphorylcholine, indicating that this second part of the bin-ding most likely reflects uptake into the platelets and further metabolism. Hence, under our experimental conditions the receptor activity is best measured at PAF concentrations of 1nM or less. Despite this handicap, it is possible to evaluate receptor activity at higher PAF concentrations by computer simulation using the experimentally obtained kinetic constants. As illustrated in Figure 2, raising the PAF concentration above 0.5 nM leads to only a slight increase in the maximal binding. More important, however, is the fact that the velocity of the binding further increases and that almost complete occupancy of the PAF receptors is obtained within 1 minute us-ing PAF concentrations of 100 nM or more.

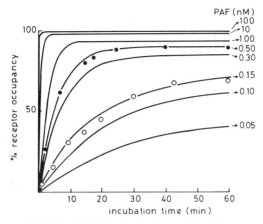

Figure 2   Time courses of the binding of platelet-activating factor calculated by computer simulation. Computer simulation of the binding of PAF to platelets based on the kinetic parameters of the binding of ^{3}H-PAF. For comparison the experimentally obtained data of 0.15 nM (open symbols) and 0.50 nM (closed symbols) ^{3}H-PAF are given. From Ref. 5, with permission.

Coupling Between the PAF Receptor and Glycoprotein IIb/IIIa

In an attempt to identify the factors that control the coupling between the binding of PAF to its receptors and the binding of fibrinogen to the glycoprotein IIb/IIIa complex, platelets were incubated with different concentrations of PAF for different periods of time in the presence of an excess of ^{125}I-labelled fibrinogen. Under these conditions the concentration of fibrinogen is not a rate-limiting factor and the number of molecules that bind to the cells depends on the exposure of binding sites. A comparison between the number of PAF molecules that occupy their receptors and the concurrent binding of fibrinogen reveals that different relationships are obtained under different experimental conditions (Fig. 3). This indicates that the number of binding sites that are exposed is not strictly controlled by the number of PAF receptors that become activated. An alternative possibility is that not the degree of occupancy of the PAF-receptors but the rate of binding between a certain number of PAF molecules and their receptors determines the biological response. Figure 4 illustrates that this is probably a correct explanation. During the initial interaction between PAF and its receptors one may neglect the dissociation of bound PAF (which is then extremely low). Thus, at a given number of platelets the number of PAF receptors is constant and the velocity of PAF binding depends on the PAF concentration. Analysis of the two types of binding not only shows the expected linear increase in PAF binding but also reveals a linear in-

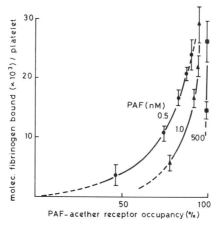

Figure 3 Comparison between occupancy of PAF-receptors and concurrent fibrinogen binding. Shown are the relationships measured by incubating platelets for various time periods with 0.5 (●-●), 1.0 (▲-▲) and 500 (■-■) nM PAF and 1 μM ^{125}I-fibrinogen. (Mean ± SD,n = 6). From ref. 5, with permission.

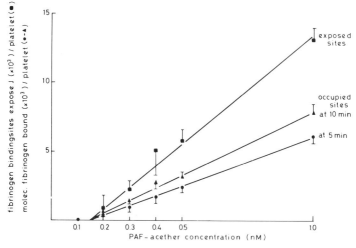

Figure 4 Exposure of fibrinogen binding sites and fibrinogen binding at different concentrations of platelet-activating factor. Platelets were incubated for 5 and 10 minutes in the presence of different concentrations of PAF and 1 μM ^{125}I-fibrinogen. The numbers of exposed sites were calculated on the assumption that exposure of sites was completed within 5 minutes. From Ref 5, with permission.

crease in fibrinogen binding. Obviously, the number of exposed binding sites is greater than the number of molecules of bound fibrinogen. Estimations based on the binding kinetics of ^{125}I-fibrinogen following 5 minutes stimulation with PAF shows that about 40% of the sites exposed at equilibrium are occupied by fibrinogen molecules.

Interference of Signal Processing by the PAF-Receptor with BN 52021

BN 52021 is known to interfere with PAF-receptor interaction in numerous cell types (8). Figure 5 illustrates the effect of different concentrations of the ginkgolide on the binding of 0.1 nM ^{3}H-labelled PAF. Following 10 minutes of platelet-PAF interaction, almost complete dissociation of bound PAF can be obtained by adding 10 μM BN 52021. Lower concentrations of the inhibitor induce incomplete dissociation of bound PAF. When the inhibitor is added at later stages during the PAF binding, the dissociation is also incomplete. Similar findings are obtained with an excess of unlabelled PAF, indicating that PAF binding to its receptors gradually becomes irreversible (3).

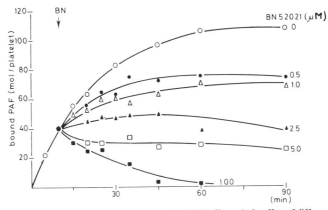

Figure 5 Disruption of PAF-receptor interaction by BN 52021. Shown is the effect of different concentrations of BN 52021 on the binding of 0.1 nM ^{3}H-PAF to platelets.

Thus, a combination of 0.1 nM PAF and a 10,000-fold excess of BN 52021 provides a means to activate the platelets for a limited period of time and to extinguish receptor-activation thereafter. Figure 6 shows the effect of BN 52021 on PAF-induced platelet aggregation, measured as single platelet disappearance at 22°C. Although optical aggregation induced by such a low dose of PAF is minimal, small aggregates are formed which can be detected electronically. When the suspension is stirred, which is a prerequisite for aggregation, about 70% of the cells have formed aggregates after 5 minutes. In an unstirred suspension, which better reflects the conditions of the binding experiments, aggregation is much slower and reaches about 60% after 90 minutes. Addition of BN 52021 at all stages leads to

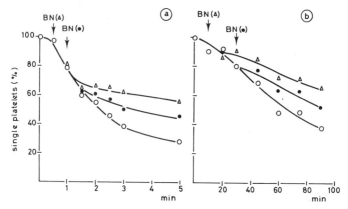

Figure 6 Effect of BN 52021 on aggregation induced by platelet-activating factor. Aggregation was measured as the disappearance of single platelets in the presence of 1 μM fibrinogen with (a) and without (b) stirring. Aggregation was initiated by addition of 0.2 nM PAF, and at times indicated in the figure, 10 μM BN 52021 (final concentrations) was added.

inhibition of aggregation, indicating that normal aggregation induced by a low dose of PAF requires continuous receptor occupancy. This fact is further illustrated by PAF-induced mobilization of cytosolic calcium ions. Following stimulation with 5 nM PAF at 22°C, there is a small increase in Quin 2 fluorescence reflecting an increase in cytosolic free Ca^{2+} content from about 60 nM to about 130 nM which mainly results from influx of extracellular ions. Thereafter, the Ca^{2+} content slowly returns to normal levels in about 6-8 minutes. Addition of 10 μM BN 52021 at 30 seconds after stimulation with PAF induces a more rapid decline and control values are reached between 2-3 minutes. This indicates that signal processing by the activated PAF receptor is interrupted when PAF is removed. Figure 7 illustrates that dissociation of the complex between PAF and its receptor also results in inhibition of fibrinogen binding. The effect is not immediate and follows after a lag time of about 15 minutes in accordance with the rather slow removal of PAF from its receptor under these conditions.

DISCUSSION

PAF-induced platelet aggregation is the result of two binding phenomena: (i) the binding of PAF to its receptors and, (ii) the binding of fibrinogen to exposed binding sites on the glycoprotein IIb/IIIa complex. The coupling between the two types of binding is mediated via a complex mechanism of signal generating pathways and still poorly understood changes in glycoproteins IIb/IIIa. Despite these uncertainties, insight into the signal generating properties of the PAF receptor can be gained by comparing the

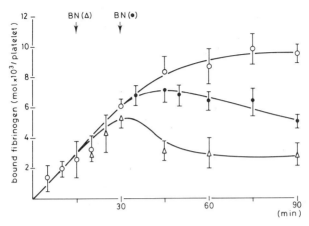

Figure 7   Effect of BN 52021 on PAF-induced binding of fibrinogen. Shown is the effect of 10 μM BN 52021 on the binding of ^{125}I-fibrinogen (1 μM) to platelets stimulated with 0.1 nM PAF.

binding of PAF with the concurrent binding of fibrinogen. The lipophilic properties of PAF and especially the high uptake capacity by the platelets partly mask the role of the PAF receptor, limiting receptor identification to a small range of PAF concentrations. Nevertheless, the receptor activity at higher concentrations can be deduced by computer simulation. A comparison of receptor binding at different PAF concentrations shows that almost complete receptor occupancy can be achieved with 0.5 nM PAF following 60 minutes incubation at 22°C. It is quite obvious that optimal aggregation and secretion require higher doses of PAF. This is already a first indication that the initial period of PAF-receptor interaction determines the biological response. Obviously, at increasing concentrations of PAF more receptors are occupied in this period, suggesting that cell activation is proportional to the number of PAF-receptor complexes. However, a comparison with concurrent fibrinogen binding demonstrates that a same percentage of occupied PAF receptors can be accompanied by different amounts of bound fibrinogen. A better correlation is observed when the rate of PAF binding is considered. Thus, PAF-induced fibrinogen binding is best described by the "rate theory", in which the rate of ligand binding determines the biological response (1). In contrast, thrombin binding to its receptor follows the "occupany theory" (11, 12) and triggers more aggregation and secretion as more ligands bind to the receptors.

On the assumption that binding site exposure is complete within 5 minutes and fibrinogen binding after 5 minutes or more follows normal ligand-receptor interaction, one can calculate that between 0.1 and 1.0 nM PAF about 40% of the number of fibrinogen binding sites that are exposed after 60 minutes are occupied after 5 minutes. The actual number of exposed binding sites is quite uncertain. Another publication (5) shows that exposed fibrinogen bindings disappear in the absence of fibrinogen. At a high dose of PAF (500 nM) the disappearance is undisturbed after 5 minutes stimulation and follows a simple exponential pattern, suggesting that exposure of binding sites is complete within the first few minutes. At a low PAF concentration, however, the disappearance is affected by the concurrent exposure of sites, providing a rough estimation of the rate of binding site exposure. These data show that following stimulation with 0.5 nM PAF about 30 minutes are required before exposure is complete. Thus, with such a low dose of PAF the number of exposed binding sites after 5 minutes is distinctly lower than after 60 minutes and the percentage of occupied fibrinogen binding sites is probably more than 40%.

These considerations provide an insight into the signal generating capacity of the PAF receptor. When a high dose of PAF is added to the platelets, the rate of PAF-receptor interaction is maximal and induces a maximal stimulus in the cell that initiates maximal binding site exposure in a matter of minutes (at 22°C). It is uncertain whether at later stages maintenance of exposed binding sites still depends on an intact PAF-receptor complex. A low dose of PAF induces slow signal processing leading to slow exposure of fibrinogen bindings sites with which other processes may interfere. Continuous receptor activation is then required. The findings with BN 52021 are in line with this concept. Following stimulation with 0.1 nM PAF a 10,000-fold excess of inhibitor added after 15 and even after 30 minutes interferes with fibrinogen binding and aggregation, probably as a result of inhibition of binding site exposure. It would be of interest to know the effect of inhibitors of PAF binding at high doses of PAF, such as 500 nM or more, but these studies await the development of more potent inhibitors of PAF-receptor interaction.

References

1. Birnbaumer, L. Pohl, S.L. *Relation of glucagon-specific binding sites to glucagon-dependent stimulation of adenylyl cyclase activity in plasma membranes of rat liver.* J Biol Chem 1973; 248: 2056-2061.

2. Kloprogge, E. et al. *Properties of PAF-acether-induced platelet aggregation and secretion.* Thromb Res 1983; 29: 595-608.

3. Kloprogge, E. et al. *Binding kinetics of PAF-acether (1-0-alkyl-2-acetyl-sn-glycero-3-phosphocholine) to intact human platelets.* Biochem J 1984; 223: 901-909.

4. Kloprogge, E. et al. *PAF--acether induces high- and low affinity binding of fibrinogen to human platelets via independent mechanisms.* Biochem J 1986; 240: 403-412.

5. Kloprogge, E. et al. *Kinetics of platelet-ativating factor 1-0-alkyl-2-acetyl-sn-glycero-3-phosphocholine-induced fibrinogen binding to human platelets.* J Biol Chem 1986; 261: 11071-11076.

6. Kloprogge, E. et al. *PAF-acether-induced fibrinogen binding to platelets depends on metabolic energy.* Biochem J 1986; 238:

885-891.

7. Kloprogge, E. et al. *Stimulus-aggreation coupling in platelets stimulated with PAF-acether.* Biochim Biophys Acta 1986; 883: 127-137.

8. Braquet, P. *The ginkgolides: Potent platelet-activating factor antagonists isolated from Ginkgo biloba L.: Chemistry, pharmacology and clinical applications.* Drugs of the Future 1987; 12: 643-699.

9. Peerschke, E.I.B. *The platelet fibrinogen receptor.* Sem Haematol 1985; 22: 241-259.

10. Pytela, R. et al. *Platelet membrane glycoprotein IIb/IIIa: Member of a family of arg-gly-asp-specific adhesion receptors.* Science 1986;

231: 1559-1562.

11. Rodbard, D. In: Receptors for Reproducing Hormones. B.N. O'Malley, A.R. Means (Eds.). Plenum: New York 1973; 342-364.

12. Tandon, N. et al. *Thrombin receptor defined responsiveness of cholesterol-modified platelets.* J Biol Chem 1983; 258: 11840-11845.

13. Tsien, R.Y. et al. *T-cell mitogens cause early changes in cytoplasmic free Ca^{2+} and membrane potential in lymphocytes.* Nature 1982; 295: 68-71.

14. Verhoeven, A.J.M. et al. *Quantification of energy consumption in platelets during thrombin-induced aggregation and secretion.* Biochem J 1984; 221: 777-787.

Ginkgolides - Chemistry, Biology, Pharmacology and Clinical Perspectives. P. Braquet (Ed.)
Copyright © 1988, J.R. Prous Science Publishers, S.A.

PAF-ACETHER ANALOGS, PLATELET ACTIVATION AND BN 52021

Eliane Coëffier

Unité de Pharmacologie Cellulaire, Unité Associée Institut Pasteur/IN-SERM 285, 25, rue du Docteur Roux, F-75015 Paris, France

INTRODUCTION

PAF-acether is a phospholipid mediator which was first described as a soluble component released from rabbit IgE-sensitized basophils upon antigen challenge and which causes rabbit platelet aggregation (2). Identification of the structure of PAF-acether as 1-O-alkyl-2-acetyl-*sn*-glyceryl-3-phosphorylcholine (3, 14) and its total chemical synthesis (17) have increased availability of PAF-acether for biological studies. Indeed, *in vitro* studies revealed that PAF-acether is active on and is formed by isolated cells and organs (platelets, neutrophils, macrophages, mast cells, monocytes, eosinophils, lung, heart, smooth muscle, kidney, spleen, liver, skin) (4, 10, 32) and *in vivo* experiments in several animal species and in man indicate that PAF-acether has a potential role in various physiopathological situations such as inflammation, asthma, thrombosis, cardiopathy and nephropathy. Research on PAF-acether antagonists is now widely developed and the availability of specific antagonists of the effects of PAF-acether is a useful tool to investigate the action of the mediator, its involvement in different pathological states and offer new therapeutic approaches. The first attempts to obtain antagonists involved the synthesis of structural analogs devoid of agonistic properties and capable of antagonizing PAF-acether effects. But effective and chemically unrelated PAF-acether antagonists have also been described (7, 15). Among them, BN 52021, a pure compound isolated from *Ginkgo biloba* (5) and which effects are described in this book, appears to be a specific inhibitor of the platelet activation as well as other biological effects induced by PAF-acether.

MATERIALS AND METHODS

Platelet Aggregating Activity

The platelet aggregating activity of PAF-acether and analogs was performed on washed rabbit platelets as previously described (26). Activity was expressed as final molar concentration of each compound required for inducing 50% of the maximum aggregation induced by a standard solution of synthetic PAF-acether.

Platelet Desensitizing Activity

The desensitizing activity of the analogs was assessed by aggregation induced with PAF-acether on phospholipid-pretreated platelets as previously described (26, 27, 38). In a first step, platelets were incubated with various dilutions of the phospholipids at 37°C without stirring. After 2 minutes (second step), they were exposed to a submaximal concentration of PAF-acether (0.7 ± 0.5 nM) and aggregation was measured under stirring.

EFFECT OF STRUCTURALY RELATED PAF-ACETHER MOLECULES ON PLATELET ACTIVATION

PAF-acether analogs have been synthesized in order to 1) determine the structural requirements for biological activity and then to specify the structure of specific binding sites, 2) enhance the possible therapeutic effects such as selective anti-hypertensive activity while eliminating undesirable effects such as platelet aggregation and bronchoconstriction, and 3) search for new antagonists devoid of agonistic properties. Synthesis of a large number of PAF-acether analogs has therefore been performed using substituents and functional variations. We present here a summary of the effects of the various changes on rabbit platelet aggregation.

Enantiomer and Positional Isomer

PAF-acether is the R enantiomer as represented by the *sn* nomenclature. Its final molar concentration required for inducing 50% of the maximum aggregation of washed rabbit platelets (EC_{50}) was 5.7×10^{-11} M. By contrast, the unnatural enantiomer (S) appears far less potent than PAF-acether ($EC_{50} = 1.7 \times 10^{-7}$ M) and the racemic mixture has an intermediate activity ($EC_{50} = 2.2 \times 10^{-10}$ M) (21). The optical specificity of the substituent at position 2 of the *sn*-glycerol is necessary for the platelet aggregating and desensitizing activity (21, 26, 38). Positional isomer of PAF-acether (1-O-hexadecyl-3-O-acetyl-*sn*-glyceryl-3-phosphorylcholine) is a weak platelet agonist and also demonstrates the critical importance of the acetyl group at position 2 (38).

Substitution of the Glycerol Backbone

CHANGES IN CARBON 1   Ether function is an absolute requirement for aggregating activity. Indeed, there is an almost complete disappearance of agonistic effect when oxygen is replaced by sulfur (22), methylene (11, 29, 42), ester (37) or various nitrogen radicals (8). The length of the fatty chain (and its consequent lipophilicity) is a key point for activity. Thus, platelet. activation (and also hypotension and thrombocytopenia) is maximum for lipophilicity corresponding to a C14 chain (16). As for lipophilicity, the presence of double bonds in the chain slightly reinforces the agonistic activity (18:2 > 18:1 > 18:0) (36).

CHANGES IN CARBON 2   The length of the substituent seems to be the main requirement for effectiveness since activity decreases rapidly as the size of the acyl group is increased, the propionyl analog being nearly as active as PAF-acether (37). However, major changes of the ester function, including methylcarbamate, do not lead to a change of activity (19). Ethoxy (37), nitrate (19) and n-propyl (43) retain a residual PAF-acether-like activity, indicating that no transfer of labile acetate group is necessary for the actions of the mediator.

CHANGES IN CARBON 3   The degree of methylation on the nitrogen base is a requirement for activity. Thus, the dimethyl-substituted phosphoglyceride is more active than the choline derivative (26, 33, 37), thereafter the monomethyl ethanolamine (26) and unsubstituted ethanolamine derivative are sequentially less active (18, 26, 33). The two analogs, N-methyl-morpholino ethanol and N-methyl-piperidinium ethanol, which carry a quaternary nitrogen group, are as effective as PAF-acether in activating platelets and in inducing bronchoconstriction. By contrast, the unsubstituted (unmethylated) derivatives, piperidino ethanol and morpholino ethanol, were less active (13; Table 1). When the nitrogen base was replaced by an ethyl group or removed and simply replaced by a hydrogen (phosphoric acid), the biological activity decreased (18, 33, 37, 39). These results may be of interest in view of the biological effect of PAF-acether, since they raise the possibility of N-methylation of the amino group of monomethyl and dimethyl derivatives (23).

The replacement of a phosphate group by a phosphonate group does not significantly modify platelet stimulation (28, 29, 41). However, deletion of the phosphoryl group or replacement by an etheroxyde (20) or a sulfonylbis-methylene moiety (41) reduces or abrogates platelet stimulating activity.

The distance between the phosphate group and the ammonium head is critical. When the length of this link is increased this leads to a gradual but progressive decrease in the hypotensive and platelet aggregating response (39, 41).

The choline head group in position 3 of the glycerol skeleton of PAF-acether is not a compulsory requirement for biological effects and N-methyl-piperidine, N-methyl-morpholine and N-methyl-pyrrolidine analogs are more effective than the N-trimethyl analog (PAF-acether itself) in inducing platelet activation (13, 31). Nevertheless, other modifications of the choline head group lead to a loss of activity (13, 18).

Table 1 Platelet activation induced by PAF-acether and analogs. Inhibition by BN 52021

Structure of Agonist CH_2-O-$(CH_2)_{17}$-CH_3 H-C-O-CO-CH_3 CH_2-O-P-O-Z $\quad$ O OH	Platelet Activation		Inhibition by BN 52021 (0.1 mM) of	
	Aggregation EC_{50} (nM)	Secretion EC_{20} (nM)	Aggregation %	Secretion %
-CH_2-CH_2-N^+(CH_3)$_3$*	0.41	0.56	94 ± 3	79 ± 11
-CH_2-CH_2-N^+ (morpholine) CH_3	0.23	0.23	99 ± 2	74 ± 10
-CH_2-CH_2-N^+ (piperidine) CH_3	0.40	0.32	83 ± 6	55 ± 19
-CH_2 (pyrrolidine) N – CH_3	0.42	1.00	88 ± 3	96 ± 3
(piperidine) N-CH_3	0.50	0.75	87 ± 3	92 ± 4
-CH_2-CH_2-N (piperidine)	3.40	4.50	93 ± 3	67 ± 15

Guinea-pig platelet activation induced by PAF-acether and analogs, inhibition by compound BN 52021. Platelet-rich plasma (PRP, 400 000 platelets/μl) was incubated for 1 min at 37°C while stirring (1100 r.p.m.) without the antagonist. Then PAF-acether or the analogs were added at different concentrations. Three minutes after the addition of the aggregating agent, a 20 μl aliquot was collected for monitoring the release of ATP. Activity was expressed as the final molar concentration of agonist required for inducing 50% of the maximum aggregation (EC_{50}) or 20% of the maximum secretion (EC_{20}). For study of the inhibition by BN 52021, PRP was incubated 1 min with antagonist then PAF-acether or analogs were added in a concentration inducing 80% of the maximal aggregation and 20-30% of the maximal ATP release measured at 3 min. Percents of inhibition were calculated from control experiments monitored at the same time and were expressed as means ± S.E.M. of 4-6 experiments. * PAF-acether.

EFFECT OF BN 52021 ON PLATELET ACTIVATION INDUCED BY PAF-ACETHER ANALOGS

Platelet aggregation induced by thrombin is mediated by at least three distinct activation pathways. The mediators for the two first pathways are ADP and arachidonic acid, whereas PAF-acether is a candidate for the third pathway (12, 40). BN 52021, a purified molecule extracted from the leaves of *Ginkgo biloba* (5), appears to be a new specific inhibitor of platelet activation induced by PAF-acether. BN 52021 inhibits the binding of PAF-acether to rabbit (5, 9) and to human (24, 30) washed platelets with an IC_{50} close to 10^{-7} M. This inhibition of PAF-acether receptor is competitive and highly specific since BN 52021 does not interact with any other known receptor (5, 9). The results of the inhibition of the aggregation of human (30) and rabbit (5, 9) platelets (washed and in PRP) or guinea-pig platelets (in PRP) (13) confirm those results obtained in the binding assays ($IC_{50} = 2.2$ μM, washed human platelets, 7.5 nM PAF-acether; $IC_{50} = 0.14$ μM, washed rabbit platelets, 2.5 nM PAF-acether). This effect is specific since no inhibition is observed with the other pro-aggregating agents (ADP, arachidonic acid, ionophore A23187, collagen and thrombin) and since BN 52021 does not inhibit arachidonic acid metabolism (5, 9). Platelet aggregation inhibition by BN 52021 is also obtained *ex vivo* (9). These data correlated with inhibition by BN 52021 in intact rabbit platelets both of reacylation of lyso analog of PAF-acether in 2-acyl derivative (25) and of the phosphatidylinositol cycle demonstrated by the fall in synthesis of phosphatidic acid (34). Furthermore, no effect is observed on acetyltransferase. The inhibition of the aggregation was also associated with a significant decrease in the mobilization of intracellular calcium and the generation of inositol triphosphate induced by PAF-acether (1, 25, 34).

In a recent report, we have described the influence of modifications of the polar head group at position 3 in the molecular structure of PAF-acether on activation (aggregation and ATP release) of guinea-pig platelets in comparison with their *in vivo* effects (bronchoconstriction, thrombocytopenia and leucopenia) (13). BN 52021 is studied as a potential antagonist of platelet activation and bronchoconstriction induced by the analogs to find out if they interact with sites in common with those of PAF-acether itself.

As shown in Table 1, PAF-acether induced concentration-dependent guinea-pig platelet aggregation and ATP release. The 3-phosphoryl-N-methyl morpholino ethanol analog is slightly more active than PAF-acether and the 3-phosphoryl-N-methyl-piperidinium ethanol, 3-phosphoryl-(N-methyl-piperidino-3')-methanol and 3-phosphoryl-(N-methyl-hydroxy-4')-piperidine analogs are equieffective to PAF-acether in activating platelets. The 3-phosphoryl piperidino ethanol analog was 8 times less active than

PAF-acether, the 3-phosphoryl-morpholino ethanol analog and the 1-O-octadecyl-2-O-acetyl-3-O-(-(trimethyl-ammonio)-propyl) glycerol were inactive up to 1 μM. Our data show that the choline head group is not a compulsory requirement for activity. When injected i.v. to propranolol-treated guinea-pigs, the platelet-activating analogs also induced bronchoconstriction, thrombocytopenia and leukopenia.

The PAF-acether antagonist, BN 52021 inhibits PAF-acether-induced platelet activation when added to PRP at the final concentration of 0.1 mM (aggregation inhibited by $94 \pm 3\%$; secretion inhibited by $79 \pm 10\%$, mean $\pm$ S.E.M., n = 4). BN 52021 inhibits platelet-activation induced by PAF-acether or its analogs under conditions where neither collagen nor arachidonic acid are affected. BN 52021 also suppresses bronchoconstriction induced by the analogs and reduces to a lower extent thrombocytopenia and leukopenia. Our results indicate that PAF-acether and the analogs studied trigger platelet activation and the consequent bronchoconstriction through mechanisms which share sensitivity to the same antagonist. BN 52021 inhibits the binding of PAF-acether to its presumed platelet receptor (rev. in 6) and our results suggest that PAF-acether and analogs trigger *in vivo* platelet activation and the consequent platelet-dependent bronchoconstriction after interacting with similar receptors.

In summary, among the new PAF-acether analogs substituted in position 3, some are endowed with platelet-stimulating and bronchoconstrictor activities equipotent to that of PAF-acether, and are inhibited by similar antagonists. Accordingly, the choline head group is not a compulsory requirement for the biological effects of PAF-acether.

CONCLUSIONS

The involvement of specific PAF-acether receptor(s) has been first suggested by the demonstration that only the naturally occurring stereoisomer (R) triggers platelet stimulation and various PAF-acether responses (21, 26, 27, 35, 37). Additional data corroborate these findings: very low concentrations (lower than 0.1 nM) are necessary to trigger biological effects, specific desensitization takes place after platelets exposure to PAF-acether, and there is specific inhibition by PAF-acether antagonists. The existence of PAF-acether receptors has recently been confirmed by binding using ^{3}H-PAF-acether (8). A putative conformation of the PAF-acether binding site was proposed by Godfroid and Braquet (8, 15) on the basis of the studies on structure-activity relationship considerations. The agonistic activity decreases when the fatty chain is shortened, whereas the introduction of a polar group in BN 52021 greatly reduces antagonism. The anchorage of the chain to the membrane and the relative position of the ether function as compared with its environment certainly change membrane metabolism and fluidity. Membrane activation may possibly derive from an electronic transfer from oxygen doublets of the ether function to an unknown membrane target. The length and the bulk of the substituents on carbon 2 are the main factor for agonistic activity. The short chain may thus take part in the anchorage of PAF-acether on its receptor, resulting in better alignment of the polar head of the mediator with that of membrane phospholipids.

Such a receptor model can accomodate BN 52021 which incorporates a tetrahydrofuran ring. Tetrahydrofuran oxygen is more basic than ether oxygen in PAF-acether and the electronic transfer to a membrane target is facilitated. The competition between the tetrahydrofuran ring of BN 52021 and the ether function of PAF-acether is sterically possible. The position of BN 52021 in the receptor site may prevent the activation of transmembrane events triggered by PAF-acether or analogs.

References

1. Baroggi, N., Etienne, A., Braquet, P. *Changes in cytosolic free calcium by platelet-activating factor in rabbit platelets: Specific inhibition by BN 52021 and structurally related compounds.* Agents and Actions 1986; 20: 87-97.

2. Benveniste, J., Henson, P.M., Cochrane, C.G. *Leukocyte-dependent histamine release from rabbit platelets: The role of IgE, basophils and a platelet-activating factor.* J Exp Med 1972; 136: 1356-1377.

3. Benveniste, J., Tencé, M., Varenne, P., Bidault, J., Boullet, C., Polonsky, J. *Semi-synthèse et structure proposée du facteur activant les plaquettes (P.A.F.): PAF-acether, un alkyl-éther analogue de la lysophosphatidylcholine.* CR Acad Sci (Paris) 1979; 289: 1037-1040.

4. Benveniste, J., Vargaftig, B.B. *An ether lipid with biological activities: Platelet-activating factor (PAF-acether).* In: Ether-Lipids: Biomedical Aspects. H.K. Mangold, F. Paltauf (Eds.). Academic Press: New York 1983; 355-376.

5. Braquet, P. *Treatment or prevention of PAF-acether disorders provoked by a new series of highly specific inhibitors.* GB Patent 84/18 424, 1984; Belg BE 901, 915.

6. Braquet, P. *The Ginkgolides: Potent platelet-activating factor antagonists isolated from Ginkgo biloba L.: Chemistry, pharmacology and clinical applications.* Drugs of the Future 1987; 12: 643-699.

7. Braquet, P., Godfroid, J.J. *Platelet activating factor (PAF-acether) specific binding sites: 2. Design of specific antagonists.* TIPS 1986; 397-403.

8. Braquet, P., Godfroid, J.-J. *Conformational properties of the PAF-acether receptor in platelets based on structure-activity studies.* In: Platelet Activating Factor. F. Snyder (Ed.). Plenum Press: New York, 1987; in press.

9. Braquet, P., Spinnewyn, B., Braquet, M., Bourgain, R.H., Taylor, J.E., Etienne, A., Drieu, K. *BN 52021 and related compounds: A new series of highly specific PAF-acether receptor antagonists isolated from Ginkgo biloba.* Blood Vessels 1985; 16: 559-572.

10. Braquet, P., Touqui, L., Shen, T.Y., Vargaftig, B.B. *Perspectives in platelet activating factor research.* Pharmacol Reviews 1987; 39: 97-145.

11. Broquet, C., Teulade, M.-P., Borghero, C., Heymans, F., Godfroid, J.J., Lefort, J., Coëffier, E., Pirotsky, E. *Structural analogues of PAF-acether I. Rac-acetyloxydocosyl phosphorylcholines.* Eur J Med Chem 1984; 19: 229-233.

12. Chignard, M., Le Couedic, J.-P., Tencé, M., Vargaftig, B.B., Benveniste, J. *The role of platelet-activating factor in platelet aggregation.* Nature 1979; 279: 799-800.

13. Coëffier, E., Borrel, M.-C., Lefort, J., Chignard, M., Broquet, C., Heymans, F., Godfroid, J.-J., Vargaftig, B.B. *Effects of*

PAF-acether and structural analogues on platelet activation and bronchoconstriction in guinea-pigs. Eur J Pharmacol 1986; 131: 179-188.

14. Demopoulos, C.A., Pinckard, R.N., Hanahan, D.J. *Platelet-activating factor. Evidence for 1-O-alkyl-2-acetyl-sn-glyceryl-3-phosphorylcholine as the active component (a new class of lipid chemical mediator).* J Biol Chem 1979; 254; 9355-9358.

15. Godfroid, J.-J., Braquet, P. *Platelet-activating factor (PAF-acether) specific binding sites: 1. A tentative approach of their structure using a Q.S.A.R. study on PAF-acether isosters.* TIPS 1986; 397-403.

16. Godfroid, J.-J., Broquet, C., Jouquey, S., Lebbar, M., Heymans, F., Redeuilh, C., Steiner, E., Michel, E., Coëffier, E., Fichelle, J., Worcel, M. *Structure-activity relationship in PAF-acether. 3. Hydrophobic contribution to the agonistic activity.* J Med Chem 1987; 30: 792-797.

17. Godfroid, J.-J., Heymans, F., Michel, E., Redeuilh, C., Steiner, E., Benveniste, J. *Platelet activating factor (PAF-acether): Total synthesis of 1-O-octadecyl-2-O-acetyl-sn-glycero-3-phosphorylcholine.* Febs Lett 1980; 116: 161-164.

18. Hadvary, P., Baumgartner, H.R. *Activation of human and rabbit blood platelets by synthetic structural analogs of platelet activating factor.* Throm Res 1983; 30: 143-156.

19. Hadvary, P., Cassal, J.M., Hirth, G., Barner, R., Baumgartner, H.P. *Structural requirements for the activation of blood platelets by analogues of platelet-activating factor (PAF-acether).* In: Proceedings of the Platelet-Activating Factor Symposium. J. Benveniste, B. Arnoux (Eds.). Elsevier Sciences Publishers: Amsterdam 1983; 57-64.

20. Heymans, F., Borrel, M.-C., Broquet, C., Lefort, J., Godfroid, J.-J. *Structure-activity relationship in PAF-acether.2.Rac 1-O-octadecyl-2-O-acetyl-3-O-((dimethylamino)propyl) glycerol.* J Med Chem 1985; 28: 1094-1096.

21. Heymans, F., Michel, E., Borrel, M.-C., Wichrowski, B., Godfroid, J.-J., Convert, O., Coëffier, E., Tencé, M., Benveniste, J. *New total synthesis and high resolution ^{1}H NMR spectrum of platelet-activating factor, its enantiomer and racemic mixtures.* Biochim Biophys Acta 1981; 666: 230-237.

22. Hillmar, I., Muramatsu, T., Zoellner, N. *Effects of a thio analog of platelet-activating factor on platelet aggregation and adenosine*

3',5'-monophosphate concentration in hepatocyte suspensions and in platelets. A comparison with the naturally occurring compound. Hoppe-Seyler Z Physiol Chem 1984; 368: 33-41.

23. Hotchkiss, A., Jordan, J.V., Hirata, F., Shulman, N.R., Axelrod, J. *Phospholipid methylation and human platelet function.* Biochem Pharmacol 1981; 30: 2089-2095.

24. Korth, R., Hirafuji, M., Benveniste, J. *Comparison of human endothelial cells in culture and platelets for ^{3}H-PAF-acether binding.* Fed Proc 1987; 46: 742 (Abst).

25. Lachachi, H., Plantavid, M., Simon, M.-F., Chap, H., Braquet, P., Douste-Blazy, L. *Inhibition of transmembrane movement and metabolism of platelet-activating factor (PAF-acether) by a specific antagonist, BN 52021.* Biochem Biophys Res Comm 1985; 132: 460-466.

26. Lalau Keraly, C., Coëffier, E., Tencé, M., Borrel, M.-C., Benveniste, J. *Effect of structural analogues of PAF-acether on platelet desensitization.* Brit J Haematol 1983; 53: 513-521.

27. Lalau-Keraly, C., Benveniste, J. *Specific desensitization of rabbit platelets by platelet activating factor (PAF-acether) and derivatives.* Brit J Haematol 1982; 51: 313-322.

28. Moschidis, M.C., Demopoulos, C.A., Kritikou, L.G. *Phosphono-platelet activating factor I. Synthesis of 1-O-hexadecyl-2-O-acetyl-glyceryl-3-(2-trimethyl ammonium methyl) phosphonate and its platelet activating potency.* Chem Phys Lipids 1983; 33: 87-92.

29. Nakamura, N., Miyazaki, H., Ohkawa, N., Koike, H., Sada, T., Asai, F., Kobayashi, S. *Synthesis and biological activities of biososteric O-carba-analogues of platelet activating factor.* Chem Pharm Bull 1984; 32: 2455-2459.

30. Nunez, D., Chignard, M., Korth, R., Le Couedic, J.-P., Norel, X., Spinnewyn, B., Braquet, P., Benveniste, J. *Specific inhibition of PAF-acether-induced platelet activation by BN 52021 and comparison with the PAF-acether inhibitors kadsurenone and CV 3988.* Eur J Pharmacol 1986; 123: 197-205.

31. Ohno, M., Fujita, K., Nakai, H., Kobayashi, S., Inoue, K., Nojima, S. *An enantioselective synthesis of platelet-activating factors, the enantiomers, and the analogues from D- and L-tartaric acids.* Chem Pharm Bull 1985; 33: 572-580.

32. Roubin, R., Tencé, M., Mencia-Huerta, J.-M., Arnoux, B., Ninio, E., Benveniste, J. *A chemically defined monokine-macrophage-defined platelet-activating factor.* In: Lymphokines. E. Pick (Ed.). Academic Press: New York 1983; 8: 249-276.

33. Satouchi, K., Pinckard, R.N., McManus, L.M., Hanahan, D.J. *Modification of the polar head group of acetyl glyceryl ether phosphorylcholine and subsequent effects upon platelet activation.* J Biol Chem 1981; 256: 4425-4432.

34. Simon, M.F., Chap, H., Braquet, P., Douste-Blazy, L. *Effect of BN 52021, a specific antagonist of platelet activating factor (PAF-acether), on calcium movements and phosphatidic acid production induced by PAF-acether in human platelets.* Thromb Res 1987; 45: 299-309.

35. Snyder, F. *Chemical and biochemical aspects of platelet activating factor: A novel class of acetylated ether-linked choline-phospholipids.* Med Res Rev 1985; 5: 107-140.

36. Surles, J.R., Wykle, R.L., O'Flaherty, J.T., Salzer, W.L., Thomas, M.J., Snyder, F., Piantadosi, C. *Facile synthesis of platelet-activating factor and racemic analogues containing unsaturation in the sn-1-alkyl chain.* J Med Chem 1985; 28: 73-78.

37. Tencé, M., Coëffier, E., Heymans, F., Polonsky, J., Godfroid, J.-J., Benveniste, J. *Structural analogs of platelet-activating factor (PAF-acether).* Biochimie 1981; 63: 723-727.

38. Tencé, M., Coëffier, E., Polonsky, J., Benveniste, J. *The enantiomer and the positional isomer of platelet-activating factor.* Biochem Biophys Acta 1983; 755: 526-530.

39. Tokumura, A., Homma, H., Hanahan, D.J. *Structural analogs of alkylacetylglycero-phosphocholine inhibitory behavior of platelet activation.* J Biol Chem 1985; 260: 12710-12714.

40. Vargaftig, B.B., Chignard, M., Benveniste, J. *Present concepts on the mechanisms of platelet aggregation.* Biochem Pharmacol 1981; 30: 263-271.

41. Wissner, A., Kohler, C.A., Goldstein, B.M. *Analogues of platelet-activating factor: 3. Replacement of the phosphate moiety with a sulforylbismethylene group.* J Med Chem 1985; 28: 1365-1367.

42. Wissner, A., Sum, P.E., Schaub, R.E., Kohler, C.A., Goldstein, B.M. *Analogues of platelet activating factor (PAF). 1. Some modifications of the alkoxy chain.* J Med Chem 1984; 27: 1174-1181.

43. Wykle, R.L., Miller, C.H., Lewis, J.C., Schmitt, J.D., Smith, J.A., Surles, J.R., Piantadosi, C., O'Flaherty, J.T. *Stereospecific activity of 1-O-alkyl-2-O-acetyl-sn-glycero-3-phosphocholine and comparison of analogs in the degranulation of platelets and neutrophils.* Biochem Biophys Res Comm 1981; 100: 1651-1658.

Ginkgolides - Chemistry, Biology, Pharmacology and Clinical Perspectives. P. Braquet (Ed.)

EFFECTS OF GINKGOLIDES ON PAF-INDUCED CALCIUM MOBILIZATION IN PLATELETS

Annie Etienne and Nicole Baroggi

Institut Henri Beaufour 72, avenue des Tropiques, F-91952 Les Ulis Cédex, France

INTRODUCTION

Platelet-activating factor (PAF, 1-O-alkyl 2(R)-acetyl glycero-3-phosphorylcholine) is a powerful activator of various cell types (11, 32) including platelets (9, 10). PAF stimulates rapid shape-change, secretion of the contents of both dense and alpha granules and induces aggregation of human platelets. The investigation of the stimulus-activity coupling processes has pointed out that the increase in cytoplasmic free calcium $[Ca^{2+}]_i$ is a critical early event in platelet activation induced by PAF, as already demonstrated with other platelet activators: ADP, thrombin (17, 24) or vasopressin (13). Specific binding sites for PAF have been shown on rabbit (15) and human (18, 31) platelets, suggesting that PAF-dependent platelet aggregation involves a receptor mediated mechanism. Furthermore, specific antagonists like BN 52021, kadsurenone or CV 3988, selectively inhibit PAF-induced platelet aggregation and binding of [³H] PAF to platelets (4, 6).

The use of the fluorescent calcium indicator dye quin 2 has allowed the $[Ca^{2+}]_i$ measurements in intact platelets at rest or during stimulation by agonists. PAF was shown to raise $[Ca^{2+}]_i$ 8- to 10-fold the basal level in a few seconds, as measured on platelets loaded with this fluorescent probe (12).

In this paper, we describe the inhibition by ginkgolides, BN 52021 and structurally related compounds (5) of the quin 2-signal induced by PAF

Address all correspondence to: Dr. A. Etienne, Institut Henri Beaufour, Dept. of General Pharmacology, 72, avenue des Tropiques, F-91952 Les Ulis Cédex, France.

on washed and loaded rabbit platelets. We compare the efficiency of these drugs in reducing $[Ca^{2+}]_i$ mobilization with that of inhibiting platelet aggregation. The specificity of their activity against PAF is also pointed out.

The increase in intracellular free calcium induced by the binding of PAF to its putative receptors on platelet membrane may be partially attributed to calcium influx but also to the discharge of intracellular calcium from internal stores (12). Indeed, PAF-induced platelet activation is also associated with a rapid degradation of inositol-phospholipids resulting in the formation of inositol 1,4,5-triphosphate $[IP_3]$, diacylglycerol and its phosphorylated product phosphatidic acid. These substances remain inside the platelets and IP_3 has been proposed as second mediator releasing calcium intracellular stores (3, 26).

Thus, in another series of experiments, ^{32}P-labelled platelets were prepared and incubated in the same conditions as in quin 2 assays. The inhibitory effect of BN 52021 on inositol phospholipids hydrolysis induced by PAF was also sought.

MATERIALS AND METHODS

Materials

A 0.5 mg/ml stock solution of PAF [1-O-hexadecyl-2(R)-acetyl-glycero-3-phosphorylcholine] in 0.5% bovine serum albumin (BSA fraction V) saline solution was used. Thrombin was solubilized in Tyrode buffer, acetyl salicylic acid in water and the calcium ionophore A 23187 in dimethylsulfoxide (DMSO). Quin 2 acetomethylester (quin 2/AM) was solubilized in DMSO and 2 μl/ml of cell suspension (final quin 2 concentration: 20 μM) were used. Digitonin was used in aqueous solution.

The PAF antagonists ginkgolides and kadsurenone were also solubilized in DMSO.

The composition of the normal Tyrode buffer was (mM): NaCl: 137; KCl: 2.7; NaH_2PO_4, $2H_2O$: 0.4; $NaHCO_3$: 12; $MgCl_2$: 1; $CaCl_2$: 1; glucose: 5.6 [BSA 0.35%, pH = 7.35]. Male New-Zealand rabbits (2.5 kg body weight) were used for platelet preparation.

Preparation of Cells

Rabbit blood was withdrawn by ear artery puncture and mixed with one-sixth volume of acid citrate/dextrose. The platelets were then isolated and washed first in a modified Tyrode buffer lacking calcium, containing 2 mM $MgCl_2$, 0.25 mM EGTA and 0.35% BSA (pH = 6.5).

They were then centrifuged at 1000 g (15 min) and suspended at a density of 5 x 10^8 cells ml^{-1} in the buffer previously described but without EGTA.

Platelet Loading with Quin 2

Platelet loading with quin 2 is generally carried out at 37°C using the lipophilic acetomethylester quin 2/AM (1, 12, 25). However, by prolonged incubation at 37°C, human platelets are made refractory to PAF routinely causing aggregation. Since we verified in preliminary studies that rabbit platelets react in the same way as human platelets, we adapted the method previously described by Hallam *et al.* (12) by performing the quin 2 loading at room temperature in all our studies.

After pretreatment by 100 μM acetylsalicylic acid at room temperature for 30 minutes, the platelets in buffer without EGTA were loaded with quin 2 by incubation at room temperature for 20 minutes with 20 μM quin 2/AM. The cells were pelleted by centrifugation, washed and gently resuspended in a normal Tyrode buffer containing 0.35% BSA.

Measurement of $[Ca^{2+}]_i$

The measurement of $[Ca^{2+}]_i$ from the fluorescence of the intracellular trapped quin 2 was similar to that previously reported (1).

Inhibitor or its solvent was added to the quin 2-loaded platelets and 0.7 ml of the mixture was placed in a cylindrical quartz cuvette of a spectrofluorometer LS 5 Perkin Elmer. The fluorescence (excitation: 339 nm, emission: 492 nm) was continously recorded.

After 5 minutes equilibration at 37°C under mild magnetic stirring, the agonists, PAF, thrombin or ionophore A 23187, were added into the cuvette through a septum. For calibration of the fluorescence signal, a sample of quin 2-loaded cells was exposed to digitonin (50 μm), a membrane permeabilizing agent, to obtain maximum fluorescence (F max); the minimum fluorescence (F min) was then obtained after adding an excess EGTA.

$[Ca^{2+}]_i$ corresponding to the measured fluorescence F of the platelet sample, was calculated using the formula:

$$[Ca^{2+}]_i = kd \ (F\text{-}F \ min)/(F \ max\text{-}F)$$

The kd value was fixed at 115 nM in the experimental conditions used (30).

Measurement of Aggregation

Washed platelets resuspended at a density of 4 x 10^8 cells ml^{-1} in the normal Tyrode buffer were used for aggregation studies. Just before agonists addition, apyrase was added to avoid aggregation by secreted ADP.

Platelet aggregation was measured as a function of light transmission with a Chronolog aggregometer; 380 μl of platelet suspension were placed in a cuvette maintained at 37°C and stirred at 1200 rpm for 2 minutes prior to the addition of the aggregating inducer.

Study of the Phosphoinositides Turnover

Platelets ^{32}P labelling was performed, as described by Mauco *et al.* (20), by incubation at 37°C for 60 minutes with [^{32}P]-O-phosphate (50 μCi ml^{-1}), simultaneously with acetylsalicylic acid 100 μM. After centrifugation, cells were washed and resuspended (5 x 10^8 platelets ml^{-1}) in a normal Tyrode-BSA buffer CaCl$_2$ 1 mM. PAF (10^{-9} M) was added to 0.5 ml aliquots, after 1 minute preincubation at 37°C. The reaction was stopped after 10 seconds or 60 seconds by addition of 1 ml chloroform/methanol (1 V/1 V) and 37 μl of EDTA 0.2 M. Lipids were extracted after acidification with 30 μl HCl 12N. ^{32}P-labelled phospholipids were separated by monodimensional thin-layer chromatography with chloroform/acetone/methanol/glacial acetic acid/water (40/15/13/12/8, respectively by volume) as described by Jolles *et al.* (16). After autoradiographic localization, the spots were scraped for liquid scintillation spectrophotometer counting (insta-gel).

RESULTS

Effect of Agonists on Free-Intracellular Calcium

At the basal level and in our experimental conditions, [Ca^{2+}]$_i$ value in washed rabbit platelets measured by quin 2 method was 135.0 ± 26.9 nM. Stimulation of platelets with various doses of PAF, in the presence of 1 mM external Ca^{2+} caused a dose-dependent and rapid increase of [Ca^{2+}]$_i$ level to a value of 2.5 to 5 μM in less than 1 minute for the highest dose of agonist (3 x 10^{-9} M); then the response declined in a few minutes (Fig. 1). A tachyphylactic effect was observed in response to PAF although cells did

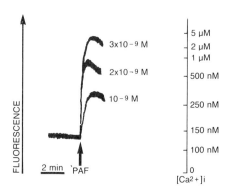

Figure 1 Dose-dependent response curves of quin 2-loaded platelets to PAF stimulation (fluorescence measurement: excitation 339 nm; emission 492 nm).

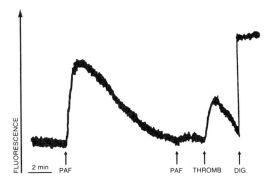

Figure 2 Tachyphylactic effect of PAF on quin 2-loaded rabbit platelets: responses to consecutive stimulations with PAF (2 applications of 2×10^{-9} M) thrombin (0.1 U/ml) and digitonine (100% fluorescence).

not aggregate; a second application of the same concentration of PAF caused no further increase in $[Ca^{2+}]_i$, whereas a subsequent addition of thrombin (0.1 U/ml) or digitonine 50 μM after PAF stimulation were still able to give a fluorescence signal (Fig. 2). The rise in $[Ca^{2+}]_i$ value induced by thrombin (0.025 U/ml) appeared slower and the fluorescence signal was wider than with PAF stimulation (Fig. 5).

Effect of PAF Antagonists on Calcium Mobilization

The three antagonists, BN 52020, BN 52021 and BN 52022, added 5 minutes before PAF (2×10^{-9} M) markedly antagonized the PAF-induced rise in the cation though they had no effect on their own at the doses used on

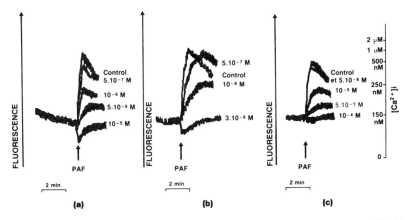

Figure 3 Fluorescence responses of quin 2-loaded rabbit platelets to stimulation with 2×10^{-9} M PAF. Inhibition by pretreatment of cells 5 minutes before PAF with (a) BN 52020, (b) BN 52021, (c) BN 52022.

the basal $[Ca^{2+}]_i$ value. The effects were dose-dependent, the most active compound being BN 52021. At the dose of 5 x 10^{-7} M of BN 52021 the PAF-induced signal appeared more slowly, whereas with higher doses, the increase in $[Ca^{2+}]_i$ was either reduced by 90% (BN 52021 = 10^{-6} M) or totally abolished (BN 52021 = 3 x 10^{-6} M) (Fig. 3b).

The PAF-acether induced fluorescence signal was also reduced with BN 52020 (Fig. 3a) and BN 52022 (Fig. 3c) (10^{-6} M and 10^{-5} M, respectively) and totally abolished for higher doses (10^{-5} M and 10^{-4} M, respectively). Like BN 52021, kadsurenone dose-dependently decreased the PAF-induced fluorescence signal with approximately the same efficiency as BN 52021. At the dose of 3 x 10^{-6} M, kadsurenone totally abolished PAF-acether effect on platelets (Fig. 4).

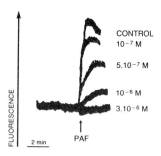

Figure 4   Fluorescence response of quin 2-loaded rabbit platelets to 2 x 10^{-9} M PAF-stimulation; dose-dependent effect of kadsurenone by pretreatment of cells 5 minutes before PAF addition.

Specificity of Action of the PAF Antagonists

BN 52021 (3 x 10^{-6} M) inhibited PAF-induced increase in $[Ca^{2+}]_i$ without modifying those induced by thrombin (0.025 U/ml) or calcium inophore A 23187 (1 x 10^{-6} M) (Fig. 5).

Similar results were obtained with BN 52020 and BN 52022 (data not shown), whereas the calcium channel blocker verapamil (10^{-4} M) impaired both PAF and thrombin stimulations. The PAF-induced signal was totally abolished by verapamil, while the one induced by thrombin was decreased by 65% (Fig. 6).

Effect of Ginkgolides on PAF-Induced Aggregation of Washed Rabbit Platelets

Two concentrations of PAF (2.5 x 10^{-10} M and 5 x 10^{-10} M) which gave submaximal and not spontaneously reversible aggregations, were used in this study.

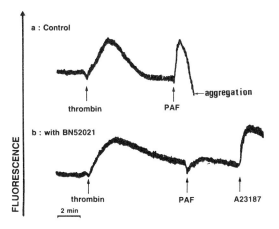

Figure 5 Effect of BN 52021 (3 x 10⁻⁶ M) on fluorescence responses of quin 2-loaded platelets to consecutive stimulations with thrombin (0.025 U/ml) PAF (2 x 10⁻⁹ M) and A 23187 (10⁻⁶ M).

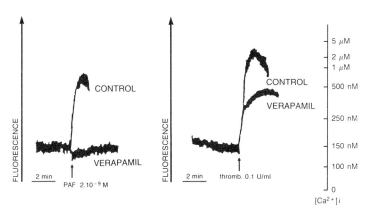

Figure 6 Effect of verapamil 10⁻⁴ M on PAF and thrombin-induced stimulations of quin 2-loaded platelets.

The three compounds studied, BN 52020, BN 52021 and BN 52022, inhibited dose-dependently the aggregation of rabbit washed platelets induced by PAF; the inhibition regression lines for the two concentrations of PAF used were nearly parallel as indicated by the slopes of the regression lines (Fig. 7). The most potent compound was BN 52021 with calculated IC$_{50}$ values of 1.4 x 10⁻⁷ M and 2.62 x 10⁻⁷ M for 2.5 x 10⁻¹⁰ M and 5 x 10⁻¹⁰ M of PAF, respectively. BN 52020 and BN 52022 were about one order of magnitude less potent, the less active compound being BN 52022.

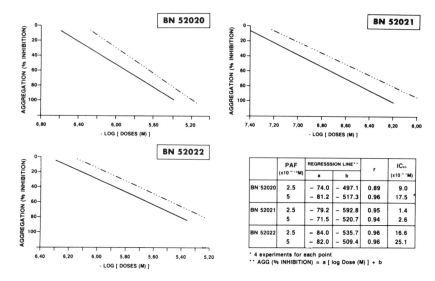

Figure 7   Dose-dependent inhibitions of PAF induced aggregation by BN 52020, BN 52021 and 52022. on rabbit washed platelets.

Effect of BN 52021 on the [^{32}P]-Phosphatidic Acid Increase Induced by PAF in Platelets

BN 52021 also dose-dependently inhibited [^{32}P] PA radioactivity increase after platelet stimulation, induced by 10^{-9} M PAF. The level of phosphatidic acid, when measured 60 seconds after stimulation was reduced by 85% with 10^{-5} M BN 52021, by 39% with 10^{-6} M BN 52021, and only by 20% with 10^{-7} M of the drug.

DISCUSSION

The increase in intracellular free calcium induced by PAF in platelets may be partially attributed to calcium influx but also to the discharge of intracellular calcium from internal stores (12). Inositol 1, 4, 5 triphosphate (IP$_3$), formed from agonist-induced hydrolysis of phosphatidylinositol bisphosphate (PIP$_2$) by phospholipase C, has been proposed as the mediator of internal calcium release (3, 26). This change in [Ca^{2+}]$_i$ is transient as indicated in our results, but a second application of PAF does not produce any signal, whereas platelets are still able to react to other stimulations reflecting PAF receptors desensitization. This phenomenon has already been described by Hallam *et al.* (12) using a similar method and is also known for other cells or tissues (19, 29); these results prove the good relationship between PAF receptor stimulation and $[Ca^{2+}]_i$ increase.

Furthermore, if concentrations higher than 2×10^{-9} M of PAF are used to induce $[Ca^{2+}]_i$ increase, a rapid aggregation occurs which shows that washed quin 2-loaded platelets are still able to react in a physiological manner, even if the quin 2 indicator exerted a partial chelation of $[Ca^{2+}]_i$ (14).

The data reported here demonstrate that ginkgolides block specifically the $[Ca^{2+}]_i$ increase in platelet cytoplasm induced by PAF stimulation with the same potency as they block aggregation. These results confirm their specific PAF receptor antagonistic properties.

Kadsurenone, another PAF-antagonist (27), has shown the same profile of activity. The activity of these compounds is highly structure-related since one OH group less or more with regard to BN 52021 decreases the effects of the drug by one order of magnitude. At doses effective on $[Ca^{2+}]_i$, BN 52021 also inhibited phosphatidic acid production induced by PAF in rabbit platelets, which proves a breaking off in the early biochemical events occurring at membrane level during platelet activation. This inhibitory effect on phosphoinositides cleavage had already been shown on human platelets by Simon *et al.* (28).

By inhibiting PAF binding to its receptor, ginkgolides may block the PAF-induced activation of a stimulatory protein for cGTP hydrolysis and thus the phospholipase C activation, enzyme which cleaves inositol phospholipids (7).

The calcium antagonist verapamil has been shown to inhibit *in vitro* [³H]-PAF binding (33) and to reduce markedly or abrogate different biologic activities induced by PAF, such as platelet activation (23), contraction of lung smooth muscle (8) or cardiac and circulatory disturbances (2).

But, contrary to ginkgolides, verapamil impaired both PAF and thrombin induced quin 2 signal because it exerts a dual effect: inhibition of calcium influx and interaction with PAF binding on its receptor.

Furthermore, verapamil possesses side effects by its own on vascular and cardiac functions.

Since a potential role for PAF has been ascribed in various pathologies such as inflammation, allergy, sepsis or thrombosis, the ginkgolides might be of therapeutic interest, not only by inhibiting the direct effects of PAF such as lung tissue contraction, vascular tone increase or aggregation, but also by blocking the formation of the other mediators, thromboxane A_2 or leukotrienes, which follows PAF receptor stimulation. In addition, the role of PAF in the late asthmatic responses has been pointed out (21), and this mediator could trigger the recruitment of inflammatory cells such as neutrophils, macrophages/monocytes and eosinophils seen in bronchial tissue from asthmatic patients (22). Ginkgolides may thus provide a new insight in the treatment of bronchial asthma. These compounds could also be useful tools for structure-activity relationship studies in order to elucidate the conformation of the binding site for PAF.

References

1. Affolter, H. et al. *Ca²⁺ as messenger of 5HT₂-receptor stimulation in human blood platelets.* Naunyn Schmiedeberg's Arch Pharmacol 1984; 325: 337-342.

2. Alloatti, G. et al. *Protective effect of verapamil on the cardiac and circulatory alterations induced by platelet-activating factor.* J Cardiovasc Pharmacol 1987; 9: 181-186.

3. Berridge, M.J. *Inositol trisphosphate and diacylglycerol as second messengers.* Biochem J 1984; 220: 345-360.

4. Braquet, P., Godfroid, J.J. *PAF-acether specific binding sites: 2. Design of specific antagonists.* TIPS 1986; 7: 397-403.

5. Braquet, P. *The Ginkgolides: Potent plateletactivating factor antagonists isolated from Ginkgo biloba L.: Chemistry, pharmacology and clinical applications.* Drugs of the Future 1987; 12: 643-699.

6. Braquet, P., Godfroid, J.J. *Conformational properties of the PAF-acether receptor in platelets based on structure-activity studies.* In: Platelet Activating Factor. F. Snyder (Ed.). Plenum Press: New York 1987; 191-236.

7. Braquet, P., Paubert-Braquet, M. *A tentative approach of platelet-activating factor membrane signalling process in platelets, using BN 52021 a specific antagonist.* Thrombosis Rev; in press.

8. Camussi, G. et al. *Platelet-activating factor mediated contraction of rabbit lung strip: Pharmacologic modulation.* Immunopharmacol 1983; 6: 87-96.

9. Cazenave, J.P. et al. *Aggregation of rabbit platelets by platelet-activating factor is independent of the release reaction and the arachidonate pathway and inhibited by membrane-active drugs.* Lab Invest 1979; 41: 275-285.

10. Fouque, F., Vargaftig, B.B. *Triggering by PAF-acether and adrenaline of cyclooxygenase independent platelet aggregation.* Br J Pharmacol 1984; 83: 625-633.

11. Goetzl, E.J. et al. *Novel effects of 1-0-hexadecyl-2-acyl-sn-glycero-3-phosphorylcholine mediators on human leukocyte function: Delineation of the specific roles of the acyl substituents.* Biochem Biophys Res Commun 1980; 94: 881-887.

12. Hallam, T.J. et al. *Stimulus-response coupling in human platelets.* Biochem J 1984; 218: 819-827.

13. Hallam, T.J. et al. *The role of cytoplasmic free calcium in the responses of quin 2 loaded human platelets to vasopressin.* Biochem J 1984; 221: 897-901.

14. Hatayama, K. et al. *Fluorescent Ca²⁺ indicator quin 2 as an intracellular Ca²⁺ antagonist in platelet reaction.* Thrombosis Res 1985; 38: 505-512.

15. Hwang, S.B. et al. *Specific receptor sites for 1-O-acetyl-sn-glycero-3-phosphocholine (platelet-activating factor) on rabbit platelet and guinea pig smooth muscle membranes.* Biochemistry 1983; 22: 4756-4763.

16. Jolles, J. et al. *Calcium-dependent turnover of brain phosphoinositides in vitro after prelabelling in vivo.* Biochem Biophys Acta 1981; 666: 90-98.

17. Kitagawa, S. et al. *Effects of four types of reagents on ADP-induced aggregation and Ca²⁺ mobilization of bovine blood platelets.* Biochem Biophys Acta 1984; 798: 210-215.

18. Kloprogge, E., Akkerman, J.W. *Binding kinetics of PAF-acether (1-O-alkyl-2-acetyl-sn-glycero-3-phosphocholine) to intact human platelets.* Biochem J 1984; 223: 901-909.

19. Maridonneau-Parini, I. et al. *Desensitization to PAF-induced bronchoconstriction and to activation of alveolar macrophages by repeated inhalations of PAF in guinea pig.* Biochem Biophys Res Commun 1985; 131(1): 42-49.

20. Mauco, G. et al. *Platelet-activating factor (PAF-acether) promotes an early degradation of phosphatidylinostiol 4,5, biphosphate in rabbit platelets.* FEBS Lett 1983; 153(2): 361-365.

21. Morley, J. et al. *The platelet in asthma.* Lancet 1984; 2: 1142-1144.

22. Nakamura, T. et al. *Platelet-activating factor in late asthmatic response.* Int Archs Allergy Appl Immunol 1987; 82: 57-61.

23. Nayler, W.G. et al. *A protective effect of verapamil on hypoxic heart muscle.* Cardiovasc Res 1976; 10: 650-662.

24. Purdon, A.D. et al. *Cytoplasmic free calcium concentration in porcine platelets. Regulation by an intracellular nonmitochondrial calcium*

pump and increase after thrombin stimulation. Biochem Biophys Acta 1984; 800: 178-187.

25. Rink, T.J. et al. *Cytoplasmic free Ca^{2+} in human platelets: Ca^{2+} thresholds and Ca-independent activation for shape-change and secretion.* FEBS Lett 1982; 148(1): 21-26.

26. Sage, S.O., Rink, T.J. *Inhibition by forskolin of cytosolic calcium rise, shape change and aggregation in quin 2-loaded human platelets.* FEBS Lett 1985; 188: 135-140.

27. Shen, T.Y. et al. *Characterization of a platelet-activating factor receptor antagonist isolated from haifenteng (Piper futokadsura): Specific inhibition of in vitro and in vivo platelet-activating factor-induced effects.* Proc Natl Acad Sci USA 1985; 82: 672-675.

28. Simon, M.F. et al. *Effect of BN 52021, a specific antagonist of platelet-activating factor (PAF acether), on calcium movements and phosphatidic acid production induced by PAF-acether in human platelets.* Thrombosis Res 1987; 45: 299-309.

29. Stimler, N.P., O'Flaherty, J.T. *Spasmogenic properties of platelet-activating factor: Evidence for a direct mechanism in the contractile response of pulmonary tissues.* Am J Pathol 1983; 113(1): 75-84.

30. Tsien, R.Y. et al. *Calcium homeostasis in intact lymphocytes: Cytoplasmic free calcium monitored with a new intracellularly trapped fluorescent indicator.* J Cell Biol 1982; 94: 325-334.

31. Valone, F.H. et al. *Specific binding of phospholipid platelet-activating factor by human platelets.* J Immunol 1982; 129: 1637-1641.

32. Vargaftig, B.B. et al. *Background and present status of research on platelet-activating factor (PAF-acether).* Ann NY Acad Sci 1981; 370: 119-137.

33. Wade, P.J. et al. *Effect of calcium and calcium antagonists on [³H]-PAF-acether binding to washed human platelets.* Thrombosis Res 1986; 41: 251-262.

Ginkgolides - Chemistry, Biology, Pharmacology and Clinical Perspectives. P. Braquet (Ed.)
Copyright © 1988, J.R. Prous Science Publishers, S.A.

PAF-ACETHER METABOLISM AND SIGNALLING PROCESS: INHIBITION BY GINKGOLIDES

Marie-Françoise Simon, Valérie Lamant, Hafida Lachachi, Monique Plantavid, Gérard Mauco, Hugues Chap and Louis Douste-Blazy

INSERM Unité 101, Biochimie des Lipides, Hôpital Purpan, F-31059 Toulouse Cédex, France

INTRODUCTION

Since its discovery, and especially after knowing its structure, platelet-activating factor, or PAF-acether (1-O-alkyl-2-acyl-*sn*-glycero-3-phosphocholine), has been considered as an autenthic chemical mediator inducing very specific biochemical events in its target cells and undergoing various metabolic conversions leading to its deactivation. Concerning its biochemical effects, evidence has now accumulated indicating that PAF-acether stimulates platelets by triggering phospholipase C activation (7, 22, 31). As reviewed elsewhere (2, 24), this leads to the generation of two intracellular messengers, diacylglycerol (DAG) and inositol-1,4,5-trisphosphate (IP3). These two compounds are derived from phosphatidylinositol-4,5-bisphosphate (PIP2) and were shown to activate protein kinase C and to mobilize calcium from sarcoplasmic reticulum (dense tubular system in the case of platelets), respectively. Accompanying these events, opening of putative receptor operated channels leads to a large influx of external calcium through the plasma membrane (14, 15), which in the case of PAF-acether

---

Address all correspondence to: Pr. Hugues Chap, INSERM Unité 101, Biochimie des Lipides, Hôpital Purpan, F-31059 Toulouse Cédex, France.

seems to represent a very critical phenomenon in the process of platelet activation (12).

On the other hand, platelets are able to deactivate PAF-acether through a metabolic conversion into its membrane precursor phospholipid, *i.e.,* 1-O-alkyl-2-acyl-*sn*-glycero-3-phosphocholine or alkylacyl GPC, which requires the subsequent action of an acetylhydrolase and of a transacylase (1, 18, 21, 26, 34, 35). Since the former enzyme displays a cytosolic localization, it could be speculated that processing of PAF-acether by platelets might require previous internalization involving transmembrane movement of PAF (on the other hand the nature of the membrane containing transacylase still remains poorly defined).

Previous studies on PAF-acether metabolism have shown that conversion into alkylacyl GPC occurs at a much slower rate than the biological response (26, 35). Moreover, this metabolism seems to be independent of platelet aggregation (35). However, the inactive deacetylated metabolite of PAF (1-O-alkyl-2-lyso-*sn*-glycero-3-phosphocholine or lyso-PAF-acether) is metabolized at a 10-fold lower rate compared to PAF-acether (26, 35). This suggests that some link might still occur between PAF metabolism and PAF biological action.

A useful tool to study a possible relationship between PAF metabolism and PAF biological effects is represented by specific antagonists acting at the receptor level, *i.e.,* at the earliest step of PAF interaction with the platelet membrane (8, 13). In this respect, ginkgolides A, B and C revealed very powerful and highly specific antagonists of PAF, inhibiting biological effects as well as specific binding of PAF to its putative membrane receptor (8). The present chapter reviews some of our recent studies dealing with the effects of ginkgolides (BN 52020, 52021 and 52022) on calcium movements and phospholipid metabolism in blood platelets (19, 20, 32). Metabolic studies involve both phosphoinositide turnover and PAF conversion into alkylacyl GPC.

EFFECT OF BN 52021 ON CALCIUM MOVEMENTS AND PHOSPHOLIPASE C ACTIVATION IN HUMAN PLATELETS

As discussed in the Introduction, cytoplasmic free calcium concentration $[Ca^{++}]_i$ suddenly increases in platelets stimulated by PAF. A convenient procedure to follow $[Ca^{++}]_i$ changes is the use of fluorescent dyes such as quin 2, which can be easily introduced into intact cells. Under these conditions, platelets stimulated by PAF in a calcium free medium (1 mM EGTA) display a small fluorescence signal corresponding to an increase of $[Ca^{++}]_i$ from the basal value (80-100 nM) to a maximal value ranging around 300 nM (15,

32). Since calcium is absent from the extracellular medium, it is currently admitted that $[Ca^{++}]_i$ raise corresponds to calcium release from dense tubular system (calcium mobilization), as a consequence of IP3 generation. However, absolute values of $[Ca^{++}]_i$ determined under these conditions are probably underestimated, owing to the high buffering capacity of quin 2 introduced in platelet cytosol in millimolar concentrations (33).

When the same procedure is applied to platelets suspended in a medium containing 1 mM calcium, $[Ca^{++}]_i$ reaches higher values in the micromolar range. This is thought to reflect a large influx of calcium through the plasma membrane by a still poorly-defined mechanism. Since platelets seem to lack voltage dependent channels, the presence of receptor operated channels has been suggested (12, 14). However, at this time, it is not yet clear whether channel opening involves GTP binding proteins or, as shown recently in sea urchin eggs (17), the formation of inositol-1,3,4,5-tetrakisphosphate (IP4), a phosphorylation derivative of IP3.

By using this experimental model, we were able to show that BN 52021, the most potent PAF antagonist among ginkgolides, was able to inhibit both calcium mobilization and calcium influx induced by PAF. Increasing doses of the drug were necessary to suppress the calcium signals evoked by increasing concentrations of PAF and both calcium mobilization and calcium influx displayed a similar sensitivity (32).

Since at least one of these events (calcium mobilization) is related to PIP2 hydrolysis by phospholipase C, we also focused on the effects of BN 52021 on phosphoinositide metabolism. PIP2 hydrolysis generates IP3 as a hydrosoluble product and DAG as a lipophilic compound. But determination of IP3 generation requires a previous labelling with [3H]inositol, which involves rather long incubation of platelets prior to stimulation studies. Moreover, IP3 is the object of a very active metabolism involving essentially a specific phosphatase (11), making difficult quantitative determinations required in pharmacological studies. The same is true for DAG, which is either deacylated by plasma membrane DAG/monoacylglycerol lipases (23) or converted into phosphatidic acid (PA) by DAG kinase (9). For these reasons, and owing to a higher metabolic stability of this phospholipid, PA synthesis, as detected by [32P] incorporation, remains the most sensitive as well as the most convenient way to detect phospholipase C activation in stimulated platelets. We also found that PA formation elicited by PAF is specifically inhibited by BN 52021, and the drug remained without effect against PA synthesis evoked by thrombin. As for calcium movements, the inhibition of PA synthesis by BN 52021 was dose-dependent (32). However, the concentrations of ginkgolide necessary to inhibit PA synthesis were significantly higher than those required to suppress calcium movements. Such a result was unexpected when considering the fact that at least calcium mobilization directly depends on PIP2 hydrolysis by phospholipase C. However, PIP2 is not the only substrate of phospholipase C, which probably also degrades phosphatidylinositol-4-phosphate (PIP) and phosphatidylinositol (PI). In agreement with this, PA synthesis displays a PAF-dose-dependence curve different from those of calcium movements, since maximal PA production is obtained at PAF concentrations about 10-fold higher than those giving a maximal calcium mobilization of calcium influx (32).

In conclusion of this first study, BN 52021 clearly appears to specifically inhibit the various biochemical events involved in membrane signal transduction following PAF interactions with its putative receptor. Since the same events triggered by thrombin remain essentially unmodified, one can propose that BN 52021 leaves intact the biochemical machinery involved in membrane signalling processes, including GTP binding proteins, calcium channels and phospholipase C. This further illustrates the specificity of BN 52021 *vis a vis* PAF and gives additional support to the view that calcium movements and phospholipase C are obligatory steps in the mechanism of platelet activation by PAF.

Another consequence of PAF interaction with platelets is the metabolic conversion by which platelets inactivate the chemical mediator. Although a link between PAF binding to its membrane receptor and PAF metabolism is apparently much less expected than the direct relationship existing with phosphoinositide metabolism, ginkgolides proved to be very useful to investigate this point.

EFFECTS OF GINKGOLIDES ON PAF-ACETHER METABOLISM IN RABBIT PLATELETS

For this purpose, rabbit platelets were chosen in view of their higher metabolic activity towards PAF. As shown previously (26, 35), rabbit platelets convert [3H]PAF into [3H]alkylacyl GPC without any accumulation of [3H]lyso-PAF. BN 52021 is able to suppress such a conversion, and [3H]PAF remains unchanged in the incubation medium, indicating that PAF metabolism is blocked at or before the step of acetylhydrolase (19).

Our incubation conditions involved the presence of bovine serum albumin in the medium (2.5 g/l), which avoided platelet aggregation at the PAF concentration used (1.6 nM). Indeed, it was verified on various platelet suspensions that around 30 nM PAF was required to induce aggregation. This observation agrees with the finding that platelet aggregation is not required for PAF metabolic conversion by intact platelets.

However, it does not mean that PAF metabolism is unrelated to its interaction with the membrane receptor, since PAF conversion can be inhibited by an antagonist competing for PAF specific binding to platelets. Besides the fact that this observation was recently confirmed with other structurally different PAF antagonists (16), three additional arguments favor the view that PAF metabolism by platelets involves in some way its previous binding to membrane receptor:

1) In a more recent study (20), we have compared the relative potencies of ginkgolides A, B and C (BN 52020, 52021 and 52022) in inhibiting PAF metabolism. The three compounds displayed the same order of potency (BN 52021 > BN 52020 > BN 52022) as that previously defined for inhibition of aggregation or of PAF specific binding (8).

2) Although lyso-PAF is metabolized at a much slower rate than PAF itself by intact platelets, BN 52021 remained inactive against lyso-PAF under these conditions (19).

3) PAF conversion by platelet lysates was unaffected by BN 52021 concentrations (up to 1 mM) giving a maximal effect in platelet suspensions. This further indicated that the ginkgolide was inactive against the two enzymes involved in PAF metabolism, *i.e.,* cytosolic acetylhydrolase and particulate transacylase. Although this has never been reported, such an effect might be expected from PAF antagonists which are structural analogs of PAF, like those used by Homa *et al.* (16).

Moreover, the latter experiments revealed that, in contrast to platelet suspension, lyso-PAF was metabolized even more rapidly than PAF itself in platelet lysates, again with no effect of BN 52021. This led us to suggest that metabolism of both PAF and its lyso derivative in intact platelets requires a previous transmembrane movement allowing accessibility to the cytosolic acetylhydrolase and (or) to the membranous transacylase. In this respect, although the precise localization of transacylase is not yet established, this enzyme has been shown to transfer arachidonic acid from diacyl phospholipids (mainly phosphatidylcholine) to 1-O-alkyl-*sn*-glycero-3-phosphocholine (18). Since we previously found that arachidonic acid containing phospholipids displays an internal localization (either the inner leaflet of the plasma membrane or other intracellular membranes) (10, 25, 28), transacylase probably also displays an internal localization.

A faster transfer of PAF, compared to lyso-PAF, through the platelet membrane might be explained by a somewhat higher hydrophobicity owing to the presence of the acetyl group in the sn2 position. Indeed, literature data are now available concerning the ability of PAF to cross the plasma membrane (4, 30). However, the specific inhibition exerted on this transfer by BN 52021 strongly suggests that interaction of PAF with its receptor is involved in some way in PAF translocation across the membrane.

At the present state of our knowledge, any interpretation of these data can only be speculative. Regardless, two different working hypotheses can be proposed to explain such a relationship between PAF specific binding to platelets and PAF internalization leading to further metabolism:

1) PAF binds to a receptor present in the external face of the membrane and, as for many other chemical mediators, hormones and growth factors, the complex PAF-receptor becomes internalized. However, this would not allow a direct interaction of PAF with the cytosolic acetylhydrolase, further processing of ligand-receptor complexes being normally achieved after fusion of the endocytotic vesicles with lysosomes (29).

2) Besides the well-known biochemical events described above leading to platelet activation (calcium movements, diacylglycerol generation, *etc.*), PAF receptor interaction also induces some change in the platelet membrane allowing a faster translocation of PAF to the cell interior. Such a transmembrane movement might esentially concern those PAF molecules inserted in a non-specific way in the external leaflet of the surface membrane.

In favor of the second hypothesis, one could recall previous studies showing that under certain conditions of platelet activation (these include stimulation of rabbit platelets by PAF), some important changes of membrane phospholipid asymmetry can occur (5, 6). These concern essentially a transfer of phosphatidylserine from the internal to the external leaflet of the platelet membrane, leading to the exposure of procoagulant phospholipids, but it is accompanied by an inverse movement of sphingomyelin (flip-flop mechanism).

Another strong argument fitting in with the second hypothesis is the observation by Pieroni and Hanahan (27) that non-radioactive PAF stimulates metabolism of [3H]lyso-PAF in rabbit platelets. By comparing with our own data, this would indicate that platelet activation by PAF could introduce some membrane change allowing lyso-PAF (as well as PAF itself) to cross the platelet membrane, thus allowing further metabolism. Such a postulated membrane change would not be specific of PAF itself, since it also occurs in thrombin-stimulated platelets (27).

So, one can reasonably conclude from the second part of these studies that the very specific antagonistic activity of ginkgolides against PAF-acether allowed us to evidence a possible relationship between PAF receptor interaction and PAF metabolism. The latter one involves a yet poorly defined membrane change allowing an accelerated exchange of this phospholipid and its lyso derivative between the two halves of the membrane. Although no additional information on this point is available so far, we shall discuss in the conclusion part some possible relationship between the two aspects of these studies concerning the two kinds of PAF-acether effects on platelet phospholipid metabolism.

CONCLUSIONS

There is no doubt that platelet activation by PAF-acether follows the rather general mechanism of membrane signal transduction described for many other chemical mediators and involving calcium movements together with phospolipase C activation (2, 24). Experimental data obtained in other studies dealing with specific binding of PAF to intact platelets or platelet membranes (8, 13), as well as the studies reported herein all fit in with this general scheme. In this respect, the discovery of various specific antagonists of PAF such as ginkgolides proved to be very useful to investigate this problem (besides the fact that they represent promising therapeutic agents for various pathological situations).

However, a main problem with PAF-acether is its lipidic nature, which probably has hampered any biochemical identification of its receptor, although very elegant photoreactive analogs were recently synthesized (3). In other words, there is not yet evidence that PAF receptor is exposed to the external face of the membrane, as in the case of other small or peptidic hydrosoluble mediators, which are virtually unable to cross the lipid bilayer. The same remark can be made for PAF-acether antagonists, which all share some hydrophobic characteristics. In this respect, the tertiobutyl group of ginkgolides has been found to be very critical for the PAF antagonistic activity (8).

The second part of the present study draws attention to the problem of PAF-acether translocation across the platelet plasma membrane. Although this event is essentially related to PAF metabolism and rather appears as a consequence of PAF interaction with its putative receptor, one should keep in mind at least one example of a lipidic mediator whose target protein displays a cytosolic localization. This is the case of phorbol esters, which specifically interact with protein kinase C, as shown either by evidence of enzyme activation or by detection of specific binding (24). So the question still remains open as to whether PAF receptor is an external or an internal protein, possibly belonging in the latter case to the group of peripheral proteins, as in the case of protein kinase C. However, this will remain speculative in the absence of any additional information.

Finally, a last question concerns, at the reverse, the possible relationship between platelet activation and the accelerated translocation of PAF and lyso-PAF through the plasma membrane. In confirmation to previous studies of Touqui *et al.* (34), we also found that PAF metabolism is unrelated to platelet aggregation. However, in the same way as various platelet responses (shape change, aggregation, secretion of various granule populations) require different threshold PAF concentrations (suggesting different requirement for receptor occupancy), we found some dose dissociation between different signalling processes, such as calcium movements, on one hand, and diacylglycerol generation (reflected by PA formation), on the other hand. This was shown both by varying PAF concentration and by following dose-dependent inhibition by ginkgolides, especially BN 52021 (32). This approach will probably provide additional interesting information allowing to better define to which PAF-acether-evoked event this membrane change is related.

References

1. Alam, I., Smith, J.B., Silver, M.J. *Metabolism of platelet-activating factor by blood platelets and plasma.* Lipids 1983; 18: 534-538.

2. Berridge, M.J. *Inositol trisphosphate and diacylglycerol as second messengers.* Biochem J 1984; 220: 345-360.

3. Bette-Bobillo, P., Bienvenue, A., Broquet, C., Maurin, L. *Synthesis and characterization of a radioiodinated, photoreactive and physiologically active analogue of platelet-activating factor.* Chem Phys Lipids 1985; 37: 215-226.

4. Bette-Bobillo, P., Luxenbourg, A., Bienvenue, A. *Interaction between blood components and a spin-labeled analogue of PAF-acether.* Biochim Biophys Acta 1986; 860: 194-200.

5. Bevers, E.M., Comfurius, P., Benveniste, J., Zwaal, R.F.A. *The effect of PAF-acether on the procoagulant activity of rabbit platelets.* Thromb Haemost 1983; 50: 14.

6. Bevers, E.M., Comfurius, P., Zwaal, R.F.A. *Changes in membrane phospholipid distribution during platelet activation.* Biochim Biophys Acta 1983; 736: 57-66.

7. Billah, M.M., Lapetina, E.G. *Platelet-activating factor stimulates metabolism of phosphoinositides in horse platelets: Possible relationship to calcium mobilization during stimulation.* Proc Natl Acad Sci USA 1983; 80: 965-968.

8. Braquet, P., Godfroid, J.J. *PAF-acether specific binding sites: 2. Design of specific antagonists.* TIPS 1986; 7: 397-403.

9. Call, F.L. II, Rubert, M. *Diglyceride kinase in human platelets.* J Lipid Res 1973; 14: 466-474.

10. Chap, H., Perret, B., Mauco, G., Plantavid, M., Laffont, F., Simon, M.F., Douste-Blazy, L. *Organization and role of platelet membrane phospholipids as studied with phospholipases*

A2 *from various venoms and phospholipases C from bacterial origin.* Toxicol 1982; 20: 291-298.

11. Connolly, T.M., Lawing, W.J., Majerus, P. *Protein kinase C phosphorylates human platelet inositol trisphosphate 5'-phosphomonoesterase, increasing the phosphatase activity.* Cell 1986; 46: 951-958.

12. Drummond, A.H., MacIntyre, D.E. *Platelet inositol lipid metabolism and calcium flux.* In: Platelets in Biology and Pathology, III. D.E. MacIntyre, J.L. Gordon (Eds.). Elsevier: Amsterdam 1987; 373-441.

13. Godfroid, J.J., Braquet, P. *PAF-acether specific binding sites: 1. Quantitative SAR study of PAF-acether isosteres.* TIPS 1986; 7: 368-373.

14. Hallam, T.J., Rink, T.J. *Agonists stimulate divalent calcium channels in the plasma membrane of human platelets.* FEBS Lett 1985; 186: 175-179.

15. Hallam, T.J., Sanchez, A., Rink, T.J. *Stimulus response coupling in human platelets. Changes evoked by platelet-activating factor in cytoplasmic free calcium monitored with the fluorescent calcium indicator quin 2.* Biochem J 1984; 218: 819-827.

16. Homa, H., Kumar, R., Hanahan, D.J. *Some unique features of the metabolic conversion of platelet-activating factor (AGEPC) to alkyl acyl PC by washed rabbit platelets.* Archiv Biochem Biophys 1987; 252: 259-268.

17. Irvine, R.M., Moor, R.M. *Micro-injection of inositol 1, 3, 4, 5-tetrakisphosphate activates sea urchin eggs by a mechanism dependent on external calcium.* Biochem J 1986; 240: 301-304.

18. Kramer, R.M., Patton, G.M., Pritzker, C.R., Deykin, D. *Metabolism of platelet-activating factor in human platelets. Transacylase-mediated synthesis of 1-O-alkyl-2-arachidono-yl-sn-glycero-3-phosphocholine.* J Biol Chem

1984; 259: 13316-13320.

19. Lachachi, H., Plantavid, M., Simon, M.F., Chap, H., Braquet, P., Douste-Blazy, L. *Inhibition of, transmembrane movement and metabolism of platelet-activating factor (PAF-acether) by a specific antagonist, BN 52021.* Biochem Biophys Res Commun 1985; 132: 460-466.

20. Lamant, V., Mauco, G., Braquet, P., Chap, H., Douste-Blazy, L. *Inhibition of platelet-activating factor (PAF-acether) metabolism by three specific antagonists from Ginkgo biloba.* Biochem Pharmacol 1987; in press.

21. Malone, B., Lee, T.C., Snyder, F. *Inactivation of platelet-activating factor by rabbit platelets. Lyso-platelet activating factor as a key intermediate with phosphatidylcholine as a source of arachidonic acid in its conversion to a tetraenoic acylated product.* J Biol Chem 1985; 260: 1531-1534.

22. Mauco, G., Chap, H., Douste-Blazy, L. *Platelet-activating factor (PAF-acether) promotes an early degradation of phosphatidylinositol-4,5-bisphosphate in rabbit platelets.* FEBS Lett 1983; 153: 361-365.

23. Mauco, G., Fauvel, J., Chap, H., Douste-Blazy, L. *Studies on enzymes related to diacylglycerol production in activated platelets. II. Subcellular distribution, enzymatic properties and positional specificity of diacylglycerol- and monoacylglycerol-lipases.* Biochim Biophys Acta 1984; 796: 169-177.

24. Nishizuka, Y. *The role of protein kinase C in cell surface signal transduction.* Nature 1984; 308: 693-698.

25. Perret, B., Chap, H., Douste-Blazy, L. *Asymmetric distribution of arachidonic acid in the plasma membrane of human platelets. A determination using purified phospholipases and a rapid method for membrane isolation.* Biochim Biophys Acta 1979; 556: 434-446.

26. Pieroni, G., Hanahan, D.J. *Metabolic behavior of acetyl glyceryl ether phosphorylcholine on interaction with rabbit platelets.* Archiv Biochem Biophys 1983; 224: 485-493.

27. Pieroni, G., Hanahan, D.J. *Effect of acetylglyceryl ether phosphocholine (platelet-activating factor) and thrombin on acylation*

of exogenous lysophosphoglycerides in rabbit platelets. Biochim Biophys Acta 1986; 877: 61-67.

28. Plantavid, M., Perret, B., Chap, H., Simon, M.F., Douste-Blazy, L. *Asymmetry of arachidonic acid metabolism in the phospholipids of the human platelet membrane as studied with purified phospholipases.* Biochim Biophys Acta 1982; 693: 451-460.

29. Schlessinger, J. *The mechanism and role of hormone-induced clustering of membrane receptors.* Trends Biochem Sci 1980; 5: 210-214.

30. Shneider, E., Haest, C.W.M., Deuticke, B. *Transbilayer reorientation of platelet-activating factor in the erythrocyte membrane.* FEBS Lett 1986; 198: 311-314.

31. Shukla, S.D. *Platelet-activating factor-stimulated formation of inositol triphosphate in platelets and its regulation by various agents including calcium, indomethacin, CV-3988 and forskolin.* Archiv Biochem Biophys 1985; 240: 674-681.

32. Simon, M.F., Chap, H., Braquet, P., Douste-Blazy, L. *Effect of BN 52021, a specific antagonist of platelet-activating factor (PAF-acether), on calcium movements and phosphatidic acid production induced by PAF-acether in human platelets.* Thromb Res 1987; 45: 299-309.

33. Simon, M.F., Chap, H., Douste-Blazy, L. *Selective inhibition of human platelet phospholipase A_2 by buffering cytoplasmic calcium with the fluorescent indicator quin 2. Evidence for different calcium sensitivities of phospholipases A_2 and C.* Biochim Biophys Acta 1986; 875: 157-167.

34. Touqui, L., Jacquemin, C., Dumarey, C., Vargaftig, B.B. *1-O-alkyl-2-acyl-sn-glycero-3-phosphorylcholine is the precursor of platelet-activating factor in stimulated rabbit platelets. Evidence for an alkylacetyl-glycerophosphorylcholine cycle.* Biochim Biophys Acta 1985; 833: 111-118.

35. Touqui, L., Jacquemin, C., Vargaftig, B.B. *Conversion of 3H-PAF-acether by rabbit platelets is independent from aggregation: Evidences for a novel metabolite.* Biochem Biophys Res Commun 1983; 110: 890-893.

Ginkgolides - Chemistry, Biology, Pharmacology
and Clinical Perspectives. P. Braquet (Ed.)
Copyright © 1988, J.R. Prous Science Publishers, S.A.

ARTERIAL THROMBOSIS INDUCED BY PAF-ACETHER (1-O-ALKYL -2-ACETYL-SN-GLYCERO-3- PHOSPHOCHOLINE) AND ITS INHIBITION BY GINKGOLIDES

René H. Bourgain[1], Roger Andries[1] and Claire Bourgain[2]

[1]Laboratorium voor Fysiologie en Fysiopathologie and [2]Laboratorium voor Experimentele Pathologie, VUB B-1090 Brussels, Belgium

ABSTRACT

The effect of PAF-acether applied in topical superfusion at 1 μM and the effect of an electrical challenge of 40 μA are described and compared to the results observed after the application of sub-effective molarities of the mediator combined to a sub-effective electrical challenge. Ultrastructural analysis clearly indicates that lesions occur in the endothelial cells such as bleb formation and cellular margin retraction, exposing subintimal tissue to the blood stream. Platelet thrombosis ensues followed by recruitment of leukocytes, in order, neutrophils, monocytic cells and later eosinophils. Blood coagulation is triggered and phagocytosis occurs. All phenomena involved except bleb formation can be inhibited by the administration of the specific PAF-acether antagonist BN 52021, indicating that the *in vivo* thrombotic process is mediated by PAF-acether.

Address all correspondence to: Prof. Dr. R. Bourgain, Lab. voor Fysiologie en Fysiopathologie, VUB Brussels, Laarbeeklaan 103, B-1090 Brussels, Belgium.

INTRODUCTION

Platelet activating factor (PAF-acether) is a very potent mediator involved in many inflammatory and allergic reactions (5, 10). Since its discovery in 1972 by Benveniste (1) it was demonstrated that this agent can induce leukopenia (7), platelet aggregation (6), plasma leakage at the venular site of the vascular compartment (4) followed by arterial hypotension and death.

We described in a previous paper (2) that thrombosis can be induced by superfusion of PAF-acether (1 μM) over a branch of the mesenteric artery in the guinea-pig on condition that the arterial segment was first challenged by an electrical current not exceeding 30 μA by itself insufficient to induce any significant thrombotic reaction. So the question then arose as to the involvement of this mediator in the initiation of arterial and venous thrombosis, as our investigations demonstrated that within minutes following topical application of the mediator, platelet thrombosis developed at the site of superfusion and over time leukocytes invaded the thrombotic mass. Although fragments frequently detached from the thrombus and embolized, its size increased and occlusion of the vascular lumen ultimately occurred. Topical or systemic administration of BN 52021, a ginkgolide extracted from the *Ginkgo biloba* tree and a specific inhibitor of PAF-acether, not only inhibited thrombus formation, but equally prevented recruitment of leukocytes and recurrence of the thrombotic phenomenon attributed to the generation of PAF-like activity in the vessel wall. The question then arose if a higher molarity of the mediator or an electrical challenge of higher intensity were by themselves capable of inducing a comparable thrombotic phenomenon.

Furthermore, in order to study the sequence of the platelet and leukocyte involvement during thromboformation, ultrastuctural analysis was performed using transmission (TEM) and scanning (SEM) electron microscopy on arterial segments challenged by the mediator, the electrical current or the combination of both in appropriate conditions of the choice of current intensity and mediator molarity.

MATERIALS AND METHODS

Male guinea-pigs weighing between 300 and 350 g were used for this investigation. The techniques practiced for anesthesia, thrombus induction, recording of the thrombotic phenomena by optoelectronic analogue computer and sampling of the arterial segments as well as the processing procedures were described in previous papers (3, 8).

PAF-acether (1-0-alkyl-2-acetyl-*sn*-glycero-3-phosphocholine) at 1 μM was applied in topical superfusion in absence of previous electrical challenge.

A DC electrical current of 40 μA was applied onto the artery for 1 minute and the polarity of the current inversed every 5 seconds in order to avoid vasospastic phenomena. Isotonic Ringer solution was applied during and after the application of the electrical challenge and following mediator superfusion.

In another series of experiments using the weak electrical current (< 30 μA), lyso-PAF was used as the co-inductor for thrombus induction.

The thrombotic phenomenon was monitored continuously by the optoelectronic device developed by Bourgain *et al.* (3) for quantification of the discriminant parameters characterizing the thrombus.

For ultrastructural study, the animals were total body perfusion fixed at physiologic pressure through the left common carotid artery using 2.5% glutaraldehyde in 0.1 M cacodylate buffer (pH 7.4, 37°C, 10 min). This fixation was preceded by a short wash (2-3 min) of the arterial tree with 0.1 M cacodylate buffer (37°C, pH 7.4). The mesenterium was excised *in toto* and overnight immersion fixed at 4°C. The arterial segment was carefully dissected out of the mesenteric tissue over a distance of about 5 mm at both sides of the thrombotic site and postfixed in 1% OsO4 for 30 minutes at room temperature.

For transmission electron microscopy, semi-thin sections were made in order to visualize the general aspect of the preparation. When in these controls, practiced every 60 μm, the area of interest was reached, thin sections were made every 2 μm.

For scanning electron microscopy, the arterial specimens were investigated according to the method of Reidy and Schwartz (9). Arterial specimens were taken at regular time intervals following the induction of the thrombus by PAF-acether. Segments were examined at different time intervals ranging from 60 seconds to 20 minutes following thrombus induction, using scanning electron microscopy and 3 specimens at 15 minutes for transmission electron microscopic investigation.

BN 52021 is a specific PAF-acether antagonist isolated from the *Ginkgo biloba* tree (4); its formula is 9H-1,7a-(epoxymethano)-1H,6aH-cyclopenta [c] furo [2,3-b] furo [3', 2': 3,4] cyclopenta [1,2-d] furan-5,9,12-(4H)-trione, 3-tert-butylhexahydro-4, —7B, —11 hydroxy-8 methyl (Inst. H. Beaufour, Le Plessis-Robinson, France). It was demonstrated by our group (5) and by other investigators (7) that this compound inhibits PAF-acether induced platelet aggregation *in vivo* and *in vitro*.

RESULTS

Control Arterial Segments

The endothelial cells demonstrated close contact and no free space could be detected in between them. The internal lamina elastica presented an uninterrupted appearance except for the fenestrae, the smooth muscle cells showed a normally developed endoplasmatic reticulum and mitochondriae. Some elastin and collagen fibers were interspersed between the smooth muscle cells (Fig. 1).

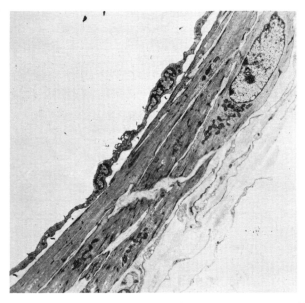

Figure 1   Transmission electron microscopic (TEM) view of normal artery (x4000). For additional information see text.

Electrical Challenge Induced Modifications

By itself the electrical challenge of the arterial wall, on condition it did not exceed 30 μA, did not induce marked changes except for some activation of the endothelium, which at restricted sites not surpassing an area of five to ten adjoining cells, consisted in the elevation of the cellular zone corresponding to the nuclear bag. The low intensity of the current proved to be insufficient to cause retraction of the cellular margins or de-endothelialization (Fig. 2).

Figure 2   Scanning electron microscopic (SEM) view of artery following the topical application of an electrical challenge. Some bleb formation is visible, the endothelial cells demonstrate activation.

Lesions Induced by Topical Application of PAF-Acether at 1 μM

Fifteen arterial specimens were investigated. The subsequent topical superfusion by PAF-acether at 1 μM which corresponds to 0.01 μM inside the vessel specifically affected the vessel wall. The first alterations were characterized by endothelial cell bleb formation. These changes appeared rapidly within the first ten to twelve minutes. The blebs containing well-defined myelin figures floating in electron translucent material underwent rupture, and in breaching the plasma membrane left extensive gaps, which allowed free communication between cytoplasm and blood stream. Some cells desquamated and in doing so greatly extended the de-endothelialized area (Fig. 3), but rarely surpassing a zone of twenty adjoining endothelial cells. The medial structures appeared normal.

Application of a weak electrical challenge (< 30 μA) followed by PAF-acether application at 0.1 μM by itself insufficient to induce thrombosis, resulted equally in extensive thrombus formation. As a result of the combined challenge, some retraction of the cell margins became apparent and platelet adhesion was initiated onto the denuded areas between the endothelial cells. Very rapidly they conflated into a thrombotic mass and

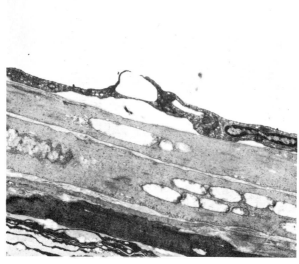

Figure 3   TEM (x10000) of arterial segment submitted to topical application of PAF-acether. Marked bleb formation is present.

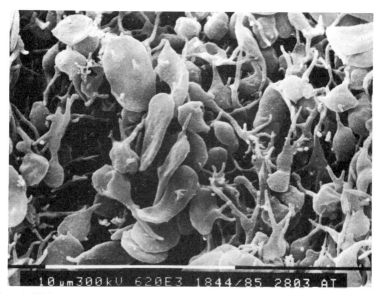

Figure 4   SEM or the induced thrombus consisting mainly of platelets. Some do demonstrate pseudopod formation and assume a spherical form typical for activation. Other platelets appear normal at the periphery of the thrombotic mass.

demonstrated conspicuous pseudopod formation and while losing their discoid form (Fig. 4), developed intercellular connections.

The thrombus did not remain confined to the area of endothelial cell injury but extended beyond that zone covering surrounding endothelium.

Degranulation of the platelets in the thrombus particularly at the periphery was a constant finding. No fibrin was detected and no leukocytes were observed within the first minutes following the onset of thrombus formation. The presence of leukocytes became detectable ten minutes later; the recruitment involved mainly neutrophils.

Thrombi examined at 15 minutes were larger and presented a different aspect. The platelets in these thrombi had become a compact mass, they were mostly degranulated and vacuolized and extended long pseudopods. Monocytes also participated in the invasion of the thrombus while marked phagocytosis of platelet remnants by leukocytes was a common observation. Eosinophilic cell recruitment occurred later; these cells, however, showed very little if any phagocytotic activity as their membranes appeared smooth, without any breaching nor pseudopod formation. In these thrombi fibrin appeared between the cells, mostly confined around the monocytes while extensive phagocytosis of cellular debris of platelet origin both by neutrophils and monocytes became a constant finding. The phagocytic cells demonstrated large phagosomes containing electron dense material which consisted mostly of platelet debris.

Some platelets assumed a balloon-shaped aspect preferentially when located around the eosinophils. Another striking feature was the phagocytosis of fibrin by monocytes; fibrin strands surrounded these cells in dense circular tufts in close apposition to the membrane (Fig. 5). Erythrocytes were found located within crevices of the thrombotic mass; they demonstrated marked deformation, became entrapped in a fibrin mesh, while some underwent phagocytosis.

Numerous apparently normal platelets were observed in the up stream part of the thrombus; however, in its immediate neighborhood, they underwent shape-change and demonstrated pseudopod formation (Fig. 6).

Ultrastructural analysis of specimens submitted to a strong electrical challenge alone also demonstrated comparable features.

Optoelectronic Observations

Inhibition by BN 52021 of the thrombotic phenomenon induced either by PAF-acether 1 μM, the combination of the weak current and the subeffective concentration of PAF-acether 0.1 μM or the challenge by the strong current alone are shown in Figures 7, 8 and 9, respectively.

The inhibition was not only confined to the initiation, development or

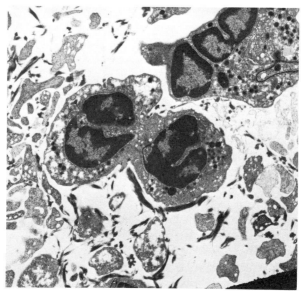

Figure 5   TEM (x10000) of a thrombus which over time becomes invaded by leukocytes demonstrating phagocytosis. Fibrin fibers are also present.

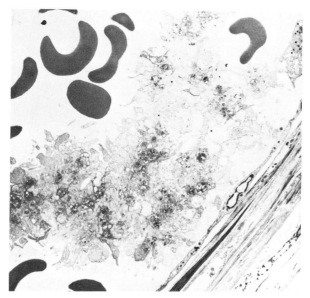

Figure 6   TEM (x4000) of arterial segment containing a platelet thrombus; most platelets are degranulated and demonstrate marked pseudopod formation.

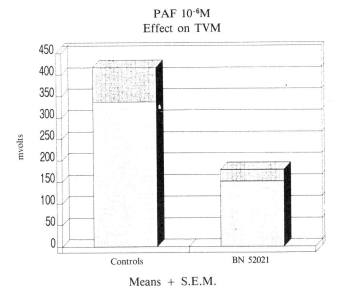

Figure 7   Effect of topical PAF 10^{-6} M on the maximum thrombotic value (TVM = mV x s). The ginkgolide BN 52021 markedly and significantly reduces thromboformation.

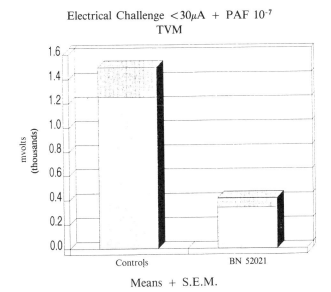

Figure 8   Thromboformation induced by weak electrical challenge (<30 μA) followed by topical superfusion of PAF 10^{-7} M (this electrical challenge and the molarity of PAF are by themselves insufficient to induce thromboformation). The thrombotic parameter TVM is markedly decreased by the ginkgolide BN 52021.

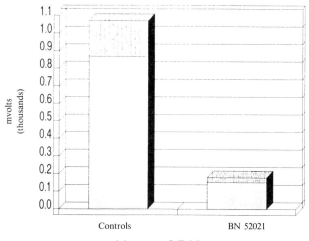

Means + S.E.M.

Figure 9   Electrical challenge (>30 μA) induces thromboformation which is PAF-mediated as it can be inhibited by the ginkgolide BN 52021.

the recurrence of thrombosis, but also to the recruitment of leukocytes. The topical superfusion by the ginkgolide BN 52021 resulted in a marked decrease of the thrombotic phenomena induced by either PAF-acether at the molarity of 1 μM, the combined effect of the weak electrical challenge (< 30 μA) and PAF-acether (0.1 μM) or the application of the electrical challenge of 40 μA.

DISCUSSION

In the guinea-pig, the topical superfusion of a branch of the mesenteric artery by PAF-acether at 0.1 μM following electrical challenge by a current not exceeding 30 μA, invariably results in the generation of a platelet thrombus at the site of superfusion: so does the application of an electrical challenge of 40 μA or the topical superfusion by 1 μM of the mediator, both inducing phenomena highly suggestive for PAF-acether mediation.

Scannig electron microscopic data clearly demonstrate that thrombus formation starts preferentially at the site of application of the electrical challenge and superfusion location.

The sequence of events herein described using electron microscopy demonstrates a well-defined pattern. The combination of the electrical challenge and the superfusion of the mediator results in retraction of the endothelial cell margins and cytoplasmic vacuolization leading to extensive bleb formation. Adhesion of platelets follows and in the process they lose their disc-shaped appearance and extend pseudopods which make contact with the neighbouring platelets developing a loose network. As a result, the whole structure assumes a sponge-like appearance and very rapidly the thrombotic mass starts to cover the surrounding endothelial cells. Most platelets degranulate extensively during this activation process.

In the early phase no leukocytes invade the thrombus, so clearly the platelet activation is independent of leukocyte derived mediators and depends solely on the presence of PAF-acether itself or a PAF-like activity, as described in our previous investigations (2).

The penetration of the neutrophils in the thrombus undoubtedly results from a chemotactic stimulus which originates in the platelets; indeed, no leukocytes are detected before platelet thrombosis occurs. As there is no precise knowledge of the chemical nature of this chemotactic factor, it is believed that PAF-acether is responsible for the leukocyte recruitment because specific antagonists of PAF-acether completely inhibit the phenomenon. Our findings are in accordance with those of O'Flaherty *et al.* (7).

The invasion by monocytic cells seems to be related to the interaction of the phagocytic neutrophils and the platelets. The appearance of the monocytes is accompanied by extensive phagocytosis of platelet debris and fibrin which over time became deposited in the thrombus. Leukotrienes or free oxygen radicals are considered possible candidates for monocytic chemotaxis.

The recruitment of eosinophils, occurring fifteen minutes following the onset of thromboformation, has not yet met any explanation. Indeed, these cells do not demonstrate any phagocytic property, at least not in the present experimental conditions. Furthermore, they do not show degranulation. They represent, however, 12% of the cells as investigated in the examined specimens. The chemotactic stimulus for these cells is not yet revealed but seems to be related to PAF-acether or possibly to an indirect effect of the latter in the process.

The presence of normal platelets in great numbers at the upstream site of the thrombus is indicative that the initial primary stimulus for platelet recruitment, possibly amplified by leukocytic factors, remains highly active in attracting the platelets to the thrombus.

The electrical current at 40 μA or the higher molarity of the mediator (1 μM) demonstrate similar ultrastructural findings and as their effects can be inhibited by specific PAF-acether antagonists such as BN 52021, it seems indicative that in these conditions PAF-like activity or the mediator itself is generated by the arterial wall.

PAF-acether induced changes appear to evolve according to a positive feedback mechanism. This can be explained on the basis of a former observation (2), in which the generation of the mediator or a PAF-like activity, demonstrated in the arterial wall, was liable to inhibition by specific antagonists such as BN 52021.

These observations clearly demonstrate that PAF-acether or a PAF-acether-like activity contributes to the development of platelet thrombosis followed by recruitment of leukocytes, starting with neutrophils, then monocytes and at a later stage eosinophils. The mechanisms of blood coagulation are equally trigered as judged from the presence of fibrin. Phagocytosis of platelets and fibrin by all invading cells except the eosinophils is very intensive at that later stage.

The propensity of the thrombus to become occlusive by the continuous apposition of newly arriving platelets probably results from the generation by the activated platelets and possibly by the endothelial cells, of PAF-acether or a PAF-like activity, which maintains the activation process. The leukocytes aiming, in view of their phagocytotic properties, at the lysis of the thrombus and repermabilization of the arterial vascular lumen, are obviously not capable of offsetting the occlusive trend.

The thrombotic phenomenon induced either by topical application of the mediator, strong electrical challenge or the combination of a weak electrical current with a sub-effective PAF-acether concentration or even with the precursor lyso-PAF (unpublished data), can be offset by topical or general administration of ginkgolides such as BN 52021.

As both lyso-PAF and the weak electrical challenge are by themselves inactive, but in combination induce the thrombotic phenomenon, suggests that the weak electrical challenge has activated the acetyl transferase pathway. This is further confirmed by the observation that the stronger electrical challenge, a full inductor by itself, activates both phospholipase A_2 and acetyl transferase. BN 52021, the ginkgolide derivative, inhibits the thrombotic phenomenon.

These observations clearly indicate that PAF-acether is a mediator involved in thrombosis, at least in our *in vivo* arterial system conditions. The induction of platelet activation, their adhesion onto small restricted denuded subintimal areas followed by conflation into a large thrombus while recruiting leukocytes and triggering blood coagulation appears to have very many features in common with a general process of inflammation mediated by PAF-acether or a PAF-like activity.

ACKNOWLEDGEMENTS

We thank Mrs. H. De Backer-De Zutter and K. Decuyper for their competent assistance. This investigation was supported by grant No. 3.0053.84 from the F.G.W.O. (National Fund for Medical Scientific Research).

References

1. Benveniste, J., Henson, P.M., Cochrane, C.G. *Leukocyte-dependent histamine release from rabbit platelets. The role of IgE, basophils and a platelet activating factor.* J Exp Med 1972; 136: 1356.
2. Bourgain, R.H., Maes, L., Braquet, P., Andries, R., Touqui, L., Braquet, M. *The effect of 1-O-alkyl-2-acetyl-sn-glycero-3-phosphocholine (PAF-acether) on the arterial wall.* Prostaglandins 1985; 30 (2): 185-196.
3. Bourgain, R.H., Six, F. *A continuous registration method in experimental thrombosis.* Thromb Res 1974; 4: 599-607.
4. Braquet, P., Vidal, M., Braquet, M., Hamard, H., Vargaftig, B.B. *Involvement of leukotriens and PAF-acether in the increased microvascular permeability of the rabbit retina.* Agents and Actions 1984; 15: 82-85.
5. Demopoulos, C.A., Pinckard, R.N., Hanahan, D.J. *Platelet-activating factor. Evidence for 1-O-alkyl-2-acetyl-sn-glycerol-3-phosphorylcholine as the active component (a new class of lipid chemical mediators).* J Biol Chem 1979; 254: 9355.
6. Hanahan, D.J., Munder, P.G., Satouchi, K., McManus, L., Pinckard, R.N. *Potent platelet stimulating activity of enantiomers of acetyl glyceryl ether phosphorylcholine and its methoxy analogs.* Biochem Biophys Res Commun 1981; 99 (1): 183-188.
7. O'Flaherty, J.T., Miller, C.H., Lewis, J.C., Wykle, R.L., Bass, D.A., McCall, C.E., Waite, M., De Chatelet, L.R. *Neutrophil responses to platelet-activating factor.* Inflammation 1981; 5 (3): 193-201.
8. Potvliege, P.R., Bourgain, R.H. *Thrombosis induced in vivo in the mesenteric artery of rats: An electron microscopic study of the initial phases.* Br J Exp Pathol 1976; 57: 722-732.
9. Reidy, M.A., Schwartz, S.M. *A technique to investigate surface morphology and endothelial cell replication of small arteries: A study in acute angiotensin-induced hypertensive rats.* Microvasc Res 1982; 24: 158-167.
10. Vargaftig, B.B., Chignard, M., Benveniste, J., Lefort, J., Wal, F. *Background and present status of research on platelet-activating factor (PAF-acether).* Ann NY Acad Sci 1981; 370: 119.

Ginkgolides - Chemistry, Biology, Pharmacology and Clinical Perspectives. P. Braquet (Ed.)
Copyright © 1988, J.R. Prous Science Publishers, S.A.

PLATELET-ACTIVATING FACTORS, NEUTROPHIL GRANULOCYTE FUNCTION AND BN 52021

János Filep, and Éva Földes-Filep

Department of Clinical Pharmacology, Hannover Medical School, Hannover, FRG

INTRODUCTION

Stimulation of certain cells including platelets, macrophages, basophil and polymorphonuclear leukocytes (PMNLs), can lead to the formation of biologically active phosphoglyceride, 1-O-alkyl-2-O-acetyl-sn-glycero-3-phosphorylcholine (platelet-activating factor, PAF) (5), which, in turn, acts itself as stimulus.

It is well documented that PAF induces chemotaxis, aggregation and degranulation of neutrophil granulocytes (9,10,13). Recently, PAF has been reported to enhance formyl-methionyl-leucyl-phenylalanine (fMLP)-stimulated respiratory burst in human neutrophils (4) and to potentiate PMNL degranulation by leukotriene B_4 (LTB_4) and 5-hydroxyeicosatetraenoate (11). PAF can, therefore, be considered as an amplifier of the activation process, and —more generally— as a mediator of inflammation. The use of specific inhibitors of the biosynthesis and/or the effects of PAF may represent useful tools to study its actions and offers new therapeutic approaches. In the last years several PAF antagonists have been developed, including CV 3988 (16), kadsurenone (14) and BN 52021 (rev. in 2). This last compound was found to be the most potent antagonist of PAF on

Address all correspondence to: Dr. János Filep, Department of Clinical Pharmacology, Hannover Medical School, P.O.B. 61 01 80, D-3000 Hannover 61, West Germany.

platelets (8). The chemistry, biology and pharmacology of BN 52021 is discussed in more detail in the other chapters of this Telesymposium.

In this chapter, we describe the direct evidence that BN 52021 specifically inhibits neutrophil responses to PAF through inhibition of PAF binding to its specific receptors.

MATERIALS AND METHODS

Reagents and Buffers

The following were purchased from Sigma Chemical Co. (Deisenhofen, FRG): PAF, fMLP, cytochalasin B, ferricytochrome c, superoxide dismutase, *Micrococcus lysodeikticus,* bovine serum albumin, β-glucuronidase kit and lactate dehydrogenase kit. Quickscint 212 (Zinsser Analytic, Frankfurt, FRG), [^{3}H]-PAF (80 Ci/mmol Amersham, UK). LTB$_4$ was a generous gift of Dr. M. Tsuboshima (ONO Pharmaceuticals, Osaka, Japan). Binding and degranulation assays were performed in a modified Hanks' balanced salt solution (MHBSS; 1.4 mM calcium chloride, 250 μg/ml bovine serum albumin, pH 7.4). Chemotaxis assay was performed in minimal essential medium (Boehringer, Mannheim, FRG).

Cell Preparation

For all experiments neutrophils were prepared from freshly drawn human blood according to the method of Bøyum (1). The resultant cell preparation contained more than 95% neutrophils, less than 5% mononuclear cells, no erythrocytes and less than 1 platelet per 100 leukocytes.

Degranulation Assay

PMNLs (5 x 10^6 cells/ml) were incubated at 37°C for 10 minutes and then the cells were pretreated with cytochalasin B (5 μg/ml) 10 minutes prior to addition of PAF, fMLP or LTB$_4$. BN 52021 was added at different times and doses as indicated. After stimulation the neutrophils were pelleted and the supernatants were retained for subsequent enzyme assay. β-glucuronidase activity was measured by a commercial kit, lysosyme was determined by a turbidimetric assay based on the ability of this enzyme to lyse suspension of *Micrococcus lysodeikticus* (15). Lactate dehydrogenase was monitored as an index of cell viability. The enzyme release obtained was corrected for background and then calculated as the percentage of total cellular enzyme content.

Superoxide Generation

Superoxide generation was determined by measuring superoxide dismutase inhibitable ferricytochrome c reduction by using an extinction coefficient of 29.5 $mmol^{-1}$ cm^{-1} for cytochrome c (3).

Chemotaxis

The spontaneous and stimulated migration of neutrophils were assayed by the methods of Nelson *et al.* (7). Chemotactic differences were calculated as described (12).

Quantification of PAF Binding

Neutrophils were suspended at a concentration of 10^7 cells/ml in MHBSS. 350 μl of the suspension was then added to microfuge tubes which contained [^{3}H]-PAF (100 pM) with or without excess unlabeled PAF, BN 52021 or the appropriate buffer. Following incubation for indicated periods at 4°C, free and bound ligands were separated using a silicone oil centrifugation method (6). Supernatants and pellets were transferred into 20 ml scintillation vials, overlaid with 350 μl of 2% Triton-X-100 for 3 hours, and mixed with 10 ml of Quickscint 212. Vials were counted for 5 minutes with an LKB 1211 scintillation counter (Turku, Finland). The system was programmed to measure each sample's quench and extrapolate from counts per minute to disintegrations per minute using tritium standards.

[^{3}H]-PAF Metabolism

10^7 PMNLs were incubated in a final volume of 1 ml with 13 nM [^{3}H]-PAF in the absence and presence of 0.2 mM BN 52021 for 100 minutes. Pelleted cells and supernatants were separately extracted with two volumes of chloroform: methanol (2:1 vol/vol). The procedure always recovered more than 90% of the radioactivity in the lower chloroform phase. Material was spotted on TLC plates and developed with chloroform: methanol: water (65:35:6, vol/vol/vol). Strips (0.5 cm) of silica gel were sequentially scraped from the plates, overlaid with 0.5 ml methanol and measured for radioactivity as described above.

RESULTS

Initial studies demonstrated that BN 52021 inhibits neutrophil degranulation (Fig. 1), superoxide production (Table 1) and migration (Table 2) in a dose-related manner with an IC_{50} of 4 x 10^{-6}, 8 x 10^{-6} and 8 x 10^{-5}M for

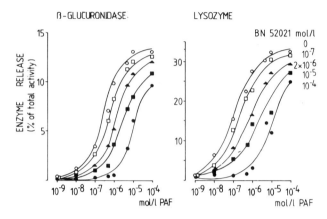

Figure 1 Dose-dependent inhibition of PAF-induced lysosomal enzyme release of neutrophil granulocytes by BN 52021. Each point represents the mean ± SE of duplicate determinations of 4-9 separate experiments.

Table 1 Specific inhibition of PAF-induced superoxide production by BN 52021

Concentration of BN 52021 (M)	Stimulus	nmoles Ferricytochrome c reduced/min/5 x 10^6 cells
0^a	0	0.46^b
0	PAF	1.31
10^{-7}	PAF	1.29
10^{-6}	PAF	1.02
10^{-5}	PAF	0.92
10^{-4}	PAF	0.51
0	fMLP	1.64
10^{-3}	fMLP	1.68
0	LTB_4	1.09
10^{-3}	LTB_4	1.06

[a] PMNLs were incubated with BN 52021 or its vehicle for 5 minutes at 37°C and were then stimulated with PAF, 10^{-6}M; fMLP, 10^{-6}M or LTB_4, 10^{-6}M.

[b] Values are means of triplicate determinations. The data are representative of three studies performed.

10^{-6}M PAF, respectively. These concentrations represent 4-to-80-fold molar excess of BN 52021 over the concentration of PAF used to challenge neutrophils. Furthermore, BN 52021 was an effective inhibitor of PAF-induced lysosomal enzyme release even when it was added to the cells at the same time as PAF (Fig. 2). The specificity of inhibition is demonstrated by the failure of 10^{-3}M BN 52021 to diminish neutrophil responses to fMLP and LTB_4 (Table 1; Fig. 3). BN 52021 in itself, even at a concentration

Table 2 Effect of BN 52021 on PAF-induced chemotaxis

Concentration of BN 52021 (M)	Chemotactic difference (μm)	% Inhibition
0 (n = 10)	887 ± 88	0
10⁻⁸ (n = 3)	895 ± 102	0
10⁻⁷ (n = 5)	873 ± 73	2
10⁻⁶ (n = 5)	810 ± 95	9
10⁻⁵ (n = 5)	745 ± 75	16
10⁻⁴ (n = 5)	638 ± 80	28
10⁻³ (n = 2)	448 ± 55	49

Chemotaxis was investigated and quantitated as described in Methods. PMNLs were preincubated with various concentrations of BN 52021 for 10 minutes at 37°C before applying the cell suspension to the wells and were challenged with PAF, 10^{-6}M for 3 hours.

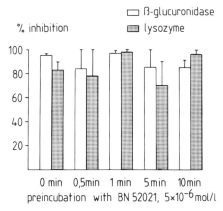

Figure 2 Time dependence of inhibition of PAF-induced enzyme release by BN 52021. Neutrophils (5 x 10⁶ cells/ml) were preincubated with BN 52021 as indicated and were then challenged with PAF, 10^{-6}M for 5 minutes. Columns represent means ± SE of duplicate measurements of 3 independent experiments.

as high as 10^{-3}M, had no neutrophil stimulating activity and did not affect cellular integrity.

In order to examine the mechanism by which BN 52021 inhibits neutrophil activation by PAF, the capability of BN 52021 and unlabeled PAF to compete with [³H]-PAF for binding to PMNL were compared. Unlabeled PAF and BN 52021 (10^{-9}-10^{-4}M) dose-dependently inhibited the specific binding of [³H]-PAF to neutrophils with IC_{50} values of 3.9 x 10^{-7} and 3.1 x 10^{-6}M, respectively (Fig. 4). The nonspecific binding (defined as the amount of binding that was not inhibited by 10^{-4}M of unlabeled PAF) was barely inhibited even by the highest dose of BN 52021 (inhibition was 2 ± 6%).

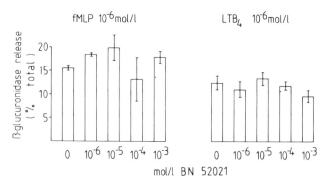

Figure 3 Lack of effect of BN 52021 on β-glucuronidase release by neutrophil granulocytes upon stimulation with fMLP or LTB₄. Columns are means ± SE of 3 experiments.

The specific binding of [³H]-PAF was reversible. Unlabeled PAF (1.5 x 10⁻⁷M) and BN 52021 (3 x 10⁻⁶M) reversed the [³H]-PAF binding in a time-dependent manner (Fig. 5).

A single peak of radioactivity was identified for supernatants and pellets obtained for PMNLs treated with BN 52021 or its vehicle. This peak coincided with the [³H]-PAF marker, indicating that no substantial metabolism of PAF occurred under the present incubation condition.

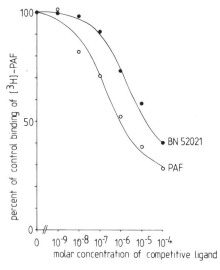

Figure 4 Inhibition of [³H]-PAF binding to human neutrophils by unlabeled PAF and BN 52021. [³H]-PAF binding in the absence of inhibitors was 20.7%. Each point is the mean of duplicate determinations. The results shown are typical of the results obtained in 3 similar experiments.

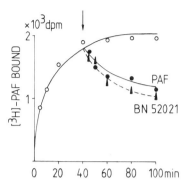

Figure 5. Reversibility of the binding of [³H]-PAF to human neutrophils. PMNLs were incubated with [³H]-PAF (100 pM) for 40 minutes at 4°C, and then unlabeled PAF (1.5 x 10⁻⁷M), BN 52021 (3 x 10⁻⁶M) or buffer was added to the medium (at the point of the arrow). Each point represents the mean of 2 experiments.

DISCUSSION

The present study demonstrates that BN 52021 specifically inhibited PAF-induced degranulation, superoxide generation and chemotaxis of neutrophils. Lysosomal enzyme release and superoxide production by 10^{-6}M PAF was inhibited 50% by 4-8 x 10^{-6}M BN 52021, whereas 10-20 fold higher concentrations were required to block PAF (10^{-6}M)-induced chemotaxis. The reason for such a discrepancy might be that BN 52021 was metabolized by PMNLs during the migration assay. Another explanation might be that PAF-induced chemotaxis is mediated, in part, by low affinity binding site, which appears not to be associated with receptor-mediated responses to PAF (17).

BN 52021 has no direct effect on neutrophils even at a concentration as high as 10^{-3}M, which is 10-fold greater than the concentration required to fully block the response to 10^{-6}M PAF.

Analysis of the mechanism by which BN 52021 inhibits the actions of PAF revealed that BN 52021 blocks binding of PAF to its receptor with a K_i of 2.1 x 10^{-6}M, about ten times higher than that for PAF itself (K_i = 2.6 x 10^{-7}M). Similarly, both PAF and twenty-fold higher concentrations of BN 52021 displaced approximately 40% of previously bound [³H]-PAF at comparable rates. The observation that BN 52021 did not affect [³H]-PAF metabolism is further evidence that BN 52021 inhibits neutrophil activation by blocking PAF binding to its receptor. BN 52021 had no effect on neutrophils *per se.* This shows that, despite its high affinity for the PAF receptor, BN 52021 does not possess any significant agonistic activity. Furthermore, BN 52021 appears to be specific for PAF as it did not interfere with the ligand binding of [³H]-fMLP (data not shown) or with the effects of fMLP and LTB₄.

In summary, the present data suggest that BN 52021 is a highly potent, specific antagonist of PAF-induced neutrophil activation, and that the inhibition of PAF-binding to its receptor is the principal mechanism by which BN 52021 blocks the actions of PAF. Therefore, BN 52021 seems to be a promising pharmacological tool in exploring the involvement of PAF in activating neutrophil granulocytes and in PMNL-mediated tissue injury.

ACKNOWLEDGEMENTS

We thank Dr. M. Tsuboshima (ONO Pharmaceuticals, Osaka, Japan) for generously supplying us with LTD₄. J.F. and É. F.-F. were visiting scientists from the Semmelweis University Medical School, Budapest, Hungary and were supported by the Boehringer-Ingelheim Foundation, Stuttgart, FRG and by the Alexander von Humboldt Foundation, Bonn, FRG, respectively.

References

1. Bφyum, A. *Isolation of lymphocytes, granulocytes and macrophages*. Scand J Immunol 1976; 5(Suppl 5): 9-15.

2. Braquet, P. *The ginkgolides: Potent platelet-activating factor antagonists isolated from Ginkgo biloba L.: Chemistry, pharmacology and clinical applications*. Drugs of the Future 1987; 12: 643-699.

3. Cox, C.Ch. et al. *Differential stimulation of the respiratory burst and lysosomal enzyme secretion in human polymorphonuclear leukocytes by synthetic diacyl glycerols*. J Immunol 1986; 136: 4611-4616.

4. Dewald, B. et al. *Activation of NADPH oxidase in human neutrophils. Synergism between fMLP and the neutrophil products PAF and LTB₄*. Biochem Biophys Res Commun 1985; 128: 297-304.

5. Hanahan, D.J. *Platelet-activating factor: A biologically active phospholipid*. Annu Rev Biochem 1986; 55: 483-509.

6. Naccache, P.H. et al. *Sodium, potassium and calcium transport across rabbit polymorphonuclear leukocyte membranes: Effect of chemotactic factor*. J Cell Biol 1977; 73: 428-435.

7. Nelson, R.D. et al. *Chemotaxis under agarose: A new and simple method for measuring chemotaxis and spontaneous migration of human polymorphonuclear leukocytes and monocytes*. J Immunol 1975; 115: 1650-1656.

8. Nunez, D. et al. *Specific inhibition of PAF-acether-induced platelet activation by BN 52021 and comparison with the PAF-acether inhibitors kadsurenone and CV 3988*. Eur J Pharmacol 1986; 123: 197-205.

9. O'Flaherty, J.T. et al. *1-O-alkyl-sn-glyceryl-3-phosphorylcholines. A novel class of neutrophil stimulants*. Am J Pathol 1981; 103: 70-78.

10. O'Flaherty, J.T. et al. *Selective desensitization of neutrophils: Further studies with 1-O-alkyl-sn-glycero-3-phosphorylcholine analogues*. J Immunol 1981; 127: 731-737.

11. O'Flaherty, J.T. *Neutrophil degranulation: Evidence pertaining to its mediation by the combined effects of leukotriene B₄, platelet-activating factor, and 5-HETE*. J Cell Physiol 1985; 122: 229-239.

12. Orr, W. et al. *Quantitation of leukotaxis in agarose by three different methods*. J Immunol Methods 1978; 20: 95-107.

13. Shaw, J.D. et al. *Activation of human neutrophils with 1-O-hexadecyl/octadecyl-2-acetyl-sn-glyceryl-3-phosphorylcholine (platelet-activating factor)*. J Immunol 1981; 127: 1250-1255.

14. Shen, T.Y. et al. *Characterization of a platelet-*

activating factor receptor antagonist isolated from haifenteng (Piper futokadsura): Specific inhibition of in vitro and in vivo platelet-activating factor induced effects. Proc Natl Acad Sci USA 1985; 82: 672-676.

15. Smith, R.J. et al. *Characterization of 1-O-hexadecyl and 1-O-octadecyl-O-acetyl-sn-glyceryl-3-phosphorylcholine-stimulated granule enzyme release from human neutrophils.* Clin Immunol Immunopathol 1983; 28: 13-28.

16. Terashita, Z. et al. *CV 3988, a specific antagonist of platelet-activating factor (PAF).* Life Sci 1983; 32: 1975-1982.

17. Valone, F.H. et al. *Specific binding by human polymorphonuclear leukocytes of the immunological mediator 1-O-hexadecyl/octadecyl-2-acetyl-sn-glycero-3-phosphorylcholine.* Immunology 1983; 48: 141-149.

Ginkgolides - Chemistry, Biology, Pharmacology and Clinical Perspectives. P. Braquet (Ed.)
Copyright © 1988, J.R. Prous Science Publishers, S.A.

PAF-ACETHER, GRANULOCYTE ACTIVATION AND BN 52021

Michel Bureau and Edouard Vannier

Unité de Pharmacologie Cellulaire, Institut Pasteur/INSERM 285, F-75015 Paris, France

INTRODUCTION

Granulocytes participate in the acute inflammatory response (24, 36) and in the late phase of anaphylaxis (21, 27). They secrete (38) and are stimulated by PAF-acether (12, 33, 41), a potential key factor for the propagation and amplification of cell responses to an initial stimulation. The *in vivo* administration of PAF-acether is followed by hypotension (26), increased vascular permeability (3, 9, 20, 22, 26), bronchoconstriction, thrombocytopenia (39) and leukopenia (11), suggesting that it displays a pathological role. Recent studies demonstrated its implication in anaphylaxis (14, 31) and endotoxinic shock (1, 34). Use of specific PAF-acether antagonists should allow investigation of the role of this mediator in inflammation and anaphylaxis.

Numerous *in vitro* effects of PAF-acether on granulocytes were described, such as chemotaxis at low concentrations, sensitization to further activation by PAF-acether itself or by other effectors (priming effect) at higher concentrations: adherence and aggregation, release of arachidonic acid metabolites, respiratory burst and enzyme release (degranulation). In this review, we will describe the effects of the gingkolide BN 52021, a PAF-acether antagonist, on different granulocyte functions stimulated by PAF-acether or other agonists.

MATERIALS AND METHODS

The methods used have been described elsewhere and include: Measurement of chemotaxis with modified Boyden chambers (4, 37) or Nelson's

---

Address all correspondence to: Dr. Michel Bureau, Unité des Venins, Unité Associée Institut Pasteur/IN-SERM No. 285, 25 rue du Docteur Roux, F-75724 Paris Cédéx 15, France.

method (migration under agarose) (28); respiratory burst studies, following the production of superoxide anion, evaluated from the superoxide dismutase-inhibitable reduction of cytochrome c (12). In other experiments the induction of chemiluminescence was assumed to be correlated to the generation of extracellular oxidative metabolites (7); evaluation of the amounts of cyclooxygenase products by thin layer chromatography (TLC) (6) and those from the lipoxygenase pathway by high pressure liquid chromatography (HPLC) (6, 7); determination of enzyme release (lysozyme and β-glucuronidase) as expression of degranulation, by standard methods (15); «Aggregation» studies. Measurement of light transmission variation through platelet suspension is a current method to evaluate their aggregation. The same method has been used by different authors with PMN suspensions (16, 19, 43). Nevertheless, the signal recorded is not clearly correlated to PMN aggregation, the increased light transmission during stimulation of the PMN being attributed in part to change in light output from the organelles (43). In this case, exocytosis should account for part of the variation of light transmission during cell activation.

RESULTS

Table I summarizes the results from the different studies analyzed.

Macrophages

Desquand et al. (12) reported that BN 52021 at a high concentration (3 10^{-4} M) supresses the production of superoxide anions by guinea-pig alveolar macrophages triggered by 10^{-8} M PAF-acether. The inhibition was partial but still significant when PAF-acether was used at 10^{-6} M. Furthermore, BN 52021 can be considered as selective since at the same concentrations of fMLP the superoxide anion production was not significantly reduced.

Eosinophils

CHEMOTAXIS Tamura et al. (37) showed that BN 52021 is a powerful inhibitor of PAF-acether-induced human eosinophil migration. With 10^{-7} M PAF-acether, the IC_{50} of BN 52021 was 5 10^{-7} M as measured from the Boyden chamber method (4).

METABOLISM OF ARACHIDONIC ACID Bruynzeel et al. (7) reported that LTC_4 production induced by 10^{-5} M PAF-acether was significantly reduced by 10^{-4} M BN 52021. BN 52021 also inhibited the LTC_4 production induced by opsonized zymosan (OZ) (5 mg/ml) and OZ (5 mg/ml) associated to fMLP (10^{-7} M) or PAF-acether (10^{-6} M).

Table 1 Inhibition by BN 52021 of different granulocyte functions induced by PAF-acether or unrelated compounds

Cell	Effector	BN	Migration	O_2^-	LT	Degranulation Lyso	β Glu	«Aggregation»
(H) PMN	PAF 10^{-6}	5 10^{-4}	50					
	PAF 10^{-8} priming fMLP 2 10^{-8}	3 10^{-6}		26.9				
(H)	''	10^{-5}		58.4				
	fMLP 2 10^{-8}	''		0				
	''	3 10^{-5}		S				
(H)	PAF 10^{-6}	2 10^{-6}				50	50	
	PAF 10^{-8}	5 10^{-7}						50
(H)	PAF 10^{-7}	5 10^{-6}						50
	PAF 5 10^{-7}	10^{-4}						50
	PAF 10^{-9}	3 10^{-4}				17.3	ϵ	60.4
	+ cyto B	''				38.4	68.4	79
	PAF 10^{-8}					21.7	32.3	51.2
	+ cyto B	''				27.1	66.8	64.4
(RT)	PAF 10^{-6}	''				27.3	43.5	33.9
	+ cyto B	''				37.5	56.5	57
	fMLP 10^{-8} and 10^{-6} + cyto B	''				ϵ	to	30
(H) EO	PAF 10^{-7}	4.9 10^{-7}	50					
	PAF 10^{-5}	10^{-4}		70	52.7			
	PAF 10^{-6} + OZ 5 mg/ml	''			54.9			
(H)	fMLP 10^{-7} + OZ 5 mg/ml	''			51			
	OZ 5 mg/ml	''				59.5		
MO	PAF 10^{-8}	3 10^{-4}		100				
	PAF 10^{-6}	''		69.4				
(GP)	fMLP 10^{-8}	''		10.7				
	10^{-6}	''		33.3				

Results are mean percent inhibition of the control response without inhibitor and are issued from the different studies analyzed (6-8, 12, 15, 37). Concentrations are in M/L. (H) for human cells, (RT) for rat cells and (GP) for guinea-pig cells. S: significant.

RESPIRATORY BURST BN 52021 at 10^{-4} M also reduced the chemiluminescence induced by 10^{-5} M PAF-acether (7). The effects of BN 52021 on OZ- or fMLP-induced chemiluminescence were not assessed.

Neutrophils

CHEMOTAXIS Foldes-Filep *et al.* (15) showed that BN 52021 is a weak antagonist of PAF-acether-induced human PMN migration as measured by the method of Nelson (28) (IC_{50} about $5 \cdot 10^{-4}$ M against 10^{-6} M PAF-acether). Up to 10^{-3} M BN 52021 did not suppress the PAF-acether-induced migration.

PRIMING EFFECT Pretreatment of human PMN with low concentrations of PAF-acether potentiates further stimulation by unrelated agonists such as fMLP, PMA, OZ, C5a as measured from superoxide anion production (2, 18), gelatinase release and endothelial cell damage (42). BN 52021 (10^{-6} M to 10^{-5} M) was shown to inhibit the PAF-acether priming effect on fMLP-induced O_2^- production (2, 40, 42) and fMLP- and PMA-induced endothelial cell damage (40, 42). At low concentrations (10^{-6} to 10^{-5} M) BN 52021 inhibited the priming effect of PAF-acether on fMLP stimulation but not stimulation by fMLP alone. Nevertheless, at $3 \cdot 10^{-5}$ M and above BN 52021 inhibited the neutrophil stimulation by fMLP, as well (2).

RESPIRATORY BURST Chemiluminescence of human PMN stimulated by 10^{-5} M PAF-acether is reduced by about 70% by 10^{-4} M BN 52021 (7).

METABOLISM OF ARACHIDONIC ACID Ionophore A23187-induced production of 5-HETE and LTB_4 is slightly reduced by 10^{-4} M BN 52021 (6) (—38% and —27%, respectively), but BN 52021 does not inhibit the cyclooxygenase pathway (6).

ENZYME RELEASE (DEGRANULATION) Inhibition by BN 52021 of PAF-acether-induced enzyme release was studied with human and rat neutrophils. With human PMN pretreated with cytochalasin B, BN 52021 tested at the concentration range of 10^{-11} M to 10^{-3} M clearly reduced β-glucuronidase and lysozyme release induced by 10^{-6} M PAF-acether (15) ($IC_{50} = 2 \cdot 10^{-6}$ M). Foldes-Filep *et al.* (15) also showed that BN 52021 does not affect the degranulation of PMN by fMLP or LTB_4.

BN 52021 may be a less powerful inhibitor of PAF-acether-induced degranulation of rat PMN (8). Indeed, at 10^{-4} M BN 52021 was only marginally effective against release of lysozyme and β-glucuronidase release triggered by 10^{-8} M or more PAF-acether. A higher concentration of BN

52021 ($3 \cdot 10^{-4}$ M) reduced enzyme release by 10^{-9} M, 10^{-8} M or 10^{-6} M PAF-acether, inhibition being enhanced when PMN were pretreated with 5 $\mu g/kg$ cytochalasin B. The inhibition of β-glucuronidase release was higher than that of lysozyme. This inhibition can be considered specific since fMLP-(10^{-8} M, 10^{-6} M) and LTB$_4$- ($2 \cdot 10^{-7}$ M) induced degranulation was non-significantly reduced by $3 \cdot 10^{-4}$ M of BN 52021.

«AGGREGATION»   Both in absence and in presence of cytochalasin B, $3 \cdot 10^{-4}$ M BN 52021 inhibited significantly rat PMN activation induced by 10^{-9} M, 10^{-8} M and 10^{-6} M PAF-acether. The inhibition was lower for the highest concentration of PAF-acether. Stimulation by fMLP or by LTB$_4$ was unaffected by BN 52021, except when fMLP was used at 10^{-6} M. At a lower concentration (10^{-4} M) BN 52021 was marginally effective against the lower dose of 10^{-9} M PAF-acether. Inhibition by BN 52021 remained unchanged when incubation with the PMN was extended from 3 to 15 minutes. Furthermore, after removal of the antagonist by washing the PMN twice about half of the inhibition of stimulation with 10^{-8} M PAF-acether persisted (8).

BN 52021 seems to be more effective against PAF-acether on human PMN (6). Indeed PAF-acether (10^{-9} to 10^{-6} M) induced PMN activation as measured by «aggregation» was reduced by BN 52021 at $5 \cdot 10^{-7}$ M. Furthermore, an inhibitory effect of BN 52021 (up to 10^{-4} M) against fMLP-induced stimulation of human PMN has not been detected. Nevertheless, human PMN were peripheral and rat PMN of the previous study were collected from the pleural cavity.

INTERACTION BETWEEN ENDOTHELIAL CELLS AND PMN   Thrombin (1 U/ml) applied to human endothelial cell monolayers enhanced O$_2^-$ generation by fMLP-(10^{-7} M) stimulated human PMN (5.73 ± 0.68 to 8.01 ± 0.85 nM O$_2^-$/15 min/10^6 PMN). This enhancement was completely inhibited by BN 52021 (42).

INTERACTION BETWEEN PMN AND PLATELETS   Coeffier et al. (10) reported that platelets are activated by a product of fMLP-stimulated neutrophils. This cell cooperation was observed in mixed cell suspension and also in whole blood. PAF-acether was assumed to be implied in this neutrophil-mediated platelet activation. Indeed, 10^{-4} M BN 52021 (and another PAF-acether antagonist, WEB 2086) reduced significantly the platelet response accompanying the fMLP-induced neutrophil activation.

DISCUSSION

In the studies summarized in this short review, BN 52021 has been shown to significantly reduce different PAF-acether-induced granulocyte responses. BN 52021 was more efficient on eosinophils than on neutrophils when PAF-acether-induced migration was evaluated. Nevertheless, chemotaxis for both types of cells was assessed by two different methods (Boyden chamber, Nelson method).

In the study of Braquet et al. (6) inhibition by BN 52021 of PAF-acether induced platelet aggregation or PMN «aggregation» were the same since in both cases the IC_{50} of BN 52021 was about 5 10^{-7} M against 10^{-8} M PAF-acether.

Efficacy of BN 52021 also varied according to the function which was evaluated. The concentration required to reduce PAF-acether-induced LTC_4 or O_2^- production by human neutrophils was higher than that needed to reduce PAF-acether-induced migration. In contrast, the concentrations of BN 52021 necessary to inhibit the PAF-acether priming effect were of the same order of magnitude as those needed to inhibit degranulation. Human neutrophils possess high and low affinity binding sites for PAF-acether (30) and for fMLP (17, 32, 35). At low concentrations fMLP binds to the only high affinity receptor, which induces chemotaxis. At higher concentrations, binding of fMLP to low affinity receptors induces other events such as degranulation, superoxide anion production, etc. (17, 32, 35). By analogy the same mechanism may operate for PAF-acether receptors and as a consequence it may be assumed that concentrations of BN 52021 needed to block neutrophil migration associated to the higher affinity receptor should be lower.

In many studies PMN were pretreated with cytochalasin B. Results of Bureau et al. (8) on rat PMN demonstrated that in most cases such PMN are not only more sensitive to activation but also to inhibition.

Finally, differences between species are expected. Braquet et al. (6) reported a 50% inhibition of human neutrophil aggregation induced by 10^{-9} M PAF-acether with 5 10^{-7} M BN 52021, whereas Bureau et al. (8) needed 3 10^{-4} M BN 52021 on rat neutrophils to reach similar results. Likewise, Foldes-Filep et al. (15) showed a 50% inhibition of human neutrophil enzyme release induced by 10^{-6} M PAF-acether with 2 10^{-6} M BN 52021, whereas on rat neutrophils more than 10^{-4} M BN 52021 were necessary for the same result. These differences may result from variations in the affinity of the PAF-acether receptor. Indeed, for example, comparing human and rabbit platelets showed such a variation (23). Meanwhile, human PMN were isolated from total blood and rat PMN were collected from the pleural cavity of a rat after intrapleural injection of isologous sera.

Binding studies with platelets have shown that BN 52021 is a competitive inhibitor of the PAF-acether receptor (6). Such studies have not been performed with granulocytes. Nevertheless, it has been shown that inhibition by a given concentration of BN 52021 decreased when the concentration of PAF-acether increased, which is in accordance with a competitive mechanism at the level of the PAF-acether binding site. Meanwhile, Bureau *et al.* (8) reported that washing the rat PMN after addition of the BN 52021 failed to restore completely their sensitivity to PAF-acether, suggesting that inhibition by this PAF-acether antagonist does not result only from reversible receptor occupancy. The same behavior was observed with human platelets (29). The difficulty to overcome inhibition by washing may be due to a strong binding of the antagonist to receptors or to their internalization, as is observed with PAF-acether for platelets (25) and neutrophils (30).

The last question to be considered is the selectivity of BN 52021 with respect to PAF-acether-induced granulocyte activation. In several studies, this selectivity was shown to be partial. Baggiolini *et al.* (2) showed that BN 52021 at the concentration of 10^{-6} M to 10^{-5} M is a selective PAF-acether antagonist but at $3 \cdot 10^{-5}$ M it significantly reduces the O_2^- production of human PMN induced by $2 \cdot 10^{-8}$ M fMLP. Further, BN 52021 selectively reduced the PAF-acether induced degranulation of human PMN ($IC_{50} = 2 \cdot 10^{-6}$ M BN 52021 for 10^{-6} M PAF-acether). In the study of Bureau *et al.* (8) with rat PMN, when a higher concentration of BN 52021 ($3 \cdot 10^{-4}$ M) was required the selectivity was less perfect. With guinea-pig macrophages BN 52021 at $3 \cdot 10^{-4}$ M seems to reduce the O_2^- production induced by fMLP (12). BN 52021 reduced somewhat the 5-HETE and LTB_4 production by human PMN induced by calcium ionophore A23187 (6). The LTC_4 production of human eosinophils stimulated by 10^{-5} M PAF-acether as well as by OZ (5 mg/ml) or fMLP (10^{-7} M) + OZ (5 mg/ml) was significantly reduced by 10^{-4} M BN 52021 (7).

Non-specific inhibition by BN 52021 could be linked to its action on receptor other than PAF-acether receptor, when the concentration applied was high. Nevertheless, an alternative hypothesis can be considered. Indeed, some authors demonstrated that PAF-acether is produced during granulocyte activation (24b, 25b, 34b). Baggiolini *et al.* (2) and others (13, 18) reported the priming effect of PAF-acether at very low concentrations (from 10^{-11} M) upon neutrophil activation by fMLP. If we assume that PAF-acether produced during cell activation contributes or amplifies it, blocking PAF-acether receptor could reduce the response to other agonists.

In conclusion, PAF-acether has been shown to stimulate different functions (chemotaxis, respiratory burst, degranulation, «aggregation», leukotriene production) of the granulocyte such as macrophages, PMN, eosinophils, which is in accordance with its role in inflammation and anaphylaxis (5).

As described in this review, the PAF-acether antagonist BN 52021 inhibits various PAF-acether induced functions of the granulocytes and accordingly is a useful tool to investigate the PAF-acether role in granulocyte mediated function and diseases, even though the question of its exact selectivity remains to be elucidated.

References

1. Adnot, S., Lefort, J., Braquet, P., Vargaftig, B.B. *Interference of the PAF-acether antagonist BN 52021 with endotoxin induced hypotension in the guinea-pig.* Prostaglandins 1986; 32: 791-802.

2. Baggiolini, M., Dewald, B. *Stimulus amplification by PAF and LTB₄ in human neutrophils.* Pharmacol Res Comm 1986; 18: 51-59.

3. Bjork, J., Smedegard, G. *Acute microvascular effects of PAF-acether, as studied by intravital microscopy.* Eur J Pharmacol 1983; 96: 87-94.

4. Boyden, S.T. *The chemotactic effect of mixtures of antibody and antigen on polymorphonuclear leukocytes.* J Exp Med 1962; 115: 453-466.

5. Braquet, P., Godfroid, J.J. *PAF-acether binding sites: 2. Design of specific antagonists.* TIPS 1986; 397-403.

6. Braquet, P.G., Spinnewyn, B., Braquet, M., Bourgain, R.H., Taylor, J.E., Etienne, A., Drieu, K. *BN 52021 and related compounds: A new series of highly specific PAF-acether receptor antagonists isolated from Ginkgo biloba L.* Blood and Vessels 1986; 16: 558-572.

7. Bruynzeel, P.L.B., Koenderman, L., Kok, P.T.M., Hameling, M.L., Verhagen, J. *Platelet activating factor (PAF-acether) induced leukotriene C4 formation and luminol dependent chemiluminescence by human eosinophils.* Pharmacol Res Comm 1986; 18: 61-69.

8. Bureau, M., Joseph, D., Vargaftig, B.B. *Desensitization and antagonism of rat polymorphonuclear leukocytes stimulated with PAF-acether.* Prostaglandins 1987; 33: 37-50.

9. Burhop, K.E., Garcia, J.G.N., Selig, W.M., Lo, S.K., Van der Zee, H., Kaplan, J.E., Malik, A.B. *Platelet-activating factor increases lung vascular permeability to protein.* J Appl Physiol 1986; 61: 2210-2217.

10. Coeffier, E., Joseph, D., Prevost, M.C., Vargaftig, B.B. *Platelet-leukocyte interaction: Activation of rabbit platelets by N-formyl-l-methionyl-l-leucyl-phenylalanine-stimulated neutrophils.* Br J Pharmacol 1987; submitted.

11. Coeffier, E., Borrel, M.C., Lefort, J., Chignard, M., Broquet, C., Heymans, F., Godfroid, J.J., Vargaftig, B.B. *Effects of PAF-acether and structural analogues on platelet activation and bronchoconstriction in guinea-pigs.* Eur J Pharmacol 1986; 131: 179-188.

12. Desquand, S., Touvay, C., Randon, J., Lagente, V., Vilain, B., Maridonneau-Parini, I., Etienne, A., Lefort, J., Braquet, P., Vargaftig, B.B. *Interference of BN 52021 (ginkgolide B) with the bronchopulmonary effects of PAF-acether in the guinea-pig.* Eur J Pharmacol 1986; 127: 83-95.

13. Dewald, B., Baggiolini, M. *Activation of NADPH oxidase in human neutrophils. Synergism between fMLP and the neutrophil products PAF and LTB₄.* Biochem Biophys Res Comm 1985; 128: 297-304.

14. Fitzgerald, M.F., Moncada, S., Parente, L. *The anaphylactic release of platelet-activating factor from perfused guinea-pig lungs.* Br J Pharmacol 1986; 88: 149-153.

15. Foldes-Filep, E., Frolich, J.C., Filep, J. *Inhibition of PAF induced activation of human neutrophils by BN 52021.* Eur J Pharmacol 1987; in press.

16. Ford-Hutchinson, A.W. *Neutrophil aggregating properties of PAF-acether and leukotriene B₄.* Int J Pharmacol 1983; 5: 17-21.

17. Gallin, J.I., Seligmann, B.E. *Mobilization and adaptation of human neutrophil chemoattractant fMeth-Leu-Phe receptors.* Fed Proc 1984; 43: 2732-2736.

18. Gay, J.C., Beckman, J.K., Zaboy, K.A., Lukens, J.N. *Modulation of neutrophil oxidative response to soluble stimuli by platelet-activating factor.* Blood 1986; 67: 931-936.

19. Hammerschmidt, D.E., Bowers, T.K., Lammi-Keefe, C.J., Jacob, H.S., Cradock, P.R. *Granulocyte aggregometry: A sensitive technique for the detection of C5a and complement activation.* Blood 1980; 55: 898-902.

20. Handley, D.A., Van Valen, R.G., Melden, M.K., Saunders, R.N. *Evaluation of dose and route effects of platelet activating factor-induced extravasation in the guinea-pig.* Thromb Haemostas 1984; 52: 34-36.

21. Holgate, S.T., Howarth, P.H., Beasly, R., Agius, R.. Church, M.K. *Cellular and biochemical events in the pathogenesis of asthma.* Eur J Resp Dis 1986; 68 (Suppl 144): 34-76.

22. Hwang, S.B., Li, C.L., Lam, M.H., Shen, T.Y. *Characterisation of cutaneous vascular permeability induced by platelet-activating factor in guinea-pigs and rats and its inhibition by a platelet-activating factor receptor antagonist.* Lab Invest 1985; 52: 617-630.

23. Hwang, S.B., Lam, M.H. *Species differences in the specific receptors of platelet activating factor.* Biochem Pharmacol 1986; 35: 4511-4518.

24. Issekutz, A.C. *Vascular responses during acute neutrophilic inflammation. Their relationship to in vivo neutrophil emigration.* Lab Invest 1981; 45: 435-441.

24b. Jouvin-Marche, E., Ninio, E., Beaurain, G., Tence, M., Niaudet, P., Benveniste, J. *Biosynthesis of PAF-acether (platelet-activating factor). VII. Precursors of PAF-acether and acetyl-transferase activity in human leukocytes.* J Immunol 1984; 133: .

25. Lachachi, H., Plantavid, M., Simon, M.F., Chap, H., Braquet, P., Douste-Blazy, L. *Inhibition of transmembrane movement and metabolism of platelet activating factor (PAF-acether) by a specific antagonist, BN 52021.* Biochem Biophys Res Comm 1985; 132: 460-466.

25b. Lynch, J.M., Lotner, G.Z., Betz, S.J., Henson, P.M. *The release of a platelet-activating factor by stimulated rabbit neutrophils.* J Immunol 1979; 123: 1219-1226.

26. Mojarad, M., Hamasaki, Y., Said, S.I. *Platelet activating factor increases pulmonary microvascular permeability and induces pulmonary edema.* Bull Eur Physiopath Resp 1983; 19: 253-256.

27. Murphy, K.R., Wilson, M.C., Irvin, C.G., Glezen, L.S., Marsh, W.R., Haslett, C., Henson, P.M., Larsen, G.L. *The requirement for polymorphonuclear leukocytes in the late asthmatic response and heightened airways reactivity in an animal model.* Am Rev Resp Dis 1986; 134: 62-68.

28. Nelson, R.D., Quie, P.G., Simon, R.L. *Chemotaxis under agarose: A new and simple method for measuring chemotaxis and spontaneous migration of human polymorphonuclear leukocytes and monocytes.* J Immunol 1975; 115: 1650-1656.

29. Nunez, D., Chignard, M., Korth, R., Le Couedic, J.P., Norel, X., Spinnewin, B., Braquet, P., Benveniste, J. *Specific inhibition of PAF-acether-induced platelet activation by BN 52021 and comparison with the PAF-acether inhibitors kadsurenone and CV 3988.* Eur J Pharmacol 1986; 123: 197-205.

30. O'Flaherty, J.T., Surles, J.R., Redman, J., Jacobson, D., Plandosi, C., Wykle, R.L. *Binding and metabolism of platelet-activating factor by human neutrophils.* J Clin Invest 1986; 78: 381-388.

31. Page, C.P., Archer, C.B., Paul, W., Morley, J. *PAF-acether: A mediator of inflammation and asthma.* TIPS 1984; 5: 239.

32. Painter, R.G., Sklar, L.A., Jesaitis, A.J., Schmitt, M., Cochrane, C.G. *Activation of neutrophils by N-formyl chemotactic peptides.* Fed Proc 1984; 43: 2737-2742.

33. Poitevin, B., Mencia-Huerta, J.M., Roubin, R., Benveniste, J. *Role of PAF-acether (platelet activating factor) in neutrophil activation.* In: The Pulmonary Circulation and Acute Lung Injury. S.I. Said (Ed.). Futura Publishing Co.: Mount Kisko, NY, 1985; 357-373.

34. Rylander, R., Beijer, L. *Inhalation of endotoxin stimulates alveolar macrophage production of platelet-activating factor.* Am Rev Resp Dis 1987; 136: 83-86.

34b. Sánchez Crespo, M., Alonso, F., Egido, J. *Platelet-activating factor in anaphylaxis and phagocytosis. I. Release from human peripheral polymorphonuclears and monocytes during the stimulation by ionophore A23187 and phagocytosis but not from degranulating basophils.* Immunology 1980; 40: 645-655.

35. Snyderman, R. *Regulatory mechanisms of a chemoattractant receptor on leukocytes.* Fed Proc 1984; 43: 2743-2748.

36. Staub, N.C., Schultz, E.L., Albertine, K.H.

Leukocytes and pulmonary microvascular injury in mechanisms of lung microvascular injury. Ann NY Acad Sci 1982; 332-343.

37. Tamura, N., Agrawal, D.K., Suliaman, F.A., ,Towley, R.G. *Effects of platelet activating factor on the chemotaxis of normodense eosinophils from normal subjects.* Biochem Biophys Res Comm 1987; 142: 638-644.

38. Vargaftig, B.B., Benveniste, J. *Platelet activating factor today.* TIPS 1983; 4: 341-344.

39. Vargaftig, B.B., Lefort, J., Chignard, M., Benveniste, J. *Platelet-activating factor induces a platelet-dependent bronchoconstriction unrelated to the formation of prostaglandin derivatives.* Eur J Pharmacol 1980; 65: 185-192.

40. Vercellotti, G.M., Huh, P.W., Yin, H.Q., Nelson, R.D., Jacob, H.S. *Enhancement of PMN mediated endothelial damage by platelet activating factor (PAF): PAF primes PMN responses to activating stimuli.* 28th Ann Meet Amer Soc Hematology 1986.

41. Wardlaw, A.J., Moqbel, R., Cromwell, O., Kay, A.B. *Platelet-activating factor. A potent chemotactic and chemokinetic factor for human eosinophils.* J Clin Invest 1986; 78: 1701-1706.

42. Wickham, N.W.R., Vercelloti, G.M., Yin, H.Q., Moldow, C.F., Jacob, H.S. *Neutrophils are primed to release toxic oxidants by contact with thrombin-stimulated endothelium: Role of endothelial cell-generated platelet activating factor.* Meet Amer Soc Clinical Investigation 1986.

43. Yuli, I., Snyderman, R. *Light scattering by polymorphonuclear leukocytes stimulated to aggregate under various conditions.* Blood 1984; 64: 649-655.

Ginkgolides - Chemistry, Biology, Pharmacology
and Clinical Perspectives. P. Braquet (Ed.)
Copyright © 1988, J.R. Prous Science Publishers, S.A.

PAF-INDUCED LEUKOTRIENE SYNTHESIS IN HUMAN POLYMORPHONUCLEAR LEUKOCYTES: INHIBITION BY GINKGOLIDE B (BN 52021)

Pierre Borgeat[1], Marie Nadeau[1], Genevieve Rouleau[1], Pierre Sirois[2], Pierre Braquet[3] and Patrice Poubelle[1]

[1]Unité de Recherche, Inflammation et Immunologie-Rhumatologie, Centre Hospitalier de l'Université Laval, Sainte-Foy, Québec, Canada; [2]Département de Pharmacologie, Centre Hospitalier de l'Université de Sherbrooke, Québec, Canada; [3]Institut Henri-Beaufour, F-92350 Le Plessis Robinson, France

ABSTRACT

Incubation of human polymorphonuclear leukocytes (PMNLs) with 1-O-octadecyl (or hexadecyl)-2(R)-acetyl-glycero-3-phosphorylcholine (PAF) results in the stimulation of 5-lipoxygenase product synthesis. Reversed phase HPLC analysis of the incubation media 5 to 60 min after stimulation with PAF showed the presence of leukotriene B_4 (LTB_4) and/or 20-hydroxy- and 20-carboxy-LTB_4. The synthesis of LTs was increased in presence of exogenous arachidonic acid. The intensity of the response (LT synthesis) of different human PMNL preparations to PAF was highly variable. Dose response studies of the effect of PAF on LT synthesis indicated a threshold concentration of 10 to 30 nM and a maximal response at 0.1-1 μM. Ginkgolide B (BN 52021), a PAF-antagonist, when added to PMNL suspensions prior to stimulation with PAF, inhibited LT synthesis in a concentration dependent manner with an IC_{50} of 3-5 μM. Ginkgolide B did not show detectable agonist activity (LT synthesis) at concentrations up to 10 μM

Address all correspondence to Pierre Borgeat, Unité de Recherche, Inflammation et Immunologie-Rhumatologie, Centre Hospitalier de l'Université Laval, Sainte-Foy, Québec, Canada GlV 4G2.

and did not inhibit LT synthesis induced by the ionophore A23187. These data indicated that PAF can stimulate LTB_4 synthesis in human PMNLs at concentrations comparable to those required to activate neutrophil functions. The data also suggest that the effect of PAF on LT synthesis is secondary to the PAF receptor activation.

INTRODUCTION

Leukotrienes (LTs) and 1-0-octadecyl (or hexadecyl)-2(R)-acetyl-glycero-3-phosphorylcholine (PAF) constitute two classes of biologically active lipids which appear to be involved in inflammation (4, 16). The biochemistry and pharmacology of PAF and LTs appear to be highly intricate. Both classes of compounds are formed in activated polymorphonuclear leukocytes (PMNLs) (12) and monocytes/macrophages (6). Moreover, it has recently been demonstrated that the action of a phospholipase A_2 on 1-0-alkyl-2-arachidonyl-glycero-3-phosphorylcholine in neutrophils causes the release of the precursor molecules for the formation of LTs and PAF, *i.e.*, arachidonic acid and lyso-PAF, respectively (7). In human neutrophils PAF and LTB_4 show similar biological activities causing degranulation, chemotaxis, aggregation and superoxide synthesis (8, 15).

PAF has also been shown to induce LTB_4 and LTC_4 synthesis in human neutrophils and eosinophils, respectively (5, 11). However, the biological significance of the PAF-induced LT synthesis is not clear. Indeed, the concentration of PAF used in these studies to elicit LT synthesis was 2 to 3 orders of magnitude higher than the concentration required to produce biological responses in the same cells (15). In the present study we have reexamined the effect of PAF on LT synthesis in human neutrophils and have studied the effect of the PAF antagonist BN 52021 (rev. in 3) on PAF and ionophore A23187-induced LT synthesis in PMNLs.

MATERIALS AND METHODS

PAF was obtained from Sigma (St. Louis, MO) in solution in chloroform. Aliquots of this stock solution were evaporated and redissolved in ethanol for addition to cell suspensions. Ginkgolide B (BN 52021, Institut Henri Beaufour) and the ionophore A23187 (Sigma) were also used as ethanolic solutions (the maximal organic solvent concentration in incubation media was 0.3%).

Preparation of PMNL Suspensions

Human blood was obtained from healthy volunteers by venous puncture and collected on citrate-phosphate-dextrose-adenine (CPDA). The blood was immediately centrifuged (200 x g, 15 min) and the platelet-rich plasma discarded. PMNLs were prepared by successive treatment with dextran for red cell sedimentation, ammonium chloride lysis for elimination of remaining red cells and separation of the mononuclear cells by centrifugation over Ficoll-Paque (Pharmacia) cushions, as described previously (10). The PMNL pellets were resuspended in Dulbecco's phosphate buffered saline (PBS) without Ca^{++} and Mg^{++}, containing 10 mM D-glucose, at the concentration of 1 or 10 x 10^6 cells/ml. The final cell suspensions had a viability of more than 95% as assessed by Trypan blue exclusion and contained 95% PMNLs (5% mononuclear cells). The platelet contamination was of 1 to 3 platelets/leukocyte.

Incubation Procedures

Aliquots of the PMNL suspensions were transferred to polypropylene test tubes and $CaCl_2$ and $MgCl_2$ were added to the final concentrations of 2 and 0.5 mM, respectively. The cell suspensions were preincubated 15 min at 37°C; when used in an experiment, the compound BN 52021 was added at the beginning of the preincubation period. The cells were then stimulated with various PAF concentrations for 5, 25, 30 or 60 min, as indicated in legends, or 2 μM ionophore A23187 for 5 min; at the end of the incubation period, the reactions were stopped by addition of 0.5 ml of a mixture of acetonitrile and methanol (50/50, v/v) containing 25 and 15 ng of pro-staglandin B_2 (PGB_2) and 19-hydroxy-PGB_2 (19-OH-PGB_2), respectively.

Analysis of Lipoxygenase Products

Analysis of lipoxygenase products was carried out by reversed phase-HPLC (RP-HPLC) as previously described (2) and using an on-line extraction procedure. Briefly, the denatured cell suspensions were centrifuged to remove the precipitated material and the supernatants were directly injected on a Radial Pak C_{18} Resolve column (5 x 100 mm, 10 μm particles, Waters Millipore) protected with a Guard Pak C_{18} cartridge (Waters Millipore, same packing as the column). The compounds were eluted using gradients of organic solvents and a change of pH of the mobile phase. Elution was monitored using fixed wavelength UV photometers at 229 and 280 nm. Compounds were identified by comparison of their retention times with that of authentic standards and by the ratio of their UV absorbances at 229 and 280 nm. Quantitation was performed by comparing peak areas of the compounds with that of PGB$_2$ (internal standard) after correction for attenuation settings and extinction coefficients.

RESULTS

Figure 1 shows the RP-HPLC analysis of the incubation media of 10 x 10^6 PMNLs stimulated with PAF. Two products of the 5-lipoxygenase pathway were formed in detectable amounts, 20-hydroxy-LTB$_4$ (20-OH-LTB$_4$) and 20-carboxy-LTB$_4$ (20-COOH-LTB$_4$). LTB$_4$ itself was not clearly detectable. Other 5-lipoxygenase products such as 5-hydroxy-eicosatetraenoic acid (5-HETE), LTC$_4$ or the trans-isomers of LTB$_4$ were not detectable. When an aliquot of the same cell suspension was incubated in absence of PAF, the two metabolites of LTB$_4$ were undetectable (not shown).

The effect of increasing concentrations of PAF on LT synthesis in human PMNLs was investigated (Fig. 2). Measurements of LTB$_4$ were carried out after 5 min of incubation while 20-OH- and 20-COOH-LTB$_4$ were measured

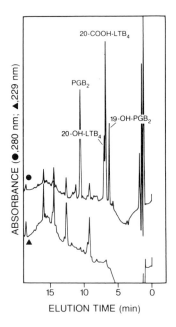

Figure 1 RP-HPLC chromatograms of the lipoxygenase products released by human PMNLs. The cells (10 x 10^6 in one ml) were incubated 60 min at 37°C in PBS in the presence 3 x 10^{-7} M PAF. The reaction was stopped by addition of 0.5 ml of a mixture of methanol and acetonitrile (50/50, v/v) containing 25 and 15 ng of PGB$_2$ and 19-OH-PGB$_2$, respectively, as internal standards. The denatured incubation medium was centrifuged to remove the precipitated material and injected directly without further purification or derivatization. Attenuation settings were of 0.05 and 0.02 absorbance unit full scale at 229 and 280 nm, respectively.

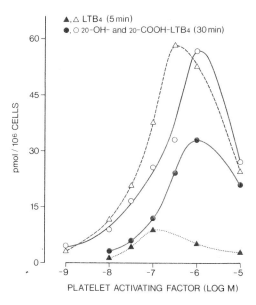

Figure 2 Effect of increasing concentrations of PAF on the generation of LTs by human PMNLs. The cells (10 x 10⁶ cells in one ml) were incubated 5 or 30 min at 37°C at the indicated PAF concentration in PBS in the absence (closed symbols) or presence of 30 μM arachidonic acid (open symbols). The lipoxygenase products were measured by RP-HPLC analysis. The effect of PAF on LTB_4 synthesis were measured after 5 min of incubation, whereas the production of the 20-OH- and 20-COOH-LTB_4 was measured in 30 min incubation periods. In absence of exogenous arachidonic acid and PAF, LT production was undetectable (at 5 and 30 min) *i.e.*, was inferior to 0.5 pmol/10⁶ cells. In presence of exogenous substrate, but in absence of PAF, LT synthesis was equivalent to that measured at 1 nM PAF. This experiment shows the values obtained with a PMNL suspension responding strongly to PAF stimulation (see Discussion).

in 30 min incubations. In absence of exogenous arachidonic acid, LT synthesis was detectable from 30 nM PAF. In presence of 30 μM exogenous substrate the stimulation of LT synthesis was detectable at 10 nM PAF, and more LTs were formed at all PAF concentrations tested. The dose response curves clearly show that the effect of PAF on LT synthesis is maximum between 0.1 μM and 1 μM according to incubation conditions, while higher concentrations of PAF led to decreased LT synthesis.

The effects of the PAF antagonist BN 52021 were then investigated on PAF-induced LT synthesis in human PMNLs. The antagonist was preincubated with the cells 15 min prior to stimulation with 0.1 μM PAF. Figure 3 shows that BN 52021 efficiently antagonizes the PAF-stimulated LT synthesis. Half-maximal inhibition of LTB_4 and 20-OH- and 20-COOH-LTB_4 occurred at a concentration of 3-5 μM. In control experiments BN 52021 at doses up to 10 μM in presence of 10 μM arachidonic acid did not in-

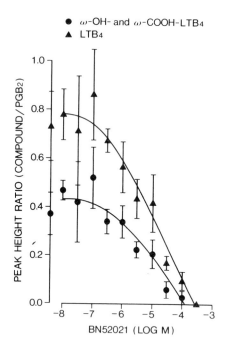

Figure 3 Effect of BN 52021 on the synthesis of LTs in human PMNLs stimulated with PAF. The cells (1 x 10⁶ cells/ml) were preincubated 15 min at 37°C in PBS in the presence of the indicated concentrations of BN 52021 before stimulation with 0.1 μM PAF for 25 min at 37°C. The lipoxygenase products were analyzed by RP-HPLC. The viability of the PMNLs at the end of the incubation period without and with 0.1 mM BN 52021 was 95 and 85%, respectively. In absence of PAF, LT synthesis was not detectable. Each data point shows the mean ± SEM of 5 separate incubations from a representative experiment.

crease LT synthesis, indicating that it does not have detectable agonist properties in this system (data not shown). BN 52021 was also tested on A23187-induced LT synthesis and did not show any inhibition at concentrations up to 10 μM, indicating that it does not act as a 5-lipoxygenase inhibitor to block the effect of PAF on LT synthesis (data not shown).

DISCUSSION

Figure 1 shows the profile of 5-lipoxygenase products generated upon stimulation of human PMNLs with PAF. The omega-oxidation metabolites of LTB₄ (13) are the main products found in incubation media. This profile is strikingly different from that obtained on stimulation of the same cells with the ionophore A23187, which induces the formation of the 20-OH- and 20-COOH-LTB₄ and other metabolites such as 5-HETE, the trans isomers of LTB_4, the 5,6-dihydroxy-eicosatetraenoic acids (5,6-di-HETEs) and small amounts of LTC_4 (from eosinophils) (2, 13). The differences in the profiles obtained with PAF and A23187 likely lie in that PAF is a weaker stimulus of LT synthesis. Under A23187 stimulation, the strong stimulation of the 5-lipoxygenase and massive release of substrate lead to formation of an amount of LTA_4 that exceeds the capacity of the LTA_4 hydrolase; in this condition non-enzymatic hydrolysis occurs resulting in the formation of the trans isomers of LTB_4 and 5,6-di-HETEs (1, 9). Under PAF stimulation the smaller amount of LTA_4 generated is almost quantitatively converted to LTB_4, which is further metabolized to omega-oxidation products.

The present study extends previous reports that PAF can induce LT synthesis in human PMNLs (5, 11). Increased LT synthesis was detectable at 30 nM and maximum at 0.1 or 1 μM (Fig. 2). Furthermore, when PAF was used in combination with 30 μM arachidonic acid, larger amounts of LT were formed than with PAF alone, and significant stimulation of LT synthesis occurred at 10 nM. These data suggest that substrate availability is limiting LT synthesis under conditions of PAF stimulation, and that PAF significantly activates the 5-lipoxygenase at concentrations as low as 10 nM. At this point, it should be emphasized that in the course of these investigations, the response (LT synthesis) of PNMLs obtained from different donors to PAF (alone) was highly variable. Some preparations responded strongly to PAF (Figs. 1 and 2), while other preparations would generate smaller amounts and frequently would not generate detectable amounts of LTs after stimulation with PAF. Similar variability in response to the chemotactic peptide formyl-methionyl-leucyl-phenylalaline (f-mlp) was also observed in our laboratory, while the different preparations of human PMNLs responded consistently to A23187 stimulation. The reasons for the variability of the PMNL response to PAF and f-mlp are not clear at this time and this phenomenon is presently the subject of investigations in our laboratory.

Ginkgolide B or BN 52021 is now recognized as a specific PAF antagonist (3). In the present study we found that the compound efficiently antagonized the stimulatory effect of PAF on LT synthesis in human PMNLs (Fig. 3); the lack of inhibitory effect of BN 52021 on A23187-induced synthesis (data not shown) clearly demonstrated that the compound does not block PAF-induced LT synthesis at the level of the 5-lipoxygenase. These data also support the interpretation that this biological effect of PAF follows the activation of the PAF receptor and is not due to a non-specific effect of PAF. The very high concentrations of PAF used in previous studies to elicit LT synthesis in neutrophils (11) and eosinophils (5) (0.9 and 10 μM, respectively) indeed raised some questions about the specificity of this effect of PAF, since other biological effects of PAF such as stimulation of migration, degranulation, aggregation and superoxide production were reported to occur at nM concentrations (14, 15, 17). In fact, the dose response curves reported herein for LT synthesis are close to those reported for the stimulatory effect of PAF on PMNL functions; interestingly, a decreased response to PAF between 1 and 10 μM was also noted in other studies (15, 17), a phenomenon that was attributed to the rapid desensitization of the PMNLs in the presence of high concentrations of PAF (15).

Yet, the present study does not answer the question of the biological significance of the stimulatory effect of PAF on LT synthesis in PMNLs. The apparent correlation between the cellular effects of PAF and LT synthesis constitutes circumstantial evidence, but this question will only be answered by studies of the cellular effects of PAF in the presence of specific inhibitors of LT syntthesis. Given the fact, however, that LTB$_4$ and PAF have similar effects on PMNL functions (8, 15), it seems likely that LTB$_4$ generated upon stimulation of the cells with PAF accounts, at least in part, for the functional responses to PAF.

References

1. Borgeat, P., Samuelsson, B. *Arachidonic acid metabolism in polymorphonuclear leukocytes: Unstable intermediate in formation of dihydroxy acids.* Proc Natl Acad Sci USA 1979; 76: 3213-3217.

2. Borgeat, P., Fruteau de Laclos, B., Rabinovitch, H., Picard, S., Braquet, P., Hebert, J., Laviolette, M. *Eosinophil-rich human polymorphonuclear leukocyte preparations characteristically release leukotriene C$_4$ on ionophore A23187 challenge.* J Allergy Clin Immunol 1984; 74: 310-315.

3. Braquet, P. *The ginkgolides: Potent platelet-activating factor antagonists isolated from Ginkgo biloba L: Chemistry, pharmacology and clinical applications.* Drugs of the Future 1987; 12: 643-699.

4. Braquet, P., Touqui, L., Shen, T.Y., Vargaftig, B.B. *Perspectives in platelet-activating factor research.* Pharmacol Rev 1987; 39: 97-145.

5. Brunynzeel, P.L.B., Koenderman, L., Kok, P.T.M., Hameling, M.L., Verhagen, J. *Platelet-activating factor (PAF-acether) induced leukotriene C$_4$ formation and luminol dependent chemiluminescence by human eosinophils.* Pharmacol Res Commun 1986; 18 (Suppl): 61-69.

6. Camussi, G., Bussolini, F., Tetta, C., Piacibello, W., Agiletta, M. *Biosynthesis and release of platelet-activating factor from human monocytes.* Int Arch Allergy Appl Immunol 1983; 70: 245-251.

7. Chilton, F.H., Ellis, J.M., Olson, S.C., Wykel, R.L. *1-0-Alkyl-2-arachidonoyl-sn-glycero-3-phosphocholine. A common source of platelet-activating factor and arachidonate in human polymorphonuclear leukocytes.* J Biol Chem 1984; 259: 12014-12019.

8. Ford-Hutchinson, A.W. *The role of leukotriene B$_4$ as a mediator of leukocyte function.* Agents Actions 1983; 12 (Suppl): 154-166.

9. Fruteau de Laclos, B., Braquet, P., Borgeat, P. *Characteristics of leukotriene (LT) and hydroxy eicosatetraenoic acid (HETE) synthesis in human leukocytes in vitro effect of arachidonic acid concentration.* Prostaglandins Leukotrienes Med 1984; 13: 47-52.

10. Laviolette, M., Coulombe, R., Picard, S., Braquet, P., Borgeat, P. *Decreased leukotriene B$_4$ synthesis in smokers' alveolar macrophages in vitro.* J Clin Invest 1986; 77: 54-60.

11. Lin, A.H., Morton, D.R., Gorman, R.R. *Acetyl glyceryl ether phosphorylcholine stimulated leukotriene B$_4$ synthesis in human polymorphonuclear leukocytes.* J Clin Invest 1982; 70: 1058-1065.

12. Ludwig, J.C., Hoppens, C.L., McManus, L.M., Mott, G.E., Pinckard, R.N. *Modulation of platelet-activating factor (PAF) synthesis and release from human polymor-*

phonuclear leukocytes (PMN): Role of ex-tracellular albumin. Arch Biochem Biophys 1985; 241: 337-347.

13. Nadeau, M., Fruteau de Laclos, B., Picard, S., Braquet, P., Corey, E.J., Borgeat, P. *Studies on leukotriene B_4 omega-oxidation in human leukocytes.* Can J Biochem Cell Biol 1984; 62: 1321-1326.

14. O'Flaherty, J.T., Miller, C.H., Lewis, J.C., Wykle, R.L., Bass, D.A., McCall, C.E., Waite, M., DeChatelet, L.R. *Neutrophil responses to platelet-activating factor.* Inflammation 1981; 5: 193-201.

15. Shaw, J.O., Pinckard, R.N., Ferrigni, K.S.,

McManus, L.M., Hanahai, D.J. *Activation of human neutrophils with 1-0-hexadecyl/octa-decyl-2-acetyl-sn-glyceryl-3-phosphorylcholine (platelet-activating factor).* J Immunol 1981; 127: 1250-1255.

16. Sirois, P., Borgeat, P. *Pharmacology of the leukotrienes.* J Pharmacol 1984; 15 (Suppl): 53-68.

17. Smith, R.J., Bowman, B.J. *Stimulation of human neutrophil degranulation with 1-0-oc-tadecyl-2-0-acetyl-sn-glyceryl-3-phosphoryl-choline: Modulation by inhibitors of arachidonic acid metabolism.* Biochem Biophys Res Commun 1982; 104: 1495-1501.

*Ginkgolides - Chemistry, Biology, Pharmacology
and Clinical Perspectives.* P. Braquet (Ed.)
Copyright © 1988, J.R. Prous Science Publishers, S.A.

ENHANCEMENT OF NEUTROPHIL-MEDIATED ENDOTHELIAL DAMAGE BY PLATELET-ACTIVATING FACTOR (PAF): POSSIBLE ROLE IN ATHEROGENESIS

Harry S. Jacob and Gregory M. Vercellotti

University of Minnesota Medical School, Minneapolis, Minnesota USA

ABSTRACT

The lipid mediator, pletelet-activating factor, not only directly activates PMNs but also in much more minuscule quantities primes PMN responses, including adhesion to endothelial cells, superoxide generation, and elastase release to stimuli such as FMLP and activated complement. Concomitantly, and of possible relevance to vascular damage pathogenesis, PAF-primed PMNs cause excessive endothelial injury *in vitro*. PAF priming is receptor mediated, requires the intact PAF molecule, and is associated with enhanced intracellular calcium flux. The PAF receptor antagonists BN 52021, kadsurenone, and L-652 inhibit PAF-primed PMN adhesion, superoxide generation, elastase release, and therefore the resulting enhancement of PMN-mediated endothelial lysis and detachment. Since thrombin-exposed endothelium produces PAF, as do stimulated neutrophils themselves, powerful paracrine and autocrine amplifications of endothelial damage may occur during blood coagulation at sites of atherosclerosis. We suggest that minuscule amounts of PAF, derived from endothelial cells perturbed by coagulation can potentiate otherwise trivial activators of PMNs so that they become lethal to endothelium, aggravating, thereby, vascular damage. We

---

Address all correspondence to: Dr. Harry S. Jacob, M.D., Division of Hematology, Box 480 UMHC, University of Minnesota Hospital and Clinics, 420 Delaware St., S.E., Minneapolis, MN 55455, USA.

181

are encouraged by our studies to suggest a possible therapeutic role for PAF inhibitors in atherosclerosis.

INTRODUCTION

Our laboratory has been interested in the mechanisms by which neutrophils damage vascular endothelium in diverse clinical syndromes, particularly in the Adult Respiratory Distress Syndrome of septic shock and as an initiating event in atherosclerosis (4,5). We previously showed that neutrophils stimulated by inflammatory mediators such as activated complement, adhere tightly to the endothelial surface. There they release toxic oxygen metabolites (*e.g.,* superoxide and peroxide) as well as lysosomal proteases, which, in turn, damage vascular endothelium. Our attention has recently turned to the possible etiologic role of platelet-activating factor (PAF) in the vascular damage seen in septic shock and in atherosclerosis. This lipid mediator, 1-O-alkyl-2-acetyl-3-phosphocholine, is produced by various activated cells including basophils, monocytes, endothelial cells, and neutrophils themselves.

Originally named because of its capacity to aggregate and degranulate platelets *in vitro,* PAF is really a far more potent neutrophil activator. For instance, PAF provokes neutrophils (PMNs) to chemotax, aggregate, release superoxide, and degranulate (6), and when infused into animals, PAF induces pulmonary sequestration of neutrophils, followed by hypotension, bronchoconstriction, and increased vascular permeability (3). Of particular relevance to atherogenesis are recent findings that thrombin induces PAF synthesis and release from endothelium (2,7).

Since PAF may play a critical role in inflammation and atherosclerosis, search for antagonists of PAF which might prove therapeutic has been undertaken. From the armamentarium of the barefoot doctors of China, several herbal remedies for ailments of the lungs and heart have been pharmaceutically purified, and 2 botanicals have been found to contain potent PAF inhibitors. The seeds and leaves of the *Ginkgo biloba* tree, or "ya-chiao-pan", are the source of a powerful PAF receptor antagonist purified by Dr. Braquet and his colleagues and known by the code number BN 52021 (1). Another Chinese herb, "haifenteng", from a plant of the nightshade family has yielded to Merck scientists the PAF antagonists kadsurenone and L-652 (8).

Recent reports indicate that rather high concentrations of PAF will directly promote neutrophil production of toxic O_2 species, such as superoxide and peroxide. In studies presented herein, we demonstrate that minuscule amounts of PAF —5 to 6 orders of magnitude lower than previously examined— can *prime* neutrophils so that they respond excessively to subsequent application of otherwise trivial stimuli; this phenomenon enhances, thereby, neutrophil-mediated endothelial injury. We also report on the mechanisms of this amplification and demonstrate that the aforementioned PAF receptor inhibitors block amplified neutrophil oxidant responses and concomitantly inhibit *in vitro* endothelial damage.

RESULTS AND DISCUSSION

PMNS were incubated or "primed" with various concentrations of PAF for 5 minutes, followed by the addition of FMLP, an oligopeptide chemotaxin which by itself is a very weak provoker of superoxide production. Minute concentrations of PAF (10^{-10} to 10^{-11}M) induce no superoxide production by PMNs when added alone, but markedly provoke superoxide production in these same cells when they are subsequently exposed to otherwise trivial levels of FMLP. Similarly PAF-primed, FMLP-stimulated neutrophils also release more tissue-damaging elastase than cells exposed to FMLP alone. Having shown that pre-incubation with non-stimulatory amounts of PAF enhances subsequent oxidant production and elastase exocytosis, we next tested whether neutrophils so primed would be more adherent to monolayers of human umbilical vein endothelium. We used a concentration of PAF that did not enhance PMN adhesion over that observed with buffer alone, and a concentration of FMLP that increased adhesion by only 5%. However, when neutrophils were first primed with PAF and then stimulated with FMLP, markedly enhanced (10-fold increased) PMN adhesion was observed.

Since PAF priming enhances PMN adhesion, superoxide production, and elastase release, we predicted that such primed PMNs would be particularly potent in causing endothelial lysis and detachment. Indeed, in virtually any concentration, PAF or FMLP when added alone causes no neutrophil-mediated lysis of ^{51}Cr-radiolabeled cultured endothelial cells. However, if first exposed to PAF and then to FMLP, PMNs now significantly lyse endothelium and even more markedly detach intact endothelial cells from their anchoring substratum. Not only does PAF prime the aforementioned responses of neutrophils to FMLP, but also primes their capacity to chemotax, aggregate, and express on their surfaces the adhesion-promoting receptor, CR3.

Priming by PAF is not stimulus specific in that PAF equally primes PMN responses to FMLP, activated complement (C5a), phorbol myristate acetate, and opsonized zymosan. Priming is maximal within 5 minutes, and once primed PAF can be washed away prior to subsequent agonist stimulation, without losing effect. However, neutrophil priming by PAF requires preexposure of neutrophils to intact PAF and involves a specific PAF receptor. In other words, if the sequence of PMN exposure is reversed —FMLP first, followed by PAF— no enhancement of superoxide production or elastase release is demonstrable. Moreover, lyso-PAF, which has an hydroxyl group instead of an acetate at the glycerol-backbone position 2, does not prime PMN functions. Finally, PAF must be taken up by PMNs by specific receptors to exert its actions; for instance, if receptor function is blocked by cold incubation (4°C), no priming occurs.

Since receptor-ligand signal transduction in diverse other cells is often mediated by changes in intracellular calcium and phosphatidyl inositol turnover, we assayed Ca^{++} fluxes of PMNs and their perturbations induced by PAF priming, using the calcium-sensitive probe, Fura-2. FMLP (10^{-7}M) alone induces a 300% increase in intracellular calcium within 20 seconds which returns to baseline in four minutes. However, neutrophils, first primed with concentrations of PAF that have minimal effects on Ca flux when used alone (10^{-7}M) and then stimulated with FMLP, manifest markedly augmented increases (over 800%) in intracellular calcium.

Finally, we investigated the recently described PAF receptor antagonists, BN 52021, kadsurenone, and L-652 for their capacity to inhibit PAF priming of neutrophils, particularly *vis a vis* their enhanced mediation of endothelial injury. All 3 inhibitors in micromolar concentrations inhibit the PAF-induced increments in neutrophil adhesion, superoxide generation, and elastase release, and as might be predicted, all significantly protect the viability of ^{51}Cr-labeled endothelium from PMN assault —BN 52021 being most efficient in this regard.

References

1. Braquet, P. *Involvement of PAF-acether in various immune disorders using BN 52021 (Ginkgolide B): A powerful PAF-acether antagonist isolated from Ginkgo biloba L.* In: Advances in Prostaglandins, Thromboxane and Leukotriene Research, Vol. 16. Raven Press: New York 1986: 179-198.

2. Camussi, G. et al. *The release of platelet-activating factor from human endothelial cells in culture.* J Immunol 1983; 131: 2397-2403.

3. Handley, D.A. et al. *Effect of platelet activating factor on endothelial permeability to plasma macromolecules.* Immunopharmacol 1984; 8: 137-142.

4. Jacob, H.S. et al. *Complement-induced granulocyte aggregation: An unsuspected mechanism of disease.* New Engl J Med 1981; 302: 789-794.

5. Jacob, H.S. *Interactions between granulocytes and the vascular wall: Ramifications for atherogenesis.* Atherosclerosis Reviews 1985; 13: 53-65.

6. O'Flaherty, J.T. et al. *1-O-Alkyl-sn-glyceryl-3-phosphorylcholines: A novel class of neutrophil stimulants.* Am J Pathol 1981; 103: 70-79.

7. Prescott, S.M. et al. *Human endothelial cells in culture produce platelet activating factor when stimulated with thrombin.* Medical Science 1984; 81: 3534-3538.

8. Shen, T.Y. et al. *Characterization of a platelet-activating factor receptor antagonist isolated from haifenteng (Piper futokadsura): Specific inhibition of in vitro and in vivo platelet-activating factor-induced effect.* Proc Natl Acad Sci 1985; 82: 672-676.

*Ginkgolides - Chemistry, Biology, Pharmacology
and Clinical Perspectives.* P. Braquet (Ed.)
Copyright © 1988, J.R. Prous Science Publishers, S.A.

PERIPHERAL BLOOD LEUKOCYTES, ISCHEMIC HEART, PAF, GINKGOLIDE B AND LEUKOTRIENE C_4

Aaron Fink[1]*, Joseph Shalev[2], Arnou Afek[1], Avi Caspi[3], Nisim Kauli[2] and Zui Bentwich[1]

[1]Ruth Ben Ari Institute of Clinical Immunology, [2]Heart Institute, [3]Intensive Coronary Care Unit, Kaplan Hospital, Rehovot, Israel (Affiliated to the Medical School of the Hebrew University and Hadassah, Jerusalem)

ABSTRACT

Leukotriene C_4 (LTC_4) and platelet-activating factor (PAF), inducers of glass non-adherence in leukocytes obtained from asthmatic individuals, can cause coronary artery spasm and myocardial ischemia in experimental animals. In order to study the role of LTC_4 and PAF in human acute and chronic ischemic heart disease, a leukocyte adherence inhibition (LAI) assay was performed in 68 patients with acute myocardial infarction, acute ischemia and chronic stable angina. LAI was induced by PAF but not by LTC_4 in peripheral blood leukocytes from 19/22 (86%) patients with acute ischemia and in 13/18 (68%) patients with chronic stable angina. In 28 patients with acute myocardial infarction, LAI was induced by LTC_4 in 17 (61%) and by PAF in 9 (32%); 4 (14%) were reactive to both PAF and LTC_4. PBL from 47 normal controls did not respond to either inducer. Induction of the LAI by LTC_4 and PAF was abrogated by pre-incubation with their respective receptor-specific antagonists, FPL 55712 and BN 52021. The results indicate that ischemic heart disease is associated with increased sensitivity to LTC_4 and PAF. They also suggest that by binding to separate

Address all correspondence to: A. Fink, M.D., Ph.D., Ruth Ben Ari Institute of Clinical Immunology, Kaplan Hospital, 76100 Rehovot, Israel.
*A. Fink is the recipient of Career Development Award ICRF, Montreal, Canada.

receptors, each ligand plays an independent role in different phases of ischemic heart disease.

INTRODUCTION

AGEPC-platelet activating factor (PAF) (1-O-hexadecyl-2-acetyl-sn-glycero-
3-phosphocholine) is a phospholipid produced by white blood cells and
platelets. PAF and the cysteinyl-containing leukotrienes (LTC$_4$, D$_4$, E$_4$),
lypoxygenase products of arachidonic acid metabolism, show vasoactive
properties in experimental animal models (13,15). Production of these compounds may be elicited by a variety of specific and non-specific stimuli,
including antigen-antibody reactions and inflammatory responses.

Certain episodes of myocardial ischemia or infarction are mediated by
PAF or LTC$_4$. When introduced into the coronary circulation, LTC$_4$ causes
coronary vasoconstriction and reduction of coronary blood flow associated
with reduced contractility of the myocard (3,12,14). Introduction of PAF
into the coronary arteries of pig heart results in a biphasic effect, namely
an initial increase followed by a decrease of coronary blood flow (4). These
findings, together with clinical observations that occlusion of epicardial
arteries is not always demonstrated in coronary artery disease, support the
hypothesis that symptoms may be caused by injury-spasm of resistance
vessels (10).

We have previously shown that leukocyte adherence inhibition (LAI) can
be mediated by LTC$_4$ (6,16). Using the LAI assay, we demonstrated that
in individuals afflicted with diseases associated with increased LTC$_4$ production, such as bronchial asthma (6) or ARDS (unpublished), leukocytes
adquire non-adherence properties when challenged with pure synthetic
LTC$_4$, suggesting that there may be an alteration in receptor density (6).
In addition, normal PBL can be sensitized to acquire non-adherence properties *in vitro* by pre-incubation with α-interferon (5) as well as with LTC$_4$
(unpublished). We postulated that increased production of LTC$_4$ induces
the expression of LTC$_4$ receptors on the cell surface in a mechanism similar
to that of α-interferon (5), manifested *in vitro* as LAI.

Thus, if coronary spasm (acute or chronic) is caused by increased production of LTC$_4$ or PAF, it is likely that leukocytes of these patients will
show increased sensitivity to these mediators. In the present study we have
tested PBL from patients with ischemic heart disease not only to demonstrate
the LAI phenomenon, but also to investigate whether LAI activity induced by these mediators correlates with the status of disease activity.

MATERIALS AND METHODS

Patients

Sixty-eight participants, selected from patients with coronary artery disease treated at the Heart Institute or admitted to the Intensive Coronary Care Unit, were divided into three groups. All patients gave their informed consent. The first group consisted of 28 patients (mean age 59, female to male ratio 9:1) within 24 hours following an acute myocardial infarction, diagnosed by clinical, electrocardiographic and laboratory criteria. The second group consisted of 22 patients (mean age 50, female to male ratio 4:18) within 24 hours of an acute ischemic event (electrocardiographic changes with no increase in enzymes). The third group consisted of 18 patients (mean age 58, female to male ratio 1:17) who had chronic stable angina, established by coronary angiography or state after MI. Patients in all groups were receiving medication as warranted for their condition. Forty-seven individuals (mean age 45, female to male ratio 14:31) with no previous complaints of coronary artery disease were chosen at random to serve as a control group for the study.

Materials

LTC$_4$ and FPL 55712 were kindly provided by Dr. U. Zor (Dept. of Hormone Research, The Weizmann Institute of Science, Rehovot, Israel). BN 52021, a PAF antagonist, was received as a generous gift from from Dr. P. Braquet (Institut Henri Beaufour). Stock solutions of FPL 55712, BN 52021 and LTC$_4$, diluted to 10^{-2}M in absolute ethanol, DMSO or Medium 199, respectively, were further diluted to working solutions of 10^{-5}M in Medium 199 and stored until further use.

Peripheral Blood Leukocyte (PBL) Preparation

Twenty ml of venous blood were drawn into a heparinized syringe and immediately transferred into 16 x 150 mm glass tubes. Cells were allowed to settle for 45 minutes in a humidified atmosphere of 95% air and 5% CO$_2$, at 37°C. The buffy coat containing PBL was aspirated with a Pasteur pipet, cells were centrifuged at 1400 rpm for 5 minutes, and contaminating erythrocytes were lysed with ice-cold buffered Tris ammonium chloride, pH 7.3. Cells were washed 3 times with Medium 199, resuspended in the same medium and the cell concentration was adjusted to 10^7/ml.

PAF- and LTC$_4$-Induced LAI

The LAI assay was performed essentially as previously described (6). Ten μl of PAF or LTC$_4$ were added to triplicate glass test tubes (16 x 150 mm, marked "A") containing 300 μl Medium 199, 100 μl PBL suspension and 100 μl fetal calf serum (FCS) at a final concentration of ~ 100 μg. A dose-response pattern was determined by titration of PAF and LTC$_4$ (final concentrations of 10^{-7}M-10^{-10}M/tube) in order to find the optimum concentration to be used in the assay. A standard dose of 10^{-7}M of each was employed. Cell viability tested by Trypan blue dye exclusion after the addition of PAF and LTC$_4$ was always > 95%. PBL control tubes, marked "B", prepared as above, did not contain PAF or LTC$_4$. To control for innate non-adherence properties, PBL were incubated with FCS in both tubes so that when cells were incubated without any external stimulus, the non-adherence index (NAI) = zero. Thus, any increase in non-adherence following addition of inducers is specific. The tubes were shaken, placed in a horizontal position with the suspended cells covering two thirds of each tube and incubated for 2 hours in a humidified atmosphere of 95% air and 5% CO_2 at 37°C. Following incubation, the tubes were placed upright, the content at the bottom stirred with a Pasteur pipet and a drop was layered onto a hemocytometer. The number of non-adherent cells was automatically enumerated by a computerized image analyzer (Model 90, Artek Corp., U.S.A.). Two fields were read for each tube; results were calculated automatically as a non-adherence index (NAI) as follows: NAI = (A-B)/(B) x 100, where A = number of non-adherent cells in the presence of PAF or LTC$_4$ and B = number of non-adherent cells in the absence of PAF or LTC$_4$. Indices > 30 for PAF and > 20 for LTC$_4$ were considered positive, based on large scale studies of LAI-induced by these compounds.

PAF- and LTC$_4$-Induced LAI in the Presence of Receptor Antagonists

Duplicate tubes marked "A" (one to serve as a positive LAI control) and one marked "B", were prepared as described for the LAI assay. Into one of the "A" tubes, 10 μl of a specific receptor antagonist (FPL 55712 for LTC$_4$ and BN 52021 for PAF) were added. Following determination of the dose-response pattern of LAI negation, performed as described for LAI induction, a standard concentration of 10^{-7}M was used. No LAI properties were attributed to the antagonists when added alone to cells. A result of inhibition was accepted only if the cells in the control tube showed a positive LAI.

Statistical Evaluation

The data are presented as mean ± SD of the NAI. Data were analyzed for significance using a Student's t test for paired data observation.

RESULTS

Dose-Response of PAF- and LTC$_4$-Induced LAI

Figures 1 and 2 show the effect of inducer concentration on the sensitivity of LTC$_4$- and PAF-induced LAI. Both vasoactive substances induced LAI at concentrations of 10^{-7}-10^{-9}M, with 10^{-7}M being optimal. Neither inducer was active at 10^{-10}M.

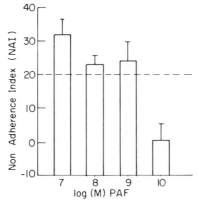

Figure 1 Dose response for PAF induced leukocyte adherence inhibition. NAI > 20 indicates positive response.

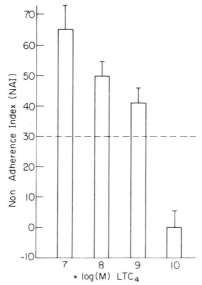

Figure 2. Dose response for LTC$_4$ induced leukocyte adherence inhibition. NAI > 30 indicate positive response.

Dose-Response of PAF Antagonist BN 52021

Figure 3 shows that a specific competitive receptor antagonist, BN 52021, abrogated in a dose-response fashion(10^{-6}-10^{-9}M), the ability of a standard dose of PAF (10^{-7}M) to induce a positive LAI. The results agree with those published elsewhere (7) using FPL 55712, the competitive antagonist for LTC_4 activity.

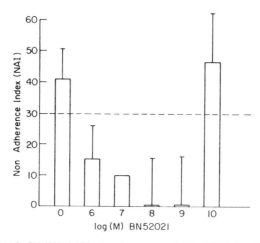

Figure 3   BN-52021 inhibits in a dose response fashion PAF-induced LAI.

PAF- and LTC₄-Induced LAI of Patients and Controls

Results of PAF- and LTC_4-induced LAI are presented in Table 1 and Figure 4. The mean NAI of PAF-induced LAI was significantly higher in the majority of the 22 patients with acute (86%) or chronic (68%) ischemic heart

Table 1   Leukocyte adherence inhibition induced by LTC_4 and PAF in PBL of 68 patients and 47 healthy subjects

Leukocyte donors	No.	LTC₄ Positive NAI (> 20)			PAF Positive NAI (> 30)		
		No.	%	Mean ± SD	No.	%	Mean ± SD
Acute ischemia	22	1	4.5	5.1 ± 10	19	86	22.9 ± 7
Chronic stable angina	18	0	0	1.8 ± 5	13	68	26.6 ± 5
Acute MI	28	17*	61	32.0 ± 6	9*	32	20.6 ± 4
Normal controls	47	0	0	-2.1 ± 10	7	14.8	3.0 ± 6

*Four of these were reactive to both ligands

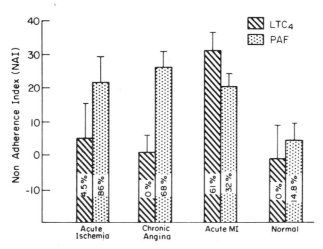

Figure 4 PAF- and LTC₄-induced LAI of patients with acute or chronic heart disease.

disease when compared to the control group. Of these, only one (4.5%), a patient with acute ischemia, had an LTC₄-induced LAI. For LTC₄-induced LAI, the mean NAI for both groups was similar to that of the control group. The pattern that emerged from PBL of patients with acute myocardial infarction (MI) was different. The mean NAI of this group was significantly higher than that observed for the control group in both LTC₄- and PAF-induced LAI.

Time Course Relationship for the LTC₄- and PAF-Induced LAI

In order to determine the time relationship for the LTC₄- and PAF-induced LAI following myocardial infarction, PBL of three consecutive MI patients were monitored for LAI reactivity at 24, 48 and 72 hours after the infarction. Table 2 shows that although PBL from acute MI patients reacted to

Table 2 Kinetics of the leukocyte adherence inhibition response to LTC₄ and PAF in three patients undergoing myocardial infarction

Time (hr)	LTC₄ Positive NAI (> 20)	PAF Positive NAI (> 30)
24	33 ± 6	22 ± 4
48	23 ± 10	32 ± 8
72	-8 ± 7	38 ± 5

LTC$_4$ as well as to PAF during the first 24 hours, the pattern changed dramatically after 48 and 72 hours. LTC$_4$ reactivity ceased, whereas PAF-induced LAI persisted and was similar to that of patients with acute ischemia or chronic stable angina.

PAF and LTC$_4$ Bind to Different Receptors

In several MI patients (4/28), PBL were reactive to both PAF and LTC$_4$. To determine whether LAI reactivity was specific for each stimulant and thus receptor-specific, PBL that were reactive to both LTC$_4$ and PAF were incubated in a criss-cross fashion with their respective receptor antagonists, FPL 55712 and BN 52021. Figure 5 shows that PAF-induced LAI is abrogated by the addition of BN 52021 but not by FPL 55712, whereas LTC$_4$-induced LAI is abrogated by the latter but not by the former. In both situations, only the addition of the specific antagonist of the appropriate stimulator reduced the NAI values below the cut-off values for positive LAI.

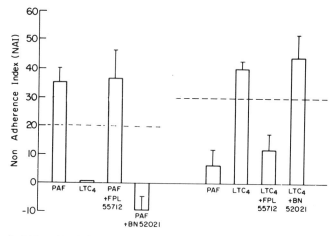

Figure 5 PAF- and LTC$_4$-induced LAI is dependent on ligand's binding to different receptors.

DISCUSSION

Leukocytes from patients undergoing a myocardial infarction appeared to respond in a specific manner to LTC$_4$ and PAF, whereas those from patients with acute or chronic ischemic heart disease responded only to the latter. While fewer MI patients responded to PAF than to LTC$_4$ within 24 hours following the attack, their mean NAI was significantly higher for both ligands when compared to those of the control group. Moreover, when followed for 72 hours, kinetics of PAF reactivity revealed that PAF-induced LAI increased with time and the mean NAI became similar to that observed in patients with acute ischemia and chronic stable angina. In contrast, LTC_4 responsiveness disappeared within 48 hours after MI and reached control values after 3 days. The results, which suggest a direct and independent action of PAF, differ from those of others (2,9,17).

In previous reports we postulated that LTC_4 induction of LAI is dependent on prior up-regulation of LTC_4 receptor density on PBL (6,16). Until now, it has not been clear whether PAF stimulates leukocytes directly, via a separate receptor, or elicits the production of LTC_4 which subsequently triggers the LAI response. In the present study, abrogation of the effects of LTC_4 and PAF by specific inhibitors, FPL 55712 and BN 52021, respectively, ruled out the possibility that PAF acted via stimulation of LTC_4 and indicated that, indeed, the LAI phenomenon can be mediated independently by either of these vasoactive substances.

This fact not only suggests that different mechanisms operate within a defined pathological process, but also provides a hypothesis about the function of LTC_4 and PAF in coronary heart disease. It appears that during myocardial necrosis (MI), LTC_4 and PAF play a major role, where PAF may also have some vasodilative effects (4). In processes without tissue damage, such as acute or chronic ischemia, PAF could be responsible for the pathologic event. Indeed, the fact that myocardial ischemia may be related to platelet-induced coronary spasm (10) supports our findings and suggests the possibility of treatment with specific PAF antagonists.

References

1. Benveniste, J., Henson, P.M. and Cochrane, C.G. *Leukocyte-dependent histamine release from rabbit platelets. The role of IgE, basophils and platelet-activating factor.* J Exp Med 1972; 136: 1356-1377.

2. Bounct, J., Thibandson, D. and Bessin, P. *Dependency of the PAF-acether-induced bronchospasm on the lipoxygenase pathway in the guinea-pig.* Prostaglandins 1983; 26: 457-466.

3. Ezra, D., Boyd, L.M., Feuerstein, G. and Goldstein, R.E. *Coronary constriction by leukotriene C₄, D₄ on guinea-pig isolated hearts.* Br J Pharmacol 1982; 76: 169-176.

4. Feuerstein, G., Boyd, L.M., Ezra, D. and Goldstein, R.E. *Effect of platelet-activating factor on coronary circulation of the domestic pig.* Am J Physiol 1984; 246: 4466-4471.

5. Fink, A., Shahin, R., Eliraz, A., Bibi, H., Berkanstadt, H., Levin, S. and Bentwich, Z. *Interferon modulates the leukotriene C₄-induced non-adherence properties of leukocytes acquisition of an asthmatic phenotype.* Immunol Letters 1985; 10: 159-163.

6. Fink, A., Bibi, H., Eliraz, A. and Bentwich, Z. *Leukotrienes (LTC₄, LTD₄) confer glass non-adherence on leukocytes of asthmatic individuals. Dependency on cyclooxygenase products and calcium ion and characterization of an asthmatic phenotype.* Immunol Letters 1985; 10: 319-323.

7. Fink, A., Bibi, H., Eliraz, A. and Bentwich, Z. *Ketotifen, disodium chromoglycate and verapamil inhibit leukotriene activity: Determination by the tube leukocyte adherence inhibition (LAI) assay.* Annals of Allergy 1986;

194 A. FINK ET AL.

57: 103-106.

8. Goetzl, E.J., Phillips, M.J. and Gold, W.M. *Stimulus specificity of the generation of leukotrienes by dog mastocytoma cells.* J Exp Med 1983; 158; 731-737.

9. Heffuer, J.E., Shoemaker, S.A., Canham, M.E., Mahesh, P., McMurty, I.F., Morris, H.C. and Repine, J.E. *Acetyl glyceryl ether phosphorylcholine stimulated human platelets cause pulmonary hypertension and edema in isolated rabbit lungs.* J Clin Invest 1983; 71: 351-357.

10. Hellstrom, H.R. *The injury spasm (ischemia-induced hemostatic vasoconstriction) and vascular autoregulatory hypothesis of ischemic disease. Resistance vessel spasm hypothesis of ischemic disease.* Am J Cardiol 1982; 49: 802-810.

11. Henson, P.M. *Release of vasoactive amines from platelets induced by sensitized mononuclear leukocytes and antigen.* J Exp Med 1970; 131: 287-306.

12. Letts, L.G. and Piper, P.J. *The action of leukotriene C_4 and D_4 on pig isolated hearts.* Br J Pharmacol 1982; 76: 169-176.

13. McManns, L.M., Hanahan, D.J., Demopoulos, C.A. and Pinekard, R.N. *Pathobiology of the intravenous infusion of acetylglyceryl ether phosphorylcholine.* J Immunol 1980; 124: 2919-2924.

14. Michelassi, F., Landa, L., Hill, R.D., Lowenstein, E., Watkins, W.D., Petkan, A.J. and Zapol, W.M. *Leukotriene D_4: Patent coronary artery vaso-constrictor associated with impaired ventricular contraction.* Science 1982; 17: 841-843.

15. Peck, M.J., Piper, P.J. and Williams, T.J. *The effect of leukotrienes C_4 and D_4 on the microvasculature of guinea-pig skin.* Prostaglandins 1981; 21: 315-321.

16. Thomson, D.M.P. *Various authentic chemoattractants mediating leukocyte adherence inhibition.* JNCI 1984; 73: 595-605.

17. Voelkel, N.F., Worthon, J.T., Henson, P.M. and Murphy, R.C. *Non-immunological production of leukotrienes induced by platelet-activating factor.* Science 1982; 218: 286-288.

Ginkgolides - Chemistry, Biology, Pharmacology
and Clinical Perspectives. P. Braquet (Ed.)
Copyright © 1988, J.R. Prous Science Publishers, S.A.

INHIBITION OF CALCIUM MOBILIZATION BY BN 52021 IN MOUSE MACROPHAGES: POSSIBLE INVOLVEMENT OF PAF-ACETHER RECEPTORS ACTING THROUGH A PERTUSSIS TOXIN-SENSITIVE GTP-BINDING PROTEIN

Ricardo Garay and Pierre Braquet[1]

INSERM U7, Hôpital Necker, F-75015 Paris; [1]Institut Henri Beaufour, F-92350 Le Plessis Robinson; France

INTRODUCTION

The interaction of PAF-acether with membrane receptors of platelets, neutrophils, macrophages and other target cells results in an increase of cytosolic free Ca^{2+} content through the opening of membrane Ca^{2+} channels and/or inositol triphosphate-dependent Ca^{2+} mobilization from internal stores (4, 7, 12-14, 22; for effects on Na^+: Ca^{2+} exchange see ref. 11).

Increases in cytosolic free Ca^{2+} contents modify the activity of several membrane ion transport systems. One of the most sensitive and physiologically relevant changes is the opening of Ca^{2+}-dependent K^+-channels (Fig. 1), which have been frequently found activated during secretory processes in a wide variety of cells (18). In particular, stimulation

Address all correspondece to: Dr. Ricardo Garay, INSERM U7, Hôpital Necker, 161 rue de Sèvres, Paris F-75015, France.

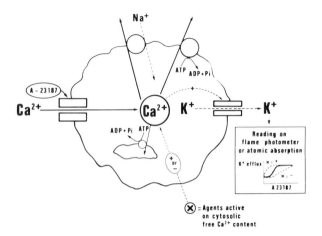

Figure 1   A model for the stimulation of K⁺ efflux by the Ca^{2+} ionophore A23187 in macrophages. This effect reflects the opening of Ca^{2+}-dependent, K⁺-channels in response to increases in cytosolic free Ca^{2+} contents. Agents that directly or indirectly act on Ca^{2+} transport systems may modulate A23187-stimulated K⁺ efflux.

of phagocytic cells with the calcium ionophore A23187, chemotactic factors or other agents provokes the opening of these Ca^{2+}-dependent K⁺-channels (2, 10, 17, 20). In line with these studies we have previously found that PAF-acether opens Ca^{2+}-sensitive K⁺-channels in mouse macrophages, an effect inhibited by BN 52021, a specific PAF-acether antagonist (7). However, we surprisingly found that BN 52021 was also able to antagonize the opening of membrane K⁺-channels induced by the calcium ionophore A23187, even in the absence of exogenous PAF-acether (7).

Some previous observations suggested to us that the antagonism between BN 52021 and A23187 involved a participation of cyclic AMP (cAMP). First, cAMP inhibits the chemiluminescence and other stimulatory phenomena induced by addition of A23187 to macrophages (15, 16). In addition, prostaglandins may exert inhibitory effects in immune cells via cAMP (1, 9). Finally, we have previously shown that several adenylate cyclase stimulators (like isoproterenol, PGE_1 and forskolin), exogenous cAMP and/or inhibition of phosphodiesterase with MIX (1-methyl-3-isobutylxanthine) were able to antagonize the opening of K⁺-channels induced by A23187 in mouse macrophages (20). These effects of cAMP likely reflect an inhibition of Ca^{2+} mobilization via: i) the stimulation of some Ca^{2+} extruding mechanism like the Ca^{2+} pump or Na^+:Ca^{2+} exchange and/or ii) the inhibition of membrane Ca^{2+} channels (19).

The above results suggested to us that BN 52021 was able to stimulate adenylate cyclase in *intact* macrophages. However, a direct demonstration of this stimulation is hampered by the particular kinetics of biochemical reactions involving cAMP in intact cells (21). For instance, the inhibition of Ca^{2+}-dependent K^+-channels by isoproterenol in macrophages is observed at much lower concentrations than those required for stimulating endogenous levels of cAMP (20).

Recently, Lad *et al.* have found that pertussis toxin (PT) inhibits PAF-acether dependent Ca^{2+} mobilization in human neutrophils (12). In addition, it appears that beta adrenergic receptors may regulate PAF-sensitivity in target cells (3, 5). These observations renewed our interest to further investigate a possible involvement of cAMP in the inhibitory mechanism of BN 52021 on A23187-stimulated K^+-channels in mouse macrophages.

MATERIALS AND METHODS

Preparation of Mouse Macrophages

Peritoneal mouse macrophages were obtained according to a previously published method (6, 7, 20). Briefly, 2-5 ml of sterile thioglycollate medium (Institut Pasteur, Paris) were injected into the peritoneal cavity of female mice 5-8 weeks old, of the 57 BL/5(H-2^b) and DBA/2 (H-2^d) inbred strains. Elicited cells were collected 3 to 5 days later by washing the peritoneal cavity with Hank's balanced salt solution (HBSS). HBSS media were freshly prepared by adding $NaHCO_3$ (final concentration: 4.2 mM) to a basal medium of the following composition (mM): 137 NaCl, 5.3 KCl, 0.34 Na_2HPO_4, 0.32 KH_2PO_4, 5.5 glucose, 1.3 $CaCl_2$ and 0.5 $MgCl_2$. The number of cells collected per mouse was $10-20 \times 10^6$ and in these more than 80% presented the morphological aspect of macrophages. A pool of 10-20 mice was used in each experiment. The collected suspension was immediately centrifuged at 1000g for 1 minute at 4°C and the supernatant was removed.

Measurement of K^+-Efflux

Macrophages, washed twice with cold 150 mM NaCl, were resuspended in a (Rb^+/Na^+)-media of the following composition (mM): 140 NaCl, 5 RbCl, 1 $CaCl_2$, 1 $MgCl_2$, 10 4-morpholinopropane sulphonic acid-Tris buffer (pH 7.4 at 37°C), 0.02 bumetanide, 0.5 MIX and 10 glucose. In order to measure internal K^+ content, 0.1 ml of the macrophage suspension were added to two tubes containing 1 ml of Acationox 0.02%. The tubes were rapidly frozen and thawed 2 or 3 times, sonicated and then centrifuged 10 min at 3000. K^+ contents were measured in the supernatants by flame photometry (Eppendorf flame photometer).

Release of cell K^+ content in the incubation medium was measured using the following method: 0.1 ml of macrophage suspension in (Rb^+/Na^+)-medium were added in the cold to four tubes containing 1 ml of (Rb^+/Na^+)-medium. The tubes were then transferred to a 37°C water bath for further incubation. At times (min) 0 and 10 a duplicate of tubes were transferred to the cold and centrifuged for 2 minutes at 1000g at 4°C. The supernatants were carefully removed and their K^+ contents were measured by flame photometry. In control experiments we verified that K^+ release was linear during at least the 10 minute incubation period.

The rate constant of K^+ efflux (k_k) was calculated using the following equation:

$$k_k = \frac{\Delta K_0}{K_i \times t} \qquad (1)$$

where ΔK_0 is the increase in external K^+ content during the incubation time t: 10 min and K_i is the reading of internal K^+ content.

Measurement of K^+-Efflux in Human Red Cells

K^+-efflux in human red cells was measured according to previously published methods (8).

Chemicals

BN 52021 (9H-1,7a-(epoxymethano)-1H, 6aH-cyclopenta[c]-furo[2,3-b]furo-[3',2':3,4]cyclopenta[1,2-d]furan-5,9,12-(4H)-trione, 3-tert-butyl-hexahydro-4,7b-11-trihydroxy-8-methyl) was produced by IHB-IPSEN Institute for Therapeutic Research (Le Plessis, France). PAF-acether was purchased from Bachem (Bubendorf, Switzerland) and stored at —80°C in a 0.5% bovine serum albumin solution. Pertussis toxin was generously provided by Françoise Megret (Institut Pasteur, Paris). Bumetanide was a gift from Leo Laboratories (Paris, France). All other chemicals were either from Merck or Sigma (distributed through Coger, Paris, France).

The effect of drugs on K^+ movements was studied using the protocols described above. Concentrated solutions in water or dymethylsulfoxide (DMSO) were freshly prepared every day. Different amounts of drugs were added directly to the flux media provided that the final concentration of DMSO had no effect *per se* on K^+ movements (final concentration of DMSO never exceeded 0.2% v/v).

RESULTS

Stimulation of K^+ Efflux by the Ca^{2+} Ionophore A23187

The rate constant of K^+ efflux (k_k) in mouse macrophages was strongly stimulated by increasing concentrations of the Ca^{2+} ionophore A23187 from a basal value of 0.67 ± 0.04 (h)$^{-1}$ up to maximal values of 2-4 (h)$^{-1}$ with an IC_{50} of 7.6 ± 1.9 μM (mean ± SEM of 6 experiments). Figure 2 shows a typical experiment. The Ca^{2+} ionophore ionomycin induced a similar maximal K^+ flux-stimulation although the IC_{50} was 3-5 fold higher (data not shown).

Inhibition of A23187-Stimulated K^+ Efflux by BN 52021

K^+ efflux was stimulated by increasing concentrations of A23187. Figure 2 shows that in presence of BN 52021 the dose-response curve is partially inhibited, particularly at high A23187 concentrations. In experiments performed at 40 μM of A23187, the "BN 52021-sensitive" K^+ efflux (defined as the fraction of K^+ efflux inhibited by BN 52021) was 0.56 ± 0.09 (mean ± SEM of 7 experiments). It is important to note that BN 52021 slightly inhibited K^+ efflux, even in the absence of A23187 (7).

In control experiments in human red cells, BN 52021 was not able to modify A23187-stimulated K^+ efflux (data not shown).

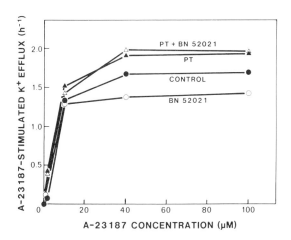

Figure 2   Stimulation of K^+ efflux by increasing concentrations of the Ca^{2+} ionophore A23187. In the presence of 10 μM of BN 52021 the dose-response curve is partially inhibited, particularly at high A23187 concentrations. Addition of pertussis toxin (PT) to the flux media at a concentration of 0.5 μg/ml completely abolished the effect of BN 52021. On the other hand, PT increased by itself the magnitude of A23187-stimulated K^+ efflux.

Antagonism Between BN 52021 and Pertussis Toxin

Addition of pertussis toxin (PT) to the flux media at a concentration of 0.5 μg/ml completely abolished the inhibitory effect of BN 52021 on A23187-stimulated K⁺ efflux (Fig. 2). In addition, careful inspection of Figure 2 shows that PT increased by itself the magnitude of A23187-stimulated K⁺ efflux.

Effect of Preincubation with PAF-Acether

Figure 3 shows BN 52021-sensitive K⁺ efflux in macrophages preincubated for 15 minutes with several concentrations of PAF-acether. It can be seen that PAF-acether exerted a biphasic effect, *i.e.*, BN 52021-sensitive K⁺ efflux was *stimulated* at very low PAF-doses (about 10^{-12}M) and *inhibited* at PAF-acether concentrations higher than 10^{-8} M.

It is important to note that the magnitude of the enhancement of BN 52021-sensitive K⁺ efflux by low PAF-acether concentrations was variable from one experiment to the other. Figure 3 represents mean values of 4 experiments performed at 40 μM of A23187. Essentially similar results were obtained in 4 other experiments carried out at other A23187 concentrations.

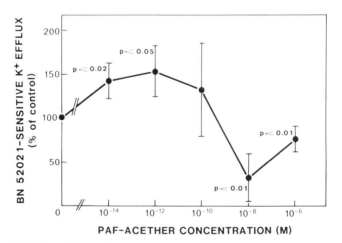

Figure 3   BN 52021-sensitive K⁺ efflux in macrophages preincubated for 15 min with several concentrations of PAF-acether. Values are given as mean ± SD of 4 experiments (p calculated by Student's *t* test). In can be seen that PAF-acether exerted a biphasic effect, *i.e.*, BN 52021-sensitive K⁺ efflux was stimulated at very low PAF-doses (10^{-12}M) and inhibited at PAF-acether concentrations higher than 10^{-8} M. It is important to note that the magnitude of the enhancement of BN 52021-sensitive K⁺ efflux by low PAF-acether concentrations was variable from one experiment to the other. Essentially similar results were obtained in 4 other experiments carried out at other A23187 concentrations.

DISCUSSION

We have confirmed previous results showing that BN 52021 partially counterbalances the opening of Ca^{2+}-sensitive K^+-channels induced by the Ca^{2+} ionophore A23187 in mouse macrophages (7). This effect may result from: i) a direct interaction of BN 52021 with the ionophore or with the K^+-channel, ii) an effect mediated via some second messenger. The first possibility seems to be excluded by the fact that BN 52021 was not able to modify A23187-stimulated K^+ efflux in human red cells.

We have previously found that isoproterenol and PGE_1 also inhibited A23187-sensitive K^+-channels in mouse macrophages (20). This effect seems mediated by cAMP which appears to counterbalance increases in cytosolic free Ca^{2+} content through the stimulation of some Ca^{2+}-extruding transport system and/or through the inhibition of membrane Ca^{2+} channels (20). Indeed, cAMP inhibits Ca^{2+} mobilization in several (but not all) cell models (19). These and other results suggested to us that BN 52021 could act through cAMP (see Introduction).

BN 52021 was not able to antagonize the opening of A23187-sensitive K^+-channels in the presence of pertussis toxin (PT). This suggests that, in contrast to isoproterenol, PGE_1 and other agents acting through the cholera toxin-sensitive GTP-binding protein (Ns), BN 52021 acts through the PT-sensitive GTP-binding protein (Ni).

Interestingly, PT enhanced the magnitude of K^+ efflux induced by A23187 in macrophages. On the other hand, it has been previously reported that A23187 stimulates cAMP generation in macrophages (15, 16). It appears, therefore, that this effect is mediated through the GTP-binding protein Ni.

Lad *et al.* have previously found that PT (at high concentrations and after 30-60 min preincubation) inhibits PAF-acether induced Ca^{2+} mobilization in human neutrophils (12). We thus performed experiments in order to see if the effect of BN 52021 on K^+-channels involved the PAF-receptor acting through the GTP-binding Ni protein. This was apparently confirmed by the observation that the effect of BN 52021 on K^+-channels was antagonized by preincubation of cells with PAF-acether concentrations of 10^{-8}-10^{-6}M. However, we noted that low concentrations of PAF-acether (10^{-12}-10^{-14}M) *enhanced* BN 52021-sensitive K^+ efflux, although the magnitude of the stimulating effect varied from experiment to experiment. On the other hand, we have also found that endotoxin, which is able to stimulate endogenous PAF-acether generation, induced a similar enhancement of BN 52021-sensitive K^+ efflux (data not shown). This may suggest that BN 52021 could displace a variable amount of endogenous PAF-acether from its receptor site, thus inducing cAMP generation and inhibition of Ca^{2+}-sensitive K^+-channels.

In conclusion, BN 52021 inhibits Ca^{2+} mobilization and the associated opening of K^+-channels induced by the Ca^{2+} ionophore A23187 in macrophages. This effect may reflect cAMP-generation by displacement of endogenous PAF-acether from a receptor acting through a GTP-binding Ni protein. Further studies are required in order to precisely determine the nature of the Ca^{2+}-transport system(s) regulated by cAMP in mouse macrophages.

ACKNOWLEDGEMENTS

We are greatly indebted to Corine Nazaret (Inserm U7, Hôpital Necker, France) for technical help.

References

1. Bonta, I.L., Adolfs, M.J.P. *Interactions between prostaglandin E_2 and prostacyclin in regulating levels of cAMP in elicited populations of peritoneal macrophages.* In: Advances in Prostaglandin, Thromboxane and Leukotriene Research, Vol. 12. B. Samuelson, R. Paoletti, P. Ramwell (Eds.). Raven Press: New York 1983; 13-17.

2. Braquet, M., Garay, R., Ducousso, R., Borgeat, P., DeFeudis, F.V., Braquet, P. *Transmembrane potassium movements and the arachidonic acid cascade: I. A study in A23187-stimulated human leukocytes.* In: Protaglandins and Membrane Ion Transport. P. Braquet, R. Garay, J.C. Frölich, S. Nicosia (Eds.). Raven Press: New York 1984; 113-121.

3. Braquet, P., Etienne, A., Clostre, F. *Down regulation of β_2-adrenergic receptors by PAF-acether and its inhibition by the PAF-acether antagonist BN 52021.* Prostaglandins 1985; 30: 721.

4. Camussi, G., Alloati, G., Montruchio, G., Meda, M., Emanuelli, G. *Effect of platelet-activating factor on guinea-pig papillary muscle.* Experientia 1984; 40: 697-699.

5. Criscuoli, M., Subissi, A. *PAF-acether-induced death in mice: Involvement of arachidonate metabolites and β-adrenoceptors.* Br J Pharmacol 1987; 90: 203-209.

6. Diez, J., Braquet, P., Verna, R., Nazaret, C., Garay, R. *The effect of cyclic AMP on Na^+ and K^+ transport systems in mouse macrophages.* Experientia 1985; 41: 666-667.

7. Garay, R., Braquet, P. *Involvement of K^+ movements in the membrane signal induced by PAF-acether.* Biochem Pharmacol 1986; 35: 2811-2815.

8. Garay, R., Nazaret, C., Diez, J., Etienne, A., Bourgain, R., Braquet, P., Esanu, A. *Stimulation of K^+ fluxes by diuretic drugs in human red cells.* Biochem Pharmacol 1984; 33: 2013-2020.

9. Gemsa, D. *Stimulation of prostaglandin E release from macrophages and possible role in the immune response.* In: Lymphokines, Vol. 4. E. Pick (Ed.). Academic Press: New York 1981;335-375.

10. Holian, A., Daniele, R.P. *Formyl-peptide stimulation of superoxide anion release from lung macrophages: Sodium and potassium involvement.* J Cell Physiol 1982; 113: 413-419.

11. Kester, M., Kumar, R., Hanahan, D.J. *Alkylacetylglycerophosphocholine stimulates Na^+-Ca^{2+} exchange, protein phosphorylation and polyphosphoinositide turnover in rat ileal plasmalemmal vesicles.* Biochim Bioph Acta 1986; 888: 306-315.

12. Lad, P.M., Olson, C.V., Grewal, I.S., Scott, S.J. *A pertussis toxin-sensitive GTP-binding protein in the human neutrophil regulates multiple receptors, calcium mobilization, and lectin-induced capping.* Proc Natl Acad Sci 1985; 82: 8643-8647.

13. Lapetina, E. *Platelet-activating factor stimulates the phosphatidylinositol cycle.* Biol Chem 1982; 257: 7314.

14. Lee, T.C., Malone, B., Blank, M.L., Snyder, F. *1-Alkyl-2-acetyl-sn-glycero-3-phosphorylcholine (platelet-activating factor) stimulates calcium influx in rabbit platelets.* Biochem Biophys Res Commun 1981; 102: 1262-1268.

15. Lim, L.K., Hunt, N.H., Eichner, R.D., Weidemann, M.J. *Cyclic AMP and the regulation of prostaglandin production by macrophages.* Biochem Biophys Res Comm 1983; 114: 248-254.

16. Lim, L.K., Hunt, N.H., Weidemann, M.J. *Reactive oxygen production, arachidonate metabolism and cyclic AMP in macrophages.* Biochem Biophys Res Comm 1983; 114: 549-555.

17. Oliveira-Castro, G.M. *Ca^{2+}-sensitive, K^+-channels in phagocytic cell membranes.* Cell Calcium 1983; 4: 475-492.

18. Petersen, O.H., Maruyama, Y. *Calcium-activated potassium channels and their role in secretion.* Nature 1984; 307: 693-696.

19. Rasmussen, H., Barrett, P.Q. *Calcium messenger system. An integrated view.* Physiol Rev 1984; 64: 938-984.

20. Rosati, C., Hannaert, P., Dausse, J.P., Braquet, P., Garay, R. *Stimulation of beta-adrenoceptors inhibits calcium-dependent potassium-channels in mouse macrophages.* J Cellular Physiol 1986; 129: 310-314.

21. Strickland, S., Loeb, J.N. *Obligatory separation of hormone binding and biological response curves in systems dependent upon secondary mediators of hormone action.* Proc Natl Acad Sci 1981; 78: 1366-1370.

22. Valone, F.H., Johnson, B. *Decay of the activating signal after platelet stimulation with 1-0-Alkyl-2-acetyl-sn-glycero-3-phosphorylcholine: Changes in calcium permeability.* Thromb Res 1985; 40: 385-392.

Ginkgolides - Chemistry, Biology, Pharmacology and Clinical Perspectives. P. Braquet (Ed.)
Copyright © 1988, J.R. Prous Science Publishers, S.A.

PAF-ACETHER AND EOSINOPHIL-MEDIATED CYTOTOXICITY. INHIBITION BY THE PAF-ACETHER ANTAGONIST BN 52021 AND RELATED GINKGOLIDES

Monique Capron[1], Jacques Benveniste[2], Pierre Braquet[3], Jean-Marie Grzych[1], Anthony E. Butterworth[4] and André Capron[1]

[1]CIBP, Unité Mixte INSERM U167-CNRS 624, Institut Pasteur, Lille, [2]Unité INSERM 200, Clamart, [3]Institut Henri Beaufour, Le Plessis-Robinson, France; [4]Department of Pathology, Cambridge University, U.K.

INTRODUCTION

The production of PAF-acether by activated eosinophils has been recently reported (10, 12). Earlier studies have shown an increased formation of PAF-acether in eosinophils from patients with eosinophilia, in response to various chemotactic factors (12). In addition, "hypodense" eosinophils, only present in blood of highly hypereosinophilic patients or more frequently in tissues, seemed to produce more PAF-acether than cells with normal density (10), a result in keeping with the fact that such hypodense eosinophils exhibited higher IgE-dependent cytotoxicity for parasite targets (8). These findings suggested that the increased production of PAF-acether in hypodense cells could be a consequence of *in vivo* activation of eosinophils and might play a role in IgE-dependent inflammatory and allergic reactions in which this cell subset participates.

Address all correspondence to: Dr. Monique Capron, CIBP, Institut Pasteur, 1, rue du Professeur A. Calmette, F-59019 Lille Cédex, France.

PAF-acether is not only synthetized by eosinophils (12) but it is also a potent activator of eosinophil functions. PAF-acether induces an eosinophil chemotactic response and is much more potent on a molar basis that other chemotactic factors, such as Eosinophil Chemotactic Factor of Anaphylaxis (ECF-A) or leukotriene B_4 (LTB_4) (16, 19). The specificity of this effect is demonstrated by the strong inhibition of PAF-acether induced chemotaxis caused by a PAF-acether antagonist, BN 52021, which suggested the presence of a receptor for PAF-acether on eosinophils (16, 19). Intracutaneous injections of PAF-acether cause a marked eosinophilic response, exclusively in allergic patients, a large number of these cells being degranulated (9). As well, intravenous injections of PAF-acether into guinea-pigs have been shown to induce a massive infiltration of the lung with eosinophils, a phenomenon antagonized by treatment with BN 52021 (13). These lines of evidence suggest that PAF-acether may participate in eosinophil recruitment both *in vitro* and *in vivo*.

In addition, PAF-acether induces LTC_4 formation by human eosinophils as well as O_2^- production and chemiluminescence (3), a phenomenon antagonized by the ginkgolide BN 52021. More recently, it has been reported that PAF-acether induces a dose-dependent enhancement of eosinophil cytotoxicity for *Schistosoma mansoni* schistosomula coated with C3b and IgG antibodies (14). This effect is also inhibited by preincubation of eosinophils with BN 52021, but no inhibition was observed on the cytotoxicity mediated by these eosinophils in the absence of PAF-acether (14).

Taken together, these results indicate that PAF-acether plays a central part in the recruitment of eosinophils. However, the eosinophil response to PAF-acether may differ according to their state of activation. Following our original observation that hypodense eosinophils could bind IgE and release cytolytic mediators (8), more recent data have indicated that eosinophil mediators could be selectively released in response to IgE or IgG-dependent stimulation, suggesting at least two different pathways of activation (11). In the present study, we have extended these findings to the generation of PAF-acether, by showing that PAF-acether is mainly produced by human eosinophils after IgE-dependent activation. In addition, we have investigated the role of several PAF-acether-antagonists, including BN 52021, on the cytotoxicity of both human and rat eosinophils against antibody-coated *S. mansoni* larvae.

MATERIALS AND METHODS

Reagents and Buffers

Monoclonal antibodies (Mab) anti-human IgE antibodies were obtained from ImmunoTech (Marseille-Luminy, France). Polyclonal anti-human IgG antibodies were purchased from Cappel Laboratories (Cochranville, PA, USA). The PAF-acether antagonists BN 52021 and other related ginkgolides (ginkgolide A: BN 52020; ginkgolide C: BN 52022) were obtained from Institut Henri Beaufour (IHB, Le Plessis-Robinson, France). Another series of PAF-acether antagonists, BN 50488 and BN 50489, were also obtained from IHB. These compounds were dissolved in dimethylsulfoxide (DMSO) and further diluted with culture medium as appropriate.

The buffer used for PAF-acether biosynthesis was Hanks medium (pH 7.4) supplemented with 2 mM $CaCl_2$ and 0.25% (w/v) fatty acid free bovine serum albumin (BSA, Sigma Chemical Co, St Louis, MO, USA). For cytotoxicity experiments, the medium was Eagle's minimum essential medium (MEM) supplemented with 1% heat-inactivated normal human serum (MEM/NHS) or normal rat serum (MEM/NRS).

Eosinophil Purification

Human eosinophils from venous blood of patients with hypereosinophilia of various etiologies were purified using centrifugation upon discontinuous metrizamide (Nyegaard, Oslo, Norway) gradient (18). Several cell fractions were collected from the gradients, according to their density (15). Eosinophils are referred to as "hypodense" when obtained in the lower density layers corresponding to metrizamide concentrations less than 23%. In some experiments, "normodense" eosinophils were obtained from normal or hypereosinophilic individuals at the top of the 25% and 24% metrizamide layers. Cell preparations were extensively washed and counted by using a coulter counter (Coultronics, Margency, France). Eosinophil purity was evaluated on cytocentrifuge preparations stained with Giemsa.

Rat eosinophil-rich populations were prepared from peritoneal cell suspensions obtained from normal rats, stimulated 48 hours previously by injection of 0.9% sterile physiological saline. Peritoneal cells were depleted from macrophage-rich adherent cells by plating for 2 hours at 37°C onto plastic petri dishes. The non adherent population was composed of 50 to 60% eosinophils and 10% mast cells, as previously described (4).

Sensitization and Stimulation of Human Eosinophils

Human eosinophils were resuspended in Hank's balanced salt solution containing 0.25% (w/v) fatty acid free BSA. The cells (5 x 10^6/ml) were either incubated for 1 hour at 37°C with anti-human IgE or anti-human IgG or with medium alone (direct activation experiments) or (passive sensitization experiments), they were first incubated for 60 minutes at + 4°C with sera from filariasis patients or with normal sera (1/10 final dilution), prior to activation by anti-IgE or anti-IgG for 1 hr at 37°C. After this incubation period, the reaction was stopped by addition of EDTA (5 mM final concentration). Ethanol was then added to the tubes in order to obtain 80% concentration (v/v). After slow agitation, ethanolic supernatants were recovered by centrifugation and desiccated under an air stream.

PAF-Acether Assay and Characterization

PAF-acether activity was determined following a modified method (1). Briefly, it was measured using an aggregometer (Icare, Marseille, France) by aggregation of aspirin-treated (0.1 mM) washed rabbit platelets in the presence of creatine phosphate (0.7 mM) and creatine phosphokinase (13.9 U/ml; Sigma). Results are expressed as the equivalent of synthetic PAF-acether in $ng/5 \times 10^6$ cells, calculated over a calibration curve established with synthetic PAF-acether.

Adherence and Cytotoxicity Assays

S. mansoni schistosomula prepared by the skin penetration procedure were used as targets of the cytotoxicity assays (4). For IgE-mediated eosinophil-dependent cytotoxicity, 50 µl aliquots of the schistosomula suspension containing 50 targets in MEM/NHS were incubated in flat-bottomed microtiter plates (NUNC, Roskilde, Denmark). Fifty µl of unheated sera from S. mansoni infected patients or normal subjects were added at a final dilution of 1:32, together with 100 µl of hypodense eosinophils purified from highly hypereosinophilic patients (5,000 effector to target ratio), according to previous reports (8). The IgG-mediated killing assay was performed with normodense eosinophils from normal or slightly hypereosinophilic individuals and heat-inactivated pools of human immune sera as a source of IgG antibodies (18).

Adherence and cytotoxicity assays were also performed with rat eosinophils, according to previously described techniques (4). Briefly, S. mansoni schistosomula were incubated with immune serum from 42 day S. mansoni infected rats. Unheated immune serum (containing the 2 effector antibodies, IgE and IgG2a) was used at the 1:64 final dilution. In order to evaluate the respective role of each anaphylactic antibody class, IgE containing serum was heated for 2 hours to 56°C and used at the 1:32 final dilution. Non adherent peritoneal cells enriched in eosinophils were then added to opsonized S. mansoni schistosomula at a ratio of 5000 cells/target.

For both human and rat eosinophils, the percentage of adherence was expressed as the percentage of schistosomula bearing closely adherent eosinophils, as compared to the total number of target parasites in each well. The percentages of adherence and cytotoxicity (% of dead schistosomula) were evaluated by microscopical observation after 24-48 hours contact between effector cells and targets at 37°C under a 5% CO_2 atmosphere.

To investigate the inhibitory activity of several PAF-antagonists, the various substances were added at defined concentrations directly to the cultures without any preincubation.

Statistical Analysis

Student's *t* tests for paired and unpaired observations were used to compare means of replicate samples.

RESULTS

Biosynthesis of PAF-Acether after IgE-Dependent Activation of Human Eosinophils

The production of PAF-acether by human eosinophils was studied in response to various stimuli. When eosinophils purified from patients with filariasis infection and presenting increased IgE levels were directly incubated with anti-IgE antibodies, significant levels of PAF-acether could be produced (Fig. 1A). In contrast no PAF-acether was detected after addition of anti-human IgG.

Since we have previously demonstrated that very little cytophilic IgG was detected on the surface of such eosinophils (7), it was necessary to use a different protocol of activation in order to trigger eosinophils by an IgG dependent mechanism. When eosinophils from patients with the hypereosinophilic syndrome (HES) and without surface IgE were passively sensitized by incubation with sera from filariasis patients, only IgE but not IgG triggering was able to induce the production of PAF-acether (Fig. 1B).

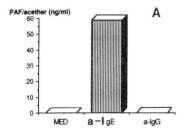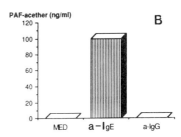

Figure 1 Production of PAF-acether by purified human hypodense eosinophils after incubation for 60 min at 37°C either with medium (MED) or with anti-human IgE (A-IgE) or anti-human IgG (a-IgG). a) Eosinophils were purified from parasite infected hypereosinophilic patients and directly activated with the various stimuli. b) Eosinophils were purified from patients with the hypereosinophilic syndrome (HES) and passively sensitized with the sera of parasite infected patients at 1:10 final dilution for 60 min at +4°C prior to incubation with the various stimuli (2 experiments in each case).

Role of PAF-Acether Antagonists in the IgE-Dependent Cytotoxicity Mediated by Human Hypodense Eosinophils

The above results led us to investigate the putative role played by PAF-acether in the effector function of eosinophils. The effect of various PAF-acether antagonists was studied both on the adherence and on the cytotoxicity of eosinophils to parasite larvae. As shown in Table 1, BN 52021, a potent PAF-acether antagonist, strongly inhibited in a dose-dependent manner the cytotoxicity induced by hypodense eosinophils and IgE antibodies towards *S. mansoni* targets. The other two ginkgolides BN 52020 and BN 52022 were less inhibitory than BN 52021 at the highest concentration. Inhibition of cytotoxicity was also obtained with 2 other PAF-acether antagonists with different chemical framework (BN 50488 and BN 50489), but to a lesser extent than with BN 52021. None of these compounds was able to significantly decrease the very high percentages of parasites bearing adherent eosinophils.

Table 1   Effect of various PAF-acether antagonists on IgE-mediated adherence and cytotoxicity of human eosinophils to parasite targets

PAF-acether	Final concentration	% Adherence[a]	% Cytotoxicity[b]
None		93.2 ± 1.7	46.8 ± 5.2
BN 52021	10^{-4}M	85.2 ± 9.8	14.0 ± 1.5[c]
	10^{-5}M	81.7 ± 4.7	30.1 ± 6.9[c]
	10^{-6}M	92.0 ± 0.5	48.2 ± 10.5
BN 52020	10^{-4}M	70.0 ± 1.9	26.7 ± 6.1[c]
	10^{-5}M	83.9 ± 7.2	30.8 ± 5.0[c]
	10^{-6}M	85.7 ± 0.9	45.9 ± 13.0
BN 52022	10^{-4}M	72.3 ± 10.3	29.6 ± 1.2[c]
	10^{-5}M	77.9 ± 0.9	33.2 ± 8.7
	10^{-6}M	79.9 ± 3.4	28.2 ± 1.7[c]
BN 50488	10^{-4}M	83.6 ± 9.1	55.2 ± 11.0
	10^{-5}M	74.6 ± 10.6	31.7 ± 10.7
	10^{-6}M	92.2 ± 7.3	56.6 ± 6.8
BN 50489	10^{-4}M	80 ± 3.6	26.9 ± 13.5
	10^{-5}M	83.4 ± 16.7	50.3 ± 5.5
	10^{-6}M	80 ± 12.3	59.3 ± 7.7

a) Expressed as the percentage of *S. mansoni* schistosomula targets with more than 20 adherent eosinophils to one target (x ± s.e.m.). b) Expressed as the percentage of dead *S. mansoni* schistosomula, 24 hrs to 48 hrs after incubation at 37°C with purified human eosinophils, IgE-containing immune sera and without or with PAF-acether antagonists. (x ± s.e.m.). c) Significant inhibition at the p < 0.05 level.

Role of PAF-Acether Antagonists in IgG-Dependent Cytotoxicity Mediated by Human Normodense Eosinophils

The difference in PAF-acether biosynthesis in response to IgE versus IgG triggering led us to evaluate the effects of PAF-acether antagonists in the case of *S. mansoni* killing mediated by IgG antibodies. Two sets of experiments were performed and the results were analyzed separately, because of some variability between the positive controls, with cells originating from different cell donors (Table 2). In the first set of experiments, BN 52021 induced a significant inhibition of the cytotoxicity mediated by normodense human eosinophils and anti-*S. mansoni* specific IgG antibodies although the differences were significant only for the highest concentration. In the second set of experiments, the other PAF-acether antagonists were shown to induce the same level of inhibition as BN 52021.

Tabla 2   Effect of PAF-acether antagonists on IgG-mediated cytotoxicity by normodense human eosinophils

PAF-acether antagonists	Final concentration	% Cytotoxicity[a]	% Inhibition[b]
1st set of experiments			
None		47.5 ± 3.5	
BN 52021	10^{-4}M	30.1 ± 2.8[c]	36.6
	10^{-5}M	43.7 ± 2.2	8
	10^{-6}M	46.6 ± 3.4	1.9
2nd set of experiments			
None		29.2 ± 0.9	
BN 52020	10^{-4}M	17.2 ± 3.5[c]	40
BN 52022	10^{-4}M	19.8 ± 3.8[c]	32.2
BN 50488	10^{-4}M	19.7 ± 2.9[c]	32.5
BN 50489	10^{-4}M	21.0 ± 7.2	28.1

a) Normodense eosinophils were added to schistosomula in the presence of heat-inactivated immune sera at 1:20 final dilution. This assay was performed in tubes and the adherence reaction was not evaluated. Results are the mean ± s.e.m. of 2 different experiments in each situation. b) The % inhibition is calculated according to the formula:

$$1 - \frac{\% \text{ cytotoxicity with inhibitor}}{\% \text{ cytotoxicity without inhibitor}} \times 100$$

c) Significant at the $p < 0.05$ level.

Inhibitory Role of PAF-Acether Antagonists in Rat Eosinophil Mediated Cytotoxicity

Rat eosinophils induce high levels of cytotoxicity against *S. mansoni* larvae in the presence of anaphylactic type immunoglobulins (IgG2a and IgE)

(4). The effects of the various PAF-acether antagonists were investigated in these cytotoxicity assays (Table 3). Both in the presence of unheated (containing IgE and IgG2a antibodies) and heat-inactivated (containing IgG2a antibodies) immune serum, a strong inhibition of cytotoxicity was observed with BN 52021 (70-80% at 10^{-4} M, 43-48% at 10^{-5} M). The other 2 ginkgolides induced a significant inhibition only at the highest concentration. A similar inhibition was obtained with BN 50488 and BN 50489. As in the case of human eosinophils, these PAF-acether-antagonists never inhibited the adherence reaction (data not shown).

Table 3 Inhibition by PAF-acether antagonists of the cytotoxicity mediated by rat eosinophils in the presence of IgE and IgG2a antibodies

PAF-acether antagonists	Final concentration	% Cytotoxicity[a]	
		Unheated immune serum (1/64)	Heat-inactivated immune serum (1/32)
None		66.4 ± 5.9	43.8 ± 7.9
BN 52021	10^{-4}M	18.6 ± 4.4[b]	9.2 ± 2.3[b]
	10^{-5}M	37.9 ± 7.5[b]	22.9 ± 5.8[b]
	10^{-6}M	71.1 ± 7.9	35.7 ± 8.7
BN 52020	10^{-4}M	29.3 ± 3.3[b]	6.6 ± 3.1[b]
	10^{-5}M	62.9 ± 12.3	40.7 ± 6.4
	10^{-6}M	77.1 ± 13.0	60.8 ± 0.1
BN 52022	10^{-4}M	39.7 ± 11.3[b]	15.5 ± 2.4[b]
	10^{-5}M	54.2 ∓ 12.4	54.8 ± 7.5
	10^{-6}M	83.8 ± 2.7	56.5 ± 3.0
BN 50488	10^{-4}M	32.9 ± 11.1[b]	13.4 ± 2.4[b]
	10^{-5}M	71.8 ± 8.7	56.0 ± 5.4
	10^{-6}M	82.4 ± 7.2	63.1 ∓ 3.4
BN 50489	10^{-4}M	49.4 ± 14.3	11.7 ± 0.9[b]
	10^{-5}M	80.4 ± 12.2	57.9 ± 7.9
	10^{-6}M	83.8 ± 9.7	50.9 ± 5.9

a) *S. mansoni* schistosomula were incubated with eosinophil-rich rat peritoneal cells obtained from normal rats, and with immune sera from *S. mansoni* infected rats. The unheated immune serum (IgE and IgG2a) was used at the 1:64 final dilution. The heat-inactivated immune serum (IgG2a) was used at a final dilution of 1:32. Results are expressed as the % of dead schistosomula after 24 hrs incubation at 37°C (mean of 3 to 7 experiments ± s.e.m.). b) Significant at the $p < 0.05$ level.

DISCUSSION

The potent role of PAF-acether as an *in vivo* and *in vitro* modulator of eosinophil functions, recently reviewed (2), led us to investigate both the production of PAF-acether after eosinophil triggering with various stimuli and the role of endogenous PAF-acether in the effector function of eosinophils. We had first reported that a subpopulation of human eosinophils, characterized by their low density, was able to produce significantly higher amounts of PAF-acether than eosinophils with normal density, in response to calcium ionophore A23187 (10). In the present study, we show that hypodense eosinophils purified from patients with increased IgE levels were able to produce significant amounts of PAF-acether after anti-IgE triggering. Since we had previously shown that surface IgE was mainly detected on tissue eosinophils (7), the present results suggest that eosinophils can release PAF-acether in response to specific stimulation with antigens, together with other potent cytolytic mediators such as eosinophil peroxydase [EPO (11)] and major basic protein [MBP (5)]. However, addition of anti-IgG antibodies to hypodense eosinophils did not induce PAF-acether formation. In order to exclude the possibility that this negative result could be due to the absence of surface IgG as previously suggested (7), experiments were conducted with eosinophils passively sensitized with immune sera containing both IgE and IgG. In this case, no PAF-acether was produced after IgG triggering. This selectively of mediators released by eosinophils in response to various immunological stimuli has been previously reported for 2 proteins normally present in the same granule compartment, EPO and eosinophil cationic protein [ECP (11)], and suggested different pathways of activation through membrane $Fc_{\epsilon}R$ or $Fc_{\gamma}R$. This concept, which has been developed in other situations, such as the release of histamine versus serotonin by mast cells (17) can therefore be extended, as shown in the present study, to the production of a newly formed mediator. However, since the biosynthesis of PAF-acether after IgE and IgG triggering has only been studied in the case of hypodense eosinophils, the possibility that normal or normodense eosinophils could produce PAF-acether was not excluded (see below).

To investigate the hypothesis that endogenous PAF-acether, produced by eosinophils in response to an IgE stimulus, could participate in eosinophil effector functions, we evaluated the effects of various PAF-acether antagonists on eosinophil-mediated cytotoxicity. The cytotoxicity of purified human hypodense eosinophils for parasite (*Schistosoma mansoni*) larvae in the presence of specific IgE antibodies was inhibited, in a dose-dependent manner by the potent PAF-acether antagonist, BN 52021. The other structurally related or unrelated PAF-acether antagonists also induced a significant inhibition of cytotoxicity. Interestingly a significant correlation was observed between their ability to inhibit the binding of ^3H PAF-acether to its receptor and the inhibition of cytotoxicity (M. Capron et al., submitted for publication). Similar results were obtained in the animal experimental model, namely cytotoxicity of rat peritoneal eosinophils mediated by anaphylactic immunoglobulins. These results raised two main questions:

1) What are the various possible mechanisms explaining the role of PAF-acether in this model? The results reported in the present study allow to postulate that PAF-acether is produced in response to interaction between $Fc_{\epsilon}R$ on eosinophil surface, specific IgE antibodies and the target antigens. PAF-acether might participate at different steps of the killing mechanisms. As recently reported (19), it might be required to bring the eosinophils in contact with the targets. The total lack of inhibition of the adherence reaction by the various PAF-acether antagonists renders this possibility unlikely. PAF-acether might be involved directly in the target killing mechanism. The inhibitory role of the PAF-acether receptor antagonists could then be explained by the existence of a PAF-acether receptor on the target membrane. Further experiments are needed to investigate this hypothesis. The third hypothesis could be the role of endogenous PAF-acether in the activation process of eosinophils. This might involve the activation of other membrane receptors, such as $Fc_{\epsilon}R$ or CR3 which have been shown to be both increased in hypodense eosinophils and required for the expression of IgE-mediated cytotoxicity (6). This could also be due to the release of cytolytic cationic proteins by PAF-acether as recently postulated (2). This would fit perfectly well with the role of PAF-acether receptor antagonists inhibiting cytotoxicity but not the adherence reaction between effector cells and targets, suggesting a dissociation between the effects of PAF-acether in chemotaxis and in eosinophil activation.

2) What is the variability in PAF-acether production after interaction with IgE or IgG immunoglobulins? The present results show a very potent inhibitory effect of the PAF-acether antagonists when eosinophils interacted with anaphylactic classes of immunoglobulins (human or rat IgE, rat IgG2a). In the case of human IgG-mediated cytotoxicity, the maximum levels of inhibition were lower but significant. This could be explained either by the fact that the cytotoxicity induced by human IgG is only partly mediated by a subclass of IgG with anaphylactic properties. This also indicates that eosinophils could produce some amounts of PAF-acether after interaction with IgG antibodies, and that the apparent discrepancies with the results presented in Figure 1 might be due to the eosinophil heterogeneity. Further experiments are needed to determine whether differences in PAF-acether production by hypodense *versus* normodense eosinophils are only due to differences in the expression of membrane receptors ($Fc_{\epsilon}R$ on hypodense *versus* $Fc_{\gamma}R$ on normodense eosinophils) or whether they can also be related to the existence of variations in the cell enzymatic equipment.

The inhibition of eosinophil-mediated cytotoxicity towards parasite by PAF-acether antagonists suggests not only the major role played by this mediator in eosinophil effector functions but also opens the way to new therapeutical strategies in the pathological situations where eosinophils are responsible for tissue damage.

References

1. Benveniste, J., Henson, P.N., Cochrane, C.G. *Leukocyte-dependent histamine release from rabbit platelets: The role of IgE, basophils and a platelet-activating factor.* J Exp Med 1972; 136: 1356-1377.
2. Braquet, P., Rola-Pleszczynski, M. *The role of PAF in immunological responses.* Immunology Today 1987; 8: 345-352.
3. Bruynzeel. P.L.B., Koenderman, L., Kod, P.T.M., Haeling, M., Verhagen, J. *Platelet-activating factor (PAF-acether) induced leukotriene C. formation and luminol-dependent chemiluminescence by human eosinophils.* Pharmacol Res Commun 1986; 18: 61-65.
4. Capron, M., Bazin, H., Joseph, J., Capron, A. *Evidence for IgE-dependent cytotoxicity by rat eosinophils.* J Immunol 1981; 126: 1764-1768.
5. Capron, M., Capron, A. *The IgE receptor of human eosinophils.* Allergy and Inflammation 1987, in press.
6. Capron, M., Kazatchkine, M., Fischer, E., Butterworth, A.E., Prin, L., Capron, A. *Role of membrane receptors in eosinophil effector function.* Proc VIth Int Immunol Cong (Toronto) 1986; N° 5-28-27, 654.
7. Capron, M., Kusnierz, J.P., Prin, L., Spiegelberg, H.L., Ovlaque, G., Gosset, P., Tonnel, A.B., Capron, A. *Cytophilic IgE on human blood and tissue eosinophils: Detection by flow microfluorometry.* J Immunol 1985; 134: 3013-3018.
8. Capron, M., Spiegelberg, H.L., Prin, L., Bennich, H., Butterworth, A.E., Pierce, R.J., Ouaissi, M.A., Capron, A. *Role of IgE receptors in effector function of human eosinophils.* J Immunol 1984; 232: 462-468.
9. Henocq, E., Vargaftig, B.B. *Accumulation of eosinophils in response to intracutaneous PAF-acether and allergens in man.* Lancet 1986; 1378-1379.
10. Jouvin-Marche, E., Grzych, J.M., Boullet, C., Capron, M., Benveniste, J. *Formation of PAF-acether by human eosinophils.* Fed Proc 1984; 1924: Abst 2966.
11. Khalife, J., Capron, M., Cesbron, J.Y., Tai, P.C., Taelman, H., Prin, L., Capron, A. *Role of specific IgE antibodies in peroxidase (EPO) release from human eosinophils.* J Immunol 1986; 137: 1659.
12. Lee, T.C., Lenihan, D.J., Malone, B., Roddy, L.L., Wasserman, S.I. *Increased biosynthesis of platelet-activating factor in activated human eosinophils.* J Biol Chem 1984; 259: 5526-5530.
13. Lellouch-Tubiana, A., Lefort, J., Pfister, A., Vargaftig, B.B. *Interactions between granulocytes and platelets with the guinea pig lung in passive anaphylactic shock. Correlation with PAF-acether induced lesions.* Int Archs Allergy Appl Immunol 1987; 83: 198-205.
14. MacDonald, A.J., Moqbel, R., Wardlaw, A.J., Kay, A.B. *Platelet-activating factor (PAF-acether) enhances eosinophil cytotoxicity in vitro.* J Allerg Clin Immunol 1986; 77: 227 (Abst.).
15. Prin, L., Capron, M., Tonnel, A.B., Bletry, O., Capron, A. *Heterogeneity of human peripheral blood eosinophils: Variability in cell density and cytotoxic ability in relation to the level and the origin of hypereosinophilia.* Int Archs Allergy Appl Immunol 1983; 72: 336-346.
16. Tamura, N., Agarwal, D.K., Suliaman, F.A., Townley, R.G. *Effects of platelet-activating factor on the chemotaxis of normodense eosinophils from normal subjects.* Biochem Biophys Res Commun 1987; 142: 638-644.
17. Theoharides, T.C., Bondy, P.K., Tsakalos, N.D., Askenase, P.W. *Differential release of serotonin and histamine from mast cells.* Nature 1982; 297: 229-231.
18. Vadas, M.A., David, J.R., Butterworth, A.E., Pisani, N.T., Siongok, T.A. *A new method for the purification of human eosinophils and neutrophils and a comparison of the ability of these cells to damage schistosomula of S. mansoni.* J Immunol 1979; 122: 1228-1236.
19. Wardlaw, A.J., Moqbel, R., Cromwell, O., Kay, A.B. *Platelet-activating factor. A potent chemotactic and chemokinetic factor for human eosinophils.* J Clin Invest 1986; 78: 1701-1705.

Ginkgolides - Chemistry, Biology, Pharmacology and Clinical Perspectives. P. Braquet (Ed.)
Copyright © 1988, J.R. Prous Science Publishers, S.A.

PLATELET-ACTIVATING FACTOR, HUMAN EOSINOPHILS AND GINKGOLIDE B (BN 52021)

*Naohiko Tamura, Devendra K. Agrawal, Robert G. Townley and *Pierre Braquet*

Allergic Disease Center, Creighton University School of Medicine, Omaha, Nebraska 68178, USA; *Institut Henri Beaufour, F-92350 Le Plessis Robinson, France

ABSTRACT

PAF-acether induced both eosinophil chemotactic and chemokinetic responses in a dose-dependent manner. The chemotactic activity of PAF-acether was much greater than chemokinesis at all concentrations. ECF-A but not LTB_4 also showed the chemotactic activity; however, PAF-acether was about two log units more potent than ECF-A. Furthermore, the magnitude of PAF-acether-induced chemotaxis was about three times greater than that induced by ECF-A. BN 52021 inhibited the PAF-acether induced chemotaxis to human eosinophils in a dose-dependent fashion. The IC_{50} value of BN 52021 to inhibit the eosinophil chemotaxis was calculated to be 0.49 μM. PAF-acether also released LTC_4 from the purified eosinophils. These studies suggest that PAF-acether released under pathological conditions by several human cell types may recruit more eosinophils. The infiltrating eosinophils become activated and generate mediators such as LTC_4, major basic protein and eosinophil cationic protein which might lead to bronchospasm and inflammation. Furthermore, since BN 52021 potently inhibited the PAF-acether-induced eosinophil chemotaxis, BN 52021 may be useful in preventing inflammation and in the treatment of bronchial asthma.

Address all correspondence to: Robert G. Townley, M.D., Allergic Disease Center, Creighton University, School of Medicine, Omaha, NE 68178, USA.

INTRODUCTION

Nonspecific airway hyperreactivity is a hallmark of asthma. However, the underlying mechanism of airway hyperreactivity is still unclear. Recent studies support the thesis that airway hyperreactivity may be due, at least in part, to the effects of inflammatory mediators which are generated as a consequence of immunological responses in the airways (15). These mediators are released from inflammatory leukocytes, including neutrophils and eosinophils. Of these two cell types, eosinophils have been a focus of research in recent years because of their close association with atopic diseases, including bronchial asthma (12, 13) and allergic rhinitis (8). Recently, Capron and colleagues (6, 7) demonstrated the presence of surface IgE on either human blood or tissue eosinophils in several pathological situations. This further strengthens the role for an IgE-eosinophil interaction in the *in vivo* effector function of these cells.

Several lines of evidence suggest that eosinophils may be activated *in vivo*. These activated eosinophils may then have the potential for a dual role; first, by releasing enzymes which are capable of degrading mast cell mediators and modulating their effects (20); and second, by releasing cytotoxic and neurotoxic mediators which may damage and/or alter the function of airways (1, 18). The enzymes released from the activated eosinophils include phospholipase D, lysophospholipase, histamine, arylsulphate and eosinophil peroxidase (11, 15). The eosinophil granule proteins which are cytotoxic and neurotoxic and may alter the function of airway smooth muscle include: eosinophil cationic protein, eosinophil-derived neurotoxin and major basic protein. Eosinophils also contain LTC_4 synthetase and the activated eosinophils have the potential to release LTC_4. Eosinophils may be activated by several mediators. Recently, a phospholipid mediator, platelet-activating factor (PAF-acether) has been described and characterized (2, 4).

PAF-ACETHER AND CHEMOTAXIS TO EOSINOPHILS

PAF-acether is a very potent mediator of inflammation and possesses a variety of biological activities (4). Various cell types are capable of synthesizing PAF-acether. These cells include basophils, neutrophils, eosinophils, platelets, macrophages and endothelium (4, 25). The stimulation of polymorphonuclear leukocytes by PAF-acether induces the release of lysosomal enzymes and superoxide anions, and induces leukocyte aggregation and chemotaxis.

Recently, we observed that PAF-acether is capable of causing chemotaxis of human eosinophils (22). In these studies, we purified blood eosinophils from healthy male volunteers. Eosinophils were separated by discontinuous percoll and Histopaque density gradient centrifugation. The density of eosinophils used in our study was 1.085 or greater and we considered them as normodense eosinophils. The purity of eosinophils was greater than 90% and the viability of the cells was greater than 96%. PAF-acether exhibited both chemotaxis and chemokinesis to human eosinophils in a dose-dependent manner. The chemotaxic activity was much greater than chemokinesis at all concentrations of PAF-acether (Fig. 1a). The threshold concentration of PAF-acether to produce chemotaxis to eosinophils was about 0.1 nM and the maximum chemotactic activity was observed at 100 nM concentration of PAF-acether.

We also examined the chemotactic activity of eosinophil chemotactic factor of anaphylaxis (ECF-A) and leukotriene B_4 (LTB_4) in our system. ECF-A showed the chemotactic activity from the concentration of 0.1 μM to 10 μM with a maximum activity at 1 μM concentration (Fig. 1b). There was a significant difference in the threshold concentrations and the maximum response elicited by PAF-acether and ECF-A. The threshold concentration of PAF-acether to produce chemotaxis to eosinophils was about two log units lower than that of the ECF-A. Furthermore, the magnitude of PAF-

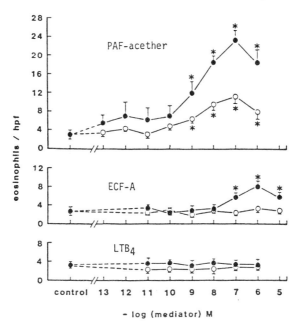

Figure 1   Eosinophil chemotactic (●) and chemokinetic (○) activities of PAF-acether, ECF-A and LTB_4. Each point represents mean ± S.E.M. of six independent experiments. Asterisk indicates significant (p < 0.05) difference from the control values. (Reproduced from Ref. 22 with permission of Academic Press, Inc.).

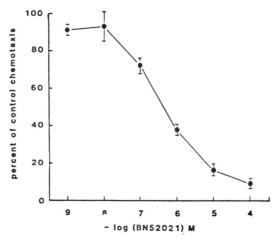

Figure 2 Effect of BN 52021 to inhibit the eosinophil chemotactic responses to 0.1 μM PAF-acether. Eosinophils were preincubated with either a specified concentration of BN 52021 or the vehicle for 20 min at 37°C before the chemotactic experiment. Each control response (in the presence of HBSS alone) was set at 100%. Each point represents mean ± S.E.M. of six individual experiments. (Reproduced from Ref. 22 with permission of Academic Press, Inc.).

acether-induced chemotaxis was about three times greater than that by ECF-A. LTB$_4$ up to 1 μM concentration did not show any chemotactic activity for eosinophils in our system (Fig. 1c).

A selective PAF-acether receptor antagonist, BN 52021, inhibited the PAF-acether-induced chemotaxis to eosinophils in a dose-dependent manner (Fig. 2). In these experiments, eosinophils were incubated with different concentrations of BN 52021 or the vehicle for 20 min at 37°C. The chemotactic response to PAF-acether (0.1 μM) was then examined. The threshold concentration of BN 52021 to elicit such response was around 10 nM and the concentration of BN 52021 to inhibit the PAF-acether-induced chemotaxis by 50% was calculated to be 0.49 μM (22). The chemotactic activity of PAF-acether was completely inhibited with 100 μM BN 52021. Without a prior incubation of human eosinophils with the PAF-acether receptor antagonist, BN 52021 only partially inhibited the chemotaxis even at very high doses. These data suggested that PAF-acether-induced chemotaxis was through their specific PAF-acether receptors, and a prior blockade of PAF-acether receptors with BN 52021 was necessary to inhibit the PAF-acether-induced chemotaxis.

Other investigators have also reported PAF-acether induced chemotaxis of eosinophils (26). Wardlaw and colleagues (26) also demonstrated PAF-acether to be a potent eosinophilotactic agent, and the eosinophil chemotactic response of LTB$_4$ and ECF-A was negligible as compared to that of

PAF-acether. However, our results with LTB_4 are at variance with those of Czarnetzki and colleagues (9), who have reported a significant eosinophil chemotactic activity of LTB_4 and only a minimal effect of PAF-acether on eosinophil chemotaxis. Although the reason for such discrepancy is not clear, differences in the purity of the eosinophils used in our study and those of Czarnetzki et al. (9) could be a contributing factor. Nevertheless, our results suggest that PAF-acether may be responsible for attracting eosinophils to the site of inflammation.

The amounts of PAF-acether used in the chemotaxis studies were in the range of 0.1 nM to 10 μM. Although PAF-acether may be generated endogenously by a number of human cell types, it is difficult to relate amounts of PAF-acether generated by cells under in vitro conditions to the concentrations of PAF-acether found at the inflammatory sites in vivo. Nevertheless, about 1 ng of PAF-acether has been demonstrated to be released from one million cells of neutrophils or normodense eosinophils in response to calcium ionophore (16, 17). In comparison, hypodense eosinophils have been shown to release about 100 ng LTC_4 per million eosinophils (16). These studies suggest that human blood cells under a proper stimulus have a considerably enhanced capacity to release PAF-acether. Such concentrations of PAF-acether in our studies and others have been shown to produce chemotaxis to eosinophils.

There is ample evidence that several cell types such as mast cells, macrophages and platelets are capable of releasing chemotactic factors. These chemotactic factors which could be released by immunological or non-immunological reactions, play a significant role in the pathogenesis of asthma by attracting the inflammatory cells including neutrophils and eosinophils in the lung tissue. Several evidence suggest that eosinophils are involved during the late phase reaction possibly by the result of eosinophils migrating to the bronchial lumen under the influence of the chemotactic factors such as PAF-acether and ECF-A (18, 20, 24). Recently, a significantly elevated eosinophil counts have been observed in the bronchoalveolar lavage fluid of asthmatic individuals (10). Eosinophilia in the lung tissue is also evident by the findings of elevated levels of eosinophil cationic protein in the lavage fluid obtained from patients during late asthmatic response. During the early phase of the asthmatic response or in the patients with only early asthmatic reaction, there was no bronchoalveolar eosinophilia (10). Booy-Noord and coworkers (3) have also observed an increase in peripheral blood eosinophils 24 h after allergen inhalation in patients with late asthmatic reaction. In this study there was no change in the blood eosinophil levels in the patients with only early asthmatic reaction (3). These results strongly support the role of eosinophils in late phase response in asthma. The infiltrated eosinophils can degranulate to release granular proteins and

newly formed mediators. These mediators may be responsible for inflammation and bronchospasm in asthma.

PAF-ACETHER AND LEUKOTRIENE C_4 RELEASE FROM HUMAN EOSINOPHILS

We have also examined the potential of PAF-acether, ECF-A and LTB_4
to synthesize and release LTC_4 from human eosinophils. Purified eosinophils
were incubated with different concentrations of PAF-acether, lyso-PAF,
ECF-A and LTB_4 for 30 min at 37°C. The released LTC_4 was measured
by a specific LTC_4 radioimmunoassay kit. PAF induced LTC_4 production
and release in a time and dose-dependent manner. Ten micromolar of PAF-
acether induced 0.74 ± 0.08 ng of LTC_4 production per million eosinophil
cells (Fig. 3). Other mediators such as lyso-PAF, ECF-A and LTB_4 even
up to a concentration of 10 μM did not induce LTC_4 production from
human eosinophils.

Several other investigators have also reported the predominant production of LTC_4 from human eosinophils in response to calcium ionophore
activation (8, 14, 19, 21, 23, 27). Shaw and colleagues (21) reported the
release of leukotrienes from human eosinophils when the cells were

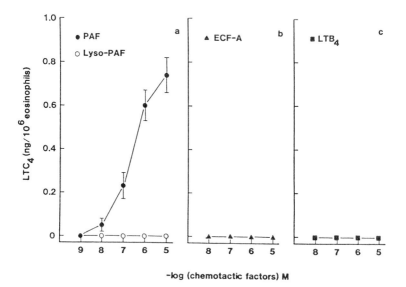

Figure 3   Direct effect of eosinophil chemotactic factors on the LTC_4 production from purified human
eosinophils. Eosinophils were incubated with different concentrations of PAF-acether, lyso-PAF, ECF-A
or LTB_4 for 30 min at 37°C. LTC_4 was measured by a specific radioimmunoassay kit. Each point represents
the mean ± S.E.M. from 4 independent experiments. There was no detectable amount of LTC_4 production
by lyso-PAF, ECF-A or LTB_4.

stimulated immunologically by an IgG-dependent mechanism, possibly mediated through the release of complement cascade-generated anaphylatoxins such as C3a and C5a. Bruijnzeel and coworkers (5) have also reported the PAF-acether-induced LTC_4 formation and luminol dependent chemiluminescence by human eosinophils. Very recently, Kauffman and colleagues (14) reported that the amount of calcium ionophore-induced LTC_4 production from hypodense eosinophils was significantly lower than those from normodense eosinophils. However, serum-treated zymosan (in the presence of glutathione) released greater amount of LTC_4 from the low-density eosinophils compared with normal density cells. There is no current evidence from the literature that PAF-acether releases LTC_4 in a greater amount from hypodense eosinophils as compared to those from normodense eosinophils. However, in view of the reports described above, it may be speculated that receptor-mediated stimulus such as zymosan and PAF-acether may release more leukotrienes from hypodense eosinophils as compared to a non-receptor mediated stimulus such as calcium ionophore. This could be responsible, at least in part, for the increased airway reactivity in bronchial asthma. In this case, selective and potent antagonists for PAF-acether, such as BN 52021, would prove fruitful in the treatment of various inflammatory processes and bronchial asthma.

ACKNOWLEDGEMENTS

This work was supported by a James M. Keck Faculty Development Award from the Health Future Foundation to D.K. Agrawal.

References

1. Barnes, N.C., Costello, J.F. *Airway hyper-responsiveness and inflammation.* Br Med Bull 1987; 43: 445-459.

2. Benveniste, J. *Platelet-activating factor, a new mediator of anaphylaxis and immune complex deposition from rabbit and human basophils.* Nature (Lond) 1974; 249: 581-582.

3. Booy-Noord, H., de Vries, K., Sluiter, H.J., Orie, N.G.M. *Late bronchial obstructive reaction to experimental inhalation of house dust extract.* Clin Allergy 1972; 2: 43-61.

4. Braquet, P., Touqui, L., Shen, T.Y., Vargaftig, B.B. *Perspectives in platelet-activating factor research.* Pharmacol Rev 1987; 39: 97-145.

5. Bruijnzeel, P.L.B., Koenderman, L., Kok, P.T.M., Hamelink, M.L., Verhagen, J.L. *Platelet-activating factor (PAF-acether) induced-leukotriene C_4 formation and luminol chemiluminescence by human eosinophils.*

Pharmacol Res Commun 1986; (Suppl) 18: 61-69.

6. Capron, M., Spiegelberg, H.L., Prin, L., Bennich, H., Butterworth, A.E., Pierce, R.J., Ouassi, M.A., Capron, A. *Role of IgE receptors in effector function of human eosinophils.* J Immunol 1984; 133: 162-168.

7. Capron, M., Kusnierz, J.P., Prin, L., Spiegelberg, H.L., Ovlaque, G., Gosset, P., Tonnel, A.B., Capron, A. *Cytophilic IgE on human blood and tissue eosinophils: Detection by flow microfluorometry.* J Immunol 1985; 134: 3013-3017.

8. Creticos, P., Peters, S., Adkinson, N., Naclerio, R., Hayes, E., Norman, P., Lichtenstein, L.M. *Peptide leukotriene release after antigen challenge in patients sensitive to ragweed.* N Engl J Med 1984; 310: 1626-1630.

9. Czarnetzki, B.M., Rosenbach, T. *Chemotaxis*

of human neutrophils and eosinophils towards leukotriene B_4 and its 20-w-oxidation products in vitro. Prostaglandins 1986; 31: 851-858.

10. De Monchy, J.G.R., Kaufman, H.F., Venge, P., Koeter, G.H., Jansen, H.M., Sluiter, H.J., de Vries, K. Bronchoalveolar eosinophilia during allergen induced late asthmatic reactions. Am Rev Respir Dis 1985; 131: 373-376.

11. Frigas, E., Gleich, G.J. The eosinophil and the pathophysiology of asthma. J Allergy Clin Immunol 1986; 77: 527-537.

12. Fukuda, T., Dunnette, S.L., Reed, C.E., Ackerman, S.J., Peters, M.S., Gleich, G.J. Increased numbers of hypodense eosinophils in the blood of patients with bronchial asthma. Am Rev Respir Dis 1985; 132: 981-985.

13. Horn, B.R., Robin, E.D., Theodore, J., Van Kessel, A. Total eosinophil counts in the management of bronchial asthma. N Engl J Med 1975; 292: 1152-1155.

14. Kauffman, H.F., van der Belt, B., de Monchy, J.G.R., Boelens, H., Koeter, G.H., de Vries, K. Leukotriene c_4 production by normal-density and low-density eosinophils of atopic individuals and other patients with eosinophilia. J Allergy Clin Immunol 1987; 79: 611-619.

15. Kay, A.B. Mediators and inflammatory cells in asthma. In: Asthma: Clinical Pharmacology and Therapeutic Progress. A.B. Kay (Ed.). Blackwell Scientific Publications: London 1986; 1-10.

16. Lee, T.-C., Lenihan, D.J., Malone, B., Roddy, L.L., Wasserman, S.I. Increased biosynthesis of platelet-activating factor in activated human eosinophils. J Biol Chem 1984; 259: 5526-5530.

17. Makoto, O., Kiyoshi, S., Yascunoja, K., Sacho, K. Molecular species of platelet-activating factor generated by human neutrophils challenged with ionophore A23187. J Immunol 1985; 134: 1090-1093.

18. Metzger, W.J., Richardson, H.B., Wasserman, S.I. Generation and partial characteriza-

tion of eosinophil chemotactic activity and neutrophil chemotactic activity during early and late-phase asthmatic response. J Allergy Clin Immunol 1986; 78: 282-290.

19. Owen, Jr. W.F., Soberman, R.J., Yoshimoto, T., Sheffer, A.L., Lewis, R.A., Austen, K.F. Synthesis and release of leukotriene C_4 by human eosinophils. J Immunol 1987; 138: 532-538.

20. Schatz, M., Wasserman, S., Patterson, R. The eosinophil and the lung. Arch Intern Med 1982; 142: 1515-1519.

21. Shaw, R.J., Crombell, O., Kay, A.B. Preferential generation of leukotriene C_4 by human eosinophils. Clin Exp Immunol 1984; 56: 716-722.

22. Tamura, N., Agrawal, D.K., Suliaman, F.A., Townley, R.G. Effects of platelet-activating factor on the chemotaxis of normodense eosinophils from normal subjects. Biochem Biophys Res Commun 1987; 142: 638-644.

23. Tamura, N., Agrawal, D.K., Townley, R.G. A specific radioreceptor assay for leukotriene C_4 and the measurement of calcium ionophore-induced leukotriene C_4 production from human leukocytes. J Pharmacol Methods 1987; 18: 327-333.

24. Taylor, K.J., Luksza, A.R. Peripheral blood eosinophil counts and bronchial responsiveness. Thorax 1987; 42: 452-456.

25. Vargaftig, B.B., Braquet, P.G. PAF-acether today: Relevance for acute experimental anaphylaxis. Br Med Bull 1987; 43: 312-335.

26. Wardlaw, A.J., Moqbel, R., Cromwell, O., Kay, A.B. Platelet-activating factor: A potent chemotactic and chemokinetic factor for human eosinophils. J Clin Invest 1986; 78: 1701-1706.

27. Weller, P.F., Lee, C.W., Foster, D.W., Corey, E.J., Austen, K.F., Lewis, R.A. Generation and metabolism of 5-lipoxygenase pathway leukotrienes by human eosinophils: Predominant production of leukotriene C_4. Proc Natl Acad Sci USA 1983; 80: 7626-7630.

Ginkgolides - Chemistry, Biology, Pharmacology and Clinical Perspectives. P. Braquet (Ed.)
Copyright © 1988, J.R. Prous Science Publishers, S.A.

EFFECTS OF BN 52021 AND CYCLOSPORIN ON PAF- OR ANTIGEN- INDUCED EOSINOPHIL MOBILIZATION IN THE RAT

Annie Etienne, Chantal Soulard, Florence Thonier, Christine Guilmard, Françoise Hecquet and Pierre Braquet

Institut Henri Beaufour, 72 avenue des Tropiques, F-91952 Les Ulis, France

INTRODUCTION

Platelet-activating factor (PAF-acether, 1-0-hexadecyl-2-acetyl-*sn*-glycero-3-phosphocholine) is a phospholipid mediator of the allergic reaction that is now recognized as a potent stimulus of acute inflammatory processes exhibiting a wide range of biological activities (1, 2), including neutrophil aggregation, secretion and chemotaxis (3, 5). PAF is produced by various inflammatory cells upon activation by immune or non-immune stimuli. In addition, PAF is a more potent chemotactic factor for human eosinophils than neutrophils, suggesting that this mediator may be involved in the recruitment of tissue and blood eosinophils, a characteristic feature of immediate type hypersensitivity reactions (6, 7). Indeed, the late-phase asthmatic reaction appears to be an inflammatory process in which eosinophils could play a critical role (8).

Clinical studies on the skin of atopic patients have demonstrated the development of a late response 6 to 12 h following antigen challenge, characterized by edema, mast cell degranulation and eosinophil and neutrophil infiltration (8, 9), a phenomenon which can be reproduced by injection of PAF into this tissue (10).

Recently, a bronchial hyperresponsiveness similar to that observed during asthma has been shown to occur in guinea-pigs and humans after PAF inhalation. In addition, the late asthmatic response to antigen is also known

Address all correspondece to: Dr. P. Braquet, Institut Henri Beaufour, 17, avenue Descartes F-92350 Le Plessis Robinson, France.

to be associated with the accumulation of inflammatory cells including eosinophils within the lung (12, 13), a reaction possibly initiated by PAF (14). Both neutrophils and eosinophils have been recovered in bronchoalveolar lavage fluid collected during the late-phase reaction (15), the latter of these cell types being predominant (16).

Similar changes in cellular composition have been observed in experimental animals. In such systems inhalation or i.v. injection of PAF or antigen induce bronchoconstriction (17) and accumulation of inflammatory cells (18, 19). These phenomena are inhibited by the PAF-antagonists BN 52021 (20) and WEB 2086 (21).

Ginkgolide BN 52021, a specific PAF receptor antagonist (22), has been shown to be a potent inhibitor of PAF-induced thrombocytopenia, bronchoconstriction (23, 24) and pulmonary anaphylaxis (25). BN 52021 also reduces hemoconcentration and the increase in total leukocyte count observed 15 min after systemic injection of PAF in the rat (26). Interestingly, these modifications are associated with a decrease in circulating neutrophil and eosinophil subsets. Furthermore, BN 52021 alone or in combination with cycloporin significantly delays grafts rejection (27), suggesting that both products affect the immune response. Cyclosporin has recently been shown to inhibit eosinophilia induced by cyclophosphamide prior to immunization (28).

Taking into account these data we have compared the effects of BN 52021 and cyclosporin on the cellular modifications, particularly eosinophilia, induced by antigen challenge or intra-peritoneal PAF injection in the rat. Since the normal rat has a low peripheral eosinophil count (absolute count in the blood < 200 cells/mm³) relative to allergic humans, rats were made hypereosinophilic by intravenous administration of Sephadex-G200 beads or high-dose cyclophosphamide before the induction of inflammatory reaction.

MATERIALS AND METHODS

Chemicals

Sephadex-G200 was obtained from Pharmacia Fine Chemicals (Uppsala, Sweden), cyclophosphamide from Endoxan-Asta 100 (Lucien, France) and complete Freund's adjuvant from Difco (Detroit, USA). Cyclosporin was kindly supplied by Sandoz (Basel, Switzerland). Bn 52021 (ginkgolide B) was prepared by I.H.B. Research Labs (Le Plessis-Robinson, France).

Induction of Eosinophilia by Cyclophosphamide Prior to Immunization

Male Sprague Dawley rats, 200 g body weight at the beginning of the experiment, were injected intraperitoneally with 150 mg/kg cyclophosphamide 48 h before immunization as described by Thomson *et al.* (28).

The animals were then immunized by a subplantar injection in one hind foot of 0.1 ml of a mixture 1:1 volume of ovalbumin in saline solution (2 mg/ml) and complete Freund's adjuvant. The animals were challenged 13 days later by an intraperitoneal injection of 1 mg ovalbumin in 1 ml saline. One half of the animals were sacrificed 4 h after challenge and the remainder 20 h later. The peritoneal cavity of each animal was lavaged with 5 ml of saline containing 6 units x ml^{-1} heparin. Immediately after, blood samples were removed from the vena cava.

Total and differential leukocyte counts were determined on blood and peritoneal washings using a Coulter counter and May-Grünwald-Giemsa-stained smears, respectively. When appropriate, the drugs were given orally from the day of sensitization until day 13, the last administration taking place 1 h before antigen challenge.

Sephadex-Induced Peripheral Eosinophilia

Male 250-300 g Sprague Dawley rats were injected intravenously with 0.5 ml of 3 x 10^3 beads/ml Sephadex-G200 suspension in 0.9% NaCl as described by Lemanske *et al.* (29). Prior to injection, the suspension, which corresponded to the maximum non-lethal volume, was autoclaved for 30 min and the bead count determined with a ZBI Coulter counter (Coultronics). Five days later, the animals were given an intraperitoneal injection of PAF 1 µg/kg. The rats were anesthetized with ether 24 h after PAF injection, their peritoneal cavities lavaged and blood samples collected as described above. Total and differential leukocytes counts in the blood and peritoneal washings were determined as previously described. The drugs under investigation were given orally as suspensions in tragacanth gum on day 4 and 5, 30 min before PAF injection. Cyclosporin and BN 52021 were both administered at a dose of 25 mg/kg.

RESULTS

Eosinophilia Induced by High-Dose Cyclophosphamide Prior to Immunization

Peritoneal injection of the antigen in actively sensitized and cyclophosphamide-pretreated rats induced an inflammatory reaction accom-

Table 1 Comparison of the effect of cyclosporin A and BN 52021 on cell recruitment induced by immune challenge in cyclophosphamide pretreated animals

Treatment	Blood		Peritoneal Fluid	
	4 h	24 h	4 h	24 h
Normal control	18200 ± 2300	22600 ± 1760	26790 ± 1760	28280 ± 1460
I-Cy	61600 ± 4550	43300 ± 4880	53900 ± 13580	30750 ± 4125
I-Cy + BN 52021	55550 ± 7750[NS]	75380 ± 16480*	50390 ± 8980[NS]	40780 ± 6930[NS]
Normal control	19360 ± 9000	18610 ± 1220	15260 ± 1560	17000 ± 2220
I-Cy	63630 ± 3470	55010 ± 2130	41690 ± 10140	32510 ± 4580
I-Cy + cyclosporin	33560 ± 2835***	30580 ± 2800***	21200 ± 1820*	21090 ± 21090[NS]

White cell counts in peripheral blood (cells/mm^3) and peritoneal washings (total cells in the exudate) 13-14 days post immunization (I-Cy) 4 h or 24 h after challenge. Treatments (day 0 → 13) BN 52021 5 mg/kg, cyclosporin 25 mg/kg. Mean values ± SEM; n = 10. Cy: cyclophosphamide injection (day - 2). Significance: ***p < 0.001; **p < 0.01; *p < 0.05. NS = Not significant.

panied after 4 h by a marked increase in total leukocyte count of the blood and peritoneal fluid (Table 1). These increases were still observed, although to a lesser extent, 24 h after challenge (Table 1).

Four hours after antigen challenge, these increases were only slightly and non-significantly reduced by chronic treatment with 5 mg/kg/day BN 52021. After 24 h this marginal effect was no longer apparent (Table 1). Administration of a higher dose of BN 52021 at a rate of 25 mg/kg/day did not affect the increase in blood and peritoneal cavity cell counts (data not shown). Treatment with cyclosporin, however, significantly reduced leukocyte levels in the blood as well as in the peritoneal fluid after 4 and 24 h (Table 1).

Determination of white cell subsets demonstrated that the circulating eosinophil count was markedly enhanced (+ 400%) 4 h after the immune challenge (Fig. 1). This increase was moderately affected by BN 52021 (—22%) and totally abolished by cyclosporin, the eosinophil count for this latter drug being below that of the controls. The number of circulating eosinophils was still higher 24 h after challenge (+ 550%) and activity of drugs was basically the same as that observed after 4 h (data not shown).

An increase in the eosinophil count in the peritoneal fluid was noted 4 h after challenge (Fig. 1). This variation was abolished by treatment with either BN 52021 or cyclosporin. In this exudate the eosinophil count in the BN 52021-treated group was lower than that of the control group and was zero in the peritoneal cavity of cyclosporin-treated animals. Although the differential eosinophil count in the peritoneal fluid was higher (about 20%) 24 h after challenge relative to that recorded at 4 h, the degree of antagonism elicited by the drugs was similar to that observed after 4 h (data not shown).

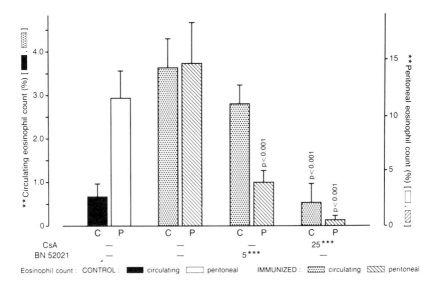

Figure 1 Comparison of the effect of cyclosporin A (CsA) and BN 52021 on hypereosinophilia induced by high dose of cyclophosphamide prior to immunization in rats. At day -2, cyclophosphamide (150 mg/kg) was injected intraperitoneally. Then at day 0 the animals were immunized by subplantar administration of ovalbumin (2 mg/ml) + Freund's adjuvant. At day 13 challenge with antigen (1 mg/ml, i.p.). At day 13 + 4 h the rats were killed and circulating and peritoneal eosinophil subsets measured**. Mean ± SEM (n = 10). ***Drugs were given (day 0 → day 13): non-immunized control groups were treated with saline.

Neutrophil counts were also dramatically enhanced in the peritoneal fluid and blood after 4 h (+ 290% and + 372%, Fig. 2) and after 24 h (+ 210% and + 150%, data not shown). No significant effect of the drugs on the neutrophil increase in these samples was detected (Fig. 2).

Effects of PAF in Rats with Sephadex-Induced Peripheral Eosinophilia

Intraperitoneal injection of PAF in normal rats induced a significant increase in the total leukocyte count of the blood after 24 h (Tabla 2). This increase was lower and non-significant in Sephadex-pretreated rats whether administered or not with BN 52021 or cyclosporin. Conversely, in peritoneal lavages, the total cell count was decreased slightly after PAF injection, possibly due to cell leakage or adherence of the cells to the tissue. Cyclosporin treatment not only reversed the alterations induced by PAF but also increased the number of cells recovered from the peritoneal cavity (Table 2).

As reported in Figure 3, analysis of differential leukocyte counts show-

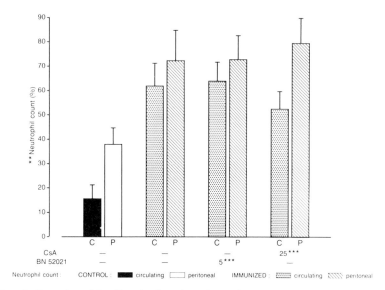

Figure 2 Comparison of the effect of cyclosporin A (CsA) and BN 52021 on neutrophil count induced by high dose of cyclophosphamide prior to immunization in rats. At day -2, cyclophosphamide (150 mg/kg) was injected intraperitoneally. Then at day 0 the animals were immunized by subplantar administration of ovalbumin (2 mg/ml) + Freund's adjuvant. At day 13 challenge with antigen (1 mg/ml, i.p.). At day 13 + 4 h the rats were killed and circulating and peritoneal neutrophil subsets measured**. Mean ± SEM (n = 10). ***Drugs were given (day 0 → day 13): non-immunized control groups were treated with saline.

ed that PAF induced a high and significant increase in eosinophils at the site of injection ($+127\%$; $p < 0.001$), a process further enhanced by Sephadex treatment ($+142\%$; $p < 0.001$). This increase was significantly reduced by pretreatment with cyclosporin ($p < 0.001$) but only moderately so by BN 52021.

Table 2 Comparison of the effect of cyclosporin A and BN 52021 on cell recruitment induced by PAF injection in Sephadex-pretreated animals

Treatment	Blood	Peritoneal Fluid
Normal control	15900 ± 690	24270 ± 2580
PAF	21780 ± 2440	20360 ± 2140
PAF + Sephadex	16920 ± 575	22980 ± 1880
PAF + Sephadex + BN 52021	18420 ± 900[NS]	16590 ± 1060*
PAF + Sephadex + cyclosporin	18220 ± 670[NS]	28220 ± 1600*

White cell counts in peripheral blood (cells/mm³) and peritoneal washings (total cells in the exudate) 24 h after i.p. PAF injection in Sephadex-induced hypereosinophil rats. Treatments t - 24 h and t - 30 min before challenge. Cyclosporin or BN 52021: 25 mg/kg. Mean values ± SEM; n = 10 or more. Significance: *$p < 0.05$. NS = Not significant.

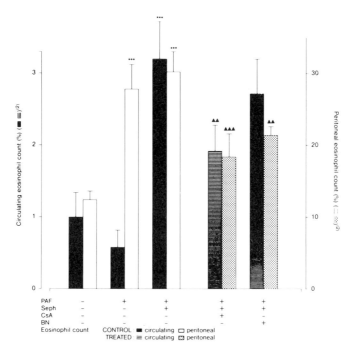

Figure 3 Comparison of the effect of cyclosporin A (CsA) and BN 52021 on hypereosinophilia induced by Sephadex particles + PAF injection in rats. At day 0, Sephadex particles G200 suspension (saline) were injected; drugs were given at day 4 and day 5, 30 min before i.p. injection of PAF (1 μg/kg). The animals were killed at day 6 and circulating and peritoneal eosinophils counted. Mean ± SEM (n = 15). ***p < 0.001 *vs.* control group; ΔΔ: p < 0.05; ΔΔΔ: p < 0001 *vs.* PAF + Sephadex - treated group.

Blood eosinophil count was not modified by intraperitoneal injection of PAF to rats. In contrast, the eosinophil count was higher in rats treated with both PAF and Sephadex (+ 220%; p < 0.001). In this latter case, cyclosporin treatment significantly reduced these alterations in eosinophil count (p < 0.05), whereas the reduction obtained with BN 52021 was low and non-significant. Neutrophil counts in blood and peritoneal lavages in Sephadex-treated animals were only moderately affected by PAF-injection (data not shown).

DISCUSSION

Several lines of evidence suggest that PAF plays a major role in the pathogenesis of bronchial asthma, brain and gastrointestinal ischemic disorders and inflammatory reactions by recruiting inflammatory cells (8, 30, 31). In asthmatic subjects this phenomenon may account for the late inflammatory phase of allergic reactions (32). The involvement of eosinophils appears to be essential in these pathophysiological processes since major basic protein (MBP), which causes respiratory epithelial damage (13), is known to be released from the granules of this cell type (33, 34). Thus, in this study we investigated the potential protective effect of the PAF antagonist BN 52021, which possesses anti-anaphylactic properties (35, 36), on PAF-or antigen-induced pro-inflammatory cell mobilization. To assess more precisely the mode of cell recruitment, this process was amplified by inducing hypereosinophilia in rats either by injection of cyclophosphamide prior to immunization or by administration of Sephadex before PAF challenge.

Provision of cyclophosphamide prior to immunization induced leukopenia over a ten-day period followed by a transient leukocytosis, with an associated increase of eosinophils from day 8 to 21. In keeping with the suppressive effect of cyclophosphamide, a lymphopenia was observed throughout the experiment (28).

In the present study, the antigen challenge was performed at day 14 and a leukocytosis with an increase in neutrophil and eosinophil counts was apparent both in blood and peritoneal lavages. As already published (37), chronic administration of cyclosporin from the time of immunization up to the challenge strongly reduced blood eosinophilia, abolished peritoneal eosinophil mobilization and reduced the circulating neutrophil count.

BN 52021 also significantly reduced peritoneal eosinophil mobilization but was only slightly effective against the increase in circulating eosinophils and did not modify neutrophil levels. Following administration of Sephadex, maximum eosinophilia occurred after 4 to 6 days with a progressive return to baseline values between days 10-14 (29). In this model, perivascular infiltrations with neutrophils and eosinophils could be observed. In contrast to antigen challenge (38), no increase in leukocyte count was detected 24 h after injection of PAF in Sephadex-treated animals. However, a marked eosinophilia was obtained in blood and peritoneal lavages.

As in the case of the immune model, cyclosporin treatment reduced blood and peritoneal eosinophilia induced by PAF in Sephadex-injected animals, whereas BN 52021 was only effective on peritoneal cell mobilization. Taken together, these results indicate that BN 52021 treatment is capable of reducing eosinophil infiltration triggered by PAF injection or anaphylactic reaction.

Although similar results were obtained with both drugs, the mode of action of cyclosporin and BN 52021 appear to be quite different. It is known that cyclosporin affects T-cell proliferation (39) and that these cells are involved in the differentiation of hematopoietic cells into eosinophils via interleukines 3 and 5 and GM-CSF production. This may provide an explanation as to why treatment with this drug affects the eosinophil count of the blood, the decrease in eosinophil mobilization probably reflecting the fact that there are less cells available for recruitment. In contrast, BN 52021, which is a specific PAF antagonist, probably elicits its effect by inhibiting the action of this mediator on eosinophil chemotaxis.

As the airway epithelium modulates the reactivity of respiratory smooth muscle (40), damage to this tissue induced by eosinophils could be responsible for bronchial hyperreactivity. The inhibitory effect of BN 52021 on eosinophil mobilization after antigen or PAF challenge may thus explain the beneficial activity of this drug observed in bronchial hyperreactivity models (41).

References

1. O'Flaherty, J.T., Wykle, R.L. *Biology and biochemistry of platelet-activating factor.* Clin Rev Allergy 1983; 1: 353-367.

2. Braquet, P., Touqui, L., Shen, T.Y., Vargaftig, B.B. *Perspectives in platelet-activating-factor research.* Pharmacol Rev 1987; 39: 97-145.

3. Ford-Hutchinson, A.W. *Neutrophil aggregating properties of PAF-acether and leukotriene B_4.* Int J Immunopharmacol 1983; 5: 17-21.

4. Baggiolini, M., Dewald, B. *Stimulus amplification by PAF and LTB_4 in human neutrophils.* Pharmacol Res Commun 1986; 18: 51-60.

5. Moodley, I., Stuttle, A. *Evidence for a dual pathway in platelet-activating factor-induced aggregation on rat polymorphonuclear leukocytes.* Prostaglandins 1987; 33: 253-263.

6. Sigal, C.E., Valone, F.H., Holtzman, M.J., Goetz, E.J. *Preferential human eosinophil chemotactic activity of the platelet-activating factor (PAF) 1-0-hexadecyl-2-acetyl-sn-glyceryl-3-phosphocholine (AGEPC).* J Clin Immunol 1987; 7: 179-184.

7. Gosset, P., Tonnel, A.B., Joseph, M., Prin, L., Mallard, A., Charn, J., Capron, A. *Secretion of a chemotactic factor for neutrophils and eosinophils by alveolar macrophages from asthmatic patients.* J Allergy Clin Immunol 1984; 74: 827-834.

8. Larsen, G.L. *Late-phase reactions: Observations on pathogenesis and prevention.* J Allergy Clin Immunol 1985; 76: 665-669.

9. Dolovich, J., Hargreave, F.E., Chalmers, R., Shier, K.J., Gauldie, J., Bienenstock, J. *Late cutaneous allergic responses in isolated IgE-dependent reactions.* J Allergy Clin Immunol 1973; 52: 38-46.

10. Henocq, E., Vargaftig, B.B. *Accumulation of eosinophils in response to intracutaneous PAF-acether and allergens in man.* Lancet 1986; i: 1378-1379.

11. Cuss, F.M., Dixon, C.M., Barnes, P.J. *Effects of inhaled platelet-activating factor on pulmonary function and bronchial responsiveness in man.* Lancet 1986; ii: 189-192.

12. Kay, A.B. In: Bronchial Asthma. E.B. Weiss, M.S. Segal, M. Stein (Eds.). Little, Brown and Co.: Boston 1985; 255-265.

13. Frigas, E., Gleich, C.G. *The eosinophil and the pathophysiology of asthma.* J Allergy Clin Immunol 1986; 77: 527-537.

14. Page, C.P., Archer, C.B., Paul, W., Morley, J. *PAF-acether: A mediator of inflammation and asthma.* TIPS 1984; 239-241.

15. Metzger, W.J., Moseley, P., Nugent, K., Richerson, H.B., Hunninghake, G.W. *Local antigen challenge and bronchoalveolar lavage of allergic asthmatic lungs.* Chest 1985; 87: 155S-156S.

16. De Monchy, J.G.R., Kauffman, H.F., Venge, P., Koeter, G.H., Jansen, H.M., Sluiter, H.J., De Vries, K. *Bronchoalveolar eosinophilia during allergen-induced late asthmatic reactions.* Am Rev Resp Dis 1985; 131: 373-376.

17. Vargaftig, B.B., Lefort, J., Chignard, M., Benveniste, J. *Platelet-activating factor induces a platelet-dependent bronchoconstriction unrelated to the formation of prostaglandin derivatives.* Eur J Pharmacol 1980; 65: 185-192.

18. Lellouch-Tubiana, A., Lefort, J., Pirotzky, E., Vargaftig, B.B., Pfister, A. *Ultrastructural evidence for extravascular platelet recruitment in the lung upon intravenous injection of platelet-activating factor (PAF-acether) to*

guinea-pigs. Br J Exp Pathol 1985; 66: 345-355.

19. Patterson, R., Harris, K.E. *The activity of aerosolized and intracutaneous synthetic platelet-activating-factor (AGEPC) in rhesus monkeys with IgE-mediated airway responses and normal monkeys*. J Lab Clin Med 1983; 102: 933-938.

20. Braquet, P., Guinot, P., Touvay, C. *The role of PAF-acether in anaphylaxis demonstrated with the use of the antagonist BN 52021*. In: Platelets, PAF and Asthma. M. Smith-Schumann, G. Menz, C. Page (Eds.). Agents Actions (Supp.) 1987; 97-117.

21. Casals-Stenzel, J., Franke, J., Friedrich, T., Lichey, J. *Bronchial and vascular effects of PAF in the rat isolated lung are completely blocked by WEB 2086, a novel specific PAF antagonist*. Br J Pharmacol 1987; 91: 799-802.

22. Braquet, P. *The ginkgolides: Potent platelet-activating factor antagonists isolated from Ginkgo biloba L. Chemistry, pharmacology, and clinical applications*. Drugs of the Future 1987; 12: 643-699.

23. Desquand, S., Touvay, C., Randon, J., Lagente, V., Vilain, B., Maridonneau-Parini, I., Etienne, A., Lefort, J., Braquet, P., Vargaftig, B.B. *Interference of BN 52021 (ginkgolide B) with the bronchopulmonary effects of PAF-acether in the guinea-pig*. Eur J Pharmacol 1986; 127: 83-95.

24. Touvay, C., Vilain, B., Carre, C., Etienne, A., Braquet, P. *Comparative effects of three orally active PAF receptor antagonists extracted from Ginkgo biloba on in vivo bronchoconstrictions and in vitro lung strips contractions induced by PAF-acether*. Abst 6th Conf Protaglandins and Related Compounds. Florence 1986; 316.

25. Touvay, C., Vilain, B., Taylor, J.E., Etienne, A., Chabrier, P.E., Braquet, P. *Proof of the involvement of platelet-activating factor (PAF-acether) in pulmonary complex immune systems using specific PAF-acether receptor antagonist BN 52021*. Prog Lip Res 1986; 25: 277-288.

26. Etienne, A., Hecquet, F., Soulard, C., Spinnewyn, B., Clostre, F., Braquet, P. *In vivo inhibition of plasma protein leakage and Salmonella enteritidis-induced mortality in the rat by a specific PAF-acether antagonist: BN 52021*. Agents and Actions 1985; 17: 368-370.

27. Foegh, M.L., Khirabadi, B.S., Rowles, J.R., Braquet, P., Ramwell, P.W. *Prolongation of cardiac allograft survival with BN 52021, a*

specific antagonist of platelet-activating factor. Transplantation 1986; 42: 86-88.

28. Thomson, A.W., Milton, J.I., Aldridge, R.D., Simpson, J.G., Davidson, J.L. *Inhibition by cycloporine of eosinophilia induced by high-dose cyclophosphamide prior to immunization*. Transplantation Proc 1986; 18: 895-897.

29. Lemanske, R.F., Kalner, M.A. *The experimental production of increased eosinophils in rat late-phase reactions*. Immunology 1982; 45: 561-568.

30. Camussi, G., Pawlowski, I., Tetta, G., Roffinello, C., Alberton, M., Brentjens, J., Andres, G. *Acute lung inflammation induced in the rabbit by local instillation of 1-0-octadecyl-2-acetyl-sn-glyceryl-3-phosphorylcholine or of native platelet-activating factor*. Am J Pathol 1983; 112: 78-88.

31. Patterson, R., Bernstein, P.R., Harris, K.E., Krell, R.D. *Airway response to sequential challenge with platelet-activating factor and leukotriene D_4 in rhesus monkeys*. J Lab Clin Med 1984; 104: 340-345.

32. Page, C.P., Guerriero, D., Sanjar, S., Morley, J. *Platelet-activating factor (PAF-acether) may account for late-onset reactions to allergen inhalation*. Agents and Actions 1985; 16: 30-32.

33. Gleich, G.L., Loegering, D.A., Kueppers, F., Bajaj, S.P., Mann, K.G. *Physiochemical and biological properties of the major basic protein from guinea-pig eosinophil granules*. J Exp Med 1974; 140: 313.

34. Frigas, E., Loegering, D.A., Solley, G.O., Farrow, G.M., Gleich, G.J. *Elevated levels of the eosinophil granule major basic protein in the sputum of patients with bronchial asthma*. Mayo Clin Proc 1981; 56: 345.

35. Braquet, P., Etienne, A., Touvay, C., Bourgain, R.H., Lefort, J., Vargaftig, B.B. *Involvement of platelet-activating factor in respiratory anaphylaxis demonstrated by PAF-acether inhibitor BN 52021*. Lancet 1985; i: 1501.

36. Touvay, C., Etienne, A., Braquet, P. *Inhibition of antigen-induced lung anaphylaxis in the guinea-pig by BN 52021, a new specific PAF-acether receptor antagonist isolated from ginkgo biloba*. Agents and Actions 1985; 17: 371-372.

37. Thomson, A.W., Milton, J.I., Aldridge, R.D., Davidson, R.J.L., Simpson, J.G. *Inhibition of drug-induced eosinophilia by*

cyclosporin A. Scand J Immunol 1986; 24: 163-170.

38. Spicer, B.A., Laycock, S.M., Smith, H. *The effects of drugs on leucocyte changes following the injection of antigen into the peritoneal cavities of actively sensitized rats.* Agents and Actions 1985; 17: 498-505.

39. Hiestand, P.C., Mekler, P., Nordmann, R., Grieder, A., Permmongkol, C. *Prolactin as a modulator of lymphocyte responsiveness provides a possible mechanism of action for cyclosporine.* Immunology 1986; 83: 2599-2603.

40. Hay, D.W.P., Farmer, S.G., Raeburn, D., Robinson, V.A., Flemming, W.W., Fedan, J.S. *Airway epithelium modulates the reactivity of guinea-pig respiratory smooth muscle.* Eur J Pharmacol 1986; 129: 11-18.

41. Touvay, C., Pignol, B., Vilain, B., Pfister, A., Mencia-Huerta, J.M., Braquet, P. *Functional and morphological alterations of guinea-pig lung induced by chronic infusion of platelet-activating factor (PAF-acether) support a role for the mediator in bronchial hyperreactivity.* Prostaglandins 1987; 34: 180.

Ginkgolides - Chemistry, Biology, Pharmacology and Clinical Perspectives. P. Braquet (Ed.)
Copyright © 1988, J.R. Prous Science Publishers, S.A.

THE EFFECT OF PAF-ACETHER ANTAGONISTS AND PLATELET SUPPRESSION ON PAF-ACETHER AND ANTIGEN-INDUCED EOSINOPHIL ACCUMULATION INTO GUINEA-PIG LUNGS

*Arielle Lellouch-Tubiana, Jean Lefort, Marie-Thérèse Simon, *André Pfister and Boris Vargaftig*

Institut Pasteur, INSERM U285, Paris, F-75015 France; *Hôpital Necker Paris, F-75015 France

INTRODUCTION

Intravenous administration of platelet-activating factor (PAF-acether) induces in the guinea-pig bronchoconstriction (1), intravascular platelet aggregation and platelet and neutrophil diapedesis (2). These features are followed within one hour by an eosinophil infiltration into the bronchial walls (2,3). PAF-acether may play an important role in eosinophil recruitment to the site of allergic reactions (4), and Frigas and Gleich (5) suggested that the eosinophil is a prime mediator of the pathophysiology of bronchial asthma. Furthermore, it has been shown recently (6) that PAF-acether is the most potent eosinophilotactic agent as compared to other potential mediators. Nevertheless, no histological studies relating PAF-acether administration to late cellular changes have been reported until now. This led us to study the bronchopulmonary effects of PAF-acether, 6 and 24 h after its injection and to compare them with those of experimental passive anaphylactic shock, which is used as a model for asthma (7) after treating the animals with two PAF-acether antagonists. Since PAF-acether is such a potent stimulator of platelet functions (8), and since it has been

---

Address all correspondence to: Dr. Arielle Lellouch-Tubiana, Institut Pasteur, 28 rue du Dr. Roux, F-75724 Paris Cédex 15, France.

suggested that platelets trigger cell recruitment during asthma (9), we pretreated the animals with either antiplatelet serum or prostacyclin, a powerful platelet protecting agent very effective against aggregation by PAF-
acether (1). We particularly studied the evolution of the eosinophilic infiltration and for this purpose made use of the technique of Luna (10), which
is based on the affinity of the eosinophil granule proteins for the acidophilic
dye Biebrich scarlet. This method for staining highlights eosinophils and
is very useful to assess quantitative changes in lung tissue eosinophilia.

Our findings strongly suggest that PAF-acether and antigen may mediate
the effects of antigen and could be responsible for the antigen-induced
eosinophil accumulation. In addition, the role of early platelet activation
is highlighted, since their depletion or protection markedly reduced
eosinophil recruitment.

MATERIALS AND METHODS

Hartley guinea-pigs of both sexes (300-500 g) were anesthesized with 30
mg/kg i.p. pentobarbitone, treated with the neuromuscular blocking agent
pancuronium (2 mg/kg i.v.) and prepared for the recording of bronchial
resistance to inflation (11). After controlling bronchial reactivity with
serotonin (5HT, 1-3 μg/kg i.v.), PAF-acether (100 ng/kg) or ovalbumin
(see below) were injected i.v. The potential antagonists were given i.v. 10
min before PAF-acether or antigen. At intervals after the administration
of ovalbumin or PAF-acether (6 and 24 h), the lungs were removed. Finally, since antigen-injected animals failed to survive consistently, in some experiments the antihistamine mepyramine was given i.v. beforehand, at 5
μg/kg, which did not interfere with the histological observations.

Histological Techniques

For light microscopy, lung tissue was fixed in 10% buffered formalin,
embedded in parafin and the sections were stained with hematoxylin-eosin-
safranin, Alcian blue and Luna's reagent for eosinophil granules (10). For
electron microscopy, tissue fragments were fixed in 2.5% glutaraldehyde
at 4°C, rinsed in phosphate buffer, post-fixed in 2% osmic acid, dehydrated
in graded alcohols and embedded in Epon. Sections two micrometers thick
were stained with toluidine blue and examined by light microscopy in order
to select suitable blocks. Ultrathin sections were cut with diamond knives
and stained with uranyl acetate and lead citrate prior to examination in
a Philips EM 300 transmission electron microscope. The number of
eosinophils was quantitated in the bronchial walls (50 fields of 62300 μm^2
each) with a Leitz Orthoplan using a 400 X magnification. These counts
are expressed as number of cells per mm^2.

Sensitization Procedure

Guinea-pigs were injected s.c. with 0.5 ml of 0.9% NaCl (saline) containing 10 μg of ovalbumin dispersed in 1 mg of Al(OH)$_3$ (modified from ref. 12). The injection was repeated after 14 days and 7-10 days later the animals were bled to provide serum for passive sensitization. In this case, 1 ml of a pooled serum was injected i.p. to naive animals, which were used 10-14 days later.

Materials

The following drugs were used: pentobarbitone (Nembutal, Lathévet, France); pancuronium (Pavulon, Organon, France); mepyramine maleate (Rhone-Poulenc); ovalbumin was from Sigma and Al(OH)$_3$ from Merck Darmstadt, FRG. PAF-acether (the hexadecanoic derivative) and lyso-PAF were gifts from Prof. J.J. Godfroid (Université Paris VII). Prostacyclin was a gift from Dr. S. Moncada (The Wellcome Research Laboratories, Beckenham, Great Britain). PAF-acether antagonists were BN 52021 (9H-1,7a-(epoxymethano)-1H,6aH-cyclopenta(c)furo(2,3-b)furo-(3',2':3,4)cyclopenta(1,2-d)furan-5,9,12-(4H)-trione,3-tert-butylhexahydro-8-methyl (13), kindly provided by Dr. P. Braquet, Institut Henri Beaufour, France, and WEB 2086 (3-[4-(2-chlorophenyl)-9-methyl-6H-thieno[3,2-f][1,2,4]triazolo-[4,3-a][1,4]-diazepin-2-yl]-1-(4-morpholinyl)-l-propanone) (14), kindly provided by Drs. Heuer and Weber, Boehringer Ingelheim, RFG. Anti-platelet serum (APS) was prepared as previously described (11).

Statistical Analysis

Data are expressed as means $\pm$ SEM. Statistical significance was calculated for $p < 0.05$ by the Student's Newman-Keuls t test.

RESULTS

Effects of PAF-Acether on Lung Parenchyma and on the Bronchial Mucosa

Electron microscopy showed epithelial damage 6 h after i.v. injection of PAF-acether. Damage consisted in degenerative changes with presence of residual bodies in the epithelial ciliated cells, which furthermore showed a marked enlargement of the mitochondrial cristae. Mucous cells showed important signs of hypersecretion (Fig. 1). Eosinophils markedly infiltrated the bronchial walls 6 h after injection of PAF-acether (Fig. 2) and persisted 24 h after administration of PAF. Isolated eosinophilic granules and

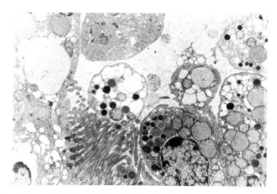

Figure 1 Electron micrograph of bronchial epithelium showing signs of important mucous hypersecretion 6 h after the injection of PAF-acether. x 11800.

cristalloids were seen in the bronchial walls, in close contact with areas of necrosed epithelial cells (Fig. 3). Eosinophils were frequently at the close vicinity of partially degranulated mast cells. Mucous plugs were observed in the bronchial lumens, containing degenerated epithelial cells and numerous eosinophils. Associated inflammatory cells (mast cells, plasma cells, neutrophils and macrophages) were found in the bronchial mucosa and submucosa. Twenty four hours after the injection of PAF-acether mucous metaplasia of bronchial epithelium was noted, indicating that regeneration was in course.

It should be noted that in no instance were these different effects observed when lyso-PAF, the inactive metabolite of PAF-acether, was injected at the same dose.

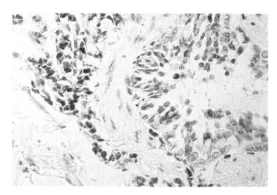

Figure 2 Light micrograph of a bronchus 6 h after the injection of PAF-acether showing a major eosinophil infiltration of the wall. Luna's staining. x 200.

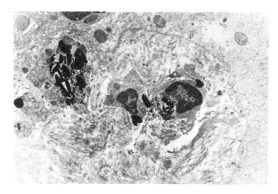

Figure 3 Electron micrograph of a bronchial wall 24 h after the injection of PAF-acether showing a necrosed epithelial area in close contact with degranulated eosinophil and free granules and cristalloids. x 14400.

Effects of Systemic Anaphylactic Shock on Lung Parenchyma and the Bronchial Mucosa

When lungs were collected 6 h after shock, the general features observed for PAF-acether were noted. Important degenerative changes were observed in the bronchial epithelial cells, which contained numerous lysosomes and showed important swelling of the cytoplasm.

Eosinophils were found within the bronchial walls and mucous plugs filled with eosiniphils in the bronchial lumens.

Interference of PAF-Acether Antagonists

The PAF-acether antagonist BN 52021 was given 10 min before i.v. administration of PAF-acether or antigen. As described (15,16), it blocked PAF-acether and ovalbumin-induced bronchoconstriction. Another PAF-acether antagonist, WEB 2086, had the same effect. Both were also effective in reducing the number of infiltrated eosinophils triggered by PAF-acether (Fig. 4) or antigen.

Interference of Platelet Depletion and of Prostacyclin with the Effects of PAF-Acether or Antigen

The total platelet counts decreased by at least 95% 1 h after administration of APS (11). when the total leucocyte counts were comparable to those observed before platelet depletion. The eosinophilic infiltration measured 6 h after injection of PAF-acether or ovalbumin to the platelet-depleted animals was significantly reduced. Similarly, no eosinophilic infiltration was

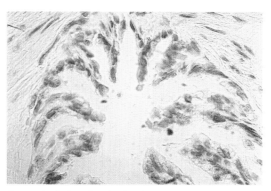

Figure 4   Light micrograph of a bronchus showing that a PAF-acether antagonist, BN 52021, markedly reduced the PAF-induced bronchial eosinophilia. Luna's staining. x 400.

observed when PAF-acether or ovalbumin were injected to guinea-pigs pretreated with a two minute infusion of 10 μg/kg of PGI$_2$ (Fig. 5).

DISCUSSION

Our results demonstrate that the responses of guinea-pig lung parenchyma to PAF-acether and antigen 6 and 24 h after i.v. administration are characterized by the presence of:

1. A major lung eosinophil infiltration, especially into the bron chial walls.
2. Isolated eosinophil granules and cristalloids in the lamina propria of the bronchi.
3. Bronchial mucous plugs, including degenerated epithelial cells and numerous eosinophils.
4. Degenerative changes of the bronchial epithelium.
5. A mucous metaplasia of the bronchial epithelium.

These histological findings, which bear a striking resemblance to the pathological features of late-phase reactions in human asthma (5,17), were never reported after PAF-acether and confirm that the latter is a potent eosinophilotactic agent (6). Eosinophil infiltration into the peribronchial vessels and the bronchial mucosa was reported by Kallos and Kallos (18) during experimental asthma in guinea-pigs, after repeated inhalations of antigen. These authors reported the presence of bronchial mucous plugs, including eosinophils and degenerated epithelial cells, and the appearance of numerous goblet cells in the bronchial epithelium associated with its mucous degeneration.

Bronchial mucous metaplasia, observed 24 h after i.v. administration of PAF-acether or antigen, is probably a transient phenomenon, secondary to epithelial damage which should be followed by epithelial regeneration. Eosinophilia is a constant finding in bronchial asthma. This is indicated by the increased number of eosinophils found in the bronchoalveolar lavage of late asthmatic reaction (19) and by recent findings of Coyle *et al.* (20) that antigen aerosolization to guinea-pigs is followed by a marked enrichment of the alveolar lavage in eosinophils, which furthermore is antagonized by BN 52021. It has been suggested that eosinophils may damage the bronchial epithelium (21) and our present identification of free eosinophil granules and cristalloids in the bronchial walls may explain the bronchial epithelial lesions now described. The resulting mucous hypersecretion may contribute to the formation of the eosinophil-enriched plugs found in our experiments.

It was not a surprise that two PAF-acether antagonists suppressed the bronchoconstrictor effects of the mediator itself and of the antigen (15,16). In addition, they also suppressed the delayed effects on eosinophils of PAF-acether itself and, more surprising, they antagonized as well the eosinophilotactic effects of antigen. Coyle *et al.* (20) also noted that BN 52021 reduces the number of eosinophils present in bronchoalveolar lavage after antigenic challenge, and it is likely that PAF-acether may mediate such an effect. Its cellular origin is as yet unknown, but the fact that two different antiplatelet treatments (immune depletion and prostacyclin administration) also abrogated eosinophil lung accumulation suggests a role for those cells.

CONCLUSIONS

Our results clearly show that PAF-acether can duplicate different histopathological features of acute pulmonary anaphylaxis, a model for asthma. These effects are suppressed by two chemically unrelated PAF-acether antagonists and by two different procedures which affect the platelet function. Sensitized animals contain more eosinophils in their bronchoalveolar lavage fluid than controls (Bachelet *et al.,* in preparation), and these cells may be activated upon antigen recognition, a process in which platelets are possibly involved (22). A complex cascade of successive cell activations involving platelets, alveolar macrophages, mast cells and eosinophils, with an essential participation of PAF-acether, accounts for the different features of experimental anaphylaxis.

References

1. Vargaftig, B.B., Lefort, J., Chignard, M., Benveniste, J. *Platelet-activating factor induces a platelet-dependent bronchoconstriction unrelated to the formation of prostaglandin derivatives.* Eur J Pharmacol 1980; 65: 185-192.

2. Lellouch-Tubiana, A., Lefort, J., Pirotzky, E., Vargaftig, B.B., Pfister, A. *Ultrastructural evidences for extravascular platelet recruitment in the lung upon intravenous injection of platelet-activating factor (PAF-acether) to guinea-pigs.* Br J Exp Pathol 1985; 66: 345-355.

3. Lellouch-Tubiana, A., Lefort, J., Pfister, A., Vargaftig, B.B. *Interactions between granulocytes and platelets with the guinea-pig lung in passive anaphylactic shock. Correlations with PAF-acether-induced lesions.* Int Archs Allergy Appl Immunol 1987; 83: 198-205.

4. Henocq, E., Vargaftig, B.B. *Accumulation of eosinophils in response to intracutaneous PAF-acether and allergens in man.* Lancet 1986; ii: 1378-1379.

5. Frigas, E., Gleich, G.J. *The eosinophil and the pathophysiology of asthma.* J Allergy Clin Immunol 1986; 77: 527-537.

6. Wardlaw, A.J.,Moqbel, R., Cromwell, O., Kay, A.B. *Platelet-activating factor, a potent chemotactic and chemokinetic factor for human eosinophils.* J Clin Invest 1986; 78: 1701-1706.

7. Carmo-Garcez, L., Cordeiro, R., Lagente, V., Lefort, J., Randon, J., Vargaftig, B.B. *Failure of a combined antihistamine and antileukotriene treatment to suppress passive anaphylaxis in the guinea-pig.* Int J Immunopharmacol 1986; 8: 985-995.

8. Benveniste, J., Henson, P.M., Cochrane, C.G. *Leukocyte-dependent histamine release from rabbit platelets: The role for IgE, basophils and a platelet-activating factor.* J Exp Med 1977; 136: 1356-1377.

9. Page, C.P., Archer, C.B., Paul, W., Morley, J. *PAF-acether: A mediator of inflammation and asthma.* TIPS 1984; 5: 239-241.

10. Luna, L.G. Manual of Histologic Staining Methods of the Armed Forces Institute of Pathology. 3rd Ed. McGraw-Hill: New York 1968.

11. Lefort, J., Vargaftig, B.B. *Role of platelets in aspirin-sensitive bronchoconstriction in the guinea-pig; interactions with salicylic acid.* Br J Pharmacol 1978; 63: 35-42.

12. Andersson, P. *Antigen-induced bronchial anaphylaxis in actively sensitized guinea-pigs.* Allergy 1980; 35: 65-71.

13. Braquet, P.G., Spinnewyn, B., Taylor, J.E., Drien, K. *Specific inhibitor of PAF-acether-induced platelet aggregation by BN 52021, a highly specific PAF-acether receptor antagonist isolated from Ginkgo biloba.* Blood and Vessels 1985; 16: 558-572.

14. Casals-Stenzel, J., Muacevic, G., Weber, K.H. *WEB 2086, a new specific antagonist of platelet-activating factor (PAF) in vitro and in vivo.* Arch Pharmacol 1986; 334: Suppl R44.

15. Braquet, P., Touvay, C., Etienne, A., Lefort, J., Bourgain, R.H., Vargaftig, B.B. *Involvement of platelet-activating factor in respiratory anaphylaxis demonstrated by PAF-acether inhibitor BN 52021.* Lancet 1985; 1501: 8444.

16. Desquand, S., Touvay, C., Randon, J., Lagente, V., Maridonneau-Parini, I., Etienne, A., Lefort, J., Braquet, P. Vargaftig, B.B. *Interference of BN 52021 (gingkolide B) with the bronchopulmonary effects of PAF-acether in the guinea-pig.* Eur J Pharmacol 1986; 127: 83-95.

17. Pagel, W. *Zur Pathologie des Asthma bronchiale.* Virchows Arch Path Anat Physiol 1932; 286: 580-590.

18. Kallos, P., Kallos, L. *Experimental asthma in guinea-pigs revisited.* Int Archs Allergy Appl Immunol 1984; 73: 77-85.

19. De Monchy, J.G.R., Kauffman, H.F., Venge, P., Koeter, G.H., Jansen, H.M., Sluiter, H.J., De Vries, K. *Bronchoalveolar eosinophilia during allergen-induced late asthmatic reactions.* Am Rev Resp Dis 1985; 131: 373-377.

20. Coyle, A.J., Urwin, S.C., Page, C.P., Touvay, C., Braquet, P. *The effect of the selective PAF antagonist BN 52021 on PAF- and antigen-induced bronchial hyperreactivity and eosinophil accumulation.* Eur J Pharmacol 1988; 148: 51-58.

21. Gleich, G.J., Frigas, E., Loegering, D.A., Wassom, D.L., Steinmuller, D. *Cytotoxic properties of the eosinophil major basic protein.* J Immunol 1979; 123: 2925-2927.

22. Capron, A., Ameisen, J.C., Joseph, M., Auriault, C., Tonnel, A.B., Caen, J. *New functions for platelets and their pathological implications.* Int Arch Allergy Appl Immunol 1985; 77: 101-114.

Ginkgolides - Chemistry, Biology, Pharmacology and Clinical Perspectives. P. Braquet (Ed.)
Copyright © 1988, J.R. Prous Science Publishers, S.A.

HUMAN ENDOTHELIAL CELLS ARE TARGET FOR PLATELET-ACTIVATING FACTOR (PAF). II. STUDIES WITH BN 52021, A SPECIFIC PAF ANTAGONIST

Federico Bussolino[1], Giovanni Camussi[2], Franco Turrini[1] and Paolo Arese[3]

[1]Dipartimento di Genetica, Biologia e Chimica Medica, Università di Torino, Italy; [2]Department of Pathology, State University of New York at Buffalo, USA; and [3]Laboratorio di Immunopatologia della Cattedra di Nefrologia Università di Torino, Italy.

ABSTRACT

Platelet-activating factor (PAF) stimulated in a dose-dependent manner the increase of cytosolic calcium in adherent human endothelial cells (ECs). The same concentrations of PAF that increase cytosolic calcium promote morphologic changes, F-actin depolymerization, and an increased clearance of albumin across EC monolayers, suggesting that cytosolic calcium plays a regulating role in these EC functions. BN 52021, a specific PAF antagonist, abolished the effects of PAF on ECs, supporting the existence of a specific mechanism of PAF-mediated activation of ECs. These results explain in part the PAF mechanism of action that induces the increase of vascular permeability *in vivo*.

Address all correspondence to: Prof. Federico Bussolino, Dipartimento di Genetica, Biologia e Chimica Medica, Università di Torino, I-10126 Torino, Italy.

INTRODUCTION

It is increasingly apparent that blood vessels are not passive containers, but a complex organ composed of cells with highly specialized functions that play important roles in health and disease. The endothelial cells (ECs) that line the luminal surface of the vessels' walls have recently received much attention in this regard (23, 27, 38-40). Autocrine mechanisms can modulate several important EC functions related to thrombosis, interaction with circulating cells, inflammation and immune competence (22, 23, 27, 38-40).

Platelet-activating factor (1-O-alkyl-2-acetyl-sn-glycero-3-phosphocholine, PAF) is one of the major autocrine substances playing an important function in cell-to-cell communication (6, 11, 19, 48). Cultured human and bovine ECs have recently added to the growing list of PAF producing and PAF sensitive cell types (7, 9, 10, 12-14, 17, 18, 34, 35, 50). Stimulated ECs synthetize PAF via activation of the acetyltransferase (13) that can be released or bound to EC membrane (12, 17, 18, 35, 50), and are able to deacetylate PAF (3). Furthermore, stereoselective affects of PAF on calcium homeostasis (7, 9, 10), cytoskeleton structures (14), and prostacyclin synthesis (9, 22) have been shown by us and others. PAF induces a rapid, dose-dependent increase of ^{45}Ca influx-efflux in adherent human ECs (9, 10) and a transient increase of cytosolic calcium Ca^{++} in suspended bovine ECs (7). Moreover, PAF induces human ECs to change their shape: ECs retract and tend to lose reciprocal contact while the distribution of F-actin changes from a stress fiber pattern to a more diffuse membrane-associated distribution (14).

The recent availability of specific PAF antagonists opens new perspectives to study the specificity of PAF-induced activation of membrane signalling systems and cellular activation (6). Natural substances, such as the terpene ginkgolide B (BN 52021) (4, 6) and the lignan kadsurenone (6), specifically interfere with the interaction between PAF and its high affinity binding sites by means of their tetrahydrofuran ring that competes with the oxygen atom of the ether linkage of PAF (6).

In the present study we report on the effect of BN 52021 on PAF-induced activation of human ECs.

MATERIALS AND METHODS

The chemicals and sources were as follows: 1-O-octadecyl-2(R)-acetyl-glycero-3-phosphocholine (PAF, [R] form) and 1-O-octadecyl-2-lyso-glycero-sn-3-phosphocholine (lyso-PAF) from Bachem Feinchemikalien (Switzerland); collagenase from *Clostridium histolyticum* from Boehringer

Mannheim GmbG (FRG); Iscove's medium and fetal calf serum from Flow Laboratories (UK); bovine serum albumin, fraction V (BSA) from Miles Labs. (USA); N-2-hydroxyethylpiperazine-N'-2 ethanesulfonic acid (HEPES), human fibronectin, quin2, EGTA, human serum albumin, fraction V and fluorescein-labelled phalloidin (F-PHD) from Sigma (USA); quin2/AM from Amersham Int. (UK); ionomycin from Calbiochem (USA); 1-O-octadecyl-2 (S)-acetyl-glycero-3-phosphocholine (enantiomer [S] form) was a gift from Drs. H.P. Kertscher and G. Ostermann (Karl Marx University, Leipzig and Medical Academy, Erfurt, GDR).

PAF and lyso-PAF were checked for purity by thin layer chromatography ($60F_{254}$, Merck, FRG) using chloroform: methanol: water (65:35:6, v/v) as solvent system and dissolved in Iscove's medium containing 0.25% BSA.

BN 52021 (a gift from Dr. P. Braquet, Institut Henri Beaufour, IPSEN, France) was dissolved in dimethylsulfoxide as 0.5 mM stock solution. In preliminary experiments, the final concentration of dimethylsulfoxide (0.1%, v/v) did not interfere with the experiments.

Human Endothelial Cell Cultures

ECs were isolated by treatment of human umbilical cord veins with 0.2% collagenase and grown in Iscove's medium containing 20% fetal calf serum as previously described (18). ECs were used at the first passage. For electron microscopy or quin2 experiments 2-3x10^4 or 1x10^5 ECs were plated on glass coverslips coated with fibronectin (14) and grown for 24 hours to obtain subconfluent or confluent monolayer, respectively. For the measure of F-actin, 6x10^5 ECs were plated on 35 mm diameter Petri dishes.

ECs were characterized by morphological criteria and immuno-fluorescence as previously described (18).

Measure of [Ca^{++}$_i$]

Culture wells containing 4 coverslips immersed in 1 ml Iscove's medium containing 20% fetal calf serum, were incubated for 30 minutes at 37°C in humidified 5% CO_2-air atmosphere in the presence of 1 μM quin 2/AM. After loading, coverslips were washed 3 times with buffered saline and kept at room temperature in Iscove's medium (without $NaHCO_3$ and buffered to pH 7.4 with 20 mM HEPES) until used. Fluorescence microscopy observations confirmed that all cells accumulated the dye, which was found to be distributed homogeneously throughout the cytoplasm. Measurements of [Ca^{++}$_i$] from the fluorescence of intracellular quin2 was performed in a Perkin-Elmer LS-5 spectrofluorimeter (Perkin - Elmer Corp., UK); the fluorimeter cuvette holder was thermostated at 37°C; standard monocromator settings were 339 nm excitation (5 nm slit) and 492 nm emis-

sion (10 nm slit). The coverslip was firmly positioned at an angle of 45°
in a quartz cuvette (10 mm square) containing 1 ml Krebs-buffer, pH 7.4.
The autofluorescence of the cells was 6.2 ± 1.6 arbitrary fluorescence units
(mean $\pm$ S.D. of 12 determinations).After quin2 loading, the fluorescence
was increased by a factor ranging from 3.7 to 4.2. Fluorescence spectral
analysis of adherent cells after loading revealed a peak at 492 nm,
demonstrating that quin2 had been readily accumulated intracellularly.
[Ca^{++}_i] measurements were performed within 30 minutes from the end of
the loading procedure: quin2 release into the medium during this period
was negligible. For calibration, the fluorescence from Ca^{++}-saturated dye
(F_{max}) was taken as the emission from cells treated with 200 nM ionomycin
in Ca^{++}-containing medium. $MnCl_2$ (2 mM), which enters the cells via the
ionophore and quenches quin2 fluorescence completely, was then added,
leaving only the autofluorescence cell signal. The final autofluorescence
signal (F_{min}) was essentially equal to the background signal obtained before
quin2 loading. [Ca^{++}_i] was calculated according to the following formula:

$$[Ca^{++}_i] = 115 \text{ x } (F\text{-}F_{min}/F_{max}\text{-}F) \text{ (42)}$$

Cellular quin2 contents were determined by comparing the fluorescence
of lysed quin2 cellls with the fluorescence of known concentration of acid
free quin2. Agonist and drugs were pipetted into the cuvette from stock
solutions to give final concentrations as indicated in the results.

Scanning Electron Microscopy

ECs were fixed for 1 hour at 4°C with 2.5% buffered glutaraldehyde,
dehydrated through graded alcohols and dried by the critical point method
with a critical point drying system (Sorvall, Model n° 49300, DuPont Company, USA). The cells were mounted on stubs and coated with gold plate
by a sputterer (Interatre Scientific-Instruments, Model PE-5000, USA). The
specimens were examined with a scanning electron microscope (JEOL
JSM-35CF) operating at 25 KV (37).

F-Actin Assay

The assay of F-actin was done by a slight modification of the method of
Rotrosen and Gallin (43). ECs were washed twice with buffered saline, fixed in 3% paraformaldehyde in phosphate-buffered saline (pH 7.6) containing 2% sucrose for 5 minutes at room temperature and made permeable
to large molecules by incubation for 5 minutes at 4°C in the following buffer (mM): NaCl 50, HEPES 20, sucrose 300, $MgCl_2$ 3 and Triton X 100

0.5% (36). ECs were stained with 200 nM F-PHD, 20 minutes at 37°C in the dark and F-actin was extracted with methanol (1 ml per well, 1 hour at 37°C in the dark). Measure of the fluorescence of intracellular F-PHD was performed with a Perkin-Elmer fluorimeter. Standard monocromator settings were 280 nm excitation (5 nm slit) and 320 nm emission (10 nm slit).

Albumin Transfer Across ECs

The albumin transfer across EC monolayer was determined by calculating the ratio of ^{125}I-albumin in the upper and lower chamber of a filter chamber assembly (Transwell, Costar, USA). Chambers were placed in plastic wells (24 mm diameter) containing 3 ml of Iscove's medium. The upper chamber was filled with 0.5 ml Iscove's medium containing 200 μM human serum albumin and 0.1 μCi ^{125}I-albumin. Stimuli were added to upper chamber and incubation was continued for 1 hour. Radioactivity was counted in the lower chamber. Results are expressed according to (14): % change albumin transfer = cpm ^{125}I-albumin after stimulus-cpm ^{125}I-albumin control/cpm ^{125}I-albumin control.

Human serum albumin was iodinated according to (14) (specific activity: 1.2 $\mu Ci/0.5$ μM albumin).

Experimental Protocol

ECs were preincubated for 15 minutes at 37°C in an incubator (CO_2 5%) in 2 ml Iscove's medium with 10% fetal calf serum or in Krebs buffer in quin2 experiments. ECs were stimulated with different concentrations of PAF (0.1-100 nM) for different times (5-30 minutes), with lyso-PAF (100 nM) or with PAF enantiomer ([S] form) (100 nM) at 37°C. In some experiments, ECs were preincubated for 5 minutes at 37°C with different concentrations of BN 52021.

RESULTS

PAF Induces Transient Increase of $[Ca^{++}_i]$

As shown in Figure 1, PAF elicited a dose-dependent increase of $[Ca^{++}_i]$ in adherent ECs in the presence of 1 mM external $CaCl_2$. The maximal rise in $[Ca^{++}_i]$ consistently occurred at PAF concentrations between 8 and 10 nM and responses to 100 nM were essentially equivalent. At 10 nM, PAF caused a rapid increase in $[Ca^{++}_i]$ from basal level of 121 ± 16 nM (n = 6) to a peak of 550 ± 41 nm (n = 7) after 20-60 seconds. Within 6-10 minutes $[Ca^{++}_i]$ had returned to the basal value. In the absence of extracellular calcium and in the presence of 2 mM EGTA, 10 nM PAF stimulated an

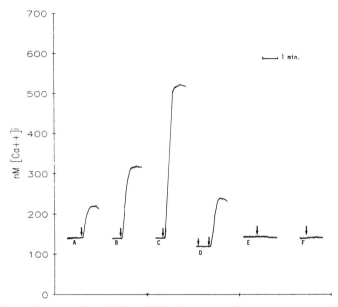

Figure 1 Dose-dependent effect of PAF on EC[Ca^{++}$_i$]. PAF was added at the arrows. A: PAF 2 nM; B: PAF 5 nM; C: PAF 10 nM; D: EGTA 2 mM (first arrow) + PAF 10 nM; E: lyso PAF 100 nM; F: S-PAF 100 nM.

equally rapid transient in [Ca^{++}$_i$] from the resting level of 110 ± 11 nM (n = 4) to a peak of 218 ± 15 nM (n = 4). In our experimental conditions (10 minutes without calcium), we did not observe any cell detachment, cell shape change or release of lactate dehydrogenase. S-PAF or lyso-PAF (100 nM) were ineffective.

BN 52021 caused a dose-dependent inhibition of the phenomenon without affecting *per se* the basal level of [Ca^{++}$_i$] (Fig. 2). The IC$_{50}$ for BN 52021 was 36.2 ± 5.0 nM with 2 nM PAF, 103 ± 8.8 nM with 10 nM PAF and 1.2 ± 0.2 μM with 100 nM PAF.

Scanning Electron Microscopy

The morphologic alterations induced by 0.1-100 nM PAF were studied by scanning electron microscopy. In basal condition, ECs were flat with a rather smooth surface and with nuclei and nucleoli protruding from the even surface (Fig. 3). Contact points between cells were well defined. In contrast, after 10 minutes of challenge with 0.1-10 nM PAF, ECs started to contract and come apart. The retraction reached a maximum after 30-60 minutes (Figs. 4 and 5). The cell body thickened as a consequence of cellular retrac-

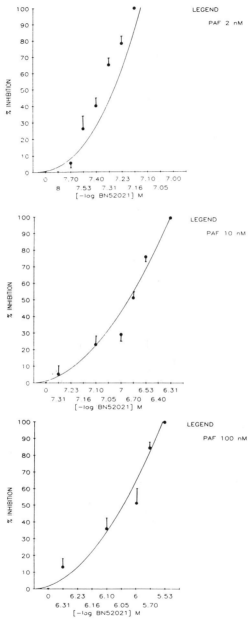

Figure 2 Dose-dependent inhibitory effect of BN 52021 on PAF-induced EC [Ca$^{++}_i$] transient. The results are expressed as % inhibition of maximal [Ca$^{++}_i$] level reached after stimulation with PAF: 2 nM (237 + 10 nM Ca$^{++}_i$), 10 nM (550 ± 41 nM [Ca$^{++}_i$] and 100 nM (561 ± 48 nM [Ca$^{++}_i$]. Mean ± S.D. of 3 experiments done in duplicate.

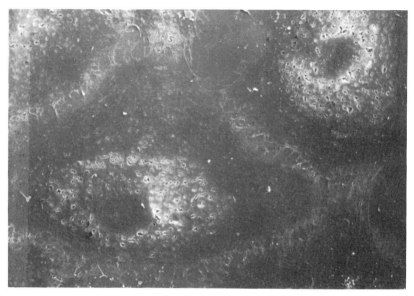

Figure 3 Scanning electron microscopy of untreated ECs. ECs show a very flattened appearance and a number of long linear reliefs outlining the underlying stress fibers (1100x).

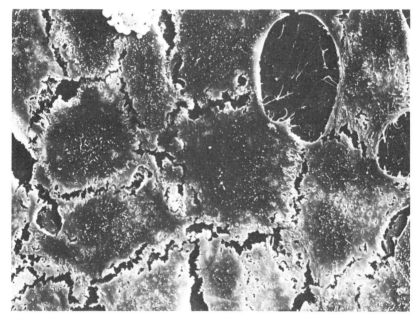

Figure 4 Scanning electron microscopy of ECs treated with 10 nM PAF for 30 minutes. ECs round up, lose their reciprocal contacts and show membrane protrusions (860x).

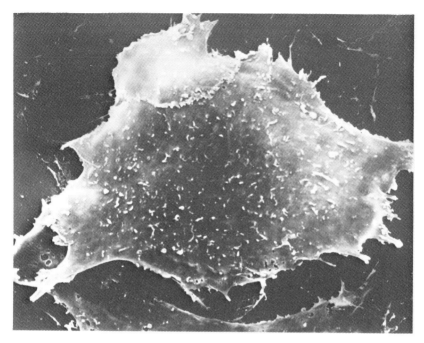

Figure 5 Scanning electron microscopy of ECs treated with 1 nM PAF for 30 minutes. EC assumes a migratory phenotype (3000x).

tion and nuclei and nucleoli were no longer visible. The cell surface show-ed a wealth of stubby microvilli. The cell retraction produced separation of contiguous ECs (Fig. 5). When ECs were stimulated with 100 nM PAF the above described alterations reached a maximum at 5-10 minutes. Ex-posures to PAF lasting up to 30-60 minutes, however, induced a marked ruffling of the EC surface and the appearance of numerous cytoplasmic blebs (Fig. 6).

The preincubation of EC with BN 52021 (10-50 fold the PAF concentra-tion) prevented the structural modification induced by PAF.

F-Actin Content in PAF Stimulated ECs

To determine whether the PAF-induced EC activation could modify the cytoskeleton structure, we stained ECs with F-PHD, which specifically binds to F-actin (49). F-actin content of ECs exposed to PAF for 30 minutes at 37°C was significantly decreased in a dose-dependent manner. Lyso-PAF and S-PAF had no effect. PAF receptor occupancy was required for PAF

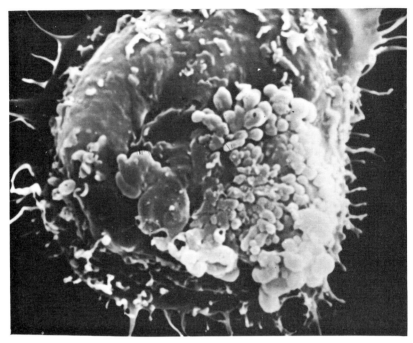

Figure 6 Scanning electron microscopy of ECs treated with 100 nM PAF for 30 minutes. ECs show evident blebs on their surface (6600x).

elicited changes in F-actin content, as inferred by the inhibitory effect of BN 52021 (Table 1).

Table 1 Change in F-actin content of ECs challenged with PAF

Stimulus	Relative F-actin content
None	1.00 ± 0.08
PAF 0.1 nM	0.96 ± 0.02
PAF 1 nM	0.89 ± 0.01
PAF 5 nM	0.78 ± 0.05
PAF 10 nM	0.66 ± 0.02
PAF 100 nM	0.63 ± 0.04
Lyso-PAF 100 nM	1.02 ± 0.01
S-PAF 100 nM	0.99 ± 0.02
BN 52021 3 μM + PAF 10 nM	0.99 ± 0.01
BN 52021 1 μM + PAF 10 nM	0.82 ± 0.03
BN 52021 100 nM + PAF 10 nM	0.70 ± 0.02

*Data are expressed as relative F-actin content normalized to a value of 1.00 for control ECs. Mean ±S.D. of 4 experiments done in duplicate.

PAF Increases[125]I-Albumin Clearance Across EC Monolayer

ECs caused a marked reduction of ^{125}I-albumin clearance as compared to filter alone. After 1 hour incubation at 37°C and 5% CO_2, the baseline permeability was determined: $3.8 \pm 1.7\%$ (n = 4) of ^{125}I-albumin added to the upper chamber was recovered in the lower chamber. The baseline permeability in absence of ECs was $59.3 \pm 1\%$ (n = 3). The effects of PAF on transendothelial albumin clearance after 30 minutes' incubation are shown in Figure 7. Compared to the normal transendothelial clearance, PAF produced a concentration dependent increase of ^{125}I-albumin clearance. The maximum increase occurred at 10-100 nM PAF. The effect of PAF began to be evident after 10 minutes' incubation and reached a plateau after 30 minutes (data not shown)

BN 52021 blocked the effects induced by 10 nM PAF in a dose-dependent manner ($p < 0.001$ at 3 μM, $p < 0.002$ at 1 μm and $p < 0.05$ at 100 nM). A 50% inhibition of the response to PAF was obtained at approximately 1 μM.

The concentrations of BN 52021 that blocked albumin transfer and F-actin depolymerization are higher than those that inhibited the increase in cytosolic calcium and the morphological shape change studied by electron

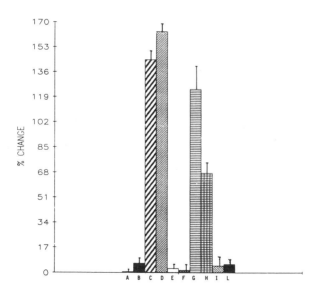

Figure 7 ^{125}I-albumin clearance across EC monolayer. A: no stimulus; B: PAF 1 nM; C: PAF 10 nM; D: PAF 100 nM; E: lyso PAF 100 nM; F: S-PAFD 100 nM; G: BN 52021 100 nM + PAF 10 nM; H: BN 52021 1 μM + PAF 10 nM; I: BN 52021 3 μM + PAF 10 nM; L: BN 52021 3 μM. Results (means ± S.D. of 4 experiments) are expressed as described in Materials and Methods.

microscopy. A possible explanation for these differences could be the higher cell number employed in the former (20-30 fold), compared with the other experiments.

DISCUSSION

The alteration of cytosolic calcium concentration is one mechanism by which extracellular agonists can activate or inactivate selected cellular responses.

By using ^{45}Ca, we have demonstrated that PAF can alter calcium homeostasis in adherent ECs (9, 10). Subsequently, Brock and Gimbrone (7) showed that PAF is able to increase cytosolic calcium in trypsin treated and suspended bovine ECs loaded with the fluorescent probe quin2. However, the protease treatment of adherent ECs affects *per se* [Ca$^{++}_i$] (25), and thus limits the extrapolation of the results obtained on such cells to the physiologic conditions. By contrast, use of ECs grown on fibronectrin-coated coverslips permits studying ECs maintained in an adherent monolayer.

The present results demonstrate that nanomolar concentrations of PAF cause an increase of [Ca$^{++}_i$] and that a 20-39% increase occurs in the absence of extracellular calcium, suggesting that a portion of the PAF-induced [Ca$^{++}_i$] transient is generated from intracellular stores. BN 52021 is able to block [Ca$^{++}_i$] transient both in the presence or absence of extracellular calcium, as previously reported for human and rabbit platelets (1, 47).

Several studies show that change in cytosolic calcium concentrations might be involved in the regulation of the physico-chemical state of cytoskeleton (33). We have previously shown by immunofluorescence technique that PAF induced a rearrangement of ECs cytoskeleton; in particular, F-actin rapidly changed from a stress fiber pattern to a more diffuse membrane-associated distribution. At the same time, vinculin, no longer visible at the stress fiber endings corresponding to focal contacts of the ventral membrane with the substratum, disappears (14). These alterations are compatible with cell retraction and also suggest the adoption of previously absent migratory properties (28-30). In fact, in non-muscle cells, an inverse correlation between the presence of the stress fibers and cell motility has been described (28, 30). Vascular ECs, studied *in situ*, present a dishomogeneous pattern in the distribution of stress fibers (28-30). The presence of these structures in different vascular sites correlates with the cell need for greater adherence capability and structural integrity to face elevated hemodynamic forces. In cultured ECs, stress fibers are present with a homogeneous pattern and have been implicated in cell spreading providing an intracellular isometric tension, and in cell adhesion to substratum (8, 15, 28).

PAF induces depolymerization of F-actin, alteration of the EC shape and increase of albumin transfer across an EC monolayer, at concentrations similar to those that are able to increase cytosolic calcium, thus suggesting a linkage between these events. Moreover, exposure of ECs to histamine (43) or oxidant stress (46) was associated to a calcium-dependent shape change, F-actin rearrangement and increased transfer of macromolecules across the EC monolayer.

After PAF exposure, ECs tend to loosen their contact with contiguous ECs. As a consequence, cell bodies round up and a wealth of stubby microvilli sprouts from their surface. These alterations are associated with depolymerization of F-actin, rearrangement of microfilaments and decreased adhesion. Therefore, EC shape changes due to F-actin depolymerization may be responsible for the increased albumin permeability observed here, as suggested by Shasby et al. (45).

The effect of PAF on ECs may also reflect EC injury. However, we did not observe release of lactate dehydrogenase at lower doses of PAF (0.05 nM-10 nM) (14). Only 100 nM PAF caused statistically significant lactate dehydrogenase release indicating some cell damage (14), also witnessed by the presence of some cytoplasmic blebs.

It has been demonstrated that several lipids act on cells by a nonspecific perturbation of plasma membrane fluidity (41). However, the following data suggest a specific mechanism for PAF action on ECs: BN 52021 which competes with PAF at the level of its high affinity binding sites, blocks the effects of PAF; PAF acts on ECs at very low concentrations; a concentration of the biologically inactive 2-lyso derivative of PAF (lyso-PAF) 1000-fold greater than the minimal active PAF concentration was ineffective on ECs, as well as the enantiomer of PAF (S-form); the ^{45}Ca influx induced by PAF was blunted by pre-exposure of the cells to PAF, consistent with deactivation by occupation of the putative PAF receptor (9). Moreover, Korth et al. recently demonstrated the presence of PAF-binding sites on human ECs (34).

As demonstrated for platelets, after binding to its receptor, PAF could activate an unknown target (GTP-regulated protein) leading to hydrolysis of GTP and activation of phospholipase C, a breakdown of phosphoinositides with formation of the second messengers inositol triphosphate and diacyl glycerol, and an increase in cytosolic calcium (6).

Our results suggest that a direct effect of PAF on ECs may be responsible for the increase in vascular permeability induced in vivo by this mediator (2, 16, 17, 20, 24, 26, 34, 44) and explain the protective effect of BN 52021 (5, 6, 21) in human and experimental pathologic conditions characterized by an increase in vascular permeability.

258   F. BUSSOLINO ET AL.

ACKNOWLEDGEMENTS

We thank Dr. P. Braquet for supplying BN 52021 and his suggestions, Drs. Kertscher and Osterman for supplying (S) PAF enantiomer. This study was supported by Ministero della Pubblica Istruzione and by grant AM 36807 from the National Institue of Arthritis, Diabetes, Digestive and Kidney Diseases. F.B. is a fellow of Regione Piemonte.

References

1. Baroggi, et al. *Changes in cytosolic free calcium induced by platelet-activating factor in rabbit platelets: Specific inhibition by BN 52021 and structurally related compounds.* Agents and Actions 1986; 20 (suppl): 87-98.
2. Bjork, J. et al. *Acute microvascular effect of PAF-acether, as studied by intravital microscopy.* Eur J Pharmacol 1983; 96: 87-90.
3. Blank, M.L. et al. *Metabolism of platelet-activating factor (1-alkyl-2-acetyl-sn-glycero-3-phosphocholine) and 1-alkyl-2-acetyl-sn-glycerol by human endothelial cells.* Biochim Biophys Acta 1986; 876: 373-378.
4. Braquet, P. et al. *BN 52021 and related compounds: A new series of highly specific PAF-acether receptor antagonists from Ginkgo biloba L.* Blood and Vessels 1985; 16: 559-572.
5. Braquet, P. et al. *Involvement of PAF-acether in various immune disorders using BN 52021 (Ginkgolide B): a powerful PAF-acether antagonist isolated from Ginkgo Biloba.* In: Advances in Prostaglandin, Thromboxane and Leukotriene Research. Raven Press: New York 1986; 179-198.
6. Braquet, P. et al. *Perspectives in platelet-activating factor research.* Pharmacol Rev 1987; 39: 97-145.
7. Brock, T.A. et al. *Platelet-activating factor alters calcium homeostasis in cultured vascular endothelial cells.* Am J Physiol 1986; 250: H1086-H1092.
8. Burridge, K. *Are stress fibers contractile?* Nature 1981; 294: 691-692.
9. Bussolino, F. et al. *Alkyl-ether phosphoglycerides influence calcium fluxes into human endothelial cells.* J Immunol 1985; 135: 2748-2753.
10. Bussolino, F. et al. *Platelet-activating factor influences calcium homeostasis into human endothelial cells.* In: Advances in Inflammation Research. F. Russo-Marie et al. (Eds.). Raven Press: New York 1985; 310-312.
11. Bussolino, F. et al. *Platelet-activating factor-*

A powerful lipid autacoid possibly involved in microangiopathy. Acta Haematologica 1986; 75: 129-140.
12. Bussolino, F. et al. *Interleukin 1 stimulates platelet-activating factor (1-O-alkyl-2-acetyl-sn-glycero-3-phosphocholine) production in cultured human endothelial cells.* J Clin Invest 1986; 77: 2027-2033.
13. Bussolino, F. et al. *Studies on the mechanism of interleukin 1 stimulation of platelet-activating factor synthesis in human endothelial cells in culture.* Biochim Biophys Acta 1987; 927: 43-54.
14. Bussolino, F. et al. *Human endothelial cells are target for platelet-activating factor (PAF). I. PAF induces changes in cytoskeleton structures.* J Immunol 1987; in press.
15. Byers, H.R. et al. *Stress fibers in cells in situ: Immunofluorescence visualization with antiactin, antimyosin and anti-alpha-actinin.* J Cell Biol 1982; 93: 804-811.
16. Camussi, G. et al. *Platelet-activating factor (PAF) in experimentally-induced rabbit acute serum sickness: Role of basophil-derived PAF in immune-complex deposition.* J Immunol 1982; 128: 86-94.
17. Camussi, G. et al. *Release of platelet-activating factor in rabbits with antibody-mediated injury of the lung: The role of leukocytes and of pulmonary endothelial cells.* J Immunol 1983; 131: 1802-1807.
18. Camussi, G. *Potential role of platelet-activating factor from the human endothelial cells in culture.* J Immunol 1983; 131: 2397-2403.
19. Camussi, G. *Potential role of platelet activating factor in renal pathophysiology.* Kidney Int 1986; 29: 469-477.
20. Chang, S. et al. *Platelet-activating factor mediates hemodynamic and lung injury in endotoxin-treated rats.* J Clin Invest 1987; 79: 1498-1509.
21. Chung, K.F. et al. *Effect of a ginkgolide mixture (BN 52063) in antagonising skin and*

platelet responses to platelet-activating factor in man. Lancet 1987; i: 248-251.

22. d'Humieres, S. et al. *PAF-acether-induced synthesis of prostacyclin by human endothelial cells.* Eur J Pharmacol 1986; 131: 13-19.

23. Folkman, J. et al. *Angiogenic factors.* Science 1987; 235: 442-447.

24. Grandel, K.E. et al. *Association of platelet-activating factor with primary cold urticaria.* New Engl J Med 1985; 313: 405-409.

25. Hamilton, K.K. et al. *Changes in cytosolic Ca^{2+} associated with von Willebrand Factor release in human endothelial cells exposed to histamine.* J Clin Invest 1987; 79: 600-608.

26. Handley, D.A. et al. *Effect of platelet-activating factor on endothelial permeability to plasma macromolecules.* Immunopharmacology 1984; 8: 137-142.

27. Harlam, J.M. *Leukocyte-endothelial interactions.* Blood 1985; 65: 513-525.

28. Herman, I.M. et al. *Relation between the cell activity and the distribution of cytoplasmic actin and myosin.* J Cell Biol 1981; 88: 84-91.

29. Herman, I.M. et al. *Contractile proteins in endothelial cells.* Ann N Y Acad Sci 1982; 40: 50-60.

30. Herman, I.M. et al. *Capillary endothelial cell migration: Loss of stress fibres in response to retina-derived growth factor.* J Muscle Res Cell Motil 1984; 5: 697-609.

31. Humphrey, D.M. et al. *Vasoactive properties of acetyl glyceryl ether phosphorylcholine and analogs.* Lab Invest 1982; 46: 422-431.

32. Ito, S. et al. *Hyperacute renal allograft rejection in the rabbit. The role of platelet-activating factor and of cationic proteins derived from polymorphonuclear leukocytes and from platelets.* Lab Invest 1984; 51: 148-161.

33. Kakiuchi, S. et al. *Control of cytoskeleton by calmodulin and calmodulin-binding proteins.* TIPS 1984; 8: 59-62.

34. Korth, R. et al. *Comparison of human endothelial cells in culture and platelets for ^3H PAF-acether binding.* Fed Proc 1987; (Abst).

35. Lynch, J.M. et al. *The intracellular retention of newly synthesized platelet-activating factor.* J Immunol 1986; 137, 2653-2661.

36. Marchisio, P.C. et al. *Cell-substratum interaction of cultured avian osteoclasts is mediated by specific adhesion structures.* J Cell Biol 1984; 99: 1696-1703.

37. Mendrick, D.L. et al. *Antibody-mediated injury to proximal tubules in Heymann nephritis.* Kidney Int 1980; 18: 328-334.

38. Mullane, K.M. et al. *Endothelium, arachidonic acid, and coronary vascular tone.* Fed Proc 1987; 46: 54-62.

39. Nathan, C.F. *Secretory products of macrophages.* J Clin Invest 1987; 79: 319-326.

40. Old, L.J. *Tumor necrosis factor.* Science 1985; 230: 630-632.

41. Quinn, P.J. *The fluidity of cell membrane and its regulation.* Prog Biophys Mol Biol 1981; 38: 1-42.

42. Rink, J. et al. *Using quin2 in cell suspension.* Cell Calcium 1985; 6: 133-144.

43. Rotrosen, D. et al. *Histamine type I receptor occupancy increases endothelial cytosolic calcium, reduces F-actin, and promotes albumin diffusion across cultured endothelial monolayers.* J Cell Biol 1986; 103: 2379-2387.

44. Sanchez-Crespo, M. et al. *Vascular actions of synthetic PAF-acether (a synthetic platelet-activating factor) in the rat. Evidence for a platelet-independent mechanism.* Immunopharmacology 1982; 4: 173-185.

45. Shasby, M. et al. *Reversible oxidant-induced increases in albumin transfer across cultured endothelium: Alterations in cell shape and calcium homeostasis.* Blood 1985; 65: 605-614.

46. Shasby, D.M. et al. *Role of endothelial cell cytoskeleton in control of endothelial permeability.* Circ Res 1982; 51: 657-661.

47. Simon, A.F. et al. *Effect of BN 52021, a specific antagonist of platelet-activating factor (PAF-acether) in Ca2+ mobilization and phosphatidic acid production induced by PAF-acether in human platelets.* Thromb Res 1987; 45: 299-309.

48. Snyder, F. *Chemical and biochemical aspects of platelet-activating factor: A novel class of acetylated ether-linked choline phospholipids.* Med Res Rev 1985; 5: 107-140.

49. Wulf, E.A. et al. *Fluoresent phallotoxin, a tool for the visualization of cellular actin.* Proc Natl Acad Sci USA 1979; 76: 4498-4502.

50. Zimmerman, G.A. et al. *Human vascular endothelial cells produce platelet-activating factor (1-alkyl-2- acetyl-sn-glycero- 3-phosphocholine): Evidence for a requirement for specific agonists and modulation by prostacyclin.* Circulation 1985; 72: 718-722.

Ginkgolides - Chemistry, Biology, Pharmacology and Clinical Perspectives. P. Braquet (Ed.)
Copyright © 1988, J.R. Prous Science Publishers, S.A.

INTERFERENCE OF BN 52021 WITH CARRAGEENIN-INDUCED INFLAMMATORY RESPONSE: IS THIS EFFECT DUE TO PAF-ACETHER ANTAGONISM?

Renato Sergio Balão Cordeiro, Marco Aurélio Martins, Patrícia Machado Rodrigues e Silva, Maria das Graças Muller Oliveira Henriques, Vivian Baseches Weg, Hugo Caire Castro Faria Neto and Marcia Coronha Ramos Lima

Fundação Oswaldo Cruz, I.O.C., Departamento de Fisiologia e Farmacodinâmica, Rio de Janeiro, Brasil

ABSTRACT

Mouse and rat pleurisy and paw edema were used to determine the interference of the ginkgolide BN 52021 with the PAF-acether- and carrageenin-induced inflammatory reaction. In mice, intraperitoneal administration of BN 52021 suppressed the carrageenin-induced inflammatory response, but had no effect on the pro-inflammatory activity of PAF-acether. In contrast, in rats, BN 52021 was effective against PAF-acether at 5-20 mg/kg. However, in rats pretreatment with the ginkgolide failed to interfere with the development of the reaction induced by carrageenin demonstrating that in this species this reaction occurs independently of PAF-acether. It is suggested that (a) compound BN 52021 has a species dependent anti-inflammatory activity and (b) this effect is not due only to the antagonism of PAF-acether.

Address all correspondence to: Dr. Renato S.B. Cordeiro, Fundação Oswaldo Cruz, I.O.C., Departamento de Fisiologia e Farmacodinâmica, Avenida Brasil, 4365, Caixa Postal 926, CEP - 20010, Rio de Janeiro, Brasil.

INTRODUCTION

With the discovery of platelet-activating factor antagonists, and of the ginkgolide BN 52021 in particular (4), a specific inhibitor of PAF-acether receptors, more in-depth investigations have been conducted on the participation of this phospholipid in physiopathological changes such as thrombosis (3), anaphylaxis (5, 10), endotoxemic shock (19, 6), gastric ulcers (26), and renal injury (17).

The involvement of PAF-acether in inflammatory phenomena has been widely reported in the literature (1, 2, 8, 13, 20, 22, 24). PAF-acether is one of the most powerful agents inducing increased vascular permeability, with an effect 100 and 1000 times more powerful than that of serotonin and histamine, respectively, on a molar basis (18). Assays involving rat paw edema and increased vascular permeability in rats and guinea pigs have demonstrated that the inflammatory signs elicited by PAF-acether are clearly independent of platelets and polymorphonuclear neutrophils and seem to result, at least in part, from a direct action of the lipid at the endothelial cell level (21).

The participation of PAF-acether in the inflammatory reaction induced by carrageenin has not been fully elucidated. Hwang *et al.* (16) have presented strong evidence that PAF-acether may be involved in the first stage of carrageenin-induced paw edema in the rat. On the other hand, Cordeiro *et al.* (8) demonstrated that successive intraplantar PAF-acether injections in rats led to a state of marked topical desensitization to stimulation with PAF-acether and 2-methyl-carbamate-PAF, under conditions in which the response to carrageenin remained unchanged.

In view of these considerations, the present study was undertaken to extend these results by investigating the possible interference of ginkgolide BN 52021 with paw edema and pleurisy produced in rats and mice by PAF-acether and carrageenin. The study showed that, in contrast to what has been observed in the rat, treatment with BN 52021 was effective in blocking the inflammatory response induced by carrageenin in the mouse, even though the ginkgolide was surprisingly ineffective in inhibiting the action of PAF-acether itself. These results suggest that compound BN 52021 has a strong anti-inflammatory action which is species-dependent and that cannot be attributed only to its anti-PAF activity.

MATERIALS AND METHODS

Animals

Outbred Wistar rats and Swiss 44 mice of both sexes weighing approximately 200 g and 25 g, respectively, were used.

Paw Edema

Rat and mouse paw edema was produced by an injection of the flogogenic agents PAF-acether and carrageenin (100 and 50 μl, respectively) diluted in sterile 0.9% NaCl solution into one of the hind paws. The contralateral paw was injected with an equal volume of saline. The edema was measured by the plethysmographic technique of Ferreira (11).

Experimental Pleurisy

PAF-acether and carrageenin diluted in 0.9% sterile saline were injected (200 μl/rat; 50 μl/mouse) by the intercostal route into the right flank of unanesthetized animals with a 6 mm-long 10x5 needle. Control animals injected with the same volume of vehicle were used and sacrificed at the same time as the experimental animals. After that, the animals were anesthetized with ether and sacrificed by cutting the cervical vessels. The skin covering the thorax was removed and saline/heparin (10Ui/ml) was injected to wash the pleural cavity. Rat and mouse pleural exudates were collected and the volumes were measured. Leukocytes were diluted in Turk's solution and counts were made using a Neubauer chamber.

Animal Treatment

For systemic treatment, BN 52021 diluted in sterile 0.9% saline was injected intraperitoneally 1 hour before PAF-acether or carrageenin injection. For *in situ* treatment, BN 52021 was diluted in the same volume as used for the inflammatory agents and injected 5 minutes before the intraplantar or intrapleural injection of the flogogenic agents.

Drugs

PAF-acether(1-O-hexadecyl-2-acetyl-*sn*-glycero-3-phosphorylcholine) was obtained from Bachem, Switzerland, carrageenin from Marine Colloids, Springfield, IL, USA, and BN 52021 was kindly provided by Dr. P. Braquet, Institut Henri Beaufour.

Statistical Analysis

Data were analyzed statistically by the Student's t test for unpaired samples. P values of 0.05 or less were considered significant.

RESULTS

The effect of BN 52021 was investigated in PAF-acether- and carrageenin-induced rat paw edema. Intraperitoneal administration of increasing

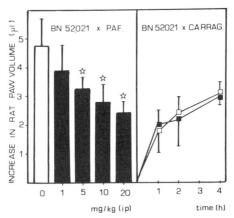

Figure 1 PAF-acether- and carrageenin-induced rat paw edema. Left side: dose-dependent effect of BN 52021 against PAF-acether (2 μg/paw) (closed columns). The analysis was performed 1 hour after the administration of PAF-acether. Each column represents the mean ± SD from at least 5 animals. Control edema: open column. *p < 0.001. Right side: absence of effect of BN 52021 (20 mg/kg, i.p.) against carrageenin (500 μg/paw) (□). Non-treated animals were indicated by (■). Each point represents the mean ± SD from at least 5 animals.

amounts of BN 52021 (1-20 mg/kg) reduced the edema induced by the intraplantar injection of PAF-acether in a dose-dependent manner (Fig. 1A). On the other hand, BN 52021 (20 mg/kg) failed to modify the edema induced by carrageenin in rats (Fig. 1B). Similar results were obtained when the ginkgolide was simultaneously injected with PAF-acether or carrageenin into the rat pleural cavity. Figure 2A shows that the pleurisy produced by PAF-acether was significantly, but not completely, blocked by intrapleural injections of 4 or 8 μg of BN 52021 under conditions in which the reaction induced by carrageenin was not affected (Fig. 2B).

In contrast to what is observed in rats, previous intraperitoneal administration (1 hour before) (Fig. 3A) or even simultaneous *in situ* administration of compound BN 52021 (Fig. 3B) did not interfere with the edematous response induced by intraplantar PAF-acether injections in mice. However, treatment of mice with BN 52021 (0.5-5 mg/kg) inhibited paw edema induced by carrageenin in a significant and dose-dependent manner (Fig. 3C). The powerful anti-carrageenin activity of compound BN 52021 was confirmed when the mouse pleurisy model was utilized. Figure 4 shows that intraperitoneal treatment with BN 52021 (10 mg/kg) markedly reduced the exudation reaction induced by the polysaccharide. However, both the intraperitoneal and *in situ* treatments failed to change the exudation reaction induced by PAF-acether (Fig. 4A and 4B). Table 1 gives the total leukocyte values obtained for the pleural exudates of rats and mice after

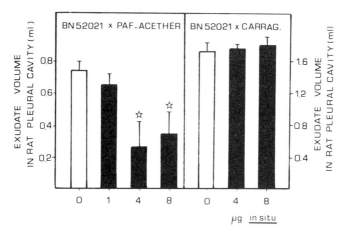

Figure 2 PAF-acether- and carrageenin-induced rat pleurisy. Left side: dose-dependent effect of BN 52021 (1-8 μg, *in situ*) against PAF-acether (1 μg, *in situ*) (closed columns). The analysis was performed 30 minutes after PAF-acether. Each column represents the mean ± SD from at least 5 animals. Control pleurisy: open column. *p < 0.001. Right side: absence of effect of BN 52021 (4 and 8 μg, *in situ*) against carrageenin (1 mg, *in situ*) (closed columns). The analysis was performed 4 hours after intrapleural injection of carrageenin. Each column represents the mean ± SD from at least 5 animals.

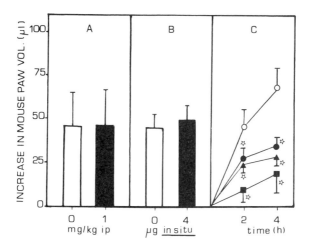

Figure 3 PAF-acether- and carrageenin-induced mouse paw edema. A- Absence of effect of BN 52021 (1 mg/kg, i.p., 1 hour before) (closed columns) against PAF-acether (2 μg/paw). B- Absence of effect of BN 52021 (4 μg, *in situ*) against PAF-acether (2 μg/paw) (closed columns). The analysis was performed 30 minutes after intraplantar injection of PAF-acether. Each column represents the mean ± SD from at least 5 animals. Control edema: open column. C- Dose-dependent effect of BN 52021 at the doses of 0.5 mg/kg (●), 1.0 mg/kg (▲), and 5.0 mg/kg (■) against carrageenin (300 μg/paw). Each point represents the mean ± SD from at least 6 animals. Control edema (○). *p < 0.05.

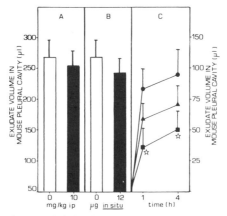

Figure 4 PAF-acether and carrageenin-induced mouse pleurisy. A- Absence of effect of BN 52021 (10 mg/kg, 1 hour before, i.p.) against PAF-acether (6 μg *in situ*) (closed columns). B- Absence of effect of BN 52021 (12 μg *in situ*) against PAF-acether (6 μg *in situ*) (closed columns). Each column represents the mean ± SD from at least 5 animals. Control pleurisy: open column. C- Dose-dependent effect of intraperitoneal BN 52021 at the dose of 5 mg/kg (▲) and 10 mg/kg (■) against carrageenin (300 μg). Each point represents the mean ± SD from at least 6 animals. Control pleurisy (●). *p < 0.005.

Table 1 Interference of BN 52021 with the changes in the total leukocyte number observed in the pleural cavity after intrapleural injection of PAF-acether or carrageenin in rats and mice.

Stimulus	Treatment	Total leukocytes in the exudate (x 10⁶)	
		Rat pleurisy	Mouse pleurisy
None	None	78.3 + 11.5	1.15 + 0.30
PAF-acether	None	24.5 + 19.1	1.00 + 0.51
PAF-acether	BN 52021	60.2 + 17.1*	1.57 + 0.12
Carrageenin	None	742.5 + 65.1	5.10 + 1.50
Carrageenin	BN 52021	791.3 + 123.0	5.40 + 2.70

In rats, 8 μg of BN 52021 were administered *in situ* 5 minutes before PAF-acether (1 μg) or carrageenin (1 mg) injection. In mice, BN 52021 (10 mg/kg) was administered intraperitoneally 1 hour before PAF-acether (10 μg) or carrageenin (300 μg) injection.
Data are the mean ± S.D. from at least 5 animals. Statistically significant differences are indicated by an asterisk (p < 0.001) and were obtained by comparing treated and non-treated groups.

stimulation with carrageenin and PAF-acether. At the doses utilized, intrapleural PAF-acether injections caused a significant reduction in the number of leukocytes present in the inflammatory exudate of rats but not of mice, an effect that was cancelled by treatment with BN 52021. Intrapleurally injected carrageenin caused a drastic increase in leukocyte number both in rats and mice, and this effect was resistant to treatment with the ginkgolide.

DISCUSSION

The ginkgolide BN 52021 is a selective and powerful PAF-acether antagonist which is extracted and purified from a crude extract of leaves of the *Ginkgo biloba* plant (4). The discovery of compounds having a recognized anti-PAF activity has been of great importance not only for a better understanding of the mechanism of action of PAF-acether, but also for the study of the real role of this phospholipid in various physiopathological alterations.

In the present study we observed that intraperitoneal treatment with compound BN 52021 reduced, though it did not fully eliminate, rat paw edema response induced by intraplantar PAF-acether injection. The inhibition shown by the compound was dose-dependent at concentrations from 1 to 20 mg/kg, with 53% blockade being reached at the maximum dose. Inappropriate concentrations of the ginkgolide at the site of action may be one of the possible causes of the only partial protective effect observed in this system. However, when BN 52021 at concentrations 4 and 8 times higher than the agonist's was administered locally 5 minutes before intrapleural PAF-acether injection, a significant, though partial, inhibition of the exudative response was again observed. These results clearly indicate that, even though it is effective in blocking the inflammatory action of PAF-acether, compound BN 52021 was unable to completely cancel these effects, suggesting that PAF-acether may be acting through at least two different mechanisms to promote increased vascular permeability in rats: one of them sensitive and the other refractory to treatment with BN 52021.

Intrapleural PAF-acether injection in rats caused a significant reduction in total leukocyte numbers in the cavity. These results confirm those previously reported by Tarayre *et al.* (23), who advanced the hypothesis that PAF-acether may induce greater cell adherence at the level of the serous membrane which lines the pleural cavity. These authors, however, did not rule out the possibility that the observed reduction was the consequence of a leukocyte aggregation phenomenon. It should be pointed out that BN 52021 fully inhibited the leukocyte reduction induced by PAF-acether, indicating that this phenomenon probably occurs through a selective drug-receptor interaction process.

In a recent study, Hwang *et al.* (16) raised the hypothesis of a significant participation of PAF-acether in the first phase of carrageenin-induced rat paw edema mainly on the basis of the protective effect shown by compound L 652,731, which also has a marked anti-PAF activity. In the present study, compound BN 52021 had no effect on the inflammatory reaction induced by intraplantar or intrapleural carrageenin injection in rats. These results agree with previous data in which successive PAF-acether injections led to a state of selective desensitization to PAF-acether itself, though full sensitivity to stimuli such as serotonin and carrageenin was maintained (8). Taken as a whole, these results indicate that carrageenin does not seem to recruit PAF-acether as a preferential pathway for triggering the inflammatory response in rats. A possible explanation for the anti-carrageenin activity exhibited by the anti-PAF compound L 652,731 (16) could be a nonspecific action of this compound.

On the other hand, in contrast to what was observed in rats, both carrageenin-induced paw edema and pleurisy of mice were drastically blocked by pre-treatment with BN 52021. There are marked differences between the inflammatory reactions provoked by carrageenin in rats and in mice, and perhaps the most outstanding one is related to the time course of the reaction. The maximum reaction provoked by carrageenin in mice invariably occurs between 48 and 72 hours both in paw edema (15) and pleurisy (data not shown), whereas in rats the peak of the response appears 4 to 6 hours after carrageenin (25). Another marked difference between the two processes is that the anti-platelet serum significantly inhibited the paw edema response induced by carrageenin in mice, suggesting the potential involvement of platelets in this system (14). However, similar studies conducted on rats have demonstrated that anti-platelet serum has no ability to effect any change in the inflammatory picture induced by carrageenin (12). It is interesting to point out that treatment with BN 52021 1 h before and at daily intervals throughout the development of the reaction also eliminated the late (48-72 hours) phase of paw edema and pleurisy induced by carrageenin in mice (data not shown).

The hypothesis that PAF-acether may be involved in the inflammatory reaction induced by carrageenin in mice, however, is impaired by the fact that treatment with BN 52021 did not interfere with the effects of PAF-acether itself suggesting that the anti-carrageenin effect shown by BN 52021 should not be exclusively attributed to its activity as an antagonist of PAF-acether receptors. The reasons for the lack of antagonist activity of BN 52021 clearly demonstrated, both after intraperitoneal and *in situ* administration, are not yet fully clear, though we cannot exclude the possibility that PAF-acether receptors markedly refractory to this antagonist may exist in mice.

It is important to emphasize that, at least during the initial phase (1-4 hours), the ginkgolide BN 52021 markedly inhibited the pleural exudate volume induced by carrageenin, though without modifying the total number of leukocytes, which is significantly increased in this process. In any case, further experiments are needed to better clarify the anti-inflammatory mechanism of action elicited by the ginkgolide BN 52021 in mice.

ACKNOWLEDGEMENTS

The authors thank Dr. Pierre Braquet for having kindly sent BN 52021, Aida R. Silva for revision of the English and Jorge Silvano da Silva for technical assistance. This study was supported by grants from Conselho Nacional de Desenvolvimiento Cientifico e Tecnologico (CNPq, Brazil) and by FINEP.

References

1. Bjork, J., Smedegard, G. *Acute microvascular effects of PAF acether, as studied by intravital microscopy.* Eur J Pharmacol 1983; 96: 87-94.

2. Bonnnet, J., Loiseau, A.M., Orvoen, M., Bessin, P. *Platelet-activating factor (PAF-acether) involvement in acute inflammatory and pain processes.* Agents and Actions 1981; 11: 558-562.

3. Bourgain, R.H., Maes, L., Andries, R., Braquet, P. *Thrombus induction by endogenic PAF-acether and its inhibition by Ginkgo biloba extracts in the guinea pig.* Prostaglandins 1986; 32: 142-144.

4. Braquet, P.G. *Treatment and prevention of PAF-acether disorders provoked by a new series of highly specific inhibitors.* 1984; GB patent 84/18.424, US patent.

5. Braquet, P., Etienne, A., Touvay, C., Bourgain, R.H., Lefort, J., Vargaftig, B.B. *Involvement of platelet factor in respiratory anaphylaxis, demonstrated by PAF-acether BN 52021.* Lancet 1985; i: 1501.

6. Braquet, P., Paubert-Braquet, M., Vargaftig, B.B. *Platelet-activating factor, a potent mediator of shock.* In: Advances in Prostaglandin, Thromboxane and Leukotriene Research 1987; 17: 818-823.

7. Camussi, G. *Potential role of platelet-activating factor in renal patho-physiology.* Kidney Int 1986; 29 469-477.

8. Cordeiro, R.S.B., Martins, M.A., Silva, P.M.R., Castro Faria Neto, H.C., Castanheira, J.R.C., Vargaftig, B.B. *Desensitization to PAF-induced rat paw oedema by repeated intraplantar injections.* Life Sci 1986; 39: 1871-1878.

9. Cordeiro, R.S.B., Silva, P.M.R., Martins, M.A., Vargaftig, B.B. *Salicylates inhibit PAF-acether-induced rat paw oedema when cyclooxygenase inhibitors are ineffective.* Prostaglandins 1986; 32: 719-727.

10. Desquand, S., Touvay, C., Randon, J.,

Lagente, V., Vilain, B., Maridonneau-Parini, I., Etienne, A., Lefort, J., Braquet, P., Vargaftig, B.B. *Interference of BN 52021 (ginkgolide B) with the bronchopulmonary effects of PAF-acether in the guinea-pig.* Eur J Pharmacol 1986; 127: 83-95.

11. Ferreira, S.H. *A new method for measuring variations of rat paw volume.* Journal of Pharmacology 1979; 31: 648.

12. Ferreira, S.H., Ubatuba, F.B., Vane, J.R. *Platelets, acute inflammation and inflammatory mediators.* Agents and Actions 1976; 6: 313-319.

13. Goldenberg, M.M., Meurer, R.D. *A pharmacologic analysis of the action of platelet-activating factor in the induction of hind paw edema in the rat.* Prostaglandins 1984; 28: 271-278.

14. Henriques, M.G.M.O., Silva, P.M.R., Martins, M.A., Cunha, F.W., Assreuy Filho, J., Flores, C.A., Cordeiro, R.S.B. *Action of platelets on mouse paw oedema elicited by carrageenin.* Proc Symp Inflammatory Mediators, Satellite Symp 9th Int Cong Pharmacol 1984; 241-242.

15. Henriques, M.G.M.O., Silva, P.M.R., Martins, M.A., Flores, C.A., Cunha, F.Q., Assreuy Filho, J., Cordeiro, R.S.B. *Mouse paw oedema. A new model for inflammation?* Brazilian J Med Biol Res 1987; 20: 243-249.

16. Hwang, S., Lam, M., Li, C., Shen, T. *Release of platelet-activating factor and its involvement in the first phase of carrageenin rat foot edema.* Eur J Pharmacol 1986; 120: 33-41.

17. Koltai, M., Lepran, I., Szekeres, L., Viossat, I., Chabrier, P.E., Braquet, P. *Effect of BN 52021, a specific PAF-acether antagonist, on cardiac anaphylaxis in Langendorff hearts isolated from passively sensitized guinea-pigs.* Eur J Pharmacol 1986; 130: 133-136.

18. Pirotzky, E., Page, C.P., Roubin, R., Pfister, A.P., Paul, W., Bonnet, J., Benveniste, J. *PAF-acether induced plasma exudation in rat*

skin is dependent of platelets and neutrophils.
Microc Endot Lymp 1984; 1: 107-122.

19. Sánchez-Crespo, M., Fernández-Gallardo, S., Nieto, M.L., Baranes, J., Braquet, P. *Inhibition of the vascular actions of Ig aggregates by BN 52021, a highly specific antagonist of PAF-acether.* Immunopharmacology 1985; 10: 69-75.

20. Silva, P.M.R., Cordeiro, R.S.B., Martins, M.A., Henriques, M.G.M.O., Vargaftig, B.B. *Platelet involvement in rat paw edema induced by 2-methoxy-PAF.* Inflammation 1986; 10: 393-401.

21. Stimler, N.P., Bloor, C.M., Hugli, T.E., Wykle, R.L., Macgali, C.E., O'Flaherty, J.T. *Anaphylactic actions of platelet-activating factor.* Am J Pathol 1981; 105: 64-69.

22. Swingle, K.F., Reiter, M.J. *Inhibition of PAF-acether induced edema of the rat's paw.* Agents and Actions 1986; 18: 359-365.

23. Tarayre, J.P., Delhon, A., Bruniquel, F., Puech, L., Tisne-Versailles, J., Couzinier, J.P. *Exudative, cellular and humoral reactions to platelet-activating factor (PAF-acether) in the pleural cavity of rats.* Eur J Pharmacol 1986; 124: 317-323.

24. Vargaftig, B.B., Ferreira, S.H. *Blockade of the inflammatory effects of platelet-activating factor by cyclo-oxygenase inhibitors.* Brazilian J Med Biol Res 1981; 14: 187-189.

25. Vinegar, R., Truax, J.F., Selph, J.L. *Some quantitative temporal characteristics of carrageenin-induced pleurisy in the rat.* Proc Soc Exp Biol Med 1973; 143: 711.

26. Wallace, J.L., Stell, G., Wittle, B.J.R., Lagente, V., Vargaftig, B.B. *Evidence for platelet-activating factor (PAF) as a mediator of endotoxin-induced gastrointestinal damage in the rat: Effects of three PAF antagonists.* Gastroenterology 1987; submitted.

*Ginkgolides - Chemistry, Biology, Pharmacology
and Clinical Perspectives.* P. Braquet (Ed.)
Copyright © 1988, J.R. Prous Science Publishers, S.A.

INTERFERENCE OF THE PAF-ACETHER ANTAGONIST BN 52021 WITH BRONCHOPULMONARY ANAPHYLAXIS. CAN A CASE BE MADE FOR A ROLE FOR PAF-ACETHER IN BRONCHOPULMONARY ANAPHYLAXIS IN THE GUINEA-PIG?

Stéphanie Desquand and B. Boris Vargaftig

Unité de Pharmacologie Cellulaire, Unité Associée Institut Pasteur/IN-
SERM 285, 25 rue du Docteur Roux, F-75015 Paris, France

INTRODUCTION

Asthma and bronchial hyperreactivity are complex illnesses in which many
different mediators are involved. Even though the mechanisms accounting
for anaphylaxis and for asthma differ (3), anaphylactic shock in guinea-
pigs is frequently used to study the mode of action of different drugs.
Systemic anaphylaxis in guinea-pigs essentially involves the release of
histamine from lungs and extra-pulmonary sources and, accordingly, antihistamine drugs are effective antagonists (2, 17). In contrast, clinical asthma
is refractory to antagonists of H_1 histamine receptors. Furthermore, even
though circulating cells may be recruited in lung tissue and participate in

---

Address all correspondence to: Prof. B. Boris Vargaftig, Unité de Pharmacologie Cellulaire, INSERM U
285, 25 rue Dr. Roux, F-75015 Paris, France.

asthma, particularly in its delayed form (4), asthma is usually a local disease in which no change in the number of circulating cells occurs. This contrasts with systemic anaphylaxis, in which leukopenia, and in some instances thrombocytopenia, are major events (16, 17). It has been established that platelet-activating factor (1-O-alkyl-2-(R)-acetyl-*sn*-glyceryl-3-phosphoryl-choline, PAF-acether) is synthetized and released by basophils sensitized to IgE and stimulated by antigen (5, 18). Production of PAF-acether accompanies immune activation of other cells such as neutrophils, vascular endothelial cells or IgE-sensitized macrophages exposed to antigen. PAF-acether causes aggregation of platelets as well as secretion of their granular content (33). Administered by intravenous route, PAF-acether induces a platelet-dependent and cyclooxygenase-independent bronchoconstriction (44), hypotension, thrombosis and early platelet migration from the vessels to extravascular spaces (8), particularly in the vicinity of the smooth muscle (25). Nevertheless, bronchoconstriction induced by aerosolized PAF-acether is tachyphylactic, inhibited by aspirin (23) and may involve alveolar macrophages (28).

Furthermore, PAF-acether is released into the rabbit circulation during anaphylactic shock (34). Since sensitized rabbit (20) and guinea-pig lungs (32, 36) release PAF-acether when challenged with antigen, PAF-acether is probably formed and rapidly metabolized. Other observations confirmed the role of PAF-acether in immediate hypersensitivity (4), late asthma (30) and shock (7, 27, 31, 34). The diversity and importance of the biological effects of PAF-acether led to intensive research for specific receptor antagonists in order to understand its role and counteract its physiopathological effects.

Extracts of *Ginkgo biloba* have been used for a long time in traditional Chinese medicine and are reported in chinese pharmacopea as «good for the heart and the lung» (12). Three ginkgolides, newly extracted from *Ginkgo biloba* leaves, have been initially described as specific inhibitors of platelet aggregation induced by PAF-acether (rev. in 9, 10). BN 52021 or ginkgolide B, the most potent of these compounds, prevents different effects of PAF-acether including its binding to platelet membranes (11, 40). On the other hand, BN 52021 has been described (14, 40) as a selective antagonist of the effects of PAF-acether on the bronchopulmonary system and on the circulating blood cells of the guinea-pig. Since PAF-acether may be involved in anaphylaxis, it was logical to further study the interference of BN 52021 with different antigen-induced reactions in the bronchopulmonary system.

MATERIALS AND METHODS

Sensitization Procedures

The effects of BN 52021 were studied against two different types of systemic anaphylaxis: active and passive shock.

Procedures used for active sensitization were: 1) Guinea-pigs were actively sensitized with a subcutaneous injection of 0.5 ml of saline containing 10 μg of ovalbumin dispersed in 1 mg of $Al(OH)_3$, a procedure slightly modified from Andersson and Brattsand (2). A booster injection was performed after 14 days and the animals were challenged by ovalbumin 7-10 days later. Serum prepared from blood of these active guinea-pigs was used for passive sensitization; 2) Guinea-pigs were actively sensitized with two injections of 50-100 mg/kg of ovalbumin and then challenged 21-30 days later; 3) Guinea-pigs were sensitized as above but one week after the two injections, they were treated with 10 mg of ovalbumin.

Procedures used for passive sensitization were: 1) In the homologous sensitization procedure, guinea-pigs were injected with serum collected from the actively sensitized guinea-pigs (see above, 1) and then challenged with ovalbumin 10-14 days later. IgG were expected to disappear after this delay, whereas IgE persisted on the sensitized cells (30). Our serum had a high IgE titer as tested on passive cutaneous anaphylaxis (17), but recent experiments demonstrated that in fact IgG (homocytotropic in guinea-pigs) remain for at least 10-14 days after the transfer; 2) In the heterologous procedure, guinea-pigs were given an intravenous injection of diluted rabbit anti-ovalbumin immune serum. The animals were challenged with ovalbumin after 24 hours.

Challenges

The following parameters were measured:

IN VIVO   1) Bronchial resistance to inflation by an intravenous injection or an aerosolization of ovalbumin to sensitized guinea-pigs; 2) Arterial blood pressure and the changes of the number of circulating platelets and leukocytes (6, 13, 22, 43). In some experiments, the amounts of circulating thromboxane B_2 were also determined (6).

IN VITRO   1) Determination of the contraction of sensitized lung strips mounted in isolated organ baths and challenged by ovalbumin with accompanying measurements of thromboxane B_2 and histamine during the contraction (15, 22, 41); 2) Determination of the release in the effluent from perfused lungs of thromboxane B_2 and histamine induced by the intraarterial administration of ovalbumin (15, 19, 22, 38).

RESULTS

Table 1 summarizes the results when BN 52021 was used against guinea-pig lung anaphylaxis.

Passive Shock

BN 52021 at 1 mg/kg has been reported (15, 21, 22, 47) to suppress bronchoconstriction induced by a perfusion of 1 mg/kg of ovalbumin without modifying the accompanying leukopenia in non-propranolol-treated, passively sensitized guinea-pigs. In contrast, when the animals were pretreated with propranolol, BN 52021, even at 3 mg/kg, did not reduce this bronchoconstriction, whereas under the same conditions it inhibited the bronchoconstriction induced by an intravenous injection of PAF-acether.

When interference by other mediators of anaphylactic bronchoconstriction was inhibited by aspirin, mepyramine and the leukotriene antagonist FPL 55712, BN 52021 did not improve inhibition, *i.e.,* suppression by propranolol of its protective effect persisted.

In guinea-pigs sensitized with heterologous serum, BN 52021 at 1 mg/kg partially inhibited the bronchoconstriction induced by 1 mg/kg of ovalbumin (11, 40, 43). Administered orally, BN 52021 (10-30 mg/kg) was also effective against bronchoconstriction (41).

In homologous passively sensitized and bivagotomized guinea-pigs, BN 52021 at 10 mg/kg reduced the bronchoconstriction induced by an aerosolization of 10 mg/ml of ovalbumin during 1 minute (13, 22).

In vitro, BN 52021 at 0.1 mM failed to reduce parenchyma lung strip contraction, thromboxane B_2 and histamine liberation triggered by 10 μg/ml of ovalbumin in the organ baths. In contrast, at 30 μM, BN 52021 inhibited the thromboxane B_2 and histamine release triggered by 10 μg of ovalbumin in the pulmonary artery of passively sensitized perfused lungs (15, 22).

Active Shock

In guinea-pigs actively sensitized with two injections of 50-100 mg/kg of ovalbumin and challenged 21-30 days later, BN 52020 and BN 52021 have been reported to inhibit the anaphylactic response in a dose-dependent manner (6). BN 52021 was more effective than BN 52020. At 4 mg/kg, BN 52021 inhibited bronchoconstriction by 90% and the liberation of thromboxane B_2 measured in plasma by 95%. The protective effect of BN 52021 on immune bronchoconstriction was associated with the recovery of blood pH, pO_2 and thromboxane B_2 level impaired by antigen challenge (6).

The effects of BN 52021 were also studied against the release of arachidonate metabolites during ovalbumin-induced IgG-dependent guinea-pig pulmonary anaphylaxis *in vitro* (19, 38). In perfused lungs actively sen-

Table 1 Effects of BN 52021 with bronchopulmonary anaphylaxis in different models

Sensitization Procedure	Model	Challenge (ovalbumin) Route	Challenge (ovalbumin) Dose	Other Inhibitors	BN 52021 Route	BN 52021 Dose	Effects on Broncho-constriction or contract.	Effects on Thromboxane B$_2$ liberation	Effects on Histamine liberation	References
Passive homologous (1)	In vivo	I.V.	1 mg/kg	—	I.V.	1 mg/kg	**			(22)
				Propranolol	I.V.	3 mg/kg	NS			(47)
										(21)
				Propranolol FPL 55712 Mepyramine	I.V.	3 mg/kg	NS			(15)
		Aerosol	10 mg/ml 1 mn	—	I.V.	10 mg/kg	*			(22)
				Propranolol	I.V.	10 mg/kg	NS			(13)
	In vitro strips		10 µg/ml			0.1 µM	NS	NS	NS	(22)
	In vitro perfused lungs		10 µg			30 µM		**	*	(15)
Passive heterologous (2)	In vivo	I.V.	1 mg/kg	—	I.V.	0.1 mg/kg	**			(11)
						1 mg/kg	**			(40)
						2 mg/kg	**			(43)
					Oral	20 mg/kg	I = 55%			(41)
Active (2)	In vivo	I.V.	5 mg/kg	—	I.V.	1 mg/kg	I = 24.0%	I = 30.1%		(6)
						2 mg/kg	I = 58.4%	I = 63.8%		
						4 mg/kg	I = 90.4%	I = 94.9%		
Active (3)	In vitro perfused lungs	I.V.	100 µg/ml			1 µg/ml		I = 30%		(19)
						3 µg/ml		I = 50%		(38)
						30 µg/ml		I = 80%		
Active (1)	In vivo	I.V.	1 mg/kg		I.V.	1 mg/kg	NS			(21)
			0.330 mg/kg		I.V.	1 mg/kg	NS			
	In vitro strips		1 µg/ml			0.3 µg	NS	NS		
	In vitro perfused lungs					30 µM		potentiation	potentiation	

(*: p < 0.05; **: p < 0.01)

sitized by procedure 3), BN 52021, at 1, 3 and 30 μg/ml reduced by 30, 50 and 80%, respectively, the amount of thromboxane B_2 recovered in the lung effluent.

In contrast, other authors (21) reported that BN 52021 failed to inhibit the *in vivo* bronchoconstriction and *in vitro* liberation of histamine and thromboxane B_2 induced by ovalbumin, respectively, in guinea-pigs actively sensitized by procedure 1) and from isolated lungs. In our laboratory, we have shown that pretreatment of these guinea-pigs by 1 mg/kg of BN 52021 did not inhibit the anaphylactic bronchoconstriction and the accompanying decrease in blood cell counts induced by a perfusion of ovalbumin (1 mg/kg, 1 min). At the same dose, BN 52021 reduced the bronchoconstriction induced by 330 μg/ml of ovalbumin.

In vitro, at 0.3 μM, BN 52021 failed to reduce the contraction and the thromboxane B_2 liberation by lung strips challenged by 1 μg/ml of ovalbumin. Furthermore, in sensitized perfused lungs, BN 52021 at 30 μM potentiated the production of thromboxane B_2 and histamine induced by 0.1 μg of ovabumin as well as the secretion of histamine due to 1 μg of ovalbumin.

Other experiments in our laboratory have shown that in guinea-pigs actively sensitized with two injections of 50-100 mg/kg of ovalbumin and then challenged 21-30 days later, BN 52021 at 10 mg/kg failed to inhibit the anaphylactic bronchoconstriction.

DISCUSSION AND CONCLUSIONS

Since bronchial asthma until now has been refractory to conventional antihistamines (anti H_1), peptido-leukotrienes have been proposed as alternative chemical mediators accounting for bronchoconstriction and pulmonary inflammation. Nevertheless, there are some reasons to moderate the enthusiasm concerning the hypothesized role of peptido-leukotrienes in allergic asthma (46). The finding that PAF-acether induces histamine and cyclooxygenase-independent bronchoconstriction (44) led to the hypothesis, supported by other findings, that PAF-acether may display the role negated to histamine and lipoxygenase metabolites. This led to the testing of PAF-acether antagonists, including BN 52021, which has been described as a specific antagonist (rev. in 9), against bronchopulmonary anaphylaxis in the guinea-pig, as a predictive model for anti-asthmatic activity.

The different protocols used with sensitized guinea-pigs may favor the selective formation of IgE. The pharmacological control of anaphylaxis should depend on the precise procedure used and the differences between passive and active sensitization have far-reaching consequences, even though in both instances histamine is the predominant mediator of acute anaphylactic bronchoconstriction. Active shock is accompanied by a marked reduction in platelet and leukocyte counts (16), whereas in passive shock this reduction involves the leukocytes, with thrombopenia being very limited (17). In agreement, the addition of ovalbumin to platelet-rich plasma of the actively sensitized animals is followed by platelet activation, which is absent in the case of passively sensitized guinea-pigs. The difference between both types of shock is probably due to a more restrictive homocytotropic selectivity in passive, as compared to active shock, in which the plasma system (complement, kallikrein) is also involved. The guinea-pig active shock model thus involves more complex mechanisms which may be less pertinent to allergic human asthma than passive shock where homocytotropic mechanisms dominate.

Given by the intravenous route at 0.1-2 mg/kg or orally at 20 mg/kg, BN 52021 inhibits both homologous (15, 21, 22, 47) and heterologous (11, 40, 41, 43) passive anaphylaxis induced by an intravenous injection of ovalbumin to guinea-pigs. Since *in vivo* passive shock is markedly histamine-dependent, the inhibition of shock by BN 52021 (which is not an antihistamine) suggests that PAF-acether might participate in histamine release during shock and that this PAF-acether antagonist might interfere with *in vivo* histamine-dependent shock by suppressing mediator release. Indeed, when tested in isolated guinea-pig lungs from passively sensitized guinea-pigs, BN 52021 blocked histamine release. Nevertheless, since PAF-acether does not release histamine from isolated lungs of naive animals, it seemed a paradox that histamine should be suppressed by a selective antagonist of a mediator unable to release it. This paradox may now be solved, since it has been demonstrated that PAF-acether becomes a histamine-releasing mediator, provided lungs used are taken from actively sensitized animals (24). Furthermore, since BN 52021 blocked bronchoconstriction resulting from the intravenous administration of ovalbumin to guinea-pigs passively transferred with anti-ovalbumin rabbit serum (heterologous shock), it has a relatively wide range of anti-anaphylactic effects not restricted to a single model. The efficacy of BN 52021 against local anaphylaxis after antigen aerosolization in homologous passively sensitized guinea-pigs (13, 15, 22) indicates that it interferes with an intrapulmonary target shared by antigen.

In actively sensitized guinea-pigs, at 2-4 mg/kg, i.v., BN 52021 has been reported to antagonize anaphylactic bronchoconstriction (6), but we failed to significantly inhibit this bronchoconstriction with up to 10 mg/kg of BN 52021, whereas the antihistamine mepyramine was effective (21). One reason for the failure of BN 52021, even when administered at high doses, to inhibit antigen-induced bronchoconstriction in actively sensitized guinea-pigs may be that histamine is released in large excess from extrapulmonary sites.

Furthermore, the ability of BN 52021 to counteract the effects of PAF-acether in non-sensitized perfused lungs is not duplicated in isolated lungs from actively sensitized animals (unpublished), which suggests that BN 52021 may lose in part its anti-PAF-acether activity when guinea-pigs are actively sensitized.

Leukopenia of anaphylactic responses is also not affected by BN 52021 (6, 22) which demonstrates that different targets independent of PAF-acether and refractory to BN 52021 are involved, since leukopenia induced by PAF-acether is suppressed. These results are in agreement with those (1) which showed that BN 52021 antagonizes hypotension induced by an intravenous injection of *Salmonella typhimurium* endotoxin without inhibition of leukopenia. BN 52021 also antagonizes the infiltration of eosinophils in lungs challenged with PAF-acether and antigen (25, 26).

Suppression by BN 52021 of prostaglandin-6-keto PGF_1, PGE_2, thromboxane B_2 and leukotrienes B_4 and D_4 formation by isolated lungs from passively (22) or actively (19, 38) sensitized guinea-pigs is not accounted for by thromboxane synthetase or cyclooxygenase inhibition since BN 52021 has no effect against arachidonic acid under similar conditions (14). This inhibitory effect of BN 52021 is explained either by a PAF-acether-independent phenomenon, since it blocks IgE-induced histamine release from rat mast cells even though PAF-acether does not activate mast cells (39, M.A. Nahori, personal communication), or by a PAF-acether-dependent phenomenon accounted for by the turning of PAF-acether into a histamine releasing agent when injected to sensitized isolated perfused lungs (24). Formation of PAF-acether by a lung component may thus account for histamine release in shock and, accordingly, BN 52021 may interfere as a PAF-acether antagonist, supporting a primary role of this mediator in the process regulating eicosanoid generation in pulmonary tissue.

BN 52021 failed to inhibit contractions of parenchyma strips isolated from passively sensitized lungs and the accompanying release of histamine and thromboxane A_2 induced by ovalbumin, even though it blocked the contraction of lung strips induced by PAF-acether (15, 42). These results also differ from those obtained on perfused lungs; however, the two models are different because more PAF-acether is required to induce contraction of the strips than to activate perfused lungs. Furthermore, the routes of administration differ in both instances; BN 52021 reaches the isolated strips by diffusion and the vascular endothelium when injected by the intravascular route.

Whatever the explanation is for the differences between both preparations, failure of BN 52021 at effective anti-PAF-acether concentrations to block passive anaphylaxis triggered on parenchyma lung strips and its effectiveness on isolated perfused lungs is a contradiction and the other points discussed below may suggest that BN 52021 is effective against anaphylaxis, not only because of its anti-PAF-acether properties, but also because it might display additional anti-anaphylactic properties. Indeed, propranolol suppresses the *in vivo* anti-anaphylactic activity of BN 52021 in passive shock (13, 22) even though the anti-PAF-acether properties are conserved in these conditions (14), BN 52021 being inert with respect to β-adrenergic receptors (10). Nevertheless, it can be argued that propranolol may modify the relative importance of mediators of anaphylactic bronchoconstriction and that shock could become less dependent on PAF-acether and, accordingly, less affected by BN 52021. In addition, the association of aspirin to mepyramine and to methysergide which blocks bronchoconstriction by PAF-acether (45) is not effective against anaphylactic bronchoconstriction.

In conclusion, the exact mechanisms of action of BN 52021 against immune bronchoconstriction require further studies. Even though it might display PAF-acether-independent anti-allergic activity, it is noteworthy that other PAF-acether antagonists, *i.e.,* WEB 2086 (35), kadsurenone (37), also possess anti-anaphylactic properties confirming that PAF-acether antagonists can counteract immune bronchoconstriction, mainly in passive anaphylaxis and that PAF-acether is involved in lung anaphylaxis.

References

1. Adnot, S., Lefort, J., Braquet, P., Vargaftig, B.B. *Interference of PAF-acether antagonist BN 52021 with endotoxin induced hypotension in the guinea-pig.* Prostaglandins 1986; 32: 791-802.

2. Andersson, P., Brattsand, R. *Protective effects of the glucocorticoid, budesonide on lung anaphylaxis in actively sensitized guinea-pigs: Inhibition of IgE- but not of IgG-mediated anaphylaxis.* Br J Pharmacol 1982; 76: 139-147.

3. Austen, K.F., Orange, R.P. *Bronchial asthma: The possible role of the chemical mediators of immediate hypersensitivy in the pathogenesis of subacute chronic disease.* Am Rev Respir Dis 1975; 112: 423-436.

4. Basran, G.S., Page, C.P., Paul, W., Morley, J. *Platelet activating factor: A possible mediator of the dual response to allergen?* Clin Allergy 1984; 14: 75-79.

5. Benveniste, J.P., Henson, P.M., Cochrane, C.G. *Leucocyte-dependent histamine release from rabbit platelets: The role of IgE, basophils and platelet-activating factor.* J Exp Med 1972; 136: 1356-1377.

6. Berti, F., Omini, C., Rossini, G., Braquet, P. *Protection by two ginkgolides, BN 25020 and*

BN 52021, against guinea-pig lung anaphylaxis. Pharmacol Res Commun 1986; 18: 775-793.

7. Bessin, P., Bonnet, J., Apffel, D., Soulard, C., Desgroux, I., Pelas, I., Benveniste, J. *Acute circulation collapse caused by platelet-activating factor (PAF-acether) in dogs.* Eur J Pharmacol 1983; 86: 403-413.

8. Bourgain, R.H., Maes, L., Braquet, P., Andries, R., Touqui, L., Braquet, M. *The effect of 1-O-alkyl-sn-glycero-3-phosphocholine (PAF-acether) on the arterial wall.* Prostaglandins 1985; 30: 185-197.

9. Braquet, P. *The Ginkgolides: Potent platelet-activating factor antagonists isolated from Ginkgo biloba L.: Chemistry, pharmacology and clinical applications.* Drugs of the Future 1987; 12: 643-699.

10. Braquet, P., Etienne, A., Touvay, C., Bourgain, R.H., Lefort, J., Vargaftig, B.B. *Involvement of platelet-activating factor in respiratory anaphylaxis, demonstrated by PAF-acether inhibitor BN 52021.* Lancet 1985a; ii: 1501.

11. Braquet, P., Spinnewyn, B., Braquet, M., Bourgain, R.H., Taylor, J.E., Nunez, D., Drieu, K. *BN 52021 and related compounds: A new series of highly specific PAF-acether*

antagonists isolated from Ginkgo biloba. Blood Vessels 1985b; 16: 559-572.

12. Chinese Pharmacopea. Peking: China 1977.

13. Cirino, M., Lagente, V., Lefort, J., Vargaftig, B.B. A study with BN 52021 demonstrates the involvement in IgE-dependent anaphylactic bronchoconstriction. Prostaglandins 1986; 32: 121-127.

14. Desquand, S., Touvay, C., Randon, J., Lagente, V., Vilain, B., Maridonneau-Parini, I., Etienne, A., Lefort, J., Braquet, P., Vargaftig, B.B. Interference of BN 52021 (ginkgolide B) with the bronchopulmonary effects of PAF-acether in the guinea-pig. Eur J Pharmacol 1986; 127: 83-95.

15. Desquand, S., Vilain, B., Lagente, V., Randon, J., Touvay, C., Lefort, J., Braquet, P., Vargaftig, B.B. Interference of PAF-acether antagonist BN 52021 with anaphylaxis in the guinea-pig. Advances in Prostaglandin, Thromboxane and Leukotriene Research. B. Samuelson, R. Paoletti, P.W. Ramwell (Eds.). Raven Press: New York 1987; 17: 814-817.

16. Detsouli, A., Lefort, J., Vargaftig, B.B. Histamine and leukotriene-independent guinea-pig anaphylactic shock unaccounted for by PAF-acether. Br J Pharmacol 1985; 84: 801-810.

17. Garcez do Carmo, L., Cordeiro, R., Lagente, V., Lefort, J., Randon, J., Vargaftig, B.B. Failure of a combined anti-histamine and anti-leukotriene treatment to suppress passive anaphylaxis in the guinea-pig. Int J Immunopharmacol 1986; 8: 985-995.

18. Hanahan, D.J., Demopoulos, C.A., Liehr, J., Pinckard, R.N. Identification of platelet-activating factor isolated from rabbit basophils as acetyl glyceryl phosphorylcholine. J Biol Chem 1980; 255: 5514-5516.

19. Harczy, M., Maclouf, J., Pradelles, P., Braquet, P., Borgeat, P., Sirois, P. Inhibitory effects of a novel platelet-activating factor (PAF) on antigen-induced prostaglandin and thromboxane formation by the guinea-pig lung. Pharmacol Res Commun 1986; 18: 111-117.

20. Kravis, T.C., Henson, P.M. IgE-induced release of platelet-activating factor from rabbit lung. J Immunol 1975; 115: 1677-1684.

21. Lagente, V., Desquand, S., Randon, J., Lefort, J., Vargaftig, B.B. Interference of PAF-acether antagonists with the effects of PAF itself and the anaphylactic shock in vitro and in vivo in guinea-pig bronchopulmonary preparations. Prostaglandins 1985; 30: 703.

22. Lagente, V., Touvay, C., Randon, J., Desquand, S., Cirino, M., Vilain, B., Lefort, J.,

Braquet, P., Vargaftig, B.B. Interference of the PAF-acether antagonist BN 52021 with passive anaphylaxis in the guinea-pig. Prostaglandins 1987; 33: 265-274.

23. Lefort, J., Vargaftig, B.B. Role of platelets in aspirin-sensitive bronchoconstriction in the guinea-pig: Interactions with salicylic acid. Br J Pharmacol 1978; 63: 35-42.

24. Lefort, J., Malenchère, E., Pretolani, M., Vargaftig, B.B. Immunisation induces bronchial hyper-activity and increased mediator release from guinea-pig lung. Br J Pharmacol 1986; 98: 768.

25. Lellouch-Tubiana, A., Lefort, J., Pirotzky, E., Vargaftig, B.B. Ultrastructural evidence for extravascular platelet recruitement in the lung upon intravenous injection of platelet-activating factor (PAF-acether) to guinea-pigs. Br J Exp Pathol 1985; 66: 345-355.

26. Lellouch-Tubiana, A., Lefort, J., Pfister, A., Vargaftig, B.B. Interactions between granulocytes and platelets in the lung in passive anaphylactic shock. Correlations with PAF-acether-induced lesions. Int Arch Allergy Appl Immunol 1987; in press.

27. Levi, R., Burke, A., Guo, Z.G., Hattori, Y., Hoppens, C.M., McManus, L.M., Hanahan, D.J., Pinckard, R.N. Acetyl glyceryl ether phosphorylcholine (AGEPC), a putative mediator of cardiac anaphylaxis in the guinea-pig. Circ Res 1984; 54: 117-124.

28. Maridonneau-Parini, I., Lagente, V., Lefort, J., Randon, J., Russo-Marie, F., Vargaftig, B.B. Desensitization to PAF-induced bronchoconstriction and to activation of alveolar macrophages by repeated inhalations of PAF in the guinea-pig. Biochem Biophys Res Commun 1985; 131: 42-49.

29. Morley, J., Page, C.P., Paul, W. Inflammatory actions of platelet-activating factor (PAF-acether) in guinea-pig skin. Br J Pharmacol 1983; 80: 503-509.

30. Ovary, Z., Kaplan, B., Kojima, S. Characteristics of guinea-pig IgE. Int Arch Allergy Appl Immunol 1976; 51: 416-428.

31. Page, C.P., Paul, W., Douglas, C.G., Casals-Stenzel, J., Morley, J. PAF-acether, platelets and bronchospasm. In: Platelet Activating Factor. INSERM Symposium, N° 23. J. Benveniste, B. Arnoux (Eds.). Elsevier Science Publishers: Amsterdam 1983; 327.

32. Parente, L., Fitzgerald, M., De Nucci, G., Moncada, S. The release of lyso-PAF from guinea-pigs lungs. Eur J Pharmacol 1977; 112: 281-284.

33. Pinckard, R.N., Halohan, M., Palmer, J.D.,

Mc Manus, L.M., Shaw, J.O., Henson, P.M. *Intravascular aggregation and pulmonary sequestration of platelets during IgE-induced systemic anaphylaxis in the rabbit. Abrogation of lethal anaphylactic shock by platelet depletion.* J Immunol 1977; 119: 2185-2193.

34. Pinckard, R.N., Farr, R.S., Hanahan, D.J. *Physiochemical and functional identity of rabbit platelet-activating factor (PAF) released in vitro from IgE sensitized basophils.* J Immunol 1979; 123: 1847-1857.

35. Pretolani, M., Lefort, J., Malanchère, E., Vargaftig, B.B. *Interference of the novel PAF-acether antagonist WEB 2086 with the bronchopulmonary responses to PAF-acether and to active and passive anaphylactic shock on guinea-pigs.* Eur J Pharmacol 1987; in press.

36. Rotillio, D., Lefort, J., Detsouli, A., Vargaftig, B.B. *Absence de contribution du PAF-acether à la réponse anaphylactique pulmonaire chez le cobaye.* J Pharmacol (Paris) 1983; 115: 1677-1684.

37. Shen, T.Y., Hwang, S.B., Chang, M.N., Doebba, T.W., Lam, M.H., Wu, M.S., Wang, X., Han, C.Q., Li, R.Z. *Characterization of a platelet activating factor receptor antagonist isolated from haifenteng (Piper futokadsura): Specific inhibition of in vitro and in vivo platelet-activating factor-induced effects.* Proc Natl Acad Sci USA 1985; 82: 672-676.

38. Sirois, P., Harczy, M., Braquet, P., Borgeat, P., Maclouf, J., Pradelles, P. *Inhibition of the release of prostaglandins, thromboxanes and leukotrienes from the anaphylactic lungs by a platelet-activating factor (PAF) antagonist and its stimulation by PAF.* Advances in Prostaglandins, Thromboxane and Leukotrienes Research. B. Samuelsson et al (Eds.). Vols. 17-18: in press.

39. Stanworth, D.R., Griffiths, H.R., Braquet, P. *Effect of PAF-acether antagonists on preformed mediator secretion from mast cells.* 2nd World Conference on Inflammation (Monte Carlo, March 19-22) 1986; Abst 193.

40. Touvay, C., Etienne, A., Braquet, P. *Inhibition of antigen-induced lung anaphylaxis in the guinea-pig by BN 52021, a new specific PAF-acether receptor antagonist isolated from Ginkgo biloba.* Agents and Actions 1985; 17: 371-372.

41. Touvay, C., Vilain, B., Carré, C., Etienne, A., Braquet, P. *Comparative effects of three orally active PAF-acether antagonists extracted from Ginkgo biloba: On in vivo bronchoconstrictions and in vitro lung strips contractions induced by PAF-acether.* 6th Conference on Prostaglandins and Related Compounds. (Florence, June 3-6) 1986a; Abst p. 316.

42. Touvay, C., Vilain, B., Etienne, A, Sirois, P., Borgeat, P., Braquet, P. *Characterization of platelet-activating factor (PAF-acether)-induced contractions of guinea-pig lung strips by selected inhibitors of arachidonic acid metabolism and by PAF antagonists.* Immunopharmacology 1986b; 12: 97-104.

43. Touvay, C., Vilain, B., Taylor, J.E., Etienne, A., Braquet, P. *Proof of the involvement of platelet-activating factor (PAF-acether) in pulmonary complex immune systems using a specific PAF-acether receptor antagonist: BN 52021.* Prog Lipid Res 1986c; 25: 277-288.

44. Vargaftig, B.B., Lefort, J., Chignard, M., Benveniste, J. *Platelet-activating factor induces a platelet-dependent bronchoconstriction unrelated to the formation of prostaglandin derivates.* Eur J Pharmacol 1980; 65: 185-192.

45. Vargaftig, B.B., Lefort, J., Chignard, M., Medeiros, M.C. *Non-steroidal anti-inflammatory drugs if combined with antihistamine and anti-serotonin agents interfere with the bronchial and platelet effects of platelet-activating factor (PAF-acether).* Eur J Pharmacol 1982; 82: 121-130.

46. Vargaftig, B.B., Borgeat, P., Braquet, P., Braquet, M., Brocklehurst, W.E., Dahlen, S.E., Drazen, S.E., Drazen, J.M., Etienne, A., Fitzpatrick, F.A., Henson, P.M., Holgate, S.T., Israel, E., Mencia-Huerta, J.M., Murphy, R.C., Robinson, C., Shore, S. *Leukotrienes and immediate hypersensitivity.* Ann Inst Pasteur: Immunol 1985; 136D: 175-228.

47. Vilain, B., Lagente, V., Touvay, C., Desquand, S., Randon, J., Lefort, J., Braquet, P., Vargaftig, B.B. *Pharmacological control of the in vivo passive anaphylactic shock by the PAF-acether antagonist compound BN 52021.* Pharmacol Res Commun 1986; 18(Suppl): 119-126.

Ginkgolides - Chemistry, Biology, Pharmacology and Clinical Perspectives. P. Braquet (Ed.)
Copyright © 1988, J.R. Prous Science Publishers, S.A.

EFFECTS OF PAF AND ANTIGEN ON GUINEA PIG LUNGS: INHIBITION BY GINKGOLIDES

Sonia Jancar[1] and Pierre Sirois[2]

[1]Dept. Immunology, University of Sao Paulo, Brazil; [2]Dept. Pharmacology, University of Sherbrooke, Canada

INTRODUCTION

The initial observation that injection of antigen into sensitized guinea pigs induces a strong and sustained bronchoconstriction has stimulated the search for the mediators released in allergic reactions which might account for the symptoms of asthma in man. Histamine was the first mediator characterized but with the advent of selective histamine antagonists (H_1), it was shown that histamine alone was not responsible for asthmatic bronchoconstriction. Another substance released from sensitized guinea pig lungs after injection of the antigen was described by Kellaway and Trethewie (13) and later named Slow-Reacting Substance of Anaphylaxis (SRS-A) because of its sustained contractile effect on guinea pig isolated ileum (6). For many years SRS-A was considered as the main mediator of allergic asthma. In 1980, SRS-A was shown to be composed of a mixture of leukotrienes C_4, D_4 and E_4 (11, 17, 20). The bronchoconstrictor activity of the synthetic leukotrienes is now well-documented (26, 27), and like SRS-A, they induce a long-lasting contraction of airway smooth muscles.

In 1972, Benveniste *et al.* (1) described an ether-linked phospholipid, unrelated to arachidonic acid, which was a potent inducer of platelet ag-

---

Address all correspondence to: Dr. Pierre Sirois, Dept. of Pharmacology, Faculty of Medicine, University of Sherbrooke, Sherbrooke, P.Q., Canada J1H 5N4.

gregation. This compound, named «Platelet Activating Factor» (PAF), was later found to be released during anaphylactic shock (23) and to induce bronchoconstriction in the guinea pig (32). Apart from its activity on pulmonary smooth muscles, PAF can also induce inflammatory changes upon administration in the lungs (7, 21). It was suggested that PAF can mimick all major features of asthma pathology including the induction of bronchial hyperreactivity (19). Nevertheless, all the mediators cited were shown to reproduce some of the symptoms of asthma, but it appears very unlikely that only one mediator could account for all the symptoms of the disease. More direct evidence for the importance of PAF in the pathological manifestations of allergic asthma have been provided by specific PAF antagonists. One of these compounds is an extract from *Ginkgo biloba* leaves, BN 52021 (3). This compound, which strongly inhibits platelet aggregation (4), is a very useful tool to analyze the real contribution of PAF to asthma symptoms. BN 52021 was found to inhibit the bronchoconstriction that follows antigen injection into sensitized guinea pig (4) and also to strongly inhibit the PAF-induced bronchoconstriction of guinea pigs *in vivo* (30, 33). In this study, we have investigated the effects of BN 52021 and BN 52020 on the response of pulmonary tissues to PAF, as well as the interactions between PAF and leukotrienes in lung anaphylaxis.

RESPONSE OF PULMONARY TISSUES TO PAF. EFFECT OF BN 52021

The *in vitro* models most commonly used to study the pharmacology of the mediators of asthma have been the isolated strips of trachea and lung parenchyma. On the guinea pig lung parenchyma, PAF induces a sustained contraction which is markedly tachyphylactic (7, 29). BN 52021 was found to inhibit PAF contractile effect on this tissue. The inhibition appeared to be competitive especially with low doses of the antagonist (9, 29). However, the response of other pulmonary tissues to PAF is less known. A new model for the study of bronchoreactivity was recently developed which consists of spiral strips of guinea pig bronchus. This preparation has been shown to be very sensitive to histamine and leukotrienes (28). We have analyzed comparatively the response of guinea pig trachea (GPT), external bronchus (GPB-ext), internal bronchus and lung parenchyma (GPLPS) to bolus injections of PAF.

As shown in Figure 1, GPLPS responds to 50 ng of PAF with a sustained but tachyphylactic contraction, whereas the bronchus and trachea respond with an initial contraction followed by relaxation. The relaxing response was not tachyphylactic and even increased after subsequent injections of PAF. In the preparation of internal bronchus (smaller bronchus),

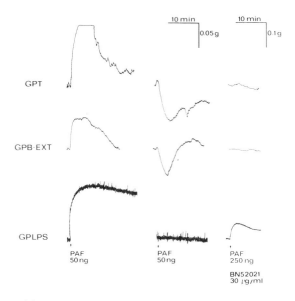

Figure 1 Characteristic responses of strips of guinea pig trachea (GPT), external bronchus (GPB-EXT) and lung parenchyma (GPLPS) to an initial bolus injection of PAF (50 ng; left hand panel), to a second injection of PAF (center panel) and to an injection of PAF in the presence of BN 52021 (30 μg/ml). The responses in the presence of the PAF antagonist were observed on tissues from a separate lung.

PAF was inactive (data not shown) (12). The compound BN 52021 (30 μg/ml) significantly reduced the response of the GPLPS to PAF (250 ng) (Fig. 2a). In the trachea and bronchus, the same dose of BN 52021 completely blocked the initial contraction as well as the subsequent relaxations elicited by PAF (Fig. 1, right hand side). BN 52021 did not affect the response to histamine, leukotriene D_4 and PGE_2 on these tissues, pointing out the specificity of the antagonistic effect of this compound (data not shown).

Compound BN 52020 at concentrations of 30 and 50 μg/ml has no effect on PAF-induced contraction of the GPLPS (Fig. 2b).

RELEASE OF SPASMOGENS FROM PAF-STIMULATED LUNGS. EFFECT OF BN 52021

Based on previous observations from our laboratories and from others, which showed that the effects of PAF on the lungs were mediated by the formation of other substances, the following experiments were done to characterize the mediators released from perfused lungs. For this purpose,

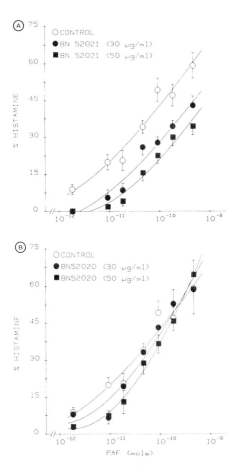

Figure 2 Effects of PAF antagonists BN 52021 (A) and BN 52020 (B) on the contractions of the guinea pig lung parenchyma strips to PAF (1.85 x 10^{-12} to 4.63 x 10^{-10} mole). Each point is the mean ± S.E.M. of 3-10 experiments. Contractions are expressed as percent of the contractile effect of 2.7 x 10^{-8} mole (5 μg) of histamine. Since the tissues develop tachyphylaxis to PAF, each dose was tested on a fresh tissue preparation.

isolated guinea pig lungs were perfused via the pulmonary artery with Krebs solution and installed over a set of isolated tissues (GPT, GPB and GPLPS) in such a way that the effluent from the perfused lungs was directed over the assay tissues. As shown in Figure 3, infusion of PAF (250 ng) into the pulmonary circulation induced the release of substances that contracted all three tissues. Since the assay tissues were previously desensitized to PAF by a continuous infusion of 50 ng/ml of PAF, the responses of the tissues

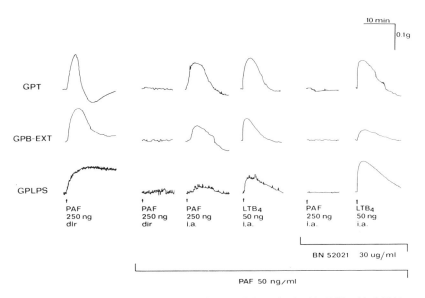

Figure 3   Release of spasmogens from the perfused guinea pig lung stimulated by PAF and its inhibition
by BN 52021. PAF (250 ng) was injected as a bolus several times either directly (dir) over strips of guinea
pig trachea (GPT), external bronchus (GPB-EXT) and lung parenchyma (GPLPS) or injected in the
pulmonary circulation (i.a.). The initial injection induced characteristic contractions of the three tissues.
The continuous infusion of PAF (50 ng/ml) produced a desensitization of the isolated tissues as evidenced
by the absence of effect of the second injection of PAF. The injection of PAF (250 ng; third panel) in
the pulmonary artery stimulated the release of spasmogens and the contraction of the isolated tissues. In
the presence of BN 52021 (30 μg/ml) the effect of PAF was completely inhibited. The injection of LTB$_4$
(50 ng) stimulated the release of prostaglandins and thromboxanes and was not affected by BN 52021. This
experiment was repeated at least 3 times.

to the lung effluent could not be due to PAF but could be regarded as being generated in the lung after stimulation. This effect of PAF was not
tachyphylactic, since the release of spasmogenic substance(s) was detected
even after several injections of PAF into the lung (data not shown). Pretreatment of the lungs with BN 52021 (30 μg/ml) completely abolished the release
of spasmogens. For comparison purposes, LTB$_4$ (250 ng) was injected into
the lungs and was also found to induce the release of contractile substances;
this effect was not affected by BN 52021, which again indicates the specificity
of the response (Fig. 3).

It appears that not only does PAF induce a direct contraction of the bronchus, but it also stimulates the release of substances which can be responsible for the bronchoconstriction observed following its injection *in vivo*. In
order to further investigate the nature of the spasmogen(s) released, specific
antagonists and inhibitors of arachidonic acid metabolism were used (data

not shown). It was found that pretreatment of the lungs with indomethacin (10 μg/ml) prior to PAF injection did not inhibit the release of contractile substances. However, when indomethacin was perfused over the assay tissues, the contractions were completely abolished. The infusion of LTA$_3$ into the perfused lungs to prevent the synthesis of LTB$_4$ inhibited the release of the contractile activity following PAF stimulation. OKY-046, a thromboxane synthetase inhibitor, perfused over the assay tissues only inhibited the contraction. The peptidoleukotriene antagonist, FPL-55712, had no effect on the contractions of the tissue to the lung effluent. Taken together, these results led us to hypothesize that PAF might induce the release of LTB$_4$ from guinea pig lungs, which in turn induces the contraction of the assay tissues via thromboxane generation (manuscript in preparation).

In accordance with this hypothesis are the data from Lefort et al. (16). The authors found that the bronchoconstriction induced by PAF injection into isolated perfused guinea pig lungs was inhibited by pretreatment with aspirin. They have also reported inhibition of bronchoconstriction by pretreatment with nordihydroguaiaretic acid but not with FPL-55712. Hamasaki et al. (10) reported that the increase in airway pressure in isolated perfused guinea pig lung stimulated with PAF, was inhibited by indomethacin. These results support the hypothesis of LTB$_4$ generation being a prerequisite for the effects of PAF in perfused lungs.

The situation in vivo seems to be different. In this case, PAF-induced bronchoconstriction is not affected by cyclooxygenase inhibitors (31, 32) but is reduced by lipoxygenase inhibitors (2). Nevertheless, aerosol administration of PAF induces bronchoconstriction which is blocked by aspirin (18). Thus, it seems likely that different spasmogens are released depending on the cell type(s) that first come(s) in contact with PAF. This probably explains the different results obtained with different routes of administration of PAF.

RELEASE OF EICOSANOIDS FROM PAF-STIMULATED LUNGS

To investigate whether injection of PAF into the pulmonary circulation would induce release of eicosanoids, the effluent was analyzed for eicosanoid content. Perfused guinea pig lungs were stimulated with solutions of PAF (1 and 6.9 μM) and the effluent collected at different intervals after stimulation to measure PGE$_2$, TxB$_2$ and 6-keto-PGF$_{1\alpha}$ by a novel enzyme immunoassay or pooled to determine LTB$_4$ and LTD$_4$ by reverse phase high performance liquid chromatography. It was found that the lungs stimulated with a solution of 6.9 μM of PAF released TxB$_2$ and PGE$_2$ (Fig. 4). Release of PGE$_2$ and TxB$_2$ was maximal 4-5 minutes after the initiation of the in-

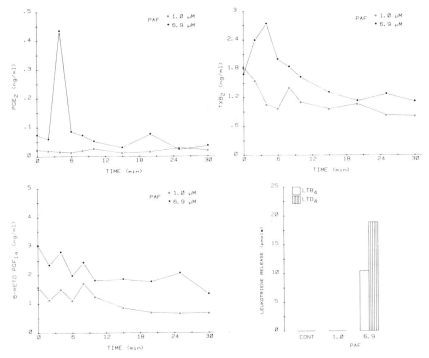

Figure 4   Effects of platelet activating factor (PAF 1.0 μM and 6.9 μM) on the kinetics of release of PGE$_2$ (upper left), TxB$_2$ (upper right), 6-keto-PGE$_{1\alpha}$ (lower left) and on the cumulative release of LTB$_4$ and LTD$_4$ (lower right) by the guinea pig lung. Values are means of 3 separate experiments.

fusion. The 6-keto PGF$_{1\alpha}$ was not elevated in the effluents in these experimental conditions. Significant amounts of LTB$_4$ and LTD$_4$ corresponding approximately to 10 pmol and 19 pmol in 30 ml of effluent were also released. At the concentration of 1 μM, PAF did not stimulate eicosanoid release (28).

RELEASE OF EICOSANOIDS FROM ANAPHYLACTIC LUNGS

Sensitized rabbit (14) and guinea pig lungs (22, 25) release PAF or its metabolite, lyso-PAF, after challenge with the specific antigen. It was also shown that bronchoconstriction that follows antigen injection is markedly reduced by treatment with BN 52021 (8, 9, 30). Similarly, bronchoconstriction that follows intravenous or aerosol administration of PAF is inhibited by BN 52021 (15). The question whether or not the release of endogenous

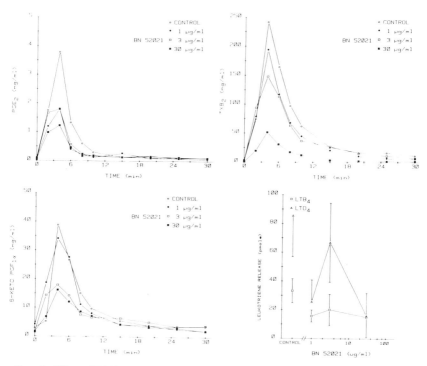

Figure 5 Effects of BN 52021 on the kinetics of release of PGE$_2$ (upper left), TxB$_2$ (upper right), 6-keto-PGF$_{1\alpha}$ (lower left) and on the cumulative release of LTB$_4$ and LTD$_4$ (lower right) by the guinea pig lung during anaphylaxis. The number of experiments is in the following order, control, BN 52021, 1 μg/ml and 30 μg/ml: for PGE$_2$, 20, 9, 10, 15; for TxB$_2$, 9, 3, 3, 3; for 6-keto-PGF$_{1\alpha}$, 16, 3, 3, 9; for leukotrienes B$_4$ and D$_4$, 9, 3, 3, 3.

PAF during anaphylaxis could in turn release eicosanoids was investigated in the following series of experiments. Sensitized guinea pig lungs were perfused via pulmonary artery and injected with the specific antigen by the same route. The effluent was collected at different time-intervals after challenge and analyzed by enzyme immunoassay for its content in prostaglandins and thromboxane. The pooled effluent collected during 30 minutes after challenge was analyzed by reverse phase high performance liquid chromatography for leukotriene B$_4$ and D$_4$ contents. It was found that the maximal concentration was reached 4-5 minutes after antigen challenge. At this time, anaphylactic lungs released approximately 250 ng/ml of TxB$_2$, 40 ng/ml of 6-keto PGF$_1$ and 4 ng/ml of PGE$_2$. It was also found that 12 ng of LTB$_4$ and 45 ng of LTD$_4$ were released during a period of 15 minutes following antigen injection. At concentrations of 1, 3 and 30 μg/ml,

BN 52021 caused a dose-dependent inhibition of the release of PGE_2, TxB_2 and 6-keto PGF_1. At the highest concentration of the antagonist, the inhibition was approximately 50, 80 and 50% for PGE_2, TxB_2 and 6-keto PGF_1, respectively. The inhibition of lipoxygenase products was only evident at the concentration of 30 μg/ml (Fig. 5). The inhibition of eicosanoid release from anaphylactic lungs by a PAF antagonist provides further evidence which suggests that antigen challenge stimulates the release of PAF from the lung.

CONCLUSIONS

In conclusion, our data show that the initial administration of PAF on strips of guinea pig trachea, bronchus and lung parenchyma elicited contractions, whereas the second and subsequent administration produce a relaxant effect on the trachea and bronchus, and no effect on the parenchyma. These effects were blocked by pretreatment of the tissues with the PAF antagonist BN 52021. The effects of PAF on isolated tissues could not account for the bronchoconstriction observed following administration of PAF *in vivo*. These findings prompted us to search for the release of secondary mediators which could be released following PAF administration. The data showed that PAF stimulated the release of spasmogens from isolated perfused guinea pig lungs. Using various pharmacological agents, we provided evidence which suggests that LTB_4 was released from the perfused lungs by PAF treatment. These results were supported by the detection of LTB_4 and LTD_4 in lung perfusates. They were also supported by the fact that BN 52021 inhibited the release of eicosanoids, including LTB_4 and LTD_4, from guinea pig lungs during anaphylaxis. Taken together, our data confirm the existence of interactions between the eicosanoids and PAF and add further support to the hypothesis suggesting that PAF stimulates leukotriene release, which in turn stimulates the formation of cyclooxygenase products.

References

1. Benveniste, J.P., Henson, P.M., Cochrane, C.G. *Leucocyte-dependent histamine release from rabbit platelets: The role of IgE, basophils and platelet-activating factor.* J Exp Med 1972; 136: 1356.

2. Bonnet, J., Thibaudeau, D., Bessin, P. *Dependency of the PAF-acether induced bronchospasm on the lipoxygenase pathway in the guinea pig.* Prostaglandins 1983; 26: 457.

3. Braquet, P.G. *Treatment and prevention of PAF-acether-induced sickness by a new series*

of highly specific inhibitors. GB Patent 1984; 8: 418.

4. Braquet, P., Spinnewyn, B., Braquet, M., Bourgain, R.H., Taylor, J.E., Nunez, D., Drieu, K. *BN 52021 and related compounds: A new series of highly specific PAF-acether antagonists isolated from Ginkgo biloba.* Blood Vessels 1985a; 16: 1.

5. Braquet, P., Etienne, A., Touvay, C., Bourgain, R.H., Lefort, J., Vargaftig, B.B. *Involvement of platelet-activating factor in respiratory anaphylaxis demonstrated by*

PAF-acether inhibitor BN 52021. Lancet 1985b; 1: 1501.

6. Brocklehurst, W.E. *Occurrence of an unindentified substance during anaphylactic shock in cavy lung.* J Physiol (Lond) 1953; 120: 16P.

7. Camussi, G., Montrucchio, G., Antro, C., Bussolino, F., Tetta, C., Emanuelli, G. *Platelet-activating factor-mediated contraction of rabbit lung strips: Pharmacological modulation.* Immunopharmacology 1983; 6: 87.

8. Cirino, M., Lagente, V., Lefort, J., Vargaftig, B.B. *A study with BN 52021 demonstrates the involvement of PAF-acether in IgE-dependent anaphylactic bronchoconstriction.* Prostaglandins 1986; 32: 121.

9. Desquand, S., Touvay, C., Randon, J., Lagente, V., Vilain, B., Maridonneau-Parini, I., Etienne, A., Lefort, J., Braquet, P., Vargaftig, B.B. *Interference of BN 52021 (ginkgolide B) with the bronchopulmonary effects of PAF-acether in the guinea pig.* Eur J Pharmacol 1986; 127: 83.

10. Hamasaki, Y., Mojarad, M., Saga, T., Tai, H., Said, S.I. *Platelet-activating factor raises airway and vascular pressures and induces edema in lungs perfused with platelet-free solution.* Am Rev Resp Dis 1984; 129: 742.

11. Hammarström, S., Murphy, R.C., Samuelsson, B., Clark, D.A., Mioskowski, C., Corey, E.J. *Structure of leukotriene C: Identification of the amino acid part.* Biochem Biophys Res Commun 1979; 91: 1266.

12. Jancar, S., Thériault, P., Braquet, P., Sirois, P. *Comparative effects of platelet-activating factor, leukotriene D₄ and histamine on guinea pig trachea, bronchus and lung parenchyma.* Prostaglandins 1987; 33: 199.

13. Kellaway, C.H., Trethewie, E.R. *The liberation of slow reacting smooth muscle-stimulating substance in anaphylaxis.* Quart J Exp Physiol 1940; 30: 121.

14. Kravis, T.C., Henson, P.M. *IgE-induced release of platelet-activating factor from rabbit lungs.* J Immunol 1975; 115: 1677.

15. Lagente, V., Desquand, S., Randon, J., Lefort, J., Vargaftig, B.B. *Interference of PAF-acether antagonists with the effect of PAF itself and on anaphylactic shock in vitro and in vivo guinea pig bronchopulmonary preparations.* Prostaglandins 1985; 30: 703.

16. Lefort, J., Rotilio, D., Vargaftig, B.B. *The platelet-independent release of thromboxane A₂ by «platelet-activating factor» from guinea*

pig lungs involves mechanisms distinct from those for leukotrienes. Br J Pharmacol 1984; 82: 565.

17. Lewis, R.A., Austen, K.F., Drazen, J.M., Clark, D.A., Marfat, A., Corey, E.J. *Slow-reacting Substance of Anaphylaxis. Identification of leukotriene C-1 and D from human and rat sources.* Proc Nat Acad Sci (USA) 1980; 77: 3710.

18. Maridonneau-Parini, I., Lagente, V., Lefort, J., Randon, J., Russo-Marie, F., Vargaftig, B.B. *Desensitization to PAF-induced bronchoconstriction and to activation of alveolar macrophages by repeated inhalation of PAF-acether in the guinea pig.* Biochem Biophys Res Commun 1985; 131: 42.

19. Morley, J., Sanjar, S., Page, C.P. *The platelet in asthma.* Lancet 1984; 17: 1142.

20. Morris, H.R., Taylor, G.W., Piper, P.J., Samhoun, M.N., Tippins, J.R. *Slow-Reacting Substances (SRSs). The structure identification of SRSs from rat basophilic leukemia cells (RBL-1).* Prostaglandins 1980; 19: 185.

21. Page, C.P., Paul, W., Douglas, G.J., Casals-Stenzel, J., Morley, J. *PAF-acether, platelets and bronchospasm.* In: Platelet Activating Factor. INSERM Symposium, No. 23. J. Benveniste, B. Arnoux (Eds.). Elsevier Science Publishers: Amsterdam 1985; 327.

22. Parente, L., Fitzgerald, M., de Nucci, G., Moncada, S. *The release of lyso-PAF from guinea pig lungs.* Eur J Pharmacol 1985; 112: 282.

23. Pickard, R.N., Farr, S.R., Hahanan, D.J. *Physicochemical and functional identity of rabbit platelet-activating factor (PAF) released in vivo during IgE anaphylaxis with PAF released in vitro from IgE-sensitized basophils.* J Immunol 1979; 123: 1847.

24. Piper, P.J., Vane, J.R. *Release of «additional factors» in anaphylaxis and its antagonism by anti-inflammatory drugs.* Nature 1969; 223: 29.

25. Rotilio, D., Lefort, J., Vargaftig, B.B. *Études préliminaires concernant le métabolisme du PAF-acether.* J Pharmacol (Paris) 1984; 14: 91.

26. Samuelsson, B., Borgeat, P., Hammarström, S., Murphy, R.C. *Leukotrienes: A new group of biologically active compounds.* Adv Prostaglandin Thromboxane, Leukotriene Res 1980; 6: 1.

27. Sirois, P. *Pharmacology of the leukotrienes.* In: Advances in Lipid Research, 21. D. Kritchevsky, R. Paoletti (Eds.). Academic Press:

New York 1985; 79.

28. Sirois, P., Prié, S., Thériault, P., Rouleau, G., Lauzière, M. *The guinea pig bronchus as a model for eicosanoid studies.* Inflammation 1987; 11: 447.

29. Touvay, C., Vilain, B., Etienne, A., Sirois, P., Borgeat, P., Braquet, P. *Characterization of platelet-activating factor (PAF)-acether-induced contractions of guinea pig lung strips by selected inhibitors of arachidonic acid metabolism and by PAF-acether antagonists.* Immunopharmacology 1986a; 12: 97.

30. Touvay, C., Vilain, B., Taylor, J.E., Etienne, A., Braquet, P. *Proof of the involvement of platelet-activating factor in pulmonary complex immune system using a specific PAF-acether receptor antagonist: BN 52021.* Prog Lipid Res 1986b; 25: 277.

31. Vargaftig, B.B., Lefort, J., Chignard, M., Benveniste, J. *Platelet-activating factor induces a platelet-dependent bronchoconstriction unrelated to the formation of prostaglandin derivatives.* Eur J Pharmacol 1980; 65: 185.

32. Vargaftig, B.B., Lefort, J., Wal, F., Chignard, M., Medeiros, M.C. *Non-steroid anti-inflammatory drugs if combined with anti-serotonin agents interfere with the bronchial and platelet effects of «platelet-activating factor».* Eur J Pharmacol 1982; 82: 121.

33. Vilain, B., Lagente, V., Touvay, C., Desquand, S., Randon, J., Lefort, J., Braquet, P., Vafgaftig, B.B. *Pharmacological control of the in vivo passive anaphylactic shock by the PAF-acether antagonist compound BN 52021.* Pharmacol Res Comm 1986; 18: 119.

Ginkgolides - Chemistry, Biology, Pharmacology and Clinical Perspectives. P. Braquet (Ed.)
Copyright © 1988, J.R. Prous Science Publishers, S.A.

BN 52021 INHIBITS THE EFFECTS OF PAF-ACETHER ON ISOLATED PERFUSED RABBIT LUNG IN SITU*

Bernard Arnoux[1] and C. Norman Gillis[2]

[1]INSERM U 200, Université Paris Sud, Clamart, France and [2]Departments of Anesthesiology and Pharmacology, Yale University School of Medicine, New Haven, CT, USA

INTRODUCTION

PAF-acether, originally isolated from antigen-stimulated rabbit basophils (2), is a phospholipid (1-O-alkyl-2-acetyl-glycerophosphocholine (3, 9, 12) with potent biological actions. Other cell types including peritoneal and alveolar macrophages (1, 18), neutrophils (17), eosinophils (16), platelets (7) and endothelial cells (6) also release this phospholipid mediator in response to specific or non-specific stimuli *in vitro*. Administration of PAF-acether *in vivo* causes bronchoconstriction in anesthetized guinea pigs (25) and paralyzed baboons (10), and bronchoconstriction and pulmonary vasoconstrictions in rabbits (21). These vascular and bronchial effects of PAF-acether are also seen in man (11).

Initial reports have suggested a strong correlation between systemic platelet changes and PAF-acether-induced pulmonary smooth muscle tone (4, 10, 11, 21). On the other hand, platelets were not required for the constrictor effects of PAF-acether on smooth muscle of isolated rat and guinea pig lung (13, 27) but were essential for PAF-acether-induced vascular responses of rabbit isolated lung (15).

Our goals in the present study were to determine whether the pulmonary vascular and airway responses induced by PAF-acether in the rabbit lung

Address all correspondence to: Dr. B. Arnoux, INSERM U200, Université Paris Sud, 32 rue des Carnets, F-92140 Clamart, France.
*This work was supported by NIH Grants HL 13315 and 07410 from the National Heart, Lung and Blood Institute.

was or was not platelet-dependent. In addition, we examined the liberation of cyclooxygenase products subsequent to a PAF-acether injection and the capacity of BN 52021, a PAF-acether receptor antagonist, to block the action of this phospholipid mediator.

MATERIALS AND METHODS

Animal Preparation

Male New-Zealand rabbits weighing 2.4 ± 0.3 kg were used. Animals were anesthetized with a mixture of allobarbital (50 mg/ml) and urethane (200 mg/ml) administered into the marginal ear vein. Before the surgical procedure, animals were given 500 IU of heparin. The trachea was intubated, after which the animal was given an overdose of anesthetic. The chest was opened, the main pulmonary artery and the left atrium were canulated. Lungs were perfused through the pulmonary artery at a flow rate of 20 ml/min with Krebs-Henseleit medium (see below) at 37°C aerated with 95% O_2 and 5% CO_2. To remove blood cells from the pulmonary vasculature, lungs were perfused for 10 minutes prior to PAF-acether challenge. Lungs were ventilated with room air at constant pressure and a frequency of 35 breaths/minute and tidal volume of 10 ml/kg by means of a respirator (Harvard Apparatus). Perfusion pressure (*i.e.*, pressure in the pulmonary artery), as well as left atrial and peak inspiratory pressure, were monitored throughout the experiment by means of pressure tranducers (Gould, type P 23 ID) and a Grass Polygraph recorder.

Perfusion Medium

Krebs-Henseleit medium was prepared freshly for each experiment and had the following composition in g/l: NaCl, 6.9; KCl, 0.35, $CaCl_2$, $2H_2O$, 0.37; KH_2PO_4, 0.16; $MgSO_4$, $7H_2O$, 0.29; $NaHCO_3$, 2.2 and D-glucose 2. The pH of the medium was adjusted to 7.4. To maintain physiological oncotic pressure 3% albumin fraction V (Sigma, St. Louis, MO, USA) was added to the perfusion medium.

Drug Treatment

To assess the possible role of arachidonic acid metabolites in PAF-acether-lung-responses, animals were treated with indomethacin (10 mg/kg, i.v.) 30 minutes before the overdose of anesthetic. The isolated lung preparations were perfused with Krebs-albumin medium supplemented by indomethacin (10 μg/ml). The potential role of thromboxane A_2 in the PAF-acether-lung-responses was analyzed by means of a thromboxane A_2 antagonist: SQ 29548 (22; gift of Dr. M. Ogletree, Squibb Institute for Medical Research, Princeton, NJ, USA). SQ 29548, dissolved in ethanol, was added into the perfusion medium to give a final concentration of 100 μM during the experimental procedure.

Challenge

PAF-acether or lyso PAF-acether were injected into the pulmonary artery. A bolus injection of either PAF-acether at a dose of 1 μg/kg of body weight (a gift of Prof. J.J. Godfroid, Université Paris VII, France) dissolved in ethanol 80%, or lyso PAF-acether, 3 μg/kg (Bachem Feinchemikalien AG. Bubendorf, Switzerland) diluted in 200 μl of the perfusion medium, was also administered via the pulmonary artery. Lung preparations were challenged 25 minutes later with a second identical dose of PAF-acether.

Analysis of Arachidonic Acid Metabolites

Five ml samples of left atrial effluent were collected 60 seconds before and 15, 30, 45, 60, 90, 180 and 600 seconds after PAF-acether challenge. Each was extracted with ethanol as described by Mencia-Huerta et al. (19). Extracts were stored at —20°C under nitrogen until analyzed by HPLC with a C-18 reverse phase column (250 x 4.6 mm; 5 μm, Rainin). Lipoxygenase metabolites were analyzed following elution with a mobile phase consisting of methanol/water (34/66%) at 254 nm; cyclooxygenase products were analyzed after elution with a mobile phase of acetonitrile/water (33/67%) at 194 nm (23). The recovery yield of the extraction procedure was tested with PGD$_2$ and ^{3}H PGB$_2$, and was 76% and 72%, respectively.

In Vitro Treatment of Isolated Lung Preparation with BN 52021

BN 52021, a specific PAF-acether antagonist was injected in the perfusion medium as a bolus (100 μg in 200 μl of perfusion medium). Treatment was done according to four different patterns.

Group one was pretreated with BN 52021 1 minute before PAF-acether challenge. Group two received an injection of BN 52021 and PAF-acether simultaneously. Group three received a BN 52021 treatment 40 seconds after PAF-acether challenge and 25 minutes later a second PAF-acether challenge was performed. A third injection of PAF-acether was performed 25 minutes later and this was followed by BN injection 40 seconds later. Group four received a BN 52021 treatment 90 seconds after PAF-acether challenge. A second PAF-acether challenge was performed 25 minutes later without BN administration. In order to verify the reactivity of the isolated lung preparation a bolus injection of U 46619 (6 pmol in 200 μl of perfusion medium) was administered five minutes after this second PAF-acether challenge.

Statistical Analysis

Data are presented as means ± SEM, and were analyzed using the Student's t test for paired and unpaired data when appropriate (24).

RESULTS

A bolus injection of PAF-acether into the pulmonary artery increased the perfusion pressure and the peak inspiratory pressure, while no alteration in the left atrial pressure was observed. The perfusion pressure reached a peak maximal effect at 90 seconds after the injection and remained constant for 20-30 seconds and slowly reversed to control pressure values within 25-30 minutes. The peak inspiratory pressure increased immediately after the challenge and decreased slowly. However, it did not reach the baseline until 30 minutes later (Table 1). A second PAF-acether challenge (25 minutes later) induced the same vascular effect as described above (Table 2). However, there was no systematic increase in airway pressure subsequent to this second injection.

Table 1   Effect of PAF-acether (1 μg/kg) on perfusion pressure and peak inspiratory pressure in isolated rabbit lungs perfused *in situ*[1]

Pressure	Time after PAF-acether challenge (sec)	
	0	90
Perfusion	8.0 ± 0.7	22.5 ± 3.0*
Airway	14.7 ± 1.2	19.0 ± 2.8*

[1]Pressure is expressed in cm H_2O. The results are reported as mean ± SEM (n = 13). Paired t test, *P < 0.05.

Table 2   Modification of perfusion pressure of isolated rabbit lung after 2 consecutive PAF-acether challenges[1]

	Time after PAF-acether challenge (sec)	
	0	90
First challenge	8.7 ± 0.9	28.9 ± 8.2*
Second challenge	10.9 ± 1.2	26.2 ± 4.2*

[1]Same legend as in Table 1. n = 3.

Lyso PAF-acether injection into the pulmonary artery did not induce any effect on vascular and airway pressure.

Drug Treatment

When animals were pretreated with indomethacin, PAF-acether induced an increase of vascular and airway pressure (Table 3). However, the magnitude of the PAF-acether lung effects were lower when compared to the effects observed in the absence of treatment (3, Table 1). U 46619 (2 pmoles/200 μl) rapidly increased perfusion pressure from 7.8 ± 2.3 to 21.8 ± 6.1 cm H_2O, but peak inspiratory pressure was unchanged. PAF-acether challenge on isolated lung preparation perfused with SQ 29548-containing Krebs albumin induced an increase of pulmonary arterial and airway pressure (Table 3). The amplitude of this effect was similar to the effect of PAF-acether in the presence of indomethacin (70 and 20% increase of perfusion pressure and peak inspiratory pressure, respectively). By contrast, the amount of SQ 29548 used in the perfusion medium completely blocked the vascular effect of a high dose of U 46619 (6 pmoles/200 μl).

Table 3 Effect of indomethacin and SQ 29548 on lung vascular and airway response to PAF-acether[1]

| | | Time after PAF-acether challenge (sec) | |
Pressure	Drug	0	90
Perfusion			
	Indo	9.1 ± 1.4	17.0 ± 2.0*
	SQ 29548	4.5 ± 0.5	7.5 ± 0.8**
Airway			
	Indo	15.7 ± 0.5	17.9 ± 0.5*
	SQ 29548	14.7 ± 0.6	17.2 ± 0.6**

[1]Same legend as in Table 1. *$P < 0.05$; **$P < 0.01$; ns = not significant.

Analysis of Arachidonic Acid Metabolites

With our system, we were unable to detect either cyclooxygenase or lipoxygenase products of arachidonic acid metabolism in the perfusion medium after PAF-acether challenge. None of the 19 peaks detected on the cyclooxygenase chromatogram co-migrated with PGE_2, PGD_2, PGF_{2a}, 6 keto PGF_{1a} or thromboxane B_2. No leukotrienes B_4, C_4 or D_4 were detected. There were no changes in any of the peaks detected after PAF-acether challenge.

Effect of BN 52021 on PAF-Acether-Lung Effects

In groups one and two, pretreatment with BN 52021 (100 μg as a bolus into the pulmonary artery) of isolated lung preparation completely blocked the PAF-acether modifications previously described. The same result was obtained when BN 52021 was injected simultaneously with PAF-acether.

Administration of BN 52021, 40 seconds after PAF-acether challenge (group three) reversed rapidly the increase of perfusion pressure. The second PAF-acether challenge induced a similar increase of perfusion pressure, as has been stated above. This pressure returned to a control baseline pressure within 25 minutes. A third challenge with PAF-acether of the same lung preparation induced vascular effects which were reversed immediately after BN 52021 administration. These results were similar to those observed after the first PAF-acether challenge of the preparation (Fig. 1).

Administration of BN 52021 90 seconds (group four) after PAF-acether challenge did not reduce the increased vascular pressure in the preparation. However, the second administration of PAF-acether 25 minutes later was completely blocked by this prior BN treatment. The administration of U 46619 to this lung preparation induced a rapid and intense response of the vascular tissue (Fig. 2).

DISCUSSION

When PAF-acether was injected into the pulmonary artery of the isolated rabbit lung perfused with blood-free medium the vascular and bronchial

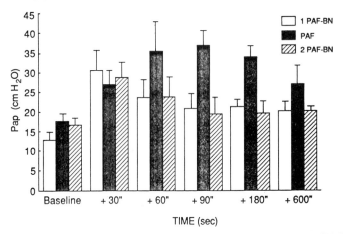

Figure 1 Effect of BN 52021 (40 seconds) on PAF-acether induced-perfusion pressure. BN 52021 (100 μg) was injected 40 seconds after PAF-acether (1 μg/kg) challenge and 25 minutes later a second PAF-acether challenge was performed. A third injection of PAF-acether was performed 25 minutes later and this was followed by BN injection 40 seconds later.

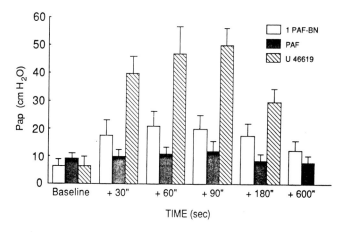

Figure 2 Effect of BN 52021 (90 seconds) on PAF-acether induced-perfusion pressure. BN 52021 (100 μg) was injected 90 seconds after PAF-acether (1 μg/kg) challenge. A second PAF-acether challenge was performed 25 minutes later without BN administration. Five minutes after this second PAF-acether challenge in order to verify the reactivity of the isolated lung preparation a bolus injection of U 46619 (6 pmol in 200 μl of perfusion medium) was administrated.

smooth muscle tone increased. Responses to PAF-acether were unaltered when preparations were challenged 3 times with the same dose. These results are in agreement with the PAF-acether effects reported on isolated perfused rat and guinea pig lungs (13, 27), but in contrast with results reported on isolated rabbit lung preparation (15). This fact could be explained by the use of ketamine anesthesia in the latter experiments. Ketamine has been reported to have vascular effects and to reverse acute bronchospasm in humans (20).

PAF-acether has a greater effect in pulmonary vascular than on airway pressure in the rabbit, while the reverse is true in guinea pig lung (14). The relative role of cyclooxygenase pathway in the PAF-acether-lung interactions was confirmed by the the use of indomethacin and/or SQ 29458. A cyclooxygenase product, possibly thromboxane A_2, seems to participate in the PAF-acether vascular and bronchial effects. Its inhibition by SQ 29548 reduced the PAF-acether effect to the same extent as indomethacin treatment. However, a specific PAF-acether effect was still present in those lung preparations. The relative importance of the cyclooxygenase pathway has been described previously in dog (8), in guinea pigs (5, 26) and in baboons (10) *in vivo* and in isolated lung tissue of guinea pigs (13). The absence of arachidonate metabolites in lung effluents suggests that they are either released in quantities too low to be measured or are not the major link between PAF-acether and the lung tissue response. BN 52021 treatment given in the absence of vasoconstriction blocked subsequent PAF-acether challenge effects. This BN action could be due to an occupancy of «PAF-acether receptors» on lung tissue (14). However, BN 52021 given during PAF-acether-induced vasoconstriction does not show the same behavior. The BN compound given during the ascendent phase of PAF-acether vasoconstriction completely reversed the increase of perfusion pressure emphasizing possible competition for the PAF-acether «receptor» between BN 52021 and PAF-acether. When BN 52021 was given at the peak effect of PAF-acether, the vasoconstriction was not reversed but any further effects during a second PAF-acether administration were prevented. BN 52021 is a powerful compound which is able to reverse and/or block the effects of PAF-acether on lung tissue.

References

1. Arnoux, B., Duval, D., Benveniste, J. *Release of platelet-activating factor (PAF-acether) from alveolar macrophages by the calcium ionophore A23187 and phagocytosis.* Eur J Clin Invest 1980; 10: 437-441.

2. Benveniste, J., Henson, P.M., Cochrane, C.G. *Leukocyte-dependent histamine release from rabbit platelets: The role of IgE basophils, and a platelet-activating factor.* J Exp Med 1972; 136: 1356-1376.

3. Benveniste, J., Tence, M., Varenne, P., Bidault, J., Boullet, C., Polonsky, J. *Semisynthesis et structure propose du facteur activant les plaquettes (PAF): PAF-acèther, un alkyl ether analogue de la lysophosphadicylcholine.* CR Acad Sci Paris, Serie D, 1979; 289: 1017-1102.

4. Bessin, P., Bonnet, J., Apffle, D., Soulard, C., Desgroux, L., Pelas, I., Benveniste, J. *Acute circulatory collapse caused by platelet-activating factor (PAF-acether) in dogs.* Eur J Pharmacol 1983; 86: 403-413.

5. Bonnet, J., Thibaudeau, D., Bessin, P. *Dependency of the PAF-acether induced bronchospasm on the lipoxygenase pathway in the guinea pig.* Prostaglandins 1983; 26: 457-466.

6. Camussi, G., Aglietta, M., Malavasi, F., Tetta, C., Piacibello, W., Sanavio, F., Bussolino, F. *The release of platelet-activating factor from human endothelial cells in culture.* J Immunol 1983; 131: 2397-2403.

7. Chignard, M., Le Couedic, J.P., Tense, M., Vargaftig, B.B., Benveniste, J. *The role of platelet-activating factor in platelet aggregation.* Nature 1979; 279: 799-800.

8. Chung, K.H., Aizawa, H., Leikauf, G.D., Ueki, I.F., Evans, T.W., Nadel, J.A. *Airway hyperresponsiveness induced by platelet-activating factor: Role of thromboxane generation.* J Pharmacol Exp Ther 1986; 236: 580-584.

9. Demopoulos, C.A., Pinckard, R.N., Hanahan, D.J. *Platelet-activating factor: Evidence for 1-O-alkyl-2-acetyl-sn-glyceryl-3-phosphorylcholine as the active component (a new class of lipid chemical mediators).* J Biol Chem 1979; 254: 9355-9358.

10. Denjean, A., Arnoux, B., Masse, R., Lockhart, A., Benveniste, J. *Acute effects of intratracheal administration of platelet-activating factor in baboons.* J Appl Physiol 1983; 55: 799-804.

11. Gateau, O., Arnoux, B., Deriaz, H., Benveniste, J. *Acute effect of intratracheal administration of PAF-acether (platelet-activating factor) in humans.* Am Rev Resp Dis 1984; 129: Abst 283.

12. Godfroid, J.J., Heymans, F., Michel, E., Redeuilh, H.C., Steiner, E., Benveniste, J. *Platelet-activating factor (PAF-acether): Total synthesis of 1-O-octadecyl-2-O-acetyl-sn-glycero-3-phosphorylcholine.* FEBS Lett 1980; 116: 161-164.

13. Hamaski, Y., Mojarad, M., Saga, T., Tai, H., Said, S. *Platelet-activating factor raises airway and vascular pressures and induces edema in lungs perfused with platelet-free solution.* Am Rev Resp Dis 1984; 120: 742-746.

14. Hwang, S.B., Ian, M.H., Shen, T.Y. *Specific binding sites for platelet-activating factor in human lung tissue.* Biochem Biophys Res

Commun 1985; 128: 972.

15. Hefner, J.E., Schoemaker, S.A., Canham, E.M., Patel, M., McMurtry, I.F., Morris, H.B., Repine, J.E. *Acetyl glyceryl ether phosphorylcholine-stimulated human platelets cause pulmonary hypertension and edema in isolated rabbit lungs.* J Clin Invest 1983; 71: 351-357.

16. Lee, T.C., Lenihan, D.J., Malone, B., Roddy, L.L., Wasserman, S.I. *Increased biosynthesis of platelet-activating factor in activated human eosinophils.* J Biol Chem 1980; 297: 329-331.

17. Lynch, J., Lotner, G.Z., Betz, S.J., Henson, P.M. *Human neutrophil-derived platelet-activating factor.* J Immunol 1980; 124: 676-684.

18. Mencia-Huerta, J.M., Benveniste, J. *Platelet-activating factor (PAF) and macrophages. I. Evidence for the release from rat and mouse peritoneal macrophages and not from mastocytes.* Eur J Immunol 1979; 9: 409-415.

19. Mencia-Huerta, J.M., Razin, E., Ringel, E.W., Corey, E.L., Hoover, D., Austin, K.J., Lewis, R.A. *Immunologic and ionophore-induced generation of leukotriene B_4 from mouse bone marrow derived mast cell.* J Immunol 1983; 130: 1885-1890.

20. McD Fisher. *Ketamine hydrochloride in severe bronchospasm.* Anesthesia 1977; 32: 771-772.

21. McManus, L.M., Hanahan, D.J., Demopoulos, C.A., Pinckard, R.N. *Pathobiology of the intravenous infusion of acetyl glyceryl ether phosphorylcholine (AGEPC), a synthetic platelet-activating fac-tor (PAF) in the rabbit.* J Immunol 1980; 124: 2919-2929.

22. Ogletree, M.L., Harris, D.N., Greenberg, R., Haslanger, M.F., Nakane, M. *Pharmacological actions of SQ 29,548, a novel selective thromboxane antagonist.* J Pharmacol Exp Ther 1985; 234: 435-441.

23. Peters, S., McGlashan, D.W., Schulman, E.S., Schleimer, R.P., Hayes, E.C., Rokack, J., Adkinson, N.F., Lichtenstein, L.M. *Arachidonic acid metabolism in purified human lung mast cells.* J Immunol 1984; 132: 1972-1979.

24. Snedecor, G.W., Cochran, W.G. Statistical Methods. 6th Ed. Iowa State University Press: Ames, Iowa 1967.

25. Vargaftig, B.B., Lefort, J., Chignard, M., Benveniste, J. *Platelet-activating factor induces a platelet-dependent bronchoconstriction unrelated to the formation of prostaglandin derivatives.* Eur J Pharmacol 1980; 65: 185-192.

26. Vargaftig, B.B., Lefort, J., Rotilio, D. *Route-dependent interactions between PAF-acether and guinea-pig bronchopulmonary smooth muscle: Relevance of cyclooxygenase mechanisms.* In: Platelet-Activating Factor and Structurally Related Ether-Lipids. J. Benveniste, B. Arnoux (Eds.). Elsevier Science Publishers: Amsterdam 1983; 307-316.

27. Voelkel, N.F., Worthen, S., Reeves, J.T., Henson, P.M., Murphy, R.C. *Nonimmunological production of leukotrienes induced by platelet-activating factor.* Science 1982; 281: 286-288.

*Ginkgolides - Chemistry, Biology, Pharmacology
and Clinical Perspectives.* P. Braquet (Ed.)
Copyright © 1988, J.R. Prous Science Publishers, S.A.

PAF, AIRWAY HYPERREACTIVITY AND ASTHMA: THE POTENTIAL OF GINKGOLIDES IN THE TREATMENT OF ASTHMA

Clive P. Page and Deirdre N. Robertson

Pharmacology Dept., King's College, London University, London, UK

ASTHMA AND AIRWAY HYPERREACTIVITY

A non-specific increase in airway responsiveness (airway hyperreactivity) is a characteristic feature of asthma whereby asthmatics have an increased bronchoconstrictor response to a wide range of stimuli compared to normal healthy individuals (24). The mechanisms involved in the pathogenesis of airway hyperreactivity are poorly understood, but elucidation of the events underlying bronchial hyperreactivity seem central to understanding the pathological basis of asthma (25). Airway hyperreactivity appears to be related to inflammatory processes occurring within the lung (17). Stimuli which cause airway hyperreactivity also induce inflammatory reactions within the airways, *e.g.*, airway hyperresponsiveness is seen in man and several animal species after exposure to the oxidant gases ozone (21, 41) and nitrogen dioxide (43), exposure to sensitizing chemicals such as toluene diisocyanate (TDI) (22, 33) and after exposure to allergens (8, 38). Cellular infiltration into the airways is associated with the late-onset airways obstruction following allergen inhalation, which is also characterized by an increased airway reactivity to histamine and methacholine (8). Studies of bronchoalveolar lavage fluid or sputum have demonstrated that many cells are present in the lungs during the late-onset response, in particular eosinophils

---

Address all correspondence to: Dr. C.P. Page, Pharmacology Dept., King's College, London University, Chelsea Campus, Manresa Road, London SW3, UK.

(38). In addition to infiltration of inflammatory cells, pathological observations have revealed that there is edema of the sub-mucosal tissue and airway wall, desquamation of the ciliated epithelial cell layer, mucus plugs with associated eosinophils and bronchial smooth muscle hyperplasia (28).

Many mediators have been proposed to play a role in both airway inflammation and bronchial hyperreactivity, including preformed mediators such as histamine, chemotactic factors, superoxide anions and adenosine, as well as mediators generated *de novo*, including leukotrienes, prostaglandins and platelet-activating factor (PAF). For any mediator to play a central role in the pathogenesis of asthma, it must be capable of eliciting the pathological features of asthma and must be released in sufficient amounts to produce such effects. This paper will review the evidence for a role for PAF in asthma and airway hyperreactivity. Additionally, the results obtained with specific PAF antagonists, in particular the ginkgolides, in models of airway hyperreactivity will be discussed in the context of these agents having potential value in the treatment of asthma.

PLATELET ACTIVATING FACTOR

Platelet-activating factor (PAF, PAF-acether, AGEPC, APRL) is a phospholipid produced by a variety of inflammatory cells including neutrophils, platelets, macrophages, eosinophils and vascular endothelial cells (39). PAF has many biological properties which have implicated it as having a role in the pathogenesis of asthma and allergic disease (5, 39).

PAF is an extremely potent bronchoconstrictor and bronchoconstriction can be produced by as little as 10 ng/kg PAF i.v. in experimental animals (40). This bronchoconstriction appears to be platelet-dependent, since it can be abrogated by prior depletion of circulating platelets using an anti-platelet anti-serum (23, 48). PAF also produces acute bronchoconstriction in man (13). Additionally, following local administration of PAF to the lungs of experimental animals, there is a progressive decrease in lung function and prolonged airway inflammation as demonstrated by pulmonary accumulation of inflammatory cells including neutrophils, macrophages (7) and eosinophils (2, 31). The mechanisms involved in the prolonged effects of PAF are of considerable interest since PAF is very rapidly metabolized to the biologically inactive de-acetylated product, lyso-PAF (46), and thus these long-term pathological changes do not reflect PAF remaining unmetabolized.

PAF is not only produced by inflammatory cells, but can also activate them. In addition to platelet activation (6), PAF stimulates neutrophil aggregation (18), chemotaxis (20), generation of superoxide radicals (29), lysosomal enzyme release and leukotriene B_4 formation (32). PAF is also a potent activator of eosinophils *in vitro* eliciting chemotaxis and the release of secondary mediators (47, 49). Toxic materials released from activated eosinophils result in the loss of airway epithelium, a process which has been postulated to lead to increased responsiveness of airways (19). Interestingly, intradermal injection of PAF into atopic individuals results in a selective accumulaton of eosinophils (27) comparable to that induced by antigen administration in the same individuals. In contrast, intradermal PAF results in an intense inflammatory response in the skin of normal volunteers but the predominant infiltrating cells are neutrophils, lymphocytes and histiocytes (1). Such observations suggest that atopic individuals respond qualitatively differently to normal individuals with respect to PAF and moreover, as eosinophils from patients with eosinophilia have been demonstrated to release large amounts of PAF compared to eosinophils from normal individuals (30), PAF may contribute to the selective eosinophilia seen in asthmatics.

In addition to recruitment of inflammatory cells, PAF administration initiates edema formation in both the bronchial (16, 42) and pulmonary circulation (26, 37). Furthermore, PAF has a variety of effects on the mucociliary esclator where it elicits increased mucous secretion (45) and effects mucociliary transport (3), both processes which may contribute to the increased bronchial responsiveness observed in asthmatics.

PAF AND AIRWAY HYPERREACTIVITY

PAF has been demonstrated to induce a long-lasting and non-specific airway hyperreactivity in both experimental animals and man (4, 9, 13, 34). PAF-induced bronchial hyperreactivity is readily demonstrable in the guinea pig and is obtained following both i.v. and aerosol administration (Fig. 1). In guinea pigs, this airway hyperreactivity can be prevented by prior depletion of circulating platelets (34) and is accompanied by a progressive pulmonary accumulation of platelets (44). However, PAF continues to induce bronchial hyperreactivity in animals rendered selectively neutropenic (14). The mechanisms behind the platelet-dependent bronchial hyperreactivity induced by PAF are not known, but other platelet agonists such as ADP, collagen or the thromboxane mimetic, U46619, cannot induce bronchial hyperreactivity in guinea pigs despite eliciting similar pulmonary platelet accumulation (44). These results may reflect the observations of Lellouch-Tubiana *et al.* (31), who have shown that PAF (but not ADP) promotes extravasation of platelets, which are then found in the proximity of the airway smooth muscle. Such observations are of considerable interest, for platelets have been observed in the lavage fluid of allergic asthmatics (35) and IgE sensitized rabbits undergoing antigen challenge (36).

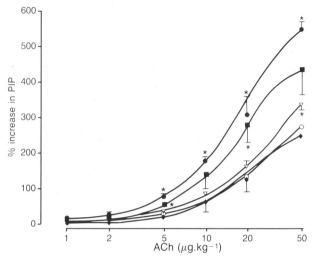

Figure 1 Airway reactivity following i.v. Ach (1-50 μg/kg) in guinea-pigs 24 hours after exposure to an aerosol of PAF (250 μg ∇, 500 μg ■, 1000 μg ●) or BSA 0.25% (▲). Airways reactivity in untreated animals are shown for comparison (○). Results are expressed as mean ± s.e.m. of % increase in pulmonary inflation pressure for groups of n = 4-7 animals. Significance (*p <0.05) against BSA treated animals determined by Mann-Whitney U test.

In the guinea pig PAF-induced bronchial hyperreactivity has been shown to be inhibited by the anti-asthma drugs disodium cromoglycate, ketotifen and glucocorticosteroids, but not by beta-adrenoceptor agonists (15), thus exhibiting a similar pharmacological sensitivity to allergic responses in sensitized asthmatics. This suggests that inhibition of PAF-induced pulmonary pathology may in part explain some of the therapeutic efficacy of prophylactic anti-asthma drugs and further study of PAF-induced bronchial hyperreactivity may, therefore, provide a better understanding of such drugs.

The contribution of PAF to airway hyperreactivity induced by antigen has recently been investigated in a number of animal models. Pre-treatment of guinea pigs with the selective PAF antagonist, the ginkgolide BN 52021, reduces airway hyperreactivity induced by aerosol PAF (Fig. 2). Moreover, in the guinea pig, antigen-induced airway hyperreactivity of a similar magnitude to that induced by PAF, is also reduced by pre-treatment with BN 52021 (Fig. 3). In the IgE sensitized rabbit, undergoing early and late-onset responses following antigen challenge, pre-treatment with BN 52021 inhibits late-onset airway obstruction while having no effect on acute bronchoconstriction (11). Both PAF and antigen-induced airway hyperreactivity are accompanied by an increase in eosinophils present in bronchoalveolar lavage fluid. Such inflammatory cell infiltration is also reduced in guinea pigs pre-treated with BN 52021 (11, 12).

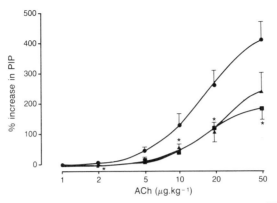

Figure 2 Airway reactivity as assessed by % increase in pulmonary inflation pressure (PIP) following i.v. acetylcholine (1-50 μg/kg) in guinea-pigs 24 hours after exposure to an aerosol of 500 μg of PAF (●), BSA (▲), or in animals pretreated with BN 52021 20 mg/kg 1 hour before exposure to 500 μg of PAF (■). Results are expressed as mean ± s.e.m. for groups of n = 6 animals. Significance (*p < 0.05) against PAF treated animals determined by Mann-Whitney U test.

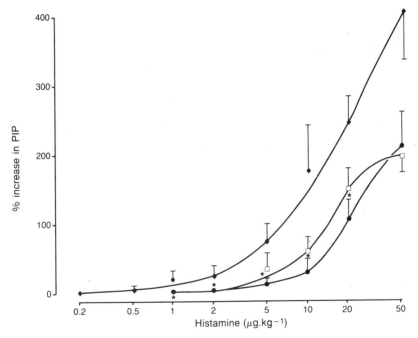

Figure 3 Airway reactivity as assessed by % increase in pulmonary inflation pressure (PIP) following i.v. histamine (1-50 μg) in guinea-pigs 24 hours after exposure to an aerosol of 250 μg of ovalbumin (▲), saline (□), or in animals pretreated with BN 52021 20 mg/kg 1 hour before exposure to 250 μg of ovalbumin (●). Results are expressed as mean ± s.e.m. for groups of n = 6 animals. Significance (*p < 0.05 against ovalbumin treated animals determined by Mann-Whitney U test.

A ROLE FOR PAF ANTAGONISTS IN ASTHMA?

Since PAF appears to play a central role in the development of antigen-induced bronchial hyperreactivity and inflammation, particularly in animal models, then it is possible that PAF antagonists may have a place as prophylactic agents for the treatment of asthma in man. It is, however, clear that during acute attacks, a bronchodilator will be necessary as PAF antagonists do not always inhibit antigen-induced bronchoconstriction (11). Although these conclusions are based largely on animal experimentation, recently BN 52063, an extract of gingkolides containing a mixture of BN 52020, BN 52021 and BN 52022, has been shown to be a selective PAF antagonist in man (10). BN 52063 inhibits PAF-induced weal and flare in human skin while having no effect on histamine-induced weal and flare responses (10). The effect of PAF antagonists in asthma have not yet been formally studied, but the availability of selective PAF antagonists for use in man should allow the role of PAF in asthma to be determined.

References

1. Archer, C.B. et al. *Accumulation of inflammatory cells in response to intracutaneous platelet-activating factor (PAF-acether) in man.* Br J Dermatol 1985; 112: 285-290.
2. Arnoux, B. et al. *Pulmonary effects of platelet-activating factor in a primate are inhibited by ketotifen.* Am Rev Resp Dis 1985; 131: A2.
3. Aursudkij, B. et al. *Reduced tracheal mucous velocity in guinea pig in vivo by platelet activating factor.* Am Rev Resp Dis 1987; 135: A160.
4. Barnes, P.J. et al. *The effect of platelet-activating factor on pulmonary beta-adrenoceptors.* Br J Pharmacol 1987; 90: 709-715.
5. Barnes, P.J. et al. *Platelet-activating factor as a mediator of allergic disease.* J Allergy Clin Immunol; in press.
6. Benveniste, J. *Leukocyte dependent histamine release from rabbit platelets: The role of IgE, basophils and a platelet-activating factor.* J Exp Med 1972; 136: 1356-1377.
7. Camussi, G. et al. *Acute lung inflammation induced in the rabbit by local instillation of 1-0-octadecyl-2-acetyl-sn-glyceryl-3-phosphorylcholine or native platelet-activating factor.* Am J Pathol 1983; 112: 78-88.
8. Cartier, A. et al. *Allergen-induced increase in bronchial responsiveness to histamine: Relationship to the late asthmatic response and change in airway calibre.* J Allergy Clin Immunol 1982; 70: 170-177.
9. Chung, K.F. et al. *Airway hyperresponsiveness induced by platelet-activating factor: Role of thromboxane generation.* J Pharmacol Exp Ther 1986; 236: 580-584.
10. Chung, K.F. et al. *Effect of a gingkolide mixture (BN 52036) in antagonising skin and platelet responses to platelet-activating factor in man.* Lancet 1987; 1: 248-251.
11. Coyle, A.J. et al. *Modification of the late asthmatic response and bronchial hyperreactivity by BN 52021, a platelet-activating factor antagonist.* Clin Res 1987; 35: A254.
12. Coyle, A.J. et al. *The effect of the selective PAF antagnist BN 52021 on PAF and antigen induced bronchial hyperreactivity and eosinophil accumulation.* Submitted for publication.
13. Cuss, F.M. et al. *Inhaled platelet-activating factor in man: Effects on pulmonary function and bronchial responsiveness.* Lancet 1986; 2: 189-192.
14. Deeming, K. et al. *PAF antagonists in asthma.* Prostaglandins 1985; 30: 706.
15. Deeming, K. et al. *Prophylactic anti-asthma drugs impair platelet accumulation within the lung.* Br J Pharmacol 1986; 87: 73P.
16. Evans, T.W. et al. *Effect of platelet-activating factor on airway vascular permeability: Possible mechanisms.* J Pharm Exp Ther, in press.
17. Fabbri, L. *Airway inflammation and asthma. Importance of arachidonate metabolites for*

airway hyperresponsiveness. Prog Biochem Pharmacol 1985; 20: 18-25.

18. Ford-Hutchinson, A.W. *Neutrophil aggregating properties of PAF-acether and leukotriene B_4.* Int J Immunopharmacol 1983; 5: 17-21.

19. Frigas, E., Gleich, G.J. *The eosinophil and the pathophysiology of asthma.* J Allergy Clin Immunol 1986; 77: 527-537.

20. Goetzl, E.S. et al. *Novel effects of 1-0-hexadecyl-2-acyl-sn-3-phosphorylcholine mediators of human leukocyte function: Deliniation of the specific roles of the acyl substitutes.* Biochem Biophys Res Commun 1980; 44: 881-889.

21. Golden, J.A. et al. *Bronchial hyperirritability in healthy subjects after exposure to ozone.* Am Rev Respir Dis 1978; 118: 287-294.

22. Gordon, T. et al. *Airway hyperresponsiveness and inflammation induced by toluene diisocyanate in guinea pigs.* Am Rev Respir Dis 1985; 132: 1106-1112.

23. Halonen, M. et al. *Differential effects of platelet depletion on the physiologic alterations of IgE anaphylaxis and acetyl ether phosphorylcholine infusion in the rabbit.* Am Rev Resp Dis 1981; 124: 416-421.

24. Hargreave, F. et al. *Bronchial responsiveness to histamine or methacholine in asthma: Measurement and clinical significance.* J Allergy Clin Immunol 1981; 68: 346-355.

25. Hargreave, F. et al. *The origin of airway hyperresponsiveness.* J Allergy Clin Immunol 1986; 78: 825-832.

26. Heffner, J.E. et al. *Acetyl glyceryl ether phosphorylcholine stimulated platelets cause pulmonary hypertension and oedema in isolated rabbit lungs.* J Clin Invest 1983; 71: 351-357.

27. Henocq, E., Vargaftig, B.B. *Accumulation of eosinophils in response to intracutaneous PAF-acether and allergens in man.* Lancet 1986; 1: 1378-1379.

28. Hogg, J.C. *The pathology of asthma.* In: Bronchial Asthma. Mechanisms and Therapeutics. E.B. Weiss, M.J. Segal, M. Stein (Eds). Little, Brown and Co.: 1985; 209-217.

29. Ingraham, L.M. et al. *Metabolic, membrane and functional responses of human polymorphonuclear leukocytes to platelet-activating factor.* Blood 1982; 59: 1259-1266.

30. Lee, T. et al. *Increased biosynthesis of platelet-activating factor in activated human eosinophils.* J Biol Chem 1984; 259:

5526-5530.

31. Lellouch-Tubiana, A. et al. *Ultrastructural evidence for extravascular platelet recruitment in the lung upon intravenous injection of platelet activating factor (PAF-acether) to guinea pigs.* Br J Exp Path 1985; 66: 345-355.

32. Lin, A.H. et al. *Acetyl glyceryl ether phosphorylcholine stimulates leukotriene B_4 synthesis in human polymorphonuclear leukocytes.* J Clin Invest 1982; 70: 1058-1065.

33. Mapp, C.E. et al. *Time course of the increase in airway responsiveness associated with late asthmatic reactions to toluene diisocyanate in sensitised subjects.* J Allergy Clin Immunol 1985; 75: 568-572.

34. Mazzoni, L. et al. *Induction of airway hyperreactivity by platelet-activating factor in the guinea pig.* J Physiol 1985; 365: 107P.

35. Metzger, W.J. et al. *Late asthmatic responses: Inquiry into mechanisms and significance.* Clin Rev Allergy 1985; 3: 145-165.

36. Metzger, W.J. et al. *Platelets in bronchoalveolar lavage fluid from asthmatics and IgE sensitised rabbits undergoing allergen-induced late phase responses.* Agents and Actions 1987; Suppl 21: 151-159.

37. Mojarad, M. et al. *Platelet-activating factor increases pulmonary microvascular permeability and induces pulmonary oedema.* Bull Europ Physiopath Resp 1983; 19: 253-257.

38. de Monchy, J.G.R. et al. *Bronchoalveolar eosinophilia during allergen-induced late asthmatic reactions.* Am Rev Respir Dis 1985; 131: 373-376.

39. Morley, J. et al. *The platelet in asthma.* Lancet 1984; 2: 1142-1144.

40. Morley, J. et al. *Pulmonary responses to platelet-activating factor.* Prog Resp Res 1985; 19: 117-123.

41. Murlas, C.G., Roum, J.H. *Sequence of pathologic changes in the airway mucosa of guinea pigs during ozone-induced bronchial hyperreactivity.* Am Rev Respir Dis 1985; 131: 314-320.

42. O'Donnell, S.R., Barnett, C.J.K. *Effects of drugs on bronchial microvascular leakage produced by platelet-activating factor in guinea pigs.* Am Rev Resp Dis 1987; 135: A161.

43. Orehek, J. et al. *Effect of short term low level nitrogen dioxide exposure on bronchial sensitivity of asthmatic subjects.* J Clin Invest 1976; 57: 301-307.

44. Robertson, D.N., Page, C.P. *Effect of platelet agonists on airway reactivity and intrathoracic*

platelet accumulation. Br J Pharmacol 1987; 92: 105-111.

45. Sasaki, T. et al. *Platelet-activating factor (PAF) increases mucus glycoprotein release from isolated tracheal submucosal gland in the presence on the platelet.* Am Rev Resp Dis 1987; 135: A160.

46. Snyder, F. *Chemical and biochemical aspects of platelet-activating factor: A novel class of acetylated ether-linked choline phospholipids.* Med Res Rev 1985; 5: 107-140.

47. Tamura, N. et al. *Effects of platelet activating factor on the chemotaxis of normodense eosinophils from normal subjects.* Biochem Biophys Res Commun 1987; 142: 638-644.

48. Vargaftig, B.B. et al. *Platelet-activating factor induces a platelet-dependent bronchoconstriction unrelated to the formation of prostaglandin derivatives.* Eur J Pharmacol 1982; 65: 185-192.

49. Wardlaw, A.J. et al. *Platelet-activating factor. A potent chemotactic and chemokinetic factor for human eosinophils.* J Clin Invest 1986; 78: 1701-1706.

Ginkgolides - Chemistry, Biology, Pharmacology and Clinical Perspectives. P. Braquet (Ed.)
Copyright © 1988, J.R. Prous Science Publishers, S.A.

THE LATE PHASE ASTHMATIC RESPONSE IN THE ALLERGIC RABBIT: A ROLE FOR PLATELET-ACTIVATING FACTOR (PAF) AND MODIFICATION BY PAF ANTAGONIST, GINKGOLIDE BN 52021

W. James Metzger[1], Kate Sjoerdsma[1], Lisa Brown[1], Tony Coyle[2], Clive Page[2] and Caroline Touvay[3]

[1]Department of Internal Medicine, East Carolina University, School of Medicine, Greenville, NC, USA; [2]Department of Pharmacology, University of Lonson, England; [3]Institut Henri Beaufour, Les Ulis, France

INTRODUCTION

In our search for insight into the pathogenetic mechanisms of allergic asthma, we are baffled by the complexities of the local mileau at the site of the allergic reaction in the lung. Yet, we continue to seek an explanation to help us understand that age-old problem recognized by Hippocrates (15) that continues presently and perhaps increasingly to bring death to the few who finally succumb to the fatigue of breathing.

Recent developments in the understanding of bronchial asthma have revealed more than ever that the persistence of allergic asthma depends upon increased nonspecific bronchial hyperresponsiveness (NSBHR), which is often "induced" by late phase asthmatic airway responses (LAR) (22). This "handle", the LAR, by which we can explore allergen triggered IgE

Address all correspondence to: W. James Metzger, M.D., Head, Section of Allergy-Immunology, School of Medicine, East Carolina University, Brody Building 3W-40, Greenville, NC 27834-4354, USA.

responses having long-lasting consequences, has revealed that asthma is more than bronchospasm; it is inflammation (22). This revelation has changed our thinking about the treatment of allergic asthma (39) and has reaffirmed the value of allergen avoidance techniques (38).

Despite the abundance of inflammatory mediators described as part of the allergic response, platelet-activating factor (PAF, PAF-acether, or AGEPC) stands out by its singular ability to recapitulate the entire asthmatic syndrome (1). PAF can increase bronchial hyperreactivity or induce an LAR with cellular inflammation (6). It has also been reported to cause vascular permeability (31) and airway smooth muscle contracture (44). It mimics anaphylaxis when injected intravenously into several animal species (2). These observations make PAF a foremost candidate as a crucial mediator for asthma and other allergically mediated diseases. It's central role as mediator of allergic asthma was hypothesized by Morley Sanjar, and Page several years ago; (33) and since then, many observations have supported their concept. This paper represents a review of the LAR using 1) the human model for inducing late phase responses and analyzing the consequences with bronchoalveolar lavage and 2) the allergic rabbit model to induce late phase cutaneous and asthmatic responses. To test the hypothesis that PAF is an important mediator for allergic asthma and produces late phase responses and bronchial airway hyperresponsiveness, we have shown that ginkgolide BN 52021 is able to inhibit the early and late cutaneous responsse (LCR), modify the late asthmatic response, block the nonspecific bronchial hyperreactivity and the inflammatory component of asthma following the onset of the late response. These data further substantiate the hypothesis that PAF plays a crucial role in the induction of asthma and that a PAF antagonist may be helpful in preventing or treating allergic asthma.

BACKGROUND

Late Phase Responses

Although Herxheimer recognized the late phase allergic response in himself many years before (14), investigators were diverted by the assumption that it was mediated by IgG-immune complexes and complement, representing the human equivalent of the Arthus reaction. But in 1972, Solley and his coworkers clearly showed that the late phase cutaneous response (LCR) was an IgE phenomena and could be produced by anti-IgE antiserum or 48-80, a direct mast cell stimulator (43). Understanding that late phase responses could account for prolonged allergic responses such as perennial allergic rhinitis, allergic asthma, or perhaps certain urticarias, was a breakthrough in our thinking, giving us the needed incentive to explore the mechanisms of chronic allergic asthma which, for the most part, had been characterized by bronchospasm and excessive mucus production.

The inflammatory nature of allergic asthma was revealed by performing bronchoalveolar lavage (BAL) on patients undergoing airway allergen challenge (24). Following the immediate airway response (IAR), there was an influx of neutrophils and eosinophils of which eosinophils were prominent and appeared to persist. IgE secreting cells were increased in the BAL (22), and helper-T cells were also elevated. Later, a more precise method of examining the local mileau of the airway was developed using local allergen challenge (LAC) followed by BAL (30). Locally, there was an immediately visible allergic response resembling the triple response of Lewis, which resulted in palor, airway edema, reactive hyperemia, and partial airway obstruction and collapse. In this case, helper-T cells were elevated five-fold, and eosinophils were found to persist up to 96 hours after a local allergen challenge, first releasing their central crystalline cores containing major basic protein, and then undergoing piece-meal degranulation (30). Activated macrophages became more numerous and were accompanied by a probable early influx of monocytes (30). The macrophages contained lamellar bodies in large phagosomes, which appeared to be incompletely degraded plasma membranes from platelets (30). The IAR and LAR were also accompanied by increased peripheral blood levels of a large molecular weight, neutrophil chemotactic factor (NCF), and a small molecular weight ($<2,000$ Daltons) eosinophilic chemotactic factor (27). NCF was also discovered in BAL (21). The LAR was a peripheral lung event involving small airways, possibly as a result of an inflammatory influx of cells, while the IAR primarily involved large airways and was found to represent a reversible bronchospastic or edematous event (25).

Based on a report by DeShazo that LCR were accompanied by fibrin deposition (41), we measured circulating levels of platelet factor 4 (PF_4), beta-thromboglobulin (β-TG), and fibrinopeptide A (FPA) as markers of platelet activation and thrombin generation. We hypothesized that platelets and/or the coagulation cascade, including kinins, participated in the asthmatic response. There was a significant elevation in BTG and FPA during the early and late phase asthmatic responses in humans, but similar changes in PF_4 did not reach significance (20, 22). Previously, however, Knauer reported that immediate responses were accompanied by a sudden and significant rise in PF_4 (17). Several particular observations influenced our thinking about late responses and asthma: 1) although mast cells were present in BAL and were degranulated by allergen challenge, their numbers were very few. Casale correlated their number following allergen challenge and increased levels of histamine with nonspecific bronchial hyperreactivity (3); 2) that platelets were present in lavage fluid, increasing briefly following the immediate response; but in peripheral blood, they decreased immediately and then decreased again, remaining low throughout the late response (29); 3) that eosinophils persisted in BAL following the late response as the prominent inflammatory cell and released their major basic protein, corroborating observations made by Gleich and coworkers (9, 10) in asthmatic airways; 4) platelets were elevated transiently in lavage fluid, but subsequent evidence implied their removal from peripheral blood and the possibility of their being ingested by macrophages, which could be activated to release other mediators such as leukotrienes, prostaglandins, or more PAF (16, 29).

Allergic Rabbit Model

The human studies were soon limited to some extent by the ability to obtain tissue for histiopathology and to test newer pharmacologic antagonists of autocoid action. Therefore, we developed a model of early and late phase asthmatic responses in the allergic rabbit, whereby neonatal rabbits were immunized on the day of birth with antigen-in-alum followed by weekly (for one month) then biweekly intraperitoneal injections after the methods of Pinkard, Halonen, and Meng (37). Although several antigens have been succesfully used, we currently immunize with ragweed extract in 10% aluminum hydroxide (AlK)$_4$ (OH)$_4$.12 H$_2$O). At the age of three to four months, these rabbits are challenged with soluble antigen (e.g., ragweed, 40,000 pnu/ml) produced by a DeVilbiss nebulizer, which aerosolizes 80% particles less than 5μ.

To produce an early and late phase obstructive airway response (23, 26), responsive rabbits generally must have PCA titers of at least a 1:40 dilution of serum and allergen-specific IgG titers of less than 20 ELISA Units (EU) (compared to a high titer and normal control rabbit serum). This is equivalent to less than 5 mm induration of full strength rabbit serum in a guinea pig PCA reaction (37). In litters of standard New Zealand White (NZW) rabbits, 40 to 50% of the immunized animals would "break through" with high titer IgG antibody responses so that their response to allergen challenge was inadequate to produce a late phase asthmatic response. Subsequently, we have used pathogen-free NZW rabbits, which more frequently respond with high IgE titers and low allergen-specific IgG antibody levels. Larsen and coworkers have developed a similar model using *Alternaria* antigen and passive transfer of serum to establish sensitization (40). They were able to show that late phase responses were blocked by high titers of IgG antibody.

Recent studies in our laboratory have shown that immunization of adult *Pasturella*-free NZW rabbits is an acceptable alternative to the neonatal model. Cyclophosphamide (100 mg/kg) is given intraperitoneally two days before immunization with ragwed extract (1 mg) and weekly injections (1 mg i.p.) for two weeks. Adult rabbits immunized in this manner produce high titers of IgE and low IgG specific antibody comparable to neonatally sensitized rabbits. Their airways are also hyperresponsive (29).

Aerosol Challenge

For aerosol challenges, allergic rabbits were anesthetized and intubated after the method of Zavala (46), and an esophageal balloon was placed to record transpulmonary pressures and flow (integrated into volume). From these data, dynamic compliance (Cdyn) and total lung resistance (R_t) were calculated after the method of Davidson (7). For measurements of NSHBR, histamine or methocholine were aerosolized at increasingly larger doses for periods of two minutes interposed by three minutes of observation. Challenges were halted when the P_tp had increased two-fold from baseline. Airway sensitivity was estimated by calculating the dose of histamine or allergen which reduced the Cdyn by 50% (PC_{50} Cdyn histamine). Airway reactivity was calculated from the slope of the dose response curve after the method of Orahek (35). The severity and duration of an LAR was calculated by digitizing the area (mm_2) under the curve described by the late response from 1 hour to 6 hours for dynamic compliance as previously described (25). Peripheral blood was obtained throughout challenges from the cannulated ear artery. Bronchial lavage was performed at various times throughout the challenge via a small polyethylene catheter inserted into the lung until resistance was felt, and suction was applied through a trap. Cells were obtained from bronchial lavage fluid and centrifuged, stained with the appropriate stain, and counted differentially.

Skin Test Responses

Skin test response to antigen and PAF were evaluated with PCA reactions in normal rabbits by transferring IgE-containing serum (0.2 cc) from allergic rabbits to the shaved backs of normal rabbits and challenging these rabbits 96 hours later with an intravenous injection of ragweed (10 pnu) and 2% Evans blue dye. Two crossed diameters of blueing were averaged to obtain a quantitative assessment of IgE activity. Direct skin testing was carried out by injection (0.2 ml intradermally) of ragweed or PAF (200 ng) directly into the shaved backs of allergic rabbits and crossed diameters of wheal (30 minutes, ICR) or induration (five hours, LCR) were averaged to quantitate the allergic skin response.

PAF Antagonist

Ginkgolide, BN 52021, a naturally occurring specific PAF antagonist (kindly donated by Dr. Pierre Braquet, Institute Henri Beaufor, Paris France) was used to block bronchial and skin responses to antigen and PAF. BN 52021 was given orally (2-100 mg/kg) in Karo® Syrup one hour before each procedure.

ASSESSMENT OF THE MODEL

Previous Work

Aerosol challenge with allergen or PAF results in an early (<1 hour) and late phase airway response (4-8 hour) consisting of an increase in R_t and a decrease in Cdyn (Fig. 1). The early response is characterized by acute airway obstruction with a small degree of cellular infiltrate consisting of sloughed tracheal epithelial cells, neutrophils, and some eosinophils. As the airway response continues, the eosinophilia of the bronchoalveolar lavage fluid increases as does the number of eosinophils in the lung. Neutrophil chemotactic activity has been found in the rabbit BAL during early and LAR (Fig. 1). These cells appear in the bronchoalveolar fluid as a result of transit through the tracheal epithelium. In some rabbits, wheezing is discernable during late phase response, which is more prolonged than the early response and is characterized by marked eosinophilia and neutrophilia.

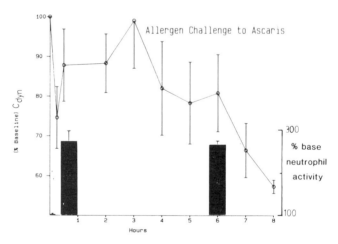

Figure 1 Airway response to ascaris aerosol challenge in immunized NZW rabbits. Percent change in dynamic compliance (Cdyn) showing an early and late phase response. Solid bars represent percent increase in neutrophil chemotactic activity found in bronchial lavage fluid.

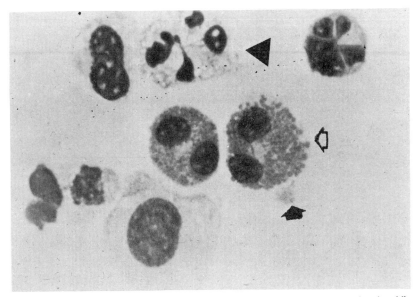

Figure 2 Photomicrograph (40x) of late phase airway response showing two central eosinophils (open arrow), a platelet (closed arrow), and neutrophils (solid triangle). The eosinophils are easily distinguished from the neutrophils by the number and shape of the nucleii and the number, size, and color of the granules.

Electron microscopy of eosinophils during the LAR reveals a central core, which degranulates in a manner similar to the human model. Changes in arterial oxygen and carbon dioxide are consistent with human asthma with a decrease in oxygen partial pressure and an increase in carbon dioxide during both early and late phase response. The inflammatory response consists of activated macrophages, platelets, eosinophils, and lymphocytes (Fig. 2).

Hyperreactive Airways

Sensitized rabbits have demonstrably hyperresponsive airways after immunization. On the average, the immunized rabbits have a PC_{35} histamine equal to 9 ± 4 mg/ml; whereas normal, nonimmunized rabbits have a PC_{35} equal to 43 ± 8 mg/ml; (Fig. 3). Twenty-four to forty-eight hours after aerosol challenge with antigen, airways hyperresponsiveness increased (Fig. 3, 4). The increase in hyperresponsiveness persisted in a few rabbits for up to two weeks (Fig. 4).

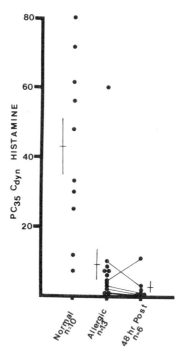

Figure 3 PC$_{35}$ histamine (mg/ml) of normal, non-immunized NZW rabbits compared to immunized rabbits. The third column shows the change in bronchial responsiveness 48 hours after allergen challenge.

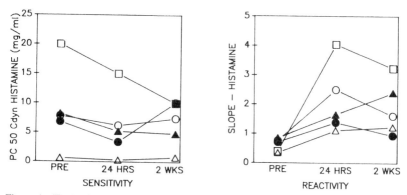

Figure 4 (Top) Airway sensitivity measured by PC$_{50}$ Cdyn for histamine (mg/ml) in five ragweed-immunized rabbits beforee ragweed challenge (PRE) (group mean = 8.7 ± 3.1 mg/ml), 24 hours later ($\bar{x}$ = 6.0 ± 2.5 mg/ml) and two weeks later ($\bar{x}$ = 6.6 ± 1.7 ng/ml). (Bottom) Airway reactivity measured by the slope of histamine dose response curve in the same five rabbits before challenge (PRE, 0.6 ± 0.1) 24 hours later (1.9 ± 0.6), and two weeks later (1.9 ± 0.4).

Evidence For Hyperreactive Muscular Contractility

The finding of nonspecific hyperresponsiveness of the airways of sensitized and challenged rabbits raised the question of whether or not airway smooth muscle was itself hyperreactive. In collaboration with Dr. Jamal Mustafa, East Carolina University School of Medicine, Department of Pharmacology, tracheal and bronchial airway smooth muscle from immunized and challenged rabbits was dissected free from the trachea and the first and second divisions of the bronchial airways (18). Muscles were suspended in isotonic muscle baths and subjected to increasing doses of histamine or methacholine (10^{-8}-10^{-4}M).

Airway smooth muscle from the trachea was unresponsive to histamine, but muscle taken from successively peripheral airways was increasingly sensitive. Muscles from all areas of the airway were responsive to methacholine. Animals which were aerosolized either acutely with antigen or chronically over a period of 8-12 weeks became more hyperresponsive *in vivo* and hyperreactive *in vitro* to histamine or acetylcholine. The response was more evident as one proceeded from central to more peripheral airways (Fig. 5). Sensitized tertiary airways were 100-fold more reactive than normal airways. These data suggest that hyperreactivity may result from a modification of the histamine and/or cholinergic receptor perhaps brought about by airway inflammation. Such airway inflammation could be a result of the release for major basic protein from eosinophil granules or toxic oxygen radicals species released from activated macrophages, eosinophils, or neutrophils (13). The correlation between *in vivo* and *in vitro* muscle hyperresponsiveness has been evident in only certain animals models (8, 42). With human muscle, a correlation has been consistently missing (4).

Tracheal Airway Epithelial Permeability

Another hypothesis for hyperreactive airways suggests that they arise from increased airway permeability. In order to test this hypothesis, tracheal epithelium obtained from immunized or challenged rabbits was compared to normal rabbit epithelium (28). Tracheal epithelium was dissected from the airways of immunized or challenged rabbits and the whole thickness preparation was placed in a Ussing chamber. The bioelectric properties of these tissues were examined with the tracheal sections mounted mucosal-side-up in the Ussing chamber and perfused with Earle's solution and 0.1% glucose. Short circuit current (Isc) and transmembrane potential difference (PD) were recorded with reversible electrodes. Transmural resistance (R_{tm}) was calculated from voltage deflexions derived by passing a bipolar current (154 mΩ/cm^2) pulse. The spontaneous resistance (Rs) was calculated

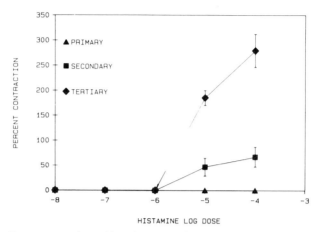

Figure 5a   Percent contraction to histamine HCl (10^{-8}-10^{-4}M) of isolated smooth from tracheal (primary) airways, secondary (diameter = 2 mm) and tertiary airways (diameter = 1 mm) from normal non-immunized rabbits.

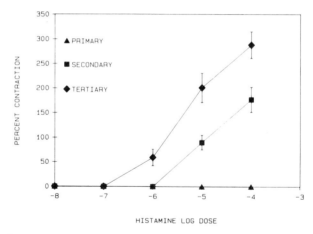

Figure 5b   Percent contraction to histamine HCl of isolated smooth muscle from primary, secondary, and tertiary airways of allergic rabbits obtained 24 hours after an allergen challenge.

from spontaneous PD/Isc and compared to R_{tm}. Recordings made from sensitized tissues showed that transmural PD was reduced compared to control rabbits, but not significantly ($p < 0.1$). The short circuit current was nearly identical for both groups of rabbits, but transmural resistance for sensitized rabbits was 25% less than that of control rabbits (75.6 ± 12.6 ohm-cm^2 *verses* 100.7 ± 7.6 ohm-cm^2 ($p < 0.02$). These data suggest that immunized tracheal epithelium possesses modified biolectric properties consistent with increased permeability to ion fluxes. These leaky membranes arise following immunization or aerosol challenge to perhaps account for an increase in airway hyperresponsiveness. They may be a result of the transmigration of inflammatory cells through tight junctions as recently demonstrated for gut epithelium (34).

STUDIES WITH PAF-ANTAGONIST, GINKGOLIDE BN 52021

Inhibition of Cutaneous Responses

Early and late phase skin test responses can be ilicited in this model by PCA or direct allergen skin testing. Late cutaneous responses (LCR) have been studied previously and were similar to the late response in the lung (23). An infiltrate of inflammatory cells began following localized edema presumably from an increase in vascular permeability. Neutrophil and eosinophils infiltrated the skin, and the response lasted generally 24 hours. Neutrophils and eosinophils were prominent at 6-8 hours; eosinophils, however, persisted while neutrophils were mostly replaced by monocytes at 24 hours.

In the present studies, we attempted to block allergen-induced skin responses using ragweed (6,000 PNU Greer Laboratories, lenoir, NC) or PAF-induced skin responses with the specific PAF antagonist, BN 52021. Initially, serum from ragweed immunized rabbits and three sham immunized (saline) rabbits was applied to the backs of two normal rabbits along with positive and negative control serum. BN 52021 given orally one hour before the skin tests were applied (20 mg/kg) had a small but significant effect on inhibiting the late phase of the PCA reaction at a 1-20 dilution of serum (ragweed, early equals 13.3 ± 1.2 mm; late = 14.9 ± 1.1 mm vs. BN 52021, early = 15.4 ± 1.0 mm, late = 13.5 ± 2.0 mm, $p < 0.01$). Others have found it difficult to inhibit a PCA reaction in the guinea pig (Caroline Touvay, personal communication), and this may be the cause for this minimal inhibition. It is more likely, however, to be a result of the small dose of BN 52021 since direct skin testing was inhibitable by larger doses (Table 1).

Direct Skin Test

Early and late phase skin test reactions to PAF (20 ng) and ragweed allergen extract (6,000 pnu) were developed in sensitized rabbits and blocked by increasing doses of BN 52021, given orally one hour before skin tests were applied. BN 52021 completely inhibited the PAF- induced early and late phase response at 20 mg/kg, but inhibited only the early ragweed response

Table 1 Modification of early and late phase cutaneous responses by PAF antagonist, BN 52021, in the allergic rabbit

Agonist (Dose)	Antagonist (Dose)	Skin Response*		Histology**	
PAF	BN 52021	ICR	LCR	ICR	LCR
(200 ng)	(20 mg/kg)	0	0	0	±
(200 ng)	(10 mg/kg)	+	±	ND	ND
(200 ng)	(5 mg/kg)	+	+	+	+
Ragweed	BN 52021				
(6,000 PNU)	(2 mg/kg)	+	+ +	ND	ND
	(5 mg/kg)	+	+ +	ND	ND
	(24 mg/kg)	0	+	+ +	+ + +
	(40 mg/kg)	0	0	0	+
	(60 mg/kg)	0	0	0	0

PAF = platelet activating factor; ICR = immediate cutaneous response; LCR = late cutaneous response. *Scale + = 10 mm wheal on induration, + + = 15 mm; + + + = 20 mm; **Scale 1 + —4 + , ± a few infiltratin neutrophils, ND = not done.

and not the late phase response at 24 mg/kg. It had no effect on the histology of the allergen-induced skin responses. At 40 mg/kg both the early and LCR was blocked by ginkgolide BN 52021, but only the early influx of cells observed histologically was inhibited (Fig. 6), and not the late phase migration. It required 60 mg/kg of BN 52021 to inhibit both the observable skin test responses and the histological appearance of cellular inflammation in these skin biopsies. It appeared, therefore, that it was somewhat easier to inhibit a PAF response with this specific PAF antagonist than to inhibit an allergen-induced response to the skin. This seems reasonable, since other mediators and a much more complex inflammatory response is probably induced by allergen than by PAF, and the pathways of inflammation are triggered differetly. PAF, nevertheless, appears to be a major mediator for the early and late phase skin response and cellular inflammation.

Modification of the Late Phase Airway Response, Bronchial Hyperreactivity, and Cellular Inflammation

In these studies, five ragweed allergic rabbits were first challenged with histamine to establish their baseline airways hyperresponsiveness (sensitivity and reactivity) and then challenged with ragweed allergen (10,000 pnu/ml)

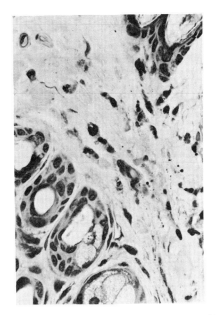 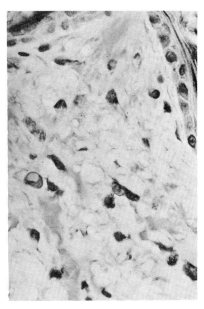

Figue 6a   Skin biopsy (40x, giemsa) of sensitized rabbit following ragweed allergen (6,000 pnu) skin test showing a marked inflammatory response including mast cells, eosinophils, and neutrophils with multiple metachromatic granules scattered throughout dermis.

Figure 6b   Skin biopsy of sensitized rabbit skin (100x) with ragweed extract (6,000 pnu) in an animal pretreated with BN 52021 (60 mg/kg), showing a lack of inflammatory cell infiltrate.

to induce an early and late phase airway response. A post challenge histamine dose-response was performed 24 hours later to establish the change in airway hyperresponsiveness. Two weeks later, each rabbit serving as its own control underwent a second allergen challenge with a pre- and post-histamine challenge but the allergen challenge was preceded by an oral dose of BN 52021 (100 mg/kg) given in Karo® Syrup. Each animal was lavaged at baseline, 30 minutes, 6 hours, and 24 hours post-challenge; neutrophils and eosinophils were differentially counted from cyto-centrifuged preparations. Platelet counts in lavage fluid and peripheral blood were obtained using the Coulter counter for the blood and Unopette® for lavage platelets. Changes in airway sensitivity and reactivity, total cell counts of neutrophils and eosinophils in lavage fluid, and the total airway response as determined by the early and late phase curve was determined for each animal with and without the protection of PAF antagonist, BN 52021.

Modification of the Late Phase Response By BN 52021

The late phase response curve (1-6 hours) following pretreatment with BN 52021 was reduced by an average of 43% compared to antigen alone (p < 0.05) (Fig. 7). The late response curve following BN 52021 was significantly reduced compared to antigen challenge from one hour through six hours post challenge. There was no observable difference in the early response curves for antigen compared to BN 52021.

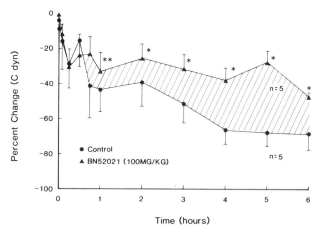

Figure 7   Modification of late phase response by BN 52021. Hatched area represents difference between unprotected allergen challenge (•) and allergen challenge following pretreatment with BN 52021 (△).

Comparison of Airways Sensitivity and Reactivity

A PC_{50} for histamine (the histamine concentration to reduce the Cdyn by 50%) was calculated for each animal pre- and post-aerosol challenge with antigen alone and after pretreatment with BN 52021. For antigen challenge, there was a small increase in sensitivity of 31%, from 8.7 to 6.0 PC_{50}, and for BN 52021, a 31% increase from 6.6 to 2.9 PC_{50} when each animal was compared and the groups averaged. The reactivity of the airways (slope of the histamine dose-response curve), was markedly increased in reactivity (315%) following allergen challenge. After BN 52021, there was a 30% decrease in reactivity (slope = 1.9 vs. 1.2) compared to allergen (slope = 0.6 vs. 1.9). Therefore, pretreatment with BN 52021 appeared to inhibit airway reactivity but not sensitivity. Orahek (35) has shown a similar phenomenon occurring in humans and has suggested that a change in reactivity may be more important to the asthmatic than a change in sensitivity. Intuitively, this seems reasonable since patients who demonstrate a gradually decreasing airway response to allergen exposure may have mild symptoms, whereas patients with an acute, reactive response to allergen challenge may present more dramatically, rapidly developing severe asthmatic symptoms.

Change In Neutrophil and Eosinophil Imflammation in Bronchial Lavage Fluid

Total cell counts for neutrophils and eosinophils were obtained from total white cell counts, and differential counts of cytospin preparations of bronchial lavage cells (Table 2). Neutrophils and eosinophils increased from baseline at 6 and 24 hours after challenge with allergen. When animals were given BN 52021, there was a marked increase at 6 hours but no significant further increase between 6 and 24 hours for either neutrophils or eosinophils. The inhibition was more obvious for eosinophils than for neutrophils when animals were given the PAF antagonist.

Table 2 Total cell counts in bronchial lavage after ragweed allergen challenge

	Neutrophils	Eosinophils	Epithelial	Lymphocytes	Macrophages
Pre-Challenge	412 ± 236	10 ± 5	409 ± 229	180 ± 82	908 ± 167
1 hrs	486 ± 130	13 ± 9	170 ± 107	19 ± 6	136 ± 60
3 hrs	1821 ± 493	53 ± 22	57 ± 17	29 ± 18	335 ± 106
6 hrs	1734 ± 857	66 ± 43	34 ± 11	30 ± 12	261 ± 128
24 hrs	6072 ± 3018	236 ± 182	85 ± 26	31 ± 10	660 ± 139

Mean total cell counts ± S.E.M. for six (6) rabbits challenged with ragweed extract (40,000 pnu/ml).

Challenge in Platelets in Lavage Fluid and Blood After Allergen Challenge

Immediately after allergen challenge, there was a decrease in peripheral blood platelets followed by a steady rise up to two hours. Subsequently, a fall in blood platelets was found for the next several hours with its nadir between 5 to 24 hours. These changes were significantly different from baseline levels. Following pretreatment with PAF antagonist BN 52021, there was less of a decrease before five hours, but there remained a significant overall decrease from baseline during late phase response. In bronchial lavage fluid, however, rabbit platelets were increased immediately after allergen challenge (p < 0.1) but decreased when the animals were pretreated with BN 52021. However, at one hour and beyond, there was no difference between allergen and PAF antagonist treated animals. Platelets in lavage fluid remained low throughout the late phase response and then rebounded at 24 hours to suprabaseline levels. These differences during the late phase response, however, were not statistically significant.

Summary of Skin and Airway Effects

Ginkgolide BN 52021 inhibited the LCR to allergen in a dose response fashion, first the visible skin response (40 mg/kg), then the histopathology with 60 mg/kg. In the case of direct skin testing, unlike the airway response, the early response was inhibited as well as the LCR at the 40 mg/kg dose. With the PCA reaction, however, the immediate bluing reaction was not modified, but the LCR was reduced a small but significant amount (12.3%, p < 0.01). This observation was similar to that for the late phase airway response (See below).

These data revealed a marked and significant ability of the naturally occurring specific PAF antagonist, BN 52021, to inhibit the late phase response but have no significant effect on the early airway response. Both the severity and the intensity of the phase response was blocked, but not completely. BN 52021 did completely inhibit the expected increase in airway hyperreactivity following allergen challenge. There was, however, no effect on airway sensitivity to allergen. Finally, there appeared to be an influx of platelets into lavage fluid immediately after allergen challenge, which was blocked by compound BN 52021. There was no difference in the reduction in platelets seen after allergen challenge in either peripheral blood or lavage fluid. Ongoing investigations are designed to potentially indentify platelets ingested by lung macrophages during the LAR (29). The difference in inhibitability between direct allergen skin testing, the PCA phenomenon, and the LAR is not clear. It may be due to a more complex mechanism for the PCA and LAR or a difference in the location of PAF receptors in the lung and skin or a greater dependence on vascular permeability in skin but on smooth muscle contraction in the lung. It was clear that PAF-induced responses were easier to inhibit than allergen-induced responses and that PAF-antagonism preferentially modified the LAR, which is presumably more relevant for the induction of clinical asthma (22).

The degree to which the LAR was modified was similar to that seen previously with allergy immunotherapy in humans (19). The observation that the LAR was not affected by PAF antagonism suggests that other mediators than PAF must be effecting the acute bronchospasm and edema characteristic of asthma during early phase response. This may not apply to skin responses since the early skin response was partially inhibited by lower doses of BN 52021. Therefore PAF may play a relatively more important role in the early skin response than the early airway response. PAF does appear to be very important, however, for the induction of the late phase response and bronchial hyperreactivity (6, 32, 36).

Blocking the influx of eosinophils and neutrophils into the airways following a LAR suggests that PAF is instrumental in furthering the inflammatory process in the lung following allergen challenge. PAF has recently been demonstrated to be chemotactic for eosinophils *in vitro* (45) and *in vivo* (12). These data suggest that PAF may contribute to lung inflammation in a manner similar to neutrophil and eosinophil chemotactic factors following their release from mast cells (27). Partial inhibition of cellular inflammation and the late phase response by BN 52021 suggests that other mediators are also important for the decrease in pulmonary function during the late phase response.

Earlier investigators have shown that PAF is essential to the production of late phase asthma and bronchial hyperreactivity (32). Others have shown that PAF antagonists, such as the glinkgolide mixture BN 52063, can antagonize skin and platelet responses by inhibiting the wheal and flare reaction to PAF (5). A mixture of three PAF antagonists, including BN 52021, has also been shown to be suitable for the relief of asthma (11). These data suggest that PAF plays a role in changes of vascular permeability, cellular inflammation, and the induction of airway hyperreactivity. The allergic rabbit model, modified to produce early and late phase airway and skin responses, has been useful to explore these hypotheses. The use of PAF antagonists will help elucidate the pathogenetic mechanisms for allergic asthma, and BN 52021 appears to be one of these pharmacologic agents which modifies both allergic skin responses and allergic asthma and will perhaps lead to improved pharmacologic treatment of allergic airway and skin diseases.

ACKNOWLEDGEMENTS

Supported by an NIH Grant R01 HL 34741, K08 AI00664 and Institut Henri Beaufour, Le-Plessis Robinson, France. Dr. Metzger is the recipient of Clinical Investigator Award K08AI00664.

References

1. Braquet, P., Touqui, L., Shen, T.Y., Vargaftig, B.B. *Perspectives in platelet research.* Pharmacol Rev 1987; 39: 97-145.
2. Braquet, P., Vargaftig, B.B. *Pharmacology of platelet-activating factor.* Transplantation Proc 1986; 18: 10-19.
3. Casale, T.B., Wood, D., Trapp, S., Richerson, H.B., Metzger, W.J., Hunninghake, G.W. *Elevated bronchoalveolar lavage (BAL) fluid histamine levels in allergic asthmatics are associated with methacholine bronchial hyperresponsiveness.* J Clin Investigation 1987; in press.
4. Cerrina, J., Ladurie, M.L., Labat, Cl., Raffestin, B., Boyol, A., Brick, C. *Comparison of human bronchial muscle responses to histamine in vitro with histamine and isoproterenol agonists in vitro.* Amer Rev Resp Dis 1986; 134: 57-61.
5. Chung, K.E., Dent, G., McCusker, M., Guinot, P.H., Page, C.P., Barnes, P.J. *Effect of ginkgolide mixture (BN 52063) in antagonizing skin and platelet responses to platelet-activating factor in man.* Lancet 1987; i: 248-251.
6. Cuss, F.M., Dixon, C.M.S., Barnes, P.J. *Effects of inhaled platelet-activating factor on pulmonary function and bronchial responsiveness in man.* Lancet 1986; ii: 189-192.
7. Davidson, J.T., Wasserman, K., Lillington, G.A., Schmidt, R.W. *Pulmonary function testing in the rabbit.* J Appl Physiol 1966; 21: 1096-1098.
8. Douglas, J.S., Ridgway, P., Brink, C. *Airway responses o the guinea pig in vivo and in vitro.* J Pharm Exp Ther 1977; 202: 116-124.
9. Filley, W.V., Holley, K.E., Kephart, G.M., Gleich, G.J. *Identification by immunofluorescence of eosinophil major basic protein in lung tissues of patients with bronchial asthma.* Lancet 1982; ii: 11-15.
10. Frigas, E., Loergering, D.A., Solley, G.O., Farrow, G.M., Gleich, G.J. *Elevated levels of the eosinophil granule major basic protein in the sputum of patients with bronchial asthma.* Mayo Clin Proc 1987; 56: 345-353.
11. Guinot, P.H., Brombilla, C., Duchies, J., Braquet, P., Cournot, K. *Effect of BN 52063, a specific PAF-acether antagonist on bronchial provocation test for allergens in asthmatic patients.* Clin Resp Physiol Bull 1987; in press.
12. Henocq, E., Vargaftig, B.B. *Accumulation of eosinophils in response to intracutaneous PAF-acether and allergens in the mouse.* Lancet 1986; i: 1378-1379.
13. Henson, P.M., Johnston, R.B. *Tissue injury in inflammation: Oxidants, proteinases, and cationic proteins.* J Clin Investig 1987; 79: 669-674.
14. Herxheimer, H. *The late bronchial reaction in induced asthma.* Int Arch Allergy Appl Immunol 1952; 3: 323.
15. *Hippocrates: Tempus iii.* In: The Aphorisms of Hippocrates. Translated by Thomas Carr. A.J. Valpy; London 1822.
16. Ishihara, T., Akizuki, S., Yokota, T., Takahasi, M., Uchino, F., Matsumoto, N. *Foamy cells associated with platelet phagocytosis.* Am J Pathol 1984; 114: 104-111.
17. Knauer, K.A., Lichtenstein, L.M., Adkinson, N.F., Fish, J.E. *Platelet activation during antigen-induced airway reactions in asthmatic subjects.* New Engl J Med 1981; 304: 1404-1407.
18. Metzger, W.J., Brown, L.A., Sjoerdsma, K.W., Mustafa, J. *Bronchial airway hyperreactivity in a rabbit model for allergic asthma: Response to histamine, acetylcholine, and platelet-activating factor.* In: Symposium on PAF and Bronchial Airway Hyperreactivity, Platelet-Activating Factor, Pulmonary Hyperreactivity, and Asthma. Karger 1987; in press.
19. Metzger, W.J., Donelley, A., Richerson, H.B. *Modification of late asthmatic responses during immunotherapy for Alternaria-induced asthma.* NER Allergy Proc 1985; 3: 270.
20. Metzger, W.J., Henriksen, R.A., Zaleski, T., Donnely, A. *Evidence for platelet release and thrombin generation in early and late asthmatic responses.* Clin Res 1983; 33: 164.
21. Metzger, W.J., Hunninghake, G.W., Wasserman, S.I., Henriksen, R., Worden, K., Richerson, H.B. *Use of bronchoalveolar lavage to study local inflammatory mediators, immunologic effector cell populations, and histopathology of effector cells in allergen-induced asthma.* Am Rev Respir Dis 1983; 127: 67.
22. Metzger, W.J., Hunninghake, G.W., Richerson, H.B. *Late asthmatic responses: Inquiry into mechanisms and significance.* Clin Rev Allergy 1985; 3: 145-165.
23. Metzger, W.J., Kregel, K., Richerson, H.B., Moore, K. *Histopathology of late responses (LR) in skin and airways of rabbits producing specific IgE.* Proc XI Int Cong Allergology, London 1982; Abst 524.

24. Metzger, W.J., Lakin, R., Richerson, H.B., Monick, M., Brady, M., Worden, K., Hunninghake, G.W. *Bronchoalveolar lavage of allergic asthmatic lungs following allergen bronchoprovocation.* Chest 1986; 89: 477-483.

25. Metzger, W.J., Nugent, K., Richerson, H.B. *Site of airway obstruction in allergen-induced late phase asthmatic responses.* Chest 1985; 88: 369-375.

26. Metzger, W.J., Richerson, H.B., Kregel, K., Barfknecht, C., Moore, K. *Late phase obstructive airways responses (LPR) in a rabbit model: Physiologic and anatomic findings.* Amer Rev Resp Dis 1982; 125: 62.

27. Metzger, W.J., Richerson, H.B., Wasserman, S.I. *Generation and partial characterization of eosinophil chemotactic activity and neutrophil chemotactic activity during early and late phase airway responses.* J Allergy Clin Immunol 1986; 72: 282-290.

28. Metzger, W.J., Scardo, J., Youmans, S., Bentzel, C. *Bioelectric properties of tracheal epithelium in allergic rabbits.* Fed Proc 1987; 46: 1043.

29. Metzger, W.J., Sjoersma, K.W., Richerson, H.B., Moseley, P., Zavala, D., Monick, M., Hunninghake, G.W. *Platelets in bronchoalveolar lavage from asthmatc patients and allergic rabbits with allergen-induced late phase responses.* Agents and Action 1987; in press.

30. Metzger, W.J., Zavala, D., Richerson, H.B., Moseley, P., Iwamota, P., Monick, M., Sjoerdsma, K.W., Hunninghake, G.W. *Local allergen challenge and bronchoalveolar lavage of allergic asthmatic lungs.* Amer Rev Resp Dis 1987; 135: 433-440.

31. Morley, J., Page, C.P., Paul, W. *Inflammatory actions of platalet-activating factor (PAF-acether) in guinea pig strain.* Br J Pharmacol 1983; 80: 503-509.

32. Morley, J., Page, C.R., Sanjar, S. *Pulmonary responses to platelet-activating factor.* Prog Resp Res 1985; 19: 117-123.

33. Morley, J., Sanjar, S., Page, C.P. *The platelet in asthma.* Lancet 1984; ii: 1142-1144.

34. Nash, S., Madara, J. *Intestinal epithelial tight junctions (TJ) open and reseal during polymorphonuclear leukocyte (PMN) transmigration.* Gastroenterollogy 1987; 92: 1549.

35. Orahek, F.J., Goyrard, P., Smith, A.P., Grimand, K., Charpin, J. *Airway response to carbacol in normal and asthmatic subjects: Distinction between bronchial sensitivity and reactivity.* Amer Rev Resp Dis 1977; 115: 937-943.

36. Patterson, R., Berstein, P.R., Harris, K.E., Krele, R.D. *Airway responses to sequential challenges with platelet-activating factor and leukotriene D_4 in rhesus monkeys.* J Lab Clin Med 1984; 104: 340-345.

37. Pinkard, R.N., Halonen, M., Meng, A.C. *Preferential expression of anti-bovine serum albumin IgE homocytotrophic antibody synthesis and anaphylactic sensitivity in the neonatal rabbit.* J Allergy Clin Immunol 1972; 49: 301-310.

38. Platts-Mills, T.A.E., Tovey, E.R., Mitchell, E.B., Mosgoro, H., Nock, P., Wilkins, S.R. *Reduction of hyperreactivity during prolonged allergen avoidance.* Lancet 1982; ii: 675-678.

39. Reed, C.E. *New therapeutic approaches in asthma.* J Allergy Clin Immunol 1986; 77: 537-543.

40. Shampain, M.P., Behrens, B.L., Larsen, G.L., Henson, P.M. *An animal model of late pulmonary responses to Alternaria challenge.* Amer Rev Resp Dis 1982; 126: 483-493.

41. deShazo, R.D., Levinson, A.I., Dvorak, H.F., Davis, R.W. *The late phase skin reaction. Evidence for activation of the coagulation system in an IgE dependent reaction in man.* J Immunol 1979; 122: 692-698.

42. Snapper, J.R., Drazen, J.M., Loring, S.H., Ingram, R.H. *Distribution of pulmonary responsiveness to aerosol histamine in dogs.* J Appl Physiol 1978; 44: 738-742.

43. Solley, G.O., Gleich, G.J., Jordon, R.E., Schroeter, A.L. *The late phase of the immediate wheal and flare skin reaction: Its dependence upon IgE antibodies.* J Clin Investigation 1976; 58: 408-420.

44. Touvay, C., Vilain, B., Etienne, A., Sirois, P., Borgeat, P., Braquet, P. *Characterization of platelet-activating factor (PAF)-acether-induced contractions of guinea pig lung strips by selected inhibitors of arachidonic acid metabolism and by PAF-acether antagonists.* Immunopharmacology 1986; 12: 87-104.

45. Wardlaw, A.J., Moqbel, R., Cromwell, O., Kay, A.B. *Platelet-activating factor. A potent chemotactic and chemokinetic factor for eosinophils.* J Clin Invest 1986; 78: 1701-1706.

46. Zavala, D., Rhodes, M. *Selective bronchial catheterization for the study of experimental lung damage in the rabbit.* Proc Soc Exp Biol Med 1973; 144: 509-512.

Ginkgolides - Chemistry, Biology, Pharmacology and Clinical Perspectives. P. Braquet (Ed.)
Copyright © 1988, J.R. Prous Science Publishers, S.A.

CLINICAL PERSPECTIVES OF PAF-ACETHER ANTAGONISTS

Kian F. Chung and Peter J. Barnes

Department of Clinical Pharmacology, Cardiothoracic Institute, Brompton Hospital, London, UK

INTRODUCTION

The discovery of platelet-activating factor (PAF) and its potent biological effects has raised the possibility that this phospholipid mediator may play an important role in several disease states, particularly those with an allergic basis. Already, with the use of currently available PAF antagonists, PAF has been implicated in several animal models of disease and this has raised the hope that specific PAF receptor antagonists may become a significant addition to the therapeutic armamentarium against a wide range of diseases. Although PAF antagonists have been recently studied in man as to their activity and specificity (13, 31), their use in human disease dates back four thousand years since the first Chinese Pharmacopeia mentioned extracts from plants which are now known to exhibit significant PAF-antagonist activity. In this review, we shall examine (i) the potent biological properties of PAF that may be clinically relevant, (ii) the experimental evidence for involvement of PAF in animal models of human disease and (iii) the therapeutic scope for PAF antagonists in clinical medicine.

BIOLOGICAL EFFECTS OF PAF OF CLINICAL RELEVANCE

Microvascular Permeability

PAF possesses several properties that indicate its possible role as an important mediator of the inflammatory response of several disease processes,

---

Address all correspondence to: Prof. P.J. Barnes, Department of Clinical Pharmacology, Cardiothoracic Institute, Brompton Hospital, Fulham Road, London SW3 6HP, England.

particularly those with an underlying allergic basis. PAF is a potent inducer of microvascular permeability and, for example in the airways, is the most potent mediator known being active at nanogram doses as low as 1 ng/kg when injected intravenously in the guinea-pig (25). Presumably, only the release of tiny amounts of PAF is needed to cause clinically significant edema, particularly in conditions such as asthma, anaphylaxis and urticaria. This effect of PAF is direct, since it is not inhibited by cyclooxygenase or lipoxygenase mediators (25). In the pulmonary vascular bed, PAF induces edema, and this effect may be partly contributory through the increase in pulmonary arterial pressures (33, 35) and partly through a direct effect on pulmonary vascular endothelium (9). Thus, PAF may be considered as a putative mediator in the acute respiratory distress syndrome.

Effects on Inflammatory Cells

In addition to increasing microvascular permeability, PAF causes chemotaxis of inflammatory cells, an effect that can be demonstrated both *in vivo* and *in vitro*. A characteristic feature of this effect is the more active chemotactic activity of PAF for eosinophils when compared to neutrophils (66). When injected into the skin of atopic volunteers, PAF predominantly causes an infiltrate of eosinophils, in contrast to neutrophil infiltration in non-atopic subjects (37). When inhaled by non-atopic volunteers, PAF causes a mild neutrophilia in bronchoalveolar lavage fluid, with activation of circulating neutrophils, as evidenced by their reduction in density. In addition, PAF causes sequestration of platelets in the lungs (51).

The fact that PAF is the most potent chemotactic agent for eosinophils supports its role in diseases where eosinophils may play a central role, such as in asthma and allergic diseases. The interaction between PAF and eosinophils may be complex, since activated eosinophils may also release PAF, thus raising the possibility of putative feedback mechanisms.

PAF may directly activate inflammatory cells to cause the generation of other newly-formed mediators and the release of oxygen radicals and lysosomal enzymes. Thus, neutrophils *in vitro* generate substantial amounts of leukotriene B_4 (45), and platelets release platelet granule factors such as platelet factor 4 and serotonin (47) on stimulation by PAF. Intravenously-administered PAF causes a fall in circulating platelets and white blood cells, thus mimicking the changes seen in anaphylactic shock (32, 46). In man, inhaled PAF causes a transient neutropenia, but has no effect on circulating platelets (17), although higher doses may do so (28).

Airway Smooth Muscle

PAF is a potent bronchoconstrictor agent in several species *in vivo* including guinea-pig (64), rabbit (32), baboon (21), dog (13) and man (20, 56), despite being a poor constrictor of tracheal and bronchial smooth muscle *in vitro* (64). In humans, PAF given by inhalation causes rapid bronchoconstriction with recovery over 1-2 hours; lyso-PAF, by contrast, has no significant effect (20). Unlike other bronchoconstrictors that have been studied, there is no relationship between the sensitivity to PAF and that to cholinergic agonists. This is particularly seen in asthmatic subjects who are hyperreactive to methacholine, but show a similar responsiveness as normal subjects to inhaled PAF (18). It is unlikely that this is a consequence of tachyphylaxis to endogenous PAF, since a similar bronchoconstrictor response is seen in normal and asthmatic subjects with PAF. A more likely possibility is that the acute airway response may be due to mechanisms in addition to airway smooth muscle contraction, such as airway edema, since PAF is a potent mediator of airway microvascular leakage (25). Thus, PAF may mimic the bronchial obstruction seen in asthma.

Hemodynamic Effects

When injected intravenously, PAF causes acute circulatory collapse with hypotension, and decreased coronary blood flow with arrythmias (5). In addition, PAF has a negative inotropic effect on the heart (41). These effects of PAF suggest that it may mediate some of the clinical features of human systemic anaphylaxis and shock.

PAF causes vasoconstriction in several systemic beds, such as skin, hamster cheek pouch, coronary circulation, small intestine and nasal mucosa (7, 38, 39, 44, 54). In the skin, intradermal injection of PAF causes immediate blanching before the appearance of the wheal and flare response (2). Although coronary vasoconstriction is not dependent on cyclooxygenase or lipoxygenase products (44), small intestinal vasoconstriction is thought to be secondarily mediated by leukotrienes (38). On the other hand, PAF can also induce dilatation of the isolated aorta of the rat precontracted with noradrenaline (12); this effect is dependent on the presence of a functionally intact endothelium. This raises the possibility for a beneficial role for PAF in peripheral vascular disease, and even in coronary artery disease (40), given the fact that PAF can be synthesised by human vascular endothelial cells (10, 55).

In pulmonary circulation, PAF causes vasoconstriction, an effect seen in the absence of platelets but potentiated by their presence (33, 35) and dependent on cyclooxygenase products (probably thromboxane A_2) (8, 33) or lipoxygenase products (65). However, extremely low doses of PAF (0.001-1.0 μg/animal) reduces the pressure of normal or precontracted pulmonary vascular bed, an effect which is independent of cyclooxygenase products but dependent on the presence of an intact endothelium (48). This complicated effect of PAF on pulmonary circulation makes it difficult to postulate a role for PAF in hypoxic pulmonary vasoconstriction.

Bronchial Hyperresponsiveness

Increased responsiveness of airways to many different stimuli is a characteristic feature of asthma and its pathogenesis is uncertain. Inflammation of the airways may underlie bronchial hyperresponsiveness and the precise contribution of inflammatory mediators remains unknown (14). Unlike the transient effect of prostaglandin D_2 or of the thromboxane-mimetic U 46619 in increasing bronchial responsiveness (1, 27), PAF is the only known mediator to cause sustained hyperresponsiveness in guinea-pig (50a), dog (13) and monkey (52). Inhaled PAF also causes bronchial hyper-responsiveness in normal and asthmatic human subjects (18, 20). The maximal increase occurs 3 days after exposure and may persist for up to 4 weeks. Because inhaled PAF is rapidly inactivated, this suggests that PAF produces its effects in airway responsiveness through a series of secondary events, such as the chemotaxis of eosinophils, damage to airway epithelium and stimulation of exposed sensory nerves.

EVIDENCE FOR A ROLE OF PAF IN MODELS OF DISEASE

Although there are now highly sophisticated techniques, such as gas chromatography and mass spectrometry, to detect picomolar amounts of PAF, the detection of PAF in biological fluids remains difficult since PAF is rapidly metabolized within seconds in these fluids. Nevertheless, evidence for PAF release has been obtained in some models of disease, such as cardiac anaphylaxis in the guinea-pig (44) and human cold urticaria (30), but full chemical and physical characterization of the PAF-like lipids detected under these circumstances have not been done. Measurement of PAF may only provide supportive evidence, since only very small amounts of PAF may be released in view of its extreme biological potency. It seems more

Table 1 Diseases in which PAF may play an important role

Asthma
Systemic anaphylaxis
Endotoxin shock
Cold urticaria
Psoriasis
Arthus responses
Ischaemic bowel disease

likely that the use of specific PAF-antagonists will provide information about the role of PAF in human disease. There is already such direct evidence emerging for several pathophysiological conditions. The following diseases will be reviewed as to the possible role of PAF (Table 1) and this is not intended to be a comprehensive list.

Anaphylaxis

A number of humoral mediators, such as histamine and leukotrienes, may mediate several features of human systemic anaphylaxis but there are several lines of evidence supporting an important role for PAF in this condition. Infusion of PAF in several species mimics many features seen in systemic anaphylaxis, including circulatory collapse with hypotension and decreased coronary blood flow, bronchoconstriction and a fall in circulating neutrophils and platelets. Release of PAF into the circulation in the rabbit (53), in the coronary circulation in the guinea-pig (44) and in the perfused guinea-pig lung (26) have been reported during anaphylaxis. Antagonists of PAF, such as BN 52021 and SRI 63072, inhibit the hemodynamic changes characteristic of anaphylaxis induced by intravenous administration of human IgG aggregates in rats, resulting in improved survival rates (34, 58). Bronchoconstriction induced by ovalbumin in sensitized animals is inhibited by PAF-antagonists (11, 62). However, the increased airway vascular permeability seen during anaphylaxis in the actively sensitized guinea-pig was not inhibited by PAF antagonists (23, 24).

Asthma

PAF can reproduce several pathological features of asthma and must, therefore, be considered as a putative mediator in this condition. PAF induces a sustained inflammatory response in the airways, with desquamation of airway epithelium and accumulation of neutrophils, macrophages, eosinophils and platelets. PAF is a potent chemotactic agent for human eosinophils *in vitro* and *in vivo* and may, therefore, account for the eosinophilic infiltration which is characteristic of asthmatic airways. The fact that eosinophils themselves may be a source of PAF raises the possibility of continued inflammation resulting from an interaction between PAF and eosinophils. PAF, being a potent inducer of microvascular leakage, may be responsible for the airway edema and extravasation of plasma described in asthmatic airways. Impaired mucociliary clearance is also seen after PAF (3) and is also a feature of asthma exacerbation.

PAF is a potent bronchoconstrictor of normal and asthmatic airways and, of greater interest, can induce a sustained increase in bronchial responsiveness. The acute bronchoconstrictor response is partially inhibited by prior

therapy with a beta-adrenergic agonist (17). The induced hyperresponsiveness is also slightly reduced, an effect similar to that seen with allergen-
induced hyperresponsiveness. On the other hand, ketotifen, which has
substantial antihistamine properties, does not affect PAF-induced bronchoconstriction or hyperresponsiveness (16). Interestingly, the same dose
of ketotifen did inhibit PAF-induced wheal and flare responses in the skin.
These studies suggest that PAF-induced effects in the airways, in contrast
to its cutaneous effects, are not mediated by histamine. Preliminary data
suggest that allergen-induced bronchial hyperresponsiveness in sensitized
guinea-pigs is inhibited by the PAF antagonist BN 52021 (19).

There is circumstantial evidence for the release of PAF into the circulation in induced bronchoconstriction in asthma. The reduction in the aggregation of circulating platelets to exogenous PAF but not to exogenous
ADP *in vitro* after antigen challenge has been used as evidence that PAF
was released *in vivo* (61). Indirect evidence of platelet involvement has been
obtained. Thus, during an antigen challenge, platelet-derived products, such
as platelet factor 4 and beta-thromboglobulin, can be detected in the circulation (42). In addition, there is a decreased survival time of a significant
proportion of circulating platelets in asthma (60). Whether these platelet
abnormalities can be ascribed to PAF remains to be determined.

Skin Diseases

Urticaria is a localized cutaneous form of anaphylaxis. In addition to raised circulating levels of histamine, platelet factor 4 and chemotactic factor
for eosinophils and neutrophils, a PAF-like lipid, has been isolated after
cold challenge in patients with cold urticaria (30). Doxepin, an H_1-receptor
antagonist, inhibits the release of PAF-like lipids, but not the release of
histamine and neutrophil chemotactic activity, and suppresses the urticaria
induced by cold challenge, suggesting that PAF release is only a secondary
event (30).

Because of its potent effect in causing microvascular leakage, it is possible that PAF is involved in eczema. PAF may also be implicated in psoriasis
with PAF production reported from psoriatic skin lesions (49).

Arthus Reactions

The Arthus reaction can be reproduced in experimental animals as a result
of local tissue interactions between an antigen and its circulating antibody.
This experimental model has several clinical counterparts, such as hypersensitivity pneumonitis or extrinsic allergic alveolitis in the lungs resulting from
inhalation of various organic dusts, like mouldy hay. In the rabbit, suppression of the cutaneous edema that occurs in antigen-antibody complex-

mediated hypersensitivity by the PAF-antagonist L-652731 has been reported (36). The cellular source of PAF in this model could be the neutrophil during the subsequent phagocytosis of immune complexes. Thus, PAF may be involved in human counterparts of the Arthus reaction.

Endotoxin-Mediated Effects

In addition to causing shock during human gram-negative bacterial infections, endotoxin has also been implicated in the occupational disease, byssinosis which results from exposure to cotton bracts. Endotoxin causes the release of PAF from alveolar macrophages *in vitro*, as demonstrated by the release of labelled serotonin from platelets (57). *In vivo* release of PAF has also been demonstrated from jejunum exposed to endotoxin (43). In this rat model, endotoxin causes hemorrhagic damage to the stomach and small intestine. Administration of endotoxin together with PAF results in morphological changes in the small intestine of the rat that are similar to human necrotizing enterocolitis (29). Endotoxin induces bronchoconstriction in animals (59) and man (63). It also causes pulmonary platelet recruitment, an effect which is inhibited by the PAF antagonist BN 52021 (4).

THERAPEUTIC SCOPE OF PAF-ACETHER ANTAGONISTS IN CLINICAL MEDICINE

It is clearly too early to assess the future impact of PAF-acether antagonists in clinical medicine, since the exact importance of this mediator in the diseases in which it has been implicated is not known. Studies are currently being undertaken in human disease. In this section, we shall speculate on the possible practical uses of PAF antagonists in the clinical setting.

The dose and frequency of administration of PAF antagonists need to be determined, but this may depend on the target organ being treated. Using the ginkgolide mixture BN 52063, a dose-dependent inhibition of the wheal response to PAF in the skin, with a maximal effect of the 120 mg dose at 2 hours after oral administration was found (15). However, the duration of effect of BN 52063 was not determined in this study, but in another study it was suggested that a three-times daily dose would be necessary for continued PAF-antagonist activity (31). It is not clear whether a similar degree of inhibition would be obtained in other organs (for example in the airways) as in the skin. Thus, it would be necessary to check the PAF-antagonist properties of each agent in each organ being targeted.

It is also possible that the oral route may not be the optimal route for obtaining maximum effects for certain organs. Thus, for the airways, it is well-recognized that drugs such as bronchodilators, when delivered by aerosol, achieve a greater effect at a lesser dose with reduced risk of side-effects when compared to the oral route. This is especially relevant for the possible use of PAF-antagonists in the control of asthma. Cells that are present in the lining of the inflamed airway, such as alveolar macrophages, neutrophils, eosinophils and lymphocytes, may be targets for activation by endogenous PAF, and inhibition of these cells may best be achieved by the aerosol route. Development of aerosols of PAF antagonists seems to be necessary not only to test the role of PAF in airway disease, but also to use therapeutically.

Release of large amounts of PAF in inflamed organs may occur locally and high concentrations of PAF antagonists may, therefore, be necessary at sites of inflammation. Delivery of PAF antagonists by liposomes may be of use in this situation, since it has recently been shown that liposomes labelled with technetium preferentially localizes at sites of inflammation, such as in joints affected by rheumatoid arthritis (67).

Experiments in rats have shown that PAF antagonists may not only prevent but can also revert already-established endotoxin-induced hypotension (22). This suggests that PAF antagonists may be used both as prophylaxis and as treatment of established disease. One area where this may be relevant is in the management of asthma, where PAF antagonists may prevent attacks of asthma, such as those resulting from exposure to environmental allergens and perhaps may act as a bronchodilator during an asthma attack. In acute anaphylaxis, immediate injection of a PAF antagonist may abrogate the accompanying hypotension, cardiac arrythmias, microvascular leakage and bronchoconstriction. Perhaps a greater effect would be obtained if the PAF antagonist were combined with an antihistamine. Since several diseases, particularly asthma, may result from an interaction of several inflammatory mediators, PAF antagonists combined with inhibition of lipoxygenase and cyclooxygenase inhibitors may be effective.

There has been no long-term clinical experience of PAF antagonists and it is difficult to predict the potential side-effects of these drugs. The crude alcoholic extract of the *Ginkgo biloba* leaf has been in use for several years in France for the treatment of peripheral vascular disease, and this has not been associated with any known side effects. Administration of a single dose of BN 52063 was not associated with any side effects (15). However, since PAF seems to be involved in many natural processes, such as the implantation of the human embryo in the uterus (50b), and since PAF is present in human amniotic fluid (6), it is worth remembering that these could be interfered with. Toxicological studies in animals with the PAF antagonist BN 52021 do not support such fears.

CONCLUSIONS

The availability of PAF receptor antagonists will make it possible to test the role of PAF in the pathophysiology of several human diseases. In addition, these drugs may prove to be clinically useful. Initial studies in man have shown that one PAF antagonist, the ginkgolide mixture BN 52063, is active and specific in the skin. Further studies in human volunteers are clearly warranted.

References

1. Aizawa, H., Chung, K.F., Leikauf, G.D., Ueki, I., Bethel, R.A., O'Byrne, P.M., Hirose, T., Nadel, J.A. *Significance of thromboxane generation in ozone-induced airway hyperresponsiveness in dogs.* J Appl Physiol 1986; 59: 1936-1940.

2. Archer, C.B., MacDonald, D.M., Morley, J., Page, C.P., Paul, W., Sanjar, S. *Effects of serum albumin, indomethacin and histamine H_1- antagonists on PAF-acether-induced inflammatory responses in the skin of experimental animals and man.* Br J Pharmacol 1985; 85: 109-113.

3. Aursudkij, B., Rogers, D.F., Evans, T.W., Alton, E.W.F.W., Chung, K.F., Barnes, P.J. *Reduced tracheal mucus velocity in guinea-pig in vivo by platelet-activating factor.* Am Rev Respir Dis 1987; 135: A160.

4. Beijer, L., Botting, J., Oyekan, A.O., Page, C.P., Rylander, R. *The involvement of PAF in endotoxin-induced pulmonary platelet recruitment.* Br J Pharmacol 1987; 90: P118.

5. Bessin, P., Bonnet, J., Apffel, D., Soulard, C., Desgroux, L., Pelas, I., Benveniste, J. *Acute circulatory collapse caused by platelet-activating factor (PAF-acether) in dogs.* Eur J Pharmacol 1983; 86: 403-413.

6. Billah, M.M., Johnson, J.M. *Identification of phospholipid platelet-activating factor (1-O-alkyl-2-acetyl-sn-glycero-3-phosphocholine) in human amniotic fluid and urine.* Biochem Biophys Res Commun 1983; 113: 51-58.

7. Bjork, J., Smedegard, G. *Acute microvascular effects of PAF-acether, as studied by intravital microscopy.* Eur J Pharmacol 1983; 96: 87-94.

8. Burhop, K.E., Van der Zee, H., Bizios, R., Kaplan, J.E., Malik, A.B. *Pulmonary vascular response to platelet-activating factor in awake sheep and the role of cyclooxygenase metabolites.* Am Rev Respir Dis 1986; 134: 548-554.

9. Burhop, K.E., Garcia, J.G.N., Selig, W.M., Lo, S.K., Van der Zee, H., Kaplan, J.E., Malik, A.B. *Platelet-activating factor increases lung vascular permeability to protein.* J Appl Physiol 1986; 61: 2210-2217.

10. Camussi, G., Aglietta, M., Malavasi, F., Tetta, C., Piacibello, W., Sanavio, F., Bussolino, F. *The release of platelet-activating factor from human endothelial cells in culture.* J Immunol 1983; 131: 2397-2403.

11. Casals-Stenzel, J. *Effects of WEB 2086, a novel antagonist of platelet-activating factor in active and passive anaphylaxis.* Immunopharm 1987; in press.

12. Cervoni, P., Herzlinger, H.E., Lai, F.M., Tanikella, T.K. *Aortic vascular and atrial responses to ±-1-O-octadecyl-2-acetylglyceryl-3-phosphorylcholine.* Br J Pharmacol 1983; 79: 667-671.

13. Chung, K.F., Aizawa, H., Leikauf, G.D., Ueki, I.F., Evans, T.W., Nadel, J.A. *Airway hyperresponsiveness induced by platelet-activating factor: Role of thromboxane generation.* J Pharmacol Exp Ther 1986; 236: 580-584.

14. Chung, K.F. *Role of inflammation in the hyperreactivity of the airways in asthma.* Thorax 1986; 41: 657-662.

15. Chung, K.F., Dent, G., McCusker, M., Guinot, P.M., Page, C.P., Barnes, P.J. *Effect of a ginkgolide mixture (BN 52063) in antagonising skin and platelet responses to platelet-activating factor in man.* Lancet 1987; 1: 248-251.

16. Chung, K.F., McCusker, M., Minette, P., Barnes, P.J. *Ketotifen inhibits the cutaneous responses but not the bronchoconstriction and bronchial hyperresponsiveness induced by PAF in man.* Thorax 1987; 42: 220.

17. Chung, K.F., Dent, G., McCusker, M. *Effect of a beta-2 adrenergic agonist on bron-*

choconstriction, airway hyperresponsiveness, neutropenia and neutrophil activation after platelet-activating factor in man. Am Rev Respir Dis 1987; 135: A181.

18. Chung, K.F., Dixon, C.M.S., Barnes, P.J. *Platelet-activating factor (PAF) and asthmatic airways: Effects on caliber, responsiveness and circulating cells.* (Abstract). Am Rev Respir Dis 1987; 135: A159.

19. Coyle, A., Page, C.P., Touvay, C., Villain, B., Braquet, P. *Effect of the selective PAF antagonist BN 52021 on antigen-induced bronchial hyperreactivity in the guinea-pig.* Am Rev Respir Dis 1987; 135: A161.

20. Cuss, F.M., Dixon, C.M.S., Barnes, P.J. *Effects of inhaled platelet-activating factor on pulmonary function and bronchial responsiveness in man.* Lancet 1986; 2: 189-192.

21. Denjean, A., Arnoux, B., Masse, R., Lockhart, A., Benveniste, J. *Acute effects of intratracheal administration of platelet activating factor in baboons.* J Appl Physiol 1983; 55: 799-804.

22. Doebber, T.W., Wu, M.S., Robbins, J.C., Choy, B.M., Chang, M.N., Shen, T.Y. *Platelet-activating factor (PAF) involvement in endotoxin-induced hypotension in rats. Studies with PAF-receptor antagonist kadsurenone.* Biochem Biophys Res Commun 1985; 127: 799-808.

23. Evans, T.W., Rogers, D.F., Roberts, N.M., Chung, K.F., Barnes, P.J. *Mediators of increased vascular permeability during anaphylaxis in sensitised guinea-pigs.* Thorax 1987; 42: 221.

24. Evans, T.W., Rogers, D.F., Aursudkij, B., Chung, K.F., Barnes, P.J. *Role of mediators in increased airway vascular permeability induced by antigen.* Am Rev Respir Dis 1987; 135: A315.

25. Evans, T.W., Chung, K.F., Rogers, D.F., Barnes, P.J. *Effect of platelet-activating factor on airway vascular permeability: Possible mechanisms.* J Appl Physiol 1987; in press.

26. Fitzgerald, M.F., Moncada, S., Parente, L. *The anaphylactic release of platelet-activating factor from perfused guinea pig lungs.* Br J Pharmacol 1986; 88: 149-153.

27. Fuller, R.W., Dixon, C.M.S., Dollery, C.T., Barnes, P.J. *Prostaglandin D_2 potentiates airway responsiveness to histamine and methacholine.* Am Rev Respir Dis 1986; 133: 252-254.

28. Gateau, O., Arnoux, B., Deriaz, H., Viars, P., Benveniste, J. *Acute effects of in-*

tratracheal administration of PAF-acether (platelet-activating factor) in humans. Am Rev Respir Dis 1984; 3: 129.

29. González-Crussi, F., Hseuh, W. *Experimental model of ischemic bowel necrosis. The role of platelet-activating factor and endotoxin.* Am J Pathol 1983; 112: 127-135.

30. Grandel, K.E., Farr, R.S., Wanderer, A.A., Eisenstadt, T.C., Wasserman, S.I. *Association of platelet-activating factor with primary acquired cold urticaria.* N Engl J Med 1985; 313: 405-409.

31. Guinot, Ph., Braquet, P., Duchier, J., Cournot, A. *Inhibition of PAF-acether induced wheal and flare reaction in man by a specific antagonist.* Prostaglandins 1986; 32: 160-163.

32. Halonen, M., Palmer, J.D., Lohman, I.C., McManus, L.M., Pinckard, R.N. *Respiratory and circulatory alterations induced by acetyl glyceryl ether phosphorylcholine, a mediator of IgE anaphylaxis in the rabbit.* Am Rev Respir Dis 1980; 122: 915-924.

33. Hamasaki, Y., Mojarad, M., Saga, T., Tai, H.H., Said, S.I. *Platelet-activating factor raises airway and vascular pressures and induces edema in lungs perfused with platelet free solutions.* Am Rev Respir Dis 1984; 129: 742-746.

34. Handley, D.A., Van Valen, R.G., Melden, M.K., Flury, S., Lee, M.L., Saunders, R.N. *Inhibition and reversal of endotoxin, aggregated IgG and PAF-induced hypotension in the rat by SRI 63072, a PAF receptor antagonist.* Immunopharmacology 1986; 12: 11-15.

35. Heffner, J.E., Shoemaker, S.A., Canham, E.M., Patel, M., McMurty, I.F., Morris, H.G., Repine, J.E. *Acetyl glyceryl ether phosphorylcholine-stimulated human platelets cause pulmonary hypertension and edema in isolated rabbit lungs.* J Clin Invest 1983; 71: 351-357.

36. Hellewell, P.G., Williams, T.J. *A specific antagonist of platelet-activating factor suppresses oedema formation in an Arthus reaction but not oedema induced by leukocyte chemoattractants in rabbit skin.* J Immunol 1986; 137: 302-307.

37. Henocq, E., Vargaftig, B.B. *Accumulation of eosinophils in response to intracutaneous PAF-acether and allergens in man.* Lancet 1986; 1: 1378-1379.

38. Hsueh, W., Gonzale-Crussi, F., Arroyave, J.L. *Release of leukotriene C_4 by isolated, perfused rat small intestine in response to platelet-*

activating factor. J Clin Invest 1986; 78: 108-114.

39. Humphrey, D.M., McManus, L.M., Satouchi, K., Hanahan, D.J., Pinckard, R.N. *Vasoactive properties of acetyl glyceryl ether phosphorylcholine and analogues.* Lab Invest 1982; 46: 422-427.

40. Jackson, C.V., Schumacher, W.A., Kunkel, S.L., Driscoll, E.M., Lucchesi, B.R. *Platelet-activating factor and the release of a platelet-derived coronary artery vasodilator substance in the canine.* Circ Res 1986; 58: 218-229.

41. Kenzora, J.L., Pérez, J.E., Bergman, S.R., Lange, L.G. *Effects of acetylglyceryl ether of phosphorylcholine (platelet-activating factor) on ventricular preload, afterload and contractility in dogs.* J Clin Invest 1984; 74: 1193-1203.

42. Knauer, K.A., Lichtenstein, L.M., Franklin Adkinson, Jr., N., Fish, J.E. *Platelet activation during antigen-induced airway reaction in asthmatic subjects.* N Engl J Med 1981; 304: 1404-1407.

43. Lagente, V., Lidbury, P., Steel, G., Vargaftig, B.B., Wallace, J.L., Whittle, B.J.R. *Role of PAF as a mediator of endotoxin-induced gastrointestinal damage.* Br J Pharmacol 1987; 90: P114.

44. Levi, R., Burke, J.A., Guo, Z.G., Hattori, Y., Hoppens, C.M., McManus, L.M., Hanahan, D.J., Pinckard, R.N. *Acetyl glyceryl ether phosphorylcholine (AGEPC): A putative mediator of cardiac anaphylaxis in the guinea-pig.* Circ Res 1984; 54: 117-124.

45. Lin, A.H., Morton, D.R., Gorman, R.R. *Acetyl glyceryl ether phosphorylcholine stimulates leukotriene B₄ synthesis in human polymorphonuclear leukocytes.* J Clin Invest 1982; 70: 1058-1065.

46. McManus, L.M., Hanahan, D.J., Demopoulos, C.A., Pinckard, R.N. *Pathobiology of the intravenous infusion of acetyl glyceryl ether phosphorylcholine (AGEPC), a synthetic platelet-activating factor (PAF), in the rabbit.* J Immunol 1980; 124: 2919-2924.

47. McManus, L.M., Hanahan, D.J., Pinckard, R.N. *Human platelet stimulation by acetyl glyceryl ether phosphorylcholine.* J Clin Invest 1981; 67: 903-906.

48. McMurtry, I.F., Morris, K.G. *Platelet-activating factor causes pulmonary vasodilation in the rat.* Am Rev Respir Dis 1986; 134: 757-762.

49. Mallet, A.I., Cunningham, F.M. *Structural*

identification of platelet-activating factor in psoriatic scale. Biochem Biophys Res Commun 1985; 126: 192-198.

50a. Mazzoni, L., Morley, J., Page, C.P., Sanjar, S. *Induction of airway hyper-reactivity by platelet-activating factor in the guinea-pig.* J Physiol 1985; 365: 107.

50b. O'Neil, C., Pike, I.L., Porter, R.N., Gidley-Baird, A.A., Sinosich, M.J., Saunders, D.M. *Maternal recognition of pregnancy prior to implantation: Methods for monitoring embryonic viability in vitro and in vivo.* Ann N Y Acad Sci 1985; 442: 429-439.

51. Page, C.P., Paul, W., Morley, J. *Platelets and bronchospasm.* Int Arch Allergy Appl Immunol 1984; 74: 347-350.

52. Patterson, R., Harris, K.E. *The activity of aerosolized and intracutaneous synthetic platelet-activating factor (AGEPC) in rhesus monkeys with IgE-mediated airway responses and normal monkeys.* J Lab Clin Med 1983; 102: 933-938.

53. Pinckard, R.N., Farr, R.S., Hanahan, D.J. *Physiochemical and functional identity of PAF release in vivo during IgE anaphylaxis with PAF release in vitro from IgE sensitized basophils.* J Immunol 1979; 123: 1847-1857.

54. Pipkorn, U., Karlsson, G., Bake, B. *Effect of platelet-activating factor on the human nasal mucosa.* Allergy 1984; 39: 141-145.

55. Prescott, S.M., Zimmerman, G.A., McIntyre, T.M. *Human endothelial cells in culture produce platelet-activating factor (1-alkyl-2-acetyl-sn-glycero-3-phosphocholine) when stimulated with thrombin.* Proc Natl Acad Sci USA 1984; 81: 3534-3538.

56. Rubin, A.E., Smith, L.J., Patterson, R. *Effect of platelet-activating factor (PAF) on normal human airways.* Am Rev Respir Dis 1986; 133: 91.

57. Rylander, R., Beijer, L. *Inhalation of endotoxin stimulates alveolar macrophage production of platelet-activating factor.* Am Rev Respir Dis 1987; 135: 83-86.

58. Sánchez-Crespo, M., Fernández Gallardo, S., Nieto, M.L., Baranes, J., Braquet, P. *BN and IgG anaphylaxis.* Immunopharm 1985; 10: 69-75.

59. Snapper, J., Hutchison, A., Ogletree, M., Brigham, K. *Effects of cyclooxygenase inhibitors on the alterations in lung mechanics caused by endotoxaemia in the unanesthetised sheep.* J Clin Invest 1983; 72: 63-76.

60. Taytard, A., Guenard, H., Vuillermin, L., Bourot, J.L., Vergeret, J., Ducasson, D., Pi-

quet, Y., Freour, P. *Platelet kinetics in stable atopic asthmatic subjects.* Am Rev Respir Dis 1986; 134: 983-985.

61. Thompson, P.J., Hanson, J.M., Bilani, H., Turner-Warwick, M., Morley, J. *Platelets, platelet-activating factor and asthma.* Am Rev Respir Dis 1984; 129: 3.

62. Touvay, C., Etienne, A., Braquet, P. *Inhibition of antigen-induced lung anaphylaxis in the guinea-pig by BN 52021 a new specific PAF-acether receptor antagonist isolated from Ginkgo biloba.* Agents and Action 1985; 17: 371-372.

63. Van der Zwan, J.C., Orie, N.G.M., Kauffman, H.F., Wiers, P.W.J., de Vries, K. *Bronchial obstructive reactions after inhalation of endotoxin and precipitinogens of Haemophilus influenzae in patients with chronic non-specific lung disease.* Clin Allergy 1982; 12: 547-559.

64. Vargaftig, B.B., Lefort, J., Chignard, M., Benveniste, J. *Platelet-activating factor induces a platelet-dependent bronchoconstriction unrelated to the formation of prostaglandin derivatives.* Eur J Pharmacol 1980; 65: 185-192.

65. Voelkel, N.F., Worthen, S., Henson, P.M., Murphy, R.C. *Non immunological production of leukotrienes induced by platelet-activating factor.* Science 1982; 218: 286-288.

66. Wardlaw, A.J., Moqbel, R., Cromwell, O., Kay, A.B. *Platelet-activating factor. A potent chemotactic and chemokinetic factor for human eosinophils.* J Clin Invest 1986; 78: 1701-1706.

67. Williams, B.D., O'Sullivan, M.M., Saggu, G.S., Williams, S.K.E., Williams, L.A., Morgan, J.R. *Imaging in rheumatoid arthritis using liposomes labelled with technitium.* Br Med J 1986; 293: 1143-1144.

Ginkgolides - Chemistry, Biology, Pharmacology and Clinical Perspectives. P. Braquet (Ed.)
Copyright © 1988, J.R. Prous Science Publishers, S.A.

THE CLINICAL EFFECTS OF BN 52063, A SPECIFIC PAF-ACETHER ANTAGONIST

Philippe Guinot, Christian Brambilla, Jacques Duchier, André Taytard and Caroline Summerhayes

Dept. of Clinical Research, IPSEN International, London, UK

INTRODUCTION

Platelet-activating factor (PAF-acether) has a wide range of biological activities in allergic diseases, and recent interest has centered on its role in the mediation of allergic inflammation and asthma (4, 11). Although bronchospasm is elicited by many other mediators of asthma, PAF is unique in that it acts as a powerful agonist for increased vascular permeability and causes an infiltration of inflammatory cells, including platelets, granulocytes and eosinophils into lung tissue. Furthermore, PAF-acether is the only mediator which has so far been shown to induce a profound and sustained bronchial hyperreactivity, the characteristic feature of asthma, in experimental animals. Therefore, it has been proposed that an antagonist of PAF could be of clinical importance in asthma.

The ginkgolides are a class of PAF antagonists which have been isolated from the *Ginkgo biloba* tree. Ginkgolide B (BN 52021), the most active PAF antagonist found in this class, is a specific and potent competitive antagonist of the binding of PAF to its membrane receptor in both human platelet (2) and lung (1) preparations. The PAF antagonist activity of ginkgolide B is significantly reinforced by combining it with ginkgolides A and C. BN 52063, a standardized mixture of ginkgolides A, B and C (BN 52020, BN 52021 and BN 52022) is the first drug which has been shown to be a potent PAF antagonist in man (9).

Address all correspondence to: Dr. Philippe Guinot, IPSEN International Ltd., 14 Kensington Square, London W8 5HH, England.

345

RATIONALE FOR DEVELOPMENT OF A PAF-ACETHER ANTAGONIST

The first clinical trials studied the safety of BN 52063 in normal healthy volunteers to find a maximum well-tolerated dose for use in the initial single and multiple dose studies. Subsequent studies confirmed the PAF-antagonist activity of BN 52063 in man, and investigated basic pharmacokinetics and pharmacodynamics and a safe dosage range. After demonstrating that BN 52063 has no direct bronchodilator activity, we used single and multiple dose trials to study the effect of the product in asthmatic patients on non-specific bronchial provocation tests to acetylcholine, carbachol and histamine. The most recent single and multiple dose studies performed have investigated the effect of BN 52036 during specific allergen challenges in atopic subjects using both intradermal and bronchial challenges with allergen.

SAFETY

Two studies have been performed which were designed to establish the comparative safety and tolerance of BN 52063 in normal healthy volunteers. In a single-blind crossover trial, five healthy male volunteers took increasing single doses of BN 52063, 20 mg, 40 mg, 80 mg, 120 mg and placebo, separated by at least one week. Clinical and laboratory parameters were closely monitored for 24 hours following each dose, and there were no significant effects of BN 52063 on the blood pressure, pulse, electrocardiogram and laboratory parameters at each dosage given (J. Duchier, unpublished results).

In a further two week double-blind, randomized, crossover study six healthy normal subjects were treated with 40 mg BN 52063 or placebo, three times a day for a week, the two treatment periods being separated by one week. Again, treatment with BN 52063 was found to be safe and well tolerated and showed no statistically significant difference to placebo treatment (C. Brambilla, unpublished results).

ANTAGONISM OF PAF

PAF-acether induces a dose-related dual inflammatory response in the skin of man, which is reminiscent of the antigen-induced dual responses in sensitized asthmatics. The effect of BN 52063 on this PAF-induced cutaneous response was studied in an initial single blind study (9) in five healthy male volunteers.

Subjects received a subcutaneous injection of PAF (400 ng in 0.1 ml 4% human albumin) in the forearm, 90 minutes after taking 80 mg BN 52063 or placebo. BN 52063, 80 mg, inhibited the acute weal and flare response

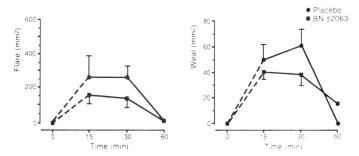

Figure 1 Effect of BN 52063 (80 mg, single dose, po, 90 min before challenge) on PAF-acether (50 ng, sc, saline)-induced flare and weal reactions in man.

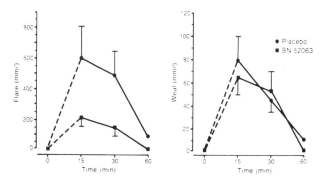

Figure 2 Effect of BN 52063 (80 mg, single dose, po, 90 min before challenge) on PAF-acether (100 ng, sc, saline)-induced flare and weal reactions in man.

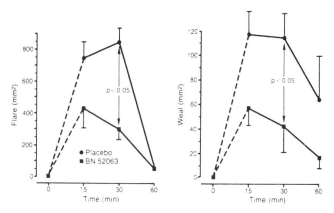

Figure 3 Effect of BN 52063 (80 mg, single dose, po, 90 min before challenge) on PAF-acether (400 ng, sc, HSA)-induced flare and weal reactions in man. Reproduced from Guinot, P. et al. *Effects of BN 52063 on PAF-acether induced weal and flare reactions in man.* In: Schmitz-Shumnann, Menz, Page. PAF, Platelets and Asthma (Birkhauser, Basel), with permission.

induced by 400 ng PAF (Figs. 1-3), and this inhibition was statistically significant 30 minutes after the injection. This was the first published report demonstrating an inhibition of the acute PAF-acether induced cutaneous response in man by a selective PAF antagonist.

In a double-blind crossover trial (8), three volunteers received single doses of 120 mg BN 52063 or placebo, and the cutaneous response to repeated subcutaneous injections of PAF 400 ng was monitored before and 1, 2, 4, 6 and 8 hours after intake of the drugs. The results on the flare reaction are shown in Figure 4.

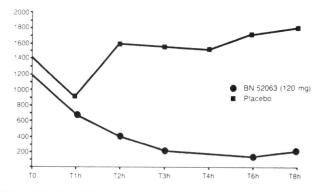

Figure 4   Effect of BN 52063 (120 mg, single dose, po) on PAF acether (400 ng, id, HSA) induced flare area at 30' (mean of three subjects).

A subsequent double-blind randomized placebo controlled crossover study confirmed these results (3). Six healthy non-atopic volunteers were administered single doses of 80 mg and 120 mg BN 52063 separated by at least a week. The effects on the weal and flare response to intradermal injections of PAF (50, 100, 200 and 400 ng) were assessed 2 hours after ingestion of BN 52063 or placebo. Weal and flare responses to 400 ng PAF were inhibited in a dose-related manner.

In the same study PAF-induced aggregation of human platelets *in vitro* was shown to be inhibited by BN 52063 (3). Both 80 ng and 120 mg BN 52063 significantly inhibited PAF-induced platelet aggregation in platelet rich plasma ($p < 0.001$). BN 52063, at concentrations up to 100 μmol/1 *in vitro*, inhibited PAF-induced platelet aggregation in a dose-dependent manner, with no modification of ADP-induced aggregation.

BRONCHODILATOR ACTIVITY

The bronchodilator activity of BN 52063 was investigated in a double-blind randomized within patient crossover study in 12 asthmatic patients (C.

Brambilla, unpublished results). The bronchodilator activity of a single dose of 120 mg BN 52063, as measured against the bronchodilator isoprenaline sulphate (Aleudrine), was compared to a single dose of placebo. There was no statistically significant difference in the spirometry measurement before and 180 minutes after a single dose of 120 mg BN 52063 or placebo, and BN 52063 had no significantly different effect from placebo. On the other hand, there was a significant increase in FEV1, FVC and FEV1/FVC values after two puffs of Aleudrine, as expected. This study demonstrated that BN 52063 has no apparent short-term bronchodilator activity.

These results were confirmed in a further double-blind randomized crossover clinical trial in six young asthmatic patients, aged 22 to 28 years taking either 40 mg BN 52063 two times a day or placebo for two weeks. The study revealed that there was no significant variation in the respiratory functions tested—FVC, FEV1 and PEF—indicating that BN 52063 appears to have no effect on bronchoconstriction in young asthmatics (J. Duchier, A. Cournot, personal communication).

NON-SPECIFIC BRONCHIAL PROVOCATION TESTS

The effects of BN 52063 on non-specific bronchial provocation tests to acetylcholine, histamine and carbachol have been investigated in acute and short term clinical trials. Bronchial hyperreactivity is a characteristic feature of asthma. Although its underlying etiology is unknown it has been suggested that it may be secondary to inflammatory events in the lungs (6). Exposure of normal subjects to inhaled PAF causes immediate bronchoconstriction and an increase in bronchial responsiveness to methacholine, which peaks 3 days after inhalation and may persist for up to 4 weeks (5).

Bronchial hyperreactivity following an acetylcholine challenge was studied in a randomized, double-blind placebo controlled crossover study in five asthmatic subjects. BN 52063 was administered either as a single dose of 80 mg, or as two days pretreatment with 40 mg BN 52063 three times a day. Bronchial resistance following an acetylcholine challenge was not modified either by a single dose or pretreatment with BN 52063 (Fig. 5) and the spirometric factors measured —FVC, FEV and PEF— showed no significant difference between placebo and BN 52063.

The effect of BN 52063 on the non-specific bronchial reactivity to histamine was examined in a double-blind, randomized, placebo controlled study in two parallel groups, which showed that the product does not inhibit bronchoconstriction following a histamine challenge (10). Five adult asthmatic patients with normal or almost normal baseline pulmonary function, an FEV1 greater than 80% of the predicted normal, were treated for one week with either 40 mg BN 52063 or placebo three times a day. BN

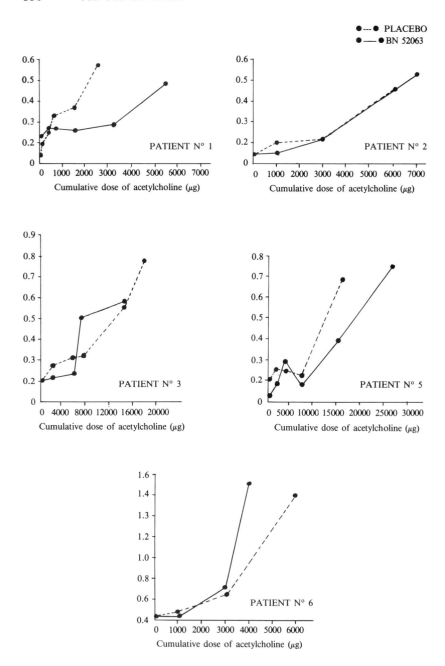

Figure 5 Airways resistance (RAW in KPa/1/s) during bronchial provocation tests to acetylcholine.

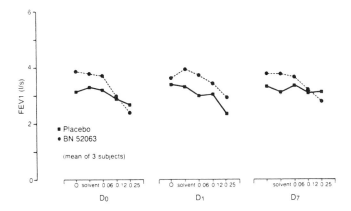

Figure 6 Bronchial provocation tests to histamine.

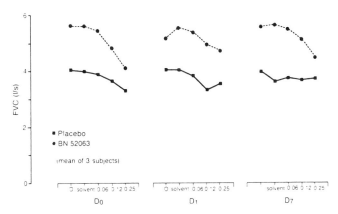

Figure 7 Bronchial provocation tests to histamine.

52063 had no significant effect on the histamine dose response curve and showed no significant difference from placebo (Figs. 6, 7).

Patients were also requested to record their peak flow, four times a day during the study, using a peak flow meter; BN 52063 did not appreciably affect these peak flow values recorded before, during and after treatment (Fig. 8). Therefore, this study confirmed the lack of bronchodilator activity.

In an open study to investigate the effect of BN 52063 on the non-specific bronchial reactivity to carbachol (C. Brambrilla, unpublished results), five asthmatic patients with an FEV1 greater than 80% of predicted normal were treated with a single dose of either 20 mg or 40 mg BN 52063. There was no significant effect in these subjects on the dose response curve to carbachol.

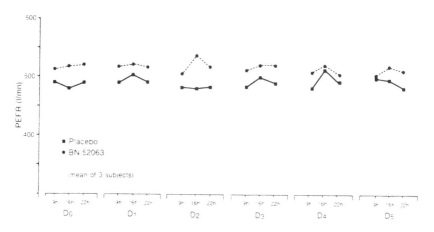

Figure 8   Effect of BN 52063 on peak flow values.

SPECIFIC ALLERGEN CHALLENGES

Skin

A randomized double-blind trial was performed to investigate the effect of BN 52063 on the biphasic cutaneous response elicited by an intradermal injection of antigen in atopic subjects. The effect of 120 mg BN 52063 or placebo taken two hours before intradermal injections of a specific antigen (low, medium and high doses), PAF (200 ng), histamine (1 μg) or diluent, was studied in 10 healthy, atopic subjects (N. Roberts, P. Barnes, personal communication). PAF and histamine elicited comparable weal and flare responses, but only the response to PAF was significantly inhibited by BN 52063.

Intradermal administration of antigen caused dose-related responses. The medium dose of antigen gave rise to a classic biphasic inflammatory response which was maximal at 1 and 8 hours and persisted for 24 hours. Pretreatment with BN 52063 resulted in a 52% decrease in the acute response and a 40% decrease in the late response, as assessed by the weal volume, reaching statistical significance at 1 and 8 hours. No significant effect was observed on flare area following pretreatment with BN 52063. These results suggest that PAF may contribute to both the acute and late onset allergic responses in the skin.

Lungs

Exposure of asthmatic subjects to inhaled antigen causes acute bronchoconstriction, which is maximal approximately 15 to 30 minutes after antigen inhalation; this is followed by a delayed response which peaks about 6 hours later. The effect of BN 52063 on the bronchial provocation test to allergen was assessed in a randomized, double-blind, placebo controlled crossover study in eight atopic, asthmatic patients (7). Patients received either 40 mg BN 52063 or placebo three times a day for 2 days. On the third day, 2 hours after receiving 120 mg BN 52063 or placebo, subjects were given a bronchial provocation test to nebulized house dust mite or pollen allergen. The two periods of drug administration, BN 52063 and placebo, were separated by an interval of one week.

The early response to bronchial allergen challenge was observed to be significantly inhibited by BN 52063 (Table 1). Residual bronchial hyper-reactivity, assessed 6 hours after the allergen challenge by a provocation test to acetylcholine, also showed a tendency to decrease during treatment, although this was not statistically significant.

Table 1 Bronchial provocation test to allergen

Patient number	Type of allergen	Quantity of allergen (μg)	
		Placebo	BN 52063
1	Pollen	15	75
2	Pollen	5	150
3	House Dust Mite	15	105
4	House Dust Mite	10	75
5	Pollen	15	40
6	Pollen	15	5
7	House Dust Mite	5	15
8	Pollen	5	10
	Mean	10.6	59.4
	SEM	1.7	18.1
		$p < 0.03$ (Wilcoxon)	

CONCLUSIONS

Pharmacological evidence for the role of PAF-acether in asthma is now accumulating. The results presented in this paper provide evidence that a PAF-acether antagonist may be of clinical interest in the treatment of asthma. It has been shown that BN 52063 is safe and well tolerated in short term treatment. Evidence for the inhibitory effect on PAF has been given by studies showing that BN 52063 antagonizes the inflammatory response induced by a subcutaneous injection of PAF and it also antagonizes PAF-induced aggregation of human platelets *ex vivo*. Further studies have demonstrated that BN 52063 does not have a direct bronchodilator effect and it has no inhibitory effect on the bronchial hyperreactivity following challenge with acetylcholine, histamine or carbachol. Pretreatment with BN 52063 attenuates the acute and late phases of the cutaneous responses to an intradermal injection of a specific antigen. Similarly, BN 52063 inhibited the early and late responses to a bronchial allergen challenge, confirming the potential interest of specific PAF-acether antagonists in the treatment of asthma.

References

1. Agrawal, D. et al. *Effect of platelet-activating factor on beta-adrenoceptors in human lung.* Biochem Biophys Res Commun; 1987; 46; 739.

2. Braquet, P. et al. *BN 52021 and related compounds: A new series of highly specific PAF-acether receptor antagonists isolated from Ginkgo biloba.* Blood & Vessels 1985; 16: 559-572.

3. Chung, K. et al. *Effect of ginkgolide mixture (BN 52063) in antagonising skin and platelet responses to platelet-activating factor in man.* Lancet 1987; 1: 248-251.

4. Cuss, F. et al. *Effects of inhaled platelet-activating factor on pulmonary function and bronchial responsiveness in man.* Am Rev Respir Dis 1986; A133: 212.

5. Cuss, F. et al. *Effect of inhaled platelet-activating factor on pulmonary function and bronchial responsiveness in man.* Lancet 1986; 2: 189-192.

6. Fabbri, L. et al. *Prednisone inhibits late asthmatic reactions and the associated increase in airway responsiveness induced by toluene diisocyanate in sensitized subjects.* Am Rev Resp Dis 1985; 132: 1010-1014.

7. Guinot, P. et al. *Effect of BN 52063, a specific PAF-acether antagonist, on bronchial provocation test to allergens in asthmatic patients.* Congres de Pneumologie de Langue Francaise, Grenoble, 11-13 June 1987; Abst.

8. Guinot, P. et al. *Effects of BN 52063 on PAF-acether induced weal and flare reaction in man.* In: PAF, Platelets and Asthma. Schmitz-Shumann, Menz, Page (Eds.). Agents Actions (Supp.) 1987; 97.

9. Guinot, P. et al. *Inhibition of PAF-acether induced weal and flare reaction in man by a specific PAF antagonist.* Prostaglandins 1986; 32: 160-163.

10. Taytard, A. et al. *Effect des ginkgolides (BN 52063) sur la stimulation bronchique non-specifique.* Congres de Pneumologie de Langue Francaise, Grenoble, 11-13 June 1987; Abst.

11. Vargaftig, B. and Braquet, P. *PAF-acether today-relevance for acute experimental anaphylaxis.* Brit Med Bull 1987; 43: 312-335.

*Ginkgolides - Chemistry, Biology, Pharmacology
and Clinical Perspectives.* P. Braquet (Ed.)
Copyright © 1988, J.R. Prous Science Publishers, S.A.

PAF, HUMAN LUNG BETA-ADRENOCEPTORS AND GINKGOLIDE B (BN 52021)

Devendra K. Agrawal and Robert G. Townley

Allergic Disease Center, Creighton University School of Medicine, Omaha, Nebraska 68178, USA

ABSTRACT

Human lung membranes contain specific [³H]PAF binding sites of high affinity and high density. Ginkgolide B (BN 52021) competed for these binding sites with very high affinity. PAF decreased the density of human lung beta-adrenoceptors which was protected by the prior incubation of the lung slices with BN 52021. In the functional studies, a subthreshold dose of PAF decreased the potency of isoproterenol to reverse the methacholine-induced contraction in human tracheal strips and histamine-induced contraction in human lung parenchymal strips. This decrease in the potency of isoproterenol induced by PAF was inhibited by BN 52021. On the basis of these data in human tissues and the data obtained by us in guinea pigs, we speculate that PAF may desensitize the responses to bronchodilators in a non-specific manner by interacting at a post-receptor site involved in receptor activation-relaxation coupling. Possible target sites have been discussed. Furthermore, because of its high affinity for the PAF receptors, ginkgolide B would prove very useful in the treatment of airway hyperresponsiveness.

INTRODUCTION

Chemical mediators are generated as a consequence of immunological responses in airways. Among the mediators, the most recently discovered

---
Address all correspondence to: Dr. Devendra K. Agrawal, Allergic Disease Center, Creighton University School of Medicine, Omaha, NE 68178, USA.

is platelet-activating factor (PAF, PAF-acether, AGEPC, [1-O-alkyl-2(R) acetyl-glycero-3-phosphorylcholine]. PAF, first described and characterized by Benveniste *et al.* (12) and Demopoulos *et al.* (21), has a broad spectrum of biological activities (25,34). In the lung, PAF can cause marked bronchoconstriction, acute inflammation and edema, platelet aggregation and degranulation, chemotaxis to neutrophils and eosinophils, and release of superoxide and lysosomal enzymes by polymorphonuclear leukocytes (29,30,40). It is a potential mediator of immediate hypersensitivity; it is released from IgE-sensitized rabbit basophils (12) and mast cells (10). The PAF induced aggregation and degranulation of platelets might amplify the anaphylactic response (16). It is also released from neutrophils, macrophages, vascular endothelium, and platelets undergoing aggregation caused by calcium ionophore A23187, collagen or thrombin (25,34).

PAF AND ASTHMA

PAF is an effective eosinophil chemoattractant and activator *in vitro* (24,38,41). *In vivo,* there is recruitment of eosinophils into the lung following intra-tracheal administration of PAF in primates or following i.v. PAF in guinea pigs (30). It is of considerable interest that eosinophils obtained from patients with eosinophilia (including asthmatics) release very large amounts of PAF in comparison with eosinophils from normal individuals (34). These findings suggest that PAF may be generated in lung tissues after immune or non-immune challenge and could participate in the bronchial response in asthma or anaphylactic shock (16,20,30). Recently it has been demonstrated that PAF (i.v. injection or an aerosol) can elicit a substantial, long-lasting and non-specific airway hyperreactivity in a variety of experimental animals including monkeys (31) guinea pigs (3,27) and dogs (18). In human subjects, an aerosol of PAF (3-200 μg) caused bronchoconstriction (19,32) and is about 37 times more potent than methacholine (32). PAF aerosol exhibited tachyphylaxis and sensitized normal human airways to methacholine. In these studies, lyso-PAF, which is an inactive metabolite of PAF, was not effective.

These studies in guinea pigs, dogs, monkeys and humans suggest that PAF increases non-specific airway reactivity and that the release of PAF may be important in increased airway reactivity in asthma. However, the underlying mechanism is not clear.

In asthmatic lymphocytes (33) we observed a down-regulation (decrease in the density of receptor and decreased c-AMP levels) of beta-adrenoceptors. In lung membranes of a guinea pig model of asthma (36) decrease in the density of beta-adrenoceptor occurred with a concomitant up-regulation (increase in the density of receptor) of alpha-adrenoceptors.

Other laboratories have also reported similar results (8,39). However, the mechanism of this phenomena is not known. Braquet and colleagues (15) earlier reported that exposure of rat cerebellar tissue to PAF *in vitro* resulted in a loss of beta-2 adrenoceptors, and this effect of PAF was prevented by prior incubation of the cerebellar tissue with BN 52021, a potent PAF antagonist. Since late-onset responses are associated with airway inflammation being susceptible to inhibition by steroids but not by beta-adrenoceptor agonists (13), we examined the effect of PAF on pulmonary beta-adrenoceptors in human trachea and lung tissue. The affinity of ginkgolide B (BN 52021) for the PAF receptors in human lung and the potency of BN 52021 to inhibit the responses to PAF in human trachea and lung parenchyma was also evaluated.

PAF RECEPTORS IN HUMAN LUNG

We have characterized the specific binding to [^{3}H]PAF in the membranes of human lung. Normal human lungs were obtained during autopsy (*within 5-6 hours after death*) from St. Joseph Hospital and V.A. Hospital in Omaha. Human lung membranes were prepared by homogenization and differential centrifugation procedure. Binding of [^{3}H]PAF was carried out in 50 mM Tris buffer (pH 7.0) containing 0.25% human serum albumin and 10 mM $MgCl_2$. Specific binding was defined as the binding displaceable by 10 μM unlabeled PAF (C_{16}-PAF). From five separate experiments, the maximum number of binding sites (Bmax) of [^{3}H]PAF was calculated to be 195 $\pm$ 20 fmoles/mg protein with an equilibrium constant (K_D) of 0.64 $\pm$ 0.3 nM (2).

In the competition studies, the Ki values of unlabeled C_{16}-PAF, BN 52021 and L-652,731 to compete for the specific binding of [^{3}H]PAF were 0.32 $\pm$ 0.15 nM, 8.2 $\pm$ 4.3 nM and 19.6 $\pm$ 5.4 nM, respectively (Fig. 1). Thus, the rank order of potency of these unlabeled compounds to compete for the [^{3}H]PAF binding sites was C_{16}-PAF < BN 52021 < L-652,731. These data suggest that human lung contains the specific receptors of PAF. Furthermore, BN 52021 is a potent antagonist of PAF receptors in human lung.

EFFECT OF PAF ON THE DENSITY OF BETA-ADRENO-CEPTORS

In the radioligand receptor binding studies for beta-adrenoceptors, preincubation of human lung slices with 0.2-0.5 μM PAF decreased the maximum number of [^{3}H]dihydroalprenolol (DHA) specific binding in the lung membranes (3,4). In the membranes of the untreated human lung, the maximum binding capacity (Bmax) and apparent equilibrium dissociation constant (K_D) of [^{3}H]DHA were 65 $\pm$ 12 fmol/mg protein and 0.5 $\pm$ 0.1 nM,

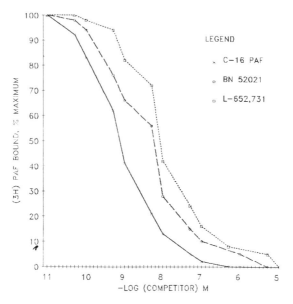

Figure 1   Inhibition of [³H]PAF specific binding by C$_{16}$-PAF, BN 52021 and L-652,731 in the human lung membranes. Each point is the mean of triplicates from 3-4 separate experiments. Concentration of [³H]PAF used in these experiments ranged between 1.2-3.5 nM. For the Ki values of the unlabeled competitors, please see text.

respectively (n = 4). However, in the PAF-treated human lung membranes Bmax and K$_D$ values for the [³H]DHA specific binding were 32 ± 11 fmol/mg protein and 0.48 ± 0.08 nM, respectively (n = 4). There was a significant (p < 0.05) difference in the Bmax of [³H]DHA binding in both the groups: PAF-treated group and PAF-untreated group (3). Prior exposure of the human lung slices with 0.5-1 μM BN 52021 protected against the PAF-induced down-regulation of beta-adrenoceptors.

EFFECT OF PAF ON FUNCTIONAL RESPONSES TO ISOPROTERENOL

Isoproterenol produced relaxation in a dose-dependent manner when added on the contractile response to methacholine or histamine in human tracheal and lung parenchymal strips. When the tissues were pre-incubated with 0.1-1 μM PAF for 30 minutes at 37°C in Krebs buffer, the maximum responses to methacholine and histamine were increased by about 30% (n = 6). However, in the PAF-treated human tracheal and lung parenchymal strips, the isoproterenol-induced relaxation on the responses to methacholine and histamine was significantly attenuated (3,5). The pD_2 values ($-\log EC_{50}$) of isoproterenol in the control trachea and lung parenchyma were 6.8 ± 0.1 and 6.56 ± 0.06, respectively. However, in the PAF-treated group the pD_2 values for isoproterenol in the trachea and lung parenchyma were 6.1 ± 0.2 and 6.03 ± 0.11, respectively (3). BN 52021 in the concentration of 0.5-1 μM protected against these PAF-induced changes (5). The decrease in the responses to isoproterenol was not due to an increase in the maximum responses to methacholine or histamine, because isoproterenol-induced relaxation on the sub-maximal doses of methacholine or histamine was also attenuated by preincubation with PAF.

DISCUSSION

The results of the radioligand binding studies suggest the presence of high affinity PAF receptors in human lung membranes. The potency of BN 52021 to compete for these receptors was observed to be higher in the human lung as compared to that reported in platelets. The reason for this is not clear. It is possible that the PAF receptors in human lung are of different characteristics. Alternatively, the presence of a complex cell system in human lung parenchyma may influence the affinity of BN 52021 for the PAF receptors. Our results for the affinity of unlabeled competitors for the [^{3}H]PAF specific binding in human lung membranes are somewhat different than those reported by Hwang and Lam (23). Such discrepancy could be due to differences in the membrane isolation, binding assay technique or even the purity of the chemicals used in the assay system.

Incubation of the human lung slices with PAF resulted in a down-regulation of the beta-adrenoceptors in human lung membranes. There was no change in the affinity of beta-adrenoceptors after PAF exposure. Prior exposure of the human lung slices with BN 52021, a very potent PAF receptor antagonist, inhibited the PAF-induced decrease in the density of beta-adrenoceptors in human lung. In the functional studies also, prior exposure of the human tracheal or lung parenchymal strips shifted the dose-response curve to isoproterenol to the right. This effect of PAF was again inhibited by BN 52021. Interestingly, prior exposure of the human tracheal or lung parenchymal strips did not decrease the magnitude of isoproterenol-induced relaxation. Since PAF decreased the number of beta-adrenoceptors to about half and also decreased the affinity of isoproterenol to produce relaxation, this suggests the presence of enormous receptor reserve for beta-adreno-ceptors in human lung.

These studies in human trachea and lung parenchyma suggest that PAF could be a mediator which alters beta-adrenergic responses. Such effect of PAF is through specific PAF receptors because (i) human lung contains

[³H]PAF specific binding sites of high affinity, and (ii) BN 52021, which is a potent antagonist of PAF receptors in human airways, inhibited the PAF-induced alterations in the beta-adrenoceptor responses. Our data are in agreement with those of Braquet and colleagues (15) who previously reported that PAF down-regulated the beta-adrenoceptors in the membranes of rat cerebellum. In another study, salbutamol (a $beta_2$-agonist) protected PAF-induced hypotension and extravasation in rats. A similar effect was seen with BN 52021, a selective and potent antagonist of PAF (14). BN 52021 did not have any effect on the beta-adrenergic receptors directly, and its beneficial effects were partially antagonized by beta-blocking agents such as propranolol or butoxamine (14).

Among the various mediators of inflammation only PAF causes an increase in non-specific airway hyperresponsiveness in non-asthmatics and the pattern of increased responsiveness was similar to that seen after allergen challenge in asthmatic subjects (19). It is therefore possible that PAF-induced down-regulation of beta-adrenoceptors in human lung could possibly induce the non-specific airway hyperresponsiveness in asthma. However, the mechanism by which PAF causes a down-regulation of beta-adrenoceptors is not clear.

Recently, Taki et al. (37) reported that increased levels of phospholipase A_2 (PLA_2) reduced beta-adrenergic responsiveness in the airways of the guinea pig model of asthma. Exogenous addition of PLA_2 decreases the density of beta-adrenergic receptors in guinea pig lung membranes (37). Indomethacin treatment has been reported to reverse the homologous desensitization of beta-adrenoceptor responses in guinea pig airways (1,17,22). It is therefore, possible that the addition of PLA_2 leads to the increased synthesis of cyclooxygenase products which in turn down-regulate beta-adrenoceptors. Furthermore, PLA_2 is also involved in the generation of PAF precursors and subsequent acetylation reactions lead to the formation of PAF (25,34). However, PAF has been reported to induce activation of phospholipase A_2 in rabbit platelets (34). Whether PAF activates phospholipase A_2 in other cells and tissues of airways is not known. Nevertheless it is reasonable to speculate that the activation of phospholipase A_2 by PAF in human lung and trachea could be a mechanism underlying PAF-induced down-regulation of beta-adrenoceptors. It is also possible that PAF could down-regulate the responses to all bronchodilators in a non-specific manner leading to non-specific airway hyperresponsiveness. If it is true, we would expect that the responses to PGE_2 and vasoactive intestinal peptide would also be desensitized by PAF. Furthermore, PAF-induced decrease in the density of beta-adrenoceptors observed in the human lung membranes could be tissue and/or species dependent.

Recently, we studied the effect of PAF on the methacholine, isoproterenol and PGE_2 responses in conscious guinea pigs as well as in the isolated tracheal rings and lung parenchymal strips of the control and ovalbumin-sensitized guinea pigs. In the isolated guinea pig tracheal rings and lung parenchymal strips, a subthreshold dose of PAF decreased the sensitivity of isoproterenol to produce relaxation (4). In our *in vivo* experiments in conscious guinea pigs, specific airway resistance (SRaw) of the lungs was monitored using a whole-body plethysmograph. PAF aerosol in its sub-threshold dose potentiated the increase in the *in vivo* specific airway resistance produced by methacholine and this airway obstruction was not reversed by isoproterenol or PGE_2 (Agrawal *et al.,* unpublished data). These effects of PAF on the responses of isoproterenol or PGE_2 were inhibited by BN 52021 in a dose-dependent fashion. Since the responses to isoproterenol and PGE_2 were both attenuated by PAF, this suggests the possibility of a non-specific desensitization of bronchodilators probably through an effect on adenylate cyclase and/or protein kinase. Whether PAF causes sensitization to other mediators to produce non-specific airway hyper-responsiveness is not known. In another study by Barnes and colleagues (9), a reduced bronchodilator responsiveness to isoproterenol in PAF-treated guinea pigs was also observed; however, there was no change in beta-adrenoceptor density or affinity in the lungs from PAF-treated guinea pigs. Although these investigators did not examine the effect of PAF on other bronchodilators, our study and the study of Barnes and colleagues suggest that PAF may produce a non-specific desensitization to bronchodilators.

PAF and arachidonic acid are released from a common precursor, 1-alkyl-2-acyl-glycero-3-phosphorylcholine, in various cells including rabbit neutrophils and rat alveolar macrophages. In both cases, the activation of phospholipase A_1 enzyme is required. It is, therefore, possible that PAF might act as a potentially potent regulator of arachidonic acid metabolism and *vice versa*. Leukotriene synthesis has been shown to be stimulated by PAF. In human neutrophils PAF can induce sufficient release of LTB_4 to account for the PAF-induced aggregation of these cells (34). The rapid vasoconstriction and edema that PAF produced in isolated rat lungs also appear to be, in part, due to the stimulation of the synthesis of LTC_4 and D_4 (34). McManus *et al.* (28) demonstrated that TXB_2 was released during anaphylaxis within 30 seconds following an i.v. antigen challenge to IgE-sensitized rabbits. The production of TXA_2 by PAF has also been reported by other investigators (34). However, whether the PAF-induced release of TXA_2 plays a role only in the early phase of the response and not on the sustained phase or the magnitude of contraction is still controversial.

Bronchodilators including isoproterenol, PGE_2 and VIP act through the adenylate cyclase system. Therefore, it is possible that the mechanism for the PAF-induced desensitization to bronchodilators could be an effect of

PAF on the adenylate cyclase system and/or a direct effect on cAMP dependent-protein kinases (cAMP-PK). Adenylate cyclase and CAMP-PK are key enzymes in the cellular response to isoproterenol, PGE_2 and VIP. cAMP activates the enzyme cAMP-PK which then catalyzes protein phosphorylation. It is possible that PAF could deactivate these enzymes to desensitize the responses to bronchodilators in a non-specific manner. Recently a novel "adenylate cyclase-coupled receptor" kinase has been reported and the translocation of this kinase from the cytosol to the plasma membrane phosphorylates adenylate cyclase-coupled receptors (11,26,35). Both beta-adrenoceptor agonists and PGE_2 induced translocation of this enzyme (35). Phosphorylation of the adenylate cyclase-coupled receptors will lead to a heterologous desensitization phenomenon. Since PAF inhibited the responses to isoproterenol and PGE_2 in guinea pigs (3), it is possible that PAF-induced heterologous desensitization is through the translocation of this enzyme. Clearly, more studies in this direction are warranted which could be helpful in understanding the PAF-induced airway hyperresponsiveness in asthma.

ACKNOWLEDGEMENTS

This work was supperted by the James M. Keck Faculty Development Award from the Health Future Foundation to D.K. Agrawal. The authors thank Dr. P. Braquet for supplying BN 52021.

References
1. Abbracchio, M.A., Daffonchio, L. and Omini, C. *Arachidonic acid metabolites and lung beta-adrenoceptor desensitization.* Pharmacol Res Comm 1986; 18: 93-110.
2. Agrawal, D.K. and Townley, R.G. *Platelet-activating factor-induced down-regulation of beta-adrenoceptors in human lung.* Proc 2nd Intl Conf on PAF (Gatlinburg, Tenn) October 1986; Abst 30, p. 117.
3. Agrawal, D.K. and Townley, R.G. *Effect of platelet-activating factor on beta-adrenoceptors in human lung.* Biochem Biophys Res Comm 1987a; 143: 1-6.
4. Agrawal, D.K. and Townley, R.G. *Effect of platelet activating factor on human pulmonary beta-adrenoceptors.* Fed Proc 1987b; 46(3): 739.
5. Agrawal, D.K. and Townley, R.G. *BN 52021, a platelet-activating factor (PAF) antagonist, protects the PAF-induced down-regulation of beta-adrenoceptors in human lung.* Am Rev Resp Dis 1987c; 135(4): A 162.
6. Agrawal, D.K., Bergren, D.R., Byorth, P.J.

and Townley, R.G. *Platelet-activating factor (PAF) and airway hyperreactivity in guinea pigs.* Proc Xth Intl Cong Pharmacol (Sydney, Australia) 1987a; in press.
7. Agrawal, D.K., Byorth, P. and Townley, R.G. *Effect of platelet-activating factor (PAF) on isoproterenol-induced relaxation in the airway.* J Allergy Clin Immunol 1987b; 79: 171.
8. Barnes, P.J., Dollery, C.T. and MacDermot, J. *Increased pulmonary alpha-adrenergic and reduced beta-adrenergic receptors in experimental asthma.* Nature 1980; 285: 569-571.
9. Barnes, P.J., Grandordy, B.M., Page, C.P., Rhoden, K.J. and Robertson, D.N. *The effect of platelet-activating factor on pulmonary beta-adrenoceptors.* Br J Pharmacol 1987; 90: 709-715.
10. Benhamou, M., Ninio, E., Salem, P., Heiblot, C., Bessou, G., Pitton, C., Liu, F.-T. and Mencia-Huerta, J.M. *Decrease in IgE Fc receptor expression of mouse bone marrow-derived mast cells and inhibition of PAF-acether formation and of beta-hexosaminidase*

release by dexamethasone. J Immunol 1986; 136: 1385-1392.

11. Benovic, J.L., Strasser, R.H., Caron, M.G. and Lefkowitz, R.J. *Beta-adrenergic receptor kinase: Identification of a novel protein kinase that phosphorylates the agonist-occupied form of the receptor.* Proc Natl Acad Sci USA 1986; 83; 2797-2801.

12. Benveniste, J., Henson, P.M. and Cochrane, C.G. *Leukocyte-dependent histamine release from rabbit platelets: The role of IgE, basophils and a platelet-activating factor.* J Exp Med 1972; 136: 1356-1377.

13. Booij-Noord, H., Orie, N.G.M. and de Vries, K. *Immediate and late bronchial obstructive reactions to inhalation of house dust and protective effects of disodium chromoglycate and prednisolone.* J Allergy Clin Immunol 1971; 48: 344-354.

14. Braquet, P. *The ginkgolides: Potent platelet-activating factor antagonists isolated from Ginkgo biloba L.: Chemistry, pharmacology and clinical applications.* Drugs of the Future 1987; 12: 643-699.

15. Braquet, P., Etienne, A. and Clostre, F. *Down-regulation of beta-2 adrenergic receptors by PAF-acether and its inhibition by the PAF-acether antagonist BN 52021.* Prostaglandins 1985; 30: 721.

16. Braquet, P., Etienne, A., Touvay, C., Bourgain, R.H., Lefort, J. and Vergaftig, B.B. *Involvement of platelet-activating factor in respiratory anaphylaxis, demonstrated by PAF-acether inhibitor BN 52021.* Lancet 1985; 1: 1501.

17. Brink, C. *Tolerance of guinea pig airway smooth muscle preparations to relaxant agonists induced by chronic exposure to isoprenaline in vivo.* Br J Pharmacol 1981; 73: 13-19.

18. Chung, K.F., Aizawa, H., Leikauf, G.D., Ueki, I.F., Evans, T.W. and Nadel, J.A. *Airway hyperresponsiveness induced by platelet-activating factor: Role of thromboxane generation.* J Pharmacol Exp Ther 1986; 236: 580-584.

19. Cuss, F.M., Dixon, C.M.S. and Barnes, P.J. *Effect of inhaled platelet-activating factor on pulmonary function and bronchial responsiveness in man.* Lancet 1986; 2: 187-192.

20. Darius, H., Lefer, D.J., Smith, J.B. and Lefer, A.M. *Role of platelet-activating factor-acether in mediating guinea pig anaphylaxis.* Science 1986; 232: 58-60.

21. Demopoulos, C.A., Pinckard, R.N. and

Hanahan, D.J. *Platelet-activating factor, evidence for 1-O-alkyl-2-acetyl-sn-glyceryl-3-phosphorylcholine as the active component (a new class of lipid chemical mediators).* J Biol Chem 1979; 254: 9355-9358.

22. Douglas, J.S., Lewis, A.J., Ridgway, P., Brink, C. and Bouhuys, A. *Tachyphylaxis to beta-adrenoceptor agonists in guinea pig airway smooth muscle in vivo and in vitro.* Eur J Pharmacol 1977; 42: 195-205.

23. Hwang, S.-B. and Lam, M.-H. *Species difference in the specific receptors of platelet-activating factor.* Biochem Pharmacol 1986; 35: 4511-4518.

24. Lee, T.C., Lenihan, D.J., Malone, B., Roddy, L.L. and Wasserman, S.I. *Increased biosynthesis of platelet-activating factor in activated human eiosinophils.* J Biol Chem 1984: 259: 5526-5530.

25. Lee, T.-C. and Snyder, F. *Function, metabolism and regulation of platelet-activating factor and related ether lipids.* In: Phospholipids and Cellular Regulation, Vol. II. J.F. Kno (Ed.). CRC Press: Boca Raton, FL 1985; 1-39.

26. Lefkowitz, R.J., Benovic, J.L., Kobilka, B. and Caron, M.G. *Beta-adrenergic receptors and rhodopsin: Shedding new light on an old subject.* TIPS 1986; 7: 444-448.

27. Mazzoni, L., Morley, J., Page, C.P. and Sanzar, S. *Induction of airway hyperreactivity by platelet-activating factor in guinea pigs.* J Physiol 1985; 369: 107P.

28. McManus, L.M., Shaw, J.O. and Pinckard, R.N. *Thromboxane B_2 (TXB$_2$) release during IgE anaphylaxis in the rabbit.* J Immunol 1980; 125: 1950-1958.

29. Page, C.P., Archer, C.B., Paul, W. and Morley, J. *PAF-acether: A mediator of inflammation and asthma.* TIPS 1984; 5: 239-241.

30. Page, C.P. and Morley, J. *Evidence favouring PAF rather than leukotrienes in the pathogenesis of asthma.* Pharmacol Res Commun 1986; 18(Suppl.): 217-237.

31. Patterson, R. and Harris, K.E. *The activity of aerosolized and intracutaneous synthetic platelet-activating factor (AGEPC) in rhesus monkeys with IgE-mediated airway responses and normal monkeys.* J Lab Clin Med 1983; 102: 933-938.

32. Rubin, A.E., Smith, L.J. and Patterson, R. *Effect of platelet-activating factor (PAF) on normal human airways.* Am Rev Resp Dis 1986; 133(Suppl): A91.

33. Sano, Y., Watt, G. and Townley, R.G.

Decreased mononuclear cell beta-adrenergic receptors in bronchial asthma: Parallel studies of lymphocyte and granulocyte desensitization. J Allergy Clin Immunol 1983; 72: 495-503.

34. Snyder, F. *Chemical and biochemical aspects of platelet-activating factor: A novel class of acetylated ether-linked choline phospholipids.* Med Res Rev 1985; 5: 107-140.

35. Strasser, R.H., Benovic, J.L., Caron, M.G. and Lefkowitz, R.J. *Beta-agonist and PGE$_1$-induced translocation of the beta-adrenergic receptor kinase: Evidence that the kinase may act on multiple adenylate cyclase-coupled receptors.* Proc Natl Acad Sci USA 1986; 83: 6362-6366.

36. Takeyama, H.F., Agrawal, D.K. and Townley, R.G. *Both allergen and histamine-induced bronchoconstrictions cause increased alpha$_1$ and decreased beta-adrenergic receptors in guinea pig lung.* 1987; submitted for publication.

37. Taki, F., Takagi, K., Satake, T., Sugiyama, S. and Ozawa, T. *The role of phospholipase in reduced beta-adrenergic responsiveness in experimental asthma.* Am Rev Resp Dis 1986; 133: 362-366.

38. Tamura, N., Agrawal, D.K., Suliaman, F.A. and Townley, R.G. *Effects of platelet-activating factor on the chemotaxis of normodense eosinophils from normal subjects.* Biochem Biophys Res Comm 1987; 142: 638-644.

39. Tashkin, D.P., Conolly, M.E., Deutsch, R.I., Hui, K.K., Littner, M., Scarpace, P. and Abrass, I. *Subsensitization of beta-adrenoceptors in airways and lymphocytes of healthy and asthmatic subjects.* Am Rev Resp Dis 1982; 125: 185-193.

40. Vergaftig, B.B., Chignard, M., Benveniste, J., Lefort, J. and Wal, F. *Background and present status of research on platelet-activating factor (PAF-acether).* Ann NY Acad Sci 1981; 370: 119-139.

41. Wardlaw, A.J., Moqbel, R., Crombell, O. and Kay, A.B. *Platelet-activating factor: A potent chemotactic and chemokinetic factor for human eosinophils.* J Clin Invest 1987; 78: 1701-1706.

Ginkgolides - Chemistry, Biology, Pharmacology
and Clinical Perspectives. P. Braquet (Ed.)
Copyright © 1988, J.R. Prous Science Publishers, S.A.

USE OF GINKGOLIDES ON PAF-ACETHER-INDUCED HYPOTENSION AND CARDIAC MODIFICATIONS

Isabelle Viossat, Jean-Michel Guillon, Eric Etiemble and Eduardo Pirotzky

Institut Henri Beaufour, 72, avenue des Tropiques, F-91952 Les Ulis Cédex, France

INTRODUCTION

Platelet-activating factor is a phospholipid mediator synthetized and released from various cell types (such as platelets, polymorphonuclear neutrophils, macrophages, mastocytes, monocytes, endothelial cells) and organs (heart, kidney) (3, 18, 20, 21). This compound shares common characteristics with the circulating vasoactive mediators of shock, and in addition to its platelet-activating properties and its role in inflammation and allergic reactions, it is known to elicit cardiovascular responses, including microcirculatory sludge (6), plasma extravasation (6), arterial hypotension (7, 16), reduction in renal blood flow (5) and coronary constriction in the isolated guinea-pig heart (2).

Ginkgolides have been shown to be effective against hemodynamic changes due to various shocks such as endotoxic shock in rats (10), mycotoxic shock in rats (11), and human IgG aggregates-induced anaphylaxis in rats (17). PAF-acether seems to play a major role in such physiopathological states (9).

In the present paper, we report the action of systemic administration of PAF-acether on arterial blood pressure, and its effect on the isolated perfused guinea-pig heart. We also analyzed the effect of ginkgolides in the above-mentioned models.

Address all correspondence to: Dr. Eduardo Pirotzky, Dept. of Vascular Pathology, Institut Henri Beaufour, 72, avenue des Tropiques, F-91952 Les Ulis Cédex, France.

MATERIALS AND METHODS

Drugs

PAF-acether (1-0-hexadecyl-2(R)-acetyl-glycero-3-phosphorylcholine) was purchased from Bachem (Bubendorff, Switzerland) and stored at —80°C in a 0.5% bovine albumin serum solution.

For *in vitro* experiments BN 52021 (ginkgolide B) or BN 52063 (ginkgolide A + B + C 40% - 40% - 20%) IHB-IPSEN Research Labs. Le Plessis-Robinson, France, was dissolved in dimethyl sulfoxide (DMSO) (Merck Schuchard).

For *in vivo* experiments BN 52063 was solubilized in DMSO then diluted to 1/10th in saline (0.9% NaCl in water) warmed to 90°C. The preparation was cooled to 37°C before injections. The same process was used to solubilize the ginkgolides A, B and C.

Indomethacin, phentolamine and propranolol were obtained from Sigma (Saint-Louis, Missouri). Indomethacin was solubilized in NaOH, N/10 (the pH was then reajusted), while phentolamine and propranolol were dissolved in saline (0.9% in water).

PAF-Acether-Induced Hypotension in Rats

Male Sprague-Dawley rats (250-260 g) were anesthetized with ethyl carbamate (1.2 g/kg i.p.). Polyethylene catheters were inserted into the left carotid artery and into the right jugular vein. Systolic and diastolic arterial blood pressure were continuously measured in the left carotid artery via a P 50 Gould transducer. Heart rate was registered with a Gould biotachometer. These parameters were recorded on a multichannel Gould polygraph (model 8000 S). PAF-acether was injected in a bolus i.v. (0.25-0.50-1 μg/kg), in the penis vein in a volume of 1 ml/kg.

BN 52063 was injected in a 15 minute venous perfusion before challenge in the jugular vein at a rate of 0.1 ml/minute (1 - 2 - 5 mg/kg). BN 52063 was also infused curatively 3 minutes after PAF-acether, either in 15 minutes venous perfusion (1 - 2 - 5 mg/kg) or in acute injections (0.5 -1 - 2 mg/kg).

Isolated Perfused Guinea-Pig Heart

Male Hartley guinea-pigs (350-450 g) were anesthetized with pentobarbital (30 mg/kg i.p.). One minute after heparin injection (1000 UI/kg i.v.) hearts were excised and rapidly cannulated through the aorta on a non-recirculating Langendorff perfusion apparatus. The heart preparations were perfused with a modified Krebs Henseleit buffer, pH 7.4 at 37°C, oxygenated with a 95% O_2-5% CO_2 gas mixture under a constant hydrostatic pressure of

80 cm of water. Hearts were first submitted to a stabilization period of 15 minutes, receiving a normal perfusion medium. They were then perfused for 10 minutes with either ginkgolides at various doses or the control medium containing 0.5% DMSO. PAF-acether was then injected in a bolus of 0.1 ml above the cannula and hearts were submitted to another 15 minutes perfusion period.

Data Analysis

Statistical comparisons were determined by Fisher-Snedecor one way analysis of variance on the experimental values. Results were presented as means ± S.E.M. or percent change of control.

RESULTS

PAF-Acether-Induced Hypotension in Normotensive Rats

Intravenous administration of PAF-acether (0.25-1.0 μg/kg) elicited a dose-related decrease in arterial blood pressure in anesthetized normotensive rats with a greater fall in diastolic blood pressure. The onset of action was within seconds and lasted for about 20 to 30 minutes, depending upon the dose of PAF-acether administered. The hypotension was associated with a normal heart rate.

Pretreatment with indomethacin (2 and 5 mg/kg i.v.), a prostaglandin cyclooxygenase inhibitor, and phentolamine (0.5 mg/kg i.v.) an α-blocking agent, 5 or 10 minutes before challenge did not modify PAF-acether-induced hypotension in the anesthetized normotensive rat.

In contrast, propranolol, a β-blocking agent injected 10 minutes before challenge reinforced the drop and the duration of PAF-acether-induced hypotension. The slight but significant potentialization at 0.5 mg/kg was particularly evident for the dose 1 mg/kg, with a more pronounced effect on systolic than on diastolic blood pressure (data not shown).

Devoid of effect *per se* on blood pressure, when perfused for 15 minutes, BN 52063 exerted a dose-dependent inhibition against PAF-acether-induced hypotension. This protection was significant already two minutes after PAF-acether injection. Against hypotension following a higher dose of PAF-acether, the antagonistic effects of BN 52063 appeared to be more durable (Fig. 1).

Among the three ginkgolides A, B and C, ginkgolide B (2 mg/kg) exerted the greatest inhibition. Ginkgolide A (2 mg/kg) also revealed a certain amount of activity, whereas ginkgolide C (1 mg/kg) was the least potent (Fig. 2).

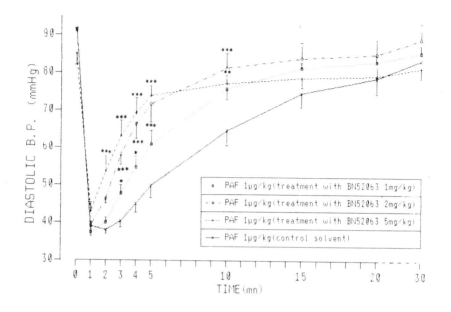

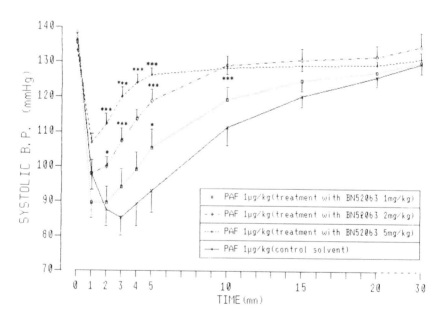

Figure 1 Effect of BN 52063 on PAF-acether-induced hypotension in the normotensive anesthetized rat (given preventively in a 15 minute perfusion). $*p<0.05$; $**p<0.01$; $***p<0.001$.

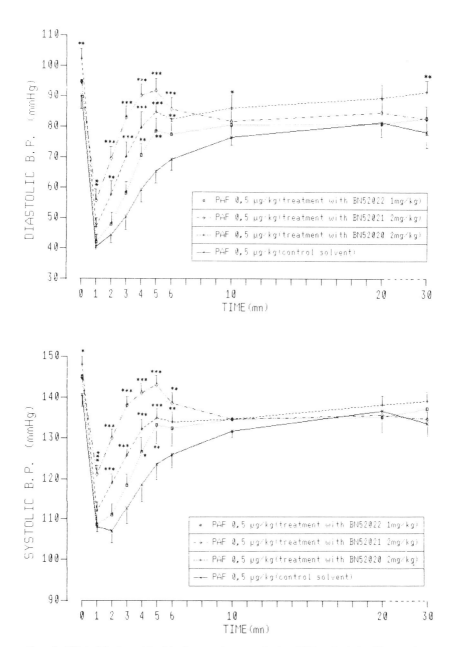

Figure 2 Effect of the three ginkgolides (in respective proportions) on PAF-acether-induced hypotension in the normotensive anesthetized rat (given preventively in a 15 minute venous perfusion). *p<0.05; **p<0.01; ***p<0.001.

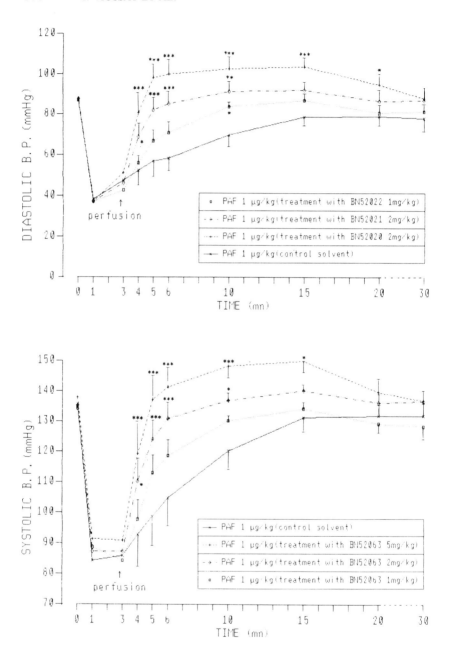

Figure 3 Effect of BN 52063 on PAF-acether-induced hypotension in the normotensive anesthetizedd rat (given preventively in a 15 minute perfusion). *p<0.05; **p<0.01; ***p<0.001.

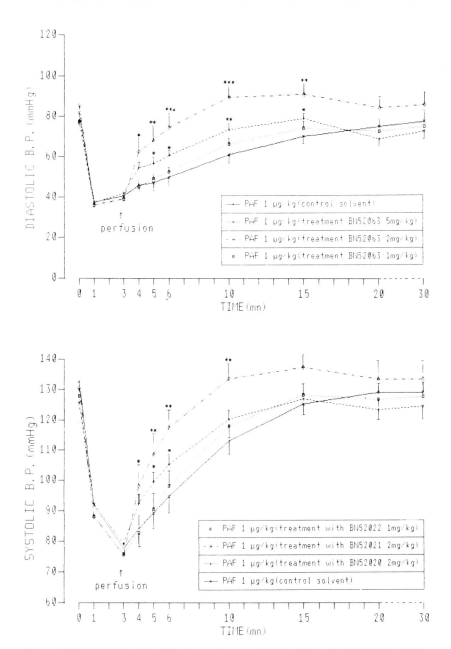

Figure 4 Effect of the three ginkgolides (in respective proportions) on PAF-acether-induced hypotension in the normotensive anesthetized rat (given preventively in a 15 minute venous perfusion). *p < 0.05; **p < 0.01; ***p < 0.001.

In curative treatment, BN 52063 also induced a dose-dependent inhibition on PAF-induced hypotension when administered in perfusion 3 minutes after PAF-acether injection (maximum hypotension time). Its effect was highly significant at the dose 5 mg/kg i.v. Two minutes after perfusion (*i.e.*, after 0.6 mg/kg of BN 52063) the arterial blood pressure exceeded its initial value and reached maximal value 10 to 15 minutes afterwards (Fig. 3).

If a comparison is made between the curative effects of BN 52063 in perfusion or in a bolus, at equal doses, it can be observed that in perfusion the protection against PAF-acether hypotension is more durable than after an acute injection.

When administered curatively, in a 15 minute venous perfusion (Fig. 4) ginkgolide B is also the most active constituent. If its action is compared with that of BN 52063, the inhibition observed with ginkgolide B is more progressive but lower than that of BN 52063 at an equivalent dose. The effect of ginkgolide A on diastolic pressure is about half that of ginkgolide B. Ginkgolide C is practically devoid of effect. Ginkgolides have a more durable effect in perfusion than in bolus at equal doses, like BN 52063.

By contrast, BN 52063 was devoid of action on diazoxide, sodium nitroprusside and diltiazem-induced hypotension (data not shown).

Isolated Guinea-Pig Heart

PAF-acether (10^{-11} up to 10^{-7} moles) provoked a dose-dependent decrease of coronary flow with a maximum 2 minutes after injection. PAF-acether also induced a fall in heart rate with a maximum after 2 minutes and a depressive effect on contractile force with a maximum occurring after 6 minutes (Table 1). At the highest dose (10^{-7} moles) of PAF-acether, we also observed arrhythmias in 40% of hearts.

In a first series of experiments, we tested the action of BN 52063 at various

Table 1 Coronary flow, heart rate and contractile force modifications after PAF-acether injection

PAF-acether (moles)		Coronary flow	Heart rate	Contractile force
10^{-11}	(n = 7)	0	$- 4 \pm 2$	$- 4 \pm 6$
5.10^{11}	(n = 4)	$-30 \pm 3**$	—	— —
10^{-10}	(n = 6)	$-55 \pm 5***$	$- 6 \pm 3$	$- 6 \pm 4$
10^{-9}	(n = 6)	$-65 \pm 4***$	$-26 \pm 2***$	$-35 \pm 4***$
10^{-8}	(n = 7)	$-85 \pm 1***$	$-34 \pm 9**$	$-30 \pm 4***$
10^{-7}	(n = 7)	$-91 \pm 4***$	$-41 \pm 7***$	$-31 \pm 8***$

Results are expressed as % change versus initial value. *p<0.05; **p<0.01; ***p<0.001.

concentrations against the effect of 10^{-8} moles of PAF-acether. BN 52063 was devoid of any effect *per se* on coronary flow and heart rate, but exhibited a slight positive inotropic effect at 10^{-4} M.

BN 52063 dose-dependently inhibited the coronary vasoconstriction caused by PAF-acether, with a significant effect at 10^{-5} M (Table 2). It also elicited a decrease in heart rate with a maximum effect after 2 minutes. This effect was antagonized by BN 52063 at 10^{-4} M.

Table 2 Inhibition by BN 52063 of PAF-acether effects on isolated heart

	Coronary flow % change	Heart rate % change	Contractile force % change
Control (n = 8)	—80 ± 3	— 24 ± 7	—41 ± 7
BN 52063 10^{-6}M (n = 6)	—77 ± 5	—30 ± 7	—33 ± 6
BN 52063 10^{-5}M (n = 6)	—63 ± 5**	—19 ± 3	—27 ± 4
BN 52063 10^{-4}M (n = 6)	—31 ± 6***	— 6 ± 9*	— 5 ± 2***

Results are expressed as % change verssus initial value. *p<0.05; **p<0.01; ***p<0.001.

PAF-acether induced a fall in contractile force with a maximum occurring after 6 minutes. This effect was also inhibited by BN 52063 at 10^{-4} M.

In another series of experiments, we used a higher dose of PAF-acether (10^{-7} moles) which provoked arrhythmias in 40% of hearts. BN 52021, at 2 x 10^{-4} M, was antiarrhythmic in this model. It also antagonized the effect of PAF-acether on coronary flow and heart rate, but not on contractile force (21).

We investigated the specificity of ginkgolides for PAF-acether-induced coronary vasoconstriction using another agent: vasopressin (2 mUI/0.1 ml). BN 52021, even at the highest dose (2 x 10^{-4} M), was ineffective against this coronary spasm (1).

DISCUSSION

PAF-acether administration was associated with a dose-dependent decrease in blood pressure. In agreement with other authors (7), our findings seemed to exclude the possibility of PAF-acether induced hypotension mediated by the synthesis and release of vasodilator prostaglandins as shown by the inefficiency of indomethacin in our model.

Furthermore, α-blockers did not modify PAF-acether hypotension. Other studies have also shown lack of interaction of PAF-acether with the α-adrenergic receptor on radioligand binding (8) and in pithed rats (19). In contrast, blockage of β-adrenoceptors prolongs and accentuates the effects of PAF-acether on arterial blood pressure.

BN 52063 elicited a dose-dependent inhibition of PAF-acether-induced hypotension in anesthetized normotensive rats. This protective effect was observed preventively and curatively. Among the three ginkgolides tested, BN 52021 was the most potent. In contrast, BN 52063 was devoid of effect against diazoxide, sodium nitroprusside and diltiazem-induced hypotension, demonstrating the specificity of the product. The inhibition of PAF-acether-induced hypotension can be ascribed to a direct interaction of BN 52063 with vascular PAF-acether receptors.

On the isolated guinea-pig heart, PAF-acether impaired cardiac function, with a decrease in coronary flow, heart rate and contractility. Some studies have reported a selective effect of PAF-acether on coronary flow and contractility with no change in heart rate: these differences can be attributed to the experimental conditions used by the various authors (2, 14, 15). PAF-acether provokes similar alterations of cardiac function as cardiac anaphylaxis (12-14). Moreover, PAF-acether seems to be released by anaphylactic hearts (13).

In our experiments, BN 52063 and BN 52021 inhibited the deleterious effects of PAF-acether on isolated guinea-pig heart. This effect is specific since the vasopressin-induced coronary vasoconstriction was not prevented by BN 52021. PAF-acether, as well as antigen-induced myocardial dysfunction, are accompanied by a release of various mediators, including TXA_2, LTC_4 and histamine (4, 14). BN 52021 protected cardiac function with a simultaneous decrease of mediators (4, 15), indicating a role of these substances in the action of PAF-acether or anaphylaxis and furthermore providing an indirect proof of the role of PAF-acether in cardiac anaphylaxis.

The use of a PAF-receptor antagonist such as BN 52063 opens prospects to investigate the role of PAF-acether in the various hemodynamic changes involved in different shock states. Futhermore, these drugs could provide a new group of potent shock treatment drugs.

References

1. Baranes, J. et al. *The effects of PAF-acether on the cardiovascular system and their inhibition by a new highly specific PAF-acether* receptor antagonist, BN 52021. Pharmacol Res Commun 1986; 18: 717-737.

2. Benveniste, J. et al. *The actions of PAF-*

acether (platelet-activating factor) on guinea-pig isolated heart preparations. Br J Pharmacol 1983; 80: 81-83.

3. Benveniste, J., Chignard, M. *A role for PAF-acether (platelet-activating factor) in platelet-dependent vascular diseases.* Circulation 1985; 72: 713-717.

4. Berti, F., Rossoni, G. *PAF, ginkgolides and active anaphylactic shock in lung and heart.* In: The Ginkgolides: Chemistry, Biology, Pharmacology and Clinical Perspectives. P. Braquet (Ed.). J.R. Prous, S.A. Barcelona 1987;

5. Bessin, P. et al. *Acute circulatory collapse caused by platelet-activating factor (PAF-acether) in dogs.* Eur J Pharmacol 1983; 86: 403-413.

6. Braquet, P. et al. *Involvement of leukotrienes and PAF-acether in the increased microvascular permeability of the rabbit retina.* Agents and Actions 1984; 15: 82-85.

7. Caillard, C.G. et al. *Hypotensive activity of PAF-acether in rats.* Agents and Actions 1982; 12 (5): 725-730.

8. Cervoni, P. et al. *Evidence for the lack of interaction between (H)-1-0-octadecyl-2-acetyl-glyceryl-3-phosphorylcholine and α-adrenoceptors in vivo and in vitro.* Br J Pharmacol 1984; 83: 511-517.

9. Doebber, T.W. et al. *Platelet-activating factor (PAF) involvement in endotoxin-induced hypotension in rats. Studies with PAF receptor antagonist kadsurenone.* Biochem Biophys Res Commun 1985; 127: 799-808.

10. Etienne, A. et al. *In vivo inhibition of plasma protein leakage and Salmonella enteritidis-induced mortality in the rat by a specific PAF-acether antagonist: BN 52021.* Agents and Actions 1985; 17(3/4): 368-370.

11. Feurstein, G. et al. *Protective effect of PAF-acether antagonist BN 52021 in trichothecene toxicosis.* J Appl Pharmacol Toxicol (Submitted).

12. Koltai, M. et al. *Effect of BN 52021, a specific PAF-acether antagonist, on cardiac anaphylaxis in Langendorff hearts isolated from passively sensitized guinea-pigs.* Eur J Pharmacol 1986; 130: 133-136.

13. Levi, R. et al. *Acetyl glyceryl ether phosphorylcholine (AGEPC). A putative mediator of cardiac anaphylaxis in the guinea-pig.* Circ Res 1984; 54: 117-124.

14. Pinckard, R.N. et al. *Intravascular and cardiovascular effects of acetyl-glyceryl-ether-phosphorylcholine (AGEPC) infusion in the baboon.* Clin Res 1980; 28: 358 A.

15. Piper, P.J., Stewart, A.G. *Antagonism of vasoconstriction induced by platelet-activating factor in guinea-pig perfused hearts by selective platelet-activating factor receptor antagonists.* Br J Pharmacol 1987; 90: 771-783.

16. Saeki, et al. *Effects of 1-0-alkyl-2-acetyl-SN-glycero-3-phosphocholine (platelet-activating factor) on cardiac function in perfused guinea-pig heart.* Life Sci 1985; 37: 325-329.

17. Sanchez-Crespo, M. et al. *Vascular actions of synthetic PAF-acether (a synthetic platelet-activating factor) in the rat: Evidence for a platelet independent mechanism.* Immunopharmacology 1982; 4: 173-185.

18. Sanchez-Crespo, M. et al. *Inhibition of the vascular actions of IgG aggregates by BN 52021, a highly specific antagonist of PAF-acether.* Immunopharmacology 1985; 10: 69-75.

19. Snyder, F. *Chemical and biochemical aspects of platelet-activating factor: A novel class of acetylated ether-linked choline phospholipids.* Med Res Rev 1985; 5: 107-140.

20. Sybertz, E. et al. *Studies on the interactions of acetyl-glyceryl-ether- phosphorylcholine with the sympathic nervous system in rats.* J Pharm Exp Ther 1982; 233: 594-598.

21. Vanhoutte, P.M., Houston, D.S. *Platelets, endothelium and vasospasm.* Circulation 1985; 72: 728-734.

22. Viossat, I. et al. *The coronary, inotropic, chronotropic and arrythmogenic effects of PAF-acether on isolated guinea-pig heart and their inhibition by BN 52021.* In: Lipid Mediators in Immunology of Burn and Sepsis. NATO ASI Series. Plenum Press: New York 1987.

23. Zimmerman, G.A. et al. *Production of platelet-activating factor by human vascular endothelial cells: Evidence for a requirement for specific agonists and modulation by prostacyclin.* Circulation 1985; 72: 718-727.

Ginkgolides - Chemistry, Biology, Pharmacology and Clinical Perspectives. P. Braquet (Ed.)
Copyright © 1988, J.R. Prous Science Publishers, S.A.

BN 52021 AS A PAF ANTAGONIST IN THE CARDIOVASCULAR SYSTEM: EXPERIMENTS IN NEWBORN PIGS AND CONSCIOUS RATS

Giora Feuerstein[1], Linda Bradley[2], Anna-Leena Sirén[1] and Robert E. Goldstein[2]

Departments of Neurology[1] and Medicine[2], Uniformed Services University of the Health Sciences, Bethesda, MD, USA

INTRODUCTION

Platelet-activating factor (PAF, acetyl-glyceryl-ether-phosphorylcholine) has already been established as an autacoid capable of producing multiple pathophysiological events in practically every species (2, 24). A major system affected by PAF is the cardiovascular system where direct cardiac, coronary, renal and vascular effects have been reported in the rat, guinea-pig, rabbit, dog and pig (1, 3, 11). The effects of PAF on the cardiovascular system produce a chain of events which leads to a state of shock characterized by low cardiac output, organ hypoperfusion and plasma extravasation in the microcirculation; these phenomena ultimately lead to death.

The cardiac and vascular effects of PAF might be the result of PAF synthesis and release by cellular elements confined to the heart and blood vessels with PAF thereby acting as a paracrine mediator. Alternatively, PAF might act as a humoral substance generated in the circulation by white blood cells or flushed into the circulation from sites of excess production. Whether produced locally or remotely, the heart and blood vessels are the primary target organs for PAF (11, 15). Therefore, blockade of the cardiac and vascular receptors of PAF is of utmost importance if protection of these

Address all correspondence to: Dr. Giora Feuerstein, Neurobiology Research Unit, Uniformed Services University of Health Sciences, 4301 Jones Bridge Road, Beethesda MD 20814 USA.

organs froms PAF effects is desired. Such situations include acute systemic or cardiac anaphylaxis, as well as endotoxic shock, where PAF levels in the circulation are elevated (5) and therefore effects on all vascular beds as well as the heart are expected.

The experiments presented in this chapter were designed to test the efficacy of a known PAF antagonist, BN 52021 (3, 21) on specific vascular beds of the newborn pig and the adult rat. Such studies might provide a basis for therapeutic interventions in situations where PAF plays a significant role in pathological processes in the cardiovascular system.

MATERIALS AND METHODS

Experiments on the Newborn Pig

The hemodynamic effects of PAF were assessed in 9 open-chest newborn piglets. Studies were performed in animals weighing 2.2-3.6 kg and aged 7-18 days. There were 4 males and 11 females.

Animals were sedated with ketamine hydrochloride (50 mg/kg iv) and anesthetized with sodium pentobarbital (30 mg/kg, iv). A tracheostomy was performed and a 3.5 mm endotracheal tube placed. An orogastric tube was inserted into the stomach for drug administration. Animals were ventilated with a volume-cycled infant respirator (Model 665, Harvard Apparatus, South Natick, MA). Respiratory rate and inspired oxygen concentration were initially adjusted to maintain arterial pO_2 100-200 mmHg, pCO_2 35-45 mmHg and pH 7.38-7.42. Blood temperature was maintained between 36.5-38.5° by an external heating blanket.

The left internal jugular vein was cannulated for PAF administration and cold saline injection. A 3.5 mm Thermocouple flow probe (Columbus Instruments, Columbus, OH) was advanced from the left carotid artery to the ascending aorta for cardiac output measurement by thermodilution using a single channel cardiac output computer (Cardiomax II, Columbus Instruments, Columbus, OH). A 4F high fidelity pressure catheter (Millar Instruments, Houston, TX) was directed from the left carotid artery to the left ventricle. A left lateral thoracotomy was performed, the internal mammary artery cannulated for systemic arterial pressure measurement, and the heart suspended in a pericardial cradle. Cannulae were placed in the right ventricle and pulmonary artery via small stab incisions. Vascular pressures were measured with pressure transducers (Model P23 ID, Gould-Statham Instruments, Hato Rey, PR) and recorded on a multichannel recorder (Model 7758A, Hewlett-Packard Instruments, Rockville, MD).

Pure synthetic PAF (1-0-hexadecyl-2-acetyl-*sn*-glycero-3-phosphorylcholine) was dissolved in 0.9% NaCl to a concentration of 1 nmol/10 μl. Aliquots were kept frozen (-70°C) until used, thawed once, and diluted to a final volume of 100 μl per injection. Pure powdered BN 52021, 5 mg/kg, was suspended in 30 ml 0.9% NaCl.

PROTOCOL Following baseline measurement of pressures and cardiac output, animals received 1 nmol PAF by intravenous injection. Pressure and cardiac dimension data were continuously recorded; cardiac outpout determinations were repeated at fixed 1 minute intervals after PAF administration. After a 30 minute recovery period, animals were randomly assigned to receive either BN 52021 (5 mg/kg via orogastric tube over 20 minutes, n = 4, age 12 ± 6 days, weight 2.9 ± 3 kg) or an equal volume of 0.9% NaCl over the same interval (n = 5, age 14 ± 2 days, weight 2.8 ± 1 kg). Sixty minutes later, after baseline measurements, 1 nmol of PAF was administered as previously described and measurements were repeated. At the conclusion of the study, animals were given an overdose of sodium pentobarbital and a lethal KCL injection.

DATA ANALYSIS All data, except cardiac output, were continuously recorded; those from mid- to end-expiration were chosen for analysis. Aortic flow was assumed to approximate cardiac output (ml/kg/min). Pulmonary vascular resistance (dynes.sec.cm^{-5}.kg) was calculated as 79.98 x (MPAP-MLVEDP)/CO where CO is cardiac output, MLVEDP is mean left ventricular end-diastolic pressure, and MPAP is mean pulmonary artery pressure. Systemic vascular resistance (dynes.sec.cm^{-5}.kg) was calculated as 79.98 x (MAP-MRVEDP)/CO with MAP being mean arterial pressure and MRVEDP being mean right ventricular end-diastolic pressure.

Data are presented as mean maximal values ± SEM for the indicated number of animals. Analysis of variance (ANOVA) followed by the Student-Newman-Keul test was used for statistical evaluation. Differences were considered significant when $P < .05$.

Experiments on the Conscious Rat

Male Sprague Dawley rats (260-360 g) were anesthetized with i.m. ketamine-acepromazine (0.13 ml/100 g of a ketamine/acepromazine solution of 100/1 mg/kg, respectively). A midline laparotomy was made and 4 mm length of the lower abdominal aorta below the left renal artery, the superior mesenteric artery and the left renal artery was exposed with the aid of an operating microscope.

Miniaturized Doppler flow probes were then sutured around each vessel. The wire leads were tunneled beneath the skin and exteriorized at the nape of the neck where they were soldered to a connector plug that was fixed to the animal's skull with small screws and dental acrylic. Polyethylene catheters (PE-50) were implanted in the femoral arteries for measurements of blood pressure and heart rate and for drug injections. The catheters were led beneath the back skin to exit at the nape of the neck and were then secured by a spring wire. The animals were allowed to recover from the surgery for 2-3 days. On the day of the experiment the rat was connected to the flow probe wire connector, and the connector line was suspended from the top of the animal's home cage to allow freedom of movements during the experiment. Regional blood flow was measured with a directional pulsed Doppler flowmeter (model 545c-3, University of Iowa Bioengineering Facility). The arterial line was attached to a pressure transducer, and the blood pressure, heart rate, and regional blood flows were continuously recorded on the Narco dynograph. Vascular resistance was calculated by dividing the mean arterial pressure by blood velocity (Doppler shift in kHz). Changes in blood flow and vascular resistance are expressed as a percent of control values.

PROTOCOL   PAF, 1 nmol/kg, was administered as a bolus injection in 200 μl of 0.9% NaCl solution. Blood pressure, heart rate and renal, mesenteric and hindquarter blood flow were continuously monitored. BN 52021, 5 mg/kg, was administered in 200 μl volume of vehicle (see below). PAF injection was repeated 15 min after BN 52021 administration. Data obtained in this experiment were analyzed by ANOVA followed by the Student-Neuman-Keul test. A $p \pm 0.05$ was considered statistically significant.

MATERIALS   PAF was kindly provided by Dr. F. Snyder, Oak Ridge Associated Universities, Oak Ridge, TN. BN 52021 was kindly provided by Dr. P. Braquet, IHB Research Laboratories, France. For administration of BN 52021 to the rat, 5 mg/kg dose of BN 52021 was first dissolved in 50 μl of 50% DMSO and further diluted with 1 ml of normal saline. The pH was adjusted to the range of 7-8 by titration with 10N NaOH.

RESULTS

Studies on the Newborn Pig

The effects of the initial bolus injection of PAF are presented in Table 1. Systemic bolus administration of PAF (1 nmol) caused increases in pulmonary artery pressure (PAP) and pulmonary vascular resistance (PVR) which were maximal 30-60 sec after PAF injection; thereafter, all these variables gradually returned to baseline levels. PAP rose from 14 ± 1 to 27 ± 3 mmHg and PVR from 7704 ± 4245 dynes. sec. cm^{-5} kg (P ± 0.01).

Table 1 Hemodynamic effects on PAF in the newborn pig (n = 9)

	Baseline	PAF
PAP (mmHg)	14 ± 1	27 ± 3*
PVR (dynes's'cm^{-5}'kg)	7704 ± 1303	25963 ± 4245*
CO (ml/kg/min)	140 ± 20	100 ± 20
MAP (mmHg)	60 ± 4	50 ± 12
SVR (dynes's'cm^{-5}'kg)	59941 ± 21448	157,86 ± 120,133

CO = cardiac outpout; MAP = mean arterial pressure; PAP = pulmonary artery pressure; PVR = pulmonary vascular resistance; SVR = systemic vascular resistance. *P < .01 *vs.* baseline.

Cardiac output declined slightly from 140 ± 20 to 100 ± 20 ml/kg/min. PAF produced no consistent effect on either mean arterial pressure or systemic vascular resistance.

The effects of PAF-receptors blockade by BN 52021 on PAF-induced circulatory derangement are presented in Table 2. Baseline values for PAP, PVR, and CO were similar between control (vehicle pretreatment) and experimental (BN 52021 pretreatment) groups. Thus, BN 52021 administration had no effect on pulmonary or systemic hemodynamics (Table 2). Orogastric administration of BN 52021 60 min before bolus injection of PAF eliminated the PAF-induced decrement in CO and almost completely abolished the PAF induced rises in PAP and PVR (Table 2).

Table 2 Hemodynamic effects of PAF after BN 52021 newborn pigs

Baseline values before PAF	BN 52021	Vehicle
PAP (mmHg)	15 ± 2	16 ± 2
PVR (dynes'sec'cm^{-5}'kg)	6487 ± 1438	7791 ± 2102
CO (ml/kg/min)	135 ± 11	162 ± 18
Changes induced by PAF		
ΔPAP (mmHg)	6 ± 3	18 ± 5*
ΔPVR (dynes'sec'cm^{-5}'kg)	2205 ± 1943	34,765 ± 4208**
ΔCO (ml/kg/min)	10 ± 10	-100 ± 10**
N	4	5

*P < .05 or **P < .01 *vs.* PAF after BN 52021. Abbreviation as in Table 1. N = number of animals in each treatment group.

Studies on the Conscious Rat

Figure 1 demonstrates that injection of PAF to the conscious rat produced a severe drop of the mean arterial pressure without a significant change

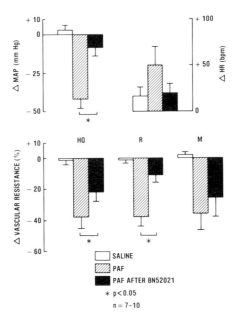

Figure 1 Effect of BN 52021 on systemic and regional hemodynamic responses to PAF. HQ = hindquarter; R = renal; M = mesenteric; MAP = mean arterial pressure; HR = heart rate; n = number of rats in each group. Asterisks indicate statistical significance between PAF BN 52021 and PAF groups (Student-Newman-Keul test).

in heart rate. The hypotensive effect of PAF was accompanied by a reduction of the vascular resistance in the hindquarters (HQ), the renal (R) and the mesenteric (M) vessels. The vasodilation produced by PAF in these vessels was highly significant when compared to the vehicle effect (p < 0.01). Administration of BN 52021 to the conscious rat did not affect the basal levels of any of these parameters nor did vehicle solutions. However, injection of the same dose of PAF (1 nmol/kg), 15 min after BN 52021, completely blocked the hypotension while substantially attenuating the vascular responses to PAF. However, some differences were noticed in the potency of BN 52021 to block the vascular effects of PAF; the order of potency for the various blood vessels was: renal > HQ > > mesenteric. In fact, only a slight tendency for blockade of PAF effects on the mesenteric circulation was noticed (Fig. 1).

DISCUSSION

The present paper confirms and extends previous reports which indicate potent vascular effects of PAF in a variety of species and organs. The present study also demonstrates for the first time the extreme potency of PAF on the pulmonary circulation of the newborn pig. Thus, a dose of 300 per kg of PAF injected into the systemic circulation of the newborn pig produced pulmonary hypertension by increasing the pulmonary vascular resistance over 300%. While the effects of PAF on the pulmonary circulation were highly consistant, systemic hemodynamic effects showed more variability. It is noteworthy that in the adult pig, the pulmonary effects of PAF, which are similar to those of the newborn pig (15, 17), are also accompanied by alterations in coronary perfusion and contractile performance (10).

The PAF antagonist BN 52021 had no effect on the pulmonary or systemic circulation *per se*. However, BN 52021 completely blocked the increase in pulmonary arterial pressure and vascular resistance as well as the decrease in cardiac output produced by PAF. Therefore, BN 52021 might be an effective drug to prevent or reverse PAF induced pulmonary derangements in the newborn pulmonary circulation.

The experiments conducted in the rat provided a unique opportunity to study peripheral organ blood flow in the conscious state using continuous and instantaneous measurement of essential organ blood flow. Additional advantages of this model are: 1) lack of respiratory complications to PAF administration; 2) prostaglandins play no role in the cardiovascular effect of PAF in the rat (8); 3) The cardiovascular effects of PAF in the rat are independent of platelet or white blood cell aggregation (20, 21).

Thus, the effect of PAF on the rat circulation seems to be a direct one. BN 52021 was very efficacious in blocking the vascular effects of PAF but in a differential manner. It seems that BN 52021 is especially potent in blocking the renal receptor of PAF. Partial blockade by BN 52021 of PAF-induced hindquarter vasodilation might be explained by the mixed type of blood vessels in the hindquarters, *i.e.*, skeletal muscle and skin blood vessels. Since PAF-induced hypotension is accompanied by immediate activation of the sympatho-adrenomedullary system and marked elevation of plasma epinephrine (8, 25), it might be possible that some vasodilation in the skeletal muscle circulation is mediated by β-adrenergic receptors. Since BN 52021 does not affect adrenergic receptors, it is conceivable that some vasodilaation seen in the hindquarter region would be resistant to PAF antagonist. However, this explanation might not be applicable to the mesenteric circulation, where catecholamines (epinephrine and norepinephrine) produce vasoconstriction through α-adrenergic receptors. Therefore, the resistance of the mesenteric PAF receptors to BN 52021 might be viewed as indication of a subtype of PAF receptors which are substantially different from the renal or hindquarter PAF receptors. The possibility of the existence of PAF receptor subtypes has already been suggested for macrophages and polymorphonuclear cells (17).

Further investigations by using other PAF antagonists and direct PAF receptor assays in the various blood vessels are necessary to substantiate this possibility. In any case, the data obtained in the rat might suggest that more than one PAF antagonist might be necessary to effectively block PAF effects on the cardiovascular system or PAF antagonists with broader blocking capacity than BN 52021 would be necessary.

The overall significance of the data presented in this study support the possibility of the potential therapeutic capacity of BN 52021 in protecting cardiovascular elements from the detrimental effects of PAF. Of special interest in this regard are disorders featuring severly increased pulmonary vascular resistance in the newborn. Persistent pulmonary hypertension syndromes remain a major source of mortality in infants; estimates vary from 20 to 50% (16). Pulmonary hypertension in the newborn is often associated with some form of aspiration syndrome (blood or meconium) (13), but can occur with gram-negative bacterial endotoxin (14, 23) or group B beta hemolytic streptococcal sepsis (19). Inflammatory substances such as leukotrienes (14, 23) and thromboxane A_2 (19) have been proposed as potential pathophysiologic mediators of pulmonary hypertension in the newborn. PAF release in response to inflammation may also be an important cause of pulmonary hypertension of the newborn, although this possibility has been little investigated. Elevated PAF levels are known to occur in endotoxemia (5).

The present study confirms that PAF can act as a potent vasoconstrictor in the pulmonary vascular bed. Current treatment modalities for persistent pulmonary hypertension are incomplete and non-specific (6). A more specific approach utilizing an effective PAF antagonist such as BN 52021 may have great therapeutic potential.

The potential therapeutic value of BN 52021 is further supported by recent studies showing reversal and protective effect of this PAF antagonist on some aspects of S. thyphimurium endotoxemia (7) as well as other immune mediated reactions (12, 21).

In summary, the data available to date are only preliminary in nature and extensive studies in other experimental models including primates would be necessary. Furthermore, the studies which are available to date include only short term effects of PAF antagonists; proof of long term protective capacity of PAF antagonists in pathological situations is still lacking.

ACKNOWLEDGEMENTS

This work was supported by USUHS protocol No. G19214 and R08346, and a grant from the Upjohn Company to Dr. G. Feuerstein. The opinions or assertions contained herein are the private ones of the author(s) and are not to be construed as official or as necessarily reflecting the views of the Department of Defense or the Uniformed Services University of the Health Sciences. There is no objection to its presentation and/or publication. The experiments reported herein were conducted according to the principles set forth in the Guide of Care and Use of Laboratory Animals, Institute of Laboratory Animal Medicine, National Research Council, DHEW Publication No. (NIH) 80-23, 1980. We wish to thank Laura L. Garza for preparing this manuscript.

References

1. Baranes, J., Hellegouarch, A., Le Hegarat, M., Viossat, I., Auguet, M., Chabrier, P.E., Braquet, P. *The effect of PAF-acether on the cardiovascular system and their inhibition by a new specific PAF-acether receptor antagonist BN 52021.* Pharmacol Res Comm 1986; 18: 717-737.

2. Benveniste, J. *PAF acether (platelet-activating factor) advances.* In: Prostaglandin Thromboxane and Leukotriene Research. Raven Press: New York 1985; 13: 11-18.

3. Braquet, P., Touqui, L., Shen, T., Vargaftig, B.*Perspectives in platelet-activating factor.* Pharmacol Rev 1987; 39: 97-145.

4. Cartwright, D., Soifer, S., Mauray, F. *Endotoxin produces acute pulmonary hypertension (PH) and thromboxane elevation in the newborn lamb.* Pediatr Res 1983; 17: 306A.

5. Doebber, T., Wu, M., Robbins, J., Choy, B., Chang, M., Shen, T. *Platelet-activating factor (PAF) involvement in endotoxin induced hypotension in rats: Studies with PAF-acether antagonist kadsurenone.* Biochem Biophys Res Comm 1985; 127: 799-808.

6. Drummond, W.H., Gregory, G.A., Heymann, M.A., Phibbs, R.A. *The independent effects of hyperventilation, tolazoline, and dopamine on infants with persistent pulmonary hypertension.* J Pediatr 1981; 98: 603-611.

7. Etienne, A., Hecquet, F., Soulard, C., Spinnewyn, B., Elostre, F., Braquet, P. *In vivo inhibition of plasma protein leakage and Salmonella ennteritidis induced mortality in the rat by a specific PAF-acether antagonist BN 52021.* Agents and Actions 1985; 17: 368-370.

8. Feuerstein, G., Zukowska-Grojec, Z., Krausz, M.M., Blank, M.L., Snyder, F., Kopin, I.J. *Cardiovascular and sympathetic effects of 1-O-hexadecyl-2-acetyl-sn-glycero-3-phosphocholine in conscious SHR and WKY rats.* Clin Exptl Hypert 1982; A4: 1335-1350.

9. Feuerstein, G., Boyd, L.M., Ezra, D., Goldstein, R.E. *Effect of platelet-activating factor on coronary circulation of the domestic pig.* Am J Physiol 1984; 246: H466-H471.

10. Feuerstein, G., Ezra, D., Ramwell, P.W., Letts, G., Goldstein, R.E. *Platelet-ativating factor as a modulator of cardiac and coronary functions.* In: Prostag Leukot Lipoxins. J.M. Bailey (Ed.).Plenum Publishing Corporation 1985; 303-310.

11. Feuerstein, G., Goldstein, R.E. *Effect of PAF on the cardiovascular system.* In: Platelet Activating Factor. F. Snyder (Ed.). Plenum: New York 1987; 403-424.

12. Feuerstein, G., Hallenbeck, J.M. *Prostaglandins leukotrienes and platelet-activating factor in shock.* Ann Rev Pharmacol Toxicol 1987; 27: 301-313.

13. Fox, W.W., Gewitz, M.H., Dinwiddie, R., Drummond, W.H., Peckman, G.J. *Pulmonary hypertension in the perinatal aspiration syndromes.* Pediatrics 1977; 59: 205-211.

14. Goldberg, R.N., Suguihara, C., Ahmed, T., Deseda de Cudemas, B., Barrios, P., Setzer, E.S., Bancalari, E. *Influence of an antagonist of slow-reacting substance of anaphylaxis on the cardiovascular manifestations of hypoxia in piglets.* Pediatr Res 1985; 19: 1201-1205.

15. Goldstein, R.E., Ezra, D., Laurindo, F.R.M., Feuerstein, G. *Coronary and pulmonary vascular effects of leukotrienes and PAF-acether.* Pharm Res Comm 1986; 18: 151-162.

16. Heymann, M.A., Hoffman, J.I.E. *Persistent pulmonary hypertension syndromes in the newborn.* In: Pulmonary Hypertension. E. Weir and J.T. Reeves (Eds.). Futura: New

York 1984; 45-71.

17. Lambrecht, G., Parnham, M.J. *Kadsurenone distinguishes between different platelet activating factor receptor subtypes on macrophages and polymorphonuclear leucocytes.* Br J Pharmac 1986; 87: 287-289.

18. Laurindo, F.R.M., Ezra, D., Czaja, J., Feuerstein, G., Goldstein, R.E. *Acute right ventricular failure due to platelet-activating factor or a thromboxane A_2 analog.* Clin Res 1985; 33: 203A.

19. Runkle, B., Goldberg, R.N., Clark, M.R. *Prostaglandins and hemodynamic events in group B beta strep (GBS) sepsis in indomethacin (I) treated piglets.* Pediatr Res 1983; 17: 333A.

20. Sanchez Crespo, M., Lonso, F., Inarrea, P., Egido, J. *Non platelet-mediated actions of 1-O-alkyl-2-acetyl-sn-3-glycerylprhosphorylcholine.* Agents and Actions 1981; 11: 565-566.

21. Sanchez Crespo, M., Alonso, F., Inarrea, P., Alvarez, V., Egido, J. *Vascular actions of synthetic PAF-acether (A synthetic platelet-activating factor) in the rat: Evidence for a platelet independent mechanism.* Immunopharmacol 1982; 4: 173-185.

22. Saunders, R.N., Handley, D.A. *Platelet-activating factor antagonists.* Ann Rev Pharmacol Toxicol 1987; 27: 237-235.

23. Stenmark, K.R., James, S.L., Voelkel, N.F., Toews, W.H., Reeves, J.T., Murphy, R.C. *Leukotriene C_4 and D_4 in neonates with hypoxemia and pulmonary hypertension.* N Engl J Med 1983; 309: 77-80.

24. Snyder, F. *Chemical and biological aspects of platelet-activating factor: A novel class of acetylated ether linked choline phospholipids.* Med Res Rev 1985; 5: 107-140.

25. Zukowska Grojec, Z., Blank, M.L., Snyder, F., Feuerstein, G. *The adrenergic system and the cardiovascular effects of platelet-activating factor (1-O-hexadecyl-2-acetyl-sn-glycero-3-phosphorylcholine) in SHR and WKY rats.* Clin Exptl Hypert 1985; A7: 1015-1031.

Ginkgolides - Chemistry, Biology, Pharmacology and Clinical Perspectives. P. Braquet (Ed.)
Copyright © 1988, J.R. Prous Science Publishers, S.A.

GINKGOLIDE B (BN 52021) AND CARDIAC ANAPHYLAXIS

Mátyás Koltai, István Leprán and László Szekeres

Department of Pharmacology, University Medical School of Szeged, Hungary

INTRODUCTION

Platelet-activating factor (PAF-acether) has been recognized by Benveniste *et al.* (6) as a polar lipid mediator influencing antigen-induced histamine release from basophil leukocytes sensitized by IgE. Since 1972, convincing evidence has been accumulated that *PAF*-acether, being chemically characterized as 1-O-hexadecyl-2-O-acetyl-*sn*-glycero-3-phosphatidylcholine (7), or acetyl-glyceryl-ether-phosphorylcholine (31), is involved in a variety of pathophysiological conditions recently reviewed by several authors (15, 17, 18, 51, 56, 63).

Research on PAF-acether has been greatly facilitated by the discovery of its antagonists which have been shown to bind specific receptors (16, 30) and inhibit platelet aggregation (49). One of the most significant representatives of such antagonists, whose effect on cardiac anaphylaxis is the main topic of this paper, is ginkgolide B (BN 52021), a natural product isolated from *Ginkgo biloba* L. (14).

PAF-acether induces characteristic effects in the heart, such as reduction of coronary blood flow, negative inotropism and increase in heart rate (8, 11). A detailed analysis of the coronary constrictor activity of PAF-

Address all correspondence to: Dr. M. Koltai, Department of Pharmacology, University Medical School of Szeged, H-6701 Szeged, P.O. Box 115, Hungary.

acether has revealed a biphasic effect, an initial increase followed by a long-lasting decrease. These alterations are related to the appearance of arachidonic acid metabolites in the perfusion fluid (11, 28, 47), and blocked by indomethacin, indicating a major role for thromboxane (Tx) A_2 in the reduction of coronary blood flow.

PAF-acether also produces a biphasic effect on myocardial contractility (3, 21, 33, 61). The effects seem to be due to an interference with slow Ca^{2+} channel (21). Negative inotropism was suspended by indomethacin (3), suggesting a role for cyclooxygenase products. The positive inotropic effect is in turn due to noradrenaline release, since it is blocked by propranolol. Similar findings were reported concerning the positive chronotropic effect of PAF-acether (23).

The effect of PAF-acether on the heart is closely related to the symptoms of cardiac anaphylaxis (5, 8, 17, 18).

The heart is known to be seriously involved in anaphylactic shock in rabbit (64), monkey (52), guinea pig (22) and man (9, 13, 24). Some clinical findings have provided additional evidence for a role of food antibodies in the pathogenesis of myocardial infarction emphasizing the significance of coronary artery constriction in systemic allergic reactions (25). It has also been reported that serious asthmatic attacks may induce myocardial infarction (32). The pathogenesis of these alterations are based on IgE-mediated cardiac hypersensitivity (43).

During anaphylactic shock evoked in isolated, perfused guinea pig heart, PAF-acether is released into the coronary effluent, and intracoronary administration of synthetic PAF-acether mimicks the symptoms of cardiac anaphylaxis, providing substantial evidence that PAF-acether is one of the mediator substances released during anaphylactic shock (44).

The marked coronary artery constriction induced by PAF-acether and cardiac antigen challenge may be indirectly mediated via the release of sulfidopeptide-leukotrienes (LTs) as suggested by studies using FPL 55712, a specific inhibitor of the receptors of Slow-Reacting Substance of Anaphylaxis (SRS-A), and BW-755C, a combined inhibitor of lipoxygenase and cyclooxygenase enzymes (28, 33, 59). In the rat, PAF-acether induces the release of 6-keto-prostaglandin (PG) $F_{1\alpha}$, $PGF_{2\alpha}$, PGE_2 and TxB_2, as well as LTC_4 and LTB_4. Coronary vasoconstriction was shown to be attenuated by indomethacin, indicating that cyclooxygenase products play only a modulatory role. FPL 55712 markedly inhibited the response, suggesting that LTs may be largely responsible for coronary vasoconstriction, while cyclooxygenase products appear to mediate the decreased contractility induced by PAF-acether (54).

It has been well established that anaphylactic shock is mediated via the release of histamine and SRS-A (19). The mediators involved in cardiac anaphylaxis were predominantly studied in actively or passively sensitized, isolated, perfused guinea pig heart which responds uniformly to antigenic challenge. Early studies provided substantial evidence that histamine has a mediator role in cardiac anaphylaxis (27, 29, 41, 65). Before its chemical characterization, SRS-A was also shown to contribute in eliciting anaphylactic symptoms in the heart (46), and a potentiating interaction between SRS-A and histamine was demonstrated (42). Potentiation by indomethacin of antigen-induced histamine and SRS-A release was also defined (46).

LTs are suggested to be mediators of cardiac anaphylaxis (1). LTD_4, LTC_4 and LTE_4 suppress contractile force in isolated guinea pig and human myocardium and profoundly decrease coronary blood flow (20). These effects proved to be long-lasting, dose-related and blocked by FPL 55712, indicating a direct effect of LTs on coronary circulation and heart muscle.

Additional arachidonic acid metabolites, such as various PGs (2, 4, 46, 53) and TxA_2 (2, 4) may have a secondary role as mediators of cardiac anaphylaxis.

The present study was undertaken to evaluate the effect of BN 52021 in isolated, perfused guinea pig hearts passively sensitized with anti-ovalbumin rabbit serum in order to have better insight into the mechanism of cardiac anaphylaxis. Passive sensitization was chosen since under this condition markedly uniform responses could be obtained.

MATERIALS AND METHODS

Hartley guinea pigs of either sex weighing 300-500 g were kept on commercial food pellets and tap water containing 1% vitamin C *ad libitum*. They were not fasted before the experiments. Anti-ovalbumin serum was produced in New Zealand rabbits. Ovalbumin (Koch-Light, Great Britain) was suspended in complete Freund adjuvant (Difco, USA), and 200 μg/kg was injected subcutaneously at different sites on the back of the rabbits. One month later the same dose of ovalbumin was given as a booster. Blood samples were withdrawn individually one week later for checking the antibody titers in the sera with precipitation probes. If the animals showed precipitation with ovalbumin in a dilution of 1:10,000 they were exsanguinated from the abdominal aorta under anesthesia induced by 35 mg/kg pentobarbitone (Mebubarbital sodique, Rhône Poulenc, France). The sera were pooled, decomplemented, and stored at —20°C. Guinea pigs were sensitized 24 hours before the experiment by a bolus of 6 ml/kg antiserum introduced intravenously into the femoral vein under light ether anesthesia.

After a blow on the neck, the guinea pigs were exsanguinated from the carotid arteries, their hearts rapidly removed and mounted in a Krebs-

Henseleit solution, containing the following substances in mM: NaCl 120, KCl 4.23, $CaCl_2$ 2.00, $MgCl_2$ 1.20, KH_2PO_4 1.17, $NaHCO_3$ 20.0, and glucose 11.0. The solution was vigorously gassed with a mixture of 5% CO_2 and 95% O_2, pH 7.40 at 38°C. The hearts were washed out with buffer, then isolated and perfused according to Langendorff (35).

The contractile force was measured isometrically by a force transducer (UC2, Gould Statham, USA). The perfusion pressure was recorded by a P23Db transducer (Gould Statham, USA). The heart rate was triggered by the force transducer. These parameters were continuously recorded by the aid of a Watanabe ink recorder (Mark V. Hugo-Sachs Electronics, FRG). Each heart was perfused with a constant flow rate adjusted to 8-12 ml/min by a peristaltic pump. The initial perfusion pressure was 35-45 mmHg, while the resting tension was set at 20 mN. The preparations were allowed to equilibrate for 20 minutes before anaphylactic challenge.

Anaphylactic shock was induced by a rapid injection of 2 mg ovalbumin dissolved in 0.2 ml buffer. BN 52021 was dissolved in DMSO, then the stock solution used in the experiments was made up by the perfusion buffer. DMSO applied in a dilution of the stock solution did not influence contractile force, coronary perfusion pressure and heart rate when injected into the perfusion stream, nor did it change the alterations induced by injection of the specific antigen. BN 52021 in various concentrations was infused before anaphylactic challenge. Since anaphlactic shock can be elicited only once, separate hearts were used for studying the effect of the PAF-acether antagonist at various concentration levels. Fifteen to 20 hearts were included in each experimental group.

The data obtained in different experimental groups were statistically analyzed by the unpaired Student's t test.

RESULTS

The injection of ovalbumin into the perfusion stream of passively sensitized Langendorff hearts produced typical changes in the parameters recorded. The most characteristic and highly reproducible alteration was the long-lasting elevation of coronary perfusion pressure due to sustained coronary artery constriction in response to the specific antigen. This was accompanied by a marked increase in heart rate, while the contractile force always showed biphasic changes, i.e., a pronounced increase was followed by a prolonged diminution.

The effect of BN 52021 was studied at five dose levels (10, 30, 60, 120 and 150 μM). Except for the higher concetrations (120 and 150 μM), which sometimes induced a slight elevation in coronary perfusion pressure and a moderate decrease in heart rate, the drug did not induce alterations in

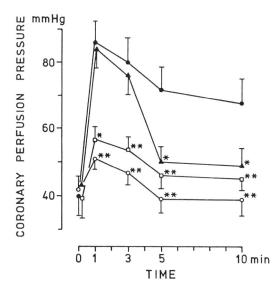

Figure 1 Effect of BN 52021 on coronary perfusion pressure in passively sensitized, isolated, perfused guinea pig heart challenged by the specific antigen. ● — — — ● control, BN 52021 ▲ — — — ▲ 10 μM, □ — — — □ 60 μM, and ○ — — — ○ 120 μM. Each dose was tested in 15 hearts. *P<0.05; **P<0.01.

the parameters recorded during the experiments. BN 52021 influenced cardiac functions during anaphylactic shock in a dose-related fashion. When it was infused before anaphylactic challenge, coronary perfusion was barely influenced. Even 10 μM BN 52021 significantly shortened coronary artery constriction. The effect was more marked at the 5th minute after challenge when a statistically significant diminution of the perfusion pressure occurred at each dose level studied (Fig. 1).

The changes in contractile force were also characteristic. BN 52021 was able to attenuate both the increase and the decrease produced by ovalbumin challenge. The effect of 10 μM was not statistically significant, while higher doses caused a contractility near the value measured before antigen challenge, especially after the third minute of ovalbumin injection (Fig. 2).

Cardiac anaphylaxis was characterized by a constant increase in heart rate (Fig. 3). This paralleled the elevation observed in coronary perfusion pressure but not the alterations in contractility. BN 52021 slightly changed tachycardia produced by the injection of the specific antigen. Higher doses (above 60 μM) caused alleviation of tachycardia.

Furthermore, an attempt was made to calculate ED_{50} values for the anti-anaphylactic effect of BN 52021 in passively sensitized, isolated, perfused Langendorff hearts. For this purpose, coronary perfusion pressure was

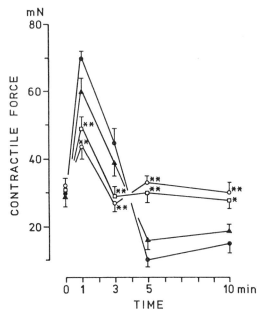

Figure 2 Effect of BN 52021 on contractile force in passively sensitized, isolated, perfused guinea pig heart in response to the specific antigen. Denotations are as in Figure 1, MN = milli-Newton.

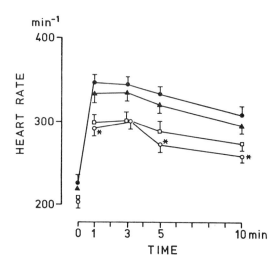

Figure 3 Effect of BN 52021 on heart rate in response to anaphylactic challenge in passively sensitized, isolated guinea pig heart. Denotations are as in Figure 1.

chosen as the most characteristically changing parameter during cardiac anaphylaxis. When log doses of BN 52021 were plotted against the percentage decrease in coronary artery perfusion pressure transformed to a probit scale, one and 3 minutes after ovalbumin challenge, the ED_{50} values for BN 52021 were found to be 30 and 28 μM, respectively, while at the 5th minute after eliciting cardiac anaphylaxis it was about 22 μM.

DISCUSSION AND CONCLUSIONS

In our study, isolated, perfused guinea pig hearts sensitized passively with anti-ovalbumin rabbit serum produced characteristic symptoms of cardiac anaphylaxis when challenged with an intracoronary bolus of the specific antigen. As described by others (22, 27, 41, 44), these were sustained reduction in coronary flow, biphasic changes in contractility (an increase followed by a long-lasting decrease), and a permanent increase in heart rate. Our results clearly show that BN 52021, administered in an intracoronary infusion before anaphylactic challenge, markedly attenuated the increase in coronary perfusion pressure and reduced negative inotropism, whereas the initial positive inotropic effect and the sustained tachycardia induced by the specific antigen remained relatively unchanged. These findings are in agreement with those previously described by using BN 52021 (5, 10, 34, 39, 45, 55, 58, 65) or other PAF-acether antagonists such as kadsurenone, L-652,731 and L-653,150 (58). Since PAF-acether exerts similar effects on isolated, perfused guinea pig heart as anaphylactic challenge (5, 8, 11, 44) and can be estimated and recovered from the coronary effluent of antigenically challenged heart preparations, the results obtained strongly suggest that PAF-acether is involved as a major mediator in cardiac anaphylaxis.

The most prominent symptom induced by anaphylaxis and PAF-acether in the heart is coronary vasoconstriction, which at least in part is responsible for negative inotropism. It appears likely that the vasoconstrictory effect of PAF-acether is indirect and mediated via cyclooxygenase products, predominantly by TxA_2. TxA_2 aggregates platelets and strongly contracts coronary vessels (49). It has also been demonstrated that TxA_2 has no direct effect on the contractile force in working myocardium (62). It seems, therefore, unlikely that TxA_2 has a major role in cardiac anaphylaxis. In contrast, it has also been shown that LTs are released either in response to PAF-acether (54) or during cardiac anaphylaxis (1). This is in favor of the concept that LTs are important mediators in anaphylactic shock (56). It has not been revealed what events determine the pathways through which PAF-acether releases cyclooxygenase products on one hand, and LTs on the other. We found that BN 52021 had no protective effect during the very early phase of myocardial infarction in coronary artery ligated conscious rats (unpublished observations, 40). In this model of acute myocardial infarction nonsteroid and steroid anti-inflammatory drugs (36, 37, 60), as well as TxA_2 synthase antagonists (38), exert beneficial effects. On the other hand, Moshonov et al. (48) have put forward the hypothesis that viral infections may sensitize the heart, whose reaction may be cardiac myocytolysis in response to the second viral infection. In other words, cardiac anaphylaxis may be an ethiological factor in the pathomechanism of myocardial infarction. Thus, BN 52021 is expected to be a protective agent even in selective cases of myocardial infarctions. Further studies are needed to get better insight in the pathogenesis of various types of PAF-induced injuries in the myocardium.

With respect to the role of histamine in cardiac anaphylaxis, there is convincing evidence that tachycardia and a delay in atrioventricular conduction are due to histamine release (41). Zavecz and Levi (65) have analyzed the factors responsible for the cardiac effect of histamine, and stated that positive inotropism is due to the stimulation of H_2 receptors (blocked by cimetidine), while a negative inotropic effect is produced on H_1 receptors (in the presence of chlorpheniramine, histamine decreases myocardial contractility). There is a synergistic interaction between histamine and SRS-A (42). More recently, Elizalde et al. (26) have reported that histamine induces positive inotropic effect through an interaction of both H_2 and H_1 receptors, mediated by an increased Ca^{2+} slow inward current and cyclic-AMP formation or through a yet unidentified mechanism, respectively.

It seems likely that H_2 receptor antagonists exert a beneficial effect in cardiac anaphylaxis (12). BN 52021, however, does not influence the positive inotropic and chronotropic effects of histamine.

In conclusion, on the basis of the results obtained in this study, BN 52021 produces a prominent, protective effect in cardiac anaphylaxis by interacting with specific PAF-acether receptor sites (30, 16) and counteracting direct and indirect effects of PAF-acether on the heart. This finding demonstrates the basic role of PAF-acether in the mediation of anaphylactic shock in the heart (44) and emphasizes the therapeutic value of BN 52021 in prevention of immediate hypersensitivity reaction.

References

1. Aehringhaus, U., Peskar, B.A., Wittenberg, H.R., Wölbling, R.H. *Effect of inhibition of synthesis and receptor antagonism of SRS-A in cardiac anaphylaxis.* Br J Pharmacol 1983; 80: 73-80.

2. Allan, G., Levi, R. *Thromboxane and prostacyclin release during cardiac hypersensitivity reactions in vitro.* J Pharmac Exp Ther 1981; 217: 157-161.

3. Alloatti, G., Montrucchio, G., Mariano, F., Tetta, C., De Paulis, R., Morea, M., Emanuelli, G., Camussi. G. *Effect of platelet-activating factor (PAF) on human cardiac muscle.* Int Arch Allergy Appl Immunol 1986;

79: 108-112.

4. Anhut, H., Bernauer, W., Peskar, B.A. *Pharmacological modification of thromboxane and prostacyclin release in cardiac anaphylaxis.* Prostaglandins 1978; 15: 889-900.

5. Baranes, J., Hellegouarch, A., Le Hegarat, M., Viossat, I., Auguet, M., Chabrier, P-E., Clostre, F., Braquet, P. *The effects of PAF-acether on the cardiovascular system and their inhibition by a new highly specific PAF-acether receptor antagonist BN 52021.* Pharmacol Res Commun 1986; 18: 717-737.

6. Benveniste, J., Henson, P.M., Cochrane, C.G. *Leukocyte-dependent histamine release from rabbit platelets: The role of IgE, basophils and a platelet-activating factor.* J Exp Med 1972; 136: 1356-1377.

7. Benveniste, J., Tencé, M., Varenne, P., Bidault, J., Boullet, C., Polonski, J. *Semisynthesis and proposed structure of platelet-activating factor (PAF): PAF-acether, and alkyl ether analog of lysophosphatidylcholine.* CRC Acad Sci 1979; 289D: 1037-1040.

8. Benveniste, J., Boullet, C., Brink, C., Labat, C. *The actions of PAF-acether (platelet-activating factor) on guinea-pig isolated heart preparations.* Br J Pharmacol 1983; 80: 81-83.

9. Bernreiter, M. *Electrocardiogram of patients in anaphylactic shock.* JAMA 1959; 170: 627-631.

10. Berti, F, Russoni, G. *PAF Ginkgolides and active anaphylactic shock.* In: The Ginkgolides: Chemistry, Biology, Pharmacology and Clinical Sciences. Ed. By P. Braquet. J.R. Prous Publishers: Barcelona 1987.

11. Bessin, P., Bonnet, J., Apffel, P., Soulard, C., Desgroux, L., Pelas, I., Benveniste, J. *Acute circulatory collapse caused by platelet-activating factor (PAF-acether) in dogs.* Eur J Pharmacol 1983; 86: 403-413.

12. Blandina, P., Brunelleschi, S., Fantozzi, R., Giannella, E., Mannaioni, P.F., Masini, E. *The antianaphylactic action of histamine H_2-receptor antagonists in the guinea-pig isolated heart.* Br J Pharmacol 1987; 90: 459-466.

13. Booth, B.H., Patterson, R. *Electrocardiographic changes during human anaphylaxis.* JAMA 1970; 211: 627-631.

14. Braquet, P. *Treatment and prevention of PAF-acether-induced sickness by a new series of highly specific inhibitors.* GB Patent 8, 4118, 1984.

15. Braquet, P. *The ginkgolides: Potent platelet-activating factor antagonists isolated from ginko biloba L.: Chemistry, pharmacology and clinical applications.* Drugs of the Future 1987; 12: 643-699.

16. Braquet, P., Godfroid, J.J. *PAF-acether specific binding sites: 2. Design of specific antagonists.* TIPS 1986; 7: 397-403.

17. Braquet, P., Vargaftig, B.B. *Pharmacology of platelet activating factor.*Transplantation Proc 1986; 18: 10-19.

18. Braquet, P., Touqui, L., Shen, T.Y., Vargaftig, B.B. *Perspectives in platelet activating factor research.* Pharmacol Rev 1987; 39: 97-145.

19. Brocklehurst, W.E. *The release of histamine and formation of slow-reacting substance (SRS-A) during anaphylactic shock.* J Physiol (Lond) 1960; 151: 416-435.

20. Burke, J.A., Levi, R., Guo, Z.G., Corey, E.J. *Leukotrienes C_4, D_4 and E_4: Effects on human and guinea-pig cardiac preparations in vitro.* J Pharmac Exp Ther 1982; 221: 235-241.

21. Camussi, G., Alloatti, G., Montrucchio, G., Meda, M., Emanuelli, G. *Effect of platelet-activating factor on guinea-pig papillary muscle.* Experientia 1984; 40: 697-699.

22. Capurro, N., Levi, R. *The heart as a target organ in systemic allergic reactions. Comparison of cardiac anaphylaxis in vivo and in vitro.* Circulation Res 1975; 36: 520-528.

23. Cervoni, P., Herzlinger, H.E., Lai, F.M. Tanikella, T.K. *Aortic vascular and atrial responses to (±)-1-O-octadecyl-2-acetyl-glyceryl-3-phosphorylcholine.* Br J Pharmacol 1983; 79: 667-671.

24. Criep, L.H., Patterson, R. *Heart in human anaphylaxis.* Ann Allergy 1971; 29: 399-409.

25. Davies, D.F., Johnson, A.P., Rees, W.G., Elwood, P.C., Anernethy, M. *Food antibodies and myocardial infarction.* Lancet 1974; 1: 1012-1014.

26. Elizalde, A., Perez-Chavez, J., Sánchez-Chapula, J. *Further characterization of the receptors involved in the positive inotropic effect of histamine on rabbit papillary muscle.* Can J Physiol Pharmacol 1986; 64: 1484-1488.

27. Feigen, G.A., Prager, D.J. *Experimental cardiac anaphylaxis: Physiologic, pharmacologic and biochemical aspects of immune reactions in the isolated heart.* Am J Cardiol 1969; 24: 474-491.

28. Feuerstein, G., Boyd, L.M., Ezra, D., Goldstein, R.E. *Effect of platelet-activating factor on coronary circulation of the domestic pig.* Am J Physiol 1984; 246: H466-H471.

29. Giotti, A., Guidotti, A., Mannaioni, P.F.,

Zilletti, L. *The influence of adrenotropic drugs and noradrenaline on the histamine release in cardiac anaphylaxis in vitro.* J Physiol (Lond) 1966; 184: 924-941.

30. Godfroid, J.J., Braquet, P. *PAF-acether specific binding sites: 1. Quantitative SA study of PAF-acether isosteres.* TIPS 1986; 7: 368-373.

31. Hanahan, D.J., Demopoulos, C.A., Liehr, J., Pinckard, R.N. *Identification of platelet-activating factor isolated from rabbit.* J Biol Chem 1980; 255: 5514-5516.

32. Jazayeri, M-R., Reen, B.M., Edwards, J.A. *Asthma induced myocardial infarction in a patient with normal coronary arteries: A case report and a pathogenetic hypothesis.* J Med 1983; 14: 351-354.

33. Kenzora, J.L., Pérez, J.E., Bergmann, S.R., Lange, L.G. *Effects of acetyl glyceryl ether phosphorylcholine (platelet-activating factor) on ventricular preload, afterload, and contractility in dogs.* J Clin Invest 1984; 74: 1193-1203.

34. Koltai, M., Leprán, I., Szekeres, L., Viossat, I., Chabrier, E., Braquet, P. *Effect of BN 52021, a specific PAF-acether antagonist, on cardiac anaphylaxis in Langendorff hearts isolated from passively sensitized guinea-pigs.* Eur J Pharmacol 1986; 130: 133-136.

35. Langendorff, O. *Untersuchungen an überlebenden Säugetierherzen.* Plügers Archiv 1895; 61: 291-332.

36. Leprán, I., Koltai, M., Szekeres, L. *Effect of non-steroid anti-inflammatory drugs in experimental myocardial infarction in rats.* Eur J Pharmacol 1981; 69: 235-238.

37. Leprán, I., Koltai, M., Szekeres, L. *Effect of actinomycin D and cycloheximide on experimental myocardial infarction in rats.* Eur J Pharmacol 1982; 77: 197-199.

38. Leprán, I., Parratt, J.R., Szekeres, L., Wainwright, C.L. *The effects of metoprolol and dazmegrel, alone and in combination, on arrhythmias induced by coronary artery occlusion in conscious rats.* Br J Pharmacol 1985; 86: 229-234.

39. Leprán, I., Braquet, P., Koltai, M., Szekeres, L. *Effect of BN 52021, a specific PAF-acether antagonist, on cardiac anaphylaxis in Langendorff hearts isolated from passively sensitized guinea pigs.* 6th Int Conf on Prostaglandins and Related Compounds, Florence, Italy, 1986; Abst p. 311.

40. Leprán, I., Koltai, M., Braquet, P., Szekeres, L. 1987; unpublished observations.

41. Levi, R., *Effects of exogenous and im-munologically released histamine on the isolated heart: A quantitative comparison.* J Pharmac Exp Ther 1972; 182: 227-238.

42. Levi, R., Burke, J.A. *Cardiac anaphylaxis: SRS-A potentiates and extends the effects of released histamine.* Eur J Pharmacol 1980; 62: 41-49.

43. Levi, R., Zavecz, J.H., Ovary, Z. *IgE-mediated cardiac hypersensitivity reactions.* Int Archs Allergy Appl Immunol 1978; 57: 529-534.

44. Levi, R., Burke, J.A., Guo, Z-G., Hattori, Y., Hoppens, C.M., McManus, L.M., Hanahan, D.J., Pinckard, R.N. *Acetyl glyceryl ether phosphorylcholine (AGEPC). A putative mediator of cardiac anaphylaxis in the guinea pig.* Circulation Res 1984; 54: 117-124.

45. Levi, R., Shen, T.Y., Yee, S.J., Robertson, D.A., Genovese, A., Isom, O.W., Krieger, K.H. Proc First Sandoz Research Symposium, New Horizons in Platelet Activating Factor Research. M. Winslow, M.L. Lee, (Eds.). J. Wiley: London 1987.

46. Liebig, R., Bernauer, W., Peskar, B.A. *Prostaglandin, slow reacting substance, and histamine release from anaphylactic guinea-pig hearts, and its pharmacological modification.* Arch Pharmacol 1975; 289: 65-76.

47. Mehta, J., Wargovich, T., Nichols, W.W. *Biphasic effects of platelet-activating factor on coronary blood flow in anesthetized dog.* Prostaglandins, Leukotrienes and Medicine 1986; 21: 87-95.

48. Moshonov, S., Ashkenazy, Y., Meshorer, A., Horwitz, N., Kauli, N., Zor, U. *Immunological challenge with virus initiates leukotriene C_4 production in the heart and induces cardiomyolysis in guinea pig.* Prostaglandins, Leukotrienes and Medicine 1986; 25: 17-26.

49. Needleman, P., Kulkarni, P.S., Raz, A. *Coronary tone modulation: Formation and actions of prostaglandins, endoperoxides, and thromboxanes.* Science 1977; 195: 409-412.

50. Nunez, D., Chignard, M., Korth, R., Le Couedic, J.P., J. *Specific inhibition of PAF-acether-induced platelet activation by BN 52021 and comparison with the PAF-acether inhibitor kadsurenone and CV-3988.* Eur J Pharmacol 1986; 123: 197-205.

51. O'Flaherty, J.T. *Biology of disease. Lipid mediators of inflammation and allergy.* Lab Invest 1982; 47: 314-329.

52. Patterson, R., Fink, J.N., Wennemark, J., Baum, J., Pruzansky, J., Nishimura, E.T.

Biologic consequences of the immediate type hypersensitivity transferred from man to monkey. J Allergy Clin Immunol 1966; 37: 295-310.

53. Peskar, B.A., Steffens, C., Peskar, B.M. *Radioimmunoassay of 6-keto-prostaglandin F_{1_α} in biological material.* In: Radioimmunoassay of Drugs and Hormones in Cardiovascular Medicine. A. Albertini, M. Daprada, B.A. Peskar (Eds.). Elsevier/North-Holland Biomedical Press: Amsterdam 1979; 239-250.

54. Piper, P.J., Stewart, A.G. *Coronary vasoconstriction in the rat, isolated perfused heart induced by platelet-activating factor is mediated by leukotriene C_4.* Br J Pharmacol 1986; 88: 595-605.

55. Piper, P.J., Stewart, A.G. *Evidence of a role for platelet-activating factor in antigen-induced coronary vasoconstriction in guinea-pig perfused hearts.* Br J Pharmacol 1986; 88: 238P.

56. Roubin, R., Mencia-Huerta, J.M., Benveniste, J. *Release of platelet-activating factor (PAF-acether) and leukotrienes C and D from inflammatory macrophages.* Eur J Immunol 1982; 12: 141-146.

57. Samuelsson, B. *Leukotrienes: Mediators of immediate hypersensitivity reactions and inflammation.* Science 1983; 220: 568-575.

58. Stewart, A.G., Piper, P.J. *Platelet-activating factor antagonists inhibit antigen-induced coronary vasoconstriction on perfused guinea-pig hearts.* 6th Int Conf on Prostaglandins and Related Compounds, Florence, Italy, 1986; Abst p. 311.

59. Sybertz, E.J., Watkins, R.W., Baum, T., Pula, K., Rivelli, M. *Cardiac, coronary and peripheral vascular effects of acetyl glyceryl ether phosphoryl choline in the anesthetized dog.* J Pharmac Exp Ther 1985; 232: 156-162.

60. Szekeres, L., Leprán, I., Boros, E., Takáts, I., Koltai, M. *The effect of non-steroid anti-inflammatory drugs and of a linoleic acid-rich diet on early arrhythmias resulting from myocardial ischaemia.* In: Early Arrhythmias Resulting from Myocardial Ischaemia. Mechanisms and Prevention by Drugs. J.R. Parratt (Ed.). Macmillan Press Ltd.: London 1982; 239-249.

61. Tamargo, J., Tejerina, T., Delgado, C., Barrigon, S. *Electrophysiological effects of platelet-activating factor (PAF-acether) in guinea-pig papillary muscles.* Eur J Pharmacol 1985; 109: 219-227.

62. Terashita, Z-I., Fukui, H., Nishikawa, K., Hirata, M., Kikuchi, S. *Coronary vasospastic action of thromboxane A_2 in isolated, working guinea pig hearts.* Eur J Pharmacol 1978; 53: 49-56.

63. Vargaftig, B.B., Chignard, M., Benveniste, J., Lefort, J., Wal, F. *Background and present status of research on platelet-activating factor (PAF-acether).* Ann NY Acad Sci 1981; 370: 119-137.

64. Wegmann, A., Renker, H., Hübsher, H. *Electrocardiographic changes in anaphylactic shock of the rabbit.* Experientia 1972; 28: 655-656.

65. Zavecz, J.H., Levi, R. *Histamine-induced negative inotropism: Mediation by H_1-receptors.* J Pharmacol Exp Ther 1978; 206: 274-280.

66. Zor, U. *The contribution of PAF to anaphylaxis of isolated guinea-pig heart and its inhibition by BN 52021.* In: Ginkgolides: Chemistry, Biology, Pharmacology and Clinical Perspectives. P. Braquet (Ed.). J.R. Prous Science Publishers: Barcelona 1988; 411-416.

*Ginkgolides - Chemistry, Biology, Pharmacology
and Clinical Perspectives.* P. Braquet (Ed.)
Copyright © 1988, J.R. Prous Science Publishers, S.A.

BN 52021, A SPECIFIC PAF RECEPTOR ANTAGONIST, PREVENTS ANTIGEN-INDUCED MEDIATOR RELEASE AND MYOCARDIAL CHANGES IN GUINEA-PIG PERFUSED HEARTS

Ferrucio Berti[1], Giovanni Galli[1], Fulvio Magni[1], Lina Puglisi[1], Giuseppe Rossoni[1] and Luigi Villa[2]

[1]Institute of Pharmacological Sciences and [2]Institute of Pharmaceutical Chemistry, University of Milan, Milan, Italy

INTRODUCTION

Direct and indirect evidence that the heart is a target organ in systemic anaphylaxis of the guinea-pig has already been provided by Capurro and Levi (9). The cardiac events in this immunological reaction, characterized by tachycardia, arrhythmias, contractile failure and coronary constriction are known to be supported by synergic interactions of various mediator release (17, 18). Between them, not only histamine and eicosanoids generated in the heart are responsible for myocardial disfunction but also platelet-aggregating-factor (PAF) has been shown to play a significant role (6).

PAF (acetyl-glyceryl-ether-phosphorylcholine, AGEPC) is a novel phospholipid that has been implicated as a mediator in different pathophysiological conditions, including acute allergic reaction (20, 24). In

Address all correspondence to: Prof. F. Berti, Università di Milano, Cattedra di Farmacologia e Farmacognosia, Via Balzaretti 9, I-20133, Milano, Italy

this regard it has been shown that intravenous administration of a pure synthetic AGEPC causes electrocardiographic changes in the rabbit which are typical manifestations of IgE-induced systemic anaphylaxis (11, 19). Furthermore, it has been documented that during guinea-pig heart anaphylaxis PAF is released in the coronary effluent in an amount sufficient to contribute, particularly with histamine and other endocoids, to cardiac crisis (16). Similar results were shown by Koltai *et al.* (12), using the specific PAF receptor antagonist BN- 52021, a ginkgolide isolated in extracts of *Gingko biloba* leaves (7). In these experiments BN 52021 dose-dependently prevented antigen-induced changes in coronary pressure and contractile force in isolated hearts from passively sensitized guinea-pigs; however, the beneficial activity of the ginkgolide was not correlated with its effect on the concomitant release of mediators. More recently, Piper *et al.* (22), using selective concentrations of BN 52021, were able to demonstrate a significant attenuation of immunological coronary vasoconstriction in guinea-pig perfused hearts. Since the increase in coronary perfusion pressure, induced by cysteinyl-containing leukotrienes (LTC_4, LTD_4) and by a thromboxane-A_2 mimetic (U-44069) was unaffected by the ginkgolide, these authors suggested that their results represent indirect evidence for PAF's role in cardiac anaphylaxis. All these experimental observations prompted us to take advantage of the present availability of BN 52021 in order to further substantiate not only the protective activity of this ginkgolide in myocardial-anaphylaxis but also to achieve more information on the role of PAF in the immunological reaction of cardiac tissues.

MATERIALS AND METHODS

Cardiac Anaphylaxis

Male Hartley guinea-pigs (300-350 g) were actively sensitized to ovalbumin (100 mg/kg i.p. plus 100 mg/kg s.c.) following the method described by Piper and Vane (21). After a period of 21 days the animals were killed by cervical dislocation and the heart, rapidly excised, was mounted in a Langendorff apparatus as reported by Berti *et al.* (3). The heart was placed in a warm chamber and after a period of equilibration it was perfused retrogradely through the aorta (peristaltic pump Gilson-M-2) with Krebs-Henseleit solution kept at 36°C and treated with a mixture of 95% O_2 and 5% CO_2. The perfusing medium composition in mM was: NaCl 118; KCl 2.8; KH_2PO_4 1.2; $CaCl_2$ 2.5; $MgSO_4$ 1.2; $NaHCO_3$ 2.5 and glucose 5.5. The hearts were perfused with constant flow at a rate adjusted to 10-11 ml/min to maintain an initial perfusion pressure of 40-45 mmHg. Left ventricular contractile force was measured using a silk thread attached to the apex of the heart and connected with an isometric force-transducer (Hewlett Packard, FTA-100-1). The resting tension was 1.7 g. Furthermore, the left ventricular contractile force was electronically differentiated in dF/dt and heart-rate (HR) using a Hewlett-Packard apparatus. Coronary perfusion presure (PP) was measured utilizing a Statham pressure-transducer (HP-1280).

Anaphylactic reactions were induced by bolus injection of 1 mg of ovalbumin in 0.1 ml of Krebs-Henseleit solution in control and treated preparations. In this respect, BN 52021 and BN 52024 dissolved in NaOH 0.5N and buffered to pH 7.4 were infused through the heart at various concentrations 30 minutes before and for a further 10 minutes following the antigen challenge. A series of 1-minute samples of coronary perfusate was collected before (2 samples) and after the challenge with antigen (10 samples) to evaluate the concentration of histamine, thromboxane-A_2 (TXA$_2$) and slow-reacting-substance of anaphylaxis (SRS-A) released from the myocardial tissues.

Histamine Bioassay

Histamine was determined in the coronary effluent by bioassay on the isolated guinea-pig ileum as reported by Levi (13) and modified according to the laminar-flow technique (10). The terminal ileum (2-3 cm) was superfused with Krebs-Henseleit solution at constant flow (0.1 ml/min) in presence of atropine (10^{-6}M), methysergide (2×10^{-9}M) and FPL-55712 (10^{-6}M). Contractions of the tissues were monitored by an isotonic force-transducer connected with a two pen Basile recorder (Gemini, 7070). A log dose response curve for histamine was determined and aliquots (30-50 μl) of perfusate suitably diluted were injected in the perfusing system in order to obtain contractions falling in the range of histamine log dose-response curve. At the end of each experiment mepyramine (10^{-6}M) was added to the perfusing medium to verify the specificity of the contractile response. The amount of histamine in the coronary effluent was expressed in μg/min.

SRS-A Bioassay

SRS-A concentration in the heart perfusate was evaluated as described for histamine. Segments of guinea-pig terminal ileum treated with mepyramine (10^{-6}M) and atropine (10^{-6}M) were perfused according to the laminar-flow technique (10).

Log dose-response curve of LTD$_4$ was determined and the amount of SRS-A found in the perfusate expressed as LTD$_4$-like activity in ng/min. At the end of each experiment FPL-55712 (10^{-6}M) was used to assure the nature of the ileum response.

TXA₂ Radioimmunoassay

The concentration of TXA$_2$ in the coronary outflow was evaluated as TXB$_2$ following the radioimmunoassay technique described by Anhut et al. (1). Thromboxane-B$_2$ [^{3}H]-RIA-KIT (NEK-007) was utilized and the results obtained were expressed in ng/min.

Drugs

For these experiments the following drugs were used: ovalbumin Grade II (Sigma Chemical Company), histamine dihydrochloridrate (Sigma Chemical Company), atropine sulfate (Sigma Chemical Company), methysergide dimaleate (Sandoz Pharmaceuticals), mepyramine dihydrochloridrate (M & B), FPL-55712 (donated by Fisons Pharmaceuticals, U.K.), BN 52021 and BN 52024 (donated by Dr. P. Braquet, Institut Henry Beaufour Res. Lab., Le Plessis-Robinson, France).

RESULTS

When the specific antigen was injected into isolated and perfused heart obtained from actively sensitized guinea-pig, a typical anaphylactic crisis was observed (Fig. 1 and 2). Heart rate increased rapidly together with a marked increase in both left ventricular contractile force and perfusion pressure. Change in heart contractility was a transient phenomenon and the positive

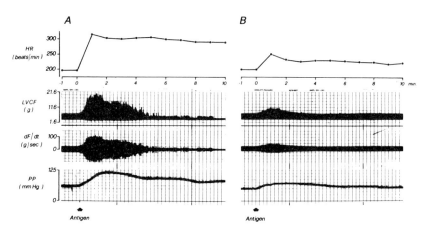

Figure 1 Typical tracing of anaphylactic response in actively sensitized guinea-pig Langendorff heart. Panel B: the heart was perfused 30 minutes before antigenic challenge with BN 52021 (40 μg/ml). At the arrow, ovalbumin (antigen) was injected as a bolus of 1 mg in 0.1 ml. HR: heart rate; LVCF: left ventricular contractile force; PP: perfusion pressure.

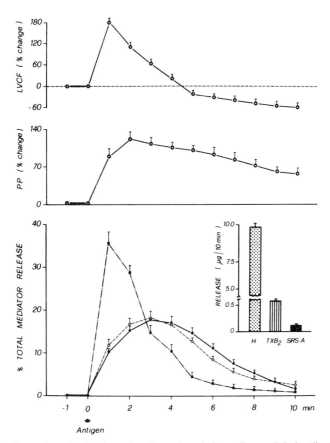

Figure 2 Changes in cardiac function and mediator release during cardiac anaphylaxis. All values represent means (±SEM) from 8 guinea-pig hearts actively sensitized to ovalbumin and challenged at the arrow
with 1 mg of ovalbumin (antigen). LVCF: percentage changes of basal values of left ventricular contractile
force; PP: percentage changes of basal values of perfusion pressure. The values of histamine (■--—--■),
TXB$_2$ (O————O) and SRS-A measured as LTD$_4$-like activity (● ———— ●) are expressed as percentage
of the total mediator released in 10 minutes. The columns indicate the total amount in µg of the three
mediators released in 10 minutes.

inotropic effect (peak in 1 minute) was followed by a prolonged negative
inotropic effect (nadir in 8-9 minutes) after antigenic challenge.

The increase in perfusion pressure, indicating coronary vasoconstriction,
reached its peak in 2 minutes and for the following 10 minutes the increase
was always 50% above the basal values. In concert with these myocardial
immunological alterations, histamine, TXB$_2$ and LTD$_4$-like activity (SRS-
A) were released in the perfusates with a kinetic profile similar to that
described by Levi *et al.* (15) (Fig. 2). Histamine release was maximal 1 minute

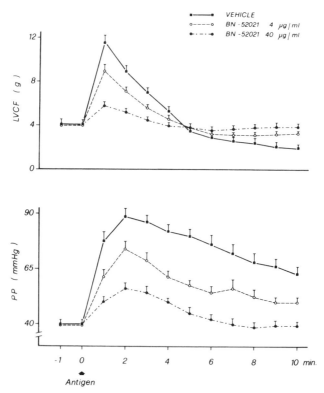

Figure 3 Protecting activity of BN 52021 on left ventricular contractile force (LVCF) and perfusion pressure (PP) changes during cardiac anaphylaxis. The values are means (± SEM) from 8 guinea-pig hearts actively sensitized and challenged with 1 mg of ovalbumin (antigen) at the arrow. The ginkgolide was infused through the hearts 30 minutes before antigenic challenge and for the following 10 minutes.

after ovalbumin injection and rapidly declined, whereas TXB_2 and SRS-A concentrations increased to a maximum in 3 minutes, decreasing slowly 10 minutes after antigenic challenge.

The 30-minute intracardiac infusion of graded doses of BN 52021 (4 and 40 µg/ml) did not modify *per se* the normal functioning of the hearts before ovalbumin injection; however, this treatment protected the hearts from anaphylactic crisis (Fig. 3). The protective activity of the ginkgolide was dose-dependent and particularly marked at the highest concentration used. In fact, as shown in Figures 1 and 3, during the anaphylactic reaction changes in ventricular contractile force and perfusion pressure were reduced and kept in a range close to basal values by BN 52021 (40 µg/ml). The beneficial activity of BN 52021 in these experiments is well correlated with

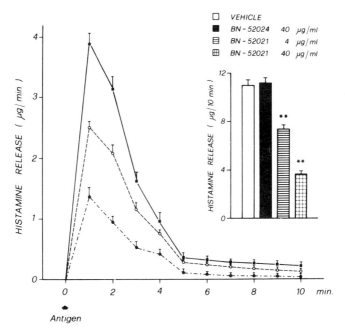

Figure 4 BN 52021 perfused at concentrations of 4 μg/ml (○————○) and 40 μg/ml (●·—·—·●) reduced histamine release during cardiac anaphylaxis. The values are means ($\pm$ SEM) of 8 guinea-pig hearts actively sensitized and challenged with 1 mg of ovalbumin (antigen) at the arrow. The compound BN 52024 was ineffective. Columns represent the total amount in μg of histamine released in 10 minutes. Asterisks denote that the values are significantly ($P < 0.001$; determined by Student's *t* test analysis) different from vehicle (■———■).

the capability of the compound to attenuate mediator release, particularly that of histamine. In fact, as shown in Figure 4, the ginkgolide infused at 4 and 40 μg/ml reduced the total amount of histamine released in 10 minutes during anaphylactic crisis by 32% and 67%, respectively.

The levels of immunoreactive TXB_2 in basal heart perfusates were below the detection limits of the radioimmunoassay; however, a significant amount of this cyclooxygenase product was found in 10 minute perfusates (580 ng) after antigen injection (Fig. 5). In the presence of BN 52021 infused at a concentration of 40 μg/ml the total quantity of TXB_2 found in 10 minutes of myocardial effluent during antigenic challenge was reduced to 320 ng, which represents 56% of the TXB_2 determined in control hearts.

The time-course of SRS-A released during anaphylactic shock of the heart was similar to that of TXB_2; however, the total amount of SRS-A evaluated in 10 minute perfusates was 5 times lower (114 ng). At the concentrations used (4 and 40 μg/ml) BN 52021 showed some difficulty in reducing the

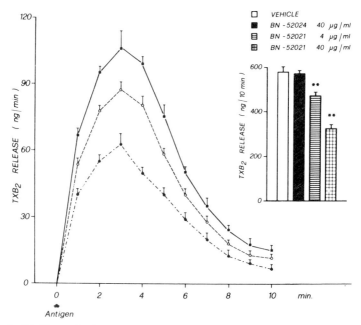

Figure 5 BN 52021 perfused at concentrations of 4 μg/ml (○————○) and 40 μg/ml (●—·—·—●) reduced TXB₂ release during cardiac anaphylaxis. The values are means (±SEM) of 8 guinea-pig hearts actively sensitized and challenged with 1 mg of ovalbumin (antigen) at the arrow. The compound BN 52024 was ineffective. Columns represent the total amount in ng of TXB₂ released in 10 minutes. Asterisks denote that the values are significantly (P<0.001) different from vehicle (■———■).

generation of this anaphylactic material and only at the highest concentration did the ginkgolide display a significant inhibitory effect of 30% (Fig. 6).

The infusion of the sensitized hearts with the ginkgolide BN 52024 at a concentration of 40 μg/ml did not prevent changes in perfusion pressure and left ventricular contractile force caused by the antigenic challenge. Also, the release of histamine, TXB₂ and SRS-A during 10 minutes of cardiac crisis was unaffected by this ginkgolide.

DISCUSSION

The present results clearly demonstrate that the ginkgolide BN 52021 displays a beneficial effect in guinea-pig heart anaphylaxis: this compound, in fact, prevents in a dose-dependent fashion changes in heart rate and left ventricular contractile force and reduces the concomitant release of mediator substances. The peculiar features of the cardiac crisis observed in these experiments reinforce the concept that not only histamine and eicosanoids

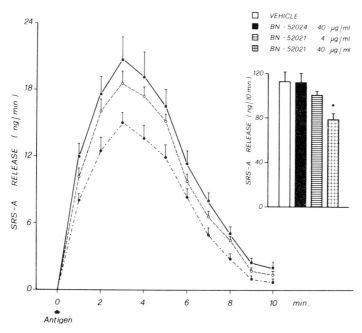

Figure 6 BN 52021 perfused at concentrations of 4 μg/ml (○————○) and 40 μg/ml (●--·--·●) attenuated SRS-A release (determined as LTD$_4$-like activity) during cardiac anaphylaxis. The values are means (± SEM) of 8 guinea-pig hearts actively sensitized and challenged with 1 mg of ovalbumin (antigen) at the arrow. Columns represent the total amount in ng of SRS-A released in 10 minutes. The compound BN 52024 was ineffective. Asterisks denote that the value is significantly (P < 0.01) different from vehicle (■——■).

are involved in these immunological events but also PAF. In fact, the capability of BN 52021 to antagonize selectively the activation of PAF receptors in various tissues (4-6) may be fundamental in explaining the preventive activity of this ginkgolide in anaphylactic shock of the heart. In this regard, PAF has been found in coronary effluent during immunological reaction of guinea-pig heart and synthetic AGEPC has been shown to mimic directly, without the participation of other mediators, the effects of endogenous PAF (16). As shown by the present experiments, however, BN 52021 is effective in reducing the release of histamine and other products of arachidonic acid metabolism. Therefore, the possibility that this compound may interfere with membrane signaling mechanisms involved in the generation of anaphylaxis mediators cannot be ruled out. This point is very important because it is not known, at the moment, if BN 52021 is capable of reducing PAF generation and release during cardiac anaphylaxis. This hypothesis should be carefully considered since the

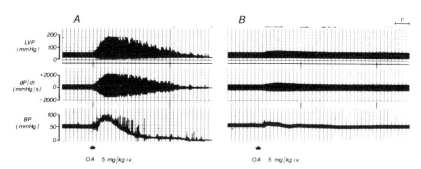

Figure 7 Typical tracing of an anaphylactic response in actively sensitized guinea-pig prepared under anesthesia for monitoring left ventricular pressure (LVP), dP/dt and arterial blood pressure (BP). At the arrow ovalbumin (OA) was injected intravenously. B: The animal was treated with BN 52021 (4 mg/kg i.v.) 3 minutes before antigen.

observed attenuation of TXB_2 and LTD_4-like activity in the heart perfusate during anaphylactic shock could be ascribed to a reduced generation of PAF caused by the ginkgolide. In this respect, Berti *et al.* (4) have already reported that PAF activates the eicosanoid system in perfused guinea-pig lung, with pronounced generation of TXA_2, suggesting that PAF may amplify its deterimental activity on cardiovascular and pulmonary systems through release of other substances derived from arachidonic acid oxidation.

The marked inhibitory effect of BN 52021 on histamine release during immunological cardiac crisis is crucial in explaining the protective activity of the compound against alterations of cardiac rhythm. It is well known that histamine through activation of H_2-histamine receptors may be responsible for tachycardia and arrhythmias, disfunctions of the heart which are potentiated and extended by SRS-A and possibly by PAF during anaphylaxis of this organ (14). Thus, it is quite conceivable that BN 52021 could be potentially useful in all conditions where histamine release from cardiac stores is an important factor for paroxysmal arrhythmias observed in man.

The mode of action of BN 52021 in preventing histamine release is an open question. Therefore, it is tempting to speculate that other effects of this ginkgolide, not necessarily related to specific PAF receptors antagonistic activity, may be involved. BN 52021 could interfere with sensitized mast cells and basophils during the early events in the histamine release reaction: at the membrane level it could either hinder the normal bridging of the antigens restraining the transient increase on phospholipid methylation and the increase of Ca^{++} influx, or it could directly effect the opening of Ca^{++} channel (23). As far as calcium movement is concerned, it has already been reported that BN 52021 and related ginkgolides are able to reduce Ca^{++} mobilization and Ca^{++} influx in rabbit platelets (2). Whatever the mechanism is, we must consider that BN 52021 protects anesthetized guinea-pigs from the dramatic course of acute anaphylactic shock resulting in death for the animals (4). This experimental observation, which is also documented in Figure 7, strongly suggests that either PAF is a key point in guinea-pig anaphylaxis or the compound BN 52021 may have a wider spectrum of activity since it is able to face a complex situation *in vivo* arising from combined effects, possibly synergistics, of various anaphylaxis mediators.

Regarding the negative results obtained with compound BN 52024, they probably could be attributed to introduction on the ginkgolide molecule of a polar group close to the lipophilic moiety: this chemical modification, as in the case of BN 52022 (5), may impair the structural requirement for a specific antagonistic activity on PAF receptors (8).

References

1. Anhut, H. et al. *Radioimmunological determination of thromboxane release in cardiac anaphylaxis.* Eur J Pharmacol 1977; 44: 85-88.
2. Baroggi, N. et al. *Changes in cytosolic Ca⁺⁺ free rabbit platelets: Specific inhibition by BN 52021 and structurally related compounds.* Agents Actions 1986; 20(Suppl): 87-98.
3. Berti, F. et al. *Defibrotide, an antithrombotic substance that preserves postsynaptic α- and β-adrenergic function in post acute infarcted rabbit hearts.* J Cardiovasc Pharmacol 1986; 8: 235-240.
4. Berti, F. et al. *Protection by two ginkgolides, BN 52020 and BN 52021, against guinea-pig lung anaphylaxis.* Pharmacol Res Commun 1986; 18: 775-793.
5. Braquet, P. et al. *BN 52021 and related compounds: A new series of highly specific PAF-acether receptor antagonists isolated from Ginkgo biloba.* Blood and Vessel 1985; 16: 557-572.
6. Braquet, P., Vargaftig, B. *Pharmacology of platelet-aggregating factor.* Transplant Proc 1986; 18: 10-19.
7. Braquet, P. *The Ginkgolides: Potent platelet-activating factor antagonists isolated from Ginkgo biloba L.: Chemistry, pharmacology and clinical applications.* Drugs of the Future 1987; 12: 643-699.
8. Braquet, P., Godfroid, J. *PAF-acether specific binding sites: 2. Design of specific antagonists.* TIPS 1986; 7: 397-403.
9. Capurro, N., Levi, R. *The heart as a target organ in systemic allergic reactions.* Circ Res 1975; 36: 520-528.

10. Ferreira, S.H., De Souza-Costa, F.S. *A laminar flow superfusion technique with much increased sensitivity for the detection of smooth-muscle stimulating substances.* Eur J Pharmacol 1976; 39: 379-381.
11. Halonen, M. et al. *Respiratory and circulatory alterations induced by acetyl glyceryl ether phosphorylcholine (AGEPC), a mediator of IgE anaphylaxis in the rabbit.* Am Rev Resp Dis 1980; 122: 915-924.
12. Koltai, M. et al. *Effect of BN 52021, a specific PAF-acether antagonist, on cardiac anaphylaxis in Langendorff hearts isolated from passively sensitized guinea-pigs.* Eur J Pharmacol 1986; 130: 133-136.
13. Levi, R. *Effect of exogenous and immunologically released histamine on the isolated heart: A quantitative comparison.* J Pharm Exp Ther 1972; 182: 227-238.
14. Levi, R., Burke, J. *Cardiac anaphylaxis: SRS-A potentiates and extends the effect of released histamine.* Eur J Pharmacol 1980; 62: 41-49.
15. Levi, R. et al. *SRS-A, leukotrienes and immediate hypersensitivity reactions of the hearts.* In: Leukotrienes and other Lipoxygenase Products. B. Samuelsson, R. Paoletti (Eds.). Raven Press: New York 1982; 215-222.
16. Levi, R. et al. *Acetyl glyceryl ether phosphorylcholine (AGEPC), a putative mediator of cardiac anaphylaxis in the guinea-pig.* Circ Res 1984; 54: 117-124.
17. Levi, R. et al. *Leukotriene C₄ is released from the anaphylactic heart: A case for its direct negative inotropic effect.* In: Prostaglandins, Leukotrienes and Lipoxins. J.M. Bailey (Ed.).

Plenum Publishing Corp. 1985; 275-288.

18. Liebig, R. et al. *Prostaglandin, slow-reacting substance and histamine release from anaphylactic guinea-pig hearts, and its pharmacological modification.* Naunyn-Schmiedeberg Arch Pharmacol 1975; 289: 65-76.

19. Mc Manus, L.M. et al. *Pathobiology of the intravenous infusion of acetyl and glyceryl ether phosphorylcholine (AGEPC), a synthetic platelet-activating factor (PAF), in the rabbit.* J Immunol 1980; 124: 2919-2924.

20. Page, C.P. et al. *PAF-acether: A mediator of inflammation and asthma.* TIPS 1984; 5: 239.

21. Piper, P.J., Vane, J.R. *Release of additional factor of anaphylaxis and its antagonism by antiinflammatory drugs.* Nature 1969; 223: 29-35.

22. Piper, P.J. et al. *Evidence of a role for platelet-activating factor in antigen-induced coronary vasoconstriction in guinea-pig perfused hearts.* Brit J Pharmacol 1986; 88: 238P.

23   Siraganian, R.P. *Histamine secretion from mast cells and basophils.* TIPS 1983; 4: 432-437.

24   Vargaftig, B.B. and Braquet, P. *PAF-acether today- relevance for acute experimental anaphylaxis.* Brit Med Bull 1987; 43: 312-335.

Ginkgolides - Chemistry, Biology, Pharmacology and Clinical Perspectives. P. Braquet (Ed.)
Copyright © 1988, J.R. Prous Science Publishers, S.A.

EFFECT OF PAF ANTAGONIST BN 52021 AND LEUKOTRIENE SYNTHESIS INHIBITOR L-652,343 ON CARDIAC ANAPHYLAXIS IN THE GUINEA PIG

Sandra Moshonov[1], Yaakov Ashkenazy[2], Arkady Chinis[2], Dan Feigel[2], Haim Shmuely[3], Yosef Rosenfeld[3] and Uriel Zor[1]

[1]Department of Hormone Research, The Weizmann Institute of Science, Rehovot, [2]Department of Internal Medicine, Wolfson Hospital, Holon and [3]Department of Internal Medicine, Beilinson Hospital, Petach Tikva, Israel

INTRODUCTION

Anaphylaxis is an immediate hypersensitivity reaction of the sensitized animal when challenged with specific antigen. Antibody-coated mast cells are stimulated by the antigen to release histamine, leukotrienes(LT), platelet-activating-factor (PAF), various prostaglandins and thromboxane, bradykinin and other hormones and enzymes. When the response is initiated in the heart *in vitro*, it is known as cardiac anaphylaxis (a parallel term to lung anaphylaxis).

This immune reaction takes place on the cell surface and causes a sharp influx of calcium ions into the cell. The high $[Ca^{2+}]_i$ activates many intracellular systems, including formation and/or release of the mediators of anaphylaxis. So, following antigen challenge to the isolated, spontaneously beating heart, several changes, some transient and others sustained, are

Address all correspondence to: Dr. U. Zor, Department of Hormone Research, The Weizmann Institute of Science, Rehovot 76100, Israel.

immediately observed. The heart develops arrhythmias, there is a rise followed by a fall in heart rate and contractile force, and, most importantly, the flow rate through the coronary arteries drops by 50%. The flow rate is a reflection of the coronary arterial resistance, and its reduction, which lingers for at least half an hour after the challenge, indicates prolonged constriction of these arteries.

Leukotrienes C_4 and D_4 were originally thought to be the major mediators of the reduced coronary blood flow in cardiac anaphylaxis. They are very powerful vasoconstrictors with a prolonged duration of action. However, PAF has very similar properties regarding its biosynthesis and pathological action and so presents itself as a complementary or even equal candidate.

Interestingly, PAF and LTs also share a surprisingly large number of other features. Neither is stored in the cell, but rather is generated upon stimulation. They can be formed in mast cells, neutrophils, basophils, eosinophils, monocytes and macrophages (1). PAF is also found in vascular endothelium (2), while LTC_4 is produced by the adventitial layer of coronary arteries (5, 7). As well as in anaphylactic states, they are both found in inflammatory exudates. PAF and LT have a common origin, membrane phospholipids. Arachidonic acid, the precursor of LT, may be derived from the acylalkylglycerophosphocholine when it is de-acylated by phospholipase A_2 to produce the unique phospholipid, PAF. Enzymes for the metabolism of PAF and LT are absolutely calcium-dependent and thus activated by high $[Ca^{2+}]_i$.

In this initial study we have tried to gauge the relative contribution, interaction and importance of LTC_4 and PAF in reducing the coronary outflow rate (CFR) during cardiac anaphylaxis.

MATERIALS AND METHODS

Antigen Challenge and Drug Administration to Sensitized Guinea Pig Hearts

Hearts isolated from guinea pigs sensitized with ovalbumin (OA) were perfused in a Langendorff system described elsewhere (4). Contractions and heart rate were recorded via a force transducer and pen recorder, and the CFR calculated from the volume of perfusate collected at 5 minute intervals. The OA challenge was introduced into the perfusion fluid close to the point where it enters the heart.

PAF antagonist, BN 52021 (30 μM) and LTC_4 synthesis inhibitor, L-652,343 (0.2 μM), were added individually or in combination to the perfusion fluid stock after the isolated heart had stabilized and control values had been measured. The heart was allowed to restabilize for a further 20 minutes before being challenged with OA. The responses to the challenge were monitored for the next 30 minutes.

PAF and LTC$_4$ on Naive Guinea Pig Hearts

Using the same Langendorff system and examining the same parameters, the effects of PAF (0.02-200 ng) and LTC$_4$ (2-200 ng) on perfused hearts taken from naive (non-sensitized) guinea pigs were measured. The hormones were given as a bolus near the point where the perfusion fluid enters the heart. The perfusates from experiments with PAF were also examined for the presence of LTC$_4$, using a standard radioimmunoassay technique.

Materials

Ovalbumin, grades II and III, and PAF, were purchased from Sigma. BN 52021, and LTC$_4$ and L-652,343 were gifts from, respectively, Dr. P. Braquet, Institut Henri Beaufour (France) and Dr. J. Rokach, Merck Frosst Canada Inc. Antibodies to LTC$_4$ were provided by Dr. F. Kohen, Hormone Research Department, Weizmann Institute of Science.

RESULTS

The Effect of OA Challenge on the Heart

The normal responses of the sensitized heart before and after challenge are shown in Table 1.

Table 1   Changes in CFR, heart rate and contractility following challenge with DA

Time after challenge (minutes)	Parameter (Relative to control value in %)		
	CFR	Heart rate	Contractility
0	100	100	100
1	—	123 ± 4	60 ± 7
5	52 ± 4	78 ± 7	188 ± 25
10	59 ± 4	83 ± 8	146 ± 23
15	59 ± 4	107 ± 6	72 ± 14
20	50 ± 3	101 ± 7	88 ± 17
Control (absolute) value	8.2 ± 0.6 ml/min	164 ± 9 beats/min	46 ± 6 mm

The Effect of BN 52021 on Anaphylaxis

The PAF antagonist, BN 52021, completely abolished the reduction in coronary flow rate over a period of at least 20 minutes (Fig. 1). Prior to challenge, it raised the basal rate by 29%. Neither changes in heart rate (initial increase followed by transient decrease) nor contractility were affected significantly by the drug.

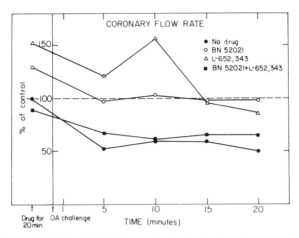

Figure 1 Effects of BN 52021 and L-652,343 on antigen-induced reduction in coronary flow rat through the perfused isolated guinea pig heart.

The Effect of BN 52021 in Combination with L-652,343 on Anaphylaxis

The leukotriene synthesis inhibitor, L-652,343, at a dose of 0.1 μg/ml, not only prevented the reduction in CFR, but actually increased it above the basal level. In fact it produced a 50% increase in CFR even before challenge with OA. Lower doses had almost no effect and a higher dose was toxic (data not presented). However, in contrast to the effect of these drugs individually, the combination of BN 52021 and L-652,343 was inactive with respect to the antigen-induced reduction of CFR (Fig. 1).

Effect of PAF and LTC$_4$ on Heart

The responses of the naive heart to PAF and LTC$_4$, and of the sensitized heart to OA challenge, are presented in comparison to one another in Table 2.

Table 2 Responses of isolated guinea pig heart to PAF and LTC_4 in terms of changes in CFR, HR and contractility

Parameter	CFR			HR			Contractility		
	A	PAF	LTC_4	A	PAF	LTC_4	A	PAF	LTC_4
Effect	—	—	—	—	—	—	+	+	—
ED_{50} (ng)	NA	5	50	NA	1	45	NA	^{a}0.02	60
Max effect (%)	50	60	70	20	35	35	90	30	80
Duration	S	S	S	T	S	S	T	S	T

A: anaphylaxis; —: reduction; +: increase; NA: not applicable; S: sustained; T: transient; ^{a}not ED_{50}; increasing dose produced progressively weaker positive inotropic effect.

DISCUSSION AND CONCLUSIONS

The only parameter, of those measured, to be affected significantly by the PAF antagonist, BN 52021, was CFR. It is the release of PAF during anaphylaxis which causes the coronary vasoconstriction and subsequent decrease in CFR. In contrast, the changes in heart rate and contractile force are probably not mediated or modulated by PAF. Since the leukotriene synthesis inhibitor also entirely prevents the fall in CFR, it is not clear how these substances operate in conjunction with each other. Both PAF and LTC_4 (LTD_4) are producing maximal vasoconstriction.

This may be readily understood if PAF works by releasing LT, as it does in certain tissues (6). But there is no evidence for this in the heart; when PAF was given to the naive isolated heart, we could detect no trace of LTC_4 in the perfusate. This should be confirmed, of course, by attempting to block the effects of PAF on the heart with a LT antagonist or synthesis inhibitor.

The contribution of PAF and LTC_4 to the changes which occur during anaphylaxis appears to focus on the effects on coronary vasoconstriction. While both lowered the heart rate the kinetics do not correspond to those of anaphylaxis. The contractile force is increased by low doses of PAF, but to a much smaller extent than by anaphylaxis, and again the kinetics for this effect do not correspond. In contrast to the response to challenge, LTC_4 produces a transient suppression of contractility.

It was anticipated that administration of a combination of BN 52021 and L-652,343 would totally inhibit the CFR reduction. Unexpectedly, the combination was quite without effect on the reduction of CFR. One may speculate that the neutralization of the major vasoconstrictors stimulates the release and action of lesser vasoconstrictors which would not otherwise be much in evidence. Among the mediators with vasoconstrictor properties are prostaglandin $F_{2\alpha}$ and thromboxane A_2. The effect of both these substances, however, is brief, unlike that of PAF and LTC_4. In summary, our study agrees with recent findings of Koltai *et al.* (3). The indirect evidence obtained by the use of specific antagonist, BN 52021, shows that PAF is released from the guinea pig heart during anaphylaxis. It has no significant inotropic or chronotropic effect but causes a marked and sustained increase in coronary arterial resistance. Even though PAF is more potent than LTC_4, under our experimental conditions both vasoconstrictors were vital, and since blocking either mediator abolished the fall in CFR, their interdependence and relative importance remain undetermined. Continuing the study with different doses of BN 52021 and LT synthesis inhibitor will provide a broader understanding of the relationship between PAF and LT in terms of coronary vasoconstriction.

Since coronary arterial spasm could be an important reason for development of acute myocardial infarction (AMI), the sustained vasoconstriction induced by PAF and LTC_4 following the immune reaction, together with PAF-stimulated platelet aggregation, constitute a major risk for AMI.

ACKNOWLEDGEMENTS

We are grateful to Rona Levin for typing this manuscript. U.Z. is the incumbent of the W.B. Graham Professorial Chair in Pharmacology.

References

1. Braquet, P., Tourqui, L., Shen, T.Y., Vargaftig, B.B. *Perspectives in platelet-activating factor research.* Pharmacol Rev 1987; 39: 97-145.
2. Camussi, G. et al. *Release of platelet-activating factor in rabbits with antibody mediated injury of the lung: The role of leukocytes and of pulmonary endothelial cells.* J Immunol 1983; 131: 1802-1807.
3. Koltai, M., Lepran, I., Szekeres, L., Viossat, I., Chabrier, E., Braquet, P. *Effect of BN 52021, a specific PAF-acether antagonist, on cardiac anaphylaxis in Langendorff hearts isolated from passively sensitized guinea-pigs.* Eur J Pharmacol 1986; 130: 133-136.
4. Moshonov, S., Ashkenazy, Y., Meshorer, A., Hurwitz, N., Kauli, N., Zor, U. *Immunological challenge with virus initiates*

leukotriene C_4 production in the heart and induces cardiomyolysis in guinea pigs. Prostaglandins Leukotrienes and Medicine 1986; 25: 17-26.
5. Piper, P.J., Letts, L.G., Galton, S.A. *Generation of a leukotriene-like substance from porcine vascular and other tissues.* Prostaglandins 1983; 25: 591-599.
6. Voelkel, N.F., Worthen, S., Reeves, J.T., Henson, P.M., Murphy, R.C. *Nonimmunological production of leukotrienes induced by platelet-activating factor.* Science 1982; 218: 286-288.
7. Wölbling, U., Aehringhaus, U., Peskar, B.M., Peskar, B.A. *Release of slow-reacting substance of anaphylaxis from layers of guinea pig aorta.* Prostaglandins 1983; 25: 823-828.

Ginkgolides - Chemistry, Biology, Pharmacology
and Clinical Perspectives. P. Braquet (Ed.)
Copyright © 1988, J.R. Prous Science Publishers, S.A.

CARDIAC ELECTROPHYSIOLOGY OF PAF-ACETHER AND PAF-ACETHER ANTAGONISTS*

Juan Tamargo, Carmen Delgado, Juan Diez and Eva Delpón

Centro Mixto de Farmacología, Facultad de Medicina, Universidad Complutense, E-28040 Madrid, Spain

INTRODUCTION

Platelet-activating factor (PAF-acether) is a low molecular weight phospholipid released by white blood cells and platelets of many species, including humans (1, 5). In the guinea-pig PAF-acether has been found to reduce coronary blood flow and contractile force and produce conduction arrhythmias (2, 23). Furthermore, it induces hypotension, increased vascular permeability and shock (3, 29). Thus, it has been proposed that PAF-acether may mediate cardiac abnormalities that occur during systemic anaphylaxis (3, 23). However, and despite all this evidence indicating that PAF-acether exerts important effects on the heart muscle, little attention has been paid to its cardiac electrophysiological effects.

In this chapter the cardiac electrophysiological effects of PAF-acether and of two specific PAF-acether antagonists, L-652,731 (15) and BN 52021 (gingkolide B) (4) will be reviewed.

MATERIALS AND METHODS

The techniques used in these experiments have been described previously. Guinea-pig papillary muscles driven at a basal rate of 1 Hz were perfused with Tyrode solution (34°C) and transmembrane action potentials were recorded with standard glass microelectrodes filled with 3 M KCl (33). Slow action potentials were elicited in papillary muscles perfused with high-K (27 mM) Tyrode solution and driven at 0.12 Hz by adding isoproterenol

Address all correspondence to: Juan Tamargo, Centro Mixto de Farmacología, Facultad de Medicina Universidad Complutense, E-28040 Madrid, Spain.
*Supported by a CAICYT Grant (N° 2074/83).

(28, 34). Intracardiac conduction times were measured in Langendorff-perfused rat hearts by simultaneous recording of the His bundle electrogram and the standard ECG (13, 35). ^{45}Ca influx and uptake were determined in guinea-pig papillary muscles driven at 1 Hz (32). ^{45}Ca efflux was determined in isolated guinea-pig septum following the technique described by Langer and Brady (21).

RESULTS

Electrophysiological Effects of PAF-Acether

EFFECT ON TRANSMEMBRANE ACTION POTENTIALS   The effects of PAF-acether on transmembrane action potentials characteristics were studied in guinea-pig papillary muscles perfused with Tyrode solution (6, 7, 32). The effects were usually evident within 1 minute after adding PAF-acether to the perfusate and reached steady state conditions within 10 minutes. As is shown in Figure 1, PAF-acether at concentrations between 10^{-11} M and 10^{-7} M produced a dose-dependent increase in the amplitude and maximal rate of rise of the upstroke (V_{max}) and shifted the resting membrane potential to less negative values. These changes reached statistically significant values ($p < 0.05$) at concentrations $> 10^{-10}$ M (32, 33). In the same preparation PAF-acether, 2×10^{-10} M caused an increase in action potential overshoot without altering the resting membrane potential, which confirms that the drug increased the amplitude of the ventricular action potential (6).

At 10^{-10} M, PAF-acether had no effect on the relationship between V_{max} and the membrane potential at the time of action, *i.e.,* membrane responsiveness (unpublished observations). These results indicated that PAF-acether did not inhibit the fast inward Na current in ventricular muscle fibres. Moreover, at 10^{-11} M PAF-acether increased the slope of phase 2 and the plateau level was shifted to more negative values. As a consequence the onset of phase 3 occurred earlier and its slope increased leading to a shortening in the action potential duration measured at both 50% (APD$_{50}$) and 90% (APD$_{90}$) level of repolarization. Further increases in PAF-acether concentration up to 10^{-7} M were not accompanied by a further shortening of the ADP. The shortening of the ADP was not observed in muscles pretreated with verapamil (10^{-6} M) and was significantly reduced in muscles pretreated with 10 mM TEA (7), which suggests that the shortening of the ADP induced by PAF-acether might be related to an increase in Ca and K conductance. Furthermore, pretreatment with propranolol (2×10^{-7} M) prevented the changes in APD induced by PAF-acether (6).

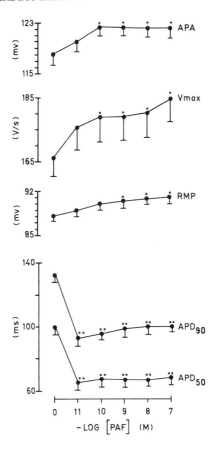

Figure 1 Effect of PAF-acether on action potential characteristics of guinea-pig papillary muscles. APA = action potential amplitude. Vmax = maximum rate of rise of the upstroke. RMP = resting membrane potential APD50 and APD90 = action potential duration measured at 50% and 90% of repolarization. Each point represents the mean ± s.e.m. of 12 experiments. *P < 0.05. **P < 0.01. From Tamargo et al. (1985).

PROARRHYTHMIC EFFECTS OF PAF-ACETHER In guinea-pig papillary muscles at all concentrations tested the shortening of the APD induced by PAF-acether was accompanied by short runs of spontaneous discharges but no change in the rate of diastolic depolarization was observed (33). The spontaneous activity induced by PAF-acether was not observed in muscles pretreated with verapamil 10^{-6} M. In isolated rat hearts PAF-acether produced ventricular extrasystoles which at 10^{-7} M denerated to ventricular fibrillation in 25% of the hearts studied (13). Atrial fibrillation has been described in the anesthetized dog at concentrations (9 nmol/kg) at which PAF-acether decreased sinus rate (3).

Conduction arrhythmias have also been observed in the Langendorff-perfused guinea-pig (23) and rat hearts (13). In perfused guinea-pig hearts, PAF-acether (10^{-12} M - 3 x 10^{-9} M) produced conduction arrhythmias ranging from second degree AV conduction block (Wenckebach phenomenon, 2:1 and 3:1 block) to complete AV dissociation with junctional rhythms, increasing the severity and duration of the AV conduction block with the concentration of PAF-acether. However, in these experiments intracardiac conduction times were not determined and thus the localization of PAF-acether-induced conduction block was unknown. More recently, González (13) studied the effects of PAF-acether on intracardiac conduction times in Langendorff-perfused rat hearts. Table 1 shows the changes induced after 30 minutes of perfusion with PAF-acether in conduction times through atria, AV node and His-Purkinje system. PAF-acether at any of the concentrations tested (10^{-9} M, - 10^{-7} M) had no effect on intraatrial (St-A interval) or intraventricular conduction times (H-V interval). In contrast, at all concentrations tested PAF-acether slowed conduction times through the AV node producing a first degree AV block as evidenced by the progressive and significative prolongation of the A-H interval. In contrast, at the same range of concentrations phosphatidic acid was able to produce second degree AV block and complete AV block in the isolated rat heart. Since in the rat heart PAF-acether never produced second degree A-V block these results suggest that the guinea-pig heart is more sensitive than the rat heart to the depressant effect of PAF-acether on the AV node.

The arrhythmogenic effects of PAF-acether were observed in hearts perfused at constant flow and thus it is unlikely that the proarrhythmogenic

Table 1 Effect of PAF acether on intracardiac conduction times in Langendorff-perfused guinea-pig heart (mean ± s.e.m., n = 8)

Drug concentration (M)	St-A (ms)	A-H (ms)	H-V (ms)
0	5.7 ± 0.3	27.2 ± 1.2	12.9 ± 0.4
10^{-9}	6.0 ± 0.4	30.0 ± 1.2	13.4 ± 0.4
10^{-8}	6.0 ± 0.4	30.1 ± 1.2*	14.0 ± 0.4
10^{-7}	6.1 ± 0.3	35.3 ± 0.8**	13.7 ± 0.6

* $p < 0.01$, ** $p < 0.001$.
(From Morales, 1987)

effect can be attributed to the reduction in coronary flow that PAF-acether produced; moreover, because cardiac arrhythmias occurred in hearts perfused with platelet-free media, they seem also to be independent of platelet aggregation or release of vasoactive amines from platelets (23).

EFFECT ON SLOW ACTION POTENTIALS   In order to ascertain whether PAF-acether modifies the slow inward Ca current, its effects were studied on the slow action potentials in guinea-pig papillary muscles perfused with high-K (22-27 mM) Tyrode solution. Under these conditions the resting membrane potential was shifted from —82.2 ± 0.8 mV to —42.8 ± 0.9 mV, the fast inward Na current was voltage-inactivated and muscles became inexcitable. When muscles were stimulated at 0.12 Hz, PAF-acether (10^{-10} M) induced in most of the experiments slowly rising overshooting electrical responses within 1-3 minutes which disappeared within 10-15 minutes and were blocked with verapamil, 10^{-6} M (7, 33). Camussi (6) studied the effects of PAF-acether (2 x 10^{-10} M) on the slow action potentials elicited in papillary muscles perfused with Tyrode solution (K = 22 mM; Ca = 6 mM). While the resting membrane potential was unchanged, PAF-acether increased within 1-3 minutes the amplitude, V_{max} and ADP of the slow action potentials but subsequently reduced all these parameters to predrug values. These effects were accompanied by a positive inotropic effect which reached its peak within 2-3 minutes, followed after 5 minutes by a marked negative inotropic effect (6). The slow action potentials and contractions elicited in partially depolarized myocardium are generally considered to be mediated by the slow channel which allows for the transmembrane influx of Ca ions (28). Therefore, from these results it was postulated (6) that PAF-acether might exert a biphasic effect on transmembrane Ca influx: first a transient increase of Ca influx across the cardiac membranes as a consequence of an enhancement of the slow inward Ca current, followed by a marked reduction as a result of an inhibitory effect on the slow Ca channels. The slow action potentials and contractions elicited by isoproterenol (10^{-6} M) were transiently enhanced but not subsequently depressed by 2 x 10^{-10} M PAF-acether. Furthermore, the depressant effects of PAF-acether on the slow action potentials and contractions were completely reversed within 2 minutes by isoproterenol. This can explain why Delgado and Tamargo (unpublished observations) were not able to show that PAF-acether decreased the amplitude of the slow contractions induced by isoproterenol.

In order to determine whether PAF-acether increased Ca influx via the slow inward Ca current, the effects of the drug were studied on the slow action potentials elicited by isoproterenol (10^{-6}) in ventricular muscles driven at 0.12 Hz. PAF-acether (10^{-11} M-10^{-7} M) produced a dose-dependent increase in amplitude and V_{max} of the upstroke of the slow action potentials induced by isoproterenol (10^{-6} M) and shifted the resting membrane potential to more negative values (33). Moreover, PAF-acether significantly lengthened the ADP of these slow action potentials, an effect which depended on the frequency of stimulation being almost absent in muscles driven at 1 Hz and persisted in muscles pretreated with phentolamine (10^{-6} M). These results suggested that PAF-acether might increase Ca influx via the slow inward Ca current and that this effect was not mediated through the stimulation of alpha-adrenoceptors.

The amplitude and V_{max} of the slow action potentials depend on the [Ca]o (28). Thus, in another group of experiments the effect of PAF-acether on the increase in the amplitude of the slow action potentials following a 10-fold increase in [Ca]o was studied (33). As is shown in Figure 2, the slope of the relationship between the amplitude of the slow action potentials and log[Ca]o was 29.2 mV per 10-fold change in [Ca]o, a value close to that predicted by the Nerst equation (30.1 mV per decade) for a Ca electrode. This value was similar to that found by others (16, 28). PAF-acether (10^{-10} M) increased the amplitude of the slow action potentials, this effect being greater as [Ca]o increased and thus shifted the slope of the relationship

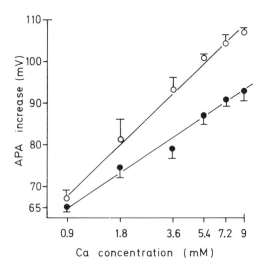

Figure 2   Relation of log[Ca]o to the increase in action potential amplitude of the slow action potentials elicited by isoproterenol in guinea-pig papillary muscles perfused with high-K (27 mM) Tyrode solution. Each point represents the mean ± s.e.m. of 12 experiments. From Tamargo et al. (1985).

to 42 mV per decade. This upward displacement suggests that PAF-acether might increase the maximum number of slow channels available for excitation or increase the conductance of the slow channels.

Electrophysiological Effects of L-652,731 and BN 52021

EFFECT ON TRANSMEMBRANE ACTION POTENTIALS The electrophysiological effects of two specific PAF-acether antagonists L-652, 731 and BN 52021, were studied in guinea-pig ventricular action potentials recorded in papillary muscles. As is shown in Figure 3, L-652,731 and BN 52021 at concentrations between 10^{-8} M and 10^{-6} M had no effect on amplitude and V_{max} of the upstroke or resting membrane potential but produced a progressive and significative shortening of the APD_{50} and APD_{90} values which reached significant values ($p < 0.05$) at concentrations $> 10^{-8}$ M.

In another group of experiments the effects of 10^{-7} M L-652,731 or BN 52021 were studied on the shortening of the APD induced by PAF-acether in ventricular muscle fibres. Results are shown in Table 2. As described above, pretreatment for 10 minutes with 10^{-10} M PAF-acether significantly shortened the APD_{50} and APD_{90} values ($p < 0.01$). When added to the per-

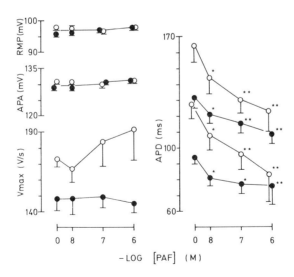

Figure 3 Electrophysiological effects of PAF-acether antagonists L-652,731 (●) and 52021 (○) on action potential characteristics in guinea-pig papillary muscles driven at 1 Hz. APA = action potential amplitude. Vmax = maximum rate of rise of the upstroke. RMP = resting membrane potential. APD = action potential duration measured at 50% and 90% level of repolarization. Each point represents the mean ± s.e.m. of at least 8-12 experiments. *P < 0.05. **P < 0.01.

fusate, L-652,731 slightly prolonged while BN 52021 produced a further shortening of the APD_{50} and APD_{90} values over the shortening induced by PAF-acether. However, changes of the APD_{50} and APD_{90} values observed when perfusing simultaneously with PAF-acether plus PAF-antagonists were not significantly different ($p > 0.05$) than those observed in the presence of PAF-acether alone.

Table 2 Effect of L-652,731 and BN 52021 on the shortening of the ventricular action potential produced by PAF acether (mean ± s.e.m., n = 8)

	APD_{50} (ms)	APD_{90} (ms)
Control	145.0 ± 5.4	179.2 ± 6.6
PAF-acether (10^{-10} M)	97.3 ± 9.9 **	129.1 ± 10.6 **
PAF-acether + L-652,731 (10^{-7} M)	114.8 ± 12.4 * . N.S.	144.9 ± 12.7 * N.S.
Control	116.9 ± 7.1	158.2 ± 8.4
PAF-acether (10^{-10} M)	83.7 ± 8.7 **	119.3 ± 9.1 ***
PAF-acether + BN 52021 (10^{-7} M)	68.7 ± 6.1 ** N.S.	104.9 ± 7.4 *** N.S.

* $p < 0.05$, ** $p < 0.01$, *** $p < 0.001$. APD_{50} and APD_{90} : action potential duration measured at 50 % and 90 % level of repolarization. NS : not significant.

EFFECT ON SLOW ACTION POTENTIALS   At concentrations between 10^{-8} M and 10^{-6} M, neither L-652,731 nor BN 52021 elicited slow action potentials in ventricular fibres partially depolarized with 27 mM K tyrode solution. This result suggested that in contrast to PAF-acether neither antagonist increased Ca influx via the slow inward Ca current.

In another group of experiments the electrophysiological effects of these two antagonists were also studied on the slow action potentials elicited by isoproterenol (10^{-6} M) in papillary muscles perfused with high K (27 mM) Tyrode solution and driven at a basal rate of 0.12 Hz. In 8 papillary muscles L-652,731 (10^{-7} M) had no effect on ventricular APD_{50} (150.0 ± 13.0 ms as compared to 150.5 ± 13.2 ms; $p > 0.05$) and APD_{90} values (172.3 ± 13.1 ms as compared to 170.2 ± 14.2 ms; $p < 0.05$), but increased the amplitude (from 79.0 ± 3.1 mV to 83.1 ± 2.3 mV; $p < 0.05$) and V_{max} of the upstroke (from 8.5 ± 1.8 V/s to 10.7 ± 1.9 V/s; $p < 0.05$) and shifted the resting membrane potential to less negative values (from —45.8 ± 1.3 mV to —48.0 ± 1.2 mV; $p < 0.05$). In contrast, at 10^{-7} M BN 52021 had no effect on the resting membrane potential and amplitude and V_{max} of the upstroke but significantly shortened the APD_{50} (from 165.0 ± 14.1 ms to 135.8 ± 14.0 ms; $p < 0.05$) and APD_{90} values (from $183.0 + 13.5$ ms to 151.8 ± 12.3 ms; $p < 0.05$). Moreover, at this concentration BN 52021 also had no effect on the amplitude, V_{max} and APD of the slow action potentials elicited by histamine (10^{-6} M). These results seem to indicate that in ventricular muscle fibres neither PAF-acether antagonist modified Ca entry through the slow channels.

Effect of PAF-acether and PAF-Antagonists on ^{45}Ca Movements

The effects of PAF-acether on ^{45}Ca movements were studied in guinea-pig papillary muscles driven at 1 Hz (8, 32). PAF-acether, 10^{-10} M, did not modify the ^{45}Ca influx at any of the time intervals studied (2, 5 and 10 minutes). However, PAF-acether at 10^{-10} M and 10^{-9} M increased ^{45}Ca uptake from 1.020 ± 0.040 mmol/kg to 1.487 ± 0.138 mmol/kg ($n = 8$; $p < 0.02$) and 1.435 ± 0.088 mmol/kg ($n = 8$; $p < 0.05$), respectively, while at 10^{-8} M PAF-acether did not increase ^{45}Ca uptake over control values (1.142 ± 0.06 mmol/kg as compared to 1.388 ± 0.141 mmol/kg $n = 6$; $p > 0.05$). These results are in agreement with previous results demonstrating that PAF-acether increases Ca uptake in mouse macrophages (12), human (37) and rabbit platelets (22) and this increase was blocked by phentolamine. Alpha-sympathomimetic agents increase the slow inward current in papillary muscles and elicit slow action potentials in partially depolarized papillary muscles (27). Thus, it could be possible that both the increase of the amplitude and V_{max} of the slow action potentials and ^{45}Ca uptake induced by PAF-acether could be related to its ability to stimulate alpha-adrenoceptors. However, this possibility seems unlikely, since an apparent alpha-adrenergic blocking action of PAF-acether has been reported (30). Moreover, in papillary muscles the effects of PAF-acether were not inhibited by pretreatment with phentolamine, which indicates that its effects were not mediated through stimulation of alpha-adrenoceptors (32).

Figure 4 shows that at 10^{-7} M L-652,731 and BN 52021 decreased ^{45}Ca uptake in guinea-pig ventricular muscle fibres from 1.020 ± 0.040 mmol/kg to 0.900 ± 0.03 mmol/kg ($n = 15$; $p < 0.05$) and 0.710 ± 0.04 mmol/kg ($n = 7$; $p < 0.001$). Furthermore, in muscles pretreated with PAF-antagonists, ^{45}Ca uptake values obtained after adding 10^{-10} M PAF-acether were not different from values obtained in the presence of L-652,731 (0.880 ± 0.11 mmol/kg $n = 11$; $p > 0.05$) or BN 52021 (0.681 ± 0.08 mmol/kg $n = 8$; $p > 0.05$), respectively. In other words, in ventricular muscle fibres both PAF-antagonists abolished the increase in ^{45}Ca uptake induced by PAF-acether.

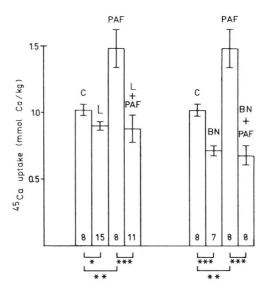

Figure 4 Effect of PAF-acether, L-652,731 (L) and BN 52021 (BN) on 45Ca uptake (mmol/kg wet weight) in guinea-pig papillary muscles driven at 1 Hz. Each column represents the mean with vertical lines showing s.e.m.; *n* is indicated by number in each column. C: controls. PAF: PAF-acether, 10⁻¹⁰M. L: L-652,731, 10⁻⁷M. BN 52021, 10⁻⁷M. *P<0.05. **P<0.01. ***P<0.001.

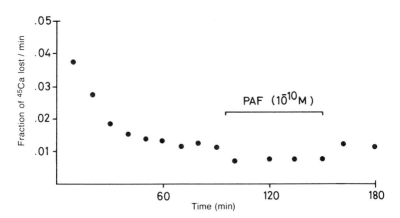

Figure 5 Effect of PAF-acether, 10-10M, on 45Ca efflux in guinea-pig papillary muscles after 2 h of incubation in radioactive Tyrode solution. Ordinate: fraction of 45Ca lost/min. Abscissa: time (min) of the washout. Each point represents the mean of 6 experiments.

Since PAF-acether increased ^{45}Ca uptake but not ^{45}Ca influx it would be of interest to study its effects on ^{45}Ca efflux. The effect of PAF-acether on ^{45}Ca efflux was studied in the isolated guinea-pig septum driven at a basal rate of 1 Hz (32). Septa were mounted and perfused at a constant flow rate of 2 ml/min and labeled with ^{45}Ca for 120 minutes. As is shown in Figure 5, PAF-acether, 10^{-10} M, when added from minute 90 to 150 of the washout period caused a significant decrease (p < 0.05) in the fraction of ^{45}Ca lost per minute, *i.e.*, decreased ^{45}Ca efflux. Thus, it seems that the increase in ^{45}Ca uptake induced by PAF-acether is due, at least partly, to a decrease in Ca efflux.

POSSIBLE MECHANISMS OF THE CARDIAC EFFECTS OF PAF-ACETHER

The mechanism(s) of the cardiac effects of PAF-acether remain(s) to be elucidated. However, from the results presented in this review it is clear that it exerted a biphasic effect.

At *low concentrations* ($\leq 10^{-10}$ M) and as a result of increased ^{45}Ca uptake and decreased ^{45}Ca efflux, PAF-acether could/might increase the intracellular calcium concentration [Ca]i. This increase in ^{45}Ca uptake could be produced by an extra Ca influx and/or to a decrease in Ca efflux. However, our experiments were not able to demonstrate that PAF-acether increased ^{45}Ca influx. The failure of PAF-acether to increase ^{45}Ca influx was not thought to necessarily mean that such an increase does not exist. It is possible that drug-induced increments in Ca exchange have escaped detection under the experimental conditions used because a cellular calcium pool of limited size has very rapidly obtained isotopic equilibrium even in the absence of PAF-acether (14). As a consequence, an additional drug-induced increase in Ca turnover could not be measured even at short exposure to ^{45}Ca (5 minutes). In fact, the increase in V_{max} and amplitude of the slow action potentials and the increase in the amplitude of the slow contractions which appeared in the first 2-5 minutes following the addition of low concentrations of PAF-acether to the perfusate in partially depolarized ventricular muscle fibres constitute indirect evidence suggesting that PAF-acether might increase Ca influx via the slow inward current, Isi (6, 33). However, there is a second possible explanation for the increase in Ca uptake, *i.e.*, a decrease in Ca efflux. Two mechanisms have been suggested for Ca extrusion through the surface membrane: an Na-Ca exchange and a Ca APTase. However, at this time the possible effect of PAF-acether on these mechanisms is unknown.

The PAF-acether-induced increase in [Ca]i may shorten the APD by increasing the time-dependent outward K current responsible for repolarization of ventricular muscle fibres (18, 19). In fact, the injection of Ca into Purkinje fibres shortened the APD and hyperpolarized the resting membrane potential (17). In our experiments (33) PAF-acether produced both effects and the shortening of the ADP was prevented in muscles pretreated with verapamil or TEA, suggesting that it might be related to an increase in K and Ca conductance. Moreover, in mouse macrophages PAF-acether was able to stimulate K efflux and this effect was blocked with quinidine, suggesting that it is due to the opening of Ca-dependent K channels (12). Thus, it can be proposed that at low concentrations PAF-acether increases ^{45}Ca uptake in guinea-pig ventricular muscle fibres, thus opening Ca-dependent K channels through an increase in [Ca]i. PAF-antagonists, L-652,731 and BN 52021 may inhibit the effects of PAF-acether by inhibiting the increase in ^{45}Ca uptake.

An increase in [Ca]i might also explain the ventricular spontaneous discharges induced by PAF-acether. It is known that any drug or condition which shortens APD is arrhythmogenic (31) and that an increase in [Ca]o (36) and hypercalcemia (11) frequently causes cardiac arrhythmias. If one assumes that elevated [Ca]o acts indirectly via an increase in [Ca]i, the spontaneous activity may also be explained by an increase in [Ca]i. Thus, verapamil might suppress the ventricular discharges induced by PAF-acether either by preventing the shortening of the APD or the increase in [Ca]i.

At *higher concentrations* (> 10^{-8} M) PAF-acether reduced peak contractile force (6, 23, 33) and did not increase ^{45}Ca uptake. The mechanism(s) responsible for these effects remain(s) to be determined, but several factors could be involved. The first possibility is that PAF-acether exerted a specific inhibitory effect on the Ca slow channel (23). In fact, an increase in [Ca]i can inhibit the Isi by reducing the driving force for Ca ions, by producing a more rapid inactivation of the Isi (26) and/or by shortening of the APD. The reduction of the Isi can explain the negative inotropic effect which accompanied the shortening of the APD and the disappearance with time of the slow action potentials induced by PAF-acether (6, 33). However, according to this hypothesis, PAF-acether should inhibit the amplitude and V_{max} of the upstroke of the slow action potentials induced by isoproterenol in K-depolarized ventricular fibres, but in contrast, in our experiments it increases these two parameters. Therefore, we would have to wait for the results of voltage-clamp experiments in order to see whether PAF-acether exhibits a biphasic effect on the Isi. A second possible explanation is that at high concentrations PAF-acether increased Ca extrusion through the surface membrane, thus decreasing the free Ca concentration in the cytoplasm. Recently, Levi (24) has proposed that the negative inotropic effect of PAF-acether appears to result from a decreased Ca availability not associated with an effect on the Isi, but secondary to a decrease in intracellular Na activity mediated by the Na-Ca exchange.

Another possibility is that the effects observed at high concentrations of PAF-acether are somehow related to the development of Ca overload. A similar explanation was offered to explain the biphasic effect on contractile force obtained in the presence of high [Ca]o or high concentrations of caffeine or cardiac steroids (20, 25). For reasons not yet understood, in the presence of Ca overload a decrease of Isi (within limits) leads to stronger contractions and increasing Isi has the opposite effect. Reciprocally, for the same Isi, contractile force becomes less if Ca overload increases. This paradoxical effect could be related to some results of Fabiato (9). In skinned cardiac fibres Ca-induced Ca release from the sarcoplasmic reticulum (SR) occurs through a channel in the SR membrane that has a time- and Ca-dependent activation and inactivation (9, 10). The Isi would release Ca from the SR by activating this channel. The activation subsides as a function of time and because of a further increase of cytoplasmic free [Ca] due to the released Ca outside the SR. Inactivation is already present and in addition when the increase of Ca outside the SR is superoptimal inactivation prevails over activation and there is little or no release of Ca from the SR. Under conditions of Ca overload, the increase of Ca needed to release Ca from the sarcoplasmic reticulum increases (10), which suggests that the same Isi would release less Ca from that structure in the presence than in the absence of Ca overload. This would account for the decrease in contractile force even if the Isi is not modified by PAF-acether.

We should like to summarize by indicating not only that some of these hypotheses must be confirmed but that it is possible that other explanations may exist for some of the cardiac effects of PAF-acether. Thus, the decrease in Ca efflux suggests that PAF-acether might exert some possible effects on intracellular events, possibly related to the release and/or uptake by the SR or on the sensibility of the contractile apparatus to [Ca]i, which must be studied in the future.

References

1. Benveniste, J., Henson, P., Cochrane, C. *Leukocyte-dependent histamine release from rabbit platelets. The role of IgE, basophils and a platelet-activating factor.* J Exp Med 1972; 136: 1356-1377.

2. Benveniste, J., Boullet, C., Brink, C., Labat, C. *The actions of PAF-acether (platelet-activating factor) on guinea-pig isolated heart preparations.* Br J Pharmacol 1983; 80: 81-85.

3. Bessin, P., Bonnet, J., Apffel, D., Soulard, C., Desgroux, L., Pelas, I., Benveniste, J. *Acute circulatory collapse caused by platelet-activating factor (PAF-acether) in dogs.* Eur J Pharmacol 1983; 86: 403-413.

4. Braquet, P. *The Ginkgolides: Potent platelet-activating factor antagonists isolated from Ginkgo biloba L.: Chemistry, pharmacology and clinical applications.* Drugs of the Future 1987; 12: 643-699.

5. Braquet, P., Touqui, B., Shen, T., Vargaftig, B.B. *Perspectives in platelet-activating factor research.* Pharmacol Rev 1987; 39: 97-145.

6. Camussi, G., Alloatti, G., Montrucchio, G., Meda, M., Emanuelli, G. *Effect of platelet activating factor on guinea-pig papillary muscle.* Experientia 1984; 40: 697-699.

7. Delgado, C., Sánchez-Crespo, M., Tamargo, J., Tejerina, T. *Electrophysiological actions of platelet activating factor on guinea-pig papillary muscles.* Br J Pharmacol 1983; 79: 239P.

8. Delgado, C., Diez, J., Tamargo, J., Sánchez-Crespo, M. *Efectos electrofisiológicos del L-652,731 en músculos papilares de cobaya.* Rev Farmacol Clin Exp 1986; 3: 198 (Abst).

9. Fabiato, A. *Time and calcium dependence of activation and inactivation of calcium-induced release of calcium from the sarcoplasmic reticulum of a skinned canine cardiac Purkinje cell.* J Gen Physiol 1985a; 85: 247-289.

10. Fabiato, A. *Rapid ionic modifications during the aequorin-detected calcium transient in a skinned canine cardiac Purkinje cell.* J Gen Physiol 1985b; 85: 189-256.

11. Fish, C. *Relation of electrolyte disturbances to cardiac arrhythmias.* Circulation 1973; 47: 408-419.

12. Garay, R., Braquet, P. *Involvement of potassium movements in the membrane signal induced by PAF-acether.* Biochem Pharmacol 1986; 35: 2811-2815.

13. González, A. *Fosfolípidos y corazón. Acciones sobre actividad eléctrica y contráctil.* Tesis Doctoral. Universidad Complutense, Madrid 1987.

14. Grossman, A., Furchgott, T. *The effects of various drugs on Ca exchange in the isolated guinea-pig left atria.* J Pharmacol Exp Ther 1964; 143: 162-172.

15. Hwang, S.-B., Lam, M.-H., Bitfu, T., Shen, T. *A synthetic competitive and specific antagonist of platelet-activating factor.* Fed Proc 1985; 44: 1435.

16. Inui, I., Imamura, H. *Restoration by histamine of the calcium-dependent electrical and mechanical response in guinea-pig papillary muscle partially depolarized by potassium.* Naunyn-Schmiedebergs Arch Pharmacol 1976; 294: 261-269.

17. Isenberg, G. *Is potassium conductance of cardiac Purkinje fibres controlled by [Ca]i?* Nature 1975; 253: 273-274.

18. Isenberg, G. *Cardiac Purkinje fibres. [Ca]i controls steady state potassium conductance.*

19. Kass R., Tsien, R. *Control of action potential duration by calcium ions in cardiac Purkinje fibres.* J Gen Physiol 1976; 67: 599-617.

20. Kotake, H., Vassalle, M. *Rate-force relationship and calcium overload in canine Purkinje fibres.* J Mol Cell Cardiol 1986; 18: 1047-1066.

21. Langer, G., Brady, A. *The effects of temperature upon contraction and ionic exchange in rabbit ventricular myocardium.* J Gen Physiol 1968; 52: 682-713.

22. Lee, T., Malone, B., Blanck, M., Snyder, F. *1-Alkyl-2-acetyl-sn-glycero-3-phosphocholine (platelet-activating factor) stimulates calcium influx in rabbit platelets.* Biochem Biophys Res Commun 1981; 102: 1262-1268.

23. Levi, R., Burke, J., Guo, Z.-G., Hattori, Y., Hoppens, C., McManus, L., Hanahan, D., Pinckard, R. *Acetyl glyceryl ether phosphorylcholine (AGEPC). A putative mediator of cardiac anaphylaxis in the guinea pig.* Circ Res 1984; 54: 117-124.

24. Levi, R. *Effects of PAF on cavian and human cardiac preparations: Mechanisms of action, antagonism and relevance to anaphylaxis* (abstract). 2nd Int Cong on PAF and Related Ether Lipids. Tennessee 1986; Abst.

25. Li, T., Vassalle, M. *The negative inotropic effect of calcium overload in cardiac Purkinje fibres.* J Mol Cell Cardiol 1984; 16: 65-77.

26. Marban, E., Tsien, R. *Enhancement of calcium current during digitalis inotropy in mammalian heart: Positive feedback regulation by intracellular calcium?* J Physiol 1981; 329: 589-614.

27. Miura, Y., Inui, J., Imamura, H. *Alpha-adrenoceptor-mediated restoration of calcium-dependent potential in partially depolarized papillary muscle.* Naunyn-Schmiedebergs Arch Pharmacol 1978; 301: 201-205.

28. Pappano, A. *Calcium-dependent action potentials produced by catecholamines in guinea-pig atrial muscle fibres depolarized by potassium.* Circ Res 1970; 27: 379-390.

29. Sánchez-Crespo, M., Alonso, F., Iñarrea, P., Alvarez, V., Egido, J. *Vascular actions of synthetic PAF-acether (a synthetic platelet-activating factor) in the rat: Evidence for a platelet independent mechanism.* Immunopharmacology 1982; 4: 173-185.

30. Smith, K., Prewitt, R., Byers, L., Muirhead, E. *Analogs of phosphatidyl choline: Alpha-adrenergic antagonists from the renal medulla.* Hypertension 1981; 3: 460-470.

Pfluggers Arch 1977; 371: 71-76.

31. Tamargo, J. *Electrophysiological mechanisms of ventricular arrhythmias.* In: Diagnosis and Treatment of Cardiac Arrhythmias. A. Bayés, J. Cosin (Eds.). Pergamon Press: Oxford 1980; 310-318.

32. Tamargo, J., Barrigón, S., Delgado, C., Tejerina, T. *Effect of PAF-acether on slow action potentials and ^{45}Ca movements in guinea-pig papillary muscles.* J Pharmacol (Paris) 1983; 14: 81.

33. Tamargo, J., Tejerina, T., Delgado, C., Barrigón, S. *Electrophysiological effects of platelet-activating factor (PAF-acether) in guinea-pig papillary muscles.* Eur J Pharmacol 1985; 109: 219-227.

34. Tamargo, J., Delgado, C. *Electrophysiological effects of propafenone on isolated guinea-pig ventricular muscle and sheep Purkinje fibres.* Eur J Pharmacol 1985; 118: 331-340.

35. Tejerina, T., Delgado, C., Valenzuela, C., Tamargo, J. *Comparative effects of oxodipine and nifedipine in the isolated guinea-pig heart.* Arch Int Pharmacodyn 1987; in press.

36. Tempte, J., Davis, L. *Effect of calcium concentration on the transmembrane potentials of Purkinje fibres.* Circ Res 1967; 20: 32-44.

37. Valone, F., Johnson, B. *Modulation of cytoplasmic calcium in human platelets by phospholipid platelet-activating factor 1-O-alkyl-2-acetyl-sn-glycero-3-phosphorylcholine.* J Immunol 1985; 134: 1120-1124.

Ginkgolides - Chemistry, Biology, Pharmacology and Clinical Perspectives. P. Braquet (Ed.)
Copyright © 1988, J.R. Prous Science Publishers, S.A.

EFFECT OF BN 52021 ON THE HEMODYNAMICS OF RATS WITH EXPERIMENTAL CIRRHOSIS OF THE LIVER

Sagrario Fernández-Gallardo, Elías Sanz, Luís Miguel Villamediana, Carlos Caramelo, Mariano Sánchez Crespo and José Miguel López Novoa

Laboratorio de Nefrología Experimental, Instituto de Investigaciones Médicas de la Fundación Jiménez Díaz (CSIC), Madrid, Spain

ABSTRACT

Previous studies from this laboratory have shown that rats with cirrhosis of the liver show a hyperdynamic status with enhaced cardiac output and decreased mean arterial pressure and peripheral vascular resistance. Cirrhotic rats also showed an increased vascular permeability. All these phenomena are similar to some of the effects of the systemic infusion of low doses of synthetic PAF-acether into the systemic circulation of normal rats. The measurement of the levels of PAF-acether in samples of blood demonstrated significantly higher levels in cirrhotic as compared to normal control rats. The hemodynamic changes induced by the i.v. infusion of BN 52021 were measured in 10 control and 10 cirrhotic male Wistar rats, using a radioactive microsphere technique. BN 52021 induced no significant hemodynamic changes in control animals. However, in cirrhotic animals it induced a significant decrease in cardiac output with an increase in peripheral vascular resistance. Mean arterial pressure increased slightly, but not significantly.

From these data it can be deduced that PAF-acether plays a role in the hemodynamic derangement shown by cirrhotic rats and that this derange-

Address all correspondence to: Dr. M. Sánchez Crespo, Laboratorio de Nefrología, Fundación Jiménez Díaz, Av. Reyes Católicos 2, E-28040-Madrid, Spain.

ment can be reversed by BN 52021, a highly specific antagonist of the PAF-acether receptor.

INTRODUCTION

The phenobarbital-carbon tetrachloride model of hepatic cirrhosis in rats is similar to human cirrhosis as regards its morphological and physiological features. These animals retain sodium and water and present a variety of hemodynamic disturbances. These changes include an increased cardiac output (CO), a reduction of the peripheral vascular resistance (PVR) and an increased extravasation of protein-rich plasma. Since the discovery of the chemical structure of platelet-activating factor (PAF, paf-acether) as 1-O-alkyl-2-acetyl-*sn*-glycero-3-phosphocholine (1, 2, 3), this phospholipid mediator has been considered to play a role in different pathological states. When infused into experimental animals, PAF-acether initiates a number of circulatory responses that are similar to the pathophysiology of the shock state (4, 5), and this also resembles the hemodynamic changes of advanced liver cirrhosis (6). In a recent paper, some of us have reported the finding of high amounts of PAF-acether in blood and ascitic fluid from cirrhotic decompensated patients (7). Interestingly, two reports have shown that rat liver generates PAF-acether in response to stimuli of Kuppfer cells such as IgG soluble aggregated and complement-coated zymosan particles (8, 9). In the last couple of years, a number of specific antagonists of the PAF-acether receptor have been developed (10) and they have been shown to be able to reverse the pathophysiological responses to bacterial endotoxin and to soluble aggregates of IgG.

All these data prompted us to search for the involvement of PAF-acether in the pathogenesis of some of the hemodynamic disturbances of experimental liver cirrhosis.

MATERIALS AND METHODS

Induction of Liver Cirrhosis

Cirrhosis was induced in male Wistar rats by inhalation of carbon tetrachloride in increasing doses and phenobarbital administration (0.4 g/l) in drinking water as described elsewhere (11, 12). The extent of hepatic cirrhosis was assessed in the "post mortem" exam in a blinded fashion and only rats showing a grade V hepatopathy according to the Gerber and Popper clasification (13) were included in the study.

Measurement and Characterization of PAF-Acether in Peripheral Blood

PAF-acether was measured in a blood sample of 1 ml obtained 48 hours before the experiment. The sample was drawn from the jugular vein and rapidly mixed with 9 ml of methanol as described (14). The methanol extract was mixed with chloroform and water to allow biphase formation. The chloroform layer was collected, evaporated under N2 stream and developed on thin layer chromatography (TLC) on silica gel plates. The lipid fraction migrating on TLC as PAF-acether was tested on [3H] serotonin labeled platelets as described (14). The chemical characterization of the platelet-activating activity as PAF-acether was performed by treatment with phospholipases and high performance liquid chromatography (14).

Hemodynamic Measurements

Rats were prepared for microsphere technique as described (4, 15). Briefly, rats were anesthetized by intraperitoneal injection of pentobarbital and tracheotomized with a polyethylene catheter. A femoral artery, a jugular vein and the right carotid artery were also cannulated. The microspheres were injected before and 20 minutes after the infusion of 5 mg/kg of BN 52021 (Institut Henri Beaufour) (16, 1)). The miscrospheres were of 15 μm and were labeled with [57]Co and [113]SN.

RESULTS

Concentration of PAF-Acether in the Blood of Rats

The blood of the animals contained a lipid fraction analogous to synthetic PAF-acether as regards its chromatographic behavior on TLC and time of retention on high performance liquid chromatography. Quantitation of the amounts of PAF-acether measured in the blood of a group of 10 cirrhotic rats showed a value of 2.69 ± 0.39 ng/ml, whereas a group of 10 control animals showed 1.5 ± 0.39 ng/ml ($p < 0.05$).

Hemodynamic Measurements

Cirrhotic rats showed a higher CO and lower PVR and mean arterial pressure (MAP) as compared to control rats. The infusion of BN 52021 at a concentration of 5 mg/kg induced a reduction of CO from 53.4 ± 5.4 to 35.9 ± 3.6 ml/min. 100 g ($p < 0.05$; n = 10); an increase of PVR from 0.86 ± 0.11 to 1.34 ± 0.17 mmHg. min. 100 g/ml ($p < 0.05$; n = 10); and an increase of MAP from 97.5 ± 5.6 to 100 ± 5.4 mmHg ($p > 0.05$; n = 10). By contrast, no significant effect of the drug was found in control rats. Cirrhotic rats showed higher values of cardiac output (53.4 ± 5.4 ml/min. 100 g) than control rats (41.1 ± 8.8; $p < 0.05$; n = 10).

DISCUSSION

The present data show that the concentration of PAF-acether is increased in blood from rats with cirrhosis of the liver as compared to control animals, and secondly that an antagonist of the PAF-acether receptor significantly reverses the hemodynamic changes accompanying experimental cirrhosis of the liver. These results, in combination with previous data showing that alterations of CO and PVR similar to those observed in cirrhotic rats are mimicked by PAF-acether infusion in normal rats (4, 5), fulfill the requirements for an autacoid to be considered as a pathogenetic factor in some of the hemodynamic changes which occur in advanced hepatic cirrhosis. A possible reason for the high levels of PAF-acether detected in the blood from cirrhotic rats could be an increased production, since the presence of blood concentrations of acetylhydrolase activity in cirrhotic patients similar to those measured in normal individuals (7) is a strong argument against a reduced catabolism of the mediator. Since cirrhotic animals often have endotoxemia because of alterations of gut permeability and hepatic degradation of endotoxemia, and bacterial endotoxin has been found to initiate the generation of PAF-acether (18), it is difficult to ascertain if in addition to endotoxin other stimuli could play a role in the generation of PAF-acether in cirrhotic animals.

It is surprising to note the reduction in CO when PVR rises to near normal values after BN 5201 infusion in cirrhotic animals. This has been previously seen in other studies in response to volume expansion (19) and angiotensin II (20). The possible mechanism involved in this reduction of CO could be a preexisting cardiomyopathy induced by a chronic hyperdynamic circulation with reduced afterload. When this hemodynamic alteration is reversed by PAF-acether receptor blockade, as shown in this paper, or by angiotensin II (20), a relative cardiac failure is then apparent.

In short, the rapid modification of the hemodynamics of cirrhotic rats by BN 52021 strongly suggests a role for PAF-acether in the regulation of peripheral vascular resistance in cirrhosis and extend the number of *in vivo* models in which PAF-acether antagonists seem to be active.

ACKNOWLEDGEMENTS

This study was supported by grants from CAICYT, Fondo de Investigaciones Sanitarias and Fundación Alvarez de Toledo.

References

1. Demopoulos, C.A., Pinckard, R.N., Hanahan, D.J. *Platelet-activating factor. Evidence for 1-0-alkyl-2-acetyl-sn-glycero-3-phosphocholine as the active component. A new class of lipid mediators.* J Biol Chem 1979; 254: 9355-9358.

2. Benveniste, J., Tence, M., Varenne, P., Bidault, J., Boullet, C., Polonski, J. *Semisynthese et structure proposee du facteur activant les plaquettes (PAF): PAF-acether, un alkyl ether analog de la lysophosphatidilcholine.* C R Acad Sci Paris 1979; 289D: 1037-1040.

3. Blank, M.L., Snyder, F., Byers, L.W., Brooks, B., Muirhead, E.E. *Antihypertensive activity of alkyl ether analog of phospahatidylcholine.* Biochem Biophys Res Commun 1979; 90: 1194-1200.

4. Sánchez Crespo, M., Alonso, F., Alvarez, V., Inarrea, P., Egido, J. *Vascular actions of synthetic PAF-acether (a synthetic platelet activating factor) in the rat. Evidence for a platelet independent mechanism.* Immunopharmacology 1982; 4: 173-185.

5. Bessin, P., Bonnet, J., Apfell, D., Soulard, C., Desgroux, I., Pelas, H., Benveniste, J. *Acute circulatory collapse caused by platelet-activating factor (PAF-acether) in dogs.* Eur J Pharmacol 1983; 86: 403-413.

6. Fernández-Muñoz, D., Caramelo, C., Santos, J.C., Blanchart, A., Hernando, L., López Novoa, J.M. *Systemic and splanchnic hemodynamic disturbances in conscious rats with experimental liver cirrhosis.* Am J Physiol 1985; 242: G236-240.

7. Caramelo, C., Fernández-Gallardo, S., Santos, J.C., Inarrea, P., Sánchez Crespo, M., López Novoa, J.M., Hernando, L. *Increased levels of platelet activating factor in blood from patients with cirrhosis of the liver.* Eur J Clin Invest 1987; 17: 7-11.

8. Inarrea, P., Alonso, F., Sánches Crespo, M. *Platelet-activating factor: An affector substance of the vasopermeability changes induced by infusion of immune aggregates in the mouse.* Immunopharmacology 1983; 6: 7-14.

9. Buxton, D.B., Hanahan, D.J., Olson, M.L. *Stimulation of glycogenolysis and platelet-activating factor by heat aggregated immunoglobulin G in the perfused rat liver.* J Biol Chem 1984; 259: 13758-13761.

10. Braquet, P., Godfroid, J.J. *PAF-acether binding sites: 2. Design of specific antagonists.* TIPS 1986; 7: 397-403.

11. López Novoa, J.M., Navarro, V., Rodicio, J.L., Hernando, L. *Cirrosis experimental de instauración rápida. Cronología de las lesiones hepáticas.* Patología 1976; 9: 233-140.

12. Lopez Novoa, J.M., Santos, J.C., Caramelo, C., Fernandez Muñoz, D., Blanchart, A., Hernando, L. *Mechanisms of the impaired diuretic and natriuretic response to a sustained and moderate saline infusion in rats with experimental cirrhosis of the liver.* Hepatology 1984; 4: 419-423.

13. Gerber, M.A., Popper, H. *Relation between central canals and portal tracts in alcoholic hepatitis.* Hum Pathol 1972; 3: 199-2C7.

14. Caramelo, C., Fernández-Gallardo, S., Marín Cao, D., Inarrea, P., Santos, J.C., López Novoa, J.M., Sánchez Crespo, M. *Presence of platelet-activating factor in blood from humans and experimental animals. Its absence in anephric individuals.* Biochem Biophys Res Commun 1984; 120: 789-796.

15. López Novoa, J.M., Ramos, B., Martín Oar, J.E., Hernando, L. *Functional compensatory changes after unilateral nephrectomy in rats. General and intrarrenal hemodynamic alterations.* Renal Physiol 1982; 5: 76-84.

16. Braquet, P., Spinnewyn, B., Braquet, M., Bourgain, R.H., Taylor, J.E., Etienne, A., Drieu, K. *BN 52021 and related compounds: A new series of highly specific PAF-acether receptor antagonists isolated from Gingko biloba.* Blood and Vessels 1985; 16: 559-572.

17. Sánchez Crespo, M., Fernández Gallardo, S., Nieto, M.L., Baranes, J., Braquet, J. *Inhibition of the vascular actions of IgG aggregates by BN 52021, a highly specific antagonist of PAF-acether.* Immunopharmacology 1985; 10: 69-75.

18. Doebber, T.W., Wu, M.J., Robbins, J.C., MaChoy, M.N., Chang, M.N., Shen, T.Y. *Platelet-activating factor (PAF) involvement in endotoxin induced hypotension in rats. Studies with the PAF-receptor antagonist kadsurenone.* Biochem Biophys Res Commun 1985; 127: 799-808.

19. Caramelo, C., Fernández Muñoz, D., Santos, J.C., Blanchart, A., Rodríguez Puyol, D., López Novoa, J.M., Hernando, L. *Effect of volume expansion in hemodynamics, capillary permeability and renal function in conscious, cirrhotic rats.* Hepatology 1986; 6: 129-134.

20. Fernández Novoa, J.M., Hernando, L. *Hemodynamic effect of angiotensin II in conscious non-ascitic cirrhotic rats.* Clin Physiol Biochem, in press.

Ginkgolides - Chemistry, Biology, Pharmacology
and Clinical Perspectives. P. Braquet (Ed.)
Copyright © 1988, J.R. Prous Science Publishers, S.A.

EFFECT OF INTRAVENOUS INJECTION OF ENDOTOXIN ON RAT MESENTERIC MICROCIRCULATION: INTERFERENCE BY PAF ANTAGONISTS

Vincent Lagente

Laboratorio de Inflamacao, Departamento de Farmacología, Instituto de Ciencias Biomédicas, Universidade de Sao Paulo, 05508 Sao Paulo, Brazil

INTRODUCTION

PAF-acether (PAF) is a potential mediator of different inflammatory and allergic reactions (4, 5). It induces a marked hypotension in several animal species which is accompanied by an increase in microvascular permeability (13). PAF induces controversial observations in microvessels. In Hamster cheek pouch microcirculation preparation a dose-dependent vasoconstriction was observed at lower doses probably due to a direct effect on endothelium (2). In contrast, it was demonstrated in the rat that topically applied PAF leads to arteriolar and venular dilatations of cremasteric muscles (19) and of mesenteric microvessels inhibited by specific PAF antagonists (14, 15). In recent studies, no significant changes in arteriolar and venular diameters on the rat gastric submucosa vasculature were noted during PAF infusion (22), in spite of the closely related slowing and stasis of blood flow.

Address all correspondence to: Dr. Vicent Lagente, Dept. of Immunology, Institut Henri-Beaufour, 72, avenue des Tropiques, F-91952 Les Ulis Cédex, France.

A direct activity of PAF by an interaction with specific membrane receptors may be a possible explanation for the PAF effect in microcirculation. PAF is included among the different autacoids which may mediate endotoxic shock. A role for PAF is supported by different results, particularly the fact that lipopolysaccharide-induced hypotension is suppressed by chemically unrelated PAF antagonists (1, 7-9, 11, 12, 20).

Microvascular dilatation may account, in part, for hypotension induced by PAF and endotoxin. We describe the vasodilatator activities of systemic endotoxin (LPS of *E. coli*) on rat mesenteric microvessels and the interference of the two PAF antagonists, BN 52021 (I.H.B. Ipsen Laboratories, France) and WEB 2086 (Boehringer-Ingelheim, FRG) (3, 6).

MATERIALS AND METHODS

General Preparation

The mesentery of anesthetized male Wistar rats (chloralhydrate 400-450 mg/kg s.c.) was exteriorized and arranged for microscopic observations as previously described (10). The animals were kept on a special board which included a transparent plate on which the tissue to be transilluminated was placed. The mesentery was maintained moist and warm by irrigating the tissue with warm (37°C) Ringer-Locke solution (pH 7.2-7.4, 300 mmol/l) containing 1% gelatin, at a controlled rate providing continuous contact with the film. In the case of intravenous injection of drugs, the jugular vein was cannulated and mean arterial blood pressure was recorded from the left carotid artery by a pressure transducer directly connected to a Narco biosystem physiograph MK-IV.

Evolution of the Diameter Changes

Microcirculation was viewed at a magnification of 3400X on the monitor screen of a closed-circuit television system. The observation was restricted to non-capillary vessels, capillaries being excluded on the basis of their diameters. Diameters of arterioles or venules at rest and under the influence of topically applied or i.v. injected drugs were determined using an image splitting micrometer adjusted to the phototube of the microscope and directly connected to the physiograph. The vessel walls were not clearly visible in these preparations and the diameter of the column of blood was determined. Only one field containing one arteriole and one venule was observed in animals.

RESULTS

Effect of I.V. Injection of Endotoxin

Injected at 10 mg/kg, endotoxin (ET) induced a small non-significant decrease in mean arterial blood pressure (MABP), accompanied by an increase of the arterial diameter, which was only significant at 2 min. When 20 mg/kg ET were used, a large decrease in MABP was observed after injection and a significant increasse of both arterioles and venules were recorded during the next 20 min (Table 1).

Table 1 Inhibition by BN 52021 and WEB 2086 of hypotension and increase in diameter of mesenteric microvessels induced by endotoxin

Treatment	Dose	Route of Administration	$\triangle$ Blood Pressure (mm/Hg)	Diameter Change (%) Arteriole	Venule
Control	—	—	24 ± 8	44 ± 9	22 ± 8
BN 52021	1 mg/kg	i.v.	34 ± 11	12 ± 10*	14 ± 10
BN 52021	5 mg/kg	i.v.	12 ± 4*	-12 ± 6**	0 ± 8*
WEB 2086	1 mg/kg	i.v.	48 ± 20	4 ± 10*	4 ± 11*
WEB 2086	5 mg/kg	i.v.	6 ± 6*	8 ± 6*	0 ± 8*
BN 52021	10^{-5}	Topic	22 ± 24	8 ± 5*	-2 ± 4*
WEB 2086	10^{-5}	Topic	32 ± 34	12 ± 10*	10 ± 10

Decrease of blood pressure (mm/Hg) and increase (%) in diameter of mesenteric microvessels 20 min after the systemic injection of 20 mg/kg of LPS of *E. coli* (endotoxin) in presence or absence of PAF antagonists (BN 52021 and WEB 2086) injected i.v. or topically applied as indicated. Results are mean ± S.E.M. *; $p < 0.05$; $p < 0.01$ (n = 4-6).

Inhibition of the Microvascular Effect of Endotoxin by the I.V. Injection of the PAF Antagonists BN 52021 and WEB 2086

Injected at 1 mg/kg i.v., 5 min before ET, both PAF antagonists slightly but significantly inhibited the increase in arterial diameter induced by ET (20 mg/kg) without interfering with the drop in MABP (Table 1). This effect was more marked when 5 mg/kg of the antagonists were used, since BN 52021 and WEB 2086 suppressed altogether the increase of arteriolar and venular diameters induced by i.v. injection of 20 mg/kg of ET. In this case, the decrease in MABP was also significantly inhibited by the antagonists (Table 1).

Interference of Topical Application of the PAF Antagonists BN 52021 and WEB 2086 with the Microvascular Effect of Systemic Endotoxin

When BN 52021 or WEB 2086 were topically applied at 10^{-5} M, a concentration which inhibited the effect of topical PAF 10^{-5} M and 10^{-4} M (15), a significant inhibition of the increase in arteriolar and venular diameter induced by ET (20 mg/kg i.v.) was observed. As expected, the local application of the PAF antagonists did not modify the ET-induced drop in MABP (Table 1).

DISCUSSION

The participation of PAF in shock is demonstrated by: 1) its infusion mimics the shock state (17); 2) it is generated during the shock state (18); and 3) PAF antagonists provide significant protection against the shock state (1, 5, 7-9, 11, 12, 20). Endotoxin shock is characterized by a systemic hypotension which occurred only at the high dose of 20 mg/kg in our experiments. A large and significant increase in both arteriolar and venular diameters was, nevertheless, observed at 10 mg/kg.

When the animals were pretreated with the PAF antagonists at 1 mg/kg, a significant inhibition of the ET-induced increase in vascular diameters was observed. At this dose, the decrease in MABP by ET was not prevented, but at 5 mg/kg both BN 52021 and WEB 2086 prevented altogether the increase in vascular diameters and the drop in MABP, confirming previous data (1, 7, 9). The increase in diameter of mesenteric microvessels inhibited by the PAF antagonists suggests that microvessel reactivity contributes, in part, to the hypotensive effect of ET, possibly involving the release of PAF at the proximity of the microvessels. This is supported by the results observed when PAF antagonists were applied topically. Indeed, BN 52021 and WEB 2086 at 10^{-5} M, a concentration which inhibits the vasodilatation of mesenteric microvessels by topical PAF, also inhibited the large increase in microvessel diameters induced by i.v. injection of ET, without interfering with the drop in MABP.

These results suggest that ET releases PAF within the mesenteric area. An increased PAF activity has been measured after ET administration to rats (8, 12) and particularly from the jejunum (16), contributing to the hypotension and gastrointestinal damage associated with endotoxin shock in rats (21).

In summary, our results demonstrate that systemic ET induces an increase in diameter of mesenteric microvessels and that this effect contributes in part to the hypotensive effect of ET.

ACKNOWLEDGEMENTS

Research was supported by FINEP and FAPESP, Sao Paulo, Brazil.

References

1. Adnot, S., Lefort, S., Lagente, V., Braquet, P., Vargaftig, B.B. *Interference of BN 52021, a PAF-acether antagonist with endotoxin-induced hypotension in the guinea pig.* Pharmacol Res Commun 1986; 18 (Suppl.): 197-201.

2. Bjork, J., Smedegard, G. *Acute microvascular effects of PAF-acether, as studied by intravital microscopy.* Eur J Pharmacol 1983; 96: 87-94.

3. Braquet, P., Spinnewyn, B., Braquet, M., Bourgain, R.N., Taylor, J.E., Etienne, A., Drieu, K. *BN 52021 and related compounds: A new series of highly specific PAF-acether receptor antagonists isolated grom Ginkgo biloba.* Blood Vessels 1985; 16: 559-572.

4. Braquet, P., Touqui, L., Shen, T.Y., Vargafting, B.B. *Perspectives in platelet-activating factor research.* Pharmacol Rev 1987; 39: 97-145.

5. Braquet, P., Paubert-Braquet, M., Vargaftig, B.B. *Platelet-activating factor: A potential mediator of shock.* Adv Prost Thromb Leuk Res 1987; 17: 818-823.

6. Casals-Stenzel, J., Huacevic, G., Weber, K.W. *WEB 2086, a new and specific antagonist of platelet-activating factor (PAF) in vitro and in vivo.* Naunyn Schmiedebergs Arch Pharmacol 1986; 334: (Suppl): R44.

7. Casals-Stenzel, J. *Protective effect of WEB 2086, a novel antagonist of platelet-activating factor, in endotoxin shock.* Eur J Pharmacol 1987; 135: 117-122.

8. Doebber, T.W., Wu, N.S., Robbins, J.C., Choy, B.M., Chang, N.N., Shen, T.Y. *Platelet-activating factor (PAF) involvement in endotoxin-induced hypotension in rats. Studies with PAF receptor antagonist kadsurenone.* Biochem Biophys Res Commun 1985; 127: 799-808.

9. Etienne, A., Hecquet, F., Soulard, C., Spinnewyn, B., Clostre, F., Braquet, P. *In vivo inhibition of plasma protein leakage and Salmonella enteritidis-induced mortality in the rat by a specific PAF-acether antagonist: BN 52021.* Agents and Actions 1985; 17: 368-370.

10. Fortes, Z.E., Garcia Leme, J., Scivoletto, R. *Vascular reactivity in diabetes mellitus: Possible role of insulin on the endothelial cells.* Br J Pharmacol 1984; 83: 635-643.

11. Handley, D.A., Van Valen, R.G., Tomesch, J.C. *Inhibition by SRI 63-441 of endotoxin- and PAF-induced responses in the rat and dog.* In: Second Int Conf Platelet-Activating Factor and Structurally Related Alkyl Ether Lipids. (October, Gatlinburg, TN) 1986; 111.

12. Iñarrea, P., Gomez-Cambranero, J., Pascual, J., Ponte, N.C., Hernando, L., Sánchez-Crespo, N. *Synthesis of PAF-acether and blood values changes in gram negative sepsis.* Immunopharmacology 1985; 9: 45-50.

13. Kasuya, Y. *Pharmacological studies of hypotensive effects of platelet-activating factor.* Adv Prost Thromb Leuk Res 1985; 15: 723-724.

14. Lagente, V., Fortes, Z.B. *Role of PAF-acether in the vascular events of inflammation.* In: PAF-Acether and Inflammation. Prog Biochem Pharmacology. Karger 1987; In press.

15. Lagente, V., Fortes, Z.B., Garcia Leme, J., Vargaftig, B.B. *Platelet-activating factor (PAF-acether) and microcirculation: Effect of lyso-PAF and PAF-antagonists.* Brazilian J Med Biol Res 1987; In press.

16. Lagente, V., Lidbury, P., Steel, G., Vargaftig, B.B., Wallage, J., Whittle, B.J.R. *Role of PAF as a mediator of endotoxin-induced gastrointestinal damage.* Br J Pharmacol 1987; 90: 114.

17. McManus, L.M., Hanahan, D.J., Demopoulos, C.A., Pinckard, R.N. *Pathobiology of the intravenous infusion of acetyl glyceryl ether phosphorylcholine (AGEPC), a synthetic platelet-activating factor (PAF) in the rabbit.* J Immunol 1980; 124: 2919-2924.

18. Pinckard, R.N., Farr, R.S., Hanahan, D.J. *Physiochemical and functional identity of rabbit platelet-activating factor (PAF) released in vivo during IgE anaphylaxis with PAF released in vitro from IgE sensitized basophils.* J Immunol 1979; 123: 1847-1857.

19. Smith, K.A., Prewitt, R.L., Byer, L.W., Muirhead, E.F. *Analogs of phospho-*

tidylcholine: Alpha-adrenergic antagonists from the renal medulla. Hypertension 1981; 3: 460-470.

20. Terashita, Z., Imuka, Y., Nishikawa, K., Sumida, S. *Is platelet-activating factor (PAF) a mediator of endotoxin shock?* Eur J Pharmacol 1985; 109: 257-261.

21. Wallace, J., Steel, G., Whittle, B.J.R., Lagente, V., Vargaftig, B.B. *Evidence for*

platelet-activating factor (PAF) as a mediator of endotoxin-induced gastrointestinal damage in the rat: Effect of three PAF antagonists. Gastroenterology 1987; 93: 765-773.

22. Whittle, B.J.R., Maishita, T., Onya, Y., Leuny, F.W., Crith, P.W. *Microvascular actions of platelet-activating factor on rat gastric mucosa and submucosa.* Am J Physiol 1986; 251.

Ginkgolides - Chemistry, Biology, Pharmacology and Clinical Perspectives. P. Braquet (Ed.)
Copyright © 1988, J.R. Prous Science Publishers, S.A.

INTERACTION BETWEEN ATRIAL NATRIURETIC FACTOR AND PAF-ACETHER

Pierre-Etienne Chabrier and Pierre Thiévant

Institut Henri Beaufour, F-91952 Les Ulis Cédéx, France

INTRODUCTION

Atrial natriuretic factor (ANF) has been recently isolated from secretory-like granules in the mammalian atria (7, 12). This peptide seems to play an important role in blood pressure and fluid homeostasis and to act as a physiological antagonist of the renin-angiotensin system through receptor mediated actions in the kidney, adrenal glands, vascular beds, brain and brain microvasculature (3, 8, 11, 14). The natriuretic effects of ANF are supposed to be mainly mediated by the increase in glomerular filtration rate (GFR) (10), although a direct tubular effect cannot be totally discarded. *In vivo*, ANF increases renal blood flow (RBF) and urinary flow, and *in vitro* in isolated perfused rat kidney, ANF increases GFR and either enhances or decreases renal vascular resistance (RVR), depending upon pre-existing vascular tone (6). In addition to natriuresis, ANF relaxes rat aortic strips (1) and reduces blood pressure in normal rats and in several models of experimentally hypertensive rats (7). These effects of ANF are independent of prostaglandins (PGs) release.

On the other hand, PAF-acether has powerful effects on cardiovascular and renal systems (5). Its intravenous infusion in rabbits produces peripheral vasodilatation, plasma leakage and arterial hypotension. Perfusion of vital

Address all correspondence to: Dr. P.E. Chabrier, Dept. of Biochemical Pharmacology, Institut Henri Beaufour, 72 avenue des Tropiques, F-91952 Les Ulis Cédex, France.

organs is, therefore, impaired, *i.e.,* renal blood flow and glomerular filtration rate are both markedly decreased as a consequence of increased renal vascular resistance (19). The effects of PAF-acether on peripheral circulation seem to be mediated by vasodilatory prostaglandins (PGs), since indomethacin prevents both plasma leakage and hypotension (13). However, the renal effects of PAF-acether are likely mediated by additional substances, since PGs synthesis inhibition does not prevent RBF, GFR and urinary sodium to fall despite adequate peripheral arterial perfusion (13).

Furthermore, PAF-acether has been shown *in vitro* to provoke contraction of rat cultured mesangial cells (6) and to induce *in vivo* the appearance in the plasma of tryptic-like activity (9).

Based on these observations, potential interactions between these two systems of mediators were investigated using the specific PAF-acether antagonist BN 52021 (4) and an anti-proteasic agent, aprotinin, in anesthetized dogs.

MATERIALS AND METHODS

Sodium pentobarbital was obtained from Clin-Midy Labs. (Paris, France) and aprotinin from Specia Labs. (Paris, France); C_{16}-PAF-acether (1-O-hexadecyl-2(R)-acetyl-glycerophosphocholine) and synthetic ANF (Ser-99-Tyr 126) were purchased from Novabiochem (Switzerland); BN 52021 (3-[1.1-dimethylethyl]hexahydro-1.4,7b-trihydroxy-8-methyl-9H-1.7α-[epoxymethanol]-1H,6αH-cyclopenta[c]furo[3',2':3.4]cyclopenta[1.2-d]furan-5,9,12[4H]-trione) was produced by Institut Henri Beaufour Research Labs. (Le Plessis-Robinson, France); all the drugs were dissolved in a saline medium (NaCl 9%) except BN 52021 in dimethyl sulfoxide (DMSO) in a volume of 0.1 ml/kg and PAF-acether in a saline-bovine serum albumin (0.5%).

Mongrel dogs of either sex (12-18 kg) purchased from Lessieux (Bray Lu, France) were anesthetized with pentobarbital (35 mg/kg, i.v.) intubated and ventilated with compressed air via a logic O_2 respirator (Minerve, France). Anesthesia was maintained by a constant pentobarbital perfusion (5 mg/kg per hour) during all the experiments. After laparotomy, each ureter was separately canulated at the base of the bladder for continuous urine collection. The experimental protocol consisted of two 15 minute periods after drug or solvent administration (i.v.). Urinary volume was measured and Na^+ and K^+ excretions were determined by flame photometry (Delhomme, France).

Five series of experiments were performed with 6 animals per group:
Group 1: Specific effect of ANF: ANF (5 μg/kg, i.v.) in saline; saline (control solvent) 5 minutes before ANF.

Group 2: Specific effect of PAF-acether: PAF-acether (0.06, 0.150, 0.300 and 0.600 μg/kg, i.v.) in saline/BSA medium; saline/BSA medium (control solvent) 5 minutes before ANF.

Group 3: Specific effect of BN 52021: BN 52021 (5 mg/kg, i.v.) in DMSO 5 minutes before saline; DMSO (control solvent) 5 minutes before saline.

Group 4: PAF-acether/ANF interactions: PAF-acether (0.1 μg/kg, i.v.) 5 minutes before ANF (5 μg/kg, i.v.); saline 5 minutes before ANF (5 μg/kg, i.v.).

Group 5: BN 52021/ANF interactions: BN 52021 (5 mg/kg, i.v.) 5 minutes before ANF (5 μg/kg, i.v.); DMSO 5 minutes before ANF (5 μg/kg, i.v.).

Group 6: Aprotinin/ANF interactions: Aprotinin (10.000 KIU/kg, or 30.000 KIU/kg, i.v.) 5 minutes before ANF (5 μg/kg i.v.); saline 5 minutes before ANF (5 μg/kg, i.v.).

In all experiments, drugs were given in a bolus. Results were given as mean ± S.E.M. Each dog was its own control. Differences between control, experimental and recovery periods were analyzed by the two way analysis of variance. Simultaneous comparisons at the different periods between pairs of groups were also made by analysis of variance.

RESULTS

Effects of ANF, PAF-Acether and BN 52021 on Diuresis and Electrolyte Excretion in the Anesthetized Dog

In the anesthetized dog, ANF produced an increase in diuresis (6 to 8 times), natriuresis (5 to 8 times), and kaliuresis to a lesser extent (2 to 3 times). This action was of short duration since the second and third collection periods were not significantly different from the control period.

After PAF-acether injection, sodium excretion was reduced by 210, 330, 600 and 960 μEq/15 minutes from baseline values at 0.060, 0.150, 0.300 and 0.600 μg/kg, respectively, showing a dose-dependent effect of PAF-acether. Sodium excretion returned to control values within 30 minutes.

BN 52021 was totally devoid *per se* of effects on diuresis and electrolyte excretion. The solvent (DMSO) was also without effect.

Interaction of PAF-Acether, BN 52021 and Aprotinin on ANF-Induced Diuresis and Electrolyte Excretion in the Anesthetized Dog

When PAF-acether was administered 5 minutes before ANF, it practically abolished the effects of the peptide. This counteracting effect was equally

Table 1   Effects of ANF, PAF-acether and BN 52021 on diuresis and electrolyte excretion in the anesthetized dog

Periods of time after ANF administration (min)	PAF-acether (μg/kg, i.v.)	Effects of diuresis and electrolytes excretions		
		Volume (ml)	Na$^+$ (NEQ)	K$^+$ (NEQ)
Control (basal values)	—	2.64 ± 0.72	560 ± 302	286.5 ± 107
0-15	—	22 ± 5***	4145 ± 1019***	964 ± 160.3***
	0.1	4.44 ± 1.81***	869 ± 385***	401 ± 148***
15-30	—	4.26 ± 0.98	965 ± 334	453 ± 141
	0.1	4.16 ± 1.27	617 ± 201	472 ± 149
30-45	—	3.28 ± 0.71	724 ± 260	386 ± 90
	0.1	4.30 ± 1.19	615 ± 195	392 ± 101

PAF-acether treated vs. ANF: ***$p < 0.001$.
Control vs.: ANF ***$p < 0.001$.

pronounced in diuresis, natriuresis and kaliuresis (Table 1). In our experiments, ANF alone induced an increase from 2.64 ± 0.72 ml/15 minutes to 22.00 ± 5.0 ml/15 minutes ($p < 0.001$). This effect was reduced to 4.4 ± 1.81 ml/15 minutes when PAF-acether was injected preventively 5 minutes beforehand ($p < 0.001$ compared with ANF alone).

In contrast to PAF-acether, BN 52021 potentiated the effect of ANF on diuresis, natriuresis and kaliuresis (Table 2). For example, concerning natriuresis, ANF increased Na$^+$ excretion approximately 6-fold. When BN 52021 was administered before ANF, natriuresis increased approximately 10-fold. Aprotinin given before ANF did not affect the duration nor the amplitude of the effect of the peptide on diuresis, natriuresis and kaliuresis (data not shown).

DISCUSSION AND CONCLUSIONS

In the anesthetized dog, ANF (Ser 99- Tyr 126) induced increases in diuresis, natriuresis and also kaliuresis to a lesser extent, as previously demonstrated in other studies (10). On the contrary, PAF-acether decreased dose-dependently sodium excretion, with only a slight effect with the dose of 0.1 μg/kg used for PAF-acether/ANF dual experiments in order to obtain only a slight effect of the ether-lipid mediator. Our results show that: 1) Pretreatment with PAF-acether 5 minutes before ANF practically abolishes the effect of the peptide on both diuresis and electrolyte excretion; 2) The PAF-antagonist BN 52021, which is devoid of effects *per se* on diuresis

Table 2 Interaction of PAF-acether, BN 52021 and aprotinin on ANF-induced diuresis and electrolyte excretion in the anesthetized dog

Periods of time after ANF administration (min)	BN 52021 (mg/kg i.v.)	Effects on diuresis and electrolytes excretions		
		Volume (ml)	Na$^+$ (NEQ)	K$^+$ (NEQ)
Control (DMSO) (basal values)	—	1.80 ± 0.684	266 ± 140	200 ± 18
Control (BN 52021) (basal values)	5	2.15 ± 0.520	316 ± 110	251 ± 53
0-15	—	12.03 ± 5.360***	1320 ± 880***	588 ± 115***
	5	19.07 ± 3.920***	3140 ± 801***	878 ± 185***
15-30	—	2.35 ± 0.775***	350 ± 150***	187 ± 33***
	5	3.48 ± 1.055***	592 ± 230	197 ± 49
30-45	—	2.12 ± 0.60	472 ± 200	210 ± 35
	5	3.10 ± 0.99	273 ± 139	117 ± 54

BN 52021 treated *vs.* ANF alone: **p < 0.05; ***p < 0.001.
Control *vs.* ANF: ***p < 0.001.

and electrolyte excretion, potentiates the effect of ANF. This is observed only with respect to amplitude but not duration. Since it has been recently shown that PAF-acether *in vivo* induces the appearance of tryptic-like activity in the plasma (9), we performed a similar experiment with aprotinin, an antiproteasic agent. However, pretreatment with aprotinin did not affect the duration nor the amplitude of the effect of ANF. Different findings were reported on anesthetized rats by Thibault *et al.* (17), who observed a prolongation of the effect of the peptide with only a slight effect on amplitude.

How does PAF-acether antagonize the effect of ANF in our experiments? A direct effect of PAF-acether on ANF specific receptors is excluded, since PAF-acether does not affect the binding of ^{125}I-ANF nor desensitizes ANF receptors (data not shown).

Among the possible hypotheses, it can be assumed that PAF-acether increases the catabolism of ANF because it induces a very rapid increase of plasma proteasic activity. This effect lasts from 15 to 20 minutes and practically disappears after 30 minutes. Another explanation is that PAF-acether acts at the kidney level by contracting glomeruli cells although it is expected that ANF will oppose this effect, as was found *in vitro* (2).

On the other hand, how can PAF-acether antagonist alone potentiate the effects of ANF? It can be assumed that PAF-acether antagonist may act by its indirect anti-proteasic effect, since, although BN 52021 does not inhibit tryptic activity *in vitro*, it counteracts PAF-acether induced proteolytic activity *in vivo*. This could strengthen the assumption that PAF-acether or PAF-acether-like compounds may be involved in the regulation of fluid homeostasis. It is also possible that ANF could raise the level or release of PAF-acether which itself inhibits the action of ANF by a feedback mechanism, as has already been demonstrated for angiotensin/prostaglandin system.

In another respect, it was recently demonstrated that PAF-acether mobilizes intracellular calcium and increases GTPases activity in platelets and consequently may affect the level of cyclic GMP (7). This contrasts with the action of ANF, which increases the level of cyclic GMP and decreases the concentration of cytosolic calcium in some vascular and renal cells. These two antagonistic effects may provide a possible explanation at the molecular level (18). However, the physiological significance of this interaction between ANF and PAF-acether needs further studies to be completely elucidated.

References

1. Auguet, M. et al. *Effects of sodium pump inhibition of the relaxation induced by synthetic atrial natriuretic factor (ANF) and sodium nitroprusside.* Regul Peptides 1985; Suppl 4: 104-109.

2. Barrio, et al. *Atrial natriuretic peptide inhibits glomerular contraction induced by angiotensin II and platelet-activating factor.* Eur J Pharmacol 1987; 135: 93-96.

3. Bianchi, C. et al. *Radioautographic localization of* ^{125}*-atrial natriuretic factor.* Histochemistry 1985; 82: 441-452.

4. Braquet P. *The ginkgolides: Potent platelet-activating factor antagonists isolated from ginko biloba L.: Chemistry, pharmacology and clinical applications.* Drugs of the Future 1987; 12: 643-699.

5. Braquet, P., Touqui, B., Shen, T.Y. and Vargaftig, B.B. *Perspectives in platelet-activating factor research.* Pharmacol Rev 1987; 39: 97-145.

6. Camargo, M.J.F. et al. *Ca^{2+}-dependent hemodynamic and natriuretic effects of atrial extract in isolated rat kidney.* Am J Physiol 1984; 246: 447-456.

7. Cantin, M. et al. *The heart and the atrial natriuretic factor.* Endocrine Rev 1985; 6: 107-127.

8. Chabrier, P.E. et al. *Specific binding site of atrial natriuretic factor in brain microvessels.* Proc Natl Acad Sci USA 1987; 84: 2078-2081.

9. Etienne, A. et al. *Inhibition of rat endotoxin-induced lethality by BN 52021 and BN 52063 compounds with PAF-acether antagonistic effect and protease inhibitory activity.* Int J Tiss Reac 1987; 9(1): 19-26.

10. Maack, T. et al. *Atrial natriuretic factor: Structure and functional properties.* Kidney Int 1985; 27: 607-615.

11. Napier, M.A. et al. *Specific membrane receptors for atrial natriuretic factor in renal and vascular tissues.* Proc Natl Acad Sci USA, 1984; 81: 5946-5950.

12. Needleman, P. et al. *Atrioptins potential mediators of an endocrine relationship between heart and kidney.* TIPS 1984; 5: 506-509.

13. Plante, G. et al. *Hemodynamic effect of PAF-acether.* Pharmacol Res Comun 1986; 18(Suppl): 173-180.

14. Saavedra, J.M. et al. *Binding of angiotensin and atrial natriuretic peptide in brain of hypertensive rats.* Nature 1986; 320: 758-760.

15. Sasaki, A. et al. *Hemodynamic effect of alpha-human atrial natriuretic polypeptide (alpha-h ANP) in rats.* Eur J Pharmacol 1985; 109: 405-407.

16. Schlondorff, et al. *Effect of platelet-activating factor and serum treated zymosan on prostaglandin E_2 synthesis, arachidonic acid and contraction of cultured mesangial cells.* J Clin Invest 1984; 73: 1227-1231.

17. Thibault, G. et al. *Atrial natriuretic factor and urinary kallikrein in the rat: Antagonist factor?* Can J Physiol Pharmacol 1984; 62: 645-649.

18. Thiévant, P. et al. *Impairment of the natriuretic and diuretic effects of atrial natriuretic factor in anaesthetized dogs by platelet-activating factor.* In: Diuretic II. Chemistry, Pharmacology and Clinical Applications. J.B. Puschett (Ed.). Elsevier 1987; 289-293.

19. Vermulapalli, S. et al. *Cardiovascular and renal action of platelet-activating factor in anesthetized dogs.* Hypertension 1984; 6: 489-493.

Ginkgolides - Chemistry, Biology, Pharmacology and Clinical Perspectives. P. Braquet (Ed.)
Copyright © 1988, J.R. Prous Science Publishers, S.A.

PAF, ENDOTOXEMIA AND GINKGOLIDES

Serge Adnot, Jean Lefort and Boris Vargaftig

Institut Pasteur, Unité de Pharmacologie Cellulaire, Unité Associée INSERM U 285, F-75015 Paris, France

INTRODUCTION

The pathophysiology of endotoxin shock involves different humoral and cellular systems (15). Evidence for the interaction of serum complement and coagulation system has been provided (2, 17) and many vasoactive substances have been incriminated including histamine, kinins, serotonin and arachidonate metabolites (2, 7-9, 17). The pathogenesis of endotoxin shock, however, remains uncertain, notwithstanding the hemodynamic, metabolic and hematologic changes observed in different animal species and in man (15). PAF-acether (1-O-hexadecyl-2-acetyl-*sn*-glycero-3-phosphocholine) displays a variety of effects likely to occur in endotoxemia such as systemic hypotension, pulmonary hypertension, increased vasopermeability, leukocyte and platelet activation (3, 6, 13, 14, 18-20). Recently, evidence has also been provided in favor of the participation of PAF-acether in anaphylaxis and in septic shock (11, 12).

The discovery of PAF-acether antagonists may help in evaluating the role of PAF-acether in endotoxic shock. Until now, two chemically distinct PAF-acether antagonists, CV 3988 and kadsurenone, have been shown to reduce the early hypotensive phase of endotoxic shock (10, 18). Since BN 52021 was previously shown to prevent the hypotension induced by i.v. PAF administration in rats (16) as well as to interfere with passive anaphylaxis in the guinea-pig (4) or with shock induced in rats by the injection of immune

Address all correspondence to: Dr. Serge Adnot, Institut Pasteur, Unité de Pharmacologie Cellulaire, Unité Associée INSERM N° 285, 25 rue du Dr. Roux, F-75015 Paris, France.

aggregates (5), we asked as to whether the participation of PAF-acether in endotoxic shock could be evaluated using BN 52021 as a PAF-acether antagonist.

The present report summarizes a previous study where interference between BN 52021 and hemodynamic and hematologic alteration produced by the i.v. administration of *Salmonella typhimurium* endotoxin were studied in the guinea-pig (1).

MATERIALS AND METHODS

Hartley guinea-pigs of either sex (300-500 g) were anesthetized with pentobarbitone and ventilated by a Palmer miniature respiratory pump. These animals were then monitored for arterial blood pressure, platelet and white blood cell counts. Experiments were conducted on paired animals, one being pretreated with BN 52021 injected intravenously and the other treated with the solvent. Ten animals received 1 mg/kg and five others 6 mg/kg BN 52021, followed within 15 minutes by 0.3 mg/kg of *Salmonella typhimurium* endotoxin as a bolus injection. This dose of endotoxin was chosen because it induced a marked hypotension as determined in preliminary experiments and enabled the animals to survive for the entire study duration. In a second series of experiments, BN 52021 was given intravenously 60 minutes after the endotoxin had been injected.

RESULTS AND DISCUSSION

A biphasic change in mean arterial pressure was elicited after endotoxin administration. Control animals showed a rapid drop in blood pressure (maximal within 10 minutes), a partial recovery at 20 minutes and a second more gradual decrease after 30 minutes. Treatment with 1 and 6 mg/kg BN 52021 injected 15 minutes prior to endotoxin reduced the initial rapid drop in blood pressure, from 44% in vehicle-treated controls (n = 15) to 27% (n = 10) and to 12% (n = 6), respectively. The more gradual secondary decrease in blood pressure recorded from 30 to 90 minutes was less reduced by both doses of BN 52021, but reached statistical significance at the 0.05 level. The early drop in blood pressure was accompanied by a drop in the number of circulating platelets which peaked at 10 minutes. This thrombocytopenia was affected by pre-treatment with BN 52021, since the 82% fall in control animals at 10 minutes was reduced to 65% (p < 0.02) with 1 mg/kg and to 60% (p < 0.01) with 6 mg/kg.

The relationship between immediate hypotension and platelet disappearance from the circulation following endotoxin administration has already been demonstrated in C3-depleted animals (3, 14). In our experiments the initial rapid change in blood pressure due to endotoxin was abbrogated in animals made thrombopenic with rabbit anti-platelet serum (platelet count < 10.000 per ul), but the late phase of shock (> 30 minutes) persisted. Although the immediate drop in blood pressure and in circulating platelets in guinea-pigs might be complement-dependent (15), complement activation was not observed with the dose of endotoxin used in this study as assessed by the absence of modifications of the CH50 (kindly performed by Mrs. F. Fouque, Institut Pasteur). Furthermore, since BN 52021 at 1 mg/kg fully suppressed the gradual hypotension of endotoxic shock in thrombopenic animals, it is clear that BN 52021 has a platelet-independent site of action.

Most importantly, the i.v. injection of BN 52021 during the prolonged secondary phase of shock (at 60 minutes) was followed by an immediate reversal of the depressed blood pressure. This curative effect was dose-dependent, and was observed also in thrombopenic animals. Furthermore, a similar antagonism has been described for PAF itself and for hypotension induced by IgG aggregates (14).

CONCLUSIONS

BN 52021 appeared to mostly interfere with changes in blood pressure in this model of endotoxic shock in guinea-pigs. Systemic hypotension following endotoxemia may be due both to myocardial depression and decreased systemic vascular resistance (15). Since the cardiac output was not measured in the present study, the mechanism by which BN 52021 prevented or corrected the endotoxin-induced systemic hypotension remains unresolved. Interference of BN 52021 with pulmonary hemodynamic alterations during endotoxemia also remains unexplored.

We do not claim that endotoxic shock is a direct consequence of the release of PAF, and of course other mechanisms and mediators are involved. Thus, the drop in the number of circulating cells (platelets and leukocytes) following the injection of endotoxin was not inhibited by BN 52021, and other effects of endotoxin may prove to be refractory as well. Furthermore, BN 52021 may not be a selective PAF antagonist, and it possibly displays other pharmacological effects relevant to shock. Nevertheless, the fact that three chemically distinct molecules, kadsurenone (9), CV 3988 (6), and BN 52021 share an anti-PAF activity, and the ability to reduce or to reverse the hypotension of endotoxic shock, is sufficient evidence to justify further studies on the involvement of PAF in the physiopathology of endotoxic and other forms of shock.

References

1. Adnot, S., Lefort, J., Braquet, P., Vargaftig, B.B. *Interference of the PAF-acether antagonist BN 52021 with endotoxin-induced hypotension in the guinea-pig.* Prostaglandins 1986; 32: 791-802.
2. Beller, F.K. *The role of endotoxin in disseminated intravascular coagulation.* Thromb Diath Haemorrh 1969; 36 (Suppl): 125.
3. Bessin, P., Bonnet, J., Apffel, D., Soulard, C., Desgroux, L., Pelas, I., Benveniste, J. *Acute circulatory collapse caused by platelet-activating factor (PAF-acether) in dogs.* Eur J Pharmacol 1983; 86: 403.
4. Braquet, P., Etienne, A., Touvay, C., Bourgain, R.H., Lefort, J., Vargaftig, B.B. *Involvement of platelet-activating factor in respiratory anaphylaxis, demonstrated by PAF-acether inhibitor BN 52021.* Lancet 1985; i: 1501.
5. Braquet, P., Spinnewyn, B., Braquet, M., Bourgain, R.H., Taylor, J.E., Etienne, A., Drieu, K. *BN 52021 and related compounds: A new series of highly specific PAF-acether receptor antagonists isolated from Ginkgo biloba L.* Blood & Vessel 1985; 16: 558.
6. Braquet, P., Touqui, L., Shen, T.Y. *Perspectives in platelet-activating factor research.* Pharmacol Rev 1987; 39: 97-145.
7. Brigham, K.L. *Mechanism of the serotonin effect on lung transvascular fluid and protein movement in awake sheep.* Circ Res 1975; 36: 761.
8. Cook, S.A., Wise, W.C., Knapp, D.R., Halushka, P.V. *Sensitization of essential fatty acid-deficient rats to endotoxin by arachidonate pretreatment: Role of thromboxane A_2.* Circ Shock 1981; 8: 69.
9. Demling, R.H., Wong, C., Fow, R., Hechtman, H., Huval, W. *Relationship of increased lung serotonin levels to endotoxin-induced pulmonary hypertension in sheep. Effect of a serotonin antagonist.* Am Rev Resp Dis 1985; 132: 1257.
10. Doebber, T.W., Wu, M.S., Robbins, J.C., Choy, B.M., Chang, M.N., Shen, T.Y. *Platelet-activating factor (PAF) involvement in PAF-receptor antagonist kadsurenone.* Biochem Biophys Res Commun 1985; 29: 799.
11. Halonen, M., Palmer, J.D., Lohman, C., McManus, L.M., Pinckard, R.N. *Respiratory and circulatory impairments induced by acetyl glyceryl ether phosporylcholine, a mediator of IgE anaphylaxis in the rabbit.* Am Rev Resp Dis 1980; 122: 915.
12. Inarrea, P., Gomez-Gambronero, J., Pascual, J., Ponte, M.C., Hernando, L., Sanchez-Crespo, M. *Synthesis of PAF-acether and blood volume changes in gram-negative sepsis.* Immunopharmacol 1985; 9: 45.
13. McManus, L.M., Hanahan, D.J., Demopoulos, C.A., Pinckard, R.N. *Pathobiology of the intravenous infusion of acetyl glyceryl ether phosphorylcholine (AGEPC), a synthetic platelet-activating factor (PAF) in the rabbit.* J Immunol 1980; 124: 2919.
14. Majarad, M., Hamasaki, Y., Said, S.I. *Platelet-activating factor increases pulmonary microvascular permeability and induces pulmonary oedema: A preliminary report.* Clin Resp Physiol 1983; 19: 253.
15. Morrisson, D.C., Ulevitch, R.J. *The effect of bacterial endotoxins on host mediation systems.* Amer J Pathol 1978; 93: 527.
16. Sanchez-Crespo, M., Fernandez-Gallardo, S., Nieto, M.L., Baranes, J., Braquet, P. *Inhibition of the vascular actions of immunoglobulin G aggregates by BN 52021, a highly specific antagonist of PAF-acether.* Immunopharmacol 1985; 10: 69.
17. Spink, W.W., Davis, R.B., Potter, R., Chartrano, S. *The initial stage of canine endotoxin shock as an expression of anaphylactic shock: Studies on complement titers and plasma histamine concentrations.* J Clin Invest 1964; 43: 696.
18. Terashita, Z., Imura, Y., Nishikama, K., Sumida, S. *Is platelet-activating factor (PAF) a mediator of endotoxin shock?* Eur J Pharmacol 1985; 109: 257.
19. Vargaftig, B.B., Lefort, J., Chignard, M., and Benveniste, J. *Platelet-activating factor induces a platelet-dependent bronchoconstriction unrelated to the formation of prostaglandin derivatives.* Eur J Pharmacol 1980; 65: 185.
20. Worthep, G.S., Goins, A.J., Mitchel, B.C., Larsen, G.L., Reeves, J.R., Henson, P.M. *Platelet-activating-factor causes neotrophil accumulation and oedema in rabbit lungs.* Chest 1983; 83: 135.

*Ginkgolides - Chemistry, Biology, Pharmacology
and Clinical Perspectives.* P. Braquet (Ed.)
Copyright © 1988, J.R. Prous Science Publishers, S.A.

THE EFFECTS OF BN 52021 ON PAF-INDUCED HYPOTENSION OR ENDOTOXIN-INDUCED HYPOTENSION IN THE CONSCIOUS RAT

J. Raymond Fletcher, Anthony Gerald DiSimone and Mark Earnest

Department of Surgery, Vanderbilt University School of Medicine, Nashville, TN, USA

INTRODUCTION

The identification of platelet-activating factor (PAF) by Benveniste in 1974 (3) has generated scientific interest in its possible role as a mediator in a wide variety of pathophysiological states. PAF is a potent phospholipid released from the cell membrane following injury. Hypotension (6), increased pulmonary artery pressure (13), increased vascular permeability (11), white blood cell and platelet activation (5, 19) are only some of the effects PAF elicits. These pathophysiological activities of PAF are similar to those which occur in endotoxemia and endotoxin shock in animals and humans (4). The recent development of specific PAF antagonists will help elucidate PAF's role in disease states.

The present study was specifically designed to: 1) determine in a conscious rat model the dose response effect of PAF on the systemic blood pressure; 2) evaluate the effects of BN 52021 on the blood pressure effects of PAF; 3) utilize endotoxemia in the rat as a model for hypotension; and 4) determine the effects of BN 52021, if any, on the blood pressure responses induced by endotoxemia in the rat.

Address all correspondence to: Prof. F. Raymond Fletcher, M.D., Ph. D., St. Thomas Hospital, 4220 Harding Road, P.O. Box 380, Nashville, TN 37202, USA.

MATERIALS AND METHODS

Animal Preparation

Male Sprague-Dawley rats (250-300 g) were obtained from Charles River Laboratories and stabilized from 2-4 days prior to experimentation. They were maintained in a 12 hour light-dark sequence and allowed water and antibiotic free rat chow *ad libitum*. On the day of the experiment, animals were placed in individual cages. Each animal was lightly anesthetized with halothane/oxygen mixture, and had an anterior neck incision followed by insertion of catheters (PE5O) into the left carotid artery and left jugular vein. Catheters were flushed with heparinized saline. Catheters were tunnelled to the dorsal neck of the rat and secured. The arterial catheter was connected to a Gould Brush physiograph via a PE23 transducer for arterial pressure monitoring. The jugular vein catheter was utilized for injections of saline or pharmacological agents. Rats were allowed to recover from the effects of anesthesia for one hour before baseline parameters were measured. At the completion of the experiments animals were sacrificed.

Pharmacological Agents and Pharmaceuticals

E. coli endotoxin (055:B5, Difco Laboratories, St. Louis, MO, USA, lyophilized) was solubilized in non pyrogenic sterile saline (0.9% w/v) and prepared fresh as a 10 mg/ml solution. The dose of endotoxin utilized, 20 mg/kg, was determined to be an LD_{100} dose for the rats. Platelet-activating factor (IHB, France) was freshly prepared in a 0.5% (w/v) albumin saline solution with a final concentration of 1 mg/ml. BN 52021 (IHB, Les Plessis Robinson, France), was dissolved in 100% dimethylsulfoxide, 70 mg/ml.

Experimental Design

PAF RESPONSE CURVE   Doses of PAF were randomized for the animals (different number of animals for each dose reported). The range of PAF was 8-800 ng/kg. The dose of PAF was injected via the jugular vein after obtaining baseline systolic and diastolic pressures. Arterial pressures were monitored continuously until the arterial pressure returned to the baseline value, then the subsequent dose was injected. In separate groups, two doses of PAF, 40 and 200 ng/kg, were utilized to determine the efficacy of different doses and variable time of administration of BN 52021. The groups were as follows: PAF alone; BN 52021, 300 μg/kg given 60 minutes before PAF; BN 52021, 5 mg/kg administered 60 minutes before PAF; BN 52021, 5 mg/kg, injected 30 minutes prior to PAF; and finally BN 52021 1 mg/kg given 1 minute before PAF. In a separate control study, DMSO alone and

0.5% albumin in saline (n = 5) demonstrated no significant effects on the systemic arterial pressures. Arterial pressures were measured in the BN 52021 treated groups in a similar manner to the PAF alone group. The data were recorded for each dose and identified as systolic and diastolic pressures. The change in mmHg of the systolic and diastolic measurements from their respective baseline measurements was determined for each dose; a mean ± SE in mmHg were determined to provide the dose response curve. Statistical evaluation was performed utilizing the paired Student's t test. A p value of 0.05 or less was considered significant.

E. coli *Endotoxemia*

Twenty rats were randomized to four groups: saline alone (no endotoxin); endotoxin (20 mg/kg) alone (saline treatment); BN 52021, 25 mg/kg, 30 minutes before endotoxin; BN 52021, 300 μg/kg, 60 minutes before endotoxin. Systolic, diastolic and mean arterial pressures were recorded at baseline, 5, 30, 60, and 120 minutes. Statistical calculations utilized the Student's t test. A p value of 0.05 or less was considered significant.

RESULTS

The effects of PAF on systolic and diastolic pressure changes in mmHg are presented in Figure 1. The mean peak effect of the most potent concentrations, 80-250 ng/kg, was 1.7 ± 0.2 minutes from the time of injec-

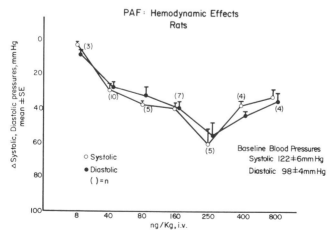

Figure 1   Dose-response of PAF and systolic and diastolic blood pressure changes in the conscious male rate. See text for details.

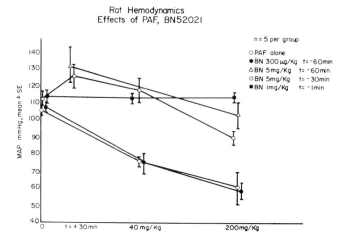

Figure 2 The effects of BN 52021, a PAF receptor antagonist, on the blood pressure changes induced by PAF. See text for details.

tion. The length of recovery time varied directly with the concentration of the PAF dose. Heart rates were variable.

The ability of the specific PAF receptor antagonist, BN 52021 to inhibit PAF-induced hypotension is illustrated in Figure 2. In separate experiments, DMSO and 0.5% albumin saline had minimal effects on mean arterial pressure (MAP) in rats (data not shown). Three observations are worthy of note. When BN 52021 is administered 30 or 60 minutes before the experiments, there is a modest, but not significant rise in the MAP. The effects of PAF on the MAP are similar in the presence of the low dose BN 52021, 300 μg/kg, to those which are observed with PAF alone. In addition, the most potent inhibitor of PAF-induced hypotension appears to be 1 mg/kg BN 52021 when administered 1 minute before PAF. The responses to PAF alone (40,200 ng/kg) are significantly greater (p < 0.01) than the responses to PAF with BN 52021 pretreatment.

Mean arterial pressure responses during endotoxemia and endotoxemia with BN 52021, a specific PAF-acether receptor antagonist, are demonstrated in Figure 3. There were no significant differences in baseline MAP amongst the groups. The endotoxin alone group clearly demonstrated the fall in MAP that occurs in this model. The values at 60 and 120 minutes are significantly different from the baseline; however, treatment with BN 52021 did not significantly improve the MAP until 2 hours following endotoxemia. The low dose of BN 52021, 300 μg/kg, had no significant effect on the decrease in MAP compared to the control values.

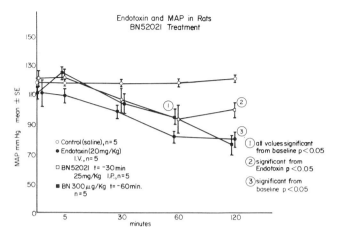

Figure 3 The effects of BN 52021, a PAF receptor antagonist on the hemodynamic events in rat endotoxemia. See text for details.

DISCUSSION

The major findings in this study are: 1) the conscious rat is exquisitely sensitive to the effects of PAF; 2) BN 52021, a specific PAF receptor antagonist, clearly and significantly attenuates the hypotension induced by PAF; 3) BN 52021 does not inhibit the early hypotensive effects of endotoxin, but does improve the later hypotension.

Dose response relationships of PAF and hypotension in rats have been reported by others (2, 6, 10, 12, 14, 16). Handley *et al.*, Baranes *et al.* (2) and Caillard *et al.* (6) performed studies in anesthetized rats. Our studies were performed in conscious rats. A number of other reports have utilized a variety of individual doses to demonstrate the hypotensive actions of PAF; however, their data do not provide an insight as to where the dose utilized fits on the dose response curve. Handley (12) and Baranes (2) began their dose response curves at 100 ng/kg and 250 ng/kg, respectively, whereas Caillard *et al.* (6) initiated their study with 60 ng/kg. All previous studies indicate a consistent decrease in the blood pressure response with increasing concentrations of PAF. In contrast, our data illustrate significant reductions in arterial pressures over the range of 40-250 ng/kg. The greater concentrations, 400 and 800 ng/kg, show a decrease in systolic pressures; however, this decrease is less than that which occurs with the 250 ng/kg concentration. One important difference in other studies and the present one is the use of anesthesia. Another difference is the random doses utilized in animals in the present study. This point is unclear in some of the other reported studies. The concern about tachyphylaxis could be raised about the present study; however, we have been unable to demonstrate this phenomenon with repeated doses in the same animal. It would appear that the dose response curves reported in this study suggest the conscious rat is sensitive to the effects of PAF and that there may be a maximal hypotensive effect elicited when compared to anesthetized animals.

That specific PAF inhibitors eliminate the hypotensive effects of PAF injections have been reported by others (1, 7, 9, 10, 12, 16-18). A variety of concentrations and times have been utilized to demonstrate their efficacy. The present study utilizing BN 52021 is essentially in agreement with the results of Baranes et al. (2) albeit their animals were anesthetized. The present data indicate that BN 52021 is effective when administered 30 to 60 minutes before the PAF challenge as well as when a smaller concentration is given 1 minute before challenge in conscious animals. The effectiveness of BN 52021 when given 1 hour prior to PAF suggests that its duration of action may be longer than 1 hour.

The use of PAF antagonists in the treatment of endotoxemia (10, 12, 15, 16) implies that PAF participates in the pathophysiology of endotoxemia. Adnot demonstrated an inhibiton of the early hypotension by administering BN 52021 15 minutes before endotoxin (1). Toth (16) utilized awake endotoxemic rats and demonstrated attenuation of the early hemodynamic events with CV3988, a PAF antagonist, given 5 minutes before the endotoxin challenge. Toyofuku (18) demonstrated effectiveness in attenuating hypotension with a PAF antagonist in sheep endotoxemia. Terashita (15) improved survival with CV3988 in endotoxemic rats, whereas Etienne (9) improved survival with BN 52021 given orally or parenterally before endotoxin. The above studies indicate that PAF antagonists attenuate the early hemodynamic events and improve the survival in different animal models of endotoxemia. It remains unclear from the reported studies what the lethality of the models were and what effects anesthesia may have had on the events in endotoxemia. The present study purposely selected an LD_{100} dose of endotoxin in order to observe the early hemodynamic events in the conscious rat. Toth et al. (16) utilized a similar model; however, the fall in MAP was significantly greater and occurred earlier than in our study. In addition, their study and the present one demonstrated effective inhibition of exogenously administered PAF with a PAF antagonist. BN 52021 significantly attenuated the endotoxin-induced hypotension only at the 2 hour observation point in the present study. This observation suggests that in rat endotoxemia the earlier hemodynamic changes may be unrelated to the effects of PAF. The difference in the induction of early MAP changes in Toth's study and the present one may be dose related. Toth utilized a 40 mg/kg concentration of endotoxin compared to 20 mg/kg in the present study.

The most unexpected finding in this study was the fact that conscious rats are very sensitive to the hypotensive effects of exogenous PAF. The present data are in contrast to other published works that show a consistent decline in blood pressure with increasing doses of PAF. The reasons for the differences between studies is unclear.

The present study supports the data of others who suggest PAF may be a mediator in endotoxemia in a number of different animal species. The PAF antagonist utilized in this study, BN 52021, inhibited the blood pressure effects of exogenous PAF and attenuated the late hypotension that occurs in endotoxemia in conscious rats. Additional, more detailed studies, must be done in other models designed to simulate sepsis in order to better define the relative importance of PAF as a mediator in these disease states.

References

1. Adnot, S., Lefort, J., Braquet, P., Vargaftig, B.B. *Interference of the PAF-acether antagonist BN 52021 with endotoxin-induced hypotension in the guinea-pig.* Prostaglandins 1985; 32: 791-802.

2. Baranes, J., Hellegouarch, A., Le Hegarat, M., Viossat, I., Auguet, P.E., Chabrier, F., Braquet, P. *The effects of PAF-acether on the cardiovascular system and their inhibition by a new highly specific PAF-acether receptor antagonist BN 52021.* Pharmacol Res Commun 1986; 18: 717-737.

3. Benveniste, J. *Platelet-activating factor, a new mediator of anaphylaxis and immune complex deposition from rabbit and human basophils.* Nature 1974; 249: 531-532.

4. Bone, R.C., Fisher, C.J., Clemmer, T.P., Slotman, G.J., Metz, C., Balk, R.A. *A controlled clinical trial of high dose methylprednisolone in the treatment of severe sepsis and septic shock.* New Engl J Med 1987; 317: 653-658.

5. Bessin, P., Bonnet, J., Apffel, D., Soulard, C., Desgroux, L., Pelas, I., Benveniste, J. *Acute circulatory collapse caused by platelet-activating factor in dogs.* Eur J Pharmacol 1983; 86: 403-413.

6. Caillard, C.G., Mondot, S., Zundel, J.L., Julou, L. *Hypotensive activity of PAF-acether in rats.* Agent and Actions 1982; 2: 725-730.

7. Doebber, T.W., Wu, M.S., Robbins, J.C., Choy, B.M., Chang, M.N., Shen, T.Y. *Platelet-activating factor (PAF) involvement in endotoxin induced hypotension in rats. Studies with PAF-receptor antagonist kad-surenone.* Biochem Biophys Res Commun 1985; 127: 799-808.

8. Duncan, S.G., Demeter, R.J., Toth, P.D. *The effects of a platelet-activating factor antagonist on endotoxin and hemmorhagic shock in dogs* (abstract). Crit Care Med 1987; 14: 413.

9. Etienne, A., Hecquet, F., Touvay, C.; Clostre, F., Braquet, P. *The relative role of PAF-acether and icosanoids in septic shock.* Pharmacol Res Commun 1986; 18: 71-79.

10. Etienne, A., Hecquet, F., Soulard, C., Spinnewyn, B., Clostre, F., Braquet, P. *In vivo inhibition of plasma protein leakage and Salmonella enteritidis-induced mortality in the rat by a specific PAF-acether antagonist: BN 52021.* Agents and Actions 1985; 17: 368-370.

11. Hamasaki, Y., Mojaiad, M., Saga, T., Tai, H., Said, S. *Platelet-activating factor raises airway and vascular pressures and induces edema in lungs perfused with platelet free solution.* Am Rev Resp Dis 1984; 126: 742-746.

12. Handley, D.A., Van Valen, R.G., Melden, M.K., Flury, S., Lee, M.L., Saunders, R.N. *Inhibition and reversal of endotoxin-aggregated IgG-and PAF-induced hypotension in the rat by SRI 63-072, a PAF-receptor antagonist.* Immunopharmacology 1986; 12: 11-16.

13. Halonen, M., Palmer, J.D., Lohman, I.C., McManus, L.M., Pinckard, R.N. *Respiratory and circulatory impairments induced by acetyl glyceryl ether phosporylcholine, a mediator of IgE anaphylaxis in the rabbit.* Am Rev Respir Dis 1980; 122: 915-924.

14. McMurtry, I.F., Morris, K.G. *Platelet-activating factor causes pulmonary vasodilation in the rat.* Am Rev Resp Dis 1986; 134: 757-762.

15. Terashita, Z., Imura, Y., Nishikawa, K., Sumida, S. *Is platelet-activating factor (PAF) a mediator of endotoxin shock?* J Pharmacol 1985; 109: 257-261.

16. Toth, P.D., Mikulaschek, A.W. *Effects of a platelet-activating factor antagonist, CV-3988, on different shock models in the rat.* Circulatory Shock 1986; 20: 193-203.

17. Wallace, J.L., Whittle, B.J.R. *Prevention of endotoxin-induced gastrointestinal damage by CV-3988, an antagonist of platelet-activating factor.* Eur J Pharmacol 1986; 124: 209-210.

18. Toyofuku, T., Kubo, K., Kobayashi, T. *Effects of ONO-6240, a platelet-activating factor antagonist, on endotoxin shock in unanesthetized sheep.* Prostaglandins 1986; 31: 271-281.

19. Worthen, G.S., Goins, A.G., Mitchel, B.C., Larsen, G.L., Reeves, J.R., Henson, P.M. *Platelet-activating-factor causes neutrophil accumulation and oedema in rabbit lungs.* Chest 1983; 83: 13S-15S.

Ginkgolides - Chemistry, Biology, Pharmacology
and Clinical Perspectives. P. Braquet (Ed.)
Copyright © 1988, J.R. Prous Science Publishers, S.A.

INTERFERENCE OF GINKGOLIDES ON NORMAL AND PATHOLOGICAL PLASMA PROTEASE ACTIVITIES IN THE RAT

Annie Etienne, Christine Guilmard, Florence Thonier and Françoise Hecquet

Institut Henri Beaufour, 72, avenue des Tropiques, F-91952 Les Ulis Cédéx, France

INTRODUCTION

Endotoxemia and gram negative sepsis remain clinically important problems since despite adapted antibiotic therapy and a great diversity of adjuvant treatments, mortality rate is still high in these diseases (28). Endotoxic shock is characterized by systemic hypotension, pulmonary hypertension, endothelial dysfunction (stretched pore phenomenon), stimulation of different plasma systems, *e.g.*, kallikrein, fibrinolysis, clotting, and circulating cells (erythrocyte sludge, stimulation of leukocyte subsets and platelets) (34).

Research in recent years has implicated many vasoactive mediators including histamine, kinins, serotonin, activated complement fragments and various metabolites of arachidonic acid in causing or maintaining the shock process (7, 11, 12, 19). Nevertheless, it is still unclear whether mediators' actions can explain all the hemodynamic, metabolic and vascular permeability changes observed after endotoxemia. This gap between endotoxin-induced alterations and specific mediators' actions may be attributable to the fact that a key mediator has not yet been considered but also that synergistic actions and/or a cascade of several mediators are involved in endotoxemia and septic shock.

Recently, the analogies between endotoxic shock and the effects of a systemic injection of platelet-activating factor (PAF, PAF-acether, AGEPC: 1-O alkyl-2 (R)-acetyl-3 phosphorylcholine) in dog (5), guinea-pig (2) or

---

Address all correspondence to: Dr. A. Etienne, Dept. of General Pharmacology, 72, avenue des Tropiques, Institut Henri Beaufour, F-91952 Les Ulis Cédex, France

rat (8) have been described, even though the platelets of the latter species do not respond to PAF (22).

The involvement of PAF in endotoxic shock was further evidenced by the use of specific PAF antagonists such as CV 3988 (36), kadsurenone (14), SRI 63441 (10), ONO 6240 (37), FR 900452 (31) and BN 52021 (16) which prevent or correct endotoxic induced disturbances in rats or guinea-pigs and by the *in vivo* appearance of PAF during experimental sepsis and endotoxic shock (10, 23). Furthermore, a pronounced proteolytic activity in plasma was observed during septic shock in man (9, 26) or in endotoxin-induced shock in animal models (32). A significant improvement is obtained in animals intoxicated by various endotoxins and treated by protease inhibitors such as aprotinin (21), S 2441 (4) or a purified urinary trypsin inhibitor (30).

For all these reasons, we searched for a possible link between PAF secretion and the increase of plasma protease activity in rats intoxicated with *Salmonella enteritidis* endotoxin. In this study the *in vitro* and *in vivo* effects of the PAF antagonists BN 52021 and BN 52063 (6) on rat trypsin-like activity were investigated in comparison with aprotinin, ε-aminocaproic acid and the soybean trypsin inhibitor.

MATERIALS AND METHODS

Salmonella enteritidis lipopolysaccharide B was supplied by Difco Lab. and solubilized in NaCl 0.9%. PAF C16 was purchased from Bachem and a stock solution (0.5 mg/ml) in 0.5% BSA saline solution was diluted in NaCl 0.9% just before use.

In Vitro *Trypsin-Like Activity Measurement*

The inhibitory action of drugs was investigated either on the basal trypsin-like activity of rat plasma, or on trypsin purified from bovine pancreas. The enzyme activity was determined using the chromogenic substrate benzoylarginine *p*-nitroanilide as described by Erlanger B.F. *et al* (1961). The hydrolysis of the substrate at 25°C in Tris buffer pH = 7.8 was quantified after 15 minutes incubation by measuring the absorbance change at 405 nm. Drugs were added simultaneously to the substrate. Each assay was performed in duplicate.

Ex Vivo *Plasma Protease Activity Measurement*

Blood of male Wistar rats (180-200 g body weight) was withdrawn from the retro-orbital sinus using heparin as anticoagulant. Trypsin-like activity was determined on the plasma as described above. In these conditions appreciable activity was measurable in rat plasma, whereas no or very low activity (0-2 U/l) was found in normal human plasma. Drugs were given orally to the animals 1 hour before blood sampling or twice a day for 3 days, the last administration taking place 18 hours before the test. Eight animals per group were used; statistical analysis of the results were performed with Student's t test.

Effects of drugs were also studied on pathological enzymes levels obtained either by PAF (1 μg/kg i.v) or endotoxin (12 mg/kg i.v or i.p) administration to male Wistar rats weighing 250-300 g. Blood was withdrawn at several time periods for plasma trypsin-like or cholinesterase (butyrylcholine as substrate) activity measurement.

RESULTS

Effect of Drugs on In Vitro Trypsin-Like Activity

As shown in Table 1, at doses of 22 μg to 220 μg neither BN 52021 nor BN 52063 exhibited any significant *in vitro* inhibitory effect on rat plasma trypsin-like activity.

Conversely, protamine sulfate decreased dose- dependently this activity with a 92% inhibitory effect at a dose of 25 μg and the soybean inhibitor

Table 1 *In vitro* effects of drugs on trypsin-like activity. Control activity of the rat plasma was 30.9 U/l (BAPNA as substrate)

Drug	Dose μg	Percentage inhibition of rat plasma trypsin-like activity
Protamine	5	34.3
sulfate	10	46.0
	25	91.6
	2.5	8
Aprotinin	5	11
	25	18.5
Soybean inhibitor	0.25	54.3
	22	4.7
BN 52021	244	5.7
	220	5.7
	22	7.6
BN 52063	44	10.9
	220	7.1

exerted an activity of 54% at 0.25 μg. Aprotinin was mildly effective on rat plasma trypsin-like activity.

BN 52021 was also studied against trypsin isolated from bovine pancreas and was totally inactive at 44 and 220 μg, whereas the soybean inhibitor at 0.25 μg exerted a complete inhibition.

Inhibition of Basal Plasma Protease Activity in Normal Rats

In our experimental conditions, the basal plasma trypsin-like activity of normal rat was about 25-35 U/l. A single oral administrastion of BN 52021 or BN 52063, one hour before blood sampling, strongly decreased this basal activity (Fig. 1). The effect of 8 mg/kg BN 52021 was about 35%.

Approximately the same activity was obtained with 2 g/kg ε-aminocaproic acid, whereas 10 mg/kg dexamethasone was devoid of activity. BN 52063 seems to have a more potent activity than BN 52021 since at 2 mg/kg it exerted a —45% highly significant inhibitory effect. However, the dose-dependent activity curve of BN 52063 presents a bell-shaped profile: above 2 mg/kg the activity decreased and was non-significant at 20 mg/kg.

BN 52021 was also administered twice a day for three days from 0.1 mg/kg to 8 mg/kg per unit dose, the last administration taking place 18 hours before blood sampling. With this schedule of administration, BN 52021 showed, like BN 52063 acutely, a bell shaped curve of activity. The inhibitory effect of BN 52063 was significant as early as 0.1 mg/kg with

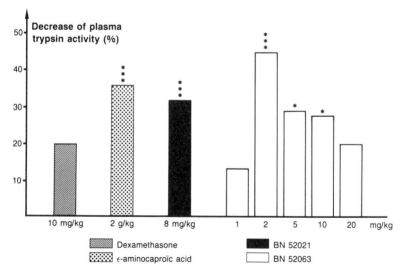

Figure 1   Inhibition of the plasma trypsin-like activity in normal rat. Drugs were given orally 1 hour before blood sampling. Statistical analysis by Student's t-test: *p<0.05; ***p<0.001; n=8.

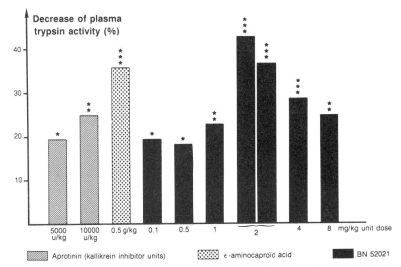

Figure 2 Inhibition of the plasma trypsin-like activity in normal rat. Drugs were given orally twice a day for three days. Statistical analysis by Student's *t*-test: *p < 0.05;; **p < 0.01; ***p < 0.001; n = 8.

a maximum effect at 2 mg/kg; at higher doses the activity was lower (Fig. 2).

After repeated administrations, 0.5 g/kg ε-aminocaproic acid showed about the same activity as 2 mg/kg BN 52021. In the same conditions, 5000 and 10,000 U/kg aprotinin was also significantly effective although administered orally.

BN 52021 was also studied acutely by subcutaneous injection (suspension in NaCl 0.9%) 30 minutes before blood sampling. The trypsin-like activity which was 38.4 ± 1.5 U/l for the control group decreased significantly to 24.4 ± 1.8 U/l (p < 0.05) for the treated animals.

Comparative Effect of I.V. Injection of PAF or Endotoxin on Plasma Trypsin-Like Activity

PAF (1 μg/kg, i.v.) induced a rapid and transient increase in plasma trypsin-like activity (Fig. 3). This parameter increased significantly at 15 minutes (+42% compared to control group; p < 0.05) and returned to basal level at about 30 minutes. In comparison with PAF, *Salmonella enteritidis* endotoxin (12 mg/kg, i.v.) induced a slower but higher and more durable increase in plasma trypsin-like activity. This increase was non-significant one hour after intoxication but became highly significant at 2 hours (+121%; p < 0.001). Plasma cholinesterase activity was not modified by PAF but it was significantly increased at 2 hours by the toxin (+38%; p < 0.01).

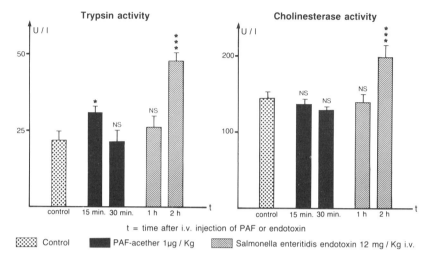

Figure 3 Comparative effects of an i.v. injection of PAF or endotoxin on plasma trypsin-like and cholinesterase activities in the rat. Statistical analysis by Student's *t*-test compared to the control group; *p < 0.05; ***p < 0.001; n = 8.

Effect of Pretreatment with BN 52063 or BN 52021 on Plasma Trypsin-Like Activity Increase Induced by Endotoxin

Oral administration of BN 52021 (8 mg/kg) or BN 52063 (10 and 20 mg/kg) just before toxin injection totally inhibited the plasma trypsin-like activity increase measured at 2 hours (Fig. 4). BN 52021 even decreased the enzyme level under that for control group (—60%; p < 0.05). Treatment with dexamethasone (10 mg/kg) did not modify the activity of the toxin.

Similarly, when the toxin was injected i.p to rats, it increased plasma trypsin-like activity which, after 2 hours, was 93% higher (p < 0.05) than that for the control group. Oral treatment of animals with 20 mg/kg BN 52063 just before the toxin injection reduced this variation which was only 28% (non-significant).

DISCUSSION

In addition to the numerous vasoactive materials released by endotoxin, a considerable increase in plasma proteolytic activity is also observed. The neutrophils have been suggested to play a central role in this phenomenon and it has been demonstrated that the release of the proteolytic enzyme elastase from the granulocytes was paralleled by the lowering of the number of circulating leucocytes observed in the early stages of the ailment (1).

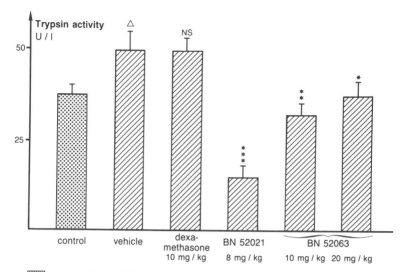

Figure 4 Effect of drugs on plasma trypsin-like activity increase induced by an i.v. injection of endotoxin. Drugs were given orally just before endotoxin injection. Statistical analysis by Student's *t*-test: p<0.05 for endotoxin-injected animals compared to control group; *p<0.05; **p<0.01; ***p<0.001 treated animals compared to vehicle group for endotoxin-injected animals.

Nevertheless, the reduced perfusion of the pancreas and other splanchnic viscera observed during septic shock and endotoxemia induce tissue hypoxia and ischemia, which are potent stimuli for lysosomal disruption and activation of zymogenic enzymes (*e.g.*, conversion of trypsinogen to trypsin) (25).

Furthermore, due to the poor substrate specificity of these proteinases, they can degrade and inactivate various plasma proteins but also by unspecific proteolysis, destroy proteinase inhibitors which represent 60% of the plasma proteins other than albumin and immunoglobins, further enhancing the plasma proteolytic activity (24).

Enhancement of plasma proteolytic activity during endotoxemia occurred steadily during the subsequent stages of the disease, increasing gradually the number of components and systems unbalanced in this pathology: clotting, fibrinolysis, complement, kallikrein-kinin system, *etc.*

Substances which inhibit the action of these proteases (cathepsin, trypsin, kallikrein and to some extent plasmin) are aprotinin, ε-aminocaproic acid and trypsin inhibitors such as that derived from soybeans, which were shown to have a beneficial effect in shock models (20). Like endotoxin, platelet-activating factor, the new mediator which could play a key role in shock states, has been shown to induce after its i.v. infusion in the rat a rapid and dose-dependent increase in plasma of lysosomal hydrolases levels (13). But this increase is almost the same in neutrophil deficient rats suggesting that another source other than granulocytes exists.

In this respect, the question arises as to whether a link could exist between PAF and the increase of proteases in endotoxin intoxication. To answer this question we checked the activity of the specific PAF antagonists, BN 52021 and BN 52063, on rat plasma trypsin-like activity in normal and endotoxin-intoxicated animals. These PAF antagonists were shown to provide significant protection against lethality induced in the rat by *Salmonella enteritidis* toxin (17), as well as on the hypotensive effect of i.v. injection of *S. typhimurium* endotoxin in the guinea-pig (2). Our results show that the PAF-antagonists (ginkgolides) did not affect protease activity *in vitro*, whereas surprisingly, they decreased normal and pathological plasma trypsin-like levels *in vivo*.

Protease inhibitors, on the contrary, were active both *in vitro* and *in vivo*. When we compared *in vivo* effects of a systemic injection of PAF or endotoxin on plasma trypsin-like activity in rats, we showed that PAF induced a rapid and transient increase of trypsin level, whereas the effect of endotoxin was delayed but more potent and long-lasting than PAF. All these data are in agreement with results already published by other authors, studying various enzymes. N-acetyl glucosaminidase has been used as a measure of lysosomal enzymes secretion induced by i.v. injection of PAF to rats (33), the maximum increase in plasma activity of this enzyme taking place 11 minutes after PAF injection. In the same way, lysosomal labilization by *Salmonella enteritidis* toxin injection to rats has been quantified by measuring β-glucuronidase and acid phosphatase activities in plasma 4 hours after endotoxin injection (3).

All these findings lead to the assumption that PAF could be released at an early stage after endotoxin injection, triggering the release of enzymes, particularly proteases. This mechanism of action, moreover, has been observed for the release of tpA (tissue plasminogen activator) by PAF, as well as by endotoxin in animals (15).

Endotoxin might act by stimulating phospholipase A_2 (27), inducing the release of membrane phospholipids, precursors of PAF. Direct leucocytes activation and/or cell injury by the synthetized PAF could lead to lysosomal enzymes release (18) and these enzymes would result in further tissue injury observed in shock states. As phospholipase A_2 can also be activated by various proteases (35) a vicious circle is created, increasing the deleterious effects of the toxin.

A scheme representing the train of events for enzymes' activation in septic shock is proposed in Figure 5.

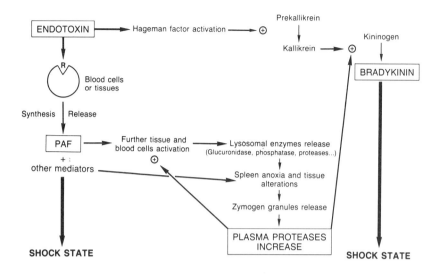

Figure 5 Mechanisms of enzymes' activation during septic shock.

In pathological states, ginkgolides may thus block the deleterious effects of PAF on various cells and tissues, which explain their beneficial activity on endotoxin-induced increase of enzymes levels. But another mechanism of action must exist to explain their inhibitory effect on normal trrypsin-like activity, otherwise we must hypothesize the existence of a basal rate of PAF in physiological conditions which could be inhibited by the ginkgolides.

On the other hand, an inhibitor of PAF has recently been isolated from rat perfused liver or isolated rat hepatocytes when a soybean trypsin inhibitor was added to the preparations, masking the detection of PAF. If this trypsin inhibitor were omitted, PAF activity could be detected. These data suggest that an enzyme sensitive to serine protease inhibition is involved in the formation and/or release of this endogenous inhibitor (29). The ginkgolides could, thus, interfere with the synthesis and release of this endogenous PAF inhibitor.

The inter-relations between PAF and proteases become more evident in septic shock and even if we cannot at present state positively that the antiprotease activity of ginkgolides is only a consequence of their PAF-antagonistic effect, these two components must account for the protective action observed with these drugs in animal models involving endotoxin. Further studies will be required on other PAF-antagonists to fully assess this assumption.

Nevertheless, as increases in plasma proteolytic activity are a feature of both clinical and experimental endotoxemia, inhibition of abnormally activated enzymes would thus provide a useful therapeutic tool, and ginkgolides BN 52021 or BN 52063, drugs with multicomponent action, seem to be of interest for the therapy of septic shock and endotoxemia.

References

1. Aasen, A.O. et al. *Alterations of plasmin activity, plasminogen levels and activity of antiplasmins during endotoxin shock in dogs.* Haemostasis 1978; 7: 164-169.

2. Adnot, S. et al. *Interference of BN 52021, a PAF-acether antagonist with endotoxin-induced hypotension in guinea-pig.* Pharmacol Res Commun 1986; 18 (Suppl): 197-200.

3. Anderegg, K. et al. *Effects of a pyridine derivative thromboxane synthetase inhibitor and its inactive isomer in endotoxic shock in the rat.* Br J Pharmacol 1983; 78: 725-732.

4. Balis, J.V. et al. *Efficacy of S-2441, a synthetic oligopeptide in a rat model of gram-negative bacteremia.* Circ Shock 1985; 15: 5-14.

5. Bessin, P. et al. *Pathophysiology of shock states caused by PAF-acether in dogs and rats.* In: Platelet-Activating-Factor and Structurally Released Ether Lipids. J. Benveniste, B. Arnoux (Eds.). Elsevier Science Publishers: Amsterdam 1983; 343-356.

6. Braquet, P. et al. *BN 52021 and related compounds: A new series of highly specific PAF-acether receptor antagonists isolated from Ginkgo biloba.* Blood and Vessels 1985; 16: 1-5.

7. Brigham, K.L. et al. *Septicemia and lung injury.* Clin Lab Med 1983; 3: 719-744.

8. Caillard, C.G. et al. *Hypotensive activity of PAF-acether in rats.* Agents and Actions 1982; 12 (5): 725-730.

9. Caridis, D.T. et al. *Endotoxemia in man.* Lancet 1972; i: 1381-1386.

10. Chang, S.W. et al. *Platelet-activating-factor mediates hemodynamic changes and lung injury in endotoxin-treated rats.* J Clin Invest 1987; 79: 1498-1509.

11. Cook, J.A. et al. *Elevated thromboxane levels in the rat during endotoxic shock.* J Clin Invest 1980; 65: 227-230.

12. Demling, R.H. et al. *Pulmonary injury and prostaglandin production during endotoxemia in conscious sheep.* Am J Physiol 1981; 240: H 348-H 353.

13. Dobber, T.W. et al. *Platelet-activating-factor intravenous infusion in rats stimulates vascular lysosomal hydrolase secretion independent of blood neutrophils.* Bioch Biophys Res Commun 1984; 125 (3): 980-987.

14. Doebber, T.W. et al *Platelet-activating-factor (PAF) involvement in endotoxin-induced hypotension in rats: Studies with PAF-receptor antagonist kadsurenone.* Biochem Biophys Res Commun 1985; 127 (3): 799-808.

15. Emeis, J.J., Kluft, C. *PAF-acether-induced release of tissue-type plasminogen activator from vessel walls.* Blood 1985; 66 (1): 86-91.

16. Etienne, A. et al. *In vivo inhibition of plasma protein leakage and Salmonella enteritidis-induced mortality in the rat by a specific PAF-acether antagonist: BN 52021.* Agents and Actions 1985; 17 (3/4): 368-370.

17. Etienne, A. et al. *Inhibition of rat endotoxin-induced lethality by BN 52021 and BN 52063, compounds with PAF-acether antagonistic effect and protease-inhibitory activity.* Int J Tiss Reac 1987; 9 (1): 19-26.

18. Godin, D.V. et al. *Plasma lysosomal enzymes in experimental and clinical endotoxemia.* Clin Invest Med 1983; 6 (4): 319-325.

19. Hagmann, W. et al. *Production of peptide leukotrienes in endotoxin shock.* FEBS Lett 1985; 180: 309-313.

20. Herlihy, B.L., Lefer, A.M. *Selective inhibition of pancreatic proteases and prevention of toxic factors in shock.* Circ Shock 1974; 1: 51-60.

21. Hughes, B., Parrat, J.R. *The effects of the protease inhibitor, aprotinin, on the course of shock induced by endotoxin in cats.* Br J Pharmacol 1985; 86: 399-403.

22. Inarrea, P. et al. *Characteristics of the bindings of platelet-activating-factor to platelets of different animal species.* Eur J Pharmacol 1984; 105: 309-315.

23. Inarrea, P. et al. *Synthesis of PAF-acether and blood volume changes in gram-negative sepsis.* Immunopharmacology 1985; 9: 45-52.

24. Jochum, M. et al. *Pathobiochemistry of sepsis: Role of proteinases, proteinase inhibitors and oxidizing agents.* Behring Inst Mitt 1986;

79: 121-130.

25. Lefer, A.M. *The pathophysiologic role of myocardial depressant factor as a mediator of circulatory shock.* Klin-Wochenshr 1982; 60: 713-716.

26. Lefer, A.M. *Lysosomes in the pathogenesis of circulatory shock.* In: Handbook of Shock and Trauma, Vol. 1. Altura, B.M. et al. (Eds.). 1983; 291-308.

27. Liu, M.S. et al. *Change in membrane lipid fluidity induced by phospholipase A_2 activation: A mechanism of endotoxic shock.* Life Sci 1983; 33: 1995-2002.

28. Lundberg, D. et al. *Intensive care treatment in septic shock.* Scand J Infect Dis 1983; Suppl 41: 187-191.

29. Miwa, M. et al. *Occurrence of an endogenous inhibitor of platelet-activating-factor in rat liver.* J Biol Chem 1987; 262 (2): 527-530.

30. Ohnishi, M. et al. *Protective effects of urinary trypsin inhibitor in experimental shock.* Japan J Pharmacol 1985; 39: 137-144.

31. Okamoto, M. et al. *Platelet-activating-factor (PAF) involvement in endotoxin-induced thrombocytopenia in rabbits: Studies with FR-900452, a specific inhibitor of PAF.* Thrombosis Research 1986; 42: 661-671.

32. Sardesai, V.M., Rosenberg, J.C. *Proteolysis and bradykinin turnover in endotoxin shock.* J Trauma 1974; 14: 945-949.

33. Shen, T.Y. et al. *Characterization of a platelet-activating-factor receptor antagonist isolated from haifenteng Piper futokadsura: Specific inhibition of in vitro and in vivo platelet-activating-factor-induced effects.* Proc Natl Acad Sci 1985; 82 (3): 672-676.

34. Shumer, W. *Pathophysiology and treatment of septic shock.* Am J Emerg Med 1984; 2 (1): 74-77.

35. Slapke, J. et al. *Protease inhibitor prevents bronchoconstriction in man.* Eur J Resp Dis 1986; 68: 29-34.

36. Terashita, Z. et al. *Is platelet-activating-factor (PAF) a mediator of endotoxin shock?* Eur J Pharmacol 1985; 109: 257-261.

37. Toyofuku, T. et al. *Effects of ONO-6240, a platelet-activating-factor antagonist on endotoxin shock in unanesthetized sheep.* Prostaglandins 1986; 31 (2): 271-231.

Ginkgolides - Chemistry, Biology, Pharmacology and Clinical Perspectives. P. Braquet (Ed.)
Copyright © 1988, J.R. Prous Science Publishers, S.A.

ROLE OF PLATELET-ACTIVATING FACTOR (PAF-ACETHER) IN THE BRONCHOPULMONARY ALTERATIONS INDUCED BY ENDOTOXIN: EFFECT ON BETA-ADRENOCEPTORS

Caroline Touvay, Béatrice Vilain, Christian Carré, Jean Michel Mencia-Huerta and Pierre Braquet

Institut Henri Beaufour, 72, avenue des Tropiques, F-91952 Les Ulis Cédéx, France

INTRODUCTION

Endotoxemia and sepsis are major pathologic manifestations associated with high morbidity that are refractory to classical treatments. The clinical symptoms are characterized by profound hemodynamic alterations such as systemic hypotension associated with a decrease in peripheral vascular resistance, cardiac failure, pulmonary hypertension, bronchoconstriction and lung edema (8). In addition, alterations in the numbers and functions of circulating platelets and leukocytes have been demonstrated, probably contributing to the circulatory disorders. The increase in vascular permeability is a determinant for the prognosis and evolution of endotoxemia since it leads to hypovolemia that enhances cardiac and pulmonary failure. The pathophysiology of endotoxemia and gram negative sepsis is unclear.

As pointed out by Morrisson and Ulevitch (13), septic shock probably relates more to the host defense to the organisms than from the aggression

Address all correspondence to: Dr. Caroline Touvay, Dept. of Immunology, Institut Henri Beaufour, 72 avenue des Tropiques, F-91952 Les Ulis Cédéx, France.

by the bacteria itself. Thus, the pathogenesis of endotoxemia probably involves various humoral and cellular components leading to the final release of inflammatory mediators such as histamine, kinins, serotonin, arachidonic acid metabolites and complement-derived peptides. Indeed, implication of these mediators in the early phase of endotoxic shock has been demonstrated (11). More recently, several lines of evidence have also indicated a role for platelet-activating factor (PAF-acether) in the *in vivo* alterations induced by endotoxin from gram-negative organisms (1, 7, 10, 16). PAF-acether infusion to rats mimics most of the symptoms observed during endotoxemia, *i.e.*, systemic hypotension, cardiac failure, pulmonary hypertension, thrombocytopenia and neutropenia, as well as severe increase in vascular permeability leading to hypovolemia (5). The role for this mediator in endotoxic shock was further strengthened by experiments showing that PAF-acether antagonists interfere with the early phase of the shock (1, 4, 7, 8, 16). We recently showed that BN 52021, a selective and specific PAF-acether antagonist (4, 5), markedly inhibited the endotoxin-induced hypotension in the guinea-pig (1) and plasma leakage and mortality in the rat (7). Thus, we further investigated the effects of endotoxin on the pulmonary response to various agonists and tempted to determine the possible involvement of PAF-acether in these alterations.

MATERIALS AND METHODS

Reagents

Histamine dihydrochloride, bovine serum albumin (BSA), isoproterenol and lipopolysaccharide (from *E. coli* 055: B5) were from Sigma (St. Louis, MO), PAF-acether (1-O-hexadecyl-2-O-acetyl-*sn*-glycero-3-phosphocholine) was from Bachem (Budendorf, Switzerland). 3-(1-1-Dimethylethyl) hexahydro-1,4,7-b-trihydroxy-8-9H-1,7 (epoxy methano)-1H,6H-cyclopenta-(c) furo (2,3b) furo (3',2':3,4) cyclopenta (1,2-d' furan-5,9,12 (4H)-trione (BN 52021) was provided by IHB (Le Plessis-Robinson, France). Stock solutions of histamine in saline and PAF-acether in 0.25% BSA (w/v) were divided in aliquots and kept frozen at —20°C. Immediately before each experiment, the various substances were diluted in the buffer of the experiment up to the appropriate concentrations.

Preparation and Assessment of the Contractile Response of Lung Parenchymal Strips from Untreated and Endotoxin-Treated Guinea-Pigs

Male Hartley guinea-pigs weighing 400-500 g were used throughout the experiments. The animals were killed by cervical dislocation and bled by section of the abdominal aorta. The lungs and the heart were immediately removed and placed in a Kreb's solution. The lung parenchyma was cut in strips (approx. 3 x 3 x 30 mm) from the margin of each lobe and placed in a superfusion system. The strips were superfused with oxygenated Kreb's solution (5 ml/min; 37°C) under a tension of 1.5 g. After a 1 hour equilibration period, the responses to various agonists were examined in the presence or in the absence of BN 52021 (0.5-30 μg/ml). Tissues were stimulated first with a fixed dose of histamine (27 nmol; 5 μg). Then, histamine, leukotriene D_4 (LTD$_4$) or PAF-acether were injected as a bolus in the medium in a cumulative manner for the first two agonists and as a single injection for the latter one. Responses were recorded isometrically with UC$_2$ Gould transducers coupled to a polygraph (8000s Gould). The contractions were either expressed as mg of tension or as percent of the contractile response of the lung parenchymal strips induced by 5 μg histamine.

In some experiments, lung parenchymal strips were obtained from endotoxin-treated guinea-pigs. Briefly, the endotoxin was suspended in isotonic saline and sonicated to ensure a homogeneous suspension. The guinea-pigs were lightly anesthetized with ether prior to endotoxin (6 mg/kg) or saline, which was injected into the penis vein. Two hours after endotoxin injection, the animals were killed. As described above, the lung strips were prepared and the contractile responses to histamine, LTD$_4$ and PAF-acether were studied.

Relaxation Induced by Isoproterenol in Lung Parenchymal Strips from Endotoxin-Treated Guinea-Pigs

Endotoxin (1.5 mg/kg i.v.) was injected 18 hours before sacrifice. Lung parenchymal strips were prepared and placed in an organ bath containing Tyrode's buffer. The tissues were submitted to 3 g tension and allowed to equilibrate for 1 hour in a Tyrode's solution at 37°C gassed with 5% CO_2 and 95% O_2. Then, the relaxation induced by isoproterenol (30 nM) was monitored using isometric transducers.

The effect of treatment of guinea-pigs with the PAF-acether antagonist, BN 52021, on the endotoxin-induced alterations was investigated. BN 52021 was given orally either at 20 mg/kg, 1 hour before endotoxin and 20 mg/kg, 1 hour before sacrifice or at 50 mg/kg, 6 hours and 1 hour before endotoxin.

Relaxation Induced by Isoproterenol after Incubation of Guinea-Pig Lung Parenchymal Strips with PAF-Acether

Lung parenchymal strips from untreated animals were prepared as described above and placed in an organ bath containing 16 ml of oxygenated Tyrode's solution at 37°C under a tension of 1 g. Prior to determining the relaxant activity of isoproterenol, the preparations were equilibrated for 1 hour. Lung parenchymal strips were stimulated with 50 μM histamine and, when the contraction reached a plateau, cumulative concentrations of isoproterenol were added to the bath and the responses were recorded isometrically.

To examine the effect of PAF-acether (0.1 μM, 1 μM and 10 μM), guinea-pig lung parenchymal strips were preincubated with PAF-acether for 20 minutes before the relaxation by isoproterenol of the histamine-induced contraction was assessed. In these experiments, control tissues from the same guinea-pig incubated with BSA were studied in parallel to determine the responses of each organ to the various agonists.

Statistical Analysis

Results are expressed as means ± SEM of the indicated number of experiments. Statistical significance was assessed using the Fisher F test.

RESULTS AND DISCUSSION

Effect of BN 52021 on the Contraction of Lung Parenchymal Strips Induced by PAF-Acether

Since PAF-acether induced tachyphylaxis, dose-response curves were constructed from the data obtained with different strips. A dose-dependent contractile response to PAF-acether was observed (Fig. 1). As previously

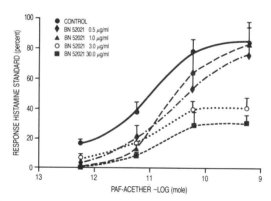

Figure 1 Dose-dependent effect of BN 52021 on the PAF-acether-induced contraction of guinea-pig lung parenchymal strips. The strips were prepared as described in the Materials and Methods section and the contractions induced by defined doses of PAF-acether, in the presence or in the absence of BN 52021, were assessed. Since PAF-acether induced tachyphylaxis the data presented in this figure were obtained from individual strips. The results are expressed as percent of the contraction induced by 5 μg histamine.

published (17), the response developed slowly and reached a maximum by 3 minutes. BN 52021, at 0.5 μg/ml and 1 μg/ml, shifted the dose response curve by almost 1 log, although the response to high concentrations of the agonist (300 ng) was unaffected. In the presence of doses of BN 52021 higher than 3 μg/ml, PAF-acether was a weak and partial agonist since the maximal response to this autacoid represented less than 40% of the maximal response induced by histamine.

These results confirmed the potent antagonistic effect of BN 52021 on the lung tissue. Indeed, this compound has been previously shown to inhibit the *in vivo* pulmonary alterations induced by PAF-acether and antigen in the guinea-pig (5). In the present experiments, the weak and partial agonist activity of PAF-acether observed in the presence of BN 52021 at concentrations above 3 μg could be due to a non-receptor-mediated action of the autacoid.

Effect of an In Vivo *Treatment of Guinea-Pigs with Endotoxin on the Contraction of Lung Parenchymal Strips Induced by Various Agonists*

Histamine induced a dose-dependent contraction of lung parenchymal strips from untreated animals (Fig. 2). The contractions of lung parenchymal strips from endotoxin-treated animals induced by low quantities of histamine (up to 1 μg) were not modified as compared to control. In contrast, the con-

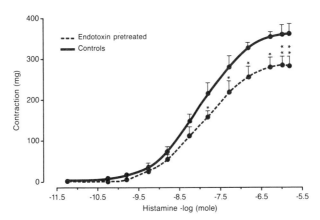

Figure 2   Dose-dependent contractions induced by histamine of lung parenchymal strips obtained from endotoxin (6 mg/kg)-treated or control guinea-pigs. The endotoxin was administered 2 hours prior to the experiments. The strips were prepared as described in the Materials and Methods section and the contractions induced by defined doses of histamine were assessed. The results are expressed as mg of tension developed upon addition of the agonist. * and ** indicated significativity at p<0.05 and p<0.01 levels, respectively.

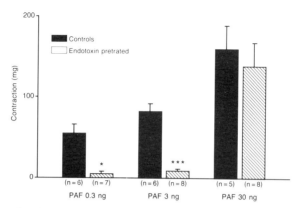

Figure 3 Dose-dependent contractions induced by PAF-acether of lung parenchymal strips obtained from endotoxin (6 mg/kg)-treated or control guinea-pigs. The endotoxin was administered 2 hours prior to the experiments. The strips were prepared as described in the Materials and Methods section and the contractions induced by defined doses of PAF-acether were assessed. The results are expressed as mg of tension developed upon addition of the agonist. * and *** indicated significativity at $p < 0.05$ and $p < 0.001$ levels, respectively.

tractions induced by amounts of histamine higher than 3 μg were significantly reduced in lung parenchymal strips from endotoxin-treated guinea-pigs with respect to those from control animals. The dose-response curves to LTD_4 obtained with lung parenchymal strips from endotoxin-treated and control animals were similar (data not shown). PAF-acether (0.3, 3, 30 and 300 ng) induced dose-dependent contractions of lung parenchymal strips from control animals (Fig. 3). When the strips were obtained from endotoxin-treated guinea-pigs, the contractions due to 0.3 ng and 3 ng PAF-acether were markedly reduced. Indeed, as compared to the controls, 91.3% ($p < 0.01$) and 76.3% ($p < 0.001$) inhibition of the contractions induced by 0.3 and 3 ng were observed, respectively. However, the contractions induced by 30 ng of PAF-acether were not significantly altered by pretreatment of the animals with endotoxin.

Endotoxin-treatment of the animals minimally affected the *ex vivo* contractions of lung parenchymal strips induced by histamine and LTD_4. In contrast, the contractions induced by PAF-acether at concentrations below 30 ng were dramatically reduced. These results demonstrated a specific desensitization of lung parenchymal strips to PAF-acether and indicated that the generation of the autacoid probably occurred upon *in vivo* endotoxin treatment. The present data are in agreement with those of several authors (6, 7, 9, 16), who demonstrated that PAF-acether plays a critical role in the pathophysiological alterations induced by endotoxin in various animal models.

Effect of Endotoxin on the Relaxation of Lung Parenchymal Strips Induced by Isoproterenol

Since part of the effects of endotoxin appeared to be mediated by PAF-acether, the possible implications of this autacoid in the regulation of beta-receptor was investigated. Thus, the relaxation by isoproterenol of lung parenchymal strips from endotoxin-treated and control animals was analyzed. As presented in Figure 4, lung parenchymal strips from endotoxin-treated guinea-pigs exhibited a significant decrease in the responsiveness to isoproterenol (13.3 ± 4.95 mg of relaxation; $n = 6$; as opposed to 110.0 ± 22.5 mg in controls). However, pretreatment of guinea-pigs with BN 52021 before endotoxin injection increased in a dose-dependent fashion the relaxing effect of isoproterenol observed on strips from endotoxin-treated guinea-pigs. *In vivo* treatment of normal animals with BN 52021 (2 x 20 mg/kg or 2 x 50 mg/kg, p.o.) prior to the sacrifice did not modify significantly the relaxation induced by isoproterenol (Table 1).

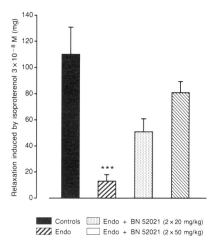

Figure 4 Isoproterenol-induced relaxation of lung parenchymal strips from untreated, endotoxin-treated or endotoxin- and BN 52021-treated guinea-pig. *** $p < 0.001$.

Down regulation of beta-receptors following endotoxin administration is well established. Indeed, bacterial injection was shown to induce a reduction in beta-receptor number in guinea-pig lung (18) and dog liver plasma membranes (12). In addition, hearts from endotoxin-treated rats are characterized by a decreased responsiveness to isoproterenol (15). The present data suggest that this phenomenon could be related to the generation of PAF-acether. Indeed, treatment of the animals with the specific PAF-

Table 1 Effect of *in vivo* treatment with BN 52021 on the relaxation of lung parenchymal strips from guinea-pigs

	n	Relaxation induced by isoproterenol
Control	6	110.0 ± 22.5 mg
BN 52021 2 x 20 mg/kg	6	87.5 ± 16.7 mg
BN 52021 2 x 50 mg/kg	5	107.0 ± 18.6 mg

acether antagonist, BN 52021, restores the capability of lung parenchymal strips to relax upon addition of isoproterenol, strengthening the role of the phospholipid mediator in endotoxemia. This phenomenon could also be explained by an alteration in receptor/adenylate cyclase coupling (14), which can be prevented by BN 52021.

Effect of In Vitro Incubation of Lung Parenchymal Strips with PAF-Acether on the Relaxation Induced by Isoproterenol

The results presented above indicate that PAF-acether was implicated in the decreased response of lung parenchymal strips from endotoxin-treated animals to beta-agonists. In the next series of experiments the effect of *in vitro* incubation of lung parenchymal strips with PAF-acether on the relaxation by isoproterenol of the contraction induced by histamine was investigated. Three PAF-acether concentrations were chosen for preincubation of the lung tissue (0.1 μM, 1 μM and 10 μM). For these experiments, a 50 μM concentration of histamine was chosen since it produces a durable contraction of guinea-pig lung strips. The amplitude of the contraction was 304.0 ± 15.5 mg (n = 24) in control strips (incubated with BSA) and represented 70 to 80% of the maximal histamine contraction. A difference in the capability of histamine to contract parenchymal strips treated with PAF-acether was observed as compared to controls (Fig. 5). Upon incubation with 1 μM and 10 μM PAF-acether, the response to histamine was reduced by 25.2% (p < 0.05) and 37.4% (p < 0.01), respectively.

The relaxation induced by isoproterenol of lung parenchymal strips from the same animal incubated either with PAF-acether or with vehicle alone were compared. The response to isoproterenol in tissues incubated with different concentrations of PAF-acether were not significantly different from those in control preparation (Table 2).

PAF-acether has been previously shown to down regulate beta-receptors in human (2) but not in guinea-pig (3) lungs, our present results being in

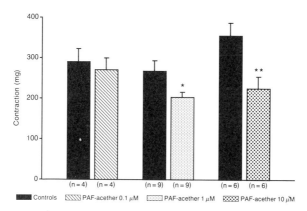

Figure 5 Histamine-induced contraction of lung parenchymal strips preincubated or not for 20 minutes at 37°C with defined concentrations of PAF-acether. The results are expressed as mg of contraction developed upon addition of 5 μg histamine. * and ** indicated significativity at $p < 0.05$ and $p < 0.01$ levels, respectively.

Table 2   Effect of incubation with PAF-acether on the pD_2 values (-log EC_{50}) of isoproterenol on guinea-pig lung parenchymal strips

	n	pD_2 Values (-log EC_{50})
Control	4	6.15 ± 0.34
PAF-acether 0.1 μM	4	6.41 ± 0.05
Control	10	6.53 ± 0.17
PAF-acether 1 μM	10	6.49 ± 0.18
Control	9	6.52 ± 0.24
PAF-acether 10 μM	9	6.62 ± 0.12

agreement with the latter work. They also indicate that the loss of sensitivity to isoproterenol of lungs from endotoxin-treated guinea-pigs could not be related to a direct effect of PAF-acether. The mechanism(s) leading to the hyporesponsiveness to isoproterenol after endotoxin treatment could be mediated by the generation of secondary mediators induced by PAF-acether. Further studies are also required to assess the mode of action of the mediator.

PAF-acether is implicated in various pathological alterations of lung functions including bronchoconstriction, hypotension, and bronchial hyperreactivity to histamine and methacholine (5). Given its broad spectrum of activities, PAF-acether appears to play a critical role in various inflammatory and allergic reactions. Its direct or indirect effects on the beta-adrenoceptors presently demonstrated suggest that its generation during bacterial infection may further contribute to the pathology of asthma.

References

1. Adnot, S. et al. *Interference of the PAF-acether antagonist, BN 52021 with endotoxin-induced hypotension in the guinea-pig.* Prostaglandins 1986; 82: 791-802.
2. Agrawal, D.K. and Townley, R.G. *Effect of platelet-activating factor on β-adrenoceptors in human lung.* Biochem Biophys Res Commun 1987; 143: 1-6.
3. Barnes, P.J. et al. *The effect of platelet-activating factor on pulmonary β-adrenoceptors.* Br J Pharmacol 1987; 90: 709-715.
4. Braquet, P.G. *Treatment and prevention of PAF-acether induced sickness by a new series of highly specific inhibitors.* G.B. Patent 1984; 8: 418-424.
5. Braquet, P. et al. *Perspectives in platelet-activating factor research.* Pharmacol Rev 1987; 39: 97-145.
6. Doebber, T.W. et al. *Platelet-activating factor (PAF) involvement in endotoxin-induced hypotension in rats. Studies with PAF-receptor antagonist kadsurenone.* Biochem Biophys Res Commun 1985; 127: 799-808.
7. Etienne, A. et al. *In vivo inhibition of plasma protein leakage and Salmonella enteritidis-induced mortality in the rat by a specific PAF-acether antagonist: BN 52021.* Agents and Actions 1985; 17: 368-370.
8. Gilbert, R.P. *Mechanisms of the hemodynamic effects of endotoxin.* Physiol Rev 1960; 40: 245-279.
9. Handley, D.A. et al. *Biological properties of the antagonist SRI 63-441 in the PAF and endotoxin models of hypotension in the rat and dog.* Immunopharmacology 1987; 13: 125-132.
10. Inarrea, P. et al. *Synthesis of PAF-acether and blood volume changes in gram-negative sepsis.* Immunopharmacology 1985; 9: 45-52.
11. Jacobs, E.R. *Overview of mediators affecting pulmonary and systemic vascular changes in endotoxemia.* In: Handbook of Endotoxin, Vol. 2. Pathophysiology of Endotoxin. J.B. Hinshaw (Ed.). Elsevier 1985; 1-15.
12. Liu, M.S. et al. *Mechanism of endotoxin-induced reduction in the number of beta-adrenergic receptors in dog livers: Role of phospholipase A.* Biochem Med 1983; 30: 295-304.
13. Morrisson, D.C. et al. *The effects of bacterial endotoxins on host mediation system.* Am J Pathol 1978; 93: 525-618.
14. Romano, F.D. et al. *Characteristics of myocardial beta-adrenergic receptors during endotoxicosis in the rat.* Am J Physiol 1986; 251: 359-364.
15. Shepherd, R.E. et al. *Mechanism of cardiac dysfunction in hearts from endotoxin-treated rats.* Circ Shock 1986; 19: 371-384.
16. Terashita, Z. et al. *Is platelet-activating factor (PAF) a mediator of endotoxin shock?* Eur J Pharmacol 1985; 109: 257-261.
17. Touvay, C. et al. *Characterization of platelet-activating factor (PAF) induced contractions of guinea-pig lung strips by selected inhibitors of arachidonic acid metabolism and by PAF-acether antagonists.* Immunopharmacology 1986; 12: 97-104.
18. Van Oosterhout, A.J. et al. *Anterior hypothalamic lesions prevent the endotoxin-induced reduction of beta-adrenoceptor number in guinea-pig lung.* Brain Res 1984; 302: 277-280.

Ginkgolides - Chemistry, Biology, Pharmacology and Clinical Perspectives. P. Braquet (Ed.)
Copyright © 1988, J.R. Prous Science Publishers, S.A.

ORAL ADMINISTRATION OF GINKGOLIDE BN 52021 DOES NOT INFLUENCE BLOOD FIBRINOLYSIS IN NORMAL AND ENDOTOXIN TREATED RATS

Anne-Marie Dosne* and Françoise Lutcher

Laboratoire d'Immunopharmacologie Experimentale UA CNRS 579, Paris, France

ABSTRACT

The effect of oral administration of BN 52021 has been investigated on blood fibrinolysis in rats. Treatment with 1-20 mg/kg did not modify the euglobulin clot lysis time in normal rats and had little influence on the early fibrinolytic activation induced by sublethal doses of endotoxin (10 mg/kg) or the hypofibrinolytic state induced by moderate doses of endotoxin (30 µg/kg).

INTRODUCTION

It has been shown that ginkgolide BN 52021 is an antagonist of platelet-activating factor (PAF) receptor (3). This compound was able to suppress several effects induced *in vivo* by PAF, thrombosis (2), cardiovascular alterations (1) and activation of fibrinolysis, namely tissue plasminogen activator release (9). The role of PAF has been proposed in various pathological situations, among them endotoxin shock, since BN 52021 decreases endotoxin

Address all correspondence to: Dr. Anne-Marie Dosne, Laboratoire d'Immunopharmacologie Experimentale UA, CNRS 579, 15 rue de l'Ecole de Médecine, F-75270 Paris Cédex 06, France.

induced lethality (11). During endotoxemia it is known that the fibrinolytic balance is disturbed in a biphasic manner. An early hyperfibrinolysis was reported in humans (15) and also in rats receiving sublethal doses (13). This was followed by a hypofibrinolytic state due to generation of a fibrinolytic inhibitor acting at the plasminogen activator level (plasminogen activator inhibitor) (4-6,8). These findings led us to question whether PAF might mediate some of the fibrinolytic responses to endotoxin and to investigate the effects of BN 52021 on blood fibrinolysis in normal and endotoxin-treated rats.

MATERIALS AND METHODS

These experiments were performed on fasting Wistar rats (270-300 g). Ginkgolide BN 52021 (Institut Henri Beaufour) was given orally as a suspension in syrup at various doses ranging from 1 to 20 mg/kg. Normal rats were bled 2 hours later. Endotoxin, lipopolysaccharide (LPS) from S-enteritidis (Difco) was injected either as a sublethal dose (10 mg/kg) or a moderate dose (30 μg/kg). Blood was then collected after either 3 minutes or 1 hour, respectively. Pretreatment with BN 52021 was performed one hour before LPS injection. Blood was withdrawn from abdominal aorta after an injection of 50 units of heparin and mixed with 1/10 volume of sodium citrate (0.1 M). Plasma was rapidly separated and frozen.

Fibrinolytic Activity of Plasma Euglobulin

Euglobulin were precipitated by acidification of the plasma to pH 5.9 with 0.01% acetic acid and then solubilized with 0.2 M borate buffer pH 7.6. Aliquots of 250 μl were clotted with 0.1 U of thrombin in the presence of 1.2 U of protamine sulfate and clot lysis time was determined.

SDS-PAGE and Fibrinoenzymography

This method was used to separate the different compounds of the fibrinolytic system by SDS electrophoresis in polyacrylamide gel under non reducing conditions and to visualize the corresponding fibrinolytic activity on a revelator gel containing agarose-bovine fibrinogen rich in plasminogen (5). The apparent molecular weights of the lysis bands were calculated with reference to calibrated proteins.

RESULTS

In normal rats receiving one oral administration of BN 52021 (1 mg to 10 mg/kg) the blood fibrinolytic activity remained unchanged as determined 2 hours later (Table 1). The euglobulin clot lysis time was comparable to

Table 1 Euglobulin clot lysis time (min) after p.o. administration of BN 52021 in normal rats

Controls	BN 52021 (mg/kg)		
	1	5	10
56(8)	59(2)	62(4)	53(7)

Mean of 3.16 values with standard deviation.

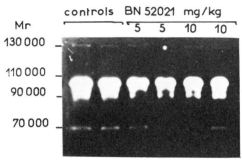

Figure 1 Fibrinoenzymographic profiles of plasma from control and BN 52021 treated rats. 4 μl of plasma diluted twice in phosphate buffered saline were submitted to SDS-PAGE in 10% acrylamide gels under non-reducing conditions. Development on fibrin-agarose plate was performed for 24 hours.

the normal values (56 min ± 8). The fibrinoenzymographic studies of plasma submitted to SDS-PAGE showed that lysis profiles were very close to those from control animals (Fig. 1). They consisted of a lysis band of Mr 70 000 corresponding to the molecular weight of tissue plasminogen activator and a large lysis area extending from Mr 90 000 to 110 000 which is considered as high molecular complexes. A very faint line of Mr 130 000 was also detected in controls and treated animals.

Rats were injected with sublethal doses of LPS in order to induce an activation of fibrinolysis which was estimated 3 minutes after LPS injection according to kinetics previously reported (13). A dose of 3 mg/kg was not sufficient to increase the fibrinolytic activity so a dose of 10 mg/kg was chosen (Table 2). Under this condition the euglobulin lysis time was shortened to 25 min ± 7. Pretreatment with BN 52021 (10 mg and 20 mg/kg) one hour before LPS had little effect on the LPS response.

Rats were also injected with a moderate dose of LPS (30 μg/kg) which has been shown to induce a deep hypofibrinolytic state (5). This resulted in a prolongation of the euglobulin clot lysis time above 240 minutes (Table 3). Pretreatment with BN 52021 (10 mg/kg) one hour before did not prevent this LPS effect.

Table 2 Euglobulin clot lysis time (min) after injection of 10 mg/kg of LPS in rats with and without pre-treatment with BN 52021 (10 and 20 mg/kg)

Controls	LPS	LPS + BN 10 mg	LPS + BN 20 mg
56(8)	25(7)	34(12)	31(6)

Blood was collected 3 minutes after LPS injection.
Mean of 5-16 values with standard deviation.

Table 3 Euglobulin clot lysis time (min) after injection of 30 μg/kg of LPS in rats pretreated with BN 25021 (10 mg/kg)

Controls	LPS	BN	LPS + BN
57(7)	>240	58(2)	>240

Blood was collected 1 hour after LPS injection.
Mean of 3-5 values with standard deviation.

DISCUSSION

The effect of ginkgolide BN 52021 has been examined on fibrinolysis in relationship to endotoxin response and a possible PAF-mediated reaction. The fact that oral administration of BN 52021 protected rats from LPS lethality (11) could suggest a role of PAF in some pathogenic mechanisms of endotoxin shock. Since both a high dose of LPS (13) and PAF injection (7) induced an increase in fibrinolytic activity, efficiency of BN 52021 to restore normal values would be an indication of PAF involvement in LPS hyperfibrinolysis. The present results did not confirm this hypothesis since shortening of the euglobulin lysis-time induced by LPS was not modified by BN 52021 pretreatment. The adrenergic stimulation following LPS injection remains a more probable mechanism for triggering this hyper-fibrinolysis (13).

It has been reported that deficient fibrinolytic activity and a high level of plasminogen activator inhibitor were associated with thrombotic disease (14). During experimental endotoxemia (4, 5, 8) and septicemia (10) a hypofibrinolytic state was found due to an increase in plasminogen activator inhibitor. This could contribute to intravascular coagulation and fatal issue.

Results of this study showed that oral treatment with BN 52021 did not prevent LPS induced hypofibrinolysis. The protective role of BN 52021 in endotoxin shock seems unrelated to fibrinolysis. BN 52021 also decreases plasma protease activity (trypsine-like) in normal and endotoxin-or PAF-treated rats (12). This had no detectable influence on the blood fibrinolytic activity.

References

1. Baranès, J. et al. *The effect of PAF-acether on the cardiovascular system and their inhibition by a new highly specific PAF-acether receptor antagonist BN 52021*. Pharmacol Res Comm 1986; 18: 717-737.

2. Bourgain, R.H. et al. *The effect of 1-0-alkyl-2-acetyl-SN-glycero-3-phosphocholine (PAF-acether) on the arterial wall.* Prostaglandins 1985; 30: 185-197.

3. Braquet, P. *The Ginkgolides: Potent platelet-activating factor antagonists isolated from Ginkgo biloba L.: Chemistry, pharmacology and clinical applications.* Drugs of the Future 1987; 12: 643-699.

4. Colucci, A.M. et al. *Generation in plasma of a fast acting inhibitor of plasminogen activator in response to endotoxin stimulation.* J Clin Invest 1985; 75: 818-824.

5. Dosne, A.M. et al. *Plasminogen activator inhibitor induced by lipopolysaccharide injection in the rat. Zymographic analysis.* Fibrinolysis 1987; 1: 45-49.

6. Dubor, F. et al. *Effect of polymyxin B and colimycin on induction of plasminogen antiactivator by lipopolysaccharide in human endothelial cell culture.* Infect Immun 1986; 52: 725-729.

7. Emeis, J.J. et al. *PAF-acether-induced release of tissue type plasminogen activator from vessel walls.* Blood, 66: 86-91.

8. Emeis, J.Y. et al. *Interleukin 1 and lipopolysaccharide induce an inhibitor of tissue type plasminogen activator in vivo and in cultured endothelial cells.* J Exp Med 1986; 163: 1260-1266.

9. Emeis, J.J. *Release of tissue type plasminogen activator from vessel walls.* 2nd World Conf on Inflammation Antirheumatics, Analgesics, Immunomodulators. Monaco, March 1986.

10. Engebretzen, L.F. et al. *Extreme plasminogen activator inhibitor and endotoxin values in patients with meningococcal disease.* Thromb Res 1986; 42: 713-716.

11. Etienne, A. et al. *In vivo inhibition of plasma protein leakage and Salmonella enteritis induced mortality in the rat by a specific PAF-acether antagonist BN 52021.* Agents and Actions 1985; 17: 368-370.

12. Etienne, A. et al. *Involvement of platelet-activating factor in the triggering of proteolysis in endotoxic shock in rats.* Workshop on Lipid Mediators in Immunology of Burn and Sepsis. Helsingor, July 1986.

13. Fracasso, J.F. et al. *Contribution of adrenalin to the fibrinolytic activity evoked by E. Coli endotoxin in the rat.* Thromb Haemost 1983; 50: 557-559.

14. Juhan-Vague, I. et al. *Deficient t-PA release and elevated PA inhibitor levels in patients with spontaneous or recurrent deep venous thrombosis.* Thromb Haemost 1987; 57: 67-72.

15. Von Kaulla, K. *Intravenous protein free pyrogen. A powerful fibrinolytic agent in man.* Circ Res 1958; 17: 187-198.

Ginkgolides - Chemistry, Biology, Pharmacology and Clinical Perspectives. P. Braquet (Ed.)
Copyright © 1988, J.R. Prous Science Publishers, S.A.

EVIDENCE FOR PLATELET-ACTIVATING FACTOR (PAF) INVOLVEMENT IN IMMUNE-COMPLEX HYPERSENSITIVITY REACTIONS PROVIDED BY BN 52021

Sonia Jancar[1], Pierre Sirois[2] and Pierre Braquet[3]

[1]Department of Immunology, Institute of Biomedical Sciences, University of Sao Paulo, Sao Paulo, Brasil; [2]Departments of Pediatrics and Pharmacology, Faculty of Medicine, University of Sherbrooke, Canada; [3]Institut Henri Beaufour, Le Plessis Robinson, France

INTRODUCTION

Immune-complex hypersensitivity reactions are caused by antibody reaction with antigen in excess to form insoluble complexes which deposit within the vascular endothelium of small vessels. These deposits of immune-complexes cause local inflammation with increase in vascular permeability, edema and subsequent infiltration of polymorphonuclear leukocytes (PMN). Products of activated leukocytes are then believed to induce further damage in the sites of immune-complex deposition. The lesions produced in different organs are responsible for the pathogenesis of serum sickness, lupus erythematosus, and rheumatoid arthritis, among other diseases.

A classical experimental model for this type of hypersensitivity is the 'Arthus reaction'' (1), which is a dermal inflammatory response induced in

Address all correspondence to: Dr. Sonia Jancar, Departamento de Inmunología, Instituto de Ciencias Biomédicas, USP, Av. Prof. Lineu Prestes, 2415, 05508, Sao Paulo, S.P., Brasil.

animals with high titers of precipitating antibody following antigen injection in the skin. The initial phase of an Arthus reaction is characterized by an increase in vascular permeability (16), transient thrombocytopenia (48), congestion of blood vessels and diapedesis of platelets (39) and accumulation of platelets at the site of the reaction (36). Massive emigration of neutrophils and eosinophils occurs reaching a maximum at 6-8 hours. This is followed by mononuclear leukocytes emigration and at 24 hours a mixed mononuclear and polymorphonuclear leukocyte infiltrate is observed. In case the reaction is more severe, thrombosis with resulting ischemic necrosis develops.

Regarding the mechanism of immune-complex induced hypersensitivity, it has been demonstrated that deposition of immune-complexes depends on local increase in vascular permeability (35). It is also known that immune-complexes activate the complement system with consequent generation of vasoactive and chemotactic peptides, which can account for the increase in vascular permeability and accumulation of PMN leukocytes. Phagocytosis of the immune-complexes by PMN leukocytes, as well as activation of these cell types by several factors, is believed to be a pivotal event in the development of tissue injury (15, 16). It is generally accepted that activation of the complement system mediates the recruitment of PMN leukocytes into inflammatory sites, through formation of C_5 fragments. Nevertheless, we have recently reported some data that suggest that the C_5 component of the complement system is not essential for PMN accumulation *in vivo*. We have comparatively analyzed the temporal profile of PMN accumulation in response to several inflammatory stimuli, including an immune-complex reaction, in coisogenic strains of mice, where one of them is genetically deficient of the C_5 complement component. It was found that the PMN influx is similar in both strains (42). Furthermore, we have observed that induction of a passive reverse Arthus reaction in the skin of C_5-sufficient and C_5-deficient mice leads to morphologically similar lesions (41).

If an initial phase of increased vascular permeability is necessary for immune-complex deposition and further development of the tissue lesions, then permeability factors other than the C_5 fragments should be responsible for this event, as well as for the accumulation of PMN leukocytes. Platelet-activating factor (PAF) can be a potential candidate, since it induces vascular permeability increase (2, 7-9, 11, 30, 38, 45, 49, 53), edema (9, 17, 23, 52) and PMN infiltration (29). It was also suggested that PAF is involved in immune-complex deposition *in vivo* (4-6, 14, 28, 36) and that it participates in glomerular immune-complex deposition in experimental serum sickness (14, 44) and in systemic lupus erythematosus (13).

Furthermore, immune-complexes can induce generation of PAF. Preformed immune-complexes stimulate PAF production *in vitro* from isolated neutrophils (12, 43) and macrophages (38). Infusion of pre-formed immune-complexes induces the release of PAF in the blood and liver (13, 31). PAF was also detected in the blood of rabbits following induction of an acute serum sickness (14) and in the joint fluid from immune-complex induced arthritis (21).

Although these data point to a link between PAF and the reactions to immune-complexes, they do not provide evidence of a mediator role for PAF in the pathological manifestations of these reactions *in vivo*. In this respect, the first evidence was given by Hellewell and Williams in 1986 (25), who showed that a putative PAF-receptor antagonist (L-652731) inhibited the edema formation in a reverse passive Arthus reaction in the rabbit. This compound was also shown to inhibit hypotension, extravasation and vascular lysosomal hydrolase release induced by infusion of immune-complexes into rats (19). The vascular actions of IgG aggregates were also inhibited by a PAF antagonist, the ginkgolide BN 52021 (47).

A mediator role for PAF in the pathogenesis of hypersensitivity reactions mediated by immune-complexes can be better investigated now that specific antagonists of PAF receptors are becoming available.

In the present study, the pathologic manifestations of immune-complex hypersensitivity were analyzed in the pancreas, peritoneal cavity and skin of rats. Use of the compound BN 52021, a potent and specific receptor antagonist (10), provided evidence for PAF involvement in immune-complex mediated reactions.

IMMUNE-COMPLEX HYPERSENSITIVITY REACTION IN THE PANCREAS

In the present study, guinea pig antibodies were employed to passively sensitize rats because these antibodies are not cytophilic for rat mast cells. It was previously shown that they do not degranulate rat peritoneal mast cells, do not induce release of histamine and 5-hydroxytryptamine from mast cells and that they are unable to induce a passive cutaneous anaphylaxis in this animal species (34). Nevertheless, they are able to reproduce a classical Arthus reaction in the rat skin. We have observed that rats passively sensitized with guinea pig hyperimmune antiserum develop an acute pancreatitis after challenge with the specific antigen (egg albumin). Hyperimmune antiserum was used in these studies because it contains high titers of antibodies of the IgG class.

A progressive and sequential series of histological changes were observed in the pancreas by light microscopy. Ten minutes after antigen challenge, there was an intense interstitial edema, congested small vessels, leukocyte margination and PMN leukocyte infiltration (Fig. 1) which progressed up

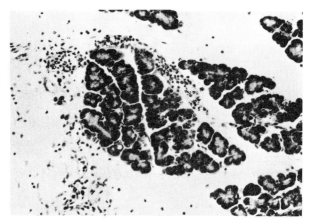

Figure 1 Photomicrograph of pancreas sections, 10 minutes after the injection of 3 mg of egg albumin into rats passively sensitized with 1.4 mg of guinea pig antibodies to egg albumin. Intense edema and infiltration of PMN leukocytes are observed, H.E. stain, x 200.

to 8 hours. From this time thereafter the edema was less prominent and a mixed PMN and mononuclear leukocytes infiltration was seen. At 24 and 48 hours the infiltrate was predominantly mononuclear and the fluid almost totally reabsorbed. There was no sign of acinar destruction or necrosis at any time examined. Slight variation in the temporal profile of PMN infiltration was seen, apparently dependent on the intensity of the reaction. This process represents an acute interstitial pancreatitis. In control animals, receiving either antiserum or antigen alone, no detectable changes could be observed in the pancreas. These pathological changes are likely to be mediated by immune-complex formation since deposits of immune-complexes around the blood vessels of the pancreas were detected by immunofluorescence technique using fluorescein conjugated sheep antibodies against guinea pig IgG2 immunoglobulins. The serum amylase levels were determined at various times after induction of the reaction. They remained unchanged and close to control levels at all times examined (10, 30, 90 minutes and 4, 24, 48 hours). These results are an indication that no functional changes occurred in the exocrine pancreas.

The immune-complex reaction was followed by a transient thrombocytopenia. The number of circulating platelets dropped to about 50% of those present in the circulation before the antigen injection and returned to normal levels 1 hour afterwards (Fig. 2). Since rat platelets were described to be unresponsive to PAF, the thrombocytopenia observed in our studies can be interpreted in two ways: a) that rat platelets are able

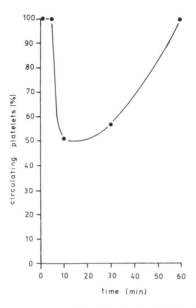

Figure 2 Temporal profile of the number of circulating platelets after injection of 3 mg of egg albumin into rats passively sensitized with 1.4 mg of guinea pig antibodies to egg albumin. Numbers are referred to as % of platelets in relation to the number before the challenge. Each point represents the mean from 6 rats.

to respond to endogenous PAF or, b) that this phenomenon is the consequence of the interaction of platelets with the immune-complexes through the Fc region of the immunoglobulin molecule (33) or through the C_3b fragment of the complement system (26, 27).

In support of the first assumption are the results from Sánchez Crespo *et al.* (44), who demonstrated that PAF obtained from rat macrophages activates rat platelets.

The vascular permeability changes in the pancreas were quantified using the Evans blue dye extravasation method. It was found that maximal extravasation occurs 10 minutes after challenge and that after 30 and 60 minutes vascular permeability is still increased. At 4 hours after challenge the permeability of pancreatic blood vessels returns to normal levels. This phenomenon is not restricted to the rat. We have observed that an acute pancreatitis develops in mice and guinea pigs passively sensitized with hyperimmune antiserum after challenge with the specific antigen.

To investigate the effect of BN 52021 on the increase in vascular permeability in the pancreas, rats were passively sensitized with guinea pig antiserum, and 30 minutes before the antigen injection, they were injected

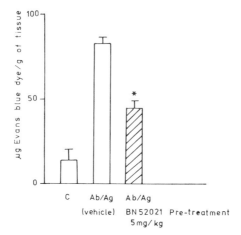

Figure 3 Measurement of Evan's blue dye extravasation in the pancreas. Rats were sensitized with 0.6 mg of guinea pig antibodies to egg albumin and challenged with 2 mg of egg albumin. Evan's blue dye (20 mg/kg) was given i.v. just before antigen injection. The animals were sacrified 30 minutes after antigen challenge, the pancreas removed and the dye extracted with formamide. The amount of dye was determined spectrophotometrically at 620 nm in the pancreas from normal rats (C); from sensitized rats, 30 minutes after challenge (Ab/Ag) and from sensitized rats, treated with 5 mg/kg of BN 52021, 30 minutes before the antigen challenge (Ab/Ag/BN 52021). Data represent the mean ± SEM.(#)* p<0.001, Student's *t* test for the difference between two means. (#) of 6-13 experiments.

i.v. with 5 mg/kg of BN 52021. It was found that the compound BN 52021 significantly inhibited the increase in vascular permeability induced by the immune-conmplex reaction in pancreas (Fig. 3).

These results provide an indirect evidence that PAF is released in immune-complex hypersensitivity reaction and is, at least in part, responsible for pancreatic edema. To further investigate this assumption, PAF was injected into the peritoneal cavity of rats and the vascular permeability changes in pancreas were measured. It was found that PAF induced extravasation of plasma proteins in the pancreas and that BN 52021 significantly inhibited extravasation (Fig. 4).

Thus, generation of PAF induced by immune-complex deposition in the pancreatic blood vessels may be an important factor in the development of acute pancreatitis.

This study is, to our knowledge, the first demonstration that immune-complex hypersensitivity reactions induce pancreatitis. Thal (50) produced an acute pancreatitis by injecting antigen into the pancreatic ducts of sensitized rabbits. Nevertheless, this method has the disadvantage of injecting the antigen intraductally, a procedure which, *per se*, induces inflammation and which does not represent the situation that is supposed to occur in

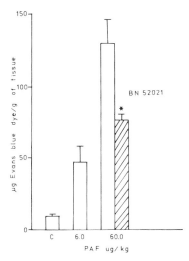

Figure 4 Evan's blue dye extravasation in the pancreas following intraperitoneal injection of PAF. Measurements of the dye were performed as described in Figure 3. BN 52021, 5 mg/kg, was injected intravenously, 10 minutes before injection of PAF (60.0 μg/kg). Data represent the mean ± SEM(#). * $p < 0.005$. Student's *t* test for the difference between two means. (#) of 3-8 experiments.

immune-complex diseases. It is also interesting to speculate whether or not pancreatic inflammation can be an additional complication in immune-complex diseases in man. A clinical study showed that in a group of 22 patients with acute pancreatitis, 40% presented immune complexes in the serum (22). There are also some case reports of acute pancreatitis associated with systemic lupus erythematosus, which is the prototype of immune-complex disease in man (3, 40).

Based on these data, we believe that it is important to consider that pancreatic inflammation may contribute to the pathologic manifestations of immune-complex diseases. Furthermore, there is growing evidence suggesting that PAF is released in immune-complex mediated reactions and that it may play an important role in the development of these reactions.

IMMUNE-COMPLEX HYPERSENSITIVITY REACTION IN THE PERITONEAL CAVITY

Induction of an Arthus reaction in the peritoneal cavity affords a better opportunity to analyze cellular events as well as the release of mediators in the inflammatory exudates. Guinea pig hyperimmune antiserum was injected into the peritoneal cavity of rats and after 2 hours the specific antigen was injected by the same route. A latent period between antibody and antigen administration was allowed in these studies since we had previously shown that under these conditions SRS activity is detected in the peritoneal exudates (34).

Following the passive Arthus reaction in the peritoneal cavity, marked hyperemia oi the omentum, mesentery and epididimum and hemorrhagic lesions in the small intestine were noted and increased in intensity during the first 4 hours. Ultrastructural examination of the omentum as early as 1 minute after antigen challenge revealed congestion of small vessels and platelet emigration at the venule site, with some platelets out of the vessels (Fig. 5).

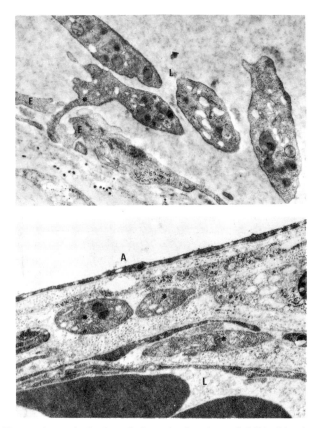

Figure 5 Electron micrographs showing a platelet passing through an endothelial cell junction and platelets in the extravascular space (*). These figures were obtained from preparations of omentum of rats sensitized with 1.7 mg of guinea pig antibodies to egg albumin, 1 minute after i.p. injection of 3.0 mg of egg albumin x 28.500.

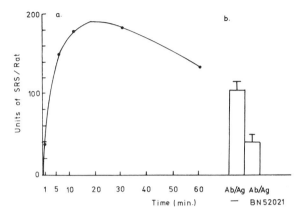

Figure 6 a) Kinetics of SRS release in the peritoneal cavity of rats passively sensitized with 1.4 mg of guinea pig antibodies to egg albumin at different times after challenge with 3 mg of egg albumin. Each point represents the mean from 12 animals. SRS activity was assayed in the guinea pig ileum according to Brocklehurst as described in (34). b) Effect of BN 52021 on the release of SRS in the peritoneal cavity of rats sensitized with 0.6 mg of guinea pig antibodies, 30 minutes after challenge with 2 mg of egg albumin. Data represent the mean ± SEM(#). One unit of SRS was considered as the contraction of guinea pig ileum equivalent to 1 ng of histamine. (#) of 6-13 experiments.

Shortly after antigen challenge, a drop in the number of peritoneal cells was noted but after 30 minutes the number of PMN leukocytes increased and reached a maximum at 6 hours; at this period, PMNs represented about 50% of the peritoneal cell population.

Induction of the Arthus reaction was also followed by a marked increase in vascular permeability and release of SRS-like substances into the peritoneal cavity. It can be seen in Figure 6a that SRS is released very early and reaches a maximum 20 minutes after challenge. Pretreatment of the rats with 5 mg/kg of BN 52021 significantly reduced the amount of SRS released 30 minutes after challenge (Fig. 6b). Similarly, the increase in vascular permeability in the peritoneal cavity following antigen challenge was reduced by 46% in the group pre-treated with 5 mg/kg of BN 52021 (Table 1).

We believe that inhibition of these two parameters of the Arthus reaction by a PAF antagonist provides an indication that PAF is released in this reaction. It can be also speculated that immune-complex formation leads to generation of PAF, which in turn induces SRS release. In fact, injection of PAF into the peritoneal cavity of rats was shown to induce the appearance of SRS in the peritoneal fluid (47). Similarly, in guinea pig lungs, PAF induces release of prostaglandins and leukotrienes B_4 and D_4 (24). These results provide further evidence of interactions between PAF and eicosanoids.

Table 1   Effect of BN 52021 on the increase in vascular permeability induced by an Arthus reaction in the rat peritoneal cavity

Groups[a]	Pretreatment	μg Evans blue dye/ml[b]
Control	—	2.85 ± 0.36
Ab/Ag	—	99.09 ± 5.64
Ab/Ag	BN 52021[c]	55.59 ± 6.78*

[a]Rats were passively sensitized with 0.6 mg of guinea pig antibodies to egg albumin and challenged with 2 mg of antigen (Ab/Ag).
[b]Evans blue dye (20 mg/kg) was given i.v. just before antigen injection. Data represent the amount of dye extravasated during a period of 30 minutes.
[c]BN 52021 in a dose of 5 mg/kg was injected i.v. into a group of sensitized rats 30 minutes before antigen challenge.
Data represent mean ± SEM of 6-13 experiments.
*p<0.001, Student's t test for the difference between two means.

Studies are in progress to analyze the type of leukotrienes responsible for SRS activity generated in this model, as well as the effect of BN 52021 on leukotriene release.

ARTHUS REACTION IN THE SKIN

A reverse passive Arthus reaction was induced in the skin of rats. Guinea pig hyperimmune serum was injected at various dilutions intradermally on the shaved back of rats and the antigen was injected intravenously. After 24 hours the animals were killed, the skin deflected and examined for the presence of hemorrhagic lesions characteristic of Arthus reaction. Measurements of the diameter of the skin lesions permitted a semi-quantitative evaluation of the lesions. One group of rats received an i.v. injection of endotoxin (100 μg of LPS from *Salmonella thyphosa*) before induction of the reaction. It was found that endotoxin pretreatment completely inhibited the development of the Arthus reaction. It is well known that systemically administered endotoxin inhibits PMN diapedesis. This phenomenon was first described by Delaunay and Pages (18). Thus, one possible interpretation of the results presented is that PMN leukocytes are essential for the development of Arthus reaction, since the lesions do not develop when PMN leukocytes are "paralyzed" by endotoxin. Nevertheless, it has been recently shown that bacterial endotoxins release PAF (20, 32), which allows a different interpretation. Release of PAF by endotoxin pretreatment can render the animals unresponsive to the PAF supposedly released by the immune-complex reaction. In support of this interpretation is the observation that lung parenchyma strips from guinea pigs treated with endotoxin are unable to respond to PAF stimulation *in vitro* (51). Studies are in progress to determine whether BN 52021 affects the development of tissue lesions of the Arthus reaction. Preliminary results were obtained in a group of rats treated with BN 52021 (5 mg/kg i.v.), before the induction of the passive Arthus reaction in rat skin. Although more experiments are needed to confirm these results, it appears that the skin lesions were less intense in the group treated with the PAF antagonist.

CONCLUSIONS

The results presented show that immune-complex hypersensitivity reaction is followed by an acute pancreatitis. Deposition of immune-complexes within the pancreatic blood vessels induced a marked increase in vascular permeability and an early influx of PMN leukocytes. The inflammatory reaction in pancreas does not seem to induce functional changes, at least as far as amylase secretion is concerned. Morphological changes in the acini were not observed. The acute intestitial pancreatitis that developed in response to immune-complex formation appeared to be reversible. The reaction was followed by a transient thrombocytopenia and circulating platelets returned to normal levels 1 hour afterwards. The mediator responsible for this rapid and severe increase in vascular permeability appears to be PAF, since a specific PAF-receptor antagonist significantly inhibited the extravasation. Furthermore, injection of PAF into the peritoneal cavity of rats induced a dose-dependent increase in vascular permeability in the pancreas; the change was also inhibited by BN 52021. Thus, immune-complex deposition within pancreatic blood vessels seems to be the triggering event for PAF release and subsequent inflammatory changes in this organ.

It is also interesting to speculate on the clinical significance of these findings. Pancreatic inflammation may be an important factor in the pathologic manifestations of immune-complex diseases. Episodes of acute pancreatitis may be an additional complication in this group of diseases.

Induction of a passive Arthus reaction in the peritoneal cavity was also followed by an increase in vascular permeability. Congestion of small vessels and diapedesis of platelets in the omentum was detected as early as 1 minute after antigen challenge. The initial drop in the number of peritoneal cells was followed by a rapid influx of PMN leukocytes. SRS activity was detected in the peritoneal exudates very early after antigen challenge. The extravasation of plasma proteins and SRS release were both significantly inhibited by BN 52021. Inhibition of these two manifestations of Arthus reaction by a PAF antagonist provides additional evidence that PAF is released in immune-complex reactions and is, at least in part, responsible for the vascular changes characteristic of the early phase of this reaction. The fact that SRS release is also inhibited by a PAF antagonist allows the speculation that release of PAF further induces generation of SRS. These findings, if confirmed by more precise assays, will provide additional evidence of interactions between PAF and eiconsanoids as demonstrated in other systems.

Although there is evidence of PAF involvement in the early phase of Arthus reaction, the role of this mediator in the later development of tissue lesions can only be speculative. Indirect evidence was provided by the inhibitory effect of endotoxin in the development of skin lesions. Moreover, preliminary results in which BN 52021 reduced the intensity of skin lesions support the hypothesis that release of PAF by immune-complex formation is a central event in the pathological manifestations of immune-complex mediated reactions.

ACKNOWLEDGEMENTS

The authors wish to express their gratitude to Dr. M. Mariano for his help in the interpretation of the histopathological findings and Dr. P. Abrahamson for the ultrastructural analyses. Their valuable criticism and helpful discussions are deeply acknowledged. We also want to thank Ms. Christel Krueger for the drawings and Ms. Karen O'Donnell for secretarial assistance. This work was partially supported by Fundacao de Amparo A. Pesquisa do Estado de Sao Paulo (FAPESP).

References

1. Arthus, M. *Injections repetees de serum de cheval chez le lapin.* CR Soc Biol (Paris) 1093; 55: 817.

2. Archer, C.B.; Page, C.P., Paul, W., Morley, J., McDonald, D.A. *Early and late inflammatory effects of PAF-acether in the skin of experimental animals and man.* J Invest Dermat 1983; 80: 346.

3. Baron, M., Brisson, M.L. *Pancreatitis in systemic lupus erythematosus.* Arthritis Rheum 1982; 25: 1006-1009.

4. Benveniste, J. *Platelet-activating factor, a new mediator of anaphylaxis and immune-complex deposition from rabbit and human basophils.* Nature 1974; 249: 581-582.

5. Benveniste, J., Egido, J., Gutierrez-Millet, V. *Evidence of the involvement of the IgE-basophil-system in acute serum sickness.* Clin Exp Immunol 1976; 26: 449-456.

6. Benveniste, M., Henson, P.M., Cochrane, C.G. *Leukocyte-dependent histamine release from rabbit platelets. The role of IgE,* basophils and platelet-activating factor. J Exp Med 1972; 136: 1356-1377.

7. Bjork, J., Lindbom, L., Gerdin, B., Smedegard, G., Arfors, K.E., Benveniste, J. *PAF-acether increases microvascular permeability and affects endothelium-granulocyte interaction in microvascular beds.* Acta Physiol Scand 1983; 119: 305-308.

8. Bjork, J., Smedegard, G. *Acute microvascular effects of PAF-acether as studied by intravital microscopy.* Eur J Pharmacol 1983; 96: 87-94.

9. Bonnet, J., Loiseau, A.M., Orvoen, M., Bessin, P. *Platelet-activating factor involvement in acute inflammatory and pain processes.* Agents and Actions 1981; 11: 559-562.

10. Braquet, P. *The Ginkgolides: Potent platelet-activating factor antagonists isolated from Ginkgo biloba L.: Chemistry, pharmacology and clinical applications.* Drugs of the Future 1987; 12: 643-699.

11. Braquet, P., Vidal, R.F., Braquet, M., Hamard, H., Vargaftig, B.B. *Involvement of leukotrienes and PAF in the increased*

microvascular permeability of the rabbit retina. Agents and Actions 1984; 15: 82-85.

12. Camussi, G., Tetta, C., Bussolino, F., Caligaris-Capio, F., Coda, R., Masera, C., Segoloni, G. *Mediators of immune-complex induced aggregation of polymorphonuclear neutrophils. II. Platelet-activating factor as the effector substance of immune-induced aggregation.* Int Arch Allergy Appl Immunol 1981; 64: 25-41.

13. Camussi, G., Tetta, C., Coda, R., Benveniste, J. *Release of platelet-activating factor in human pathology. Evidence for the occurrence of basophil degranulation and release of platelet activating factor in systemic lupus erythematosus.* Lab Invest 1981; 44: 241-251.

14. Camussi, G., Tetta, C., Deregibus, M.C., Bussolino, F., Segoloni, G., Vercellone, A. *Platelet-activating factor in experimentally induced serum sickness: Role of basophil derived PAF in immune-complex deposition.* J Immunol 1982; 128: 86-94.

15. Cochrane, C.G. *Immunologic tissue injury mediated by neutrophilic leukocytes.* Adv Immunol 1968; 9: 97.

16. Cochrane, C.G., Janoff, A. *The Arthus reaction: A model of neutrophil and complement-mediated injury.* In: The Inflammatory Process, Vol. III. B.W. Zweifach, L. Grant, R.T. McCluskey (Eds.). Academic Press: New York 1974; 85.

17. Cordeiro, R., Martins, M.A., Henriques, M.O., Vargaftig, B.B. *Desensitization of PAF-induced rat paw oedema by repeated intra plantar injections.* Life Sci 1987; in press.

18. Delaunay, A., Pages, J. *L-inhibition de diapédèse par les endotoxines bactériennes et son mécanisme.* Ann Inst Pasteur 1945; 71: 431-439.

19. Doebber, T.W., Wu, M.S., Biftu, T. *Platelet-activating factor mediation of rat anaphylactic responses to soluble immune-complexes. Studies with PAF receptor antagonist L-652,731.* J Immunol 1986; 136: 4659-4667.

20. Doebber, T.W., Wu, M.S., Robins, J.C., Machoy, B., Chang, M.N., Shen, T.Y. *Platelet-activating factor (PAF) involvement in endotoxin-induced hypotension in rats. Studies with PAF-receptor antagonist kadsurenone.* Biochem Biophys Res Comm 1985; 127: 799-808.

21. Fitzgerald, M.F., Henderson, B., Higgs, G.A., Parente, L., Pettipher, E.R. *The levels of PAF and lyso-PAF in the joint fluids of rabbits with antigen-induced arthritis.* Br J Pharmacol 1985; 86: 442 P.

22. Foy, A., Smart, C., Duggan, J.M., Major, G.A.C., Clancy, R. *Immune-complexes in acute pancreatitis.* Aust N Z J Med 1981; 11: 605-609.

23. Goldenberg, M.M., Meurer, R.D. *A pharmacologic analysis of the action of platelet-activating factor in the induction of hindpaw edema in the rat.* Prostaglandins 1984; 28: 271-278.

24. Harczy, M., Maclouf, J., Pradelles, P., Braquet, P., Borgeat, P., Sirois, P. *Inhibitory effects of a novel platelet-activating factor antagonist (BN 52021) on antigen-induced prostaglandin and thromboxane formation by the guinea pig lung.* Pharmacol Res Comm 1986; 18 (Suppl): 111-119.

25. Hellewell, P.G., Williams, T.J. *A specific antagonist of platelet-activating factor suppresses oedema formation in an Arthus reaction but not oedema indued by leukocyte chemoattractants in rabbit skin.* J Immunol 1986; 137: 302-307.

26. Henson, P.M. *The adherence of leukocytes and platelets induced by fixed IgG antibody and complement.* Immunology 1969; 16: 107.

27. Henson, P.M. *Mechanisms of release of constituents from rabbit platelets by antigen-antibody complexes I. Lytic and non-lytic reactions.* J Immunol 1970; 105: 476.

28. Henson, P.M., Cochrane, C.G. *Acute immune-complex disease in rabbits: The role of complement and of a leucocyte-dependent release of vasoactive amines from platelets.* J Exp Med 1971; 133: 554-571.

29. Humphrey, D.M., Hanahan, D.J., Pinckard, R.N. *Induction of leukocytic infiltrates in rabbit skin by acetyl glyceryl ether phosphorylcholine.* Lab Invest 1982; 47; 227-234.

30. Humphrey, D.M., MacManus, L.M., Satouchi, K., Hanahan, D.J. Pinckard, R.N. *Vasoactive properties of acetyl glyceryl ether phosphorylcholine and analogues.* Lab Invest 1982; 46: 422-427.

31. Inarrea, P., Alonso, F., Sánchez-Crespo, M. *Platelet activating factor: An effector substance of the vasopermeability changes induced by infusion of immune aggregates in the mouse.* Immunopharmacolgy 1983; 6: 7-14.

32. Inarrea, P., Gómez-Cambronero, J., Pascual, J., del Carmen Ponte, M., Hernando, L., Sánchez-Crespo, M. *Synthesis of PAF-acether and blood volume changes in gram-negative sepsis.* Immunopharmacol 1985; 9: 45-52.

33. Israels, E.D., Nishi, G., Paraskevas, F., Israels, Z.G. *Platelet Fc receptor as a mechanism of Ab-Ag complex-induced*

platelet injury. Tromb Diathes Haemorrh (Stuttgart) 1973; 29: 434.

34. Jancar, S., Akimura, O.K., Dias da Silva, W. *Formation of slow-reacting substance by guinea pig immunoglobulins.* Am J Pathol 1976; 85: 531-537.

35. Kniker, W.T., Cochrane, C.G. *The localization of circulating immune complexes in experimental serum sickness: The role of vasoactive amines and hydrodynamic forces.* J Exp Med 1968; 127: 119.

36. Kravis, T.C., Henson, P.M. *Accumulation of platelet at sites of antigen-antibody mediated injury: A possible role for IgE antibody and mast cells.* J Immunol 1977; 118: 1569-1573.

37. Mencia-Huerta, J.M., Benveniste, J. *Platelet-activating factor and macrophages. II. Phagocytosis associated release of PAF-acether from rat peritoneal macrophages.* Cell Immunol 1981; 57: 281.

38. Morley, J., Page, C.P., Paul, W. *Inflammatory actions of platelet-activating factor in guinea pig skin.* Br J Pharmacol 1983; 80: 503-509.

39. Movat, H.Z., Fernando, N.V.P. *The earliest fine structural changes at the blood-tissue barrier during antigen-antibody interaction.* Am J Pathol 1963; 42: 41.

40. Reynolds, J.C., Inman, R.D., Kimberly, R.P., Chuong, J.H., Kovacs, J.E., Walsh, M.B. *Acute pancreatitis in Systemic Lupus Erythematosus: Report of twenty cases and a review of the literature.* Medicine 1982; 61: 25-32.

41. Riffo-Vásquez, Y., Isaac, L., Jancar, S. *Relationship between leukocyte diapedesis, increase in vascular permeability and tissue injury.* Brazilian J Med Biol Res 1986; 19 (4-5): 661A.

42. Russo, M., Arruda, A.M.S., Jancar, S. *C_5 fragments: Are they important in polymorphonuclear leucocyte diapedesis?* Res Commun Chem Pathol and Pharmacol 1986; 52: 361-369.

43. Sánchez-Crespo, M., Alonso, F., Egido, J. *Platelet activating factor in anaphylaxis and phagocytosis. Release from human peripheral polymorphonuclear and monocytes during the stimulation by ionophore A 23187 and phagocytosis, but not from degranulating basophils.* Immunology 1980; 40: 645-655.

44. Sánchez-Crespo, M., Alonso, F., Barat, A., Egido, J. *Rat serum sickness: Possible role of inflammatory mediators allowing deposition of immune-complexes in the glomerular basement membrane.* Clin Exp Immunol 1982; 49: 631-638.

45. Sánchez-Crespo, M., Alonso, F., Inarrea, P., Alvarez, V., Egido, J. *Vascular actions of synthetic PAF-acether in the rat. Evidence for a platelet independent mechanism.* Immunopharmacol 1982; 4: 173-185.

46. Sánchez-Crespo, M., Fernández-Gallardo, S., Nieto, M.L., Baranes, J., Braquet, P. *Inhibition of the vascular actions of IgG aggregates by BN 52021, a highly specific antagonist of PAF-acether.* Immunopharmacol 1985; 10: 69-75.

47. Spicer, B.A., Ross, J.W., Nunn, B. *An investigation of the involvement of PAF in the non-histamine immediate hypersensitivity reaction in the rat peritoneal cavity.* Agents and Actions 1985; 16: Abst.

48. Stetson, C.A. *Similarities in the mechanisms determining the Arthus and Shwartzman phenomena.* J Exp Med 1951; 94: 347.

49. Stimler, N.P., Bloor, C.M., Hugli, T.E., Wykle, R.L., McCall, C.E., O'Flaherty, J.T. *Anaphylactic actions of platelet-activating factor.* Am J Pathol 1981; 105: 64-69.

50. Thal, A. *Studies on pancreatitis. II. Acute pancreatic necrosis produced experimentally by the Arthus sensitization reaction.* Surgery 1955; 37: 911-917.

51. Touvay, C., Vilain, B., Braquet, P. *Desensitization to PAF-acether of lung parenchymal strips from endotoxin-treated guinea pigs.* 2nd Int Conf on PAF and Structurally Related Alkyl Ether Lipids. Gatlinburg, TN (USA), Oct. 1986; Abst p 140.

52. Vargaftig, B.B., Ferreira, S.H. *Blockade of the inflammatory effects of platelet-activating factor by cyclooxyenase inhibitors.* Brazilian J Med Biol Res 1981; 14: 187-189.

53. Wedmore, C.V., Williams, T.J. *Platelet-activating factor, secretory product of polymorphonuclear leukocytes, induces increases in vascular permeability in the rabbit skin.* Br J Pharmacol 1981; 74: 916 P.

Ginkgolides - Chemistry, Biology, Pharmacology and Clinical Perspectives. P. Braquet (Ed.)
Copyright © 1988, J.R. Prous Science Publishers, S.A.

INHIBITION OF THE VASCULAR ACTIONS OF AGGREGATED IMMUNOGLOBULINS BY BN 52021

Mariano Sánchez Crespo, Sagrario Fernández-Gallardo and María Luisa Nieto

Laboratorio de Nefrología Experimental, Instituto de Investigaciones Médicas de la Fundación Jiménez Díaz, CSIC, Madrid, Spain

ABSTRACT

The effect of BN 52021 was studied in normotensive rats challenged with PAF-acether. Sudden death was observed in animals receiving an i.v. dose of 10 μg/kg of PAF-acether and this was prevented by previous treatment with BN 52021 i.v. at a dose of 5 mg/kg. BN 52021 also reduced the fall of mean arterial pressure induced by PAF-acether, and the extravasation of protein-rich plasma, measured by the intravascular clearance of iodine-labeled bovine serum albumin. To extend these findings to a model of endogenous production of PAF-acether, other animals were challenged with soluble aggregates of human IgG. In these experiments, the development of hypotension and of extravasation was more protracted than in the case of PAF-acether treated animals, which is consistent with the requirement of a time lag to generate the endogenous mediator. BN 52021 at a dose of 5 mg/kg was at least as effective in preventing hypotension and extravasation as in the case of PAF-acether treated animals. When BN 52021 was injected after the challenge with either PAF-acether or aggregates, arterial pressure rapidly recovered, which indicates that BN 52021 not only prevents but also reverses the action of PAF-acether. In summary, the present data extend to *in vivo* models the pharmacological properties of BN 52021 and provide additional evidence as to the involvement of PAF-acether in shock states initiated by immunological challenge.

Address all correspondence to: Dr. M. Sánchez Crespo, Laboratorio de Nefrología, Fundación Jiménez Díaz, Av. Reyes Católicos 2, E-28040 Madrid, Spain.

INTRODUCTION

Immunoglobulin aggregates are similar to immune complexes in many aspects. Both interact with the same type of cell receptors and activate the complement system, which may initiate the formation of humoral mediators, leading to the production of inflammatory changes such as vasodilation, extravasation of protein-rich plasma and leukocyte infiltration. On this basis, the association of the pathophysiological responses to aggregates with the formation of endogenous mediators allows a better understanding of the inflammatory reactions and a rationale for the use of pharmacological tools in experimental and clinical conditions. Among these mediators, eicosanoids, PAF-acether, interleukin-1 and anaphylatoxins appear to play a central pathogenic role.

In the past years the involvement of PAF-acether in the reactions initiated by immune complexes and in the pathogenesis of the shock state has been documented by the accumulation of direct and indirect data from different authors. For instance, Pinckard and coworkers (1) have demonstrated a central role for PAF-acether in anaphylaxis in rabbits, and Camussi and coworkers (2) have been able to detect this compound in the peripheral blood of rabbits with acute serum sickness.

In this report, using a specific antagonist of the PAF-acether receptor, we associate some of these pathophysiological responses with the generation of PAF-acether by mononuclear phagocytes.

MATERIALS AND METHODS

Materials

BN 52021 was obtained from Institut Henri Beaufour-IPSEN, Le Plessis-Robinson, France. It was dissolved in dimethylsulfoxide at a concentration of 70 mg/ml and then diluted in isotonic sodium chloride at a final concentration of 5 mg/ml. PAF-acether (hexadecyl) was from Bachem Feinchemikalien, Bubendorf, Switzerland. IgG was obtained from human gamma globulin (purchased from Sigma Co., Saint Louis, MO, USA) by precipitation with 33% saturated ammonium sulfate and anion exchange chromatography in a column of DE-52 cellulose (Whatman) using 0.01 M sodium phosphate buffer, pH 8. IgG was finally diluted at a concentration of 10 mg/ml and aggregated for 20 minutes at 65°C in a shaking bath (3). Insoluble aggregates were discarded by centrifugation at 3000 x g for 20 minutes and soluble aggregates of about 1-2 MDa were separated from monomeric IgG by gel filtration chromatography through an Ultrogel AcA 22 column (LKB, France).

Hypotension and Vascular Permeability Assays

Systemic arterial pressure was measured through a femoral catheter, whereas a jugular vein was used for infusion of drugs and agonists. Vessel hyperpermeability was measured by using iodine-labeled bovine serum albumin (BSA) as an intravascular probe. For this purpose, labeled BSA was injected about 20 minutes prior to the injection of PAF-acether, immune aggregates or control solutions. At different times thereafter, blood samples were drawn into plastic tubes containing EDTA, measured and counted by scintillation. Extravasation changes are reported as percent changes on initial values.

RESULTS

The intravenous infusion of doses of PAF-acether higher than 5 μg/kg induced a dose-dependent increase of vascular permeability, as judged from the extravasation of iodinated BSA. Doses of PAF-acether higher than 5 μg/kg induced sudden death. This was prevented by previous administration of BN 52021 (data not shown).

Intravenous injection of soluble aggregates of IgG also induced extravasation of protein-rich plasma, but the kinetic pattern of this change showed a more protracted course. Again, this extravasation was prevented by previous treatment with BN 52021 (Fig. 1).

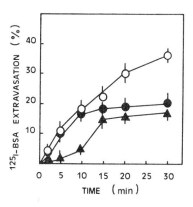

Figure 1   Time-course of the extravasation of iodinated-BSA in response to soluble aggregates of human IgG and its inhibition by BN 52021. Rats were pretreated with vehicle (○) or 5 mg/kg (●) or 1 mg/kg (▲) BN 52021. At time 0, the challenge was performed with 40 mg/kg of aggregated IgG. At the times indicated, blood samples were taken from a femoral artery and extravasation expressed as percent reduction on initial counting. Iodinated-BSA was injected 30 minutes prior to the challenge with PAF-acether. Spontaneous fall of iodinated-BSA counting was less than 5%. Data represent M ± SEM (from Sánchez Crespo *et al.*, ref. 9, with permission).

Intravenous administration of a bolus dose of 2.5 µg/kg of PAF-acether induced a profound and long-lasting arterial hypotension. This was significantly blunted by previous treatment with BN 52021. The same experiments were performed with aggregates of human IgG. In this case, the hypotensive response was slightly slower than that observed in response to PAF-acether; spontaneous recovery of the arterial pressure was not observed during the period of recording (at least one hour) in those animals receiving a challenge dose of 40 mg/kg of aggregated IgG. In contrast, recovery of the basal arterial pressure was observed in those animals which received BN 52021 after the challenge with either PAF-acether of aggregated IgG (Fig. 2). Interestingly, BN 52021 was not active as regards the hypotensive action of both diazoxide and sodium nitroprusside.

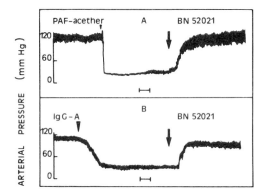

Figure 2 Reversal of hypotension induced with PAF-acether and IgG aggregates by intravenous injection of BN 52021. (A) A normal rat received an intravenous bolus dose of 2.5 µg/kg of PAF-acether, and at the time indicated, an intravenous injection of 5 mg/kg of BN 52021 was administered. (B) A normal rat received a bolus dose of 40 mg/kg of aggregated IgG; at the time indicated a bolus dose of 5 mg/kg of BN 52021 was infused. This represents a typical experiment of three with similar results. The bar under each trace represents 1 minute (from Sánchez Crespo *et al.,* ref. 9, with permission).

DISCUSSION

The present data show that the new PAF-acether receptor antagonist BN 52021, obtained from the *Ginkgo biloba* tree (4), is a powerful inhibitor of both extravasation and hypotension induced by the infusion of synthetic PAF-acether in rats. This action seems to be specific since no protection was observed as regards hypotension induced by either diazoxide or sodium nitroprusside. The biological significance of these findings is enhanced by the observation of a similar effect in animals challenged with a stimulator of the production of endogenous PAF-acether.

The release of PAF-acether *in vivo* has been demonstrated in the rabbit by Camussi and coworkers (2) during anaphylaxis and serum sickness, and by Iñarrea and coworkers (5) in rodents following the infusion of soluble aggregates of human IgG analogous to those used in this study and in a model of sepsis induced by gram negative bacteria (6). Handley and coworkers (7), using another antagonist of the PAF-acether receptor, compound SRI-63-072, have reported similar results as to the reversal of hypotension induced by immunoglobulin aggregates and bacterial endotoxin. Doebber and coworkers (8), using the compound L-652,731, have antagonized hypotension and extravasation of protein-rich plasma induced by soluble immune complexes. The conclusions obtained from all these studies indicate that PAF-acether is an important mediator of anaphylactic shock (1, 9), gram negative sepsis (6, 10) and vascular responses to the infusion of immune aggregates (7, 8, 11).

ACKNOWLEDGEMENTS

S. Fernández-Gallardo is a recipient of a grant from «Fundación Conchita Rabago». M.L. Nieto is a recipient of a grant from «Fondo de Investigaciones Sanitarias». This study has been supported by grants from CAICYT, FIS and «Fundación Alvarez de Toledo».

References

1. Pinckard, R.N., Halonen, M., Palmer, J.D., Butler, C., Shaw, J.O., Henson, P.M. *Intravascular aggregation and pulmonary sequestration of platelets during IgE-induced systemic anaphylaxis in the rabbit. Abrogation of lethal anaphylactic shock by platelet-depletion.* J Immunol 1977; 199: 2185-2190.

2. Camussi, G., Tetta, C., DeRegibus, M., Bussolino, F., Vercellone, A. *Platelet-activating factor (PAF-acether) in experimentally-induced rabbit acute serum sickness. Role of basophil-derived PAF-acether in immune complex deposition.* J Immunol 1982; 128: 86-93.

3. Sánchez Crespo, M., Alonso, F., Iñarrea, P., Alvarez, V., Egido, J. *Vascular actions of synthetic PAF-acether (a synthetic platelet-activating factor) in the rat: Evidence for a platelet-independent mechanism.* Immunopharmacology 1982; 4: 173-185.

4. Braquet, P., Spinnewyn, B., Braquet, M., Bourgain, R.N., Taylor, J.E., Etienne, A., Drieu, K. *BN 52021 and related compounds: A new series of highly specific PAF-acether receptor antagonists isolated from Ginkgo biloba.* Blood Vessels 1985; 19: 559-572.

5. Iñarrea, P., Alonso, F., Sánchez Crespo, M. *Platelet-activating factor: An effector substance of the vasopermeability changes induced by the infusion of immune aggregates in the mouse.* Immunopharmacology 1984; 6: 7-14.

6. Iñarrea, P., Gómez Cambronero, J., Pascual, J., Ponte, M.C., Hernando, L., Sánchez Crespo, M. *Synthesis of PAF-acether and blood volume changes in gram negative sepsis.* Immunopharmacology 1985; 9: 45-52.

7. Handley, D.A., Van Valen, R.G., Melden, M.K., Flury, S., Lee, M.L., Saunders, R.N. *Inhibition and reversal of endotoxin-, ag-*

gregated IgG- and PAF-induced hypotension in the rat by SRI 63-072, a PAF receptor antagonist. Immunopharmacology 1986; 12: 11-16.

8. Doebber, T.W., Wu, M.S., Biftu, T. Platelet-activating factor (PAF) mediation of rat anaphylactic responses to soluble immune complexes. Studies with PAF-receptor antagonist L-652,731. J Immunol 1986; 136: 4659-4668.

9. Darius, J., Lefer, D.H., Bryan Smith, J., Lefer, A.M. Role of platelet-activating factor in mediating guinea pig anaphylaxis. Science 1986; 239: 58-60.

10. Terashita, Z., Tshushima, S., Yoshioka, Y., Nomoto, H., Inada, Y., Nishikawa, K. CV 3988: A specific antagonist of platelet-activating factor. Life Sci 1985; 3?: 1975-1978.

11. Sánchez Crespo, M., Fernández-Gallardo, S., Nieto, M.L., Baranes, J., Braquet, P. Inhibition of the vascular actions of IgG immune aggregates by BN 52021, a highly selective antagonist of PAF-acether. Immunopharmacology 1985; 10: 65-72.

Ginkgolides - Chemistry, Biology, Pharmacology and Clinical Perspectives. P. Braquet (Ed.)
Copyright © 1988, J.R. Prous Science Publishers, S.A.

BN 52021: PAF, ENDOTOXIN AND ELLAGIC ACID IN RATS

Jacques Damas

Institut Léon Fredericq, Physiologie Humaine Normale et Pathologique, Faculté de Médecine, Université de Liège, Place Delcour 17, B-4020 Liège, Belgium

INTRODUCTION

Activation of the Hageman factor and the prekallikrein-kinin system during endotoxin-induced reactions has been reported several times (6). Intravenous injection of endotoxin in rats induces a decrease in plasma levels of the Hageman factor and prekallikrein (11-13). Thus, the involvement of the contact system of plasma (5) in the endotoxin-induced reactions has been suggested (6). However, PAF-acether antagonists prevented endotoxin-induced hypotension and gastrointestinal ulcerations in rats (10,16,17). Moreover, analogies between endotoxic shock and the effects of PAF-acether have been presented in rats (2). So we wonder if there is a link between PAF-acether and the contact system of plasma. To answer this question, we studied the influence of BN 52021 and two other related PAF-acether antagonists (1) on the effects of ellagic acid, a Hageman factor activator (15). In fact, we have shown that the injection of ellagic acid in rats induces intravascular coagulation with decreases of prekallikrein, high molecular weight kininogen, fibrinogen and plasminogen levels and also of blood platelet content. Simultaneously, a large congestion of the spleen and the lymph nodes occurs (6-9).

513

MATERIALS AND METHODS

General Procedures

We used Wistar rats of both sexes. The mean weight of the animals was 240 g. In these non-anesthetized rats, endotoxin (3 mg/kg) or ellagic acid (30 mg/kg) was injected in a tail vein. One hour later, the animals were anesthetized with sodium pentobarbital (50 mg/kg; i.p.). Blood was taken by cardiac puncture and 0.1 vol., 3.8% citrate was added. Macroscopic examination of lymph nodes and of the bowel was carried out. Spleen was removed and weighed.

To quantify the congestion of lymph nodes, four anatomical groups were systematically examined: anterior cervical and submaxillary lymph nodes, axillary nodes, intestinal nodes and Peyer patches. An arbitrary scale of swelling was used: a value from 0 to 3 was attributed to each group. The results were expressed as the sum, 0 to 12, of the four values recorded in each rat.

To quantify the congestion of the bowel, an arbitrary value 0 to 3 was attributed to each animal, 0 = no congestion, 1 = congestion of less than half of the small intestinal wall, 2 = congestion of at least half of the length of the small intestine; 3 = congestion of the entire intestinal length from the stomach to the caecum.

Blood platelet content was determined using Unopette (Becton Dickinson), Thoma's plates and phase contrast microscopy.

In other animals, after anesthesia with pentobarbital (35 mg/kg; i.p.), a tracheostomy was performed and a jugular vein and a carotid artery were cannulated. The mean blood pressure was measured with a Harvard 50-8952 transducer connected to a Harvard Universal Oscillograph. The animals were heparinized (4 mg/kg).

Drugs

We used PAF-acether (1-O-octadecyl-2-acetyl-sn-glycero-3-phosphorylcholine), from Bachem, BN 52021, BN 52020 and BN 52022 from Institut Henri Beaufour, bovine serum albumin and endotoxin (lipopolysaccharide from *E. coli*) from Sigma, ellagic acid from Janssen, heparin from Roche. Ellagic acid was dissolved in Tris HCl (0.15 M, pH 7.8), lipopolysaccharide and heparin in physiological saline, PAF-acether in ethanol as stock solution, and then diluted in 0.25% bovine serum albumin in physiological saline. BN 52021, BN 52020 and BN 52022 were dissolved in DMSO (8 mg/ml) and then diluted to 1/10 either in hot physiological saline for intravenous injection or in arabic gum (2.5%) for oral administration.

Statistical Analysis

Results were expressed as mean ± SEM. For statistical evaluation, unpaired Student's t test was used, and for the quantification of the congestion of the lymph nodes and of the small intestine, Wilcoxon's test was used. Significance was accepted at the 0.5 probability level.

RESULTS

Intravenous injection of PAF-acether (1.8 μg/kg) induced an immediate decrease of 51.1 ± 4.5% of the mean blood pressure (n = 6). That hypotensive response was inhibited by BN 52021 and BN 52020. Three minutes after the intravenous injection of these antagonists (3 mg/kg), the decrease of the mean blood pressure induced by PAF-acether was 8.5 ± 2.1% (n = 4; p < 0.001) and 17 ± 9.8% (n = 4; p < 0.01), respectively. In these experiments, BN 52021 was two times more potent than BN 52020. That result agrees with the pharmacological studies of Braquet et al. (1,2).

One hour after the intravenous injection of lipopolysaccharide (3 mg/kg) in non-anesthetized rats, macroscopic examination of the small intestine showed extensive regions of hyperemia and hemorrhage. The jejunum and terminal ileum were the most severely effected regions, while in most instances, the hyperemia extended from the pyloric region to the caecum. The stomach and the colon were devoid of damage. The Peyer patches and the intestinal lymph nodes were drowned in the intestinal hyperemia. No changes were observed in other lymph nodes. The spleen weight was not significantly reduced. These changes were not modified by the intravenous injection of DMSO (0.2 ml), but were largely inhibited by BN 52021 (6 mg/kg) given intravenously five to ten minutes before lipopolysaccharide. They were also inhibited by heparin (4 mg/kg). These results are shown in Table 1.

The intravenous injection of ellagic acid (30 mg/kg) induced a large congestion of all the lymph nodes and of the Peyer patches and a swelling of the spleen. That congestion is dependent of an intravascular coagulation elicited by the activation of the Hageman factor (8,9). The intravascular coagulation resulted in a long-lasting thrombocytopenia. Sometimes that congestion was accompanied by edema and thrombosis of the ilum, of the spleen and of the gastric and intestinal walls. However, the gastric and intestinal lesions were very variable: they were found in 0 to 55% of the treated animals, according to the series. The congestion of the lymphoid tissues, as well as the intravascular coagulation, was inhibited by heparin (9). We tried to modify the congestion of the lymphoid tissues by using the three PAF-acether antagonists. BN 52021, the most potent, was administered in-

Table 1 Modification of the effects of lipopolysaccharide on small intestine, intestinal lymph nodes, Peyer patches and spleen by BN 52021 and heparin

Agents	Small intestine Score	Lymphoid tissues Score	Spleen Weight/body weight
No treatment (n = 10)	0	0	0.342 ± 0.015
Lipopolysaccharide (n = 10)	2.8 ± 0.1	4.2 ± 1.1	0.258 ± 0.041
DMSO (n = 5)	2.8 ± 0.2 NS	3.8 ± 0.3 NS	0.298 ± 0.023 NS
BN 52021 (n = 6)	1 ± 0.3 p < 0.01	0.4 ± 0.4 p < 0.01	0.297 ± 0.016 NS
Heparin (n = 8)	1.3 ± 0.3 p < 0.01	3.0 ± 0.4 NS	0.249 ± 0.010 NS

travenously at doses of 2, 4 and 8 mg/kg five minutes before ellagic acid or orally (p.o.) two hours before. The other two, BN 52020 and BN 52022, were administered orally two hours before. None of these agents modified the swelling of the spleen and the congestion of the lymph nodes. BN 52021 did not inhibit the thrombocytopenia (Table 2). PAF-acether has no aggregating effect on rat platelets (4).

Table 2 Lack of influence of PAF-acether antagonists on the effects of ellagic acid on the lymph nodes, spleen and platelets

Agents	Lymph nodes Score	Spleen Weight/body weight	Platelets $10^3/\mu l$
Ellagic acid n = 24	5.1 ± 0.7	0.550 ± 0.027	402 ± 40
BN 52021 8 mg/kg i.v. n = 10	5.2 ± 1.4	0.561 ± 0.033	448 ± 33
10 mg/kg p.o. n = 6	4.7 ± 0.7	0.525 ± 0.082	
BN 52020 40 mg/kg p.o. n = 10	4.2 ± 0.5	0.614 ± 0.023	
BN 52022 40 mg/kg p.o. n = 10	5.5 ± 1.1	0.548 ± 0.052	

DISCUSSION

The hypotensive effect of PAF-acether and the intestinal lesions induced by endotoxin in rats were inhibited by BN 52021 and related compounds. These results agree with previous observations made by several authors (2). However, the intestinal lesions induced by endotoxin were also inhibited by heparin. Endotoxin injection in rats activates the Hageman factor and elicites intravascular coagulation with formation of kinins (12,13). Activation of the Hageman factor with ellagic acid induced congestion of lymph nodes, Peyer patches and a swelling of the spleen. These modifications are quite different from the intestinal lesions elicited by endotoxin. Moreover, the congestion of lymphoid tissues induced by ellagic acid was not modified by the PAF-acether antagonists. Thus, the involvement of PAF-acether in endotoxin-induced reactions does not follow the activation of the Hageman factor. Therefore, two links could unite PAF-acether with the Hageman factor and the kinin system. First, endotoxin injection could elicite separately the activation of the contact system of plasma on the one hand and the release of PAF-acether on the other hand. That release might be triggered by the activation of the complement system (3,14). The two chains of events add their effects resulting in endotoxic intestinal lesions and shock, though in the rat, PAF-acether seems to be the most potent effector agent. Alternatively, PAF-acether could initiate the development of the reactions with plasma exudation resulting in activation of the Hageman factor and kinin formation. In that case, the activation of the Hageman factor would take place locally in the initial lesions elicited by PAF-acether and not in the systemic vascular tree.

CONCLUSIONS

The congestion of the lymphoid tissues induced by activation of the Hageman factor with ellagic acid was not modified by BN 52021. That indicates that PAF-acether is not involved in the reactions elicited by activation of the Hageman factor contrary to its contribution to the shock induced by endotoxin.

ACKNOWLEDGEMENTS

Thanks are expressed to Dr. Braquet who gave us the PAF-acether antagonists. This paper is the fifth of a series of six papers on the reactions induced by ellagic acid. This series is dedicated to Prof. Lecomte.

References

1. Braquet, P.G. et al. *BN 52021 and related compounds: A new series of highly specific PAF-acether receptor antagonists isolated from Ginkgo biloba L.* Blood & Vessel 1985; 16: 558-572.

2. Braquet, P.G. et al. *Perspectives in platelet activating factor research.* Pharmac Rev 1987; 39: 97-145.

3. Camussi, G. et al. *Mediators of immune complex induced aggregation of polymorphonuclear neutrophils. II. Platelet-activating factor as the effector substance of immune-induced aggregation.* Int Arch Allergy Appl Immunol 1981; 64: 25-41.

4. Chignard, M. et al. *L'agrégation plaquettaire et le platelet-activating factor.* J Pharmacol 1980; 11: 371-377.

5. Cochrane, C.G. and Griffin, J.H. *The biochemistry and pathophysiology of the contact system of plasma.* Adv Immunol 1982; 33: 242-306.

6. Colman, R.W. and Wong, P.Y. *Kallikrein-kinin system in pathological conditions.* Handb Exp Pharmacol 1979; 25(Suppl): 569-607.

7. Damas, J. and Remacle-Volon, G. *The thrombopenic effect of ellagic acid in the rat. Another model of platelet stimulation in vivo.* Thrombosis Res 1987; 45: 153-163.

8. Damas, J. et al. *Studies on the hematological and vascular changes induced by ellagic acid in rats.* Agents and Action; in press.

9. Damas, et al. *Mechanism of the congestion of lymph nodes induced by ellagic acid, in rats.* Agents and Action; in press.

10. Doebber, T.W. et al. *Platelet-activating factor (PAF) involvement in endotoxin-induced hypotension in rats. Studies with PAF-receptor antagonist kadsurenone.* Biochem Biophys Res Commun 1985; 127: 799-808.

11. Latour, J.G. *Modulation of disseminated intravascular coagulation (DIC) by steroidal and non-steroidal anti-inflammatory drugs.* Agents and Actions 1983; 13: 487-495.

12. Latour, J.G. et al. *Activation of Hageman factor and initiation of hepatic vein thrombosis in the hyperlipemic rat.* Amer J Path 1974; 76: 179-190.

13. Latour, J.G. et al. *Activation of the Hageman factor-prekallikrein system in the pathogenesis of the generalized Shwartzman reaction and of hepatic vein thrombosis phenomenon in the rat.* Lab Invest 1979; 41: 237-246.

14. Müller-Berghaus, G. *The role of platelets, leukocytes, and complement in the activation of intravascular coagulation by endotoxin.* In: Platelets, a Multidisciplinary Approach. G. de Gaetano and S. Garattini (Eds.). Raven Press: New York 1977; 303-320.

15. Ratnoff, D. and Crum, J.D. *The activation of Hageman factor by solutions of ellagic acid.* J Lab & Clin Med 1964; 63: 359-372.

16. Terashita, A. et al. *Is platelet-activating factor (PAF) a mediator of endotoxin shock?* Eur J Pharmacol 1985; 109: 257-261.

17. Wallace, J.L. and Whittle, B.J.R. *Prevention of endotoxin-induced gastrointestinal damage by CV-3988, an antagonist of platelet-activating factor.* Eur J Pharmacol 1986; 124: 209-210.

Ginkgolides - Chemistry, Biology, Pharmacology and Clinical Perspectives. P. Braquet (Ed.)
Copyright © 1988, J.R. Prous Science Publishers, S.A.

THE EFFECT OF A PLATELET-ACTIVATING FACTOR ANTAGONIST, GINKGOLIDE BN 52021, ON HEPATIC GLYCOGENOLYSIS AND ALLOXAN-DIABETES IN RATS

Paloma Hernando[1], Jesús Egido[1], Jesús González[1], Eduardo Pirotzky[2], David Hosford[2] and Pierre Braquet[2]

[1]Laboratorio de Nefrología, Fundación Jiménez Díaz, Universidad Autónoma Madrid, Centro Asociado al C.S.I.C.; [2]Institut Henri Beaufour, F-92350 Les Plessis Robinson, France

EFFECT OF PAF ANTAGONISTS ON HYPERGLYCEMIA INDUCED BY DRUGS AND HORMONES

Platelet-activating factor (PAF) is a highly potent mediator of inflammation and anaphylaxis (3). This phospholipid is generated by macrophages, basophils, neutrophils, platelets and many other cells (3). PAF is also an activator of phosphoinositide metabolism and promotes hepatic glycagon breakdown (29).

Shukla *et al.* have recently demonstrated that PAF has a pronounced effect on glycogenolysis in the perfused rat liver (29). This process is dose-dependent and requires the presence of calcium ions at levels comparable to those needed for platelet activation. The glycogenolytic effect of PAF seems to be mediated via different receptors to those which act as binding sites for catecholamines and glucagon. It has also been shown that sequential infusion of PAF into rat liver causes a decrease in the glucogenolytic

Address all correspondence to: J. Egido, M.D., Laboratorio de Nefrología, Fundación Jiménez Díaz, Avenida Reyes Católicos 2, E-28040 Madrid, Spain.

response (4), an effect which is not seen when the liver is stimulated with PAF in the presence of phenylephrine or glucagon.

The availability of specific antagonists of PAF has allowed examination of the potential role of this phospholipid in the hyperglycemia induced by different diabetogenic agents. The injection of drugs such as alloxan or streptozotocin results in a triphasic glycemic response; an initial hyperglycemia at 2-4 hours, a period of marked hypoglycemia between 6-12 hours, and finally a diabetic state at 24 hours (25). The early hyperglycemia seems to be due to depletion of liver glycogen which occurs during this period. However, when PAF antagonists are administered 30 min before the injection of the drugs, a different pattern of changes in blood glucose levels is observed. BN 52021 (10 mg/kg i.p.) completely abolishes alloxan-induced hyperglycemia (Fig. 1). Alprazolam (6.5 g/kg i.p.) produces a similar effect. In contrast, no significant effect of either PAF antagonist was noted on hyperglycemia induced by streptozotocin. Since the mechanism of hepatic glycogenolysis and toxicity on the B-cell pancreatic islet by alloxan and streptozotocin is poorly understood (25), we do not have a clear explanation of the different effects of PAF antagonists on the early hyperglycemia induced by these drugs.

Since the hepatocytes contain nearly all the liver glycogen, we studied the response of these cells to alloxan. Hepatocytes were isolated from the liver of well nourished rats and incubated for different periods with alloxan (26). After 5 min incubation, the glucose output of alloxan-treated cells was 7-fold greater than that of cells incubated without the drug (Fig. 2). The addition of BN 52021 to alloxan-treated cells provoked glucose production at levels similar to the control values. Therefore, the *in vivo* and *in vitro* studies with alloxan suggest that the alloxan-induced glycogenolysis might be PAF-mediated. However, Fisher *et al.* have shown that in contrast to the glycogenolytic effect of PAF in the perfused rat liver, the addition of PAF to isolated rat hepatocytes did not provoke the release of glucose (12). These authors suggest that other hepatic cells might be involved in PAF production. Furthermore, Iñarrea *et al.* have shown that PAF can be detected in mouse liver following *in vivo* infusion of immune aggregates (16). The hepatic uptake of immune aggregates is chiefly effected by Kupffer cells (19) and accordingly, Buxton *et al.* have studied the influence of aggregated IgG on the glycogenolytic process in rat liver (5). These authors showed that the heat aggregated IgG elicited glucose release in a dose-dependent manner. The repeated infusion of immune aggregates led to a desensitization similar to that caused by PAF. In addition, the aggregates stimulated the production of the mediator. These observations suggest that the mononuclear phagocytic system may be a site of formation of this agonist. Importantly, the infusion of two specific PAF antagonists, prior to or simultaneously with the mediator, effectively inhibited the hepatic glycogenolysis (6). As in our studies, these PAF antagonists were ineffective as inhibitors of the action of the α-adrenergic agonist, phenylephrine, on the glycogenolytic process (6).

Although in our *in vitro* studies the presence of non-parenchymal cells (endothelial and Kupffer cells) was less than 1%, we cannot completely disregard the possibility that alloxan may have induced generation of PAF from Kupffer cells, as was demonstrated by the experiments of Buxton *et al.* (5). Hepatocytes possess Fc receptors and are able to bind to IgG immune aggregates (26). In fact, hepatocytes have higher binding capacity to IgG immune aggregates than Kupffer cells (26). Experiments are in progress to study the possible interaction between hepatocytes and Kupffer cells in the glycogenolitic process.

BN 52021 AND GLYCEMIA

As shown in Figures 1 and 3, a single administration of BN 52021, 10 mg/kg i.p., induced a progressive increase in glycemia, which reached a maximum after 4 hours (Fig. 3). The injection of the vehicle alone, dimethylsulfoxide (DMSO), did not produce any significant alteration of glycemia (Fig. 3).

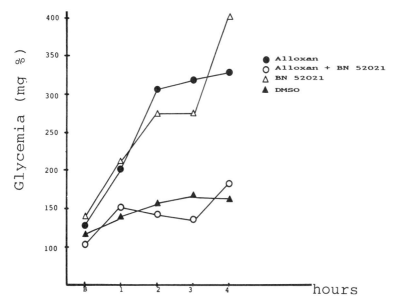

Figure 1 Effect of PAF receptor antagonist, BN 52021, on early hyperglycemia induced by alloxan. Each point is the mean of 5 animals. DMSO, dimethylsulfoxide, was used as solvent of BN 52021.

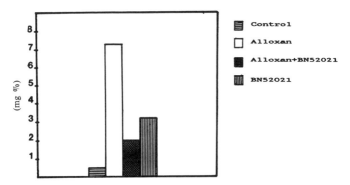

Figure 2 Glucose output by isolated hepatocytes from normal rats incubated with alloxan and/or BN 52021 for 5 min.

The apparent contradictory effects of BN 52021 on glycemia, when administered alone, prior to or simultaneously with alloxan, may be explained by the observation that PAF receptor antagonist can exhibit partial agonistic properties. Thus, although various PAF antagonists are effective in inhibiting PAF-induced hypotension in rats, some of them cause a transient hypotension when administered i.v. For instance, BN 52021 at 5 mg/kg i.v. causes a 12% decrease in diastolic pressure in rats (2).

As shown in Figure 3, the elevated glycemia induced by a single injection of BN 52021 returned to normal values after 24-48 h. The above data suggest that BN 52021 could have a glycogenolitic effect, probably by acting on PAF receptors.

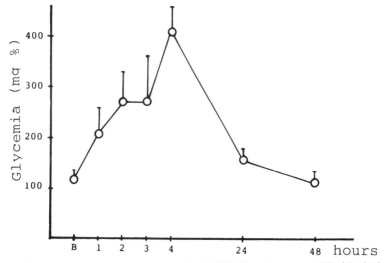

Figure 3 Glycemia levels in normal rats injected with BN 52021 (10 mg/kg) mean ± SD of 5 animals.

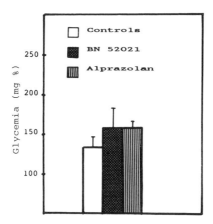

Figure 4 Glycemia levels in normal rats treated with BN 52021 (10 mg/kg) or alprazolam (6.5 mg/kg) for 4 weeks. Mean ± SD. BN 52021 (n = 15 animals) and alprazolam (n = 6).

In order to determine whether long-term administration of PAF antagonists could exert a deleterious effect on pancreatic B cells, normal Wistar or Sprague-Dawley rats were injected daily for 1 month with either BN 52021, 10 mg/kg, or alprazolam, 6.5 mg/kg. No significant differences in glycemia in relation to the controls were observed (Fig. 4).

Since PAF antagonists inhibit the early hyperglycemia phase induced by alloxan, we investigated the effect of PAF antagonists on alloxan-induced diabetes. Hyperglycemia is initiated between 24-48 h after alloxan injection. This phase can be attributed to the destruction of B-cells and the subsequent insulin deficiency. BN 52021, 10 mg/kg, afforded significant protection against alloxan-induced hyperglycemia (Table 1). No changes were noted in alloxan-treated rats when administered with diclofenac. Four weeks after the induction of diabetes the protection afforded by BN 52021 was more pronounced and mortality was not observed in the group of rats treated with BN 52021 and alloxan (Table 1).

The mechanism by which alloxan damages B-cells is not clearly defined. Since several hydroxyl radical scavengers, administered prior to alloxan, are able to prevent the diabetic state (15), the cell membrane injury might be mediated by generation of free radical oxygen. Although alloxan may induce production of these cytotoxic radicals by a series of reactions it is possible that PAF could also be released by pancreatic cells upon stimulation with alloxan (8). Since PAF induces the release of free radical oxygen (28), one can hypothesize that the partial protection from alloxan diabetes afforded by BN 52021 might be due to the inhibition of this mechanism. However, BN 52021 did not induce a significant decrease in glycemia when

Table 1   The effect of PAF antagonists on glycemia and mortality in alloxan diabetic rats

		48 Hours			4 Weeks	
	n	Glycemia (mg%)	% of rats with values in the normal range	n	Glycemia (mg%)	Mortality (%)
Control	7	132 ± 16[+]		7	137 ± 12[+]	0
Alloxan injected rats	15	396 ± 263	0	9	267 ± 204	64
Rats injected with Alloxan + BN 52021	7	133 ± 36*	100	7	157 ± 18**	0
Rats injected with Alloxan + Diclofenac	5	759 ± 507	0	2	147 ± 21	60

[+]mean ± 1 SD. *$p < 0.005$ in relation to alloxan-treated rats. **$p < 0.01$ in relation to alloxan-treated rats.

administered 48 h after alloxan injection. This data contrasts with that showing the protective effect of BN 52021 when given prior to or concomitantly with alloxan, suggesting that the effect of the antagonist may also occur at the pancreatic islet level.

EFFECT OF PAF ANTAGONISTS ON EICOSANOID SYNTHESIS BY ISOLATED GLOMERULI FROM RATS WITH EXPERIMENTAL DIABETES

The primary hemodynamic alterations of diabetes mellitus are an increase in both glomerular hydrostatic pressure and single nephron plasma flow (31). These modifications are thought to initiate glomerulosclerosis, which is characteristic of advanced diabetes mellitus nephropathy. Although the mechanisms leading to the hemodynamic alterations in diabetes are uncertain, several data suggest that the eicosanoids might play an important role. Increased production of thromboxane A_2 has been found both in human and in rat platelets during diabetes (14). Furthermore, experimentally induced diabetes in rats is accompanied by marked increase in urinary TxB_2 excretion (24).

Accordingly, we have measured the production of some eicosanoids by glomeruli isolated from rats with alloxan-induced diabetes. As shown in Figure 5, diabetic rats have a 4-fold increase in the TxB_2 production in relation to normal rats. Interestingly, the administration of PAF antagonists (BN 52021 or alprazolam) from the beginning of the diabetes induced a normalization of the TxB_2 production. A similar effect was noted in animals treated with diclofenac, a cyclooxygenase inhibitor.

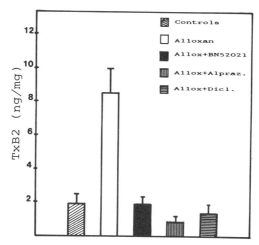

Figure 5 Thromboxane production by isolated glomeruli from diabetic rats (4 weeks after alloxan injection). Controls (n = 4); alloxan + alprazolam (n = 4); alloxan + diclofenac (n = 4); alloxan (n = 5). Alloxan + BN 52021 (n = 4).

The role of TxB_2 in the induction of proteinuria remains to be established. However, in diabetes as well as in other glomerulopathies, rats injected with alloxan and treated with BN 52021 had significantly reduced proteinuria relative to non-treated rats (9). This phenomenon could be due to the inhibition of increased glomerular permeability induced by PAF, as demonstrated in experimental nephrosis (7). The fact that alloxan diabetic rats treated with diclofenac also had proteinuria in the normal range suggests that intrarenal hemodynamic alterations could be important in the appearance of proteinuria in the early stages of diabetes. It has been shown that PAF induces the release of TxB_2 and prostaglandins from rat glomerular cells and isolated rat kidney (27). This effect is inhibited by BN 52021 (22). Since BN 52021 is able to inhibit the release of prostaglandins, thromboxanes and leukotrienes (30), our results on TxB_2 production by isolated glomeruli from diabetic rats provide further evidence for the indirect action of PAF in diabetes nephropathy. Taking into account the complex interactions between PAF and eicosanoids, further studies in this area are required.

PAF ANTAGONISTS AND DIABETES TYPE I. FUTURE PERSPECTIVES

A number of reports suggest that insulin-dependent diabetes mellitus (IDDM) has an autoimmune origin and involves T-cells either as helper or effector cells (10). Recently, the development of several animal models of

IDDM has provided evidence of the pathogenesis of the disease and allowed therapeutic trials. In experimental models of induced or spontaneous diabetes, electron microscopic studies of pancreas reveal that immediately prior to the appearance of the diabetes, an infiltration of the islets by lymphocytes and macrophages occurs (18, 20). Moreover, a passive transfer of insulinitis from spontaneous diabetic rats to the nude mouse by lymphocytes (21) suggests that a cell-mediated immune reaction is important in these models.

Support for the immune origin of these diabetes is further provided by the fact that successful therapeutic trials have been performed with anti-lymphocyte serum, total lymphoid irradiation and cyclosporine. A randomized placebo controlled trial has demonstrated that cyclosporine can induce remission in type I diabetes in humans (1). This effect is highly dose-dependent and therefore the limitations of cyclosporine therapy of this pathology are largely based on the potential nephrotoxicity of the drug. Recently, it has been demonstrated that PAF antagonists, when given simultaneously with low doses of cyclosporine, delay the appearance of rejection in the cardiac graft (13). Furthermore, BN 52021 exerts a significant protective effect on *in vitro* lymphocyte cytotoxicity against rat Langerhans islets (11). Recently, we have observed that BN 52021 decreases by around 50% the interstitial infiltrate (T-lymphocytes and macrophages) observed in experimental nephrosis in rats. In the same model, cyclosporine also induces a similar percentage decrease in cell infiltration (in preparation). Furthermore, as BN 52021 decreases the nephrotoxicity induced by cyclosporine (23), one could speculate that the administration of PAF antagonists and low doses of cyclosporine could constitute a novel approach to the treatment of autoimmune diseases, like IDDM, and may also be effective in preventing graft rejection.

ACKNOWLEDGEMENTS

We want to thank Mª Asunción de la Cruz Alonso for excellent technical assistance.

References

1. Bach, J.F. et al. *Clinical and immunological effects of cyclosporine in Type I diabetes*. In: The Immunology of Diabetes Mellitus. Elsevier Science Publisher BV: Amsterdam 1986; 337-344.
2. Baranès, J. et al. *The effects of PAF-acether on the cardiovascular system and their inhibition by a new highly specific receptor antagonist BN 52021*. Int J Immunopharmacol 1985; 7: 385.
3. Braquet, P. et al. *Perspectives in platelet-activating factor research*. Pharmacol Rev 1987; 39: 97-147.
4. Buxton, D.B. et al. *Stimulation of hepatic glycogenolysis by acetyl glyceryl ether phosphorylcholine*. J Biol Chem 1984; 259: 1468-1471.
5. Buxton, D.B. et al. *Stimulation of glycogenolysis and platelet-activating factor production by heat aggregated im-*

munoglobulin G in the perfused rat liver. J Biol Chem 1984; 13759-13761.

6. Buxton, D.B. *Specific antagonists of platelet-activating factor-mediated vasoconstriction and glycogenolysis in the perfused rat liver.* Biochem Pharmacol 1986; 35: 893-897.

7. Egido, J. et al. *Role of platelet-activating factor in adriamycin-induced nephropathy in rats.* Eur J Pharmacol 1987; 138: 119-123.

8. Egido, J. et al. *PAF, adriamycin-induced nephropathy and ginkgolide B.* In: Ginkgolides-Chemistry, Biology, Pharmacology and Clinical Perspectives. P. Braquet (Ed.). J.R. Prous Science Publishers: Barcelona 1988; 631-640.

9. Egido, J. et al. *A possible role of platelet-activating factor (PAF) in the hyperglycemia induced by alloxan in rats.* In: Trends in Lipids Mediators Research. P. Braquet (Ed.); In press.

10. Eisanberth, G.S. *Type I diabetes mellitus. A chronic autoimmune disease.* New Engl J Med 1986; 314: 1360-1368.

11. Farkas, G. et al. *Graft protective effect of BN 52021, a specific PAF-acether antagonist in an in vitro Langerhans islet-splenic lymphocyte model.* In: Ginkgolides- Chemistry, Biology, Pharmacology and Clinical Perspectives. P. Braquet (Ed.). J.R. Prous Science Publishers: Barcelona 1988.

12. Fisher, R.A. et al. *The effect of acetyl glyceryl ether phosphorylcholine on glycogenolysis and phosphatidyl inositol-4,5 bisphosphate in rat hepatocytes.* J Biol Chem 1984; 59: 8685-8688.

13. Foegh, et al. *Prolongation of cardiac allograft survival with BN 52021, a specific antagonist of platelet-activating factor.* Transplantation 1986; 42: 86-88.

14. Halushka, P.V. et al. *Increased platelet thromboxane synthesis in diabetes mellitus.* J Lab Clin Med 1981; 97: 87-96.

15. Heikkila, R.E. et al. *Protection against alloxan-induced diabetes in mice by the hydroxyl radical scavenger dimethylurea.* Eur J Pharmacol 1978; 52: 57-60.

16. Iñarrea, P. et al. *Platelet-activating factor: An effector substance of the vasopermeability changes induced by the infusion of immune aggregates in the mouse.* Immunopharmacology 1983; 6: 7-14.

17. Ketterer, H. et al. *Effect upon insulin secretion of physiologic doses of glucagon administered in the portal vein.* Diabetes 1967; 16: 283-288.

18. Like, A.A. et al. *Streptozotocin-induced pancreatic insulinitis: New model of diabetes mellitus.* Science 1976; 193: 415-417.

19. Mannick, M. et al. *Studies on antigen-antibody complexes. I. Elimination of soluble complexes from rabbit circulation.* J Exp Med 1971; 133: 713-739.

20. Nakhooda, A.F. et al. *The spontaneously diabetic Wistar rat. Metabolic and morphologic studies.* Diabetes 1976; 26: 100-112.

21. Nakhooda, A.F. et al. *Passive transfer of insulinitis from the BB rat to the nude mouse.* Endocrinology 1981; 109: 2264-2266.

22. Neuwirth, R. et al. *Stimulation of PGE_2 synthesis by platelet-activating factor in mesangial cells is inhibited by BN 52021 and kadsurenone.* In: Sixth Int Conf Prostaglandins and Related Compounds. (Florence, Italy) 1986; 320.

23. Pirotzky, E. et al. *Cyclosporine-induced nephrotoxicity: Preventive effect of a PAF-acether antagonist: BN 52063.* Trans Proc 1988; In press.

24. Quilley, J. et al. *Arachidonic acid metabolism and urinary excretion of prostaglandins and thromboxane in rats with experimental diabetes mellitus.* J Pharmacol Exp Ther 1985; 234: 211-216.

25. Rerup, C.C. *Drugs producing diabetes through damage of the insulin secreting cells.* Pharmacol Rev 1970; 22: 485-518.

26. Sancho, J. et al. *Binding kinetics of monomeric and aggregated IgG to Kupffer cells and hepatocytes of mice.* Immunology 1984; 53: 283-289.

27. Schlondorff, D. et al. *Effect of platelet-activating factor and serum-treated zymosan on prostaglandin E_2 synthesis, arachidonic acid release, and contraction of cultures rat mesangial cells.* J Clin Invest 1984; 73: 1227-1231.

28. Sedor, J.R. et al. *Platelet-activating factor stimulates oxygen radical release by cultured rat mesangial cells.* Kidney Int 1985; 27: 222.

29. Shukla, S.D. et al. *Acetyl glyceryl ether phosphoinositide metabolism and glycogenolysis.* J Biol Chem 1983; 258: 10212-10214.

30. Sirois, P. et al. *Inhibition of the release of prostaglandins, thromboxanes and leukotrienes from anaphylactic lungs by a platelet-activating factor (PAF) antagonist and its stimulation by PAF.* In: Advances in Prostaglandin, Thromboxane and Leukotriene Research, Vol. 17. B. Samuelsson, R. Paoletti, P.W. Ramwell (Eds.). Raven Press: New York 1987; 1033-1037.

31. Viberti, G.C. et al. *The kidney in diabetes: Significance of the early abnormalities.* Clin Endocrinol Metab 1986; 15: 753-782.

Ginkgolides - Chemistry, Biology, Pharmacology and Clinical Perspectives. P. Braquet (Ed.)
Copyright © 1988, J.R. Prous Science Publishers, S.A.

PAF - AND ENDOTOXIN-INDUCED GASTROINTESTINAL ULCERATION: INHIBITORY EFFECTS OF BN 52021

John L. Wallace

Department of Physiology, Faculty of Medicine, Queen's University, Kingston, Ontario, K7L 3N6, Canada

INTRODUCTION

The sequence of events which follow the phagocytosis of invading bacteria and ultimately lead to septic shock are poorly understood (13). It is clear that several potent substances are released into the blood stream which mediate many of the systemic and localized effects encountered in the septic shock patient. In recent years, substantial evidence has accumulated in support of a role for platelet-activating factor (PAF) as a mediator of many of the symptoms of septic shock. Injection of PAF into laboratory animals produces many effects also seen in the septic shock patient, including systemic hypotension, pulmonary hypertension, bronchoconstriction, increased vascular permeability and stimulation of blood coagulation (4). Gastrointestinal hemorrhage is another feature associated with septic shock which can also be produced in several species by injection of PAF (2,7,10,12,19,21).

A second line of evidence supporting a role for PAF in septic shock comes from animal studies in which shock was induced by administration of bacterial endotoxin. Several groups have now reported significant increases in PAF release elicited by administration of endotoxin to laboratory animals. For instance, Inarrea *et al.* (8) found that PAF appeared in the peritoneum and spleen following intraperitoneal injection of endotoxin. Doebber *et al.* (6) reported a marked rise in circulating blood levels of PAF 10 minutes after intravenous administration of endotoxin to rats. Lagente *et al.* (9) recently reported a 17-fold increase in release of PAF from the rat jejunum following intravenous endotoxin administration. Furthermore, several groups have reported that PAF receptor antagonists can block the hypotension and some of the other systemic effects induced by endotoxin in the rat or guinea-pig (1,5,6,15). Significant reduction of the gastrointestinal damage induced by endotoxin in the rat has been demonstrated with several structurally different PAF antagonists, including CV-3988, Ro-193704 and BN 52021 (17,18).

In the present study, the role of PAF as a mediator of the gastrointestinal damage associated with endotoxin shock has been further investigated. The specific PAF antagonist, BN 52021 (3), has been assessed for its ability to block both PAF- and endotoxin-induced gastrointestinal damage, systemic hypotension and hemoconcentration. Gastrointestinal damage has been assessed macroscopically, histologically and by measuring intestinal plasma protein leakage.

METHODS

Male, Wistar rats weighing 180-210 g were used. The rats were deprived of food for 18-20 hours prior to an experiment. During that time, tap water remained available *ad libitum*. After anesthetizing the rats with sodium pentobarbitone (60 mg/kg i.p.), a carotid artery was cannulated for measurement of systemic arterial blood pressure (BP) and a 25 gauge needle was inserted into a tail vein for injection of drugs, PAF or endotoxin. At the beginning of all experiments, a 100 μl blood sample was collected from a tail vein into a heparinized capillary tube, which was then centrifuged for 4 minutes in a Clay Adams Microhematocrit Centrifuge. The basal hematocrit was determined from this blood sample. Twenty minutes after beginning the measurement of BP, the rat received an intravenous injection of BN 52021 (20 mg/kg) or vehicle. Five minutes later, the rat received either an intravenous bolus injection of endotoxin (*E. coli* 0111:B4; Sigma) at a dose of 25 mg/kg, or a 10-minute infusion of PAF (100 ng/kg/min). A second blood sample (100 μl) was drawn from the carotid cannula thirty minutes after administration of endotoxin or completion of the PAF infusion and again the hematocrit was determined. The animal was then killed by exsanguination.

At the end of the experiment the abdomen was opened and the stomach and segments of the proximal duodenum, jejunum and distal ileum were excised and fixed in neutral buffered formalin. Macroscopically visible damage was scored by an observer unaware of the treatment using the following criteria: 0 = no damage; 1 = diffuse hyperemia; 2 = patches of focal hyperemia; 3 = extensive hyperemia and hemorrhage. This scoring system has previously been found to correlate well with histological scoring of PAF-induced gastric damage (14). Samples of the fundic region of the fixed stomach and of the segments of small intestine were excised and processed by routine techniques prior to embedding in paraffin and staining with hematoxylin and eosin. Thick sections (4-7 μm) were mounted on glass slides, coded to avoid observer bias and examined under a light microscope. Damage was scored on a 0 to 3 scale using the following criteria: 0 = no damage; 1 = superficial cell exfoliation and/or subepithelial vasocongestion; 2 = vascular congestion extending deeper than the gastric pits; 3 = vascular congestion extending down to the muscularis mucosae and/or mucosal necrosis and hemorrhage. At least three sections from each region of the gastrointestinal tract were scored and the overall score for the rat was taken as the mean of the scores for each section.

In order to determine small intestinal plasma protein leakage, rats were prepared as described above. At the beginning of the experiment the rats received an intravenous injection of 125I-bovine serum albumin (10 μCi). At the end of the experiment, a blood sample was drawn from the carotid artery and was centrifuged for 2 minutes (9000 xg) in an Eppendorf microfuge. An aliquot of the plasma was transferred to a plastic tube for counting on a γ-spectrometer (Micromedic). Leakage of labelled albumin into the small intestinal tissue and lumen was determined as described previously (16). Briefly, 8 cm segments of duodenum, jejunum and ileum were clamped and excised. The segment of duodenum was that adjacent to the pylorus, while the segment of ileum was that proximal to the ileocaecal valve. The jejunal segment was taken from the region 10-15 cm distal to the pylorus. The segments were transferred to a glass vial containing 2.0 ml of 0.9% saline and opened by a longitudinal incision. After mixing, 1.0 ml of the "luminal" fluid was transferred to a plastic tube for counting on a γ-spectrometer. The tissue samples were blotted dry, weighed and transferred to a plastic tube for determination of radioactivity, as above. The number of cpm per μl of plasma obtained counting the plasma sample was used to calculate the volume of plasma which leaked into the intestinal lumen and into the tissues themselves.

Materials

BN 52021 (9H-1,7a-(epoxymethano)-1H,6aH-cyclopenta(c)furo (2,3-b)furo-(3',2':3,4)cyclopenta(1,2-d)furan-5,9,12-(4H)-trione,3-tert-butylhexahydro-8-methyl), an extract from *Gingko biloba* leaves (IHB-IPSEN Research Laboratories, Le Plessis Robinson, France), was dissolved in 0.1 N sodium hydroxide, neutralized with 0.1 N hydrochloric acid and then diluted with

0.9% saline to a final concentration of 10 mg/ml. Endotoxin from *E. coli* was dissolved in 0.9% saline at a concentration of 25 mg/ml. Platelet-activating factor (1-O-alkyl-2-O-acetyl-*sn*-glyceryl-3-phosphorylcholine; Sigma) was stored as a stock solution (2 mg/ml) in chloroform at −20°C. On the day of an experiment, an aliquot of PAF was evaporated under a stream of nitrogen and the residue was then dissolved in 0.25% bovine serum albumin/0.9% saline. PAF was infused at a rate of 0.1 ml/min using a Sage syringe pump. Bovine serum albumin (Sigma) was labelled with 125-iodine (New England Nuclear) using the chloramine-T method and was purified on a Sephadex G-75 column prior to use.

Statistical Analysis

All data are expressed as the mean ± SEM. The Student's *t* test was used to compare groups of parametric data, while the Wilcoxon Rank-Sum test was used for comparing groups of non-parametric data. With both types of analyses, an associated probability (p value) of 5% or less was considered as significant.

RESULTS

Gastric Damage

Infusion of PAF for a period of 10 minutes (100 ng/kg/min) resulted in extensive gastric mucosal hyperemia, sometimes with focal regions of hemorrhage. The hyperemia was usually observed in the fundic region of the stomach, and the most common site of damage was on the lesser curvature, near the border of the fundus and antrum. There was often copious yellow fluid present in the lumen. The mean macroscopic damage score for the animals treated with PAF was 2.0 ± 0.3. Histologically, the damage induced by PAF was characterized by extensive vascular engorgement and stasis. The surface epithelium was often discontinuous and cellular debris was visible in the lumen. In some regions, mucosal necrosis with hemorrhage was observed. Where necrosis was observed, it did not extend deeper than the muscularis mucosae. Marginated polymorphonuclear leukocytes were frequently observed in the submucosal layer. Pretreatment with BN 52021 prior to PAF resulted in complete prevention of macroscopically visible gastric damage (Table 1).

Administration of *E. coli* endotoxin also resulted in extensive hyperemia and hemorrhage of the stomach. As with PAF, the damage was of a focal nature and was primarily confined to the fundic region. Another similarity to the damage induced by PAF was that the lesser curvature was a com-

Table 1 Macroscopical and histological assessment of gastric and intestinal damage induced by *E. coli* endotoxin or PAF

	Gastric		Intestinal	
	Macroscopical	Histological	Macroscopical	Histological
PAF	2.0 ± 0.3	NS	2.4 ± 0.3	NS
BN 52021 + PAF	0 ± 0 ***	NS	0.8 ± 0.3***	NS
LPS	2.8 ± 0.6	2.3 ± 0.2	2.5 ± 0.3	2.7 ± 0.2
BN 52021 + LPS	0.6 ± 0.4**	0.4 ± 0.2***	1.1 ± 0.1***	0.5 ± 0.2***

Macroscopical and histological damage were scored on a 0 (normal) to 3 (severe damage) scale and were assigned by an observer unaware of the treatment. Each value represents the mean ± SEM of 8 or more experiments. Asterisks denote groups which differ significantly from the corresponding control (PAF or LPS) group (**$p < 0.01$; ***$p < 0.001$; Wilcoxon Rank-Sum test). PAF = platelet-activating factor; LPS = endotoxin from *E. coli;* NS = not studied.

mon site of the gastric damage induced by endotoxin. The mean damage score for the endotoxin-treated rats was 2.8 ± 0.6 (Table 1).

Pretreatment with BN 52021 significantly ($p < 0.001$) reduced macroscopically visible gastric damage induced by endotoxin (Table 1). Histologically, damage was limited to surface epithelial cell damage and some superficial vascocongestion.

Intestinal Damage and Plasma Protein Leakage

Leakage of radiolabelled albumin into the small intestine of untreated control rats ranged between 10 and 14 μl/g for luminal samples, and 20 to 30 μl/g for tissue samples. Infusion of PAF for 10 minutes resulted in a highly significant increase ($p < 0.001$) in plasma protein leakage in both types of samples (Fig. 1). There was copious yellow fluid present in the lumen of the gut, which frequently contained blood. The samples of gut themselves were hyperemic, and histological analysis revealed extensive mucosal necrosis and hemorrhage (Table 1). Hyperemia and hemorrhage were also observed in the caecum, but the distal colon appeared normal.

Pretreatment with BN 52021 prior to PAF infusion resulted in a significant ($p < 0.01$) reduction in plasma protein leakage in both types of samples (Fig. 1). In fact, the levels of luminal plasma protein leakage observed in the BN 52021-pretreated rats were not significantly different from those observed in untreated, control rats. Macroscopically, damage to the small intestine of BN 52021-treated rats was limited to diffuse hyperemia, which was usually confined to the duodenum (Table 1).

Gastrointestinal plasma protein leakage was also significantly ($p < 0.001$) increased by endotoxin administration. As in the PAF experiments, copious

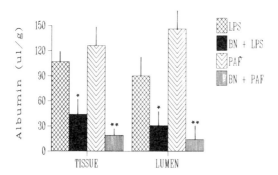

Figure 1 Leakage of [125]iodine labelled albumin into the small intestinal lumen and into the tissue itself (*i.e.* interstitium). Each bar represents the mean ± SEM of 4 to 9 experiments. Rats were pretreated with either vehicle or BN 52021 (20 mg/kg i.v.) 5 minutes before recieving an intravenous injection of endotoxin (LPS) from *E. coli* or an intravenous infusion of platelet-activating factor (PAF; 100 ng/kg/min for 10 minutes). Asterisks denote groups which differ significantly from the corresponding vehicle-pretreated group (*p < 0.05; **p < 0.01; Student's *t* test).

yellow fluid, sometimes containing blood, was frequently observed in the lumen of the segments of gut. Marked hyperemia characterized the macroscopic appearance of the small intestine of endotoxin-treated rats, while histologically, vasocongestion and mucosal necrosis were observed (Table 1). Pretreatment with BN 52021 resulted in a significant (p < 0.05) reduction in intestinal plasma protein leakage (Fig. 1). The levels of plasma protein leakage in the BN 52021-pretreated rats were not significantly different from those observed in untreated, control rats. Macroscopically, damage to the intestine of rats pretreated with BN 52021 was limited to diffuse hyperemia (Table 1). As in the PAF studies, the most affected region was the duodenum. Histological examination of the intestinal samples revealed superficial vasocongestion and occasionally subepithelial edema at the tip of villi. Another similarity to the PAF studies was that endotoxin caused hyperemia and hemorrhage in the caecum, but the distal colon appeared to be spared of damage.

Hemoconcentration and Hypotension

Resting mean systemic arterial blood pressure remained between 100 and 120 mmHg. The resting hematocrit was 43.7 ± 1.0 (n = 21). Infusion of PAF resulted in an almost immediate fall in BP of 45-60 mmHg (Fig. 2). The blood pressure often fell further during the PAF infusion and invariably the pulse pressure narrowed during this time. Following completion of the

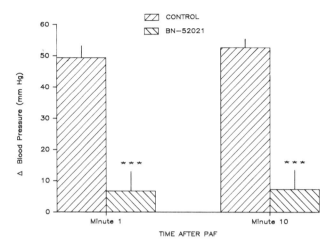

Figure 2 Effects of pretreatment with BN 52021 (20 mg/kg i.v.) on hypotension induced by an intravenous infusion of platelet-activating factor (PAF; 100 ng/kg/min for 10 minutes). Each bar represents the mean ± SEM (n = 9) decrease in systemic arterial blood pressure from resting levels to the point 1 and 10 minutes after beginning the infusion of PAF. Asterisks denote that BN 52021 significantly reduced PAF-induced hypotension at both points (***p < 0.001; Student's *t* test).

PAF infusion, BP gradually recovered towards control levels. However, in many experiments, the BP had not completely recovered at the time that the rat was sacrificed, 30 minutes after completion of the infusion. In blood samples taken immediately before sacrifice, the hematocrit had risen significantly (p < 0.001) to a mean of 56 ± 2% (Fig. 3). Pretreatment with BN 52021 resulted in significant reductions in several of the effects induced by PAF. PAF-induced hypotension was almost completely blocked by BN 52021, and on average, BP had recovered to resting levels within one minute of terminating the PAF infusion. Furthermore, the hemoconcentration observed following PAF administration was not observed in rats pretreated with BN 52021 (Fig. 3).

Endotoxin administration resulted in a biphasic fall in systemic arterial BP (Fig. 4). There was invariably an immediate fall in BP upon administration of the endotoxin. The magnitude of this fall was very much dependent on the rate of injection of the endotoxin. In fact, if the endotoxin was injected quickly, the rat often died. After the initial hypotensive effect of endotoxin administration, the BP usually increased towards resting levels. A second hypotensive effect was observed 3 to 8 minutes after injection of the endotoxin. The mean blood pressure 10 minutes after administration of endotoxin was 41 ± 7 mmHg below resting levels. While the BP usually increased towards resting levels during the final 10-20 minutes of

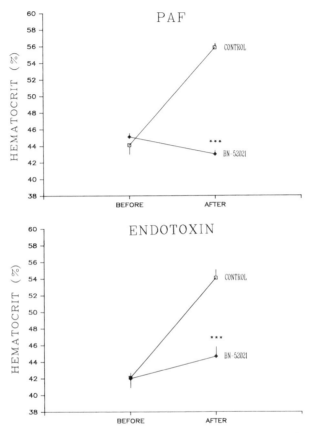

Figure 3 Effects of pretreatment with vehicle (control) or BN 52021 (20 mg/kg i.v.) on the hemoconcentration induced by intravenous injection of endotoxin from *E. coli* (bottom panel) or that induced by intravenous infusion of platelet-activating factor (PAF; top panel) for 10 minutes (100 ng/kg/min). The blood samples were taken 20 minutes before (BEFORE) and 30 minutes after (AFTER) PAF or endotoxin administration. Asterisks denote that BN 52021 significantly reduced the hemoconcentration in both models (***p < 0.001; Student's *t* test).

these experiments, complete recovery of BP was not observed in any of the rats studied (n = 9). As in the PAF experiments, a significant (p < 0.001) increase in hematocrit was observed in blood samples taken 30 minutes after endotoxin administration (Fig. 3). Pretreatment with BN 52021 did not significantly affect the initial decrease in BP induced by endotoxin injection. However, BN 52021 completely abolished the secondary phase of endotoxin-induced hypotension (mean decrease in BP: 1.1. ± 3 mmHg; p < 0.001). The hemoconcentration induced by endotoxin was also significantly reduced by pretreatment with BN 52021 (Fig. 3).

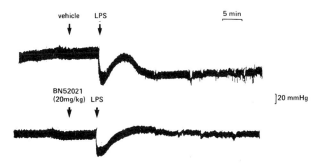

Figure 4 Systemic arterial blood pressure traces from rats pretreated with vehicle (upper) or BN 52021 (lower) prior to receiving endotoxin (LPS) from *E. coli* (25 mg/kg). Note that BN 52021 pretreatment had no effect on the initial hypotension induced by endotoxin, but completely prevented the secondary phase of the hypotension observed in the control rat. (This figure is taken from reference 17).

DISCUSSION

The present study confirms that the specific PAF-antagonist, BN 52021, can significantly reduce the gastrointestinal damage, hypotension and hemoconcentration which accompanies endotoxic shock in the rat. In previous studies, we demonstrated that this and other PAF-antagonists could prevent macroscopically and histologically assessed gastrointestinal damage (17,18). In the present study, the ability of BN 52021 to prevent endotoxin-induced plasma protein leakage in the small intestine has been demonstrated.

The ability of BN 52021 to inhibit several of the features of endotoxic shock adds further support to the hypothesis that platelet-activating factor is an endogenous mediator of this syndrome. Such a role is further supported by the observed similarity in the effects of PAF and endotoxin on the gastrointestinal tract. Both agents produced damage in the stomach, the caecum and throughout the small intestine, but not the distal colon. The reason for this tissue selectivity is not known. Endotoxin and PAF, at the doses used, also produced very similar effects on hematocrit. The observed hemoconcentration may be in large part due to the substantial loss of plasma from the gastrointestinal tract. However, despite the similarity in effects of endotoxin and PAF, there were some distinct differences suggesting that not all of the actions of endotoxin are mediated via PAF. For instance, the initial fall in blood pressure induced by endotoxin was not affected by pretreatment with BN 52021. This initial hypotension, therefore, does not appear to be mediated by PAF. Furthermore, the hemoconcentration induced by endotoxin could not be blocked completely by BN 52021. This suggests that either the endotoxin produces some of these effects independent of any role of PAF, or that the dose of BN 52021 used in this study was insufficient to accomplish complete receptor blockade. Further studies using higher doses of BN 52021 will have to be performed in order to answer this question. However, the observation that the dose of BN 52021 used in the present study (20 mg/kg) was sufficient to reduce endotoxin-induced gastrointestinal leakage to levels not significantly different from those observed in untreated control rats, suggests that the degree of receptor blockade accomplished was sufficient to inhibit any actions of the endotoxin that were mediated by PAF.

There is evidence in the literature that the dose of PAF used in the present study may be in the range of those found in the plasma following endotoxin administration. Doebber *et al.* (5) reported circulating levels of PAF of up to 4.7 nM when blood samples were taken 10 minutes after intravenous administration of *E. coli* endotoxin (50 mg/kg). In the present study, the total dose of PAF administered to a rat was of the order of 200 ng (less than 4 picomoles).

The mechanism by which PAF produces gastrointestinal damage is still unknown. We have previously suggested that mucosal vascular congestion secondary to an increase in vascular permeability is the precipitating event (12,20). Clearly, both PAF and endotoxin do produce marked increases in vascular permeability in the gastrointestinal tract. It is interesting that the region of the GI tract which we have previously noted (19) is spared of PAF-induced damage is also resistant to PAF- and endotoxin-induced plasma protein leakage. Increased vascular permeability may occur because of direct effects of PAF on the endothelium. Alternatively, the increased leakiness of blood vessels may be due to actions of such mediators as leukotrienes, which may be released as a consequence of PAF-induced neutrophil degranulation. The latter mechanism is supported by the observation that PAF-induced hemoconcentration and gastrointestinal damage can be significantly reduced by glucocorticoids or the dual cyclooxygenase/lipoxygenase inhibitor, BW755c (20).

Much more evidence is required before a role for PAF in septic shock can be established. The development of specific PAF receptor antagonists which are safe for use in man will be of tremendous benefit for future assessments of such a role of PAF. The ginkgolides may well prove to be the first such antagonists used clinically for this purpose. Whatever the role of PAF in septic shock, there is a clear need for improvement of its treatment. Mortality from septic shock has been estimated to range from 10% to 70%, and accounts for approximately 100,000 deaths per year in the U.S.A. alone (11,13).

References

1. Adnot, S., Lefort, J., Braquet, P. and Vargaftig, B.B. *Interference of the PAF-acether antagonist BN-52021 with endotoxin-induced hypotension in the guinea-pig.* Prostaglandins 1986; 32: 791-802.
2. Bessin, P., Bonnet, J., Thibodeau, D., Agier, B., Beaudet, Y. and Gilet, F. *Pathophysiology of shock states caused by PAF-acether in dogs and rats.* In: Platelet-Activating Factor. J. Benveniste, B. Arnoux (Eds.). INSERM Symposium No. 23. Elsevier: Amsterdam 1983; 343-356.
3. Braquet, P., Spinnewyn, B., Braquet, M., Bourgain, R., Taylor, J.E., Etienne, A. and Drieu, K. *BN-52021 and related compounds: A new series of highly specific PAF-acether receptor antagonists isolated from Ginkgo biloba L.* Blood and Vessel 1985; 16: 558-572.
4. Braquet, P., Touqui, L., Shen, T.Y. and Vargaftig, B.B. *Perspectives in platelet-activating factor research.* Pharmacol Rev 1987; 39: 97-145.
5. Doebber, T.W., Wu, M.S., Robbins, J.C., Choy, B.M., Chang, M.N. and Shen, T.Y. *Platelet-activating factor (PAF) involvement in endotoxin-induced hypotension in rats. Studies with PAF-receptor antagonist kadsurenone.* Biochem Biophys Res Comm 1985; 127: 799-808.
6. Etienne, A., Hecquet, J., Soulard, D., Spinnewyn, B., Clostre, F. and Braquet, P. *In vivo inhibition of plasma protein leakage and Salmonella enteritidis-induced mortality in the rat by a specific PAF-acether antagonist: BN 52021.* Agents Actions 1985; 17: 368-370.
7. Gonzalez-Crussi, F. and Hsueh, W. *Experimental model of ischemic bowel necrosis. The role of platelet-activating factor and endotoxin.* Am J Pathol 1983; 112: 127-135.
8. Inarrea, P., Gomez-Cambronero, J., Pascual, J., Ponte, M.C., Hermando, I. and Sanchez-Crespo, M.S. *Synthesis of PAF-acether an blood volume changes in gram-negative sepsis and blood.* Immunopharmacol 1985; 9: 45-52.
9. Lagente, V., Lidbury, P., Steel, G., Vargaftig, B.B., Wallace, J.L. and Whittle, B.J.R. *Role of PAF as a mediator of endotoxin-induced gastrointestinal damage.* Br J Pharmacol 1987; 90: 114P.
10. Lees, I.W., Payne, A.N., Wallace, J.L. and Whittle, B.J.R. *Cardiopulmonary and gastric effects of intravenous PAF in anaesthetized cats.* Br J Pharmacol 1986; 89: 504P.
11. Lundberg, D., Alestig, K., Haglund, U. and Hellman, A. *Intensive care treatment in septic shock.* Scand J Infect Dis 1983; Suppl 41: 187.
12. Rosam, A.-C., Wallace, J.L. and Whittle, B.J.R. *Potent ulcerogenic actions of platelet-activating factor on the stomach.* Nature 1986; 319: 54-56.
13. Shumer, W. *Septic shock.* JAMA 1979; 242: 1906-1907.
14. Steel, G., Wallace, J.L. and Whittle, B.J.R. *Failure of prostaglandin E_2 and its 16,16-dimethyl analogue to prevent PAF-induced gastric damage.* Br J Pharmacol 1987; 90: 365-372.
15. Terashita, Z.-I., Imura, Y., Nishikawa, K. and Sumida, S. *Is platelet-activating factor (PAF) a mediator of endotoxin shock?* Eur J Pharmacol 1985; 109: 257-261.
16. Wallace, J.L., Steel, G. and Whittle, B.J.R. *Gastrointestinal plasma leakage in endotoxic shock. Inhibition by prostaglandin E_2 and by a platelet-activating factor antagonist.* Can J Physiol Pharmacol 1987; 65: 1428-1432.
17. Wallace, J.L., Steel, G., Whittle, B.J.R., Lagente, V. and Vargaftig, B.B. *Evidence for platelet-activating factor (PAF) as a mediator of endotoxin-induced gastrointestinal damage in the rat: Effects of three PAF antagonists.* Gastroenterology 1987; 93: 765-773.
18. Wallace, J.L. and Whittle, B.J.R. *Prevention of endotoxin-induced gastrointestinal damage by CV-3988, an antagonist of platelet-activating factor.* Eur J Pharmacol 1986; 124: 209-210.
19. Wallace, J.L. and Whittle, B.J.R. *Profile of gastrointestinal damage induced by platelet-activating factor.* Prostaglandins 1986; 32: 137-141.
20. Wallace, J.L. and Whittle, B.J.R. *Effects of inhibitors of arachidonic acid metabolism on PAF-induced gastric mucosal necrosis and haemoconcentration.* Br J Pharmacol 1986; 89: 415-422.
21. Whittle, B.J.R., Kauffman, G.L. and Wallace, J.L. *Gastric vascular and mucosal-damaging actions of PAF in the canine stomach.* Adv Prost Leuk Res 1987; 17: 285-292.

PREVENTION OF THE PLATELET-ACTIVATING FACTOR-INDUCED GASTROINTESTINAL DAMAGES BY BN 52021 AND BN 52063

François Clostre, Annie Etienne, Jean-Michel Mencia-Huerta and Pierre Braquet

Institut Henri Beaufour Research Laboratories, F-92350 Le Plessis Robinson, France

INTRODUCTION

Besides being a potent platelet aggregating agent and a mediator of allergic and inflammatory processes (6, 10), platelet-activating factor (PAF-acether) has recently been shown to also be a potent ulcerogenic agent in the stomach (19, 23). This ulcerogenic property of PAF is neither mediated via platelet activation or generation of cyclooxygenase products, nor via stimulation of histamine or adrenogenic receptors (19).

PAF-acether-induced ulcerations are similar to the gastrointestinal impairments observed after endotoxin administration (3, 4, 19): like endotoxin, PAF-acether-induced hemorrhagic damage is associated with vascular congestion in the mucosa of stomach and small intestine but not in that of the distal colon (24). Further evidence for such a role was provided by the demonstration that intravenous administration of endotoxin to rats resulted in the release of PAF-acether into the bloodstream (13). A role for PAF-acether as a mediator of gastrointestinal ulceration is supported by the observation that PAF-acether-induced gastric necrosis in the rat stomach at doses as low as 50 μM/kg (19), while doses as low as 2 μM/kg significantly

Address all correspondence to: Dr. Pierre Braquet, Institut Henri Beaufour, 17 avenue Descartes, F-92350 Le Plessis Robinson, France.

predisposed the rat stomach to damage induced by topically applied 20%
ethanol (25). Other inflammatory mediators, such as thromboxane A_2 and
leukotriene C_4, have been suggested to have pro-ulcerogenic actions in the
gastric mucosa because of their potent vasoconstrictor actions (26, 27). While
PAF-acether has not been demonstrated to have vasoconstrictor actions
in the rat stomach, it does cause vascular congestion (19). It is, therefore,
possible that doses of PAF-acether which do not themselves produce ulceration may still have significant pro-ulcerogenic actions and, therefore,
predispose the mucosa to ulceration.

BN 52021 (3-[1, 1-dimethylethyl] hexahydro-1,4,7b-trihydroxy-8-methyl-
9H, 7α[epoxy methanol-1H,6αH-cyclopenta [c] furo[2,3-b] furo[3',2':3,4]
cyclopenta [1,2-D] furan-5, 9, 12 [4H]-trione) and BN 52063 (composed
of BN 52020, BN 52021 and BN 52022; molar ratio 2:2:1) are specific PAF-
acether antagonists isolated from a crude *Ginkgo biloba* extract (5, 9).
Besides specific inhibition of PAF-acether-induced platelet aggregation and
[³H] binding on platelet membranes and lung tissue, these compounds have
been shown to inhibit endotoxin-induced mortality in the rat (14, 10), as
well as hypotension and pulmonary alterations following endotoxin injection in the guinea-pig (1). Thus, we analyzed the effect of these antagonists
on PAF-acether- and endotoxin-induced gastric mucosal damage in comparison with several etiopathogenic models in the rat: 1) gastric hypersecretion induced by pylorus-ligation; 2) stress- and aspirin- induced ulcerations;
and 3) gastric mucosal damage caused by ethanol.

MATERIALS AND METHODS

For each set of experiments the rat strain was chosen in accordance with
the original description. The sex and weight of each group of animals, optimal for the development of gastric and/or intestinal damages, were determined in preliminary experiments. Control animals received only the solvent of the drugs.

Gastric and Intestinal Mucosal Damage Caused by PAF-Acether

Male Wistar rats (210-230 g) were injected via the penis vein with 5 ml/kg
of a saline solution containing defined concentrations (0.1-2.0 mg/ml) of
PAF-acether. Twenty minutes later, the rats were killed, the stomach and
small intestines (duodenum, jejunum) were removed and then opened. Prior
to mucosa alterations they were quantified upon microscopic observation
and scored using a coefficient relating to the severity of ulcerations: 0: normal mucosa; 1: small hemorrhage; 2: large hemorrhage; 3: hemorrhage + 1

to 3 necrotic areas; 4: hemorrhage + large necrosis; 5: perforated stomach. The effects of BN 52021 (5, 10, 20 mg/kg) and BN 52063 (10, 20, 50 mg/kg) were investigated against 2 μg/kg PAF-acether. Oral administration of the drug was carried out 30 minutes before PAF-injetion.

Gastric and Intestinal Damage Caused by Endotoxin

A similar protocol as for PAF-acether was used: the rats were injected with either saline or with a bolus of *Salmonella enteritidis* endotoxin (16 mg/kg). Twenty minutes later, the rats were sacrificed, the stomachs and the intestines were removed and opened. Mucosa alterations were scored as described for PAF-acether BN 52021 (5, 10 and 20 mg/kg) was administered orally 30 minutes before endotoxin administration.

Gastric Hypersecretion in Pylorus-Ligated Rats (Shay Rats)

Experiments were carried out on male Sprague Dawley rats (180-200 g) fasted for 24 hours. Rats were either treated or not orally with either BN 52021 (2 and 10 mg/kg) or atropine (2.5 mg/kg) 24 hours and 1 hour before pylorus ligation. In accordance with the method of Shay *et al.* (20), as modified by Del Taca *et al.* (12), the pylorus was tied under light ether anesthesia. Four hours after ligation the animals were sacrificed, the cardia was ligated, the whole stomach was removed and the accumulated gastric juice was carefully collected. After the volume of gastric juice was measured, acidity was determined by an Autotitrator pH meter (TTT 85, Radiometer, Copenhagen-DK).

Stress-Induced Gastric Damage

IN THE YOUNG MALE RAT   Male COBS/Wistar rats (70-90 g) were starved for approximately 23 hours prior to the experiments. Water was freely available until administration of the drug (BN 52021 8, 20 and 40 mg/kg or ranitidine 5 mg/kg p.o.). Groups of 12 rats received treatment 1 hour before and 6 hours after application of the plaster of Paris bandage. The plaster of Paris bandage was placed so as to leave only the head and the tail free. All animals were then checked to ensure that none had wriggled before the bandage had fully hardened. After a further 18 hour period the animals were sacrificed, the stomachs removed, opened along the greater curvature, lightly rinsed and pinned out on a cork block.

IN THE ADULT FEMALE RAT   Female Sprague Dawley rats (220-245 g) were fasted 24 hours but not deprived of water. The animals received food for the 2 hours preceeding the experiment. After light anesthesia, the rats were placed in a tight fitting wire gauze tube and the legs were fixed with adhesive tape for immobilization. The animals received oral treatment with BN 52021 (10, 20 and 50 mg/kg), triazolam (25 and 50 mg/kg) or atropine sulfate (25 and 50 mg/kg) 1 hour before the experiment and 3 hours after the beginning of the restraint period (half of the dose each time). After an 18 hour immobilization period (2 p.m. to 8 a.m. the next day), the animals were killed with i.p. injection of thiopental and the stomachs were collected and fixed in 10% formol in a saline solution prior to gastric mucosa examination.

In both cases the stomachs were examined on a blind basis for gastric damage, which was scored as indicated for PAF-acether.

Aspirin-Induced Gastric Damage

One day prior to the experiments, male COBS/Wistar rats (100-125 g) were allocated into body weight ranges and fasted. Water was freely available until administration of the drugs (BN 52021: 8, 20, 40 mg/kg or ranitidine: 5 mg/kg, p.o.). Ten minutes later, aspirin (60 mg in 1.0 ml of 0.5% carboxymethylcellulose) was given orally. Five hours after aspirin administration the rats were sacrificed and the stomachs removed, opened along the greater curvature, gently rinsed and pinned out on a cork block. The stomachs were then examined on a blind basis for gastric damage, which was scored as indicated for PAF-acether.

Ethanol-Induced Gastric Damage

Male Wistar rats (fasted overnight with free access to water) were treated orally with BN 52021 (5, 10, 25 and 50 mg/kg) and after 30 minutes, 1.5 ml of absolute ethanol was instilled intragastrically. Five minutes later the rats were killed by cervical dislocation, the stomachs were removed, opened and mucosal damage was scored as indicated for PAF-acether.

RESULTS AND DISCUSSION

Gastric and Intestinal Mucosal Damage Caused by PAF-Acether

Intravenous injection of PAF-acether to rats induced severe damage in the gastric and intestinal mucosa. These alterations appeared early (10 min) and were dose-dependent (Fig. 1A). The macroscopic aspect of the mucosal erosions was totally different from that observed after administration of non steroidal anti-inflammatory drugs: PAF-acether induced mucus hypersecretion, severe hyperemia, particularly at the intestinal level but clear necrosis areas were of limited frequency. A peeling of the mucosa seemed

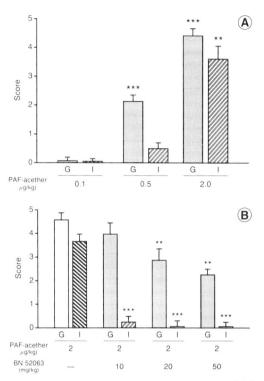

Figure 1 Gastrointestinal ulcerations induced by PAF-acether in the rat (A) and their prevention by BN 52063 (B). Rats were pretreated orally with BN 52063 30 min before intravenous administration of PAF-acether (2 μg/kg). Damage was scored as indicated in the Methods section in a randomized, blind manner. Ulcerations (G = gastric; I = intestinal) are expressed as the mean ±SEM of 10 different experiments. Asterisks denote groups which differ significantly from the corresponding control group (Student *t* test; *p<0.05; **p<0.01; ***p<0.001). Rats not treated with PAF-acether had a nil score.

to occur. Pretreatment of rats with BN 52021 (Table 1) or BN 52063 (Fig. 1B) almost totally inhibited PAF-acether-induced alterations in the intestinal mucosa at the three doses studied. The PAF-acether antagonists also decreased in a dose-dependent fashion the gastric mucosa alterations, although to a lesser extent.

These results confirm the previous reports by Rosam *et al.* (19) and Wallace and Whittle (23) that i.v. infusion of PAF-acether in the rat induces extensive hemorrhagic damage to the gastrointestinal mucosa characterized by severe hyperemia and mucus hypersecretion. Extensive damage to the surface epithelium was also noted with focal regions of deeper necrosis. The damage appeared more pronounced in the stomach than in the intestine where clear necrosis areas were of limited frequency. Never-

Table 1 BN 52021 inhibitory effect on PAF-acether-induced gastric and intestinal mucosa alterations in the rat (PAF-acether 2μg/kg i.v.)

Treatment	BN 52021 (a) (mg/kg)	Damage score (b) gastric mucosa	intestinal mucosa
PAF-acether control	—	4.35 ± 0.076	3.50 ± 0.211
PAF-acether + BN 52021	5	3.74 ± 0.212 NS	0.14 ± 0.148*
	10	3.14 ± 0.244**	0.07 ± 0.081**
	20	2.08 ± 0.204**	0.00***

(a) Oral treatment was performed 30 min before PAF-acether injection.
(b) Mean ± SEM. Statistical analysis with Student t test compared to PAF-acether control group.
*p<0.05; **p<0.01; ***p<0.001. Rats not treated with PAF-acether had a nil score. Each group was composed of 10 animals.

theless, macroscopic alterations of the jejunum and ileum mucosa were observed whereas the distal colon remained intact, as already observed by Wallace and Whittle (23).

Gastric Damage Induced by Salmonella enteritidis Endotoxin

The impairments of gastric and intestinal mucosa were similar to those produced by PAF-acether. All of the endotoxin-treated rats had extensive damage in the stomach and small intestine. As in the PAF-acether experiments, the distal colon was spared of damage. The lumen of the stomach and small intestine contained copious fluid and blood. Histologically, endotoxin-induced damage was very similar to that observed after PAF-acether. There was extensive vascular congestion throughout the stomach and small bowel. Overt bleeding and extensive necrosis were also evident, particularly in the duodenum and jejunum. In regions of the stomach in which the epithelium was intact, subepithelial edema was frequently observed.

BN 52021 given p.o. dose-dependently reduced endotoxin-induced impairments in both stomach and small intestine. Neither necrosis nor hyperemia was observed in animals treated with the highest dose of the PAF-acether antagonists (Fig. 2).

Ulcerations of the stomach and duodenum in shock like burn and sepsis were noted and several lines of evidence suggest the involvement of PAF-acether in such phenomenon: 1) Intravenous infusion of PAF-acether induces many of the symptoms of endotoxic or septic shock, including gastrointestinal ulcerations (3, 4, 15); 2) PAF-acether is not present in the blood of control animals but appears in that of rats treated with endotoxin (13, 8); 3) At doses which inhibit PAF-acether-induced shock, BN 52021 (1, 14) also inhibited endotoxin-induced hemodynamic changes in animals;

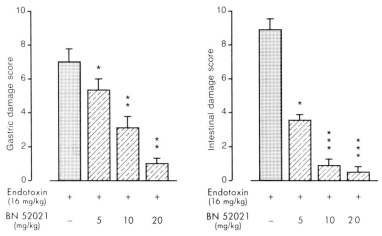

Figure 2 Effect of oral administration of BN 52021 on endotoxin-induced gastrointestinal damage. Rats were pretreated orally with BN 52021 30 min before intravenous administration of endotoxin (15 mg/kg). Damage was scored as indicated in the Methods section in randomized, blind manner. Ulcerations are expressed as the mean ± SEM of 12 different experiments. Asterisks denote groups which differ significantly from the corresponding control group (Saline infusion; Student t test; *p < 0.05; **p < 0.01; ***p < 0.001). Rats not treated with *Salmonella enteritidis* endotoxin had a nil score.

4) BN 52021 inhibits platelet accumulation in the guinea-pig after endotoxin-aerosol (2); and 5) Guinea-pig lung parenchymal strips from endotoxin-treated animals are desensitized to PAF-acether (22).

As already described for CV 3988 (24), the PAF-acether antagonists BN 52021 and BN 52036 prevent gastrointestinal damage induced by endotoxin. The protection is more evident in the intestinal tract where the two highest doses of PAF-acether antagonists afford almost total protection. A further argument for PAF-acether involvement in endotoxin-induced gastrointestinal alterations is that both endotoxin and the autacoid cause severe hyperemia and mucus hypersecretion associated with severe bleeding and extensive necrosis. In addition, mucosal degradation was absent in the distal part of intestine. However, whereas the lesions are predominant in the stomach wih PAF-acether, necrosis is mainly observed in the jejunum and duodenum with endotoxin.

Gastric Hypersecretion in Pylorus-Ligated Rats

In contrast to atropine, BN 52021 at 2, 10 and 20 mg/kg p.o. exerted only a mild and statistically non-significent decrease of the volume and free and total acidity of gastric secretion. Furthermore, this moderate effect of BN 52021 was not dose-related. However, at 40 mg/kg p.o. only a low but significant (p > 0.05) decrease in the total acidity was observed.

Stress-Induced Gastric Damage

IN THE YOUNG MALE RAT   The major impairment of the mucosa observed was the presence of numerous small ulcers with only a few small hemorrhages and large ulcers. Oral administration of BN 52021 had no protective effect against stress-induced gastric damage in the young male rat (damage score ranging from 6.8 to 7.8 *vs.* 6.5 ± 0.9 in the vehicle-treated animals, n = 10). In contrast, administered twice orally at a dose of 5.0 mg/kg, ranitidine caused a notable and statistically significant inhibition (48%) of stress-induced gastric damage.

IN THE ADULT FEMALE RAT   After an 18 hour restraint stress period, 93% of the control rats exhibited damage to the gastric mucosa. The number of impaired areas per rat was reproducible and of medium severity. BN 52021 (50 mg/kg p.o.) decreased the number of rats presenting ulcers, with about 45% protection (Fig. 3). Nevertheless, the severity of the remaining gastric damage in animals treated with BN 52021 was similar to that observed in the control group. Atropine sulfate and triazolam [a triazolobenzodiazepine exhibiting PAF-acether antagonistic activity (17)] also reduced the number of rats presenting gastric damage (Fig. 3).

Aspirin-Induced Gastric Damage

Aspirin damage consisted primarily in numerous small ulcers. BN 52021 (8, 20 and 40 mg/kg p.o.) exhibited little if any protective effect on aspirin-

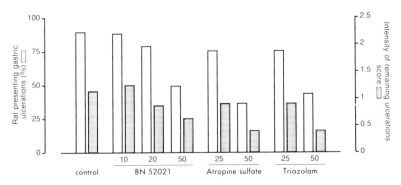

Figure 3   Effect of PAF-acether antagonists (BN 52021 and triazolam) and atropine sulfate on restraint stress- induced gastric ulcerations in the adult female rats. Rats were pretreated orally with the drugs 1 hour before the test and 3 hours after the beginning of the restraint period (half dose each time). The open bars express the percentage of rats presenting gastric ulterations. The hatched bars express the intensity of the remaining ulcerations scored as indicated in Methods in a randomized, blind manner. Asterisks denote groups which differ significantly from the corresponding control group (Student *t* test; *p < 0.05; **p < 0.01; ***p < 0.001).

induced gastric damage since only 11% and 10% reduction of gastric damage, respectively, were observed with the two highest doses of the antagonist. The reference standard ranitidine, at 5.0 mg/kg p.o., caused a statistically significant (p > 0.01) 39% decrease in aspirin-induced gastric damage.

Ethanol-Induced Gastric Damage

BN 52021 given orally 30 minutes before intragastric ethanol instillation reduced in a dose-dependent fashion the alteration of the mucosa: a slight non significant inhibitory effect appeared at 5 mg/kg and became significant at 25 mg/kg affording 50% protection. Surprisingly, the highest dose of BN 52021 (50 mg/kg) was almost ineffective (Table 2).

The possible involvement of PAF-acether in other types of gastrointestinal ulceration is not so evident. BN 52021 afforded partial protection vs. ethanol- and restraint stress-induced gastric damage. In the latter model, another PAF-acether antagonist, triazolam (17), also appeared to be partially effective and, as for BN 52021, this protection was only observed in the female rat. In these two experimental models of gastrointestinal alterations, atropine sulfate is more active than the two PAF-acether antagonists. The protection afforded by BN 52021 on ethanol-induced gastric damage is difficult to interpret since the effect of the drug follows a bell shape curve with a maximal activity at 25 mg/kg, the highest dose (50 mg/kg) being almost ineffective. A similar observation has been recently made by Peskar et al. (18), who also showed that the ethanol-induced formation of LTC_4 tended to be reduced by BN 52021 (25 mg/kg, orally), even though this effect was not stastically significant.

Table 2   Effects of BN 52021 on gastric mucosal damage caused by ethanol in the rat

Oral treatment[a]	Dose (mg/kg)	Group mean gastric[b] damage score	% Inhibition of gastric damage
Vehicle (1% tragacanth)	—	7.5 ± 0.57	—
BN 52021	5	7.3 ± 0.92	3
BN 52021	10	5.7 ± 0.96*	23
BN 52021	25	3.6 ± 0.62**	52
BN 52021	50	6.3 ± 1.04	16

(a) Oral treatment 30 min before 1.5 ml 100% ethanol; (b) mean ± SEM. Significance of difference from vehicle group (ethanol-treated) using; analysis of variance (log-transformed data): *p < 0.05; **p < 0.01. Each group was composed of 10 animals.

In contrast, PAF-acether does not appear to be involved in gastric hypersecretion in pylorus-ligated rats and in aspirin-induced gastric damage where, in contrast with ranitidine, BN 52021 only afforded a mild or nil protection regardless of the dose administered.

CONCLUSIONS

Although PAF-acether is a very potent ulcerogenic agent, the present results demonstrate that it is not involved in all types of ulceration of the gastrointestinal tract. Although its involvement appears undisputed in endotoxemia, its implication in ethanol- and stress-induced gastric impairments is probably minimal. Our results also demonstrate the lack of a role of this autacoid in the ulcerations induced by aspirin and in gastric hypersecretion in shay rats. The present data indicate a potential therapeutic use of PAF-acether antagonists such as BN 52021 and BN 52063 in gastrointestinal ulcerations induced by sepsis or stress in man.

References

1. Adnot, S., Lefort, J., Lagente, V., Braquet, P., Vargaftig, B.B. *Interference of BN 52021, a PAF-acether antagonist, with endotoxin-induced hypotension in the guinea-pig.* Pharmacol Res Commun 1986; 18: 197-200.

2. Beijer, L., Botting, J., Crook, P., Oyekan, A.O., Page, C., Rylander, P. *The involvement of PAF in endotoxin-induced pulmonary platelet recruitment.* Br J Pharmacol 1987; 92: 803-808.

3. Bessin, P., Bonnet, J., Apffel, D., Soulard, C., Desgroux, L., Pelas, I., Benveniste, J. *Acute circulatory collapse caused by platelet-activating factor (PAF-acether) in dogs.* Eur J Pharmacol 1983; 86: 403-413.

4. Bonnet, J., Thiboudeau, D., Agier, B., Beaudet, Y., Gilet, F. *Pathophysiology of shock states caused by PAF-acether in dogs and rats.* In: Platelet-Activating Factor. INSERM Symposium n° 23. J. Benveniste, B. Arnoux (Eds.). Elsevier: Amsterdam 1983b.

5. Braquet, P., Spinnewyn, B., Braquet, M., Bourgain, R.H., Taylor, J.F., Etienne, A., Drieu, K. *BN 52021 and related compounds: A new series of highly specific PAF-acether receptor antagonists isolated from Ginkgo biloba.* Blood Vessels 1985; 6: 559-572.

6. Braquet, P., Vargaftig, B.B. *Pharmacology of platelet-activating factor.* Transpl Proc 1986a; XVIII 5 (Suppl 4): 10-19.

7. Braquet, P. *Proofs of involvement of PAF-acether in various immune disorders using BN 52021 (gingkolide B): A powerful PAF-acether antagonist isolated from Ginkgo biloba.* In: Advances in Prostaglandin, Thromboxane and Leukotriene Research. U. Zor (Ed.). Raven Press: New York 1986b; 16: 179-198.

8. Braquet, P., Paubert-Braquet, M., Vargaftig, B.B. *Platelet-activating factor, a potential mediator of shock.* In: Advances in Prostaglandin, Thromboxane, and Leukotriene Research, Vol. 17. Raven Press: New York 1987; 818-823.

9. Braquet, P. Godfroid, J.J. *PAF-acether specific binding sites: 2. Design of specific antagonists.* TIPS 1986d; 397-403.

10. Braquet, P., Touqui, L., Vargaftig, B.B., Shen, T.Y. *Perspectives in platelet-activating factor research.* Pharmacol Review 1987; 39: 97-145.

11. Czaja, A.J., McAlhany, J.C., Andes, W.A., Pruitt, B.A. Jr. *Acute gastric disease after cutaneous thermal injury.* Arch Surg 1975; 110: 600-609.

12. Del Taca, M., Soldani, G., Bernardini, C., Pierini, P., Giomini, M.L. *The inhibitory action of ketamine on the rat's gastric secretion.* Arch Int Pharmacodyn 1978; 231: 308-314.

13. Doebber, T.W., Wu, M.S., Robbins, J.C., Choy, B.M., Chand, M.N., Shen, T.Y.

Platelet-activating factor (PAF) involvement in endotoxin-induced hypotension in rats. Studies with PAF-receptor antagonist kadsurenone. Biochem Biophys Res Commun 1985; 127: 799-808.

14. Etienne, A., Hecquet, F., Soulard, C., Spinnewyn, B., Clostre, F., Braquet, P. *In vivo inhibition of plasma protein and Salmonella enteritidis-induced mortality in the rat by a specific PAF-acether antagonist: BN 52021.* Agents and Actions 1985; 17: 368-370.

15. Gonzalez-Crussi, F., Hsueh, W. *Experimental model of ischemic bowel necrosis. The role of platelet-activating factor and endotoxin.* Am J Pathol 1983; 112: 127-135.

16. Hsueh, W., Gonzalez-Crussi, G., Arroyave, J.L., Anderson, R.C., Lee, M.L., Houlihan, W.J. *Platelet-activating factor-induced ischemic bowel necrosis: The effect of PAF-antagonists.* Eur J Pharmacol 1986; 123: 79-83.

17. Kornecki, E., Ehrlich, Y.H., Lenox, R.H. *Platelet-activating factor-induced aggregation of human platelets specifically inhibited by triazolobenzodiazepines.* Sciences 1984; 226: 1454-1456.

18. Peskar, B., Lande, K., Hoppe, U., Peskar, B.A. *Ethanol stimulates formation of leukotriene C_4 in rat gastric mucosa.* Prostaglandins 1986; 31: 283-293.

19. Rosam, A., Wallace, J.L., Whittle, B.J.R. *Potent ulcerogenic actions of platelet-activating factor on the stomach.* Nature 1986; 19: 54-56.

20. Shay, H., Sun, D.C., Gruenstein, M. *A quantitative method for measuring spontaneous gastric secretion in the rat.* Gastroenterology 1954; 26: 906-913.

21. Terashita, C., Imura, Y., Nishikawa, K., Sumida, S. *Is platelet-activating factor (PAF) a mediator of endotoxin shock?* Eur J Pharmacol 1985; 109: 257-261.

22. Touvay, C., Vilain, B., Braquet, P. *Desensitization to PAF-acether of lung parenchymal strips from endotoxin-treated guinea-pigs.* Second Int Conference on Platelet-Activating Factor and Structurally Related Alkyl Ether Lipids. Gattlinburg, TN: USA 1986; Abst 76.

23. Wallace, J.L., Whittle, B.J.R. *Profile of gastrointestinal damage induced by platelet-activating factor.* Prostaglandins 1986; 31: 989-998.

24. Wallace, J.L., Whittle, B.J.R. *Prevention of endotoxin induced gastrointestinal damage by CV 3988, an antagonist of platelet-activating factor.* Eur J Pharmacol 1986; 124: 209-210.

25. Wallace, J.L., Whittle, B.J.R. *Potentiation of ethanol induced gastric mucosal damage by platelet-activating factor.* Br J Pharmacol 1986; 87 (Suppl): 92P.

26. Whittle, B.J.R., Kaufman, G.L., Moncada, S. *Vasoconstriction with thromboxane A_2 induces ulceration of the gastric mucosa.* Nature 1981; 292: 472-473.

27. Whittle, B.J.R., Oren-Wolman, N., Guth, P.H. *Gastric vasoconstrictor actions of leukotriene C_4, $PGF_{2\alpha}$, and thromboxane mimetic U-46619 on rat submucosal microcirculation in vivo.* Am J Physiol 1985; 248: G580.

*Ginkgolides - Chemistry, Biology, Pharmacology
and Clinical Perspectives.* P. Braquet (Ed.)
Copyright © 1988, J.R. Prous Science Publishers, S.A.

BN 52021 AMELIORATES MUCOSAL DAMAGE ASSOCIATED WITH SMALL INTESTINAL ISCHAEMIA IN RATS

Christer Tagesson[1,2,3], Mats Lindahl[2,3] and Theophilus Otamiri[1,4]

[1]Clinical Research Center and [2]Departments of Occupational Medicine, [3]Clinical Chemistry, and [4] Surgery, Linköping University Hospital, Linköping, Sweden

ABSTRACT

We have examined how PAF-acether and its specific antagonist, BN 52021, influence the damaging effects of ischaemia in the small intestinal mucosa. We used a rat experimental model in which a ligated loop of the distal ileum was subjected to ischaemia and revascularization and the ensuing mucosal damage was assessed by lysosomal enzyme release and intestinal permeability measurements. We also determined the mucosal content of malondialdehyde —a lipid peroxidation product— and the mucosal activity of myeloperoxidase, a neutrophil granulocyte marker. Ischaemia and revascularization alone caused increased mucosal permeability to sodium fluorescein, increased N-acetyl-β-glucosaminidase release from the mucosa into the lumen, increased malondialdehyde content in the mucosa, and increased myeloperoxidase activity in the mucosa. Intravenous injection of 1 μg PAF-acether caused a significant potentiation of all these effects of ischaemia, although it had no damaging effects on the mucosa of animals not subjected to ischaemia. On the other hand, BN 52021 significantly reduced the permeability increase following ischaemia and also reduced the increases in N-acetyl-β-glucosaminidase release and malondialdehyde accumulation. By contrast, the increase in myeloperoxidase activity follow-

Address all correspondence to: Dr. Christer Tagesson, MD, Department of Occupational Medicine, University of Linköping, S-581 85 Linköping, Sweden.

ing ischaemia was unaffected by BN 52021. These findings suggest a role for PAF-acether in ischaemic intestinal injury and demonstrate that BN 52021 can ameliorate this kind of damage. The possibility that PAF-acether promotes ischaemic injury by stimulating neutrophil-dependent free-radical generation is discussed.

INTRODUCTION

The mechanisms underlying mucosal injury due to small intestinal ischaemia have not been elucidated. Oxygen-derived free radicals produced in the tissue during a post-occlusive hyperemia have been put forward (11) but the precise molecular mechanisms by which the free radicals might injure the intestinal mucosa have not been substantiated. Recently (7), we found that the intestinal permeability increase following ischaemia was potentiated by lyso-phosphatidylcholine, a potentially membrane-damaging surfactant occurring naturally in the gut (13) but also known to induce mucosal injury at higher concentrations (18). We also found that ischaemia and revascularization in the small intestine caused not only increased lipid peroxidation and accumulation of malondialdehyde in the mucosa, but also increased activity of phospholipase A_2, decreased activity of lysophospholipase, and increased ratio between lysophosphatidylcholine and phosphatidylcholine. Moreover, the intestinal mucosa could be protected against ischaemic injury by quinacrine, a phospholipase A_2 inhibitor (9). These findings, taken together, suggest that activation of phospholipase A_2 may play a role in ischaemic intestinal injury, a possibility that would be consistent with the recent findings that lysophosphatidylcholine and other lysophospholipids accumulate in the heart following ischaemia (15).

The reason why phospholipase A_2 activation may be important in mediating ischaemic intestinal injury is unclear. Phospholipase A_2 is involved in the formation of several inflammatory-promoting and tissue-damaging agents, such as arachidonic acid metabolites, lysophospholipids, and platelet-activating factor (PAF-acether). Little is known, however, about the precise role of PAF-acether in ischaemic intestinal injury. The present investigation was therefore conducted with a view to get more detailed information about the role of phospholipase A_2 activation and PAF-acether formation in this condition. To this end, we examined the influence of PAF-acether and its specific antagonist, BN 52021, on ischaemic damage to the intestinal mucosa; we also studied the influence of BN 52021 on lipid peroxidation and leukocyte infiltration in the mucosa after ischemia and revascularization. Our findings indicate that at least part of the ischaemic damage is due to PAF-acether and that one way by which PAF-acether could contribute to the ischaemic injury is by stimulating the generation of free radicals in invading leukocytes.

MATERIALS AND METHODS

Chemicals

The materials and their sources were as follows: PAF-acether (1-O-alkyl-2-acetyl-sn-glycero-3-phosphorylcholine) was purchased from Calbiochem-Behring Corp., La Jolla, Ca, USA). Stock solution in ethanol was kept at $-70°C$ and working solution in saline with 2.5 mg/ml bovine serum albumin was prepared fresh daily. BN 52021 was generously provided by Dr. P. Braquet of IHB-IPSEN Research Laboratories, Le Plessis Robinson, France. Sodium fluorescein was from E. Merck, Darmstadt, FRG.

Animals and Experimental Design

A rat experimental model described in detail elsewhere (8) was used. The model is based on tenting the mesenteric vessels to a ligated loop of the ileum and after a certain time, lowering the vessels down again. Previous studies have shown that this procedure causes ischaemia and revascularization in the small intestinal mucosa (8) and that the ensuing mucosal damage can be assessed by determining lysosomal enzyme release and increase in mucosal permeability (8,9).

In order to study how ischaemic damage was influenced by PAF-acether or its antagonist BN 52021, anesthetized rats were given 500 μl of a saline solution containing the agent under study. The solution was given intravenously 30 minutes before preparing the ligated loop. Thereafter, to create total ischaemia in the loop, the mesenteric vessels were heightened 2 cm and kept in that position for 2 hours. The vessels were then brought down again and the gut segment revascularized for 5 minutes. Control animals were prepared the same way, but the mesenteric vessels were left untreated for 2 hours and 5 minutes. The extent of mucosal damage was then assessed by determining the activity of N-acetyl-β-glucosaminidase in the gut lumen. In addition, the mucosal contents of malondialdehyde and myeloperoxidase were determined.

For these chemical determinations, the loop was excised and the luminal contents gently removed. After centrifugation of the luminal fluid at 2800 g for 5 minutes, the supernatant was withdrawn and kept at $-20°C$ until analyzed. The mucosa was washed with cold saline and scraped off with a curette; special precaution was taken to remove only the superficial layers of the mucosa. The mucosal cells were suspended in 150 mM NaCl, weighed, and disintegrated in a Dounce homogenizer by 5 strokes with a Teflon pestle. The homogenized cells were also kept at $-20°C$ until analyzed. N-acetyl-β-glucosaminidase, malondialdehyde, and myeloperoxidase were determined as described elsewhere (4,6,12,16). Protein was determined according to Lowry et al. (4).

Permeability Measurements

Experiments were also designed to assess the mucosal damage by determining the passage of permeability marker molecules across the gut wall (8,17). Animals were prepared as above and the ileal loop subjected to total ischaemia for 30 minutes. The portal vein was then cannulated with a venflon cannula (diameter 1.00 mm) and 3.3 mM sodium flourescein in 1 ml 150 mM NaCl was instilled in the ligated loop. Blood samples (100 μl) were withdrawn from the portal vein before deposition and at 10 minute intervals for 30 minutes. The samples were mixed with 1.9 ml Tris (50 Mm)-NaCl (150 mM), pH 10.3, centrifuged (2800 g, 5 minutes) and the supernatant analyzed for sodium flourescein using fluorescence spectrometry (17).

Statistical Analysis

Significance of differences were calculated using Student's t test.

RESULTS

Influence on N-Acetyl-β-Glucosaminidase, Mucosal Malondialdehyde and Mucosal Myeloperoxidase

The effects of PAF-acether on luminal N-acetyl-β-glucosaminidase, mucosal malondialdehyde and mucosal myeloperoxidase in the ischaemic and non-ischaemic intestine are shown in Table 1. Thus, PAF-acether (1 μg i.v.) did not influence the values obtained in non-ischaemic control animals, but it significantly increased the values obtained in animals subjected to ischaemia.

The influence of BN 52021 on luminal N-acetyl-β-glucosaminidase and mucosal malondialdehyde after ischaemia is shown in Table 2. Thus, BN 52021 caused dose-dependent decreases in luminal N-acetyl-β-glucosaminidase and mucosal myeloperoxidase levels as compared to ischaemic controls. On the other hand, the highest dose of BN 52021 tested (4.8 mg/kg) did not influence the mucosal myeloperoxidase activity after ischaemia (data not illustrated).

Table 1 Influence of PAF-acether on luminal N-acetyl-β-glucosaminidase, mucosal malondialdehyde and mucosal myeloperoxidase activity in ischaemic and non-ischaemic rat small intestine. The animals were pretreated with intravenous injections of PAF-acether (1 μg) or saline, and the intestine either subjected to ischaemia or left untreated. Values are means $\pm$ SD of 5 animals in each group

Treatment	N-Acetyl-β-glucosaminidase[a]	Malondialdehyde[b]	Myeloperoxidase[c]
Saline + ischaemia	1.9 $\pm$ 0.27	5.7 $\pm$ 0.67	141.2 $\pm$ 19.07
	***	*	**
PAF-acether + ischaemia	3.1 $\pm$ 0.3	6.9 $\pm$ 0.4	176.4 $\pm$ 9.8
Saline + no ischaemia	0.2 $\pm$ 0.1	1.3 $\pm$ 0.3	11.5 $\pm$ 2.0
	NS	NS	NS
PAF-acether + no ischaemia	0.3 $\pm$ 0.1	1.3 $\pm$ 0.3	13.6 $\pm$ 4.1

[a]nkat/ml; [b]nmol/mg protein; [c]units/mg protein
NS = not significantly different from the non-ischaemic control; * = p < 0.05; ** = 0.01; *** = p < 0.001

Table 2 Influence of BN 52021 on luminal N-acetyl-β-glucosaminidase and mucosal malondialdehyde in the rat small intestine following ischaemia. The animals were pretreated with intravenous injections of the different concentrations of BN 52021 and the small intestinal segment subjected to ischaemia and revascularization

Treatment	N-Acetyl-β-glucosaminidase[a]	Malondialdehyde[b]
Saline + ischaemia	1.9 $\pm$ 0.2	5.7 $\pm$ 0.6
BN 52021 (1.6 mg/kg) + ischaemia	1.5 $\pm$ 0.2*	4.5 $\pm$ 0.5*
BN 52021 (3.2 mg/kg) + ischaemia	0.9 $\pm$ 0.1***	3.7 $\pm$ 1.0**
BN 52021 (4.8 mg/kg) + ischaemia	0.9 $\pm$ 0.1***	3.6 $\pm$ 0.6***
Saline + no ischaemia	0.2 $\pm$ 0.1***	1.3 $\pm$ 0.3***

[a]nkat/ml; [b]nmol/mg protein
* = p < 0.05; ** = p < 0.01; *** = p < 0.001 vs. ischaemic control

Influence on Mucosal Permeability

The passage of sodium fluorescein across the gut wall in differently treated animals is illustrated in Figure 1. The ischaemia caused a significantly increased passage in animals given saline. In animals given BN 52021, however, the increase was much less prominent. BN 52021 thus caused a dose-dependent reduction in the permeability increase obtained after ischemia.

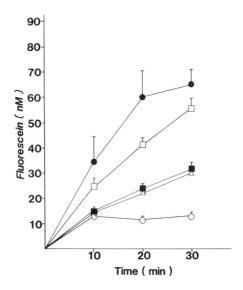

Figure 1. Influence of BN 52021 on small intestinal permeabiliy after ischaemia. Rats were given intravenous injections of BN 52021 (□ = 1.6, ■ = 3.2, and △ = 4.8 mg/kg) or saline (●) and the gut segment subjected to total ischaemia for 30 minutes. The gut segment was then filled with sodium fluorescein and the concentration of fluorescein in the portal blood determined at various times thereafter. Means of 5 animals in each group; vertical bars indicate standard deviation. ○ = non-ischaemic control animals given saline.

DISCUSSION

Recent findings indicate that phospholipase A_2 activation plays an important role in mediating ischaemic injury to the small intestinal mucosa (9). The question arises, therefore, which product(s) of phospholipase A_2 activation could cause this damage. In the present investigation, we applied biochemical determinations and permeability measurements to quantitatively assess the effects of PAF-acether, that is, a phospholipase A_2-dependent phospholipid. We used lysosomal enzyme (N-acetyl-β-glucosaminidase) release and intestinal permeability increase as indices of mucosal damage, and malondialdehyde level as an indicator of lipid peroxidation in the mucosa. In addition, we determined the mucosal activity of myeloperoxidase, a specific marker of polymorphonuclear leukocytes (1). This was because infiltrating leukocytes have previously been shown to play important parts in ischaemic tissue injury.

This investigation showed that ischaemia and revascularization alone caused increased mucosal permeability to sodium fluorescein, increased N-acetyl-β-glucosaminidase release from the mucosa into the lumen, increased malondialdehyde content in the mucosa, and increased myeloperoxidase activity in the mucosa. It was also demonstrated that PAF-acether (1 μg) significantly potentiated these effects of ischaemia, although it had no damaging effects on the mucosa of animals not subjected to ischaemia. These findings are in accordance with those of others, in that intra-aortic injections of 1 μg PAF-acether in rats caused no bowel necrosis, whereas injections of 2 μg indeed did (2). PAF-acether has also been shown to be a potent damaging agent in the gastrointestinal mucosa in a number of other studies (3,14,19).

Our findings that PAF-acether potentiated the damaging effects of ischaemia might be explained by increased mucosal sensitivity to potentially tissue-damaging agents (like PAF-acether) after ischaemia, or by the ability of PAF-acether to activate or promote the tissue-damaging action of inflammatory cells invading the mucosa during revascularization. The potentiating effect observed after interaction between ischaemic intestine and 1 μg PAF-acether could also be due to the fact that PAF-acether was formed in the mucosa and that the PAF-acether so produced, together with that injected, caused the greater injury. This possibility is supported by the finding that BN 52021, a specific PAF-acether antagonist, significantly reduced the permeability increase after ischaemia and reduced the increases in N-acetyl-β-glucosaminidase release and malondialdehyde accumulation. The findings, therefore, indicate that PAF-acether is formed in intestinal mucosa subjected to ischaemia and revascularization, and that PAF-acether contributes to the mucosal damage in this condition. Accordingly, this damage could be ameliorated by BN 52021, a PAF-acether antagonist.

The mechanism by which PAF-acether contributes to ischaemic intestinal injury was not clarified. Injection of PAF-acether caused an increment in the malondialdehyde accumulation after ischaemia and revascularization (from 5.7 $\pm$ 0.7 to 6.9 $\pm$ 0.4 nmol/mg protein), suggesting that PAF-acether promoted the peroxidation of lipids in the mucosa. It is likely that much of this lipid peroxidation was dependent on the infiltrating leukocytes and the increase in malondialdehyde accumulation could, therefore, be due to increased numbers of leukocytes in the mucosa. This possibility would be consistent with the findings that the ischaemic mucosal myeloperoxidase activity was increased after PAF-acether injection, indicating that the number of leukocytes in the mucosa was indeed increased and suggesting that PAF-acether contributed to the recruitment of leukocytes into the mucosa during revascularization. Alternatively, PAF-acether could have caused the increased malondialdehyde formation more directly by stimulating the generation of free radicals in the mucosal leukocytes. Indeed, the observation that BN 52021 reduced the malondialdehyde accumulation (Table 2) without decreasing the myeloperoxidase activity favors this latter possibility and supports the notion that PAF-acether stimulates the generation and release of toxic oxidants by leukocytes (5). Accordingly, it has recently been reported that neutrophils are primed to release toxic oxidants by contact with thrombin-stimulated endothelium and that this is due to endothelial cell-generated PAF-acether (20).

We have thus obtained some evidence to indicate that PAF-acether plays a definite role in mediating ischaemic injury to the intestinal mucosa. We have also demonstrated that B 52021 ameliorates mucosal damage associated with small intestinal ischaemia in rats, although not to the same extent as phospholipase A_2 inhibitors (10). Further studies are now in progess to investigate the ability of different ginkolides and the *Ginkgo biloba* extract to protect against ischaemic intestinal injury and related conditions.

ACKNOWLEDGEMENTS

We thank Professor David Lewis for valuable support. This work was supported by grant B87-17X-05983-07B from the Swedish Medical Research Council.

References

1. Engler, R., Dahlgren, M., Morris, D., Peterson, M., Schmid-Schönbein, G. *Role of leukocytes in response to acute myocardial ischaemia and reflow in dogs.* Am J Physiol 1986; 251: H314-H322.

2. Gonzalez-Crussi, F., Hsueh, W. *Experimental model of ischaemic bowel necrosis. The role of platelet-activating factor and endotoxin.* Am J Pathol 1983; 112: 127-135.

3. Hsueh, W., Gonzalez-Crussi, F., Arroyave, J.L. *Platelet-activating factor-induced ischaemic bowel necrosis. An investigation of secondary mediators in its pathogenesis.* Am J Pathol 1986; 122: 231-239.

4. Lowry, O.H., Rosebrough, N., Farr, A., Randell, A.R. *Protein measurement with the Folin phenol reagent.* J Biol Chem 1951; 193: 265-275.

5. O'Flaherty, J.T. *Lipid mediation of acute allergic and inflammatory reactions.* In: Inflammatory Cells and Lung Disease. CRC Press 1983; 1-27.

6. Ohkawa, H., Ohisih, N., Yagi, K. *Assay for lipid peroxides in animal tissues by thiobarbituric acid.* Analytical Biochem 1979; 95: 351-358.

7. Otamiri, T., Sjödahl, T., Tagesson, C. *Lysophosphatidylcholine potentiates the increase in mucosal permeability after small intestinal ischaemia.* Scand J Gastroenterol 1986; 21; 1131-1136.

8. Otamiri, T., Sjödahl, R., Tagesson, C. *An ex-*

perimental model for studying reversible intestinal ischaemia. Acta Chir Scand 1987; 153: 51-56.

9. Otamiri, T., Lindmark, D., Franzén, L., Tagesson, C. *Increased phospholipase A₂ and decreased lysophospholipase activity in the small intestinal mucosa after ischaemia and revascularization.* Gut, in press.

10. Otamiri, T., Lindahl, M., Tagesson, C. *Phospholipase A₂ inhibition prevents mucosal damage associated with small intestinal ischaemia in rats,* submitted for publication.

11. Parks, D., Bulkley, G., Granger, D., Hamilton, S., McCord, J. *Ischaemic injury in the cat small intestine. Role of superoxide radicals.* Gastroenterology 1982; 82: 9-15.

12. Peters, U., Heath, J.R., Wansbrough-Jones, M.H., Doe, W.F. *Enzyme activities and properties of lysosomes and brush borders in jejunal biopsies from control subjects and patients with coeliac disease.* Clin Sci Mol Med 1975; 48: 259-267.

13. Porter, H.P., Sandersaw, D.R. *Isolation of the aqueous phase of human intestinal contents during the digestion of a fatty meal.* Gastroenterology 1971; 997-1007.

14. Rosam, A.C., Wallace, J.L., Whittle, B.J.R. *Potent ulcerogenic actions of platelet-activating factor on the stomach.* Nature 1986; 319: 54-56.

15. Sobel, B., Corr, P.B., Robinson, A., Goldstein, R., Witkowski, F., Klein, M. *Accumulation of lysophosphoglycerides with arrhythmogenic properties in ischaemic myocardium.* J Clin Invest 1978; 62: 546-553.

16. Tagesson, C., Stendahl, O., Magnusson, K.E., Edebo, L. *Disintegration of single cells in suspension. Isolation of rabbit polymorphonuclear leukocyte granules.* Acta Path Microbiol Scand Section B 1973; 81: 464-472.

17. Tagesson, C., Sjödahl, R., Thoren, B. *Passage of molecules through the wall of the gastrointestinal tract. 1. A simple experimental model.* Scand J Gastroenterol 1978; 13: 519-524.

18. Tagesson, C., Franzén, L., Dahl, G., Weström, B. *Lysophosphatidylcholine increases rat ileal permeability to macromolecules.* Gut 1985; 26: 369-370.

19. Wallace, J.L., Whittle, B.J.R. *Profile of gastrointestinal damage induced by platelet-activating factor.* Prostaglandins 1986; 32: 137-141.

20. Wickham, N.W.R., Vercellotti, G.M., Yin, H.Q., Moldow, C.F., Jacob, H.S. *Neutrophils are primed to release toxic oxidants by contact with thrombin-stimulated endothelium: Role of endothelial cell-generated platelet-activating factor.* Clin Res 1987; 35: 603.

Ginkgolides - Chemistry, Biology, Pharmacology and Clinical Perspectives. P. Braquet (Ed.)

INVOLVEMENT OF PLATELET-ACTIVATING FACTOR IN RAT ISCHEMIA REPERFUSION GASTRIC DAMAGE

Marie-Thérése Droy-Lefaix[1], Yvette Drouet[2], Gérard Geraud[3] and Pierre Braquet[1]

[1]Institut Henri Beaufour, 17 avenue Descartes, Le Plessis Robinson, France; [2]Laboratoire d'Histologie, Faculté de Médecine Pitie Salpetriere, 105 boulevard de l'Hopital, Paris, France; [3]Laboratoire de Pathologie Cellulaire, 15 rue de l'Ecole de Médecine, Paris, France

ABSTRACT

Ischemia reperfusion was responsible for gastrointestinal damage with oxygen-derived free radical production and neutrophil infiltration. Platelet-activating factor (PAF-acether), one of the most potent ulcerogenic mediators, is released from various cell types including neutrophils. In addition, neutrophils are potent producers of oxygen-derived free radicals. The purpose of this study was to determine the potential involvement of PAF-acether in rat gastric post-ischemic lesions, using a PAF-acether receptor antagonist, BN 52021. The activity of BN 52021 at different doses was compared with that of superoxide dismustase and allopurinol, which are known to provide similar protection against ischemia reperfusion damage. In rat stomach, 1 h of ischemia and 24 h reperfusion induced important mucosal injury with mucus adherent spinability drop, necrotic and hemorrhagic lesion formation into the mucosa; edema and neutrophils invasion into the mucosa, submucosa and muscularis mucosa. Pretreatments with

Address all correspondence to: Dr. M.T. Droy-Lefaix, Institut Henri Beaufour, 17 avenue Descartes, F-92350 Le Plessis Robinson, France.

superoxide dismutase, allopurinol and BN 52021 showed a protective effect against mucosal damage. With BN 52021 a dose-response effect was noted. These results suggest a possible pathological role of oxygen-derived free radicals and PAF-acether in gastric mucosal ulceration. Similar results were obtained with free radical scavengers and PAF-acether antagonists; BN 52021, which is not a free radical scavenger, significantly reduces gastric post-ischemic damage. This study shows that PAF-acether antagonists provide a new approach to the therapy of ischemic and inflammatory diseases of the gastrointestinal tract.

INTRODUCTION

It is now well-known that ischemia reperfusion induces severe tissue damage (15, 18, 24, 27).

Current information suggests that reperfusion oxygen-derived free radical genesis, superoxide anion (O_2), hydrogen peroxide (H_2O_2) and hydroxyl radical (OH'), play an important role in the pathogenesis of the gastrointestinal mucosa (7, 8, 12, 13, 17, 22, 24, 27, 28). This ischemic and reflow injury seems to be associated with accumulation of neutrophils (6, 14, 18, 27).

Several recent studies have demonstrated that activated neutrophils synthesize both superoxide anion and hydrogen peroxide. These active oxygen species may interact to form the reactive hydroxyl radical (OH'), particularly toxic for tissue (5, 10, 16, 27).

Platelet-activating factor (PAF-acether) is a potent endogenous mediator (3) of anaphylaxis and shock may be generated from activated polymorphonuclear leukocytes (19, 26).

PAF-acether is reported to increase chemotaxis and neutrophil adherence and to stimulate oxidative metabolism with superoxide anion production (11). It has recently been shown that PAF-acether induces gastrointestinal damage (25) with neutrophil aggregation and extensive necrosis of the mucosa (4, 32, 33). In the present investigation, to assess the role of PAF-acether upon ischemia reperfusion rat gastric damage, we used a PAF-acether receptor antagonist, the ginkgolide BN 52021 (2), known to inhibit endotoxin induced mortality in the rat (9). We compared the effects of BN 52021 with the results obtained with allopurinol, an inhibitor of xanthine oxidase and superoxide dismutase (SOD), a scavenger of superoxide radicals.

MATERIALS AND METHODS

Experimental Procedure

Female Sprague-Dawley rats weighing 180 to 200 g (Charles Rivers, France) were randomly divided into 9 groups (n = 10). They were anesthetized with sodium pentobarbital (50 mg/kg, i.p.). A midline abdominal incision was made and the stomachs were extirpated. The coeliac artery was rapidly occluded during one hour and reperfused for 24 hours. After 18 h fasting the rats were sacrificed by prolonged ether anesthesia. The stomachs were removed, opened along the greater curvature, pinned out on a piece of cork board and rapidly washed with 0.15 M NaCl in water at animal body temperature.

Administration of Drugs

ALLOPURINOL   Allopurinol (Sigma Chemical Co., St. Louis, MO) was dissolved in distilled water by addition of the molar equivalent of lN NaOH. A dose of 50 mg/kg was administered by gavage for two days before the arterial occlusion.

SUPEROXIDE DISMUTASE (SOD)   SOD (bovine liver, Sigma Chemical Co., St. Louis, MO) was given in a 0.9% saline solution at a dose of 15,000 U/kg by direct intravenous injection into the tail vein, 45 minutes before arterial occlusion.

BN 52021   BN 52021 (IHB/Ipsen Research Laboratories, Le Plessis Robinson, France) was maintained in suspension in distilled water with 1% tragacanth and given by gavage at doses of 2.5, 5, 10, 15 and 20 mg/kg, 45 minutes before arterial occlusion.

CONTROL GROUP   Ischemia reperfusion control group received no pretreatments.

Evaluation of Gastric Mucosal Damage

GROSS MUCOSAL APPEARANCE   Gross mucosal necrosis was scored on a blind basis according to the following scale: grade 0: no lesions; grade 1; congestive mucosa, hyperhemia; grade 2: one to four superficial ulcerations about 1 mm in diameter; grade 3: atrophic mucosa, more than four ulcerations or one ulceration larger than 3 mm in diameter; grade 4: more than four deep ulcerations; grade 5: multiple deep ulcerations.

RHEOLOGY   The thread-forming properties of mucus, or spinability, a rheological parameter reflecting the glycoprotein polymerization (1), was measured with an automatic apparatus (Sefam, Nancy, France). On the gastric mucosa surface, the adherent mucous gel was gently scraped off with a fine spatula, then introduced into the measurement cell. Spinability was immediatly evaluated on a calibrated volume of 10 μl. Two measurements were performed on each animal.

MORPHOLOGICAL STUDIES   For mucosal histology, gastric wall samples were fixed in Bouin liquid and stained with Masson trichrome. Coded mucosal specimens were analyzed qualitatively by light microscopy (Leitz).

For scaning electron microscopy, coded samples were fixed using Trump liquid (21). They were then dried by a CO_2 critical point, covered with a gold-palladium mixture and examined with a Jeol 100 CX scanning microscope.

RESULTS

Gross Mucosal Appearance

Macroscopically, the ischemia reperfusion induced gastric mucosal necrotic lesions with large hemorrhages (Fig. 1). The severity of the lesions was higher in the fundus than in the antrum.

The lesions score values showed a significant drop ($p < 0.001$) from 0.25 ± 0.25 in the control group to 3.62 $\pm$ 0.44 in the ischemia reperfusion group.

In rats pretreated with SOD, allopurinol and BN 52021, no necrotic and hemorrhagic lesions were observed. The gastric mucosa retained a normal

Figure 1   Rat stomach gross appearance after ischemia reperfusion with deep, hemorrhagic and necrotic lesions.

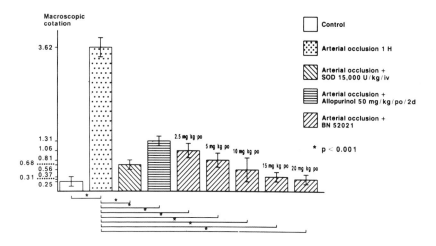

Figure 2 Effect of a PAF-acether antagonist (BN 52021), allopurinol and superoxide dismutase (SOD) on macroscopic necrosis of the rat gastric mucosa induced by 1 h arterial occlusion and 24 h reperfusion.

aspect. The lesion score was near that of the control group. With BN 52021 a dose effect response was noted (Fig. 2).

Mucus Spinability Measurement

As shown in Figure 3, the ischemia reperfusion adherent mucus samples exhibited a significant decrease in spinability from 7.93 ± 0.30 mm in the control to 3.62 ± 0.44 mm after arterial occlusion ($p < 0.001$) according to the lesions extension.

With drug pretreatment a significant increase ($p < 0.001$) in spinability was observed (Fig. 4). With SOD (7.52 < 0.41 mm), allopurinol (10.35 < 1.59 mm), BN 52021 2.5 mg/kg (7.06 ± 0.61 mm), 5 mg/kg (7.92 ± 0.46 mm), 10 mg/kg (8.06 ± 0.68 mm), 15 mg/kg 8.47 ± 0.76 mm), 20 mg/kg (9.4 ± 0.9 mm), the values remained normal.

Histological Examination

With ischemia reperfusion, sections of rat stomach showed acute necrotic gastric mucosal damage (Fig. 4), especially in the glandular part. This injury was characterized by disruption and exfoliation of the surface epithelium, deep necrotic lesions in the full thickness of the gastric mucosa and total gland disorganization. Extensive vascular congestion with hemorrhages was seen in mucosa and submucosa. Large edema was observed in

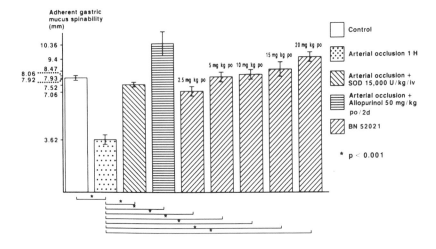

Figure 3 Effect of a PAF-acether antagonist (BN 52021), allopurinol and superoxide dismutase (SOD) on rat adherent mucus spinability drop induced by 1 h arterial occlusion and 24 h reperfusion.

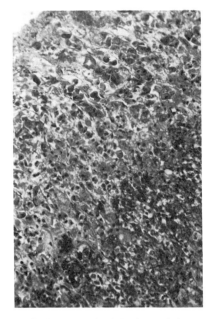

Figure 4 Histology of the rat fundic mucosa after ischemia reperfusion: prominent and deep mucosal necrosis with substantial neutrophil invasion (X 250).

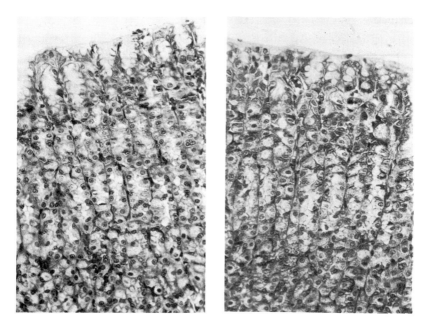

Figure 5   Histology of the rat fundic mucosa. a) Pretreatment with SOD (15,000 μ/kg/45 min i.v. before ischemia reperfusion (X 250). b) Pretreatment with allopurinol (50 mg/kg/2d/p.o.) before ischemia reperfusion (X 250). No prominent and deep necrosis with neutrophil infiltration occurred.

the mucosa, the submucosa and the muscularis mucosae with prominent neutrophil invasion.

A large quantity of mucus with blood and cellular debris was released into the lumen.

Pretreatments with SOD (Fig. 5a), allopurinol (Fig. 5b) and BN 52021 considerably reduced gastric lesion formation.

No hemorrhagic and necrotic lesions with inflammatory cellular infiltrate were observed.

With BN 52021, a dose-effect response was observed. A maximum protection was seen with BN 52021 20 mg/kg (Fig. 6a); gastric mucosa had a normal aspect and was covered with a thick layer of adherent mucus. With BN 52021 2.5 mg/kg, the protection was reduced (Fig. 6b); slight surface erosion was apparent and in some parts of the mucosa vascular congestion remained.

Scanning Electron Microscopy

Ischemia reperfusion induced severe damage of the gastric mucosal sur-

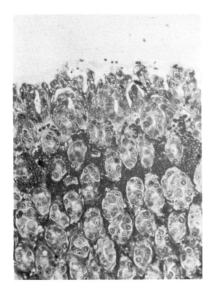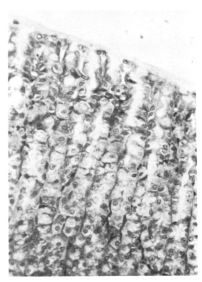

Figure 6 Histology of the rat fundic mucosa. a) Pretreatment with BN 52021 (2.5 mg/kg/45 min/p.o.) before ischemia reperfusion. Protection was reduced with cell exfoliation and mucosa vascular congestion (X 250). b) Pretreatment with BN 52021 (20 mg/kg/45 min/p.o.) before ischemia-reperfusion. Gastric mucosa was normal with a thick adherent mucus gel (X 250).

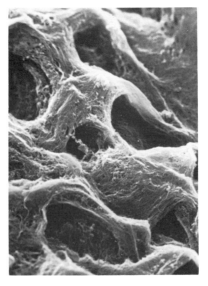

Figure 7 Scanning electron micrograph of rat fundic mucosal surface with deep craters and lamina propria totally denuded (X 1500).

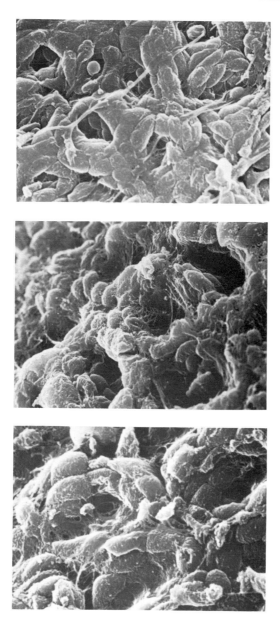

Figure 8 Scanning electron micrographs of rat fundic mucosal surface. a) Pretreatment with allopurinol (50 mg/kg/2d/p.o.) before ischemia reperfusion (X 1000). b) Pretreatment with SOD (15,000 U/kg/45 min/i.v.) before ischemia reperfusion (X 1500). c) Pretreatment with BN 52021 (20 mg/kg/45 min/p.o.) before ischemia reperfusion (X 1500). Gastric mucosal surface was normal with epithelial cells lining the openings of the glands.

face, especially in the fundus. The lesion areas were extended and the lamina propria was totally denuded and necrotic.

With SOD, allopurinol and BN 52021 pretreatments, no prominent changes were noted. Cell extrusion from the surface was considerably diminished and the epithelial cells lined the luminal surface, masking the gland openings.

DISCUSSION

The results clearly show that oxygen-derived free radicals and platelet-activating factor (PAF-acether) play a role in the pathogenesis of ischemic rat gastric injury. Damage to the stomach was characterized by a drop in adherent mucous gel spinablity, a rheological parameter reflecting the state of glycoprotein polymerization (1). Mucus alteration was accompanied by severe necrotic mucosa lesion formation, considerable vascular congestion with bleeding, extensive edema with substantial neutrophil infiltration into the mucosae, the submucosae and the muscularis mucosae.

It is well-recognized that ischemia reperfusion is associated with tissue lesions. The penomenen of reperfusion injury is caused in large part by oxygen-free radicals of both sources, xanthine oxidase (14, 22, 27) and polymorphonuclear leukocytes such as neutrophils (12, 14, 24). Furthermore, recent experimental results have implied a role for PAF-acether during post-ischemia reperfusion damage (25).

PAF-acether, a potent activator of neutrophils, is known to stimulate chemotactic factors and to enhance the ability of neutrophils to release $O_2.-$ at sites of inflammation (11). Low doses of PAF-acether injection have been demonstrated to induce gastrointestinal lesions (25, 30). Mucus hypersecretion, surface epithelium exfoliation, deep necrosis vascular congestion with bleeding were also noted (4, 33). Vascular congestion and hemorrhage may be explained by an effect of PAF-acether on neutrophil aggregation (20).

In this study, accumulation of neutrophils in the tissue adds support to the hypothesis that release of superoxide radicals are induced by PAF-acether stimulation (34).

Rats pretreated with the PAF-acether receptor antagonist, BN 52021, which is not a free radical scavenger, confirmed production of PAF-acether during ischemia reperfusion.

In vitro BN 52021 inhibited polymorphonuclear superoxide radical production after cells were stimulated by C5A and FMLP in the presence of PAF-acether. *In vivo* prevention of stroke by BN 52021 has been described in cerebral post-ischemic phase (29).

CONCLUSIONS

These results suggest that PAF-acether antagonists, and particularly BN 52021, may be used alone or in association with free radical scavengers to protect tissues from post-ischemia oxidative damage.

References

1. Arnould, J.P. et al. *A new apparatus for measuring the thread-forming property (spinability) of biological fluids.* Biorheology 1984; 1: 123.

2. Braquet, P. et al. *BN 52021 and related compounds: A new series of highly specific PAF-acether receptor antagonists isolated from Ginkgo biloba.* Blood Vessels 1985; 16: 558-572.

3. Braquet, P. et al. *Perspectives in platelet-activating factor research.* Pharmacol Review 1987; 39: 97-145.

4. Braquet, P. et al. *Possible role of platelet-activating factor in gastrointestinal ulcerations as evidenced by the use of the specific antagonists, BN 52021 and BN 52063.* Eur J Pharmacol 1988; in press.

5. Briggs, R.T. et al. *Superoxide production by polymorphonuclear leukocytes.* Histochemistry 1986; 84: 371.

6. Chatelain, P. et al. *Neutrophil accumulation in experimental myocardial infarcts: Relation with extent of injury and effect of reperfusion.* Circulation 1987; 75: 1083-1090.

7. Droy-Lefaix, M.T. et al. *Radicaux libres et tube digestif.* Cah Nutr Diet 1987; 22: 44-50.

8. Droy-Lefaix, M.T. et al. *Importance of oxygen-derived free radicals in ischemia with reperfusion gastric mucosal rat damage.* A.G.A. Congress, Chicago 1987.

9. Etienne, A. et al. *In vivo inhibition of plasma protein and Salmonella enteritis-induced mortality in the rat by a specific PAF-acether antagonist: BN 52021.* Agents Actions 1985; 17: 368-370.

10. Fantone, J.C. et al. *Role of oxygen-derived free radicals and metabolites in leukocyte-dependent inflammatory reactions.* Am J Pathol 1982; 107: 397.

11. Gay, J.C. et al. *Modulation of neutrophil oxidative responses of soluble stimuli by platelet-activating factor.* Blood 1986; 67: 931.

12. Granger, D.N. et al. *Superoxide radicals in feline intestinal ischemia.* Gastroenterology 1981; 81: 22-29.

13. Granger, D.N. et al. *Ischemia-reperfusion injury: Role of oxygen-derived free radicals.* Acta Physiol Scand 1986; 548: 47-63.

14. Grisham, M.B. et al. *Xanthine oxidase and neutrophil infiltration in intestinal ischemia.* Am J Physiol 1986; 251: G567.

15. Hallenbeck, J.M. et al. *Polymorphonuclear leukocyte accumulation in brain regions with low blood flow during the early post-ischemic period.* Stroke 1986; 17: 246-253.

16. Hoffstein, S.T. et al. *Neutrophils may directly synthesize both H_2O_2 and O_2^- since surface stimuli induce their release in stimulus specific ratios.* Inflammation 1985; 9: 425-437.

17. Itoh, M. et al. *Role of oxygen-derived free radicals in hemorrhagic shock-induced gastric lesions in the rat.* Gastroenterology 1985; 88: 1162-1167.

18. Jolly, S.R. et al. *Reduction of myocardial infarct size by neutrophil depletion, effect of duration of occlusion.* Am Heart J 1986; 112: 682-690.

19. Lee, T.C. et al. *Increased biosynthesis of platelet-activating factor in activated human eosinophils.* J Biol Chem 1984; 259: 5526-5530.

20. Lepran, I. et al. *Ischemia aggravating effects of platelet-activating factor in acute myocardial ischemia.* Basic Res Cardiol 1985; 80: 135.

21. MacDowell, E.M. et al. *Histologic fixatives suitable for diagnostic light and electron microscopy.* Arch Path Lab Med 1976; 100: 405-414.

22. McCord, J.M. et al. *The pathophysiology of superoxide: Roles in inflammation and ischemia.* Can J Physiol Pharmacol 1982; 60: 1346-1352.

23. Parks, D.A. et al. *Role of oxygen-derived free radicals in digestive tract diseases.* Surgery 1983; 94: 415-422.

24. Parks, D.A. et al. *Oxygen radicals: Effects on intestinal vascular permeability.* Am J Physiol 1984; 247: 67-70.

25. Rosam, A. et al. *Potent ulcerogenic actions of platelet-activating factor on the stomach.* Nature 1986; 310: 54-56.

26. Sanchez Crespo, M. et al. *Synthesis of*

platelet-activating factor from human polymorphonuclear leukocytes: Regulation and pharmacological approachs. Int J Tiss Reac 1985; 7: 345-349.

27. Simpson, P.J. et al. Free radical scavengers in myocardial ischemia. Fed Proc 1987; 46: 2413-2421.

28. Smith, S.M. et al. Gastric mucosal injury in the rat. Role of iron and xanthine oxidase. Gastroenterology 1987; 92: 950-956.

29. Spinnewyn, B. et al. Involvement of platelet-activating factor (PAF) in cerebral post-ischemic phase in Mongolian gerbils. Prostaglandins 1987; 87: 30.

30. Wallace, J.L. et al. Picomole doses of platelet-activating factor predispose the gastric mucosa to damage by topical irritants. Prostaglandins 1986; 31: 989-998.

31. Wallace, J.L. et al. Effects of inhibitors of arachidonic acid metabolism on PAF-induced gastric mucosal damage and haemoconcentration. Br J Pharmacol 1986; in press.

32. Wallace, J.L. et al. Inhibition of endotoxin-induced gastrointestinal plasma leakage by PGE and a PAF-antagonist. Gastroenterology 1987; 92: 1685.

33. Whittle, B.J.R. et al. Microvascular actions of platelet-activating factor on rat gastric mucosa and submucosa. Am J Physiol 1986; 251: G772-G778.

34. Wickam, N.W.R. et al. Neutrophils are printed to release toxic oxidants by contact with thrombin-stimulated endothelium: Role of endothelial cell-generated platelet-activating factor. Fed Proc 1987; in press.

*Ginkgolides - Chemistry, Biology, Pharmacology
and Clinical Perspectives.* P. Braquet (Ed.)
Copyright © 1988, J.R. Prous Science Publishers, S.A.

PLATELET-ACTIVATING FACTOR IN RENAL PHYSIOLOGY AND PATHOPHYSIOLOGY. INTEREST OF THE GINKGOLIDES

Gerard E. Plante and Richard L. Hebert

Department of Physiology and Pharmacology, University of Sherbrooke, Sherbrooke, Québec, Canada, JIH 5N4

PRODUCTION OF PAF IN THE KIDNEY

The normal kidney possesses the required machinery to produce and to metabolize the platelet-activating factor (PAF). The substrate 1-alkyl-2-acyl-glycero-phosphocholine, upon which phospholipase A_2 acts to release Lyso-PAF and arachidonic acid, is present in renal membrane preparations (18, 31, 74). The critical enzyme responsible for the production of PAF from Lyso-PAF, a specific CoA-dependent acetyltransferase, was also found in glomerular, as well as in medullary interstitial cells (74). The enzyme which inactivates PAF by transformation to Lyso-PAF, the acetyl-hydrolase, is also present in renal tissue. Camussi and coworkers (20) were able to demonstrate that rabbit renal slices produce PAF-like material when incubated at pH 10.6, whereas Pirotzky *et al.* (73) showed that the isolated rat kidney releases PAF-related material as well as leukotrienes, when appropriately stimulated. More recently, Schlondorff and his colleagues (97) identified the mesangial cells as the main source of PAF-like material in the glomerulus.

The kidney is not only capable of producing PAF under experimental *in vitro* conditions, but also of releasing this material in urine under physiological and pathological conditions. Sánchez-Crespo *et al.* demonstrated the presence of a hypotensive and platelet-activating phospholipid in normal human urine specimens (91). The normal urinary excretion of PAF-like material has even been established by these investigators to approximate 50 ng/24 hours. Using bioassay determinations, the group of Sánchez-Crespo (23) was able to evaluate the normal blood concentration of PAF in the rat, the rabbit and the human species.

EFFECTS OF PAF ON RENAL HEMODYNAMICS

Renal Blood Flow

The effects of PAF on peripheral hemodynamics have been examined in several animal species using a large range of doses. Following the infusion of PAF, a number of vascular disturbances were described, from cardiovascular collapse to minor disturbances in the skin microcirculation (4, 5, 55, 66). The fall in peripheral blood pressure which follows PAF infusion was found to be associated with plasma extravasation in the interstitial compartment, a phenomenon accompanied by a marked rise in peripheral blood hematocrit (39, 78). PAF-induced hypotension has also been ascribed to a fall in cardiac output due to the vasoconstrictor effect of the glycerophospholipid on coronary arteries (35).

The renal hemodynamic disturbances which occur during systemic PAF infusion have been attributed to the well-described peripheral vascular collapse induced by the phosoholipid (46). The sequence of events, as well as the potential mechanisms involved in these phenomena, were summarized in an excellent review recently published (96). It appears, however, that PAF exerts a direct influence on the renal microcirculation, independent therefore, of any peripheral influence. We first reported that *in situ* perfusion of the dog renal artery with small doses of PAF, ranging between 2 and 20 ng/kg/min, resulted in a progressive dose-dependent reduction of renal plasma flow. Systemic blood pressure, as well as contralateral renal parameters, remained unchanged in this experimental model (78). Renal plasma flow was measured by the para-amino-hippurate (PAH) clearance and appropriate corrections for the renal extraction of this marker (53) were made to ascertain any effect of PAF on intrarenal redistribution of plasma flow. In our studies no significant change in PAH extraction ratio was documented, indicating therefore, a uniform fall of renal plasma flow in both the cortical and the juxtamedullary regions of the kidney. The effect of PAF on renal plasma flow was found to be reversible at all doses used in our studies, administered either as continuous infusions or in single bolus (43, 78). When higher doses were administered in the peripheral circulation, irreversible shock and renal circulatory collapse have been documented (4). Using a similar *in situ* renal artery perfusion model, another group recently confirmed our results suggesting a direct effect of PAF on renal blood flow (92).

Glomerular Filtration

During systemic or intrarenal infusion of PAF, glomerular filtration rate declined as renal blood flow decreased (46, 78, 92). This finding has been reported during continuous perfusion or single bolus of PAF (43, 78). The consequences of these changes in renal plasma flow and glomerular filtration on the filtration fraction (11), a major determinant of peritubular capillary protein concentration (56), have not been consistently reported, and when examined, did not appear to change in a uniform manner (96). In our studies, a greater fall in renal plasma flow than in glomerular filtration has been documented, although the magnitude of changes in filtration fraction was not always of pathophysiological significance (43, 78). The consistent direction of changes in filtration fraction observed in our studies may suggest that PAF exerts a predominant vasoconstrictor effect on the efferent arteriole, a site also suggested for angiotensin II (87). The precise site of action on the glomerular microcirculation has not been directly examined yet.

Electrolyte Transport

Urine flow and urinary excretion of sodium were both reduced during PAF infusion (43, 78). These changes occurred in parallel with the fall in renal plasma flow and glomerular filtration. In most experimental conditions where absolute and fractional excretion were measured, a significant reduction in both parameters was noticed, suggesting that the changes in urinary sodium excretion not only resulted from the fall in the filtered load of this ion, but also from changes in the net tubular transport of sodium (43, 78, 96). It becomes evident, therefore, that PAF altered urinary excretion of sodium through an effect on glomerular filtration and filtered sodium, as well as through a direct or indirect effect on the tubular transport of this cation (43). The pattern of changes observed in urinary excretion of sodium and water following the infusion or bolus injection of PAF differed from that seen during recovery of renal hemodynamics: while renal plasma flow and glomerular filtration returned exactly to control values after PAF, urinary sodium excretion overshooted above control levels by approximately 60% (43). This phenomenon again suggests that PAF altered urinary excretion of sodium not only via hemodynamic factors but also by direct and/or indirect tubular mechanisms.

The effect of PAF on renal excretion of other electrolytes has not been consistently reported (96). In our own studies, urinary excretion of phosphate, calcium, chloride and potassium was examined. Urinary calcium excretion changed in parallel with urinary sodium, but the magnitude of changes observed was much less for calcium than for sodium (42). In most experimental conditions, urinary excretion of potassium was not statistically influenced by PAF infusion. Similarly, changes in urinary excretion of phosphate failed to reach significance in most experimental conditions: in those instances where urinary phosphate excretion was altered by PAF, the changes occurred in the same direction as described for sodium.

The combined influence of PAF on renal plasma flow, glomerular filtration rate, filtration fraction, and urinary excretion of sodium, both absolute and fractional, in normal anesthetized dogs administered an intrarenal bolus injection of the glycerophospholipid, is depicted in Figure 1. The parallel fall and recovery of renal plasma flow and filtration rate during and following PAF infusion, which determined minimal changes in filtration fraction, is well illustrated. Urinary sodium excretion fell along with the marked decrease of renal hemodynamics, but in contrast to the latter parameters, urinary sodium exceeded control values during recovery.

CONDITION	RPF ml/min	GFR ml/min	FF %	U Na V uEq/min	U/F Na %
CONTROL	52±4	28±2	53±2	69±6	1.8±0.1
PAF	26±2	11±1	42±2	25±3	1.5±0.1
RECOVERY	51±3	22±2	43±1	72±4	2.3±0.1
	58±4	28±2	48±2	93±6	2.4±0.2
	60±4	28±3	46±2	115±7	2.9±0.3
	58±3	27±3	46±2	118±8	3.1±0.4
	59±4	26±3	44±2	117±6	3.2±0.3

Figure 1 Effect of PAF on renal hemodynamics. Consequences on urinary excretion of sodium. RPF: renal plasma flow, GFR: glomerular filtration, FF: filtration fraction, U Na V and U/F Na: absolute and fractional excretion.

MECHANISMS OF PAF ACTIONS ON THE KIDNEY

Potential Mediators

PROSTAGLANDINS As several other important humoral substances known to modify the vascular tone or to alter the transport of electrolytes across epithelia, it is likely that PAF exerts its actions through the release of autacoids and/or cell mediators: among these potential mediators, metabolites of arachidonic acid, such as prostaglandins and leukotrienes, must be regarded as privileged candidates to explain the renal effects of PAF. With respect to eventual interactions between PAF and these mediators, it is of interest to recall that the production of Lyso-PAF, the immediate precursor of PAF, occurs in parallel with the production of arachidonic acid, the precursor of prostaglandins and leukotrienes (103). It is also important to remember that the production of angiotensin II can be stimulated indirectly by PAF-induced prostaglandin synthesis (25) and that angiotensin II *per se* is a potent stimulus of PAF release (20, 63). The vasodilatory effect of peripheral PAF infusion côuld be related to the production of vasodilatory mediators, such as prostaglandins, leukotrienes, or a mixture of these metabolites of arachidonic acid. Circulatory neutrophils were shown to release leukotriene B_4 upon stimulation by PAF (60), and, more recently, the kidney was found to be a potential source of prostaglandin E_2 following PAF in experimental models using either the isolated kidney (117) or cultured mesangial cells (93). We have been able to abolish completely the peripheral effects of PAF infusion by blocking prostaglandin synthesis with indomethacin (43): the reduction of blood pressure and the rise in hematocrit due to peripheral vasodilatation and plasma leakage in the interstitium failed to obtain following 0.78 μg/kg intrafemoral bolus injection of PAF in anesthetized dog pretreated with indomethacin. In these experiments, however, inhibition of prostaglandin synthesis failed to protect renal hemodynamics, since plasma flow and glomerular filtration decreased markedly despite the maintenance of systemic blood pressure (43). It is likely, therefore, that the glomerular microcirculation responded to a balance of mediators that happened to be predominantly vasoconstrictors. The fact that renal plasma flow and filtration rate decreased during PAF does not exclude the possibility of local production of prostaglandins, as demonstrated in other models (93, 117). The experimental results obtained *in vivo* during PAF infusion only indicate that the renal microcirculation was under the predominant influence of vasoconstrictor mediators. With respect to eventual PAF-induced production of renal prostaglandin E_2, a potent natriuretic substance (36), it should be pointed out that the peculiar rebound natriuresis obtained following PAF bolus injection, observed in our studies (43), is compatible with such an effect.

LEUKOTRIENES Leukotrienes represent another important category of mediators potentially involved in the PAF actions on renal hemodynamics. The kidney possesses the substrates and the required lipoxygenases controlling the production of leukotrienes, especially the C_4 and the D_4 series (114). These metabolites of arachidonic acid are potent vasoactive autacoids that were reported to vasoconstrict the glomerular microcirculation and reduce filtration rate (1, 76). PAF was demonstrated to be a potent stimulus for leukotriene production and release in glomerular immune injury (90). The renal hemodynamic effects of PAF infusion on renal plasma flow, glomerular filtration rate, and the effect of this substance on urinary sodium could be explained by a direct or indirect *in situ* stimulation of leukotriene C_4 and/or D_4 production and release. In previous experiments from our group, leukotriene D_4 was associated with a fall in renal hemodynamics and urinary sodium, qualitatively similar to that induced by PAF (76). However, more recent studies performed in our laboratory with a new receptor antagonist of thromboxane/prostaglandin endoperoxide (Merck-Frosst L 655,240), indicate that these mediators can also be involved in the response of the dog kidney to PAF infusion (80). Animals receiving intravenous doses of this antagonist failed to respond to repeated bolus injections of PAF: renal plasma flow, glomerular filtration and urinary sodium excretion remained identical to control values when 6 mg/kg of L 655,240 was administered intravenously, as shown in Figure 2.

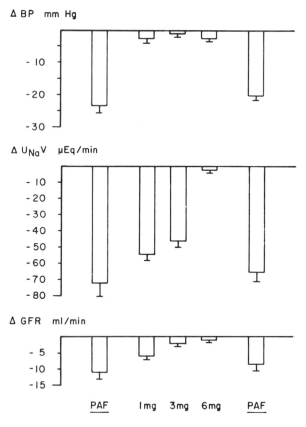

Figure 2 Inhibition of PAF-induced renal disturbances. Effect of L 655,240, a thromboxane/prostaglandin antagonist. BP: blood pressure, other symbols as in 1.

OTHER MEDIATORS   Other potential mediators could also be responsible for the observed renal actions of PAF, but have not yet been directly examined in physiological experimental models. *In vitro* PAF was shown to cause a transient increase of intracellular calcium (16, 67), presumably under the influence of triphosphoinositol (69, 93), an important intracellular mediator, which appears to control fluxes of calcium across the mitochondrial membrane (33). Generation of phosphoinositides and mobilization of calcium from extracellular fluid or mitochondrial stores represent early cellular events in the response of given organs following the binding of PAF to its specific receptor (47). The production and release of the potential mediators described above presumably occur simultaneously, and perhaps independently, but the precise sequence of events with respect to the physiological effects of PAF on specific organs, in particular the kidney, has not yet been established.

Potential Interactions of PAF

ANGIOTENSIN II   The renin-angiotensin system plays a critical role in the control of renal hemodynamics, not only through its effect on whole body sodium homeostasis (15), but also, and perhaps more importantly, through its intrarenal effects via the tubulo-glomerular feedback loop (109). Important interactions were described between angiotensin II and intrarenal prostaglandins (32), angiotensin II and PAF (78, 109), and prostaglandins and PAF (93). It is expected, therefore, to find that some of the physiological effects of PAF are inhibited by antagonists of angiotensin II, such as saralasin. We examined the relationship between PAF and angiotensin II in the normal anesthetized dog (79). As shown in Figure 3, intravenous infusion of saralasin (100 mg/kg) *per se* resulted in a slight increment of glomerular filtration, from 44 ± 2 to 51 ± 3 ml/min, while renal plasma flow remained relatively stable, as well as urinary sodium excretion. During angiotensin II receptor blockade, PAF infusion had no effect whatsoever on renal plasma flow and glomerular filtration, yet urinary sodium excretion decreased from 132 ± 10 to 67 ± 6 μEq/min. These results suggest that the local release of angotensin II, directly or indirectly induced by PAF injection, could be responsible for the predominant vasoconstrictor renal response that occurred during infusion of the glycerophospholipid.

ATRIAL NATRIURETIC PEPTIDE   Research on the atrial natriuretic peptide (ANP) has been prolific since its isolation from cardiac myocytes and its chemical characterization. Recent papers reviewed the present knowledge concerning the physiological effects of this new peptide, in particular on renal hemodynamics and electrolyte transport (2, 30). Intriguing experimen-

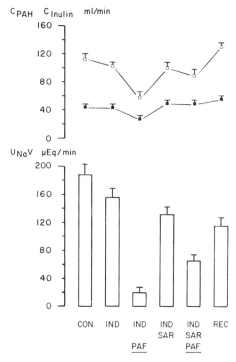

Figure 3 Interactions of angiotensin II and prostaglandins in the renal response to PAF. C PAH: renal plasma flow (open symbols), C inulin: glomerular filtration (closed symbols), CON: control, IND: indomethacin, SAR: saralasin, REC: recovery.

tal observations suggested to us that PAF and ANP may interact in the peripheral vascular system, as well as in the kidney (88). When PAF is administered in volume expanded dogs, its expected effects on renal hemodynamics and urinary sodium excretion is significantly attenuated (58). Since acute extracellular volume expansion is associated with a rise in plasma ANP levels (89), and since this peptide increases glomerular filtration rate, as well as sodium excretion (2, 30), it is reasonable to conclude that the consequences on renal function of PAF injection under such physiological conditions could be reduced because of elevated levels of plasma ANP. This phenomenon could, in turn, antagonize PAF receptors in the kidney or alter the cellular response to the glycerophospholipid. Thievant *et al.* (107) examined the renal response of the anesthetized dog to intravenous ANP during PAF receptor blockade with ginkgolide B (BN 52021): a synergistic effect of ANP and PAF blockade on urinary sodium excretion was noticed, but the effect of these manoeuvres on renal hemodynamics was not reported. According to the authors, these results rule out the participation of PAF (or the Muirhead PAF-related factor) in the natriuresis induced by ANP. In similar experiments performed in the rat, we found that ginkgolide B *per se* increased urinary sodium excretion with minimal change in glomerular filtration (82). In addition, as depicted in Figure 4, when ANP injection was superimposed to PAF receptor blockade, no further increment in glomerular filtration and urinary sodium excretion was obtained. The latter results, in contrast to those reported in the dog (107), would support the existence of a close interaction between ANP and PAF receptors. It is of interest that ANP infusion in normal human volunteers is associated with a slight plasma extravasation from the vascular to the interstitial space (25). This finding is similar to the effect of PAF on plasma leakage and hematocrit, documented by most investigators who administered PAF *in vivo* (4, 43, 78). This similarity of action of ANP and PAF on peripheral vascular permeability also suggests possible interactions, or at least common cellular pathways, for these two important endogenous compounds.

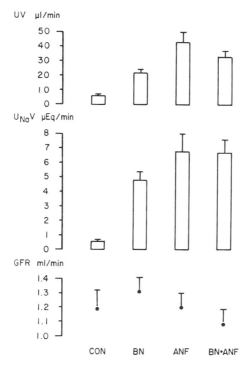

Figure 4 Interactions of ANP and PAF. Effect of BN 52021, a PAF receptor antagonist, on GFR, urinary sodium and urine flow.

ENDOGENOUS LIGNANS   Lignans are natural compounds derived from ox-
ydative dimerization of monomeric phenols. Some of these substances have
been identified in higher plants, and more recently, some lignans, mostly
of the enterolactone series, were discovered in mammalian urine (98, 105).
Braquet and co-workers (7) recently reported that mammalian lignans share
some structural properties with two important categories of pharmacological
agents: *first*, some selective antagonists of PAF receptor, in particular the
synthetic L-652,731, possess a tetra-hydrofurane ring (48); *second*, the
digitalis drugs are characterized by a butenolide ring (64). These chemical
similarities suggested to us that mammalian lignans could influence PAF
receptor sites, and perhaps play a role on the sodium-potassium pump. In
fact, all lignans tested so far inhibit the PAF-induced platelet aggregation,
as well as the sodium-potassium pump activity of human red blood cells
(7). We examined the effect of increasing doses of prestegane B, a synthetic
lignan, in the anesthetized normal rat. As shown in Figure 5, urine flow
increased in a dose-related manner by 2.8 ± 0.3, 4.5 ± 0.5, 7.7 ± 0.4, and
18.7 ± 0.8 $\mu l/min$ over control values, following 0.5, 1.0, 2.0 and 5.0 mg
of intrafemoral prestegane B injection. Urinary sodium excretion increased similarly after each dose of the lignan-related compound. Of interest,
these changes in urine flow and sodium excretion occurred in the absence
of alteration in renal hemodynamics. In particular, glomerular filtration

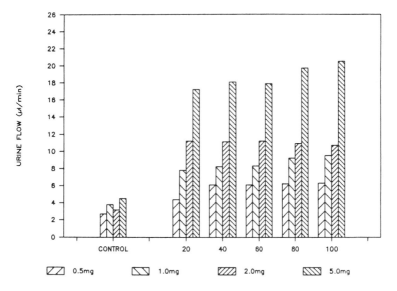

Figure 5   Diuretic properties of lignans. Effect of prestegane B, a synthetic lignan on urine flow at four
different doses (0.5, 1.0, 2.0 and 5.0 mg IV).

remained exactly the same before and after prestegane B (83). These findings suggest that the diuretic and natriuretic properties of this lignan resemble those of other endogenous natriuretic compounds, such as the ANP (30), but the renal mechanisms and the sites of action along the nephron of prestegane B are certainly different, due in particular to the absence of any renal hemodynamic effect obtained with the lignan. It is reasonable to suggest that prestegane B may influence the renal excretion of sodium through an anti-PAF effect.

Effects of the Ginkgolides (BN 52021)

The demonstration of PAF receptors on the plasma membrane of platelets (47, 112), polymorphonuclear cells (113), as well as in the ileum (47) and renal mesangial cells (68), enhanced the interest of developing PAF receptor antagonists. Besides a large number of non-specific inhibitors of PAF, including calcium channel antagonists (99), calmodulin inhibitors (27), calcium chelators (63), local anesthesic agents (24), and a variety of compounds affecting cyclic nucleotides, specific receptor antagonists of synthetic or natural origin were also developed during the recent years (8).

In our *in vivo* renal perfusion model we used ginkgolide B (BN 52021), one of the natural PAF receptor antagonists (9), to examine its inhibitory characteristics on the physiological abnormalities induced by the glycerophospholipid (43). As shown in Figure 6, there was a dose-dependent reduction in the response of peripheral blood pressure, glomerular filtration, and urinary sodium excretion to systemic PAF bolus injections (0.78 μg/kg). Intravenous doses of BN 52021 required to abolish completely the fall of blood pressure and urinary sodium induced by PAF was 25 μg/kg. Of intrest, lower doses of BN 52021 were efficient in blocking the effect of PAF on glomerular filtration, suggesting again that the reduction of urinary sodium excretion occurred independently of alterations in renal hemodynamics. Using the same PAF receptor antagonist, Neuwirth *et al.* were able to block the PAF-induced prostaglandin synthesis in primary cultures of mesangial cells (106). In this model (93), as well as in the isolated glomeruli preparation (94), PAF causes a shape change of mesangial cells, or a decrease in the planar surface of glomeruli which can be interpreted as resulting from contraction of the mesangium. This population of glomerular cells, arranged in a sort of contractile syncithium, appears to play a critical role in regulating the glomerular capillary surface, and therefore, glomerular filtration (65). The PAF-induced production of PGE_2 documented in these *in vitro* preparations is similar to that observed with angiotensin II (95), and can be interpreted as the expression of a feedback inhibition for the constrictor effect of the glycerophospholipid. When

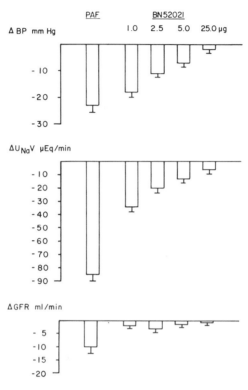

Figure 6 Effect of BN 52021 on the dog renal response to PAF. The reduction from control values of BP (blood pressure), urinary sodium, and GFR, during PAF alone, and during PAF and increasing doses of BN, is illustrated.

cultured mesangial cells are contracted with PAF, prior inhibition of prostaglandin synthesis results in enhanced changes in cell shape, whereas readdition of exogenous PGE$_2$ partially reverses this phenomenon (93). *In vivo*, we found that the combined infusion of prostaglandin E$_2$ and PAF was associated with increased natriuresis instead of the marked reduction observed characteristically with PAF alone (74). The complete inhibition by BN 52021 of all the physiological effects of PAF, the direct depressing effects on renal hemodynamics and sodium excretion, as well as the rebound phenomena presumably secondary to prostaglandin release, strongly support the hypothesis that the binding of PAF to its membrane receptor is an early, if not the first, step initiating the cascade of cellular mediators responsible for the physiological disturbances on the target organs, such as the glomeruli and the different segments of the nephron.

Role of the Renal Microcirculation

The predominant action of PAF as described in previous sections of this paper is on the blood vessel, in particular, on the vascular permeability of most microcirculation networks so far examined. This phenomenon has been carefully studied in the cutaneous vascular network of experimental animals. Changes in the permeability were measured with Evans Blue (49). Plasma exudation induced by PAF was found to be 1000 times more important than that obtained with other potent vasodilators, such as bradykinin and histamine. The effect of PAF on the permeability of the renal microcirculation as a whole was studied by Pirotzky *et al.*, using the isolated kidney preparation (75). A dose-dependent PAF-induced radioactive fibrinogen accumulation in the renal tissue was documented. Real hemodynamic parameters were not reported in these experiments. We performed similar studies in the intact anesthetized rat using radioactive albumin as a marker of plasma leakage in different organs (86). A simultaneous bolus injection of PAF and radioactive albumin was administered in the femoral vein, and renal parameters, as well as tissue specimens, were obtained thirty minutes after. A group of paired rats receiving only the PAF vehicle and the radioactive albumin was used as control. The expected fall of glomerular filtration and urinary sodium excretion was documented. As depicted in Figure 7, radioactive albumin trapping, ex-

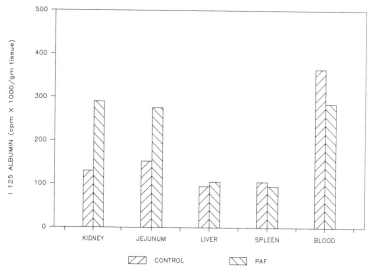

Figure 7 Tissue albumin sequestration induced by PAF. Uptake of radioactive albumin in the rat liver, spleen, jejunum and kidney following PAF, as compared to uptake values obtained in control rats. Blood levels of albumin are indicated for reference.

pressed per gram of tissue, was markedly increased in the kidney and the jejunum of animals receiving PAF. In contrast, albumin trapping in the liver and spleen was similar in the PAF-treated and control animals, despite adequate and comparable plasma levels of the marker. This experiment confirms the results of Pirotzky *et al.* (75) obtained in the kidney and further indicates that PAF exerts an heterogeneous effect on the vascular permeability of specific organs.

The renal microcirculation consists of two networks in series, the glomerular and the peritubular, and this peculiar arrangement is rather unique in higher mammalian species (13). As described in the above paragraphs, the effect of PAF on the glomerular part of the renal microcirculation is characterized by a new vasoconstriction and a decreased glomerular filtration (8, 43, 93, 94). That is not to say that changes in permeability, similar to those just reviewed (49), do not occur in the glomerular capillary. As a matter of fact, increased leakage of the glomerular barrier to plasma proteins, with significant proteinuria as a consequence, has been reported with PAF (35, 75). On the contrary, the effect of PAF on the peritubular part of the renal microcirculation has not yet been directly examined. It is reasonable to imagine that PAF may influence in a specific manner the peritubular capillary, which possesses ultrastructural and permeability characteristics different from those of the glomerular capillary (28, 110). The massive renal albumin trapping which occurred following

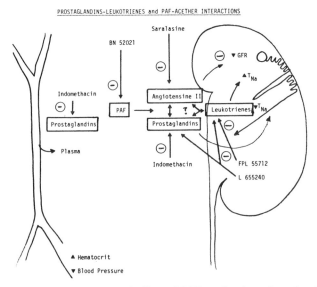

Figure 8 Hypothesis to explain the reported effects of PAF on the glomerular and peritubular microcirculation.

PAF in the experiments described above (86) most probably resulted from plasma leakage in the interstitial space because of the large volume normally occupied by the tubular mass in the rat kidney, and because of the fact that glomerular circulation was reduced in these animals. It is likely, therefore, that the disturbances in the net tubular reabsorption of sodium and water documented in these (86), as well as in other studies (43), resulted from the physical alteration of the peritubular environment. It is of interest in that respect that the peritubular protein concentration was shown to influence the active (3) as well as the passive (5) reabsorption of filtrate in the isolated proximal tubule. This hypothesis is summarized and illustrated in Figure 8.

EXTRARENAL EFFECTS OF PAF (RELATED TO ELECTROLYTES)

Body Fluid Distribution

Because of its major effect on microcirculation and vascular permeability (39, 78), it is expected that PAF may influence the distribution of body fluid between the intravascular and interstitial volumes, as well as between the latter compartments and the intracellular space. It is evident that in pathophysiological states, such as anaphylactic shock, cardiovascular collapse and pulmonary edema (55, 66), important redistribution of body fluid takes place between extracellular and intracellular volumes. The question one may ask, however, concerns the eventual role of PAF in the physiological regulation of body fluid distribution. Up to this point in time this question has not yet been addressed, to our knowledge. We examined some aspects of this question in normal anesthetized dogs using isotonic sodium chloride extracellular expansion (EXP) as a tool to challenge the regulation of body fluid homeostasis. This well-known manoeuvre, utilized to study the renal mechanisms of sodium excretion (10), has recently been shown to stimulate ANP synthesis and release (59) and perhaps other endogenous natriuretic substances, such as ouabain-like material (29). Since the latter humoral substance possesses anti-PAF activity (7), it seemed of interest to study the effect of PAF on body fluid volumes during extracellular expansion. As shown in Figure 9, the fall in hematocrit, which reflects the degree of intravascular dilution during EXP, was more important when PAF was added to the saline volume challenge, as compared to the expected dilution seen in the control conditions. These findings indicate, first, that EXP prevents the rise in hematocrit normally encountered during PAF infusion (39, 78); second, that a larger fraction of the saline load administered

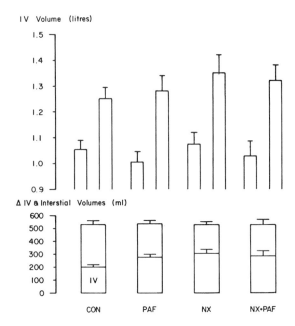

Figure 9   PAF and body fluid distribution. Changes in IV (intravascular volume) and interstitial volume following acute extracellular saline expansion, in CON (control) conditions and following PAF.

remains in the intravascular compartment during PAF, as compared to the amount normally observed under EXP alone. The calculated distribution of the saline load between body fluid compartments, taking into account the renal losses under these two experimental conditions, is also illustrated in Figure 9. The larger retention of the saline load within the extracellular compartment (including the intravascular and interstitial spaces) observed during PAF is more likely related to a reduced «buffering» capacity of the intracellular volume taken as a whole. Under normal conditions, the intracellular compartment retains a fraction of the saline load administered, perhaps because of a reduction of sodium and water extrusion from the cell mass due to inhibition of active transport by circulating antinatriuretic factors (29, 59). If PAF antagonized the sodium and water extrusion from the intracellular volume to the extracellular space, presumably under the control of ANP and the ouabain-like factors, it is reasonable to conclude that the greater intravascular dilution observed during EXP + PAF was the result of a net «impermeability» of the cellular compartment (84). It is of interest that BN 52021 antagonized these effects of PAF in volume expanded dogs (84). In this respect, PAF could be regarded, together with the endogenous natriuretic factors, as a potential regulator of body fluid compartments, at least during the experimental conditions described.

Peritoneal Microcirculation

The surface of the peritoneal cavity that can be exposed for fluid and electrolyte exchange during the course of peritoneal dialysis is quite large and roughly approximates the total body skin surface (71). In contrast to the latter surface area, however, the amount of blood entering the microcirculation of the peritoneal cavity (including of course, the gastrointestinal tube, almost entirely covered by the peritoneal membrane), is much more important and approximates 20% of the cardiac output (similar to the fraction received by the two kidneys), as compared to about 5% for the total skin surface (100). Since peritoneal clearance of fluid and solutes is mainly determined by splanchnic blood flow (70), and since this vascular network is relatively important and subjected to a variety of vasoactive influences (40), we found that it could be of interest to examine the effect of PAF on peritoneal clearance. Normal anesthetized rats were utilized for these acute clearance experiments, and 1.5% dextrose Dianeal fluid was used for peritoneal lavage. As shown in Figure 10, the intravenous infusion of PAF increased slightly the amount of fluid removed from the peritoneal cavity, but more importantly, the quantity of urea and phosphate withdrawn, suggesting that the permeability of the peritoneal barrier to these solutes was significantly increased by PAF. We also examined the renal parameters during these peritoneal measurements and found the expected results on glomerular filtration and urinary sodium excretion, which fell markedly during PAF. In addition, these experiments also revealed that BN 52021 further increased the peritoneal clearance of urea and phosphate while renal hemodynamic parameters were being restored. These findings may indicate that PAF receptors in the renal and splanchnic microcirculation are different or that the physiological expression of PAF mediators is different. The effect of PAF on splanchnic blood flow was not determined in the present study, but recent *in vivo* regional blood flow measurements by Siren *et al.* (101) indicate a biphasic response during systemic PAF infusion: first,

CONDITION	VOLUME ml/20 m	UREA mg/20 m	PHOSPHATES mg/20 m
CONTROL	9.5+0.3	8.9+1.0	302+37
PAF	10.7+0.5	11.9+1.2	517+46
BN 52021	10.0+0.3	11.4+0.8	494+38

Figure 10   Influence of PAF on peritoneal clearance. Fluid, sodium, urea and phosphate removal per 20 minute peritoneal cycles using 1.5% dextrose peritoneal solutions in normal anesthetized rats.

a brisk increment in the splanchnic blood flow is obtained, then a slow and progressive reduction is observed. These authors interpreted their results as an expression of two different types of PAF receptors (101). If the peritoneal clearance of fluid and solutes increases despite a significant fall in splanchnic microcirculation, it is likely that a more important rise in urea and phosphate clearances should take place if this regional blood flow was maintained stable, or in preference, increased above normal values.

PAF IN RENAL PHYSIOLOGY AND PATHOPHYSIOLOGY

Control of Sodium Excretion

It is still too early to consider PAF as an important and critical mediator of sodium homeostasis. There are, however, a number of indirect evidences supporting the influence of PAF in the control of sodium excretion: first, the eventual role of PAF in mediating movements of fluid and solutes between body compartments (84) may influence the delivery of sodium for excretion by the kidney; second, because of important interactions existing between PAF and potent natriuretic factors such as ANP (107), and the ouabain-like substances (7, 64), the glycerophospholipid may also be considered as a mediator of renal sodium excretion; third, the fact that PAF receptor blockade with BN 52021 is associated with significant natriuresis in the absence of changes in renal hemodynamics, supports, at least in the rat kidney, the existence of a baseline production of PAF, the inhibition of which results in an augmentation of urinary sodium losses (82).

Control of Blood Pressure

The profound hypotension that follows PAF infusion (39, 78) and the protection of peripheral hemodynamics with PAF antagonists such as BN 52021 (43) do not represent a formal evidence for a role of this lipid mediator in the maintenance of peripheral blood pressure, even though PAF was found to depress cardiac output and, consequently, blood pressure (35). These findings are more in relation with the role of PAF in the pathophysiology of severe shock. In the early studies of Muirhead and his associates, however, it was thought that the alkyl ether analogs of phosphatidylcholine extracted from the renal medulla were involved in the control of blood pressure (66). The eventual role of these compounds in the physiological regulation of peripheral hemodynamics and intravascular pressure remains to be determined. It is of interest, however, that the chemical manipulation of certain PAF antagonists resulted in the expression of specific antihypertensive molecules that were even found to normalize blood pressure of the spontaneously hypertensive rat (72). Finally, preliminary results obtained in chronic hypertensive «uremic» rats (Bricker model) indicate that BN 52021 administered orally for three weeks (30 mg/kg) attenuated the progressive rise of systolic blood pressure in contrast to animals that received the vehicle, and which developed a more pronounced hypertension (85). The mechanism involved in this sort of response are not evident at this point in time and could as well result from an effect of PAF on the smooth muscle reactivity (66) as from a cascade of humoral events involving the kidney and body fluid homeostasis (85, 61).

PAF as a Mediator of Renal Disease

GLOMERULAR IMMUNE INJURY Several laboratories have presented evidences supporting the critical role of PAF in mediating renal immune injury (19, 21) indirectly through activation of blood cells (platelets and leukocytes), or directly by activation of mesangial cells which are able to contract and alter the permeability of the glomerular barrier (34). Some potential triggers for PAF-induced renal injury were also identified and include circulating antibodies (22), complement activation (22), and endocytosis reactions (93). The cellular events responsible for increased vascular permeability in the glomerular microcirculation have been examined in the isolated perfused kidney (75), and more recently in cell cultures, where it was found that PAF may act as a modulator of the cytoskeleton (17), a critical component of cell geometry and motion (104).

HYPERFILTRATION AND RENAL INSUFFICIENCY The concept of glomerular hyperfiltration as a critical initiating step which leads to progressive renal insufficiency has received significant experimental confirmation over the past years (45). There are, however, a number of controversial issues with respect to the dietary elements that may precede hyperfiltration (12, 50, 77), as well as the eventual mediators of this hemodynamic «adaptation» (57). Several vasoactive substances known to influence glomerular microcirculation were examined with respect to their potential role in this adaptive phenomenon (6, 118). To our knowledge, no one has yet looked at the potential role of PAF in initiating or maintaining the deleterious consequences of hyperfiltration. Since this abnormality is early associated with mild and then more severe proteinuria, it is reasonable to consider PAF as a potential candidate, PAF being a mediator capable *per se* of increasing the vascular permeability to proteins (39, 78) and even capable of inducing proteinuria (21, 75). Using the Bricker model for producing experimental renal failure in the rat (102), we examined the effect of block-

	CONTROL	D 5%	CONTROL	BN52021
Weight gm	191± 4	201± 7	192± 2	209± 3
BP mmHg	159±11	236±15	159±11	196± 5
BUN g/dl	78± 5	101±18	73± 2	95± 7
PO4 mg/dl	4.6±0.3	4.4±0.4	5.1±0.4	3.7±0.1
U/F PO4 %	79± 7	127± 9	69± 4	131±14
UNaV uEq/m	0.4±0.1	1.2±0.2	0.5±0.1	0.5±0.1
U/F Na %	0.9±0.2	2.2±0.2	0.7±0.1	0.9±0.1

Figure 11 Potential role of PAF in experimental uremia. Effect of BN 52021 on renal parameters and blood pressure after 3 weeks, as compared to control rats values.

ing PAF receptors with BN 52021 (30 mg/kg) administered orally for three weeks, on body weight, blood pressure, and some renal parameters (85). The results of these experiments are presented in Figure 11. As compared to values obtained in the control animals, paired fed and receiving only the vehicle of BN 52021, no difference in whole body and kidney weight was noted at the moment of sacrifice. Blood pressure was lower (196 ± 8 mmHg) in animals treated with BN 52021 than in untreated animals (236 ± 15 mmHg). Glomerular filtration was comparable in the two groups and not different than that measured before treatment. The most striking difference between the two groups with respect to renal parameters was related to sodium excretion: «uremic» rats treated with BN 52021 had urinary excretion comparable to values measured before treatment, whereas control «uremic» animals increased absolute and fractional urinary sodium excretion from 0.43 ± 0.11 to 1.20 ± 0.25 μEq/min, and from 0.85 ± 0.18 to 2.15 ± 0.19%, respectively, from the first to the second clearance periods. These findings point to an eventual role of PAF in the adaptation of the remnant portion of the renal mass to sodium excretion: in the remnant kidney, increased urinary output of sodium is reputed to develop under such experimental circumstances. The present results indicate that PAF may be an important mediator of this «adaptation», which appears to be deleterious on the long term evolution (14).

URETERAL OBSTRUCTION Acute and chronic unilateral or bilateral ureteral obstruction is associated with peculiar physiological changes that were reviewed on several occasions, and more recently in the perspective of humoral mediators which protect the renal microcirculation against irreversible damage (41). In a recent paper, Weisman *et al.* presented results indicating that PAF contributes to the pathophysiology of unilateral ureteral obstruction (116). They suggest that PAF induces a dose-dependent release of prostaglandins following acute ureteral obstruction which may be blocked by PAF antagonists (115). The initial step of the renal hemodynamic adaptation which occurs following acute obstruction of the ureter is characterized by glomerular vasodilatation and elevation of the glomerular capillary hydrostatic pressure. The latter phenomenon will tend to maintain the normal positive gradient across the glomerular filtration barrier (81). This adaptive mechanism may explain why glomerular filtration of contrast material can be visualized in the urinary tract of completely obstructed kidneys (111). It would appear that vasodilatory mediators such as prostaglandins (41), and perhaps ANP, lignans, and possibly other endogenous compounds capable of responding to a sudden arrest of urine output, play a critical role in the early phase of ureteral obstruction. Afterwards, the net effect of obstruction on glomerular filtration is characterized by a progressive reduction of renal hemodynamics (41), compatible with a predominent vasoconstrictor effect on glomerular microcirculation: PAF would be an ideal candidate for such a performance and could, thus, participate in the complex pathophysiology of ureteral obstruction (43).

RENAL VEIN OCCLUSION   Partial or complete obstruction of the renal vein is a relatively frequent complication of the nephrotic syndrome (108) and has been attributed to the hypercoagulable state that characterizes nephrotic patients. In particular, the accelerated hepatic synthesis of coagulation proteins has been described (38). The role of PAF in the pathogenesis of this renal complication has not been examined and no PAF antagonist was administered in renal vein obstruction (RVO) experimental models. The subject is of interest on several aspects: first, urinary protein loss is frequently aggravated when RVO develops and may reach values in the order of 20 to 40 mg/day (59); second, renal hemodynamics is reduced (52) in a manner similar to that observd during the continuous intrarenal infusion of PAF (43); third, urinary excretion of sodium decreases markedly in disproportion with the small changes of glomerular filtration (52), again mimicking the PAF-induced antinatriuresis (43).

TRANSPLANT REJECTION   Recent studies indicate that PAF is released during acute allograft rejection (37). The glycerophospholipid appears to originate from the glomerular capillary endothelial wall because of an antibody and complement fixation reaction, a well-known trigger of PAF release (22). Cardiac transplantation experiments were performed in the rat by Foegh *et al.* (37). Treatment of allograft recipients with BN 52021 (10 mg/kg/day) significantly reduced the incidence and severity of graft rejection, even when the PAF antagonist was administered as the only immunosuppressive agent. This subject is of considerable importance for the understanding of the pathophysiology of graft rejection, and also of critical interest because of the potential use of PAF antagonists alone or in combination with traditional drug regimens in the prevention and treatment of kidney transplant rejection (37).

PERSPECTIVES AND CONCLUSIONS

A number of questions and several problems related to the physiological and pathophysiological effects of PAF on the kidney remain pending at this point in time, and will require certainly a few more years of research. With respect to methodology, the fact that a precise and reproducible method for measuring PAF and its metabolites in biological fluids is not yet available, limits considerably the study of PAF metabolism and implications in normal physiology as well as in diseases.

With respect to the physiological effects of PAF on the kidney, the study of the respective contributions of renal hemodynamics and tubular function to the disorders of electrolyte excretion will also require additional studies using isolated tubules or cells preparations. The interactions of PAF and other mediators or humoral agents produced in the kidney must be determined in a more direct manner. The heterogeneity of PAF actions in different vascular networks must be examined since the apparent specific response of certain organs to PAF stimulation could be related to a nonspecific reaction of the glycerophospholipid on the microcirculation of these organs.

The role of PAF in pathophysiology also appears to be ubiquitous. It is reasonable, therefore, to consider this endogenous substance as an important early responder to a variety of aggressions taking place on blood vessel walls or within the blood vessels, in the plasma or blood corpuscules. The apparent response of given organs to PAF could result from activation of one or several different types of mediators, such as the metabolites of arachidonic acid, cyclic nucleotides, phosphoinositides, or ionic messengers. The apparent involvement of PAF in diseases as different one from the other, such as infertlity, arterial hypertension, renal insufficiency and asthma, could be more easily explained in this manner.

Finally, the development of PAF antagonists has been of great help to the biochemist, cell biologist or physiologist interested in this important subject of biomedical sciences. The future development of natural or synthetic anti-PAF compounds should help to define the moieties within the molecular structure of PAF, or PAF receptors on the cell membranes, responsible for the prolific manifestations of this unique lipid mediator. The end result of basic and physiological research in this area will certainly allow in the near future the establishment of more specific treatment in a variety of morbid medical and surgical conditions.

References

1. Badr, K.F., Baylis, C., Pfeffer, J.M., Pfeffer, M.A., Soberman, F.J., Lewis, R.A., Austen, K.F., Corey, E.J., Brenner, B. *Renal and systemic hemodynamic responses to intravenous infusion of leukotriene C4 in the rat.* Circ Res 1984; 54: 492-498.

2. Ballermann, B.J., Brenner, B.M. *Biologically active atrial peptides.* J Clin Invest 1985; 76: 2041-2048.

3. Baum, M., Berry, C. *Evidence for neutral transcellular NaCl transport and neutral basolateral chloride exit in the rabbit proximal convoluted tubule.* J Clin Invest 1984; 74: 205-211.

4. Bessin, P., Bonnet, D., Apffel, D., Soulard, C., Desgroux, L., Pelas, I., Benveniste, J. *Acute circulatory collapse caused by platelet-activating factor (PAF-acether) in dogs.* Eur J Pharmacol 1983; 86: 403-413.

5. Blank, M.L., Snyder, F., Byers, L.W., Brooks, B., Muirhead, E.E. *Antihypertensive activity of an alkyl ether analog of phosphatidylcholine.* Biochem Biophys Res Commun 1979; 90: 1194-1200.

6. Blantz, R.C., Tucker, B.J., Gushwa, L.C., Peterson, O.W., Wilson, C.B. *Glomerular immune injury in the rat: The influence of angiotensin II and α-adrenergic inhibitors.* Kid Int 1981; 20: 452-461.

7. Braquet, P., Senn, N., Robin, J.P., Esanu, A., Godfraind, T. and Goray, R. *Inhibition of the erythrocyte Na⁺, k⁺ pump by mammalian lignans.* Pharmacol Res Commun 1986; 18: 227-237.

8. Braquet, P. Godfroid, J.J. *Conformational properties of the PAF-acether receptor in platelets based on structure-activity studies.* In: Platelet-Activating Factor. F. Snyder (Ed.). Plenum Press: New York 1988; 191-236.

9. Braquet, P., Spinnewyn, B., Braquet, M., Bourgain, R.H., Taylor, J.E., Etienne, A., Drieu, K. *BN 52021 and related compounds: A new series of highly specific PAF-acether receptor antagonists isolated from Ginkgo biloba.* Blood Vessels 1985; 16: 558-572.

10. Brenner, B.M., Falchuk, K.H., Keimowitz, R.I., Berliner, R. *The relationship between peritubular capillary protein concentration and fluid reabsorption by the renal proximal tubule.* J Clin Invest 1969; 48: 1519-1531.

11. Brenner, B.M., Troy, J.L., Daugharty, T.M., Deen, W.M., Robertson, C.R. *Dynamics of glomerular ultrafiltration in the rat. II.*

Plasma flow dependence of GFR. Am J Physiol 1972; 223: 1184-1190.

12. Brenner, B.M., Meyer, T.W., Hostetter, T.H. *Dietary protein intake and the progressive nature of kidney disease.* N Engl J Med 1982; 307: 652-659.

13. Bresler, E.H. *Ludwig's theory of tubular reabsorption: The role of physical factors in tubular reabsorption.* Kid Int 1976; 9: 313-322.

14. Bricker, N.S., Fine, L.G., Kaplan, M., Epstein, M., Bourgoignie, J.J., Light, A. *«Magnification phenomenon» in chronic renal disease.* N Engl J Med 1970; 299: 1287-1293.

15. Brunner, H.R., Laragh, J.H., Baer, L., Newton, M.A., Goodwin, F.T., Krakoff, L.R., Bard, R.H., Buhler, F.R. *Essential hypertension: Renin and aldosterone, heart attack and stroke.* N Engl J Med 1972; 286: 441-449.

16. Bussolino, F., Aglietta, M., Sanavio, F., Stacchini, A., Lauri, D., Camussi, G. *Alkyl-ether phosphoglycerides influence calcium fluxes into human endothelial cells.* J Immunol 1985; 135: 2748-2753.

17. Bussolino, F., Camussi, G., Aglietta, M., D'Urso, N., Bosia, A., Pescarmona, G.P., Marchisio, P.C. *PAF induces a reorganization of the microfilaments in human endothelial cells.* Proc Second International Conference of Platelet-Activating Factor and Structurally Related Alkyl Ether Lipids. Gatlinburg, Tennessee, USA; 1986.

18. Cabot, M.C., Blank, M.K., Welsh, C.J., Horan, M.J., Cress, E.A., Snyder, F. *Metabolism of 1-alkyl-2-acetyl-sn-glycero-3-phoshocholine by cell cultures.* Life Sci 1982; 31: 2891-2898.

19. Camussi, G., Tetta, C., Derigitus, C., Bussolino, F., Segolomi, G., Vercellone, A. *Platelet-activating factor (PAF) in experimentally-induced rabbit acute serum sickness: Role of basophil-derived PAF in immune complex deposition.* J Immunol 1982; 128: 86-94.

20. Camussi, G., Aglietta, M., Malavasi, F., Tetta, C., Piacibello, W., Sanavio, F., Bussolino, F. *The release of platelet-activating factor from human endothelial cells in culture.* J Immunol 1983; 131: 2397-2403.

21. Camussi, G., Tetta, C., Coda, R., Segoloni, G.P., Vercellone, A. *Platelet-activating factor-induced loss of glomerular anionic charges.* Kid Int 1984; 25: 73-81.

22. Camussi, G. *Role of platelet-activating factor*

released from endothelium in the pathophysiology of the inflammatory reaction. In: Proceedings of the First Sandoz Research Symposium. New Horizons in Platelet-Activating Factor Research. C.M. Winslow, M.L. Lee (Eds.); in press.

23. Caramelo, C., Fernández-Gallardo, S., Marin-Cao, D., Inarrea, P., Santos, J.C., López-Novoa, J.M., Sánchez-Crespo, M. *Presence of platelet-activating factor in blood from humans and experimental animals. Its absence in anephric individuals.* Biochem Biophys Res Commun 1984; 120: 789-796.

24. Cazenave, J.P., Benveniste, J., Mustard, J.F. *Aggregation of rabbit platelets by platelet-activating factor is independent of the release reaction and the arachidonate pathway and inhibited by membrane-active drugs.* Lab Invest 1979; 41: 275-285.

25. Chilton, F.H., Ellis, J.M., Olson, S.C., Wykle, R.L. *1-O-alkyl-2-sn-glycero-3-phosphocholine. A common source of platelet-activating factor and arachidonate in human polymorphonuclear leukocytes.* J Biol Chem 1984; 259: 12014-12019.

26. Cody, R.J., Atlas, S.A., Laragh, J.H., Kubo, S.H., Covit, A.B., Ryman, K.S., Shaknovich, A., Pondolfino, K., Clark, M., Camargo, M.J.F., Scarborough, R.M., Lewicki, J.A. *Atrial natriuretic factor in normal subjects and heart failure patients. Plasma levels and renal responses to peptide infusion.* J Clin Invest 1986; 78: 1362-1374.

27. Coeffier, E., Cerrina, J., Jouvin-Marche, E., Benveniste, J. *Inhibition of rabbit platelet aggregation by the Ca-antagonists verapamil and diltiazem and by trifluoroperazine.* Thromb Res 1983; 31: 565-576.

28. Crone, C. *The permeability of capillaries in various organs as determined by use of the «indicator diffusion» method.* Acta Physiol Scand 1963; 58: 292-305.

29. De Wardener, H.E., Clarson, E.M. *Concept of natriuretic hormone.* Physiol Rev 1985; 65: 658-759.

30. DeBold, A.J., Borenstein, H.B., Veress, A.T., Sonnenberg, H. *A rapid and potent natriuretic response to intravenous injection of atrial myocardial extract in rats.* Life Sci 1981; 28: 89-94.

31. Diagne, A., Fauvel, J., Record, M., Chap, H., Douste-Blazy, L. *Studies on ether phospholipids: II. Comparative composition of various tissues from human, rat and guinea pig.* Biochim Biophys Acta 1984; 793: 221-231.

32. Dunn, M.J., Wood, V.L. *Prostaglandins and the kidney.* Am J Physiol 1977; 233: F169-F184.

33. Exton, J.H. *Role of calcium and phosphoinositides in the actions of certain hormones and neurotransmitters.* J Clin Invest 1985; 75: 1753-1757.

34. Farquhar, M.G. *The primary glomerular filtration barrier: Basement membrane or epithelial slits.* Kid Int 1975; 8: 197-211.

35. Feuerstein, G., Boyd, L.M., Ezra, D., Goldstein, R.E. *Effect of platelet-activating factor on coronary circlation of domestic pig.* Am J Physiol 1984; 246: H466-H471.

36. Fine, L.G., Trizna, W. *Influence of prostaglandins on sodium transport of isolated medullary nephron segments.* Am J Physiol 1977; 232; F383-F390.

37. Foegh, M.L., Khirabadi, B.S., Rowles, J.R., Braquet, P., Ramwell, P.W. *Prolongation of cardiac allograft survival with BN-52021, a specific antagonist of platelet-activating factor.* Transplantation 1986; 42: 86-95.

38. Glassock, R.J. *The nephrotic syndrome.* Hosp Pract 1979; 14: 105-111.

39. Goldstein, B.M., Gabel, R.A., Huggins, F.J., Cervoni, P., Crandall, D.L. *Effects of platelet-activating factor (PAF) on blood flow distribution in the spontaneously hypertensive rat.* Life Sci 1984; 35: 1373-1378.

40. Granger, D.N., Norris, C.P. *Role of adenosine in local control of intestinal circulation in the dog.* Circ Res 1980; 46: 764-770.

41. Harris, R.H., Gill, J.M. *Changes in glomerular filtration rate during complete ureteral obstruction in rats.* Kid Int 1981; 19: 603-608.

42. Hebert, R.L. *Les interactions des principaux métabolites de l'acide arachidonique et du PAF-acether sur la fonction rénale.* Thesis. University of Sherbrooke; 1986.

43. Hebert, R.L., Sirois, P., Braquet, P., Plante, G.E. *Hemodynamic effects of PAF-acether on the dog kidney.* Prostaglandins, Leukotrienes and Medicine 1987; 26: 189-202.

44. Hebert, R.L., Sirois, P., Plante, G.E. *Reversal of PAF-induced renal dysfunctions with prostaglandin E_2.* J Lipid Mediators; in press.

45. Hostetter, T.H., Olson, J.L., Rennke, H.G., Venkatachalam, M.A., Brenner, B.M. *Hyperfiltration in remnant nephrons: A potentially adverse response to renal ablation.* Am J

Physiol 1981; 241: F85-F93.

46. Humphrey, D.M., McMannus, L.M., Satouchi, K., Hanahan, D.J., Pinckard, R.N. *Vasoactive properties of acetyl glyceryl ether phosphorylcholine and analogues.* Lab Invest 1982; 46: 422-427.

47. Hwang, S.B., Lee, C.S.C., Chear, M.J., Shen, T.Y. *Specific receptor sites for 1-O-alkyl-2-O-acetyl-sn-glycero-3-phosphocholine (platelet-activating factor) on rabbit platelet and guinea pig smooth muscle membrane.* Biochemistry 1983; 22: 4756-4763.

48. Hwang, S.B., Biftu, T., Doebber, T.W., Lam, M.H.T., Wu, M.S.M., Shen, T.Y. *A synthetic pseudolignan derivative as potent and specific PAF-acether receptor antagonist.* Prostaglandins 1985; 30: 689.

49. Hwang, S.B., Li, C.L., Lam, M.H., Shen, T.Y. *Characterization of cutaneous vascular permeability induced by platelet-activating factor in guinea pigs and rats and its inhibition by a platelet-activating factor receptor antagonist.* Lab Invest 1985; 52: 617-630.

50. Ibels, L.S., Alfrey, A.C., Haut, L., Huffer, W.E. *Preservation of function in experimental renal disease by dietary restriction of phosphate.* N Engl J Med 1978; 298: 122-126.

51. Imai, M., J.P., Kokko, J.P. *Effect of peritubular protein concentration on reabsorption of sodium and water in isolated perfused proximal tubules.* J Clin Invest 1972; 51: 314-325.

52. Ito, S., Camussi, G., Tetta, C., Milgrom, F., Andres, G. *Hyperacute renal allograft rejection in the rabbit: The role of platelet-activating factor and cationic proteins derived from polymorphonuclear leukocytes and from platelets.* Lab Invest 1984; 51: 148-161.

53. Jobin, J., Nawar, T., Caron, C., Plante, G.E. *Effect of acetazolamide on renal bicarbonate reabsorption in volume expanded dogs.* Am J Physiol 1977; 232: F484-F489.

54. Jobin, J., Hemmings, R., Plante, G.E. *Effect of renal vein pressure on urinary sodium and hydrogen excretion.* Can J Physiol Pharmacol 1978; 56: 30-38.

55. Kamitani, T.M., Katamoto, M., Matsumi, M., Katsura, K., Ono, T., Kikachi, H., Kamada, S. *Mechanisms of the hypotensive effect of 1-O-octadecyl-2-acetylglycero-3-phosphorylcholine.* Eur J Pharmacol 1984; 98: 357-366.

56. Knox, F.G., Mertz, J.I., Burnett Jr, J.C., Haramati, A. *Role of hydrostatic and oncotic pressures in renal sodium reabsorption.* Circ Res 1983; 52: 491-500.

57. Kreisberg, J. *Contractile properties of the glomerular mesangium.* Fed Proc 1983; 42: 3053-3060.

58. Lamoureux, C., Hebert, P., R.L., Braquet, P., Sirois, P., Plante, G.E. *Influence du PAF-acéther sur les volumes de l'organisme.* Union Méd Can 1986; 115: 575.

59. Lang, R.E., Tholken, H., Gaten, D., Luft, F.C., Ruskoaho, M., Unger, T. *Atrial natriuretic factor: A circulating hormone stimulated by volume loading.* Nature (Lond) 1985; 314: 264-266.

60. Lin, A.H., Morton, D.R., Gorman, R.R. *Acetyl glyceryl ether phosphorylcholine stimulates leukotriene B4 synthesis in human polymorphonuclear leukocytes.* J Clin Invest 1982; 70: 1058-1065.

61. London, G.M., Levenson, J.A., London, A.M., Simon, A.C., Safar, M.E. *Systemic compliance, renal hemodynamics, and sodium excretion in hypertension.* Kid Int 1984; 26: 342-350.

62. McIntyre, D.E., Shaw, A.M. *Phospholipid-induced human platelet activation: Effects of calcium channel blockers and calcium chelators.* Thromb Res 1983; 31: 833-844.

63. McIntyre, T.M., Zimmerman, G.A., Satoh, K., Prescott, S.M. *Cultured endothelial cells synthesize both platelet-activating factor and prostacyclin in response to histamine, bradykinin and adenosine triphosphate.* J Clin Invest 1985; 76: 271-280.

64. Messerschmidt, A. *Ouabain C29H44O2.* Cryst Struct Commun 1980; 9: 1185-1194.

65. Michael, A.F., Keane, W.F., Raij, L., Vernier, R.L., Mauer, S.M. *The glomerular mesangium.* Kid Int 1980; 17: 141-154.

66. Muirhead, E.E., Folkow, B., Byers, L.W., Desiderio, D.M., Thoren, P., Gothberg, G., Dow, A.W., Brooks, B. *Cardiovascular effects of antihypertensive polar and neutral renomedullary lipids.* Hypertension 1983; 5 (Suppl) I: I112-I118.

67. Naccache, P.H., Molski, M.M., Volpi, M., Becker, E.L., Shaafi, R.I. *Unique inhibitory profile of platelet-activating factor induced calcium mobilization, phosphoinositide turnover and granule enzyme secretion in rabbit neutrophils towards pertussis toxin and phorbol ester.* Biochem Biophys Res Commun 1985; 130: 677-684.

68. Neuwirth, R., Singhal, P., Satriano, J.A., Braquet, P., Schlondorff, D. *Effect of*

platelet-activating factor antagonists on cultured rat mesangial cells. J Pharmacol Exp Therap 1987; 243: 409-414.

69. Nishizuka, Y. *Phospholipid degradation and signal translation for protein phosphorylation.* Trends Biochem Sci 1983; 8: 13-16.

70. Nolph, K.D., Miller, F.N., Pyle, W.K., Popovich, R.P., Sorkin, M.I. *An hypothesis to explain the ultrafiltration characteristics of peritoneal dialysis.* Kid Int 1981; 20: 543-548.

71. Nolph, K.D. *Peritoneal dialysis.* In: The Kidney. Brenner and Rector (Eds.). Saunders: Philadelphia 1986; 1847-1906.

72. Ohno, M. *Molecular design toward biologically significant compounds based on platelet-activating factor: The first selective agonist as a potential antihypertensive agent.* Proc Second International Conference on Platelet-Activating Factor and Structurally Related Alkyl Ether Lipids. Gatlinburg, Tennessee, USA; 1986;

73. Pirotzky, E., Bidault, J., Burtin, C., Cubler, M.C., Benveniste, J. *Release of platelet-activating factor, slow reactive substance and vasoactive species from isolated rat kidneys.* Kid Int 1984; 25: 404-410.

74. Pirotzky, E., Ninio, E., Bidault, J., Pfister, P., J. Benveniste, J. *Biosynthesis of platelet-activating factor: VI. Precursor of platelet-activating factor and acetyl transferase activity in isolated rat kidney cells.* Lab Invest 1984; 51: 567-572.

75. Pirotzky, E., Page, C., Morley, J., Bidault, J., Benveniste, J. *Vascular permeability induced by PAF-acether (platelet-activating factor) in the isolated perfused rat kidney.* Agents and Actions 1985; 16: 1-2.

76. Plante, G.E., Hebert, R., Maheux, P., Braquet, P., Sirois, P. *Leukotriene D4 influences the renal transport of ions.* In: Prostaglandins and Membrane Ion Transport. P. Braquet (Ed.). Raven Press: New York 1984; 271-280.

77. Plante, G.E., Hebert, R.L., Braquet, P., Sirois, P. *Effect of platelet-activating factor on renal hemodynamics and sodium excretion.* Prostaglandins 1985; 30: 708.

78. Plante, G.E., Sobh, M., Briere, N., Petitclerc, C. *Autoregulation of glomerular filtration: Role of phosphate.* Mineral and Electrolyte Metab 1985; 11: 23.

79. Plante, G.E., Hebert, R.L., Lamoureux, C., Braquet, P., Sirois, P. *Hemodynamic effects of PAF-acether.* Pharmacol Res Commun 1986; 18: 173-179.

80. Plante, G.E., Hebert, R.L., Sirois, P. *Inhibition of PAF-induced renal vasoconstriction by L-655,240 a thromboxane/prostaglandin endoperoxide antagonist.* International Symposium on Renal Eicosanoids. Capri, Italy; 1987.

81. Plante, G.E., Gagne, E.R. *Unilateral development of glomerular filtration after contralateral release of ureteral obstruction.* J Urol; in press.

82. Plante, G.E., Prevost, C., Braquet, P. *Interactions between ANP, PAF, and the PAF Antagonist BN 52021.* J Lipid Mediators; in press.

83. Plante, G.E., Prevost, C., Chainey, A., Braquet, P., Sirois, P. *Diuretic and natriuretic properties of prestagane B, a mammalian lignan.* Am J Physiol 1987; 253: R375-R378.

84. Plante, G.E., Lamoureux, C., Hebert, R.L., Braquet, P. *The platelet-activating factor may be involved in the maintenance of body fluid volumes.* Kid Int 1987; 31: 283.

85. Plante, G.E., Lussier, Y., Chainey, A., Boisclair, L., Sirois, P., Braquet, P. *BN 52012 reduces the development of hypertension and prevents hypernatriuresis «uremic rats».* Prostaglandins, Leukotrienes and Medicine; in press.

86. Provost, C., Chainey, A., Sirois, P., Braquet, P., Plante, G.E. *Mécanismes de l'action anti-natriurétique du PAF-acéther.* Union Méd Can 1986; 115: 575.

87. Regoli, D., Gauthier, R. *Site of action of angiotensin and other vasoconstrictors on the kidney.* Can J Physiol Pharmacol 1971; 49: 608-612.

88. Rocchini, A.P., Gallagher, K.P., Botham, M.J., Lemmer, J.H., Szpunar, C.A., Behrendt, D. *Prevention of fatal hemorrhagic shock in dog by pretreatment with chronic high salt diet.* Am J Physiol 1985; 249: H577-H584.

89. Salazar, F.J., Romero, J.C., Burnett, Jr., J.C., Schryver, S., Granger, J.P. *Atrial natriuretic peptide levels during acute and chronic saline loading in conscious dogs.* Am J Physiol 1986; 251: R499-R503.

90. Sánchez-Crespo, M., Alonso, F., Barat, A., Egido, J. *Rat serum sickness: Possible role of inflammatory mediators allowing deposition of immune complexes in the glomerular basement membrane.* Clin Exp Immunol 1982; 49: 631-638.

91. Sánchez-Crespo, M., Inarrea, M.P., Alvarez,

V., Alonso, F., Egido, J., Hernando, L. *Presence in normal urine of a hypotensive and platelet-activating phospholipid.* Am J Physiol 1983; 244: F706-F711.

92. Scherf, H., Nies, A.S., Scgwertschlag, U., Hughes, M., Gerber, J.G. *Hemodynamic effects of platelet-activating factor on the dog kidney in vivo.* Hypertension 1986; 9: 82-89.

93. Schlondorff, D., Satriano, J.A., Hagege, J., Pérez, J., Baud, L. *Effect of platelet-activating factor and serum-treated zymosan on prostaglandin E_2 synthesis, arachidonic acid release and contraction of cultured rat mesangial cells.* J Clin Invest 1984; 73: 1227-1231.

94. Schlondorff, D., Goldwasser, P., Satriano, J.A. *Synthesis of platelet-activating factor by isolated glomeruli and cultured mesangial cells of rat kidney.* Clin Res 1985; 33: 588A.

95. Schlondorff, D., Ardaillou, R. *Prostaglandins and other arachidonic acid metabolites in the kidney.* Kid Int 1986; 29: 108-119.

96. Schlondorff, D., Neuwirth, R. *Platelet-activating factor and the kidney.* Am J Physiol 1986; 251: F1-F11.

97. Schlondorff, D., Goldwasser, P., Neuwirth, R., Satriano, J.A., Clay, K.L. *Production and identification of platelet-activating factor in glomeruli and cultured glomerular mesangial cells.* Am J Physiol 1986; in press.

98. Setchel, K.D.R., Lawson, A.M., Mitchel, F.L., Adlercreutz, H., Kirk, D.N., Axelson, M. *Lignans in man and in animal species.* Nature 1980; 287: 740-742.

99. Shaw, J.O., Lyons, R.M. *Requirements for different Ca pools in the activation of rabbit platelets. I. Release reaction and protein phosphorylation.* Biochem Biophys Acta 1982; 714: 492-499.

100. Shepherd, A.P., Riedel, G.L., Maxwell, L.C., Kiel, J.W. *Selective vasodilators redistribute intestinal blood flow and depress oxygen uptake.* Am J Physiol 1984; 247: G377-G384.

101. Siren, A.L., Snyder, F., Feuerstein, G. *Hemodynamic effects of platelet-activating factor in the conscious rat.* Proc Second International Conference on Platelet-Activating Factor and Structurally-Related Alkyl Ether Lipids. Gatlinburg, Tennessee, USA; 1986.

102. Slatopolsky, E., Caglar, S., Gradowska, L., Canterbury, J., Reiss, E., Bricker, N.S. *On the prevention of secondary hyperparathyroidism in experimental chronic renal disease using «proportional reduction» on dietary phosphorus intake.* Kid Int 1972; 2: 147-151.

103. Snyder, F. *Chemical and biochemical aspects of platelet-activating factor: A novel class of acetylated ether-linked choline phospholipids.* Med Res Rev 1985; 5: 107-140.

104. Stephens, R.E., Edds, K.T. *Microtubules: Structure, chemistry and function.* Physiol Rev 1976; 56: 709-777.

105. Stitch, S.R., Toumba, J.K., Groen, M.B., Funke, C.W., Leemhuis, J., Vink, J., Woods, G.F. *Excretion, isolation and structure of a new phenolin constituent of female urine.* Nature 1980; 287: 738-740.

106. Stork, J.E., Shen, T.Y., Dunn, M.J. *Stimulation of prostaglandin E_2 and thromboxane B_2 production in cultured rat mesangial cells by platelet-activating factor: Inhibition by a specific receptor antagonist.* Kid Int 1985; 27: 267A.

107. Thievant, P., Banares, J., Guilmard, C., Braquet, P. *Platelet-activating factor-induced impairment of the effect of atrial natriuretic factor in anesthetized dog.* Proc Second International Conference on Platelet-Activating Factor and Structurally Related Alkyl Ether Lipids. Gatlinburg, Tennessee, USA; 1986.

108. Thomson, C., Forbes, C.D., Prentice, C.R.M., Kennedy, A.C. *Changes in blood coagulation and fibrinolysis in the nephrotic syndrome.* Q J Med 1974; 43: 399-456.

109. Thurau, K., Dahlheim, H., Gruner, A., Mason, J., Granger, P. *Activation of renin in the single juxtaglomerular apparatus by sodium chloride in the tubular fluid at the macula densa.* Circ Res 1972; 30-31 (Suppl II): 182-186.

110. Trainor, C., Silverman, M. *Transcapillary exchange of molecular weight markers in the postglomerular circulation: Application of a barrier-limited model.* Am J Physiol 1982; 242: F436-F446.

111. Trew, P.A., Biava, C.G., Jacobs, R.P., Hopper, J. *Renal vein thromboses in membranous glomerulopathy. Incidence and association.* Medicine 1978; 57: 69-82.

112. Valone, F.H., Coles, E., Reinhold, V.R., Coetzl, E.J. *Specific binding of phospholipid platelet-activating factor by human platelets.* J Immunol 1982; 129: 1637-1641.

113. Valone, F.H., Goetzl, J. *Specific binding by human polymorphonuclear leukocytes of the immunological mediator 1-O-hexadecyl/octadenyl-2-acetyl-sn-glycero-3-phosporylcholine.* Immunology 1983; 48: 141-149.

114. Van Pragg, D., Barber, J.J. *Biosynthesis of cyclooxygenase and lipoxygenase metabolites*

of arachidonic acid by rabbit renal microsomes. Prostaglandins, Leukotrienes and Medicine 1983; 12: 29-47.

115. Vaughan, E.D., Jr., Shenasky, J.H., Gillenwater, J.Y. *Mechanism of acute hemodynamic response to ureteral occlusion.* Invest Urol 1971; 9: 109-116.

116. Weisman, S.M., Felsen, D., Vaughan, E.D. *Platelet-activating factor is a potent stimulus for renal prostaglandin synthesis: Possible significance in unilateral ureteral ligation.* J Pharmacol Exp Ther 1985; 235: 10-15.

117. Weisman, S.M., Felsen, D., Vaughan, Jr., E.D. *Kadsurenone differentially affects platelet-activating factor (PAF) and peptide stimulated prostaglandin (PG) release in unilateral ureteral obstruction (UUO).* In: Proc First Sandoz Research Symposium. New Horizons in Platelet-Activating Factor Research. C.M. Winslow, M.L. Lee (Eds.). 1987; 329-334.

118. Wilson, C.B., Gushwa, L.C., Peterson, O.W., Tucker, B.J., Blantz, R.C. *Glomerular immune injury in the rat: Effect of antagonists of histamine activity.* Kid Int 1981; 20: 628-635.

*Ginkgolides - Chemistry, Biology, Pharmacology
and Clinical Perspectives.* P. Braquet (Ed.)
Copyright © 1988, J.R. Prous Science Publishers, S.A.

EFFECT OF GINKGOLIDE BN 52021 ON PAF-INDUCED CONTRACTION OF ISOLATED RAT GLOMERULI AND CULTURED MESANGIAL CELLS

Gabriel de Arriba, Diego Rodríguez-Puyol, Vicente Barrio, Anna Olivera, Santiago Lamas and Jośe M. López-Novoa

Laboratory of Renal Physiopathology, Medical Research Institute, Fundación Jiménez Díaz, Madrid, Spain

INTRODUCTION

Platelet-activating factor (PAF) is an alkyl phosphoglyceride with growing interest in renal physiopathology (14, 15).

Intrarrenal infusion of PAF causes a dose-dependent decrease in blood flow and glomerular filtration rate (5). The synthesis of PAF by the kidney is based on the following results: 1) PAF has been found in human urine (13); 2) PAF has been reported to be present in blood from normal subjects, but absent in blood from binephrectomized ones (6); and 3) PAF formation has been demonstrated in isolated perfused kidney, isolated glomeruli and cultured mesangial cells (10, 16).

This work has been undertaken to evaluate whether the effects of PAF on glomerular filtration rate (GFR) and renal blood flow (RBF) could be based on the contraction of kidney glomeruli and mesangial cells as well as to elucidate some of the mechanisms of these actions.

Address all correspondence to: Prof. José M. López-Novoa, Ph.D., Fundación Jiménez Díaz, Avda. Reyes Católicos 2, E-28040 Madrid, Spain.

MATERIALS AND METHODS

Obtention of Isolated Rat Kidney Glomeruli

Renal glomeruli were isolated from Wistar rats weighing 150-200 g, according to a previously published technique based on the ability of glomeruli to pass through a 105 μm sieve and to be retained in a 75 μm sieve (12). At least two rats were used in each experiment. Glomerular suspension was obtained with a tubular contamination lower than 3%.

Culture of Rat Mesangial Cells

Mesangial cells were obtained after collagenase treatment of glomeruli as previously described (10). The culture medium consisted of RPMI 1640 supplemented with 10% fetal calf serum, L-glutamine (1 mM), penicillin (0.66 μg/ml), streptomycin sulfate (60 μg/ml), and buffered with Hepes, pH 7.2. Culture media was changed every two days. Epithelial cells grew rapidly, whereas mesangial cells grew slowly, with a peak of mesangial cell density at 22 days. Studies were performed on day 21 or 22, at which time epithelial cells were no longer detected in the culture flasks.

Incubation of Glomeruli

Glomeruli were suspended in a buffer containing Tris 20 mM. NaCl 130 mM, KCl 10 mM, sodium acetate 10 mM and glucose 5 mM (pH 7.45), and placed in polyestyrene tubes. Samples of 100 μl of glomeruli suspension were placed in glass excavated slides and observed with a 150 power Photomicroscope (Zeiss RS). Microphotographs were taken in each experiment in basal conditions and after the substances were added.

In the first set of experiments glomeruli were incubated in the presence or absence of PAF (PAF-acether, Bachem Feinchemikalien, A.G., Bubendorf), at a final concentration of 10^{-6} M. Calcium (CaCl$_2$ 2.5 mM final concentration) and a minimal amount of ethanol (0.5% of final concentration) were present in all the incubation media. Microphotographs were taken at 8, 15, 30 and 45 minutes of incubation. In another group of experiments, glomeruli were incubated for 20 minutes with several doses of PAF ranging between 10^{-6} to 10^{-10} M and microphotographs were taken at the end of incubation.

In additional experiments, isolated glomeruli were incubated simultaneously with PAF (final concentration of 10^{-9} M), and a PAF antagonist, BN 52021 (Institut Henri Beaufour, Paris), at two different final concentrations (10 μg.ml^{-1} and 50 μg.ml^{-1}).

Moreover, the effect of PAF 10^{-6} M was tested in presence of verapamil

(10^{-5} M Knoll Iberica, Madrid, Spain) and in a medium pre-treated by EGTA and thus calcium free (2 mM, Sigma, St. Louis, MO). Finally, isolated glomeruli were incubated for 20 minutes with PAF 10^{-6} mM and acetyl salycilate of lysine 10^{-3} M (ASL, Almirall Lab., Barcelona, Spain).

Incubation of Rat Mesangial Cells

Direct observation of mesangial cells grown in conventional plastic culture flasks was carried out at room temperature under phase contrast with an inverted Olympus photomicroscope. Serial photographs of the cells were analyzed per photograph.

Mesangial cells were incubated in presence or absence of PAF 10^{-9} M along time in a medium containing calcium (Cl_2Ca, 2.5 mM) and ethanol (0.5%), and microphotographs were taken at 0, 8, 15, 30, 45 and 60 minutes.

In another experiment mesangial cells were incubated for 30 minutes with several concentrations of PAF (10^{-6} to 10^{-12} M).

Finally, mesangial cells were incubated with PAF 10^{-9} M and the PAF inhibitor BN-52021 (final concentration 20 μg/ml).

Determination of Glomerular Cross-Sectional Area (GCSA) and Planar Surface Area of Mesangial Cells (PSA)

Apparent GCSA or PSA were measured on the microphotographs using a computerized technique (Cardio 80, Kontron Medical, West Germany) which calculates the surface as a function of the glomerular or cellular perimeter. Then, the actual GCSA or PSA were calculated using the adequate correction factors for the microscope and the microphotographs processing. Measurements were performed by two different investigators in a blind fashion.

Statistical Analysis

Results are expressed as mean ± S.E.M. Student's t test for unpaired data or two way analysis of variance and Scheffe's multiple comparisons test were used as adequate to analyze the differences between the groups. A $p < 0.05$ was considered statistically significant.

RESULTS

Glomeruli incubated without PAF in the reported conditions did not show any change in cross-sectional area along time of incubation. PAF 10^{-6} M elicited a decrease in GCSA which was significant at 15 minutes and progressed along time with respect to the control group (Fig. 1). When isolated

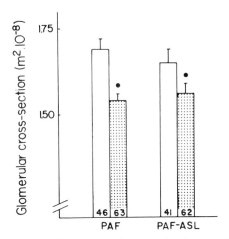

Figure 1 Platelet-activating factor effect on glomerular cross-sectional area as a function of the incubation time. Open circles, control glomeruli; closed circles, glomeruli incubated with platelet-activating factor (10⁻⁶ M). *p<0.05 *vs.* control glomeruli. Each point represents the average of at least 30 glomeruli.

glomeruli were incubated with different concentrations of PAF a significant decrease in GCSA was noted after 20 minutes of incubation with concentrations of 10^{-6} to 10^{-8} M, but this effect was not seen with lower levels (Fig. 2). ASL did not modify the changes in GCSA induced by PAF.

The effect of PAF 10^{-8} mM was inhibited by the addition of BN 52021 to the medium at both concentrations tested (Fig. 3).

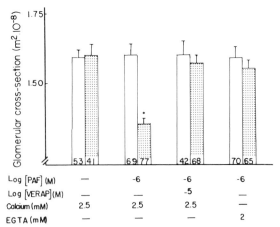

Figure 2 Glomerular cross-sectional area of isolated glomeruli after 20 minutes of incubation with variable concentrations of platelet-activating factor. Open bars, glomerular cross-sectional area before adding platelet-activating factor (time 0); dotted bars, glomerular cross-sectional area after adding platelet-activating factor (20 min). Within bars, number of glomeruli analyzed in each case. *p<0.05 *vs.* time 0.

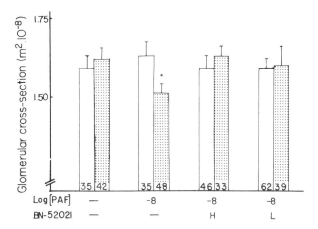

Figure 3 Effect of platelet-activating factor 10^{-8} M on the glomerular cross-sectional area of isolated glomeruli in the presence of the platelet-activating factor antagonist BN 52021. Open bars, glomerular cross-sectional area before adding the reactives (time 0); dotted bars, glomerular cross-sectional area after adding the reactives (20 min). Within the bars, number of glomeruli measured in each case. H, high concentration (50 μg/ml); L, low dose (10 μg/ml). *$p < 0.05$ *vs.* time 0.

The effect of PAF 10^{-6} M was not observed when verapamil 10^{-5} M was added to the incubation medium or when the incubation was done in a calcium-free medium with EGTA 2 mM (Fig. 4).

In mesangial cells PAF 10^{-9} M induced a shortening and narrowing of the cell projections that resulted in a decrease in plasma cell surface area.

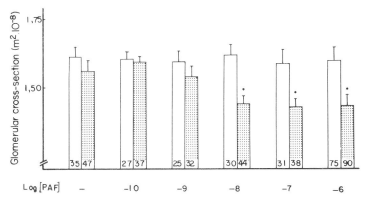

Figure 4 Effect of platelet-activating factor 10^{-6} M on the glomerular cross-sectional area of isolated glomeruli in the presence of verapamil (10^{-5} M) or in a free calcium medium supplemented with EGTA (2 mM). Open bars, glomerular cross-sectional area before adding the substances (time 0); dotted bars, glomerular cross-sectional area after adding the reactives (20 min). Within the bars, number of glomeruli measured in each case. *$p < 0.05$ *vs.* time 0.

Cell contraction was significant from 30 minutes of incubation onwards and progressed along time. Cells incubated in control conditions did not modify PSA (Fig. 5).

The PAF effect was evident along time and remained so up to 60 minutes of incubation (Fig. 7).

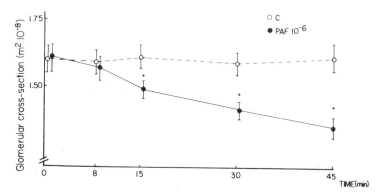

Figure 5   Effect of platelet-activating factor (PAF) 10^{-6} M on the glomerular cross-sectional area of isolated glomeruli in the presence or absence of acetyl salicylate of lysine. Open bars, glomerular cross-sectional area before adding the reactives. Dotted bars, glomerular cross sectional area after adding the reactives (20 min). Within the bars, number of glomeruli measured in each case. *p<0.05 *vs.* time 0.

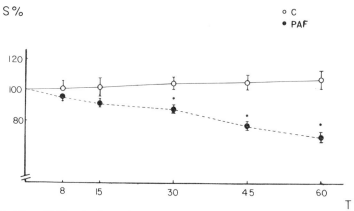

Figure 6   Effect of PAF on the planar cell surface area (S) of cultured mesangial cells. Each point represents the average of at least 30 cells. Data are percent of changes with respect to basal values (100%). Asterisks represent significant changes in S (p<0.05) with respect to basal values.

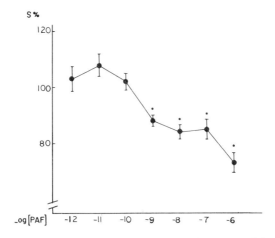

Figure 7 Changes on the planar cell surface area (S) of cultured mesangial cells in response to several doses of PAF. Symbols as in Figure 6.

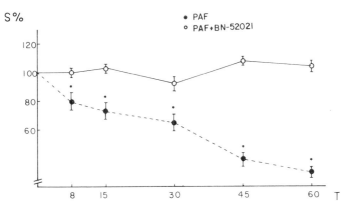

Figure 8 Effect of BN 52021 on the PAF-induced changes in planar cell surface area (S) of cultured mesangial cells. Symbols as in Figure 6.

DISCUSSION

Our results showed that platelet-activating factor reduced glomerular cross-sectional area in a dose and time dependent manner from a concentration of 10^{-8} M. This effect could be linked to a contraction of the mesangium as confirmed by our results in cultured mesangial cells that also showed a time-dependent decrease in planar surface area. We also demonstrated that this decrement was dependent on the concentration of PAF in the media. These results confirm those of Schlondorff et al. (17) and previous ones from this laboratory (2).

The effect of PAF on glomeruli and mesangial cell contraction seems to be mediated by the interaction of PAF with a specific receptor. This conclusion is supported by the fact that treatment of glomeruli or mesangial cells with BN 52021 reversed the PAF-induced contraction. Although to our knowledge no specific receptors have been demonstrated in glomeruli, this ginkgolide inhibits the union of PAF to its receptor, and the cellular response induced by PAF in other cellular systems (3).

The PAF-induced decrease in glomerular cross-sectional area seems to be mediated by calcium, as shown by the results with verapamil and the calcium-free media. Studies in platelets (18), neutrophils (9) and cultured endothelial cells (4) have shown that PAF causes a rapid increase in cytosolic free calcium. This increase could be due to increase of calcium influx through the receptor-activated calcium channels and the release of calcium from the intracellular stores originated by the breakdown of phosphoinositides (3).

The reduction in GCSA observed with PAF seems to be independent of the cyclooxygenase pathway by products derived from arachidonic acid, since ASL did not modify the glomerular response to incubation with PAF. Schlondorff et al. (12) have claimed that the inhibition of prostaglandin (PG) synthesis increased the contractile response of cultured rat mesangial cells to PAF, suggesting that PGE_2 could modulate the contractile function of mesangial cells in the presence of PAF. We have been unable to confirm those results, but glomerular structures are a more complex system than cultured mesangial cells, and it is possible that some physiological interactions are not as evident in isolated glomeruli as in cultured cells.

In summary, PAF induced a decrease in isolated glomeruli cross-sectional area and planar surface area of mesangial cells which seems to be linked to an interaction between PAF and an hypothetical specific glomerular receptor, mediated by calcium. These observations suggest that PAF acether could induce a decrease in GFR not only by decreasing the RPF or modifying systemic hemodynamics, but also by inducing a decrease in glomerular surface and thus, a decrease in ultrafiltration coefficient. Presumably, the local generation of PAF by glomerular cells could explain some of the characteristic functional alterations observed in some physiopathological conditions.

ACKNOWLEDGEMENTS

We wish to thank the Photography Department of the Jiménez Díaz Foundation for their assistance with the image processing. We are indebted to

Dr. P. Braquet for supplying BN 52021. This work was partially supported by grants from the National Institute of Health of Spain (FIS n° 751/86) and CAICYT (grant n° 594/84). V. Barrio and S. Lamas are fellows of the Iñigo Alvarez de Toledo Foundation. A. Olivera is a Fellow of the Ministerio de Educación y Ciencia. We thank Liselotte Gulliksen for secretarial assistance. Data on glomerular contraction are published with permission from the European Dialysis and Transplant Association - European Renal Association.

References

1. Baud, et al. *Reactive oxygen production by cultured rat glomerular mesangial cells during phagocytosis is associated with stimulation of lipoxygenase activity.* J Exp Med 1986; 158: 1836-1852.

2. Barrio, V. et al. *Atrial natriuretic peptide inhibits glomerular contraction induced by angiotensin II and platelet-activating factor.* Eur J Pharmacol 1987; 135: 93-96.

3. Braquet, P. *The Ginkgolides: Potent platelet-activating factor antagonists isolated from Ginkgo biloba L.: Chemistry, pharmacology and clinical applications.* Drugs of the Future 1987; 12: 643-699.

4. Bussolino, F. et al. *Alkyl-ether phosphoglycerides influence calcium fluxes into human endothelial cells.* J Immunol 1985; 135: 2748-2753.

5. Camussi, G. et al. *Potential role of platelet-activating factor in renal pathophysiology.* Kidney Int 1986; 29: 469-477.

6. Caramelo, C. et al. *Presence of platelet-activating factor in blood from humans and experimental animals. Its absence in anephric individuals.* Biochem Biophys Res Commun 1984; 120: 789-796.

7. Kreisberg, et al. *Contractile properties of cultured glomerular mesangial cells.* Am J Physiol 1985; 241: F457.

8. López Novoa, J.M. et al. *Adenosine induces a calcium dependent glomerular contraction.* Eur J Pharmacol 1987; 134: 365-367.

9. Naccache, P.H. et al. *Unique inhibitory profile of platelet-activating factor induced calcium mobilization, polyphosphoinositide turnover and granule enzyme secretion in rabbit neutrophils towards pertussis toxin and phorbol ester.* Biochem Biophys Res Commun 1985; 130: 677-684.

10. Pirotzky, E. et al. *Release of platelet-activating factor slow reacting substance and vasoactive species from isolated rat kidneys.* Kidney Int 1984; 25: 404-410.

11. Pirotzky, E. et al. *Biosynthesis of platelet-activating factor. VI. Precursor of platelet-activating factor and acetyl transferase activity in isolated rat kidney cells.* Lab Invest 1984; 51: 567-572.

12. Rodríguez Puyol, D. et al. *Lack of a direct regulatory effect of atrial natriuretic factor on prostaglandins and renin release by isolated rat glomeruli.* Biochem Biophys Res Commun 1986; 138: 496-506.

13. Sánchez Crespo, M. et al. *Presence in normal human urine of a hypotensive and platelet-activating phospholipid.* Am J Physiol 1983; 214: F706-F711.

14. Santos, J.C. et al. *Effect of PAF-acether on renal function in dogs.* Kidney Int 1985; 28: 587(a).

15. Schlondorff, D. et al. *Platelet-activating factor and the kidney.* Am J Physiol 1986; 251: F1-F11.

16. Schlondorff, D. et al. *Synthesis of platelet-activating factor by isolated glomeruli and cultured mesangial cells of rat kidney.* Clin Res 1985; 33: 588A.

17. Schlondorff, D. et al. *Effect of platelet-activating factor and serum treated zymosan on prostaglandin E_2 synthesis, arachidonic acid release and contraction of cultured rat mesangial cells.* J Clin Invest 1984; 74: 1227-1231.

18. Valone, F.H. et al. *Modulation of cytoplasmic calcium in human platelets by the phospholipid platelet-activating factor 1-O-alkyl 2-acetyl-sn-glycero-3 phosphorylcholine.* J Immunol 1985; 134: 1120-1124.

Ginkgolides - Chemistry, Biology, Pharmacology and Clinical Perspectives. P. Braquet (Ed.)
Copyright © 1988, J.R. Prous Science Publishers, S.A.

PLATELET-ACTIVATING FACTOR AND THE RENAL GLOMERULUS

Robert Neuwirth and Detlef Schlondorff

Albert Einstein College of Medicine, Bronx, New York, USA

INTRODUCTION

PAF can be generated in the kidney, both by renal cells and infiltrating inflammatory cells, and exerts potent physiologic effects on renal function. We will briefly review PAF's potential role in the kidney, and discuss some of our results on PAF in the glomerulus.

PRODUCTION BY RENAL CELLS

Camussi *et al.* reported that rabbit kidney slices were capable of producing bioactive PAF (3). Later, Pirotzky *et al.* demonstrated release of PAF bioactivity from the isolated perfused rat kidney stimulated by the calcium ionophore A23187 (10). These same authors also demonstrated generation of bioactive PAF material from isolated glomeruli and suspensions of rat tubules and medullary cells upon stimulation (11).

We have utilized rat glomerular mesangial cells in culture as a model for studying the control of platelet-activating factor production by glomerular cells. We demonstrated production of platelet-activating factor by both glomeruli and cultured glomerular mesangial cells stimulated by the calcium ionophore A23187, both by bioassay and gas chromatography and mass spectrometry (15). In these experiments mesangial cells cultured from explanted rat glomeruli were used in their second to fifth sub-culture, and after washing with buffer were exposed to the calcium ionophore A23187 for 30 minutes. Cells and buffer together were extracted via the method of Bligh and Dyer and the lipid extract passed over an open silicic acid col-

Address all correspondence to: Dr. Detlef Schlondorff, M.D., Albert Einstein College of Medicine, Division of Nephrology, 1300 Morris Park Ave., Bronx, NY 10461, USA.

umn. The fractions containing labeled PAF tracer ([3H] PAF) were collected, dried under a stream of nitrogen and then tested for bioactivity, using the washed rabbit platelet aggregation assay. Mesangial cells were found to produce 30 ± 8 pmol PAF per mg protein. In order to demonstrate the structural identity of the lipid causing platelet aggregation, samples were further purified by reverse phase HPLC and subjected to fast atom bombardment spectrometry, then derivitized and examined by mass spectrometry and gas chromatography. The PAF produced was identified as the 1-O hexadecyl form (C-16 PAF). In the absence of calcium ionophore mesangial cells do not produce PAF.

We next examined the effect of angiotensin II, a potent stimulus for phospholipase A_2 activation and prostaglandin production by mesangial cells *in vivo* and *in vitro*. As PAF formation requires phospholipase A_2 activation and an increase in intracellular calcium, we thought that angiotensin II may stimulate PAF production by mesangial cells in culture. Mesangial cells were stimulated with angiotensin II, and then the buffer and cells were extracted and tested separately to determine if the PAF produced was released into the buffer or remained cell associated. In these experiments we found that PAF production was stimulated by angiotensin II in a dose dependent manner, with no production demonstrable at doses of angiotensin II lower than 10^{-9}M. The amount of PAF produced was maximal at five minutes, decreasing rapidly over the next twenty-five minutes (Table 1). The PAF produced remains mostly cell associated, with little bioactivity demonstrable in the buffer at five minutes (Fig. 1). The structural identity of this lipid product with hexadecyl PAF was confirmed by negative ionization mass spectrometry.

We had shown previously that mesangial cells in culture are capable of the specific endocytosis of IgG containing macromolecules, and that this uptake was accompanied by the production of PGE_2 (21). We next examined whether this was also associated with stimulation of PAF production in mesangial cells. Mesangial cells were incubated with colloidal gold particles

Table 1   Platelet activating factor production pmol PAF/mg cellular protein

	Angiotensin II (10^{-8} M)	Immune complex colloidal gold	A23187 (10^{-6} M)
PAF in Cells	19 ± 6 pmol	15 ± 4 pmol	27 ± 13 pmol

	Time course of PAF production in response to angiotensin II pmol PAF/mg cellular protein		
	5 minutes	15 minutes	30 minutes
PAF in Cells	25.2 ± 8.4	8.7 ± 2.0	12.0 ± 3.0
PAF in Buffer	3.8 ± 2.3	0.5 ± 0.3	0.8 ± 0.5

coated with BSA-anti-BSA immune complexes, or immune complexes formed with the F(ab')2 portion of the antibody. After fifteen minutes of exposure of mesangial cells to the immune complexes 15 pmol/mg protein
PAF was produced by the cells, whereas those exposed to the FAB fragment were negative for PAF. In these experiments all PAF remained cell
associated, with no PAF being demonstrable in the buffer. These PAF
results have again been confirmed by negative ionization mass spectrometry.
The mesangial cell occupies a central position in the glomerulus and is exposed to all macromolecular constituents of plasma. Thus, the finding of
PAF production by these cells on stimulation by endocytosis is of obvious
importance as a potential proinflammatory mechanism in immune mediated
glomerulonephritis.

METABOLISM OF PAF BY MESANGIAL CELLS

Metabolism of PAF by mesangial cells cultured from rat and human
glomeruli proceeds mainly via activity of an acetylhydrolase enzyme, with
consequent production of lyso-PAF (Neuwirth *et al.*, in preparation). Acylation of lyso-PAF to alkylacyl-GPC then occurs at a very slow rate. We
have found that the acetylhydrolase activity is located predominantly at
the outer surface of the cell membrane. This activity can be released into
the buffer after treatment of cell with trypsin, suggesting that the
acetylhydrolase enzyme may represent an ectoenzyme anchored in the
plasma membrane but directed towards the outside. This may represent a
protective mechanism whereby cells rapidly inactivate PAF derived from
other cells, perhaps even of circulating PAF, thus limiting the
pathophysiologic consequences.

EFFECTS OF PAF ON MESANGIAL CELLS

Mesangial cells in culture respond in a dose- and time-dependent manner
to stimulation with PAF. Following binding of PAF to its membrane receptor, there is rapid activation of phospholipase C, perhaps via a guanine
nucleotide binding protein intermediary, with consequent release of IP3 and
increase in intracellular calcium (16). Following this rise in calcium, there
is activation of phospholipase A_2, causing rappid release of [^{14}C]-arachidonic
acid from prelabeled cells, and production of PGE_2. Mesangial cells exhibit a marked contractile response to PAF *in vitro*, a response consistent
with the effect of PAF to decrease glomerular blood flow and filtration
rate *in vivo*. Both whole glomeruli, as well as mesangial cells in culture respond to PAF stimulation by production of reactive oxygen metabolites,
including superoxide and hydrogen peroxide (18). Clearly, all these effects
may contribute to a local inflammatory effect of PAF in the glomerulus.

EFFECT OF PAF RECEPTOR BLOCKERS ON THE MESANGIAL RESPONSE TO PAF

Elucidation of the role of PAF in a variety of pathophysiological conditions has been facilitated considerably by the development of PAF antagonists. We undertook a series of experiments to assess the specificity and dose response characteristics of three different receptor blockers on PAF effects on glomerular mesangial cells, as an initial step in the evaluations of PAF's role in glomerular function (9). We used three antagonists: BN 52021, kadsurenone and SRI 63-072. BN 52021 and kadsurenone are compounds purified from different Chinese medicinal plants. Both are structurally unrelated to PAF, but act as PAF receptor antagonists. BN 52021 is purified from *Ginkgo biloba* L. and kadsurenone from *haifenteng (Piper futokadsura)*. In contrast, SRI 63-072 is a structural analog of PAF, that also acts as a receptor blocker.

EFFECT OF PAF BLOCKERS ON PGE$_2$ GENERATION

Addition of PAF (1×10^{-6} M) causes a 5-6 fold increase in PGE$_2$ production by mesangial cells. BN 52021 and SRI 63-072 inhibited PAF-induced PGE$_2$ production in a dose-dependent fashion over the dose range of 10^{-7} M to 10^{-5} M. Kadsurenone also decreased PGE$_2$ production in cells stimulated with PAF, but this decrement reached statistical significance only at 10^{-5} M kadsurenone (Table 2).

The specificity of the PAF antagonists was tested by comparing their effects on PGE$_2$ stimulation by PAF, angiotensin II and A23187. PGE$_2$ production in response to these agents increased by five to 10-fold over

Table 2 Effect of PAF blockers on PGE$_2$ generation PGE$_2$ ng/culture dish/10 min

Basal		PAF(10^{-6} M)				Ang II(10^{-8} M)		A23187(10^{-6} M)	
Control	BN52021 10^{-5} M	Control	10^{-7} M	10^{-6} M	10^{-5} M	Control	BN52021 10^{-5} M	Control	BN52021 10^{-5} M
0.8	0.8	6.1	4.9*	3.2*	2.2*	7.6	7.6	8.5	8.0
±0.1	±0.1	±1.0	±1.1	±0.6	±0.9	±1.8	±1.9	±1.9	±2.5
Control	SRI63-072 10^{-5} M	Control	10^{-7} M	10^{-6} M	10^{-5} M	Control	SRI63-072 10^{-5} M	Control	SRI63-072 $10_{,}$ M
0.8	0.9	4.2	3.4*	2.3*	1.5*	5.6	5.2	8.7	8.9
±0.2	±0.1	±0.2	±0.6	±0.5	±0.4	±0.6	±0.6	±0.3	±0.5
Control	Kadsurenone 10^{-5} M	Control	10^{-7} M	10^{-6} M	10^{-5} M	Control	Kadsurenone 10^{-5} M	Control	Kadsurenone 10^{-5} M
1.0	0.8	5.6	3.7	4.3	1.4*	8.4	4.6	10.7	4.9
±0.4	±0.2	±1.1	±0.8	±1.2	±0.4	±2.0	±1.5	±1.7	±1.3

*p<0.05 or better, as compared to group control

basal values. Pretreatment for ten minutes with any of the three PAF receptor blockers at doses of 10^{-5} M had no effect on basal PGE_2 production, but markedly inhibited PGE_2 production stimulated by PAF. BN 52021 and SRI 63-072 had no significant effect on PGE_2 production in cells stimulated with angiotensin II or A23187, indicating that they selectively blocked PAF's effect (Table 2). Kadsurenone, however, tended to inhibit PGE_2 production by cells stimulated with angiotensin II and A23187, indicating a lesser degree of specificity.

EFFECTS OF BN 52021 and SRI 63-072 on [^{14}C] ARACHIDONATE RELEASE

The release of arachidonic acid from cellular phospholipids is generally considered to be a major limiting factor for prostaglandin synthesis. In order to examine whether the inhibitory effect of BN 52021 and SRI 63-072 on PGE_2 synthesis is due to a decrease in arachidonate release, experiments were performed in cells prelabeled with [^{14}C] arachidonic acid. Stimulation of the cells with angiotensin II, the calcium ionophore A23187, or PAF, results in release of radiolabel. Neither PAF blocker exhibited any effect on basal [^{14}C] release (Table 3). Both BN 52021 and SRI 63-072 decreased [^{14}C] release in response to PAF (10^{-6} M) in a dose-dependent fashion (Table 3). Surprisingly, in response to both angiotensin II and the calcium ionophore A23187 there was a significant increase of [^{14}C] release from cells pretreated with BN 52021 or SRI 63-072 (both 10^{-5} M) when compared to cells stimulated under control conditions, in spite of no increase in the PGE_2 production. We have no explanation for this finding at present, which may, however, relate to an effect of PAF blockers on reincorporation of arachidonic acid released in response to the stimuli

Table 3 Effect of BN 52021 and SRI 63-072 on [^{14}C]-arachidonic release CPMx10^3/10 min period/10^5CPM incorporated

Basal		PAF(10^{-6} M)				Ang II(10^{-8} M)		A23187(10^{-6} M)	
Control	BN52021 10^{-5} M	Control	10^{-7} M	BN52021 10^{-6} M	10^{-5} M	Control	BN52021 10^{-5} M	Control	BN52021 10^{-5} M
0.7	0.7	2.2	1.6*	1.2*	0.7*	2.2	4.5*	4.5	8.3*
±0.04	±0.03	±0.1	±0.08	±0.03	±0.4	±0.6	±0.6	±0.5	±0.8
Control	SRI63-072 $10_.5$ M	Control	10^{-7} M	SRI63-072 10^{-6} M	10^{-5} M	Control	SRI63-072 10^{-5} M	Control	SRI63-072 $10_.5$ M
1.1	1.1	4.9	2.6*	2.3*	1.8*	3.5	8.5*	6.2	12.6*
±0.1	±0.03	±0.7	±0.1	±0.2	±0.1	±0.2	±0.4	±0.1	±0.2

*p 0.05 or better, as compared to group control

EFFECTS OF BN 52021 ON PAF-INDUCED MESANGIAL CELL CONTRACTION

In vivo mesangial cell contraction may influence glomerular filtration characteristics. Cultured glomerular mesangial cells have characteristics of smooth muscle cells, including actomyosin filaments and a contractile response to vasoactive agents, including PAF (7, 14, 19, 20). The contractile response of mesangial cells to PAF (10^{-6} M) was completely blocked by pretreatment with BN 52021 and SRI 63-072 (both 10^{-5} M), although neither agent alone had an effect on resting cell tension. The contractile response of these cells to angiotensin II stimulation was not altered by either agent.

These findings are similar to findings in other systems, where PAF induces a contractile response of smooth muscle, such as the rat portal vein (1), the guinea pig lung strip (22) and the porcine carotid artery (6). The PAF blockers BN 52021, SRI 63-072 and kadsurenone have all been shown to inhibit contraction in one or all of these systems, again in a dose-dependent and reasonably specific manner. Our results confirm this finding in single, cultured mesangial cells. The fact that BN 52021 and SRI 63-072 interferred both with PAF-induced PGE_2 formation and cell contraction, yet had no effect on either parameter in cells stimulated with angiotensin II, is consistent with blockade of an early step of PAF mechanism of action such as receptor binding.

As shown above, we have demonstrated that three structurally different PAF antagonists BN 52021, SRI 63-072 and kadsurenone are able to block PAF stimulation of PGE_2 production by the cultured mesangial cell. We also demonstrated that BN 52021 and SRI 63-072 decreased the PAF-induced release of [^{14}C] arachidonate from prelabeled cells and interfere with PAF-induced mesangial cell contraction, but do not inhibit response to either the calcium ionophore A23187 or angiotensin II.

PHYSIOLOGIC EFFECTS OF PAF ON THE KIDNEY

Infusion of platelet- activating factor into experimental animals results in profound changes in blood pressure, cardiac output, peripheral resistance and blood volume, all of which can exert obvious effects on renal function. Therefore, the direct effect of PAF on renal function has not been easy to delineate. Dogs receiving PAF via direct intrarenal artery infusion, in doses that do not exert effect on the systemic blood pressure or cardiac function, demonstrate a dose-dependent and reversible decrease in renal blood flow (12, 13). This is accompanied by a marked decline in glomerular filtration rate, urinary flow rate and sodium excretion. The contralateral, non-infused kidney exhibited no such changes. There was no change in platelet count across the renal vascular bed, and pretreatment of these animals with indomethacin made the changes in renal function even more dramatic, suggesting that these changes were not secondary to *in situ* platelet aggregation with thromboxane release, but rather that renal vasodilatory prostaglandins were produced that blunted the effect of the infused PAF, and when this was blocked by indomethacin, the effect of PAF was enhanced.

Infusion of PAF into the isolated perfused rat kidney produces a somewhat different picture. In this model there is some evidence that PAF is vasodilatory, although the applicability of this data to other systems is unknown (17). Rat kidneys perfused with PAF in a blood free buffer do exhibit an increase in protein excretion and loss of glomerular basement membrane anionic sites, a finding often associated with proteinuria *in vivo*.

INVOLVEMENT OF PAF IN EXPERIMENTAL MODELS OF RENAL DISEASE

At present, given the difficulties involved with measuring PAF reliably in biological samples, and the local action of PAF, involvement of PAF in the pathophysiology of experimental diseases must be inferred through the use of PAF receptor blocking agents. The importance of PAF has thus been recognized in a variety of non-renal diseases such as experimentally induced septic shock in cirrhotic animals, anaphylaxis induced by a number of different means, and cardiac transplant rejection in rats (2). As PAF can be produced both by renal cells and infiltrating inflammatory cells, and as we have shown, the effects of PAF on the mesangial cell are specifically blocked by a variety of PAF receptor blockers, the influence of these agents on the outcome of a variety of experimentally induced forms of renal disease is of obvious interest. Livio *et al.* (8) studied the influence of a PAF receptor blocker on the progression of an experimentally induced form of nephrotoxic serum nephritis, and showed marked decrease in the progression to the more severe crescentic stage. Similarly, Camussi *et al.* (4) examined the effect of PAF receptor blockade on the course of acute serum sickness nephritis in rabbits, with similar beneficial results. More recently, Camussi *et al.* (5) have examined the influence of PAF on a form of inflammatory renal injury induced by the *in situ* deposition of immune complexes. In these studies, rats were immunized with cationized human IgG, and then underwent unilateral renal artery perfusion with cationized IgG, to allow the development of unilateral glomerulonephritis resulting from the deposition of the IgG and subsequent reaction with rat anti-human antibodies. In these studies, the amount of antibody deposition was identical between rats treated with PAF receptor blockers and control; however, the inflammatory sequelae to this insult (proteinuria and glomerular cellular proliferation) were markedly decreased in the PAF blocker rats. These authors also studied the circulating levels of PAF in plasma extracts, and found that the amount of PAF in the circulation of the PAF blocker treated animals was decreased as compared to the controls, and therefore deduced that PAF is an important mediator of the *in situ* immune complex mediated form of acute glomerulonephritis in the rat.

Wang and Dunn (23) have studied the effect of a platelet-activating factor antagonist on an endotoxin induced form of acute renal insufficiency, and found that the fall in glomerular filtration rate, renal plasma flow and filtration fraction seen in animals given a bolus of endotoxin was abolished by pretreatment of the animals with the PAF blocker.

DIRECTIONS FOR FUTURE STUDIES

As reviewed above, PAF seems to be an important mediator of inflammation in the glomerulus for a number of reasons: 1) It is produced by glomerular mesangial cells, not only under extraordinary conditions (ionophore stimulation), but when exposed to more potentially physiologic stimuli, such as angiotensin II, exposure to bacterial endotoxin or endocytosis of IgG containing macromolecules; 2) Glomerular cells respond to exogenous PAF by contraction, release of arachidonic acid with subsequent production of prostaglandins, and increase in intracellular calcium, all of which may in some circumstances be linked to inflammatory responses; 3) Glomerular cells are active in the metabolism of PAF; and 4) There is increasing evidence through the use of PAF receptor blockers that PAF is important in specific disease models of glomerulonephritis.

References

1. Baranes, J. et al. *The effects of PAF-acether on the cardiovascular system and their inhibition by a new highly specific PAF-acether antagonist BN 52021*. Pharmacol Res Commun 1986; 18: 717-737.
2. Braquet, P. *The ginkgolides: Potent platelet-activating factor antagonists isolated from ginkgo biloba L.: Chemistry, pharmacology and clinical applications*. Drugs of the Future 1987; 12: 643-699.
3. Camussi, G. et al. *Release of platelet activating factor and histamine: I. Effect of immune complexes, complement and neutrophils on human and rabbit mastocytes and

basophils. Immunology 1977; 33: 523-534.
4. Camussi, G. et al. *Platelet-activating factor in experimentally induced rabbit acute serum sickness: Role of basophil derived PAF in immune complex deposition*. J Immunol 1982; 128: 86-94.
5. Camussi, G. et al. *A receptor antagonist of platelet-activating factor inhibits inflammatory injury induced by in situ formation of immune complexes in renal glomeruli and the skin*. J Lab Clin Med; in press.
6. Kester, M. et al. *Potentiation of arterial contraction with platelet-activating factor*. Pflugers Archiv 1984; 400: 200-202.

7. Kreisberg, J.I. et al. *Contractile responsiveness of cultured glomerular mesangial cells in response to vasoactive agents.* Fed Proc 1985; 44: 1016.

8. Livio, M. et al. *Role of platelet-activating factor in nephrotoxic nephritis demonstrated by a PAF-receptor antagonist.* Kidney Int 1986; 29: Abst 282A.

9. Neuwirth, R. et al. *Effect of platelet-activating factor antagonists on cultured rat glomerular mesangial cells.* J Pharmacol Exp Ther; in press.

10. Pirotzky, E. et al. *Release of platelet-activating factor, slow reacting substance and vasoactive amines from isolated rat kidney.* Kidney Int 1984; 25: 404-410.

11. Pirotzky, E., Bidault, J. *Formation of PAF-acether by rat kidneys.* In: Platelet Activating Factor. INSERM Symposium No. 23. J. Benveniste, B. Arnoux (Eds.). Elsevier Sci. Publ.: Amsterdam 1983; 117-122.

12. Plante, G.E., Hebert, R.L. *Platelet-activating factor in renal physiology and pathophysiology. Interest of the ginkgolides.* Ginkgolides - Chemistry, Biology, Pharmacology and Clinical Perspectives. P. Braquet (Ed.). J.R. Prous Science Publishers: Barcelona 1988; 575-602.

13. Scherf, H. et al. *Hemodynamic effects of platelet-activating factor in the dog kidney in vivo.* Hypertension 1986; 8: 737-741.

14. Schlondorff, D. et al. *Effect of platelet-activating factor and serum treated zymosan on prostaglandin E_2 synthesis, arachidonic acid release and contraction of cultured rat mesangial cells.* J Clin Invest 1984; 73: 1227-1231.

15. Schlondorff, D. et al. *Production of platelet-activating factor in glomeruli and cultured glomerular mesangial cells.* Am J Physiol 1986; F1123-1127.

16. Schlondorff, D., Neuwirth, R. *Platelet-activating factor and the kidney.* Am J Physiol 1986; 251: F1-F11.

17. Schwertschlag, U. et al. *L-platelet activating factor induced changes on renal vascular resistance, vascular reactivity and renin release in the isolated perfused rat kidney.* Kidney Int 1986; 29: Abst 388A.

18. Sedor, J.R., Abboud, H.E. *Platelet-activating factor stimulates oxygen radical release by cultured rat mesangial cells.* Kidney Int 1985; 27: Abst 222A.

19. Singhal, P., Hays, R.M. *Actin filaments demonstrated by fluorescence in cultured mesangial cells.* Clin Res 1985; 598A.

20. Singhal, P. et al. *Direct determination of cultured mesangial cell contraction and relaxation on a silicone rubber surface.* Kidney Int 1986; 30: 862-873.

21. Singhal, P. et al. *Endocytosis by cultured mesangial cells and associated changes in prostaglandin E_2 synthesis.* Am J Physiol 1987; 252: F627-634.

22. Touvay, C. et al. *Characterization of platelet-activating factor (PAF)-acether-induced contractions of guinea-pig lung strips by selected inhibitors of arachidonic acid metabolism and PAF-acether antagonists.* Immunopharmacology 1986; 12: 97-104.

23. Wang, J., Dunn, M.J. *Platelet-activating factor mediates endotoxin induced acute renal insufficiency in the rat.* Am J Physiol; in press.

24. Woodward, D.S. et al. *The final step in the novo biosynthesis of platelet-activating factor: Properties of a unique CDP-choline: 1-alkyl-2-acetyl-sn-glycerol choline phosphotransferase in microsomes from the renal inner medulla of rats.* J Biol Chem 1987; 262: 2520-2527.

Ginkgolides - Chemistry, Biology, Pharmacology and Clinical Perspectives. P. Braquet (Ed.)
Copyright © 1988, J.R. Prous Science Publishers, S.A.

PAF-ACETHER-INDUCED ACUTE RENAL FAILURE: EFFECT OF THE GINKGOLIDE B, BN 52021

Eduardo Pirotzky[1], Philippe Colliez[2], Christine Guilmard[1], Jeanne Schaeverbeke[2] and Jean-Michel Mencia-Huerta[1]

[1]Institut Henri Beaufour, 72, avenue des Tropiques, Les Ulis, France and [2]Laboratoire de Biologie Cellulaire, Université de Paris VII, Paris, France

INTRODUCTION

PAF-acether (platelet-activating factor) is a potent mediator of allergic and inflammatory reactions (20). Its injection in experimental animals mimics the pathological alterations observed in anaphylactic shock (15), and its role in endotoxemia was further demonstrated (8, 9). Although acute renal failure (ARF) is a major cause of mortality and morbidity during shock, the mechanism of renal injury is not fully understood. A number of mediators have been implicated in the regulation of hemodynamic alterations of ARF, among which various fatty acids and more specifically the metabolites of arachidonic acid have an important regulatory role (1). Whether PAF-acether contributes to the renal pathology associated with shock has not yet been determined. We have already reported that isolated perfused rat kidney actively releases PAF-acether in the venous system either after ionophore A23187 or antigen stimulation (17, 20). PAF-acether has also been demonstrated to cause contraction of mesangial cells, increase local PGE_2 production and glomerular permeability (19, 21), some of these effects being specifically inhibited by the use of PAF-acether antagonists (3). BN 52021 (ginkgolide B) is the most active PAF-acether antagonist described

Address all correspondence to: Dr. Eduardo Pirotzky, Dept. of Vascular Pathology, Institut Henri Beaufour, 72, avenue des Tropiques, F-91952 Les Ulis Cédéx, France.

in the ginkgolide group and has been shown to inhibit all the biological activities induced by PAF-acether *in vitro* and *in vivo* in experimental animals and man (3, 7).

In view of the possible role for PAF-acether in ARF, we injected rats with this mediator and measured urinary flow rate (UFR), glomerular filtration rate (GFR) and proteinuria. In addition, renal tissue was taken in order to be analyzed by electron microscopy. In these experiments, the renal effects of PAF-acether were antagonized by the specific antagonist BN 52021.

MATERIALS AND METHODS

Reagents

PAF-acether (1-O-hexadecyl-2-O-acetyl-*sn*-glyceryl-3-phosphorylcholine) was obtained from Novabiochem (Läufelfingen, Switzerland). One mg/ml solution was made in 0.15 M NaCl containing 0.25% bovine serum albumin (BSA) (Sigma Chemical Company, St. Louis, Missouri, USA). BN 52021 (Institut Henri Beaufour, Le Plessis-Robinson, France) was dissolved to 2 mg/ml in arabic gum and diluted in 0.15 M NaCl solution for oral administration.

Experimental Protocol

Adult male Wistar rats (209 ± 12 g) were placed in individual metabolic cages 24 hours before ARF induction. Rats were maintained on a standard rat pellet diet and allowed free access to water. Urine was collected free of food and feces, 24 hours before and 24 hours after ARF induction. Blood samples were obtained at the midpoint of each period from the artery of the eye. Serum and urine creatinine concentrations were determined with a commercial kit (Abbot Laboratories, Rungis, France). Urinary protein concentration was determined using the method of Lowry *et al.* (14). Hemoconcentration was assessed by measuring the hematocrit (Hct). Rats were allocated into 5 groups receiving the following treatment. Group 1: Control, these animals received an i.v. injection of 0.5 ml of the vehicle alone; Group 2: Rats received a bolus i.v. injection of 2 μg/kg PAF-acether; Group 3: Rats were pretreated with 25 mg/kg BN 52021, p.o. 30 minutes before 2 μg/kg PAF-acether injection; Group 4: Rats received a bolus i.v. injection of 4 μg/kg PAF-acether; and Group 5: Rats were pretreated with 25 mg/kg BN 52021 30 minutes before injection of 4 μg/kg PAF-acether.

Electron Microscopy Studies

Kidneys removed 15 minutes and 6 hours after PAF-acether injection were decapsulated, sliced and fixed for 3 hours in 2% glutaraldehyde, 2% paraformaldehyde, 0.25% NaCl in cacodylate buffer 0.12 M, pH 7.4. These specimens were cryoprotected in 10% dimethylsulfoxide in cacodylate buffer 0.2 M, snap frozen and stored at —80°C. Cryostat sections (20 μm) were immersed in the colloidal iron suspension at pH 1.7 for 3 hours and successively rinsed for 1 minute in 12% acetic acid and in distilled water, postfixed in 1% osmium tetroxide in distilled water, contrasted with 1% uranyl acetate in Palade buffer, dehydrated and embedded in epoxy resin (EPON 812). Colloidal iron particles are small-sized cationic probes, so they allow the detection of slight variation in anionic charges distribution (11). The ultrathin sections were obtained with a Reichert ultramicrotome (Ultracut E, Reichert-Jung, Paris, France) and examined with an Hitachi HS8 electron microscope at 50 KV (Hitachi Ltd., Tokyo, Japan). At least 3 glomeruli randomly selected from 2 animals in each group were examined by electron microscopy. Semi-quantitative evaluation of the ultrastructural appearance of cortical sections were performed in a blind fashion by a single observer.

Statistical Analysis

To perform statistical analysis, the Student's paired t test was used. A p value greater than 0.05 was considered not to be statistically significant (NS). Results are expressed as means ± 1 SD of the indicated number of experiments.

RESULTS AND DISCUSSION

In preliminary experiments, 100% lethal effect was observed when rats were injected with 6 μg/kg PAF-acether and the use of this dose was discontinued. Administration of 2 μg/kg or 4 μg/kg PAF-acether produced 23% and 57% increase in Hct, respectively, at 15 minutes. Hct returned to baseline value 6 hours after PAF-acether injection. In the BN 52021-pretreated rats, no variation in Hct was observed and death was completely prevented. The Hct increase after PAF-acether injection seems to be secondary to plasma volume loss, resulting from its vasopermeability-elicited effect.

Injection of 2 μg/kg or 4 μg/kg PAF-acether induced a reduction in UFR at 6 hours and a significant increase at 24 hours (Table 1). Administration of 2 μg/kg or 4 μg/kg PAF-acether also resulted in a marked fall in GFR

Table 1   Urinary flow rate and glomerular filtration rate during PAF-acether-induced acute renal failure

Group	Number of animals	UFR (μl/min)		GFR (ml/min)	
		6 h	24 h	6 h	24 h
Control	(6)	13.5 ± 4.1	9.5 ± 3.4	1.12 ± 0.2	1.15 ± 0.3
PAF-acether 2 μg/kg	(6)	*6.4 ± 1.6	19.1 ± 2.5	*0.49 ± 0.3	1.22 ± 0.4
PAF-acether 2 μg/kg BN 25 mg/kg	(6)	*4.8 ± 2.9	10.2 ± 3.2	*0.39 ± 0.3	0.97 ± 0.2
PAF-acether 4 μg/kg	(7)	0	25.9 ± 4.3	0	1.18 ± 0.4
PAF-acether 4 μg/kg BN 25 mg/kg	(9)	*6.4 ± 2.4	15.2 ± 3.1	*0.48 ± 0.4	0.91 ± 0.2

*$p < 0.05$ compared to control

at 6 hours and a return to control values within 24 hours. The increase in UFR at 24 hours, which reached values similar to those of the control group was not observed in the BN 52021-protected animals. Rats pretreated with BN 52021 and injected with 2 μg/kg or 4 μg/kg PAF-acether exhibited decreased values in UFR and GFR within 6 hours, but a complete recovery was observed at 24 hours.

A possible role for PAF-acether in mediating reactions of acute renal failure is supported by these results, but whether it promotes prerenal or intrarenal processes cannot be completely defined. Indeed, the rapid reduction in UFR and GFR suggests that hemodynamic alterations could have been responsible in part for the renal effects observed. Bessin *et al.* reported that PAF-acether injection to dogs is associated with plasma exudation and hypovolemic shock (2). The authors described decrease of UFR and creatinine and para-aminohippuric acid clearance. Since injection of PAF-acether to rats induced dose-dependent hypotensive responses (12), the prerenal hemodynamic alterations cannot be completely excluded. The demonstration of a pathophysiological role of PAF-acether mediating intrarenal processes is supported by several reports. Recently, we demonstrated that PAF-acether is released from isolated perfused rat kidney (17) together with histamine and PGE_2 (19). The potential role of the mediator in renal pathophysiology is also supported by the work of Schlondorf *et al.*, who demonstrated that PAF-acether induces contraction of glomerular cells (21). In addition, Friedlander *et al.* (10) demonstrated that PAF-acether infused in rats at doses that did not decrease glomerular filtration rate or hypotension, still induced an increase of Na^+, Ca^{++}, Mg^{++} reabsorption. Therefore,

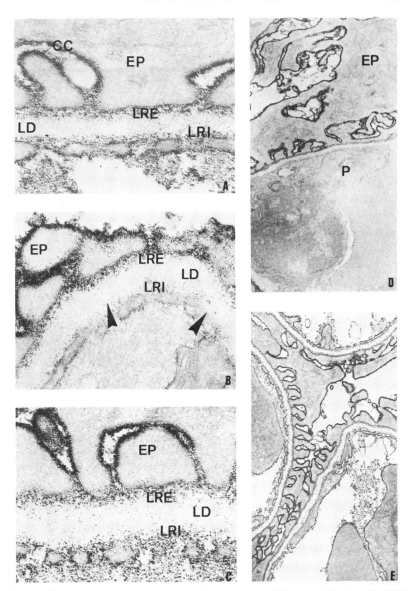

Figure 1 Electron micrographs of the glomerular filtration barrier. A) Regular distribution of colloidal iron binding to anionic sites on the cell coat (CC) and in the laminae rarae (LR) in control rats. B) 15 minutes after PAF-acether injection: marked decrease of colloidal iron staining in the laminae rarae interna (LRI) (arrow head). C) PAF-acether injected rats pretreated with BN 52021. Most of the changes observed in group B are prevented by BN 52021 treatment. Anionic sites are almost normally distributed (x 120.000). D) Low magnification of glomerular capillary in PAF-acether injected rats. Note the decrease of anionic charges in the area of proximity between platelets (P) and glomerular basement membrane (x 17.500). E) Low magnification of glomerular capillaries in BN 52021-treated rats (x 17.500).

it seems likely that PAF-acether in kidney can mediate reactions through the presence of specific receptors in different sites of the nephron. The demonstration that treatment with BN 52021 accelerates the recovery of GFR and UFR, is suggestive of the presence of such specific receptors of PAF-acether in kidney.

Electron microscopy examination revealed a loss of anionic charges in the glomerular basement membrane (Fig. 1 A-C). In addition, the presence of platelets in contact with endothelial cells was observed (Fig. 1D). In fact, platelets were observed in glomeruli of PAF-acether treated rats 15 minutes after administration but not after 6 hours, neither in BN 52021-pretreated rats nor in vehicle-injected animals. This observation supports the role of platelets in the loss of anionic charges in the glomerular basement membrane. The possibility is considered that the activation of platelets in the proximity of endothelial cells of the glomeruli induces the release of cationic proteins which contribute to neutralization of fixed anionic charges. Although rat platelets are insensitive to PAF-acether *in vitro* (6, 16), the injection of the mediator *in vivo* induced thrombocytopenia (13). This latter result suggests that PAF-acether may recruit platelets via the secondary generation of aggregating substances such as arachidonic acid metabolites. The present data also show that PAF-acether-induced loss of anionic charges was reduced by BN 52021. The loss of anionic charges in the glomerular capillary wall has already been described in rabbits after PAF-acether injection (5). Camussi *et al.* (5) have demonstrated that the loss of glomerular anionic charges is associated with reversible proteinuria. Besides species difference, the absence of increased proteinuria in the present experiments could be related to the fact that PAF-acether was injected in a peripheric vein and not in the aorta, as in the experiments performed by Camussi *et al.* (5).

Ginkgolide BN 52021 is known to exhibit several systemic effects in various experimental models or cells. In humans, the ginkgolide mixture BN 52063, given orally inhibits PAF-acether-induced platelet aggregation and skin responses in a dose-dependent manner in normal volunteers (7). BN 52021 inhibits the binding of radiolabelled PAF-acether to platelets and neutrophils, as well as the oxygen radical production by human neutrophils and human eosinophils (4). Clinical trials with this specific PAF-acether antagonist will help to determine whether or not it can prevent platelet or leukocyte activation and/or infiltration in renal tissue. The use of BN 52021 could be a useful tool to elucidate the role of PAF-acether in human and experimental renal diseases.

ACKNOWLEDGEMENTS

The authors thank Mrs. C. Borot-Laloi for excellent technical assistance with electron microscopy preparations.

References

1. Badr, K.F. et al. *Roles for thromboxane A_2 and leukotrienes in endotoxin-induced acute renal failure.* Kidney Int 1986; 30: 474-480.
2. Bessin, P. et al. *Pathophysiology of shock states caused by PAF-acether in dogs and rats.* INSERM Symposium (Platelet-Activating Factor Structurally Related Ether-Lipids). Elsevier Science Publishers: Amsterdam 1983; 23: 343-356.
3. Braquet, P. *The ginkgolides: Potent platelet-activating factor antagonists isolated from ginkgo biloba L.: Chemistry, pharmacology and clinical applications.* Drugs of the Future 1987; 12: 643-699.
4. Braquet, P. et al. *Perspectives in platelet-activating factor research.* Pharmacol Rev 1987; 39: 97-145.
5. Camussi, G. et al. *Platelet-activating factor-induced loss of glomerular anionic charges.* Kidney Int 1984; 25: 73-81.
6. Chignard, M. et al. *L'agrégation plaquettaire et le platelet-activating factor.* J Pharmacol 1980; 11: 371-377.
7. Chung, K.F. et al. *Effect of a ginkgolide mixture (BN 52063) in antagonising skin and platelet responses to platelet-activating factor in man.* Lancet 1987; 248-251.
8. Doebber, T.W. et al. *Platelet-activating factor (PAF) involvement in endotoxin-induced hypotension in rats. Studies with PAF-receptor antagonist kadsurenone.* Biochem Biophys Res Commun 1985; 29: 799-808.
9. Etienne, A. et al. *The relative role of PAF-acether and eicosanoids in septic shock.* Pharmacol Res Commun 1986; 18: 71-79.
10. Friedlander, G. et al. *Renal effects of platelet-activating factor in the rat.* Agents and Actions 1987; in press.
11. Gasic, G.J. *Positive and negative colloidal iron as cell surface electron stains.* Lab Invest 1968; 18: 63-71.
12. Humphrey, D.M. et al. *Vasoactive properties of acetyl glyceryl ether phosphorylcholine and analogues.* Lab Invest 1982; 46: 422-427.
13. Lanara, E. et al. *Response of mice and mouse platelets to acetyl-glyceryl-ether-phosphorylcholine.* Biochem Biophys Research Commun 1982; 109: 1148-1156.
14. Lowry, O.H. et al. *Protein measurement with folin phenol reagent.* J Biol Chem 1981; 193: 265-275.
15. McManus, L.M. et al. *Pathobiology of the intravenous infusion of acetyl-glyceryl-ether-phosphorylcholine (AGEPC), a synthetic platelet-activating factor (PAF) in the rabbit.* J Immunol 1980; 124: 2919-2924.
16. Namm, D.H. et al. *Species specificity of the platelet responses to 1-O-alkyl-2-acetyl-sn-glycero-3-phosphocholine.* Thromb Research 1982; 25: 341-350.
17. Pirotzky, E. et al. *Release of platelet-activating factor, slow-reacting substance, and vasoactive amines from isolated rat kidneys.* Kidney Int 1984; 25: 404-410.
18. Pirotzky, E. et al. *Vascular permeability induced by PAF-acether (platelet-activating factor) in the isolated perfused rat kidney.* Agents and Actions 1985; 16: 17-18.
19. Pirotzky, E. et al. *Renal anaphylaxis. I. Antigen-initiated responses from isolated perfused rat kidney.* Kidney Int 1987; 32: 233-237.
20. Roubin, R. et al. *A chemically-defined monokine-macrophage-derived platelet-activating factor.* In Lymphokines. E. Pick (Ed.). Academic Press: New York 1983; 8: 249-276.
21. Schlondorff, D. et al. *Production of platelet-activating factor in glomeruli and cultured glomerular mesangial cells.* Am J Physiol 1986; 250: 1123-1127.

Ginkgolides - Chemistry, Biology, Pharmacology and Clinical Perspectives. P. Braquet (Ed.)
Copyright © 1988, J.R. Prous Science Publishers, S.A.

PAF, ADRIAMYCIN-INDUCED NEPHROPATHY AND GINKGOLIDE B

Jesús Egido, Francisco Ramírez, Antonio Robles, Arturo Ortíz, Gabriel de Arriba, María-José Rodríguez, Francisco Mampaso Celia Fierro[1] and Pierre Braquet[2]

Nephrology Division, Fundación Jiménez Díaz, Universidad Autónoma, Madrid; [1]Dept. of Pathology, Hospital Ramón y Cajal, Madrid, Spain; [2]Institut Henri Beaufour, Le Plessis Robinson, France

INTRODUCTION

Previous works have suggested that PAF could play a role in the pathogenesis of certain glomerulopathies. Indeed, in rabbit acute serum sickness, the deposition (or formation) of immune complexes in glomeruli is preceded by basophil degranulation (1) and by the intravascular release of PAF-acether from this cell type (4). In the chronic serum sickness of rats, coincidentally with the appearance of immune deposits in the capillary wall, there was a specific desensitization of platelets to PAF (15).

The administration of adriamycin (doxorubicin) to rats induces an intense proteinuria accompanied by podocyte alterations consisting in the progressive loss of foot processes (2). At variance with the two experimental models described above, where there is an important glomerular infiltration by two cell types known to release PAF, namely polymorphonuclear cells and monocytes, adriamycin nephropathy, that has a clinico-histolopathological picture similar to that observed in minimal change glomerulonephritis in humans, constitutes a good model to study whether PAF generated by intrinsic glomerular cells could be implicated in the pathogenesis of this disease.

Address all correspondence to: Prof. J. Egido, M.D., Departamento de Nefrología, Fundación Jiménez Díaz, Avda. Reyes Católicos 2, E-28040 Madrid, Spain.

In a recent paper we have shown that adriamycin-injected rats treated with PAF-antagonists (ginkgolides BN 52021 and triazolobenzodiazepines) for 4 weeks presented a low, if any, proteinuria and no ultrastructural glomerular changes (8). In the present paper we have extended these preliminary results by treating rats at different periods of adriamycin nephropathy with BN 52021. Furthermore, we have studied whether an altered glomerular metabolism of arachidonic acid exists in this model, as well as the *in vitro* effect of adriamycin on the production of thromboxane A_2 (TxA$_2$), prostaglandin E_2 (PGE$_2$) and PAF by isolated glomeruli from control rats.

MATERIALS AND METHODS

Substances

Adriamycin (Farmiblastina) was purchased from Farmitalia, Carlo Erba (Milan, Italy) and BN 52021 was prepared by Institut Henri Beaufour (France). (^{3}H)-PGE$_2$ and (^{3}H)-TxB$_2$ were purchased from Amersham (U.K.). Specific antibodies and PG standards were purchased from Seragen (Seragen Inc., Boston, MA). Synthetic PAF was obtained from Biochem (Switzerland).

Animal Experiments

Adriamycin was administered in a single intravenous dose of 7.5 mg/kg to male Sprague-Dawley rats weighing 200-225 g. Animals were allocated randomly into 4 groups. In group I rats did not receive any treatment. In group II, rats received BN 52021 5 mg/kg twice daily i.p. from day 0 (the day of administration of adriamycin) up to 4 weeks. In group III, rats also received BN 52021 but only from days —1 to + 1. In group IV, rats received BN 52021 from the second to fourth weeks of adriamycin injection (that is, when nephrotic syndrome is fully developed). All animals were allowed unlimited access to both water and conventional rat chow throughout the study. At day 5, 12, 19 and 26, each rat was placed in a metabolic cage for two days prior to the collection of urine for 24 hours. The amount of protein was quantified by means of the sulfosalicylic acid method. On the day of sacrifice, blood was taken to assess renal function as measured by serum creatinine content. Renal tissue specimens for light and electron microscopy were prepared as previously published (7, 15).

Isolation and Incubation of Glomeruli

Renal glomeruli were isolated according to a previously published technique based on the ability of glomeruli to pass through a 105 μm sieve and to be retained in a 75 μm sieve (4). Glomerular suspension was obtained with a tubular contamination less than 3%. Isolated glomeruli were incubated for 5 and 60 minutes at 37°C with continuous agitation in 1 ml of a buffer containing Tris 20 mM, ClNa 130 mM, ClK 10 mM, sodium acetate 10 mM, Cl_2Ca 2.5 mM, and glucose 5 mM (pH 7.4). Incubations were stopped by centrifugation at 300 g for 3 minutes at 4°C. Supernatants were collected and frozen until PG radioimmunoassays were performed. Protein concentration was determined according to Lowry *et al.* (10). For the measurement of PAF the glomeruli were incubated in the same buffer containing Cl_2Ca 1 mM and 2.5 mg/ml of fatty acid free bovine serum albumin (BSA). For *in vitro* experiments isolated glomeruli from normal rats were incubated with doses of adriamycin ranging from 10 μg to 1 mg/ml for 5 and 60 minutes.

Prostaglandins and PAF Determination

Prostaglandin levels were measured directly in the protein-free supernatant of incubation media by RIA, without previous extraction (6, 16).

The quantitative bioassay for PAF was a modification of the assay described previously (11), employing the release of (^{3}H) serotonin from rabbit platelets. A standard curve of response to synthetic PAF was made and the amount of PAF obtained from glomeruli was quantified by using the linear portion of the standard curve. To analyze the glomeruli-associated PAF levels a methanol extraction was performed (3, 12).

Statistical Analysis

Results were analyzed by unpaired Student t tests.

RESULTS

In animals injected only with adriamycin (group I), protein excretion began to increase on the 7th day after i.v. administration (Fig. 1). All animals were heavily proteinuric on days 14, 21 and 28 (Fig. 1). Rats receiving BN 52021 for 4 weeks (group II) either did not present proteinuria or only to a very low extent ($p < 0.0005$). Rats receiving BN 52021 for 3 days (group III) had more proteinuria than those from group II; however, it was significantly lower than from group I (Fig. 2). Rats receiving BN 52021 once the nephrotic syndrome was fully developed (group IV) presented significantly less proteinuria than group I at 5 weeks of adriamycin injection (not shown).

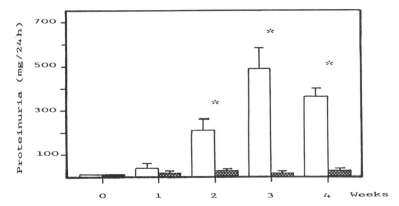

Figure 1 Urinary protein excretion in adriamycin-injected rats (n = 8) (open columns) and in BN 52021 treated rats (n = 11) for 4 weeks after the administration of adriamycin (group II; dashed columns). *Statistically significant. Mean ± SD.

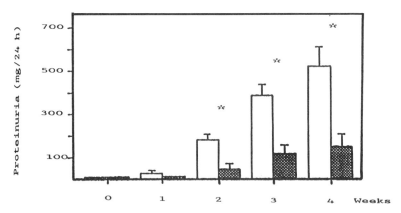

Figure 2 Urinary protein excretion in adriamycin-injected rats (n = 4) (open columns) and in BN 52021 treated rats (n = 8) days —1 to + 1 of adriamycin injection = day 0) (group III; dashed columns). Mean ± SD.

The mortality rate of rats treated with BN 52021 in the three groups was considerably lower than in the non-treated group.

At the end of each experiment renal tissue from representative animals was examined by electron microscopy. Animals injected with adriamycin (group I) showed striking abnormalities of glomerular epithelial cells with extensive fusion of foot processes, increased number of reabsorption vacuoles and segmental detachment of epithelial cells from the underlying basement membrane (Fig. 3). In contrast, in animals treated with BN 52021

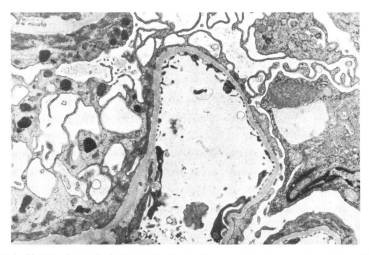

Figure 3   Electron micrograph of a glomerulus of a rat with adriamycin nephrosis not treated. The epithelial cells show important changes characterized by the presence of vacuoles, osmiophilic substances and podocyte effacement.

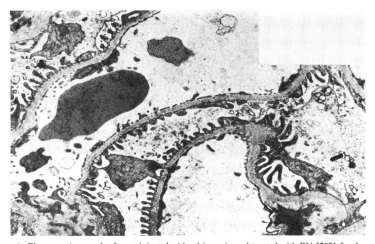

Figure 4   Electron micrograph of a rat injected with adriamycin and treated with BN 52021 for 4 weeks. Note the normal morphological appearance of the capillary wall with a well preserved foot process.

for 4 weeks (group II) no alterations in epithelial cells were observed (Fig. 4). Less impressive ameliorations were noted in rats from group III (not shown).

Isolation glomeruli were studied from rats given a single i.v. injection of adriamycin (group I), rats treated with BN 52021 for 4 weeks (group II) and normal rats. As shown in Figure 5, at 1 week after i.v. injection

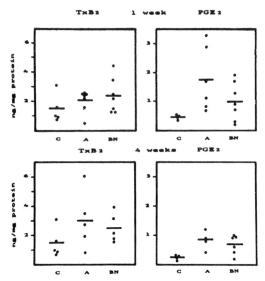

Figure 5 Glomerular TxB_2 and PGE_2 production by control rats (C), animals injected with adriamycin (A) and rats injected with adriamycin and treated with BN 52021 over the period of study (BN). Isolated glomeruli were studied at 1 week (upper panel) and at 4 weeks (lower panel) after a single i.v. injection of adriamycin in groups A and BN.

of adriamycin (A versus C) there was a slight increase in the mean of TxB_2 and PGE_2 production from isolated glomeruli (around 3 times the rates of control glomeruli for PGE_2; $p < 0.05$). Moreover, at 4 weeks of adriamycin injection, when animals are heavily proteinuric, isolated glomeruli from most of these rats synthesized more TxB_2 than those from control rats. No significant changes in the TxB_2 and PGE_2 production were noted in rats treated with BN 52021. As shown in Figures 6 and 7, at 4 weeks of adriamycin injection no correlation between the amount of proteinuria and the synthesis of TxB_2 and PGE_2 isolated glomeruli was noted.

To observe whether adriamycin alone could act on the glomerular structure inducing the release of arachidonic metabolites and PAF synthesis, experiments incubating normal glomerular preparation with adriamycin were performed. As shown in Figure 8, the lower doses of adriamycin (10 μg/ml) induced a certain increase in TxB_2 production and a decrease in PGE_2 synthesis. The most striking data were in the PAF synthesis, in the sense that the rates of PAF-associated glomeruli were 4 times higher in the glomerular samples incubated with adriamycin than those in the control glomeruli incubated only with buffer. As noted recently with various cell types (12), the majority of newly synthetized PAF appeared retained with the glomeruli and not released.

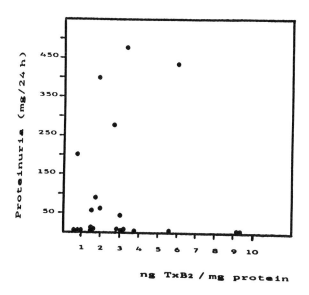

Figure 6   Relationship between the glomerular TxB$_2$ production and proteinuria.

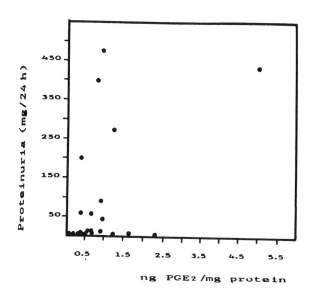

Figure 7   Relationship between the glomerular PGE$_2$ production and proteinuria.

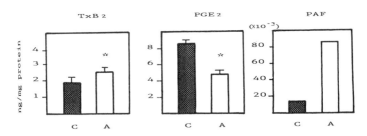

Figure 8 In vitro effect of adriamycin (10 mg/ml) on TxB₂, PGE₂ and PAF production by isolated glomeruli from normal rats. C = glomeruli incubated only with buffer; A = incubated with adriamycin. Higher concentrations of adriamycin induced a lower production of prostanoids and PAF (not shown). Mean ± SD. Results of PAF express mean of 3 incubations.

DISCUSSION

The pathogenesis of adriamycin nephropathy is not clear. It has been assumed that adriamycin induces glomerular epithelial cell damage and proteinuria, which is due to a defect in the size selective barrier function of the glomerular capillary wall (19).

In this paper we have afforded some new data in favor of PAF as an important mediator released early during kidney damage in this model. Thus, PAF antagonists like BN 52021 abrogate adriamycin-induced proteinuria, and PAF is synthetized following the incubation of isolated glomeruli from normal rats with adriamycin.

The fact that the effect of PAF-antagonist was seen mainly if administered early after adriamycin injection is in agreement with *in vitro* studies, and further suggests that PAF can be a mediator released early during glomerular injury. Moreover, the discrete response of proteinuria to BN 52021, once the nephrotic syndrome was fully developed, suggests that PAF could induce a cascade of mediators release expanding the possibility of further tissue damage. However, since the follow-up period after the initiation of treatment with BN 52021 in group IV was only 3 weeks, it is possible that longer observations are needed in order to assess the validity of this PAF-antagonist in this particular situation. On the whole, the protection on the appearance of proteinuria afforded by BN 52021 in this model is reminiscent of that seen in humans suffering minimal change disease, in the sense that early treatment favors a better and more rapid disappearance of proteinuria.

The contribution of glomerular production of arachidonic acid metabolites, mainly TxB₂ (the stable metabolite of TxA₂) and PGE₂, to glomerular dysfunction in renal disease remains unresolved and controversial. Previous studies in this and other models of experimental nephritis have suggested a correlation between damage of the glomerular filtration barrier and TxB_2 (9, 13). Our data, by showing a lack of correlation between this prostanoid released by isolated glomeruli, and the amount of proteinuria, as well as the fact that BN 52021 does not inhibit the release of prostanoids by isolated glomeruli while reducing or abolishing the proteinuria, do not suggest an important role for TxB_2 in mediating glomerular injury in this model. However, they do not exclude a certain role for TxB_2 in regulating glomerular hemodynamics. In fact, glomerular filtration rate and renal plasma flow were slightly affected by adriamycin, with a decrease of 20 and 15%, respectively (19). It is possible that the enhanced glomerular production of TxB_2 and PGE_2 in this model reflects a response of glomerular cells to adriamycin injury. In this sense, in the experiments of isolated glomeruli incubated with adriamycin, the PAF rate production was increased four-fold in relation to controls, suggesting that PAF could cause release of arachidonic acid and PGE_2 formation by glomerular cells (17).

The absence of infiltrating cells in the glomeruli of rats injected with adriamycin suggest that PAF must be generated by intrinsic glomerular cells. In this sense, glomerular cells, and particularly the mesangial cells, can release PAF upon stimulation with appropriate stimuli (18). It is, thus, conceivable that adriamycin, a highly cationic charged molecule, could interact with these cells and induce the release of PAF, as shown in this paper.

How PAF itself or through the release of other mediators can alter the glomerular basement permeability is not clear. Camussi *et al.* (5) have shown that PAF infusion into rabbit abdominal aorta induced proteinuria concommitantly with the loss of fixed anionic changes and focal disappearances of the foot processes.

The present data further strengthen previous reports (8) concerning the role of PAF in the pathogenesis of experimental nephrosis with a clinicopathological picture similar to that of minimal change disease in humans. Since no glomerular proliferation exists in this model, our results indirectly suggest an important role for this mediator (released by glomerular resident or infiltrating cells) as a common pathway of kidney injury in immune and non-immune glomerulopathies. The use of PAF-antagonists such as BN 52021, alone or in combination with other drugs, could afford a new approach to the treatment of such diseases.

ACKNOWLEDGEMENTS

A. Robles is a fellow of the Fundación Iñigo Alvarez de Toledo (FIAT). We thank Liselotte Gulliksen for secretarial assistance. This paper was supported in part by a grant from FISS.

References

1. Benveniste, J. et al. *Evidence for the involvement of the IgE basophils system in acute serum sickness of rabbits.* Clin Exp Immunol 1976; 26: 449-456.

2. Bertani, T. et al. *Adriamycin-induced nephrotic syndrome in rats. Sequence of pathologic events.* Lab Invest 1982; 46: 16-23.

3. Bligh, E.G. et al. *A rapid method of total lipid extraction and purification.* Can J Biochem Physiol 1959; 37: 911-917.

4. Camussi, G. et al. *Platelet-activating factor (PAF) in experimentally-induced rabbit acute serum sickness: Role of basophil-derived PAF in immune complex deposition.* J Immunol 1982; 128: 86-94.

5. Camussi, G. et al. *Platelet-activating factor-induced loss of glomerular anionic changes.* Kidney Int 1984; 25: 73-81.

6. Chaumet-Riffaud, P. et al. *Altered PGE₂ and PGF₂ production by glomeruli and papilla of sodium-depleted and sodium-loaded rats.* Am J Physiol 1981; 241: F517-F524.

7. Egido, J. et al. *Absence of an anaphylactic vasopermeability mechanism for the immune complexes deposition in the Heymann nephritis of rats.* Clin Exp Immunol 1980; 42: 99-106.

8. Egido, J. et al. *Role of platelet-activating factor in adriamycin-induced nephropathy in rats.* Eur J Pharmacol 1987; 138: 119-123.

9. Kelley, V.E. et al. *Increased renal thromboxane production in murine lupus nephritis.* J Clin Invest 1986; 77: 252-259.

10. Lowry, O.H. et al. *Protein measurement with the folin phenol reagent.* J Biol Chem 1951; 193: 265-275.

11. Lynch, J.M. et al. *The release of a platelet-activating factor by stimulated rabbit neutrophils.* J Immunol 1979; 123: 1219-1226.

12. Lynch, J.M. et al. *The intracellular retention of newly synthetized platelet-activating factor.* J Immunol 1986; 137: 2653-1661.

13. Remuzzi, G. et al. *Increased glomerular thromboxane synthesis as a possible cause of proteinuria in experimental nephrosis.* J Clin Invest 1985; 75: 94, 101.

14. Rodriguez-Puyol, D. et al. *Lack of a direct regulatory effect of atrial natriuretic factor on prostaglandins and renin release by isolated rat glomeruli.* Biochem Biophys Res Commun 1986; 138: 496-506.

15. Sánchez-Crespo, M. et al. *Rat serum sickness: A possible role for inflammatory mediators in the shift from mesangial into subepithelial deposition of immune complexes.* Clin Exp Immunol 1982; 49: 631-638.

16. Schlondorff, D. et al. *Prostaglandin synthesis by isolated rat glomeruli: Effect of angiotensin II.* Am J Physiol 1980; 239: F486-F495.

17. Schlondorff, D. et al. *Effect of platelet-activating factor and serum treated zymosan on prostaglandin E₂ synthesis, arachidonic acid release and contraction of cultured rat mesangial cells.* J Clin Invest 1984; 74: 1227-1231.

18. Schlondorff, D. *Production of platelet-activating factor in glomeruli and cultured glomerular mesangial cells.* Am J Physiol 1986; 250: F1123-F1127.

19. Weenig, J.J. et al. *Glomerular permeability and polyanion in adriamycin nephrosis in the rat.* Kidney Int 1983; 24: 152-159.

Ginkgolides - Chemistry, Biology, Pharmacology and Clinical Perspectives. P. Braquet (Ed.)
Copyright © 1988, J.R. Prous Science Publishers, S.A.

EFFECT OF BN 52063 ON ALTERATIONS IN BLOOD PRESSURE AND RENIN ACTIVITY INDUCED BY CYCLOSPORINE

Eduardo Pirotzky, Philippe Colliez, David Hosford, Christine Guilmard, Jesus Egido*, Etienne Chabrier and Pierre Braquet

Institut Henri Beaufour, 72 avenue des Tropiques, Les Ulis, France; *Fundación Jiménez Díaz, Servicio de Nefrología, Madrid, Spain

INTRODUCTION

The therapeutic value of cyclosporine is limited by a nephrotoxic side effect of the drug; however, the mechanism of renal damage is poorly understood. Platelet-activating factor (PAF) is known to mediate numerous inflammatory reactions including those occurring in renal tissue (2,16). However, until now, PAF has not been demonstrated to participate in cyclosporine-induced nephrotoxicity. The production of PAF from various kidney cell types has indicated a role for this mediator in renal physiopathological processes (10,11). It is known to be a potent inducer of glomerular permeability, contraction of mesangial cells, local PGE_2 production (18), activates inflammatory cells and decreases plasma renin activity (PRA) (19) and glomerular filtration rate (GFR) (15). In a previous study, it has been reported that renal transplant recipients treated with cyclosporine demonstrated suppressed plasma renin activity (1). Thus, we examined the effect of a PAF antagonist, BN 52063 on the regulation of PRA in cyclosporine-induced nephrotoxicity.

MATERIALS AND METHODS

Male spontaneous hypertensive rats (SHR) were treated for 26 days with cyclosporine (Sandoz Pharmaceuticals, Basel, Switzerland), alone or in

---

Address all correspondence to: Dr. E. Pirotzky, Dept. of Vascular Pathology, Institut Henri Beaufour, 72 avenue des Tropiques, F-91952 Les Ulis Cédéx, France.

association with BN 52063 (IHB, Le Plessis-Robinson, France). A group of animals received the vehicle of cyclosporine and BN 52063. Two groups of animals received cyclosporine treatment; 25 mg/kg/day or 50 mg/kg/day p.o. Two other groups of rats were similarly treated with cyclosporine but also received BN 52063 50 mg/kg/day p.o.

Plasma cyclosporine was measured by radioimmunoassay (6) and the antibody response against sheep erythrocytes was determined at day 19 by injection of 0.5 ml erythrocytes diluted in 10% saline. Blood samples were obtained after 7 days and the sera were tested for the presence of antibodies against sheep erythrocytes by the haemaglutination assay.

Blood Pressure and Plasma Renin Activity Determination

Systolic blood pressure was determined by the tail-cuff method after warming the animals to 37°C for 20 min (Shingomanometer and Physiograph, Narco, France). The values are the mean of three determinations. For determination of PRA, 500 μl of each plasma sample was mixed with 5 μl phenylmethylsulphonyl-fluoride and 50 μl maleate buffer (pH 6.0) at 4°C. Following incubation of 250 μl of the mixture for 90 min at 37°C; angiotensin I levels were assayed using a Clinical Assays Gamma Coat radioimmunoassay kit. PRA was expressed as ng/ml/h of generated angiotensin I.

Light Microscopy Studies

Fragments of renal cortex were fixed in Dubosq-Brazil Fluid (80% alcohol, 150 ml; 40% formol, 60 ml; acetic acid, 0.5 ml; picric acide, 1 g) and embedded in paraffin. Sections of 5 μm were prepared and stained successively with hematoxylin, phloxin and chromotrope aniline blue.

RESULTS

Cyclosporine 25 mg/kg/day or 50 mg/kg/day caused a reduction in GFR and an increase in serum urea (BUN) (Table 1). A significant dose-dependent decrease of body weight was observed. At the end of the experiment (day 22), the weight loss reached 27.2 ± 7.3 g for the group of rats receiving 25 mg/kg/day of cyclosporine and 59.5 ± 9.2 g for the group receiving 50 mg/kg/day of cyclosporine. When rats were treated with cyclosporine and BN 52063, body weight increased in a similar manner to that of the control group. The amount of protection afforded by BN 52063 was dependent on the dose of cyclosporine used. Treatment with vehicle or BN 52063 alone had no effect on PRA. Treatment with cyclosporine at 25 μg/kg/day produced a significant increase in PRA. Cyclosporine 50 mg/kg/day did not significantly modify PRA. In both groups of animals treated con-

Table 1 Treatment effect of cyclosporine and BN 52063

Group	Number of animals	GFR (ml/min)	Serum BUN (mg/l)	Blood Pressure (mm/Hg)	PRA (ng/ml/h)
Control group					
11	8	0.35 ± 0.022	0.20 ± 0.014	199.6 ± 2.55	—
22	8	1.02 ± 0.228	0.20 ± 0.016	196.8 ± 4.87	4.01 ± 0.538
BN 52063 (50 mg/kg/day)					
11	8	0.38 ± 0.019	0.22 ± 0.011	198.9 ± 3.76	—
22	8	1.28 ± 0.432	0.20 ± 0.011	193.9 ± 5.72	4.32 ± 0.293
Cyclosporine (25 mg/kg/day)					
11	9	0.27 ± 0.018	0.31 ± 0.018***	202.6 ± 3.66	—
22	9	0.81 ± 0.180	0.30 ± 0.015***	194.7 ± 4.81	9.89 ± 0.951*
Cyclosporine (50 mg/kg/day)					
11	9	0.25 ± 0.018	0.41 ± 0.018***	185.6 ± 3.52*	—
22	8	0.77 ± 0.134	0.35 ± 0.023***	168.4 ± 4.61***	4.99 ± 0.672
Cyclosporine (25 mg/kg/day) + BN 52063					
11	8	0.26 ± 0.014	0.22 ± 0.012	207.8 ± 6.36	—
22	8	0.62 ± 0.072	0.23 ± 0.022	199.1 ± 5.76	11.43 ± 2.003**
Cyclosporine (50 mg/kg/day) + BN 52063					
11	9	0.26 ± 0.018	0.28 ± 0.016***	195.8 ± 5.99	—
22	9	1.14 ± 0.294	0.31 ± 0.027***	192.7 ± 4.58	17.95 ± 2.841***

The results are means ± 1 SD. *$p < 0.05$; **$p < 0.01$; ***$p < 0.001$. Significance was calculated over the control group.

comitantly with cyclosporine and BN 52063 significantly elevated PRA was observed.

BP was not modified by 25 mg/kg/day cyclosporine, but with higher doses it was significantly reduced. Animals treated with BN 52063 and cyclosporine showed no modification in BP. The concomitant administration of BN 52063 (50 mg/kg/day p.o.) with cyclosporine did not alter the immunosuppressive effect of the latter drug. Indeed, the antibody response against sheep erythrocytes was similar in all groups of treated rats which showed a negative haemaglutination titer as compared to a positive haemaglutination in untreated rats (1/64). In addition, the concentration of plasma cyclosporine was unchanged in all groups of treated rats. On day 26, the rats were killed and the kidneys processed for optical studies. The histological changes caused by cyclosporine were mainly located in the renal cortex. These changes were dose and time-dependent and consisted of tubular atrophy and dilatation, slight cell infiltration and fibrosis (Fig. 1). In the 50 mg/kg/day cyclosporine group, lesion development was more evenly distributed throughout the tissue as compared to that observed in animals treated with 25 mg/kg/day cyclosporine. The administration of BN 52063 markedly reduced the tubular and interstitial damage.

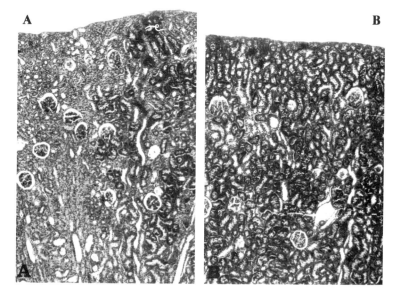

Figure 1 (A) Light micrograph of renal cortex of rat treated with cyclosporine (25 mg/kg/day) showing tubular atrophy and dilatation, and interstitial fibrosis (CAB x 80). (B) Light micrograph of renal cortex of rat treated with cyclosporine (25 mg/kg/day) and BN 52063 (50 mg/kg/day). No morphological alterations are observed (CAB x 80).

DISCUSSION

Our aim in this study was to examine the possible effects of BN 52063 on cyclosporine-induced renal dysfunction and alterations in PRA. Following 22 days of treatment, decreased renal function and tubular cell damage were dose-related up to 50 mg/kg/day cyclosporine. Nephrotoxicity was not demonstrated in animals treated with lower doses, 10 mg/kg/day (data not shown). The observed modifications in PRA were not dose-related. Elevation of PRA activity was detected in both groups of animals treated with cyclosporine and the PAF- antagonist. Increased PRA has also been reported by various authors in rats treated with 10-50 mg/kg cyclosporine (6,17). Our results agree with those of Siegl et al. who reported that in rats 20 mg/kg/day cyclosporine increased PRA more effectively than 50 mg/kg/day (20). Siegl et al. concluded that PRA was one factor participating in cyclosporine-induced nephrotoxicity; however, our studies suggest that there is no relationship between morphological alterations and increased PRA. In fact, groups of animals treated with BN 52063 and cyclosporine possessed significantly increased PRA but did not display any morphological alterations.

Our data also suggests a role for PAF in the pathogenesis of cyclosporine-induced nephrotoxicity. Recent data indicate that PAF infused intrarenally to anesthetized dogs caused renal vasoconstriction leading to a reduction in renal blood flow (15). In a recent publication, we reported that intravenous injection of PAF into rats decreased GFR and urinary flow rate (14). Bessin et al. also reported that intravenous injection of PAF into anesthetized dogs decreased creatinine and para-aminohippurate clearance (13). When administered via the femoral vein into dogs, PAF also reduced renal plasma flow. Investigations on isolated perfused rat kidney demonstrate the importance of PAF in renal pathology independently to that produced by circulating cells. Indeed, we first reported an increase of glomerular permeability after PAF injection into the renal artery (12). We have also recently demonstrated that proteinuria and PAF generation may occur in IgE-sensitized kidneys after antigen stimulation (13). PAF stimulates the release of other mediators such as leukotrienes and prostaglandins from various cell types and organs. Indeed, Weissman et al. showed that isolated perfused rabbit kidney stimulated with PAF generated PGE_2 concomitant with cellular contraction (21). These observations suggest that the reduction of GFR during glomerular injury may result from a sequential generation of various inflammatory mediators.

BN 52063, a mixture of ginkgolides A, B and C (molar ratio 2:2:1) is a potent PAF antagonist (5). In several experimental models *in vitro* or *in vivo,* BN 52063 inhibits most of the biological effects induced by PAF.

In man, BN 52063 has been shown to inhibit PAF-induced skin plasma exudation and platelet aggregation (9). In the dog, ginkgolide B, another PAF antagonist (BN 52021), inhibited the decrease of GFR and urinary sodium excretion induced by PAF injection (15). Using the same antagonist, we were able to block the acute renal failure induced by PAF in the rat (14). Bertani *et al.* reported a reduction by PAF antagonists of the glomerular damage in anti-glomerular basement membrane glomerulonephritis (3). BN 52021 has also been shown to protect proteinuria and glomerular damage in adriamycin nephrosis (7).

The histologic alterations induced by 25 mg/kg/day cyclosporine were completely prevented by BN 52063. These results suggest that PAF may be generated by renal cells during cyclosporine treatment. Therefore, the mechanism by which BN 52063 exerts its protective effect on cyclosporine nephrotoxicity may be explained by the various renal actions of the mediator. In addition, the data reported by Foegh *et al.* support the protective effect of the PAF antagonist in graft rejection (8). These authors demonstrated a beneficial effect of ginkgolides in prolonging heart graft survival. BN 52021 alone or in combination with azathioprine or cyclosporine significantly delayed graft rejection.

In conclusion, cyclosporine-induced nephrotoxicity in the rat is effectively inhibited by BN 52063 without altering cyclosporine biodisponibility. However, while BN 52063 afforded protection against cyclosporine-induced renal damage, it did not reduce PRA. Further studies are needed to determine the pathogenesis of cyclosporine-induced nephrotoxicity.

ACKNOWLEDGEMENTS

We thank P. Plas for plasma renin measurements.

References

1. Bantle, J.P. et al. *Effects of cyclosporine on the renin-angiotensin-aldosterone system and potassium excretion in renal transplant recipients.* Arch Intern Med 1985; 145: 505-508.

2. Benveniste, J. et al. *Leukocytes-dependent histamine release from rabbit platelets: The role of IgE, basophils and a platelet-activating factor.* J Exp Med 1972; 136: 1356-1377.

3. Bertani, T. et al. *Platelet-activating factor (PAF) as a mediator of injury in nephrotoxic nephritis.* Kidney Int 1987; 31: 1248-1256.

4. Bessin, P. et al. *Pathophysiology of shock states caused by PAF-acether in dogs and rats.* INSERM Symp Platelet-Activating Factor and Structurally Related Ether-Lipds, Vol. 23. Elsevier: Amsterdam 1983; 343-356.

5. Braquet, P. *The ginkgolides: Potent platelet-activating factor antagonists isolated from ginkgo biloba L: Chemistry, pharmacology and clinical applications.* Drugs of the Future 1987; 12: 643-699.

6. Donatsch, P. et al. *A radioimmunoassay to measure cyclosporin A in plasma and serum samples.* J Immunoassay 1981; 2: 19-23.

7. Egido, J. et al. *Role of platelet-activating factor in adriamycin induced nephropathy in rats.* Eur J Pharmacol 1987; 138: 119-123.

8. Foegh, M. et al. *Prolongation of cardiac*

allograft survival with BN 52021. A specific antagonist of platelet-activating factor. Transplantation 1986; 42: 86-88.

9. Guinot, Ph. et al. Inhibition of PAF-acether-induced weal and flare reaction in man by specific PAF-antagonist. Prostaglandins 1986; 32: 160-163.

10. Pirotzky, E. et al. Release of platelet-activating factor, slow-reacting substance, and vasoactive amines from isolated rat kidneys. Kidney Int 1984; 25: 404-410.

11. Pirotzky, E. et al. Biosynthesis of platelet-activating factor. VI. Precursor of platelet-activating factor acetyltransferase activity in isolated rat kidney cells. Lab Invest 1984; 51: 567-572.

12. Pirotzky, E. et al. Vascular permeability induced by PAF-acether (platelet-activating factor) in the isolated perfused rat kidney. Agents and Actions 1985; 16: 17-18.

13. Pirotzky, E. et al. Renal anaphylaxis, I. Antigen-initiated responses from isolated perfused kidney. Kidney Int 1987; 32: 223-237.

14. Pirotzky, E. et al. Protection of platelet-activating factor-induced acute renal failure by BN 52021. Br J Exp 1988; In press.

15. Plante, G.E. et al. Hemodynamic effects of PAF-acether. Pharmacol Res Commun 1986; 18: 173-179.

16. Roubin, R. et al. A chemically monokine-macrophage-defined platelet-activating factor. In: Lymphokines. E. Pick (Ed.). Academic Press: New York 1983; 8: 249-276.

17. Ryffel, B. et al. Nephrotoxicity of cyclosporine in spontaneously hypertensive rats: Effects on blood pressure and vascular lesions. Clin Nephrol 1986; 25(Suppl. 1): S193-S198.

18. Schlondorff, D. et al. Production of platelet-activating factor in glomeruli and cultured glomerular mesangial cells. Am J Physiol 1986; 250: 1123-1127.

19. Schwertschlag, V. et al. L-platelet-activating factor induces changes on renal vascular resistance, vascular reactivity, and renin release in the isolated perfused rat kidney. Circ Res 1987; 60: 534-539.

20. Siegl, H. et al. Cyclosporine, the renin-angiotensin-aldosterone system and renal adverse reactions. Transplant Proc 1983; 15(Suppl. 1): 2719-2725.

21. Weisman, S.M. et al. Platelet-activating factor is a potent stimulus for renal prostaglandin synthesis. Possible significance in unilateral uretral obstruction. J Pharmacol Exp Ther 1985; 235: 10-15.

Ginkgolides - Chemistry, Biology, Pharmacology and Clinical Perspectives. P. Braquet (Ed.)
Copyright © 1988, J.R. Prous Science Publishers, S.A.

EFFECTS OF TWO PLATELET-ACTIVATING FACTOR ANTAGONISTS, BN 52063 AND ALPRAZOLAM, ON FORCED SWIMMING-INDUCED BEHAVIORAL DESPAIR IN MICE

François Clostre, Martine Millerin, Colette Betin, Nicolas Bazan* and Pierre Braquet

Institut Henri Beaufour, Le Plessis-Robinson, France; *LSU Eye Center, New Orleans, LA, USA

ABSTRACT

In addition to possessing antianxiety effects, the triazolobenzodiazepine, alprazolam, has been reported to have antidepressant and antipanic properties in man. Furthermore, as alprazolam has shown specific inhibition of platelet-activating factor (PAF)-induced activation of human platelets, we compared the psychopharmacological profile of both alprazolam and BN 52063 —a potent and specific PAF antagonist— on open-field behavior, tetrabenazine-induced ptosis and the depression-like syndrome of forced swimming-induced behavioral despair in mice.

In acute oral administration 1 hour before the tests, alprazolam (0.25-0.50 mg/kg^{-1}) and BN 52063 (50 mg/kg^{-1}) increased the number of transits significantly in open-field behavior without interfering with tetrabenazine-induced ptosis in mice.

BN 52063 (2-50 mg/kg^{-1} po) and alprazolam (0.0625-1 mg/kg^{-1} po) — but not diazepam (0.625-2 mg/kg^{-1} po) nor triazolam (0.9625-1 mg/kg^{-1}

Address all correspondence to: Dr. P. Braquet, 17 avenue Descartes, F-92350 Le Plessis Robinson, France.

po)— significantly and dose-dependently reduced the duration of immobility of mice exposed to a mildly adverse situation.

Prazosin (3 mg/kg^{-1} sc), an α_1-antagonist, clonidine (0.1 mg/kg^{-1} ip), an α_2-antagonist and yohimbine (1 mg/kg^{-1} sc), an α_2-antagonist, did not modify the decrease in immobility duration in mice induced either by alprazolam (0.0625 mg/kg^{-1} po) or by BN 52063 (5 mg/kg^{-1} po). In contrast, propranolol (5 mg/kg^{-1} ip), a β antagonist, butoxamine (5 mg/kg^{-1} ip), a β_2 antagonist, and atenolol (5 mg/kg^{-1} ip) a β_1 antagonist, totally reversed the immobility-reducing effects of alprazolam and BN 52063. Pimozide (0.25 mg/kg^{-1} ip), a dopamine antagonist, antagonized the immobility-reducing effects of alprazolam and BN 52063. Methysergide (1 mg/kg^{-1} sc), a serotonin agonist and antagonist, and ketanserine (1 mg/kg^{-1} sc), a serotonin 5-HT$_2$ antagonist, almost completely inhibited the effect of alprazolam and BN 52063 on the duration of immobility by forced swimming-induced despair behavior in mice.

The alkylxanthine phosphodiesterases inhibitor 3-isobutylmethylxanthine (IBMX) (15 mg/kg^{-1} and 25 mg/kg^{-1} po) potentiated the effects of BN 52063 (1 mg/kg^{-1} po) and alprazolam (0.25 mg/kg^{-1} po) on the immobility time for doses where alprazolam and BN 52063 were inactive on this parameter.

As β-adrenoceptors agonists (but not α-adrenoceptors), dopamine and serotonin (5-HT$_2$) agonists are known to stimulate guanine nucleotide-binding regulatory component (Ns) which enhances the conversion of ATP into cAMP, and as phosphodiesterase inhibitors were shown to potentiate the effect of PAF antagonists like BN 52063, it can be believed that the disinhibitory effects of the two PAF antagonists, alprazolam and BN 52063, on forced swimming-induced behavioral despair in mice may be explained by the relationship between PAF receptor and cAMP cascade system. The opposite effects of PAF receptors and β-adrenergic receptors on this system may be one of the explanations for the interactions between PAF and β-adrenergic system.

INTRODUCTION

A potential role for platelet-activating factor (PAF), (1-O-alkyl-2-acetyl-sn-glyceryl-3-phosphorylcholine) in the central nervous system was suggested by the discovery that triazolobenzodiazepines (T-BDZ), especially alprazolam, triazolam (18), brotizolam (11) and WEB 2086 (34), exert a specific inhibition of PAF-induced activation of human platelets: alprazolam and triazolam inhibit PAF-induced changes in shape, aggregation and secretion by platelets, whereas other benzodiazepines, diazepam or chlordiazepoxide are not active (18).

In the course of clinical development, alprazolam was discovered to have useful antidepressant activity (24) in addition to potent anxiolytic properties that may be conferred by the triazol ring (28, 30, 33). Another group of potent PAF antagonists is formed by terpenes isolated from the Chinese tree *Ginkgo biloba* L.: ginkgolides A (BN 52020), B (BN 52021), C (BN 52022) (5-7). BN 52021, the most potent of them, inhibits PAF-binding to rabbit (5) and human (19) washed platelets, PAF-induced aggregation and degranulation of human isolated neutrophils (5), PAF-induced contraction of guinea-pig lung parenchymal strips (32) or IgG induced hypotension, hemoconcentration and extravasation in the rat (27). BN 52021 is also effective in different complex models: it counteracts preventively and curatively the hypotension induced by *Salmonella enteritidis* in the rat (14) or by *S. typhimurium* in the guinea-pig (1), antagonizes PAF-induced bronchoconstriction (13), and heterologous or homologous passive bronchospasm (8) and significantly reduces the stroke index after unilateral ligation of carotid artery in gerbils (28a).

The purpose of this study was to investigate in the depression-like syndrome of forced swimming-induced behavioral despair in mice (22), the effects of two kinds of PAF antagonists: alprazolam, a triazolobenzodiazepine with antidepressant component, and BN 52063, a standardized mixture of ginkgolides A, B and C. The present experiments were also designed to evaluate some possible influences of BN 52063 on the behavioral pattern in two classical models: mouse open-field behavior and tetrabenazine-induced ptosis in mice. A variety of pharmacological interactions with α-adrenergic agonists and antagonists, β-adrenergic, dopaminergic and serotoninergic antagonists were also investigated to determine precisely the mechanisms of the effects of alprazolam and BN 52063.

MATERIALS AND METHODS

Open-Field Test

Male CD-1 mice (Charles River Ltd.) weighing 20-22 g were used. The animals were placed in an open-field box (optovarimex 3) (30 x 30 cm) consisting of 16 squares with infra-red photocells. Activity was characterized by the total number of squares explored (distance travelled during 4 minutes and 27 seconds) and by the total number of rearings during the same time of observation. The drugs were administered at the rate of 0.5 ml/20 g in a suspension of tragacanth, 1 hour before beginning of observation.

Tetrabenazine-Induced Ptosis in Mice

Male CD-1 mice (Charles River Ltd.) weighing 20-22 g were used. Tetrabenazine (80 mg/kg, sc) was administered 45 minutes before test and

1 hour after administration of drugs by oral route, dispersed in a suspension of tragacanth.

Ptosis was rated on a scale from 0-4 with the eyelid opening score system according to Rubin *et al.* (26): 0: eyelids completely closed; 1: eyelid 1/4 opened; 2: eyelids 1/2 opened; 3: eyelids 3/4 opened; 4: eyelids completely opened.

Ptsosis was assessed 1 hour and 45 minutes after drug administration, *i.e.*, 45 minutes after tetrabenazine injection.

Forced Swimming-Induced Despair Behavior in Mice

Male CD-1 mice (Charles River Ltd.) weighing 22-25 g were used. Upon arrival, the mice were housed 20-25 per cage with food and water available *ad libitum*. For the despair test, they were weighed and housed in groups of 8. All experiments were performed in the same two hours.

The procedure is the same as that described by Porsolt *et al.* (23). The animals were forced to swim individually in a 10 cm high glass jar containing fresh water and maintained at room temperature (22-25°C).

After an initial 2-minutes period of vigorous activity, each animal assumed a typical immobile posture. A mouse was said to be immobile when it ceased struggling and made minimal movements with its limbs to keep its head above water. The total duration of immobility was recorded during the following 4 minutes of a total 6-minute test.

The drugs were either dissolved in distilled water or dispersed in a suspension of tragacanth. Mice were treated (po) 1 hour before the swimming test with alprazolam, triazolam, imipramine and BN 52063. The other drugs used were given in one dose, by oral route and with one pretreatment time reported to have a significant effect on adrenergic, serotoninergic and dopaminergic mechanism: clonidine, 0.1 mg/kg ip for 15 minutes before; prazosin, 3 mg/kg sc 60 minutes; yohimbine, 1 mg/kg 30 minutes; dl propranolol, 5 mg/kg ip 45 minutes; butoxamine, 5 mg/kg ip 45 minutes; atenolol, 5 mg/kg 120 minutes; methysergide, 1 mg/kg sc 60 minutes; pimozide, 0.25 mg/kg sc 120 minutes.

Stastistics

All data were analyzed by analysis of variance (ANOVA) followed by F test.

Drugs

The drugs used in the present investigation were obtained from the following manufacturers: tetrabenazine (Hoffmann-LaRoche), alprazolam and triazolam (Upjohn), imipramine, clonidine hydrochloride and atenolol

(Sigma), prazosin hydrochloride (Pfizer), dl-propranolol (ICI-pharma), butoxamide hydrochloride (Burroughs-Wellcome), pimozide (Cassenne), methysergide (Sandoz), and 3-isobutylmethylxanthine (Sigma).

RESULTS

Open-Field Test

The results of drug testing are expressed in terms of the total number of transits and the total number of rearings made by eight animals at each dose (Table 1).

BN 52063 increased the number of transits significantly ($p < 0.05$) at 50 mg/kg^{-1} po. The total number of rearings was not significantly improved by BN 52063 at 20 and 50 mg/kg^{-1} po. Alprazolam increased the number of transits significantly ($p < 0.05$ and $p < 0.001$) at 0..25 and 0.50 mg/kg^{-1} po, respectively. The total number of rearings was not significantly improved at these two doses.

Table 1   Effects of alprazolam and BN 52063 on open-field activity in mice

Drug	Dose[a] (po)	Total number of squares[b]	Total number of rearings[b]
Controls	—	137.58 (112.77-162.40)	37.25 (29.70-44.80)
Alprazolam	0.0625 mg/kg	153.67 (120.03-195.30)	38.50 (20.07-56.93)
	0.125 mg/kg	149.83 (126.29-173.37)	41.00 (31.78-50.22)
	0.250 mg/kg	183.20* (132.15-234.24)	41.17 (28.85-67.48)
	0.500 mg/kg	235.50*** (163.78-307.23)	53.67 (38.86-68.47)
Controls	—	87.87 (59.63-116.12)	18.75 (10.78-26.71)
BN 52063	20 mg/kg	90.37 (59.35-121.39)	22.25 (12.28-32.22)
	50 mg/kg	122.87* (92.18-153.17)	28.00 (20.20-35.80)
	100 mg/kg	79.37 (61.77-96.98)	15.87 (8.69-23.06)

[a]Mice received saline or drugs in a volume of 0.5 ml/20 g 1 hr before the open-field test.
[b]Total number of squares and rearings during 4 min.20 sec (time of observation).
Range limits in parentheses. *$p < 0.05$ *versus* control (F test); **$p < 0.01$; ***$p < 0.001$

Tetrabenazine-Induced Ptosis in Mice

Neither BN 52063 (20-100 mg/kg^{-1} po) nor alprazolam (0.0625-0.5 mg/kg^{-1} po) modified tetrabenazine-induced ptosis in mice (Table 2).

Table 2   Actions of BN 52063 and alprazolam on tetrabenazine-induced ptosis in mice

Drug and dose	Means of ptosis (scores of Rubin et al.)
Tetrabenazine (80 mg/kg sc)	6.1
Tetrabenazine (80 mg/kg sc) + Imipramine (10 mg/kg po)	1.4
Tetrabenazine (80 mg/kg sc) + BN 52063 (20 mg/kg po)	6.3
Tetrabenazine (80 mg/kg sc) + BN 52063 (50 mg/kg po)	7.4
Tetrabenazine (80 mg/kg sc) + BN 52063 (100 mg/kg po)	7.5
Tetrabenazine (80 mg/kg sc)	6.2
Tetrabenazine (80 mg/kg sc) + Alprazolam (0.0625 mg/kg po)	6.7
Tetrabenazine (80 mg/kg sc) + Alprazolam (0.125 mg/kg po)	6.9
Tetrabenazine (80 mg/kg sc) + Alprazolam (0.250 mg/kg po)	6.2
Tetrabenazine (80 mg/kg sc) + Alprazolam (0.500 mg/kg po)	5.0

Drugs were administered 1 hr before tetrabenazine. Tetrabenazine was administered 45 min before observations. The score system for eyelid opening is that of Rubin *et al.* (26): 0: eyelids completely closed; 1: eyelids 1/4 opened; 2: eyelids 1/2 opened; 3: eyelids 3/4 opened; 4: eyelids completely opened.

Forced Swimming-Induced Despair Behavior in Mice

Diazepam (0.0625-2 mg/kg^{-1} po) did not influence the duration of immobility in mice exposed to a forced adverse situation. Triazolam (0.0625-1 mg/kg^{-1} po) significantly elevated immobility duration. This effect was not dose-dependent. Alprazolam (7.8-125 μg.kg^{-1} po) significantly decreased immobility duration in mice (Table 3).

BN 52063 (2-50 mg/kg^{-1} po) significantly and dose-dependently reduced immobility duration in mice exposed to a mildly adverse situation from 2 mg/kg^{-1} to 10 mg/kg^{-1}. For the highest doses (20-50 mg/kg^{-1}), we observ-

Table 3 Effect of diazepam, triazolam and alprazolam on forced swimming-induced despair behavior during 4 min of the 6 min test in mice

Drug	Dose	n	Immobility duration (mean ± SE) (sec)	p*
Saline	0.4 ml/20 g	20	213.9 ± 2.9	
Diazepam	0.0625 mg/kg	10	206.9 ± 8.6	NS
	0.125 mg/kg	10	205.7 ± 8.6	NS
	0.250 mg/kg	10	216.9 ± 7.5	NS
	0.500 mg/kg	10	218.5 ± 4.2	NS
	1 mg/kg	10	215.1 ± 7.3	NS
	2 mg/kg	10	204.8 ± 7.4	NS
Saline	0.4 ml/20 g	20	206.7 ± 4.8	
Triazolam	0.0625 mg/kg	10	223.9 ± 7.8	p < 0.05
	0.125 mg/kg	10	218.3 ± 10	p < 0.05
	0.25 mg/kg	20	229.7 ± 3	p < 0.01
	0.50 mg/kg	10	227.3 ± 2.9	p < 0.01
	1 mg/kg	10	232.9 ± 3.3	p < 0.01
Saline	0.4 ml/20 g		213.7 ± 2.8	
Alprazolam	3.9 μg/kg		206.6 ± 10.0	NS
	7.9 μg/kg		177.6 ± 8.6	p < 0.001
	15.6 μg/kg		179.2 ± 6.8	p < 0.001
	31.2 μg/kg		165.6 ± 10.8	p < 0.001
	62.5 μg/kg		146.2 ± 10.2	p < 0.001
	125 μg/kg		183.0 ± 10.1	p < 0.001
	250 μg/kg		205.3 ± 4.7	NS
	500 μg/kg		206.5 ± 3.8	NS

*As compared to control group.

Table 4 Effect of BN 52063 on forced swimming-induced despair behavior during 4 min of the 6 min test in mice

Drug	Dose (p.o.)	n	Immobility duration (mean ± SE) (sec)	p*
Saline	0.4 ml/20 g	38	210.6 ± 3.9	—
Imipramine	10 mg/kg	10	184.4 ± 10.7	N.S.
	20 mg/kg	20	120.4 ± 15.9	p < 0.001
BN 52063	1 mg/kg	8	219.5 ± 5.8	N.S.
	2 mg/kg	18	169.8 ± 9.6	p < 0.01
	5 mg/kg	10	127.7 ± 21.2	p < 0.001
	10 mg/kg	20	91.7 ± 11.1	p < 0.001
	20 mg/kg	20	132.2 ± 9.8	p < 0.001
	50 mg/kg	10	135.0 ± 13.7	p < 0.001

*As compared to control group.

ed a plateau (Table 4). As shown in Tables 5 and 6, prazosin (3 mg/kg^{-1} sc), an α_1-antagonist, clonidine (0.1 mg/kg^{-1} ip), an α_2-agonist, and yohimbine (1 mg/kg^{-1} sc), an α_2-antagonist, did not modify the decrease in immobility duration in mice induced either by alprazolam (0.0625 mg/kg^{-1} po) or by BN 52063 (5 mg/kg^{-1} po). In contrast, propranolol (5 mg/kg^{-1} ip), a β-antagonist, butoxamine (5 mg/kg^{-1} ip), a β_2-antagonist, and atenolol

Table 5   Influence of α-adrenergic agents on the immobility-reducing action of alprazolam (0.0625 mg/kg po, 1 hr before test)

Drug	Dose	Total duration of immobility (sec/6 min)	
		saline	alprazolam (0.0625 mg/kg po)
Control	—	209.7 ± 7.0	$168.5 \pm 10.5^{**}$
Prazosin	3 mg/kg	202.7 ± 6.1 ns	190.8 ± 10.7 NS
Control	—	215.0 ± 5.4	$146.2 \pm 10.2^{+++}$
Clonidine	0.1 mg/kg i.p.	183.8 ± 10.7 ns	143.3 ± 16.6 NS
Control	—	209.2 ± 8.6	$135.0 \pm 16.8^{+++}$
Yohimbine	1 mg/kg sc	209.5 ± 13 ns	149.2 ± 11.0 NS

Each value is the mean $\pm$ SEM of 8 animals.

n.s. compared with respective saline group; $^{++}$p < 0.01 compared with respective saline group; $^{+++}$p < 0.001 compared with respective saline group.

NS compared with vehicle + alprazolam group; **p < 0.01 compared with vehicle + alprazolam group; ***p < 0.001 compared with vehicle + alprazolam group.

Table 6   Influence of α-adrenergic agents on the immobility-reducing action of BN 52063 (5 mg/kg po 1 hr before test)

Drug	Dose	Total duration of immobility (sec/6 min)	
		saline	BN 52063 (5 mg/kg po)
Control	—	209.7 ± 7.0	$156.4 \pm 8.7^{+++}$
Prazosin	3 mg/kg sc	202.7 ± 6.1 ns	166.4 ± 12.4 NS
Control	—	214.7 ± 6.5	$147.9 \pm 10.7^{+++}$
Clonidine	0.1 mg/kg ip	$178.9 \pm 7.9^{+}$	172.5 ± 12.7 NS
Control	—	209.1 ± 8.4	$124.1 \pm 13.9^{+++}$
Yohimbine	1 mg/kg sc	212.0 ± 11.9 ns	114.2 ± 12.4 NS

Each value is the mean $\pm$ SEM of 8 animals.

n.s. compared with respective saline group; $^{+}$p < 0.05 compared with respective saline group; $^{++}$p $<$ compared with respective saline group; $^{+++}$p < 0.001 compared with respective saline group.

NS compared with vehicle + BN 52063 group; **p < 0.01 compared with vehicle + BN 52063 group; ***p < 0.001 compared with vehicle + BN 52063 group.

(5 mg/kg^{-1} ip) a β_1-antagonist, totally reversed the immobility-reducing effects of alprazolam and BN 52063 (Tables 7 and 8). Pimozide (0.25 mg/kg^{-1} ip), a dopamine antagonist, antagonized the immobility-reducing effects of alprazolam and BN 52063 (Tables 9 and 10). Methysergide (1 mg/kg^{-1} sc), a serotonin agonist and antagonist, and ketanserine (1 mg/kg^{-1} sc), a 5-HT$_2$-antagonist, almost completely inhibited the effect of alprazolam and

Table 7   Influence of β-adrenergic agents on the immobility-reducing action of alprazolam (0.0625 mg/kg po, 1 hr before test)

Drug	Dose	Total duration of immobility (sec/6 min)	
		saline	alprazolam (0.0625 mg/kg po)
Control	—	210.3 ± 7.0	$138.2 \pm 5.3^{+++}$
Propranolol	5 mg/kg ip	213.6 ± 5.5 n.s.	$206.5 \pm 7.0^{***}$
Control	—	229.6 ± 2.8	$139.0 \pm 9.7^{+++}$
Butoxamine	5 mg/kg ip	223.7 ± 3.4 n.s.	$219.4 \pm 8.1^{***}$
Control	—	211.8 ± 6.0	$151.9 \pm 13.5^{+++}$
Atenolol	5 mg/kg ip	215.2 ± 4.7 n.s.	$195.8 \pm 9.1^{***}$

Each value is the mean ± SEM of 8 animals.
n.s. compared with respective saline group; $^{++}$p$<$0.01 compared with respective saline group; $^{+++}$p$<$0.001 compared with respective saline group.
NS compared with vehicle + alprazolam group; **p$<$0.01 compared with vehicle + alprazolam group; ***p$<$0.001 compared with vehicle + alprazolam group.

Table 8   Influence of β-adrenergic agents on the immobility-reducing action of BN 52063 (5 mg/kg po 1 hr before test)

Drug	Dose	Total duration of immobility (sec/6 min)	
		saline	BN 52063 (5 mg/kg po)
Control	—	224.9 ± 5.1	$159.0 \pm 6.3^{+++}$
Propranolol	5 mg/kg ip	226.7 ± 5.0 n.s.	$209.1 \pm 9.1^{***}$
Control	—	213.5 ± 8.4	$114.6 \pm 23.8^{++}$
Butoxamine	5 mg/kg ip	204.0 ± 5.0 n.s.	$211.1 \pm 4.3^{**}$
Control	—	212.0 ± 5.3	$145.2 \pm 9.0^{+++}$
Atenolol	5 mg/kg ip	221.9 ± 5.3	$206.9 \pm 7.1^{***}$

Each value is the mean ± SEM of 8 animals.
n.s. compared with respective saline group; $^{+}$p$<$0.05 compared with respective saline group; $^{++}$p$<$0.01 compared with respective saline group; $^{+++}$p$<$0.001 compared with respective saline group.
NS compared with vehicle + BN 52063 group; **p$<$0.01 compared with vehicle + BN 52063 group; ***p$<$0.001 compared with vehicle + BN 52063 group.

Table 9   Influence of dopaminergic agents on the immobility-reducing action of alprazolam (0.0625 mg/kg po, 1 hr before test)

Drug	Dose	Total duration of immobility (sec/6 min)	
		saline	alprazolam (0.0625 mg/kg po)
Control	—	224.0±4.0	162.5±11.1[+++]
Pimozide	0.25 mg/kg ip	231.6±2.3 n.s.	229.4± 5.3***

Each value is the mean ± SEM of 8 animals.
n.s. compared with respective saline group; [++]p<0.01 compared with respective saline group; [+++]p<0.001 compared with respective saline group.
NS compared with vehicle + alprazolam group; **p<0.01 compared with vehicle + alprazolam group; ***p<0.001 compared with vehicle + alprazolam group.

Table 10   Influence of dopaminergic agents on the immobility-reducing action of BN 52063 (5 mg/kg po 1 hr before test)

Drug	Dose	Total duration of immobility (sec/6 min)	
		saline	BN 52063 (5 mg/kg po)
Control	—	224.0±4.0	154.1±16.7[+++]
Pimozide	0.25 mg/kg ip	231.6±2.3 n.s.	221.9± 6.0***

Each value is the mean ± SEM of 8 animals.
n.s. compared with respective saline group; [+]p<0.05 compared with respective saline group; [++]p<0.01 compared with respective saline group; [+++]p<0.001 compared with respective saline group.
NS compared with vehicle + BN 52063 group; **p<0.01 compared with vehicle + BN 52063 group; ***p<0.001 compared with vehicle + BN 52063 group.

Table 11   Influence of serotoninergic agents on the immobility-reducing action of alprazolam (0.0625 mg/kg po, 1 hr before test)

Drug	Dose	Total duration of immobility (sec/6 min)	
		saline	alprazolam (0.0625 mg/kg po)
Control	—	214.1± 9.8	147.7± 7.7[+++]
Methysergide	1 mg/kg sc	211.3±11.4 n.s.	226.3± 4.1***
Control	—	224.0± 4.0	161.5±11.1[+++]
Ketanserine	1 mg/kg sc	218.1± 7.1 n.s.	221.6± 8.6***

Each value is the mean ± SEM of 8 animals.
n.s. compared with respective saline group; [++]p<0.01 compared with respective saline group; [+++]p<0.001 compared with respective saline group.
NS compared with vehicle + alprazolam group; **p<0.01 compared with vehicle + alprazolam group; ***p<0.001 compared with vehicle + alprazolam group.

BN 52063 on the duration of immobility by forced swimming-induced despair behavior in mice (Tables 11 and 12).

The alkylxanthine phosphodiesterases inhibitor 3-isobutylmethylxanthine (IBMX) (15 mg/kg^{-1} and 25 mg/kg^{-1} po) potentiated the effects of BN 52063 (1 mg/kg^{-1} po) and alprazolam (0.25 mg/kg^{-1} po) on the immobility time at doses where either alprazolam or BN 52063 were inactive on this parameter (Tables 13 and 14).

Table 12 Influence of serotoninergic agents on the immobility-reducing action of BN 52063 (5 mg/kg po 1 hr before test)

Drug	Dose	Total duration of immobility (sec/6 min)	
		Saline	BN 52063 (5 mg/kg po)
Control	—	214.1 ± 9.8	$151.1 \pm 8.5^{+++}$
Methysergide	1 mg/kg sc	213.4 ± 7.0 n.s.	209.1 ± 6.6***
Control	—	224.0 ± 4.0	$154.1 \pm 16.7^{+++}$
Ketanserine	1 mg/kg sc	218.1 ± 7.1 n.s.	209.1 ± 7.3***

Each value is the mean $\pm$ SEM of 8 animals.

n.s. compared with respective saline group; $^+p < 0.05$ compared with respective saline group; $^{++}p < 0.01$ compared with respective saline group; $^{+++}p < 0.001$ compared with respective saline group.

NS compared with vehicle + BN 52063 group; **$p < 0.01$ compared with vehicle + BN 52063 group; ***$p < 0.001$ compared with vehicle + BN 52063 group.

Table 14 Interaction between isobutylmethylxanthine (IBMX) and alprazolam on forced swimming-induced despair behavior in mice

Drug	Dose and route	Immobility duration (mean $\pm$ SE (sec))	p
Control (saline)	—	226.7 ± 7.4	—
Control (ethanol)	—	220.1 ± 7.4	NS (versus saline)
IBMX	15 mg/kg ip	209.8 ± 9.6	NS (versus ethanol)
IBMX	25 mg/kg ip	196.6 ± 4.4	NS (versus ethanol)
Alprazolam	0.25 mg/kg po	206.9 ± 8.5	NS (versus saline)
Alprazolam + IBM X	0.25 mg/kg po 15 mg/kg ip	174.5 ± 11.5	$p < 0.01$ (versus alprazolam) $p < 0.001$ (versus IBMX 15 mg/kg ip)
Alprazolam + IBMX	0.25 mg/kg po 25 mg/kg ip	181.3 ± 8.7	$p < 0.05$ (versus alprazolam) NS (versus IBMX 25 mg/kg ip)

IBMX was dissolved in 1.7% ethanol and administered 2 h before test and 1 h before alprazolam.
8 animals per group.

DISCUSSION

The results of this study show that the PAF antagonistic activity of triazolodiazepines is independent of their classical effects on CNS (anxiolytic, sedative and hypnotic actions) but may be related to the antidepressant component for alprazolam. A benzodiazepine without the triazol ring, diazepam, which did not inhibit PAF-induced platelet activation (18), and a benzodiazepine with a triazol ring but without antidepressant effect, triazolam —used as a short-acting sleep medication in humans— are ineffective on the time of immobility in mice by forced swimming-induced despair behavior. Moreover, triazolam increases the immobility time in mice. These results confirm the observation of Casals-Stenzel and Weber (12), *i.e.,* a dissociation between the PAF-antagonistic and CNS activities of triazolodiazepines. However, we cannot conclude that there is the same dissociation between the antidepressant component and PAF antagonist activity. Indeed, alprazolam and BN 52063, a PAF antagonist with neither anxiolytic nor sedative effects (9), show the same profile in the forced swimming test with or without interactions with agonists or antagonists having noradrenergic, dopaminergic and serotoninergic functions.

BN 52063 is a standardized mixture of ginkgolides from *Ginkgo biloba* extract. It showed a specific effect on the noradrenergic system and on beta adrenoceptors (10). In the mice open-field behavior test, BN 52063 increased the number of transits significantly ($p < 0.05$) at 50 mg/kg^{-1}. At the same dose, BN 52063 increased (non significantly) the number of rearings. No disinhibitory activity was observed with 20 or 100 mg/kg^{-1}. These observations suggest that BN 52063 disinhibits punished behavior in a non dose-related manner and without a sedative effect. Unlike imipramine, BN 52063 did not modify tetrabenazine-induced ptosis in mice indicating clearly that the disinhibitory action of BN 52063 is mechanistically distinct from the effects of imipramine-like antidepressants.

Like alprazolam, but unlike triazolam, BN 52063 showed a significant and dose-related (2-10 mg/kg^{-1}) reduction of the duration of immobility in mice exposed to forced swimming-induced behavioral despair. This despair behavior in mice was shown to be related to the central catecholamine system (23): immobility was decreased by drugs which enhance dopaminergic and α-adrenergic activity and was increased by agents which reduce the prior activity. Moreover, central β_1- and β_2- subtypes of adrenoceptors may be acting in opposite directions to modify behavioral despair: activation of β_1-adrenoceptors may lead to enhanced behavioral despair, whereas a reverse effect may be observed on β_2-adrenoceptor activation (21). On the other hand, blockade of dopamine transmission prevents the effects of antidepressants in the behavioral despair test (4).

Therefore, we investigated the effects of different pharmacological agents which selectively increase or decrease the activity of central noradrenaline, dopamine and serotonin with the effects of alprazolam and BN 52063 on the duration of immobility in forced swimming-induced despair behavior in mice. The actions of alprazolam and BN 52063 were not modified by the pretreatment with α_1-adrenergic antagonist, prazosin, presynaptic α_2-adrenergic agonist, clonidine, and presynaptic α_2-adrenergic blocker, yohimbine. These results are consistent with the studies of Kitada *et al.* (16), who reported that the action of isoproterenol and desipramine were not affected by pretreatment with yohimbine and clonidine. In contrast, α_1-adrenergic blockers, like phenoxybenzamine, were reported to completely inhibit the action of desipramine on this test (17). Indeed, it was demonstrated that tricyclic antidepressant drugs act by activating central noradrenergic neurons in the forced swimming test (23). The lack of interaction of α_1-adrenergic blocker with the effects of alprazolam and BN 52063 in the forced swimming test may be explained by other mechanisms between these two drugs and tricyclic antidepressants as suggested above.

In contrast, the effects of alprazolam and BN 52063 on forced swimming-induced despair behavior in mice was antagonized by a β-adrenergic blocker, propranolol, a β_1-adrenergic blocker, atenolol, a β_2-adrenergic blocker, butoxamine, a dopamine antagonist, pimozide, 5-HT agonist and antagonist, methysergide and a 5-HT$_2$-antagonist, ketanserine.

Evidence of β-adrenergic involvement in forced swimming-induced behavioral despair in mice was suggested by many authors (4, 17, 21, 23). It was reported that activation of central β_1-adrenoceptors might lead to enhanced behavioral despair, whereas a reverse effect might be observed on β_2-adrenoceptor activation (21). Our observations show that either β_1-adrenergic blocker (atenolol) or β_2-adrenergic blocker (butoxamine) inhibit the actions of alprazolam and BN 52063 in the forced swimming test. As propranolol removed the *in vivo* anti-anaphylactic activity of BN 52063 in passive shock (20), although BN 52063 did not interfere with the binding of beta adrenergic ligands to their receptor (5), this suggests an indirect interaction between β-adrenergic blockers and BN 52063. Even though involvement of serotoninergic system in behavioral despair test was not demonstrated (2, 23), we observed that methysergide and ketanserine somewhat inhibited the effects of alprazolam and BN 52063 in the forced swimming test. This could be explained by the relationship between membrane effects of PAF and β_1, β_2, dopamine and serotonin receptors through the interactions of their respective antagonists. As β-adrenoceptor agonists (but not α-adrenoceptor), dopamine and serotonin (5-HT$_2$) agonists are known to stimulate guanine nucleotide-binding regulatory component (Ns) which enhances the conversion of ATP into cAMP (25, 29), and as phosphodiesterase inhibitors were shown to potentiate the effect of PAF antagonists like BN 52063 (15), we investigated if the enhanced availability of brain cAMP, by pretreatment with the phosphodiesterase inhibitor, isobutylmethylxanthine (IBMX), would potentiate the effects of the PAF antagonists, alprazolam and BN 52063. Our results show that IBMX (15 mg/kg^{-1} and 25 mg/kg^{-1}) potentiates the effects of BN 52063 and alprazolam on the immobility time at doses where either BN 52063 or alprazolam were inactive on this test.

In conclusion, it is clear that the disinhibitory effects of the two PAF antagonists alprazolam and BN 52063 on forced swimming-induced behavioral despair in mice may be explained by the relationships between PAF receptor and cAMP cascade system. PAF modulates a drop in intracytosolic cAMP level which appears to be mediated via the activation of (Ni) component of the hormone-sensitive adenylate cyclase system. This antagonistic equilibrium between the effects of PAF receptors and cAMP may be one of the explanations for the interactions between PAF and β-adrenergic system.

References

1. Adnot, S., Lefort, J., Lagente, V., Braquet, P., Vargaftig, B.B. *Interference of BN 52021, a PAF-acether antagonist, with endotoxin-induced hypotension in the guinea-pig.* Pharmacol Res Commun 1986; 18(Suppl.): 197-200.

2. Araki, H., Kawashima, K., Ushiyama, Y., Aihara, H. *Involvement of amygdaloid catecholaminergic mechanism in suppressive effects of desipramine and imipramine on duration of immobility in rats forced to swim.* Eur J Pharmacol 1985; 113: 313-318.

3. Baranes, J., Hellegouarch, A., Le Hegarat, M., Viossat, I., Auguet, M., Chabrier, P.E., Clostre, F., Braquet, P. *The effects of PAF-acether on the cardiovascular system and their inhibition by a new highly specific PAF-acether receptor antagonist: BN 52021.* Pharmacol Res Commun 1986; 18: 717-737.

4. Borsini, F., Nowakowska, E., Pulvirenti, L., Samanin, R. *Repeated treatment with amitriptyline reduces immobility in the behavioural «despair» test in rats by activating dopaminergic and β-adrenergic mechanisms.* J Pharm Pharmacol 1985; 37: 137-138.

5. Braquet, P., Spinnewyn, B., Braquet, M., Bourgain, R.H., Taylor, J.E., Etienne, A., Drieu, K. *BN 52021 and related compounds: A new series of highly specific PAF-acether receptor antagonists isolated from Ginkgo*

biloba. Blood Vessels 1985; 16: 559-572.

6. Braquet, P. *Treatment or prevention of PAF-acether disorders provoked by a new series of highly specific inhibitors.* GB Patent 84/18 424 (July 19, 1984) Belg. BE 901, 915 (see CA 103: 189808d, 1985).

7. Braquet, P. *Involvement of PAF-acether in various immune disorders using BN 52021 (ginkgolide B): A powerful PAF-acether antagonist isolated from Ginkgo biloba L.* In: Advances in Prostaglandin, Thromboxane and Leukotriene Research, Vol. 16. Raven Press: New York 1986; 179-198.

8. Braquet, P., Guinot, Z.P., Touvay, C. *The role of PAF-acether in anaphylaxis demonstrated with the use of the antagonist BN 52021.* Agents and Actions 1987; in press.

9. Braquet, P. *The ginkgolides: Potent platelet-activating factor antagonists isolated from Ginkgo biloba L. Chemistry, Pharmacology and Clinical Applications.* Drugs of the Future 1987; 12: 643-699.

10. Brunello, N., Racagni, G., Clostre, F., Drieu, K., Braquet, P. *Effects of an extract of Ginkgo biloba on noradrenergic systems of rat cerebral cortex.* Pharmacol Res Commun 1985; 17: 1063-1072.

11. Casals-Stenzel, J. *Inhibition of PAF-induced effects by brotizolam and related compounds.* Naunyn Schmiedeberg's Arch Pharmacol

1986; 332 (Suppl): R71.

12. Casals-Stenzel, J., Weber, K.H. *Triazolodiazepines: Dissociation of their PAF (platelet-activating factor) antagonistic and CNS activity.* Br J Pharmacol 1987; 90: 139-146.

13. Desquand, S., Touvay, C., Randon, J., Lagente, V., Maridonneau-Parini, I., Lefort, J., Etienne, A., Braquet, P., Vargaftig, B.B. *Interference of ginkgolide B (BN 52021) with the bronchopulmonary effects of PAF-acether in the guinea-pig.* Eur J Pharmacol 1986; 127: 83-95.

14. Etienne, A., Hecquet, F., Soulard, C., Spinnewyn, B., Clostre, F., Braquet, P. *In vivo inhibition of plasma protein leakage and Salmonella enteritidis-induced mortality in the rat by a specific PAF-acether antagonist: BN 52021.* Agents and Actions 1985; 17: 368-370.

15. Garay, R., Braquet, P. *Involvement of K+ movements in the membrane signal induced by PAF-acether.* Biochem Pharmacol 1986; 35: 2811-2815.

16. Kitada, Y., Miyauchi, T., Kosasa, T., Satoh, S. *Further studies on the suppressing effect of isoproterenol on the immobility-reducing action of desipramine in the forced swimming test.* Japan J Pharmacol 1983; 33: 867-873.

17. Kitada, Y., Miyauchi, T., Kanazawa, Y., Nakamichi, H., Satoh, S. *Involvement of α- and β₁-adrenergic mechanisms in the immobility-reducing action of desipramine in the forced swimming test.* Neuropharmacology 1983; 9: 1055-1060.

18. Kornecki, E., Ehrlich, Y.E., Lenox, R.H. *Platelet-activating factor-induced aggregation of human platelets specially inhibited by triazolobenzodiazepines.* Science 1984; 226: 1454-1456.

19. Kuster, L.J., Filep, J., Frolich, J.C. *Mechanism of PAF-acether-induced platelet aggregation in man.* Thrombosis Research 1986; 43: 425-433.

20. Lagente, V., Touvay, C., Randon, J., Desquand, S., Cirino, M., Vilain, B., Lefort, J., Braquet, P., Vargaftig, B.B. *Interference of the PAF-acether antagonist BN 52021 with passive anaphylaxis in the guinea-pig.* Prostaglandins 1987; 33: 265-274.

21. Parale, M.P., Chakravarti, S., Kulkarni, S.K. *Evidence of β-adrenergic involvement in forced swimming-induced behavioral despair of mice.* Meth and Find Exptl Clin Pharmacol 1987; 9: 35-38.

22. Porsolt, R.D., Bertin, A., Jalfre, M. *Behavioural despair in rats and mice: Strain*

differences and the effects of imipramine. Eur J Pharmacol 1978; 51: 291-294.

23. Porsolt, R.D., Bertin, A., Blavet, N., Deniel, M., Jalfre, M. *Immobility induced by forced swimming in rats: Effects of agents which modify central catecholamine and serotonin activity.* Eur J Pharmacol 1979; 57: 201-210.

24. Rickels, K. *Alprazolam and imipramine in depressed outpatients. A controlled study.* Curr Ther Res 1982; 32: 157-164.

25. Ross, E.M., Gilman, A.G. *Biochemical properties of hormone-sensitive adenylate cyclase.* Ann Rev Biochem 1980; 49: 533-564.

26. Rubin, B., Malone, M., Waugh, M., Burke, J.C. *Effects of reserpine in mice.* J Pharmacol Exp Ther 1957; 120: 125.

27. Sanchez-Crespo, M., Fernandez-Gallardo, S., Nieto, M.L., Baranes, J., Braquet, P. *Inhibition of the vascular actions of IgG aggregates by BN 52021, a highly specific antagonist of PAF-acether.* Immunopharmacol 1985; 10: 69-75.

28. Sethy, V.H., Hodges, D.H. *Alprazolam in a biochemical model of depression.* Biochem Pharmacol 1982; 31: 3155-3157.

28a. Spinnewyn, B., Blavet, N., Clostre, F. *Effet de l'extrait de Ginkgo biloba sur un modèle d'ischémie cérébrale chez la gerbille.* La Presse Médicale 1986; 15: 1511-1515.

29. Takada, T., Oinuma, M., Ui, M. *Mechanisms for inhibition of the catalytic activity of adenylate cyclase by the guanine nucleotide-binding proteins serving as the substrate of islet-activating protein, pertussis toxin.* J Biol Chem 1986; 261: 5215-5221.

30. Thiebot, M.H., Doare, L., Puech, A.J., Simon, P. *U-43.465F: A benzodiazepine with antidepressant activity? Interaction with Ro 15-1788 and dl-propranolol.* Eur J Pharmacol 1982; 84: 103-106.

31. Touvay, C., Vilain, B., Taylor, J.E., Etienne, A. *Proof of the involvement of platelet-activating factor (PAF-acether) in pulmonary complex immune systems using a specific PAF-acether receptor antagonist: BN 52021.* Prog Lip Res 1985; 25: 277-288.

32. Touvay, C., Vilain, B., Etienne, A., Sirois, P., Borgeat, P., Braquet, P. *Characterization of platelet-activating factor (PAF-acether) induced contractions of guinea-pig lung strips by selected inhibitors of arachidonic acid metabolism and by PAF-acether antagonists.* Immunopharmacology 1986; 12: 97-104.

33. Von Voigtlander, P.F., Puech, A.J. *U-43.465F: A triazolobenzodiazepine with pronounced antidepressant-like as well as anx-*

iolytic activities in animals. Arch Int Pharmacodyn Ther 1983; 266: 70-76.

34. Weber, K.H., Harreus, A., Stransky, W.G., Bechtel, W.D., Casals-Stenzel, J. *Structure-activity relationship of 1,4-diazepines with PAF-antagonistic activity and absence of CNS-effects.* 2nd Int Conf Platelet-Activating Factor and Structurally Related Alkyl Ether Lipids. Gatlinburg TN (USA) October 1986; p. 29, Abst.

Ginkgolides - Chemistry, Biology, Pharmacology and Clinical Perspectives. P. Braquet (Ed.)
Copyright © 1988, J.R. Prous Science Publishers, S.A.

PROTECTIVE EFFECTS OF GINKGOLIDES IN CEREBRAL POST-ISCHEMIC PHASE IN MONGOLIAN GERBILS

Brigitte Spinnewyn, Nadine Blavet, François Clostre and Pierre Braquet

Institut Henri Beaufour, F-92350 Le Plessis-Robinson, France

INTRODUCTION

Clinical and experimental studies which examine cerebrovascular disease indicate that periods of hypoxia or disruption of blood flow result in impairments of neuronal function (41) and in behavioral disorders (44). Among other mediators, catecholamines, serotonin, angiotensin, histamine, thrombine and oxygen free radicals may participate in the development of ischemic cerebral failure (1, 16, 35). Moreover, the onset of cerebral ischemia causes a breakdown of cellular lipids and an increase in the levels of free fatty acids in the brain (2, 49, 51). There is growing evidence that cerebral ischemia leads to an accumulation of arachidonic acid products (20) and phospholipids (32, 41).

Since the discovery of platelet-activating factor, extensive studies have been devoted to examine its physiopathologic role (12). Platelet-activating factor (PAF, PAF-acether, AGEPC) is a naturally occurring ether phospholipid (1-O-alkyl-2(R)-acetyl-glyceryl-3-phosphorylcholine) that is generated by specific activation of rabbit basophils, human and rabbit polymorphonuclear leukocytes (PMNLs), human macrophages and eosinophils (12).

Address all correspondence to: Dr. F. Clostre, Institut Henri Beaufour, 17, avenue Descartes, F-92350 Le Plessis-Robinson, France.

Generation of PAF-acether during anaphylaxis and/or shock leads to chemotaxis, aggregation and degranulation of polymorphonuclear cells and activation of eosinophils (27, 46).

Recently, it was demonstrated that PAF-acether might contribute to the aggravation of ischemic cellular damage (32) and might be a promoting factor of brain edema (37).

A standardized extract of the Chinese tree *Ginkgo biloba* (GBE 761) has been demonstrated to improve cerebral metabolism (26), to antagonize cerebral edema induced by microembolization in rats (30) and to possess regulatory effects on blood vessels (14). GBE 761 also improves cerebral ischemia in gerbils (42). Beck *et al.* (4) demonstrated that it is the non-flavone fraction of GBE 761 which exerts beneficial action on cerebral energy metabolism. BN 52021 (ginkgolide B) and related compounds, *i.e.,* BN 52020 (ginkgolide A), BN 52022 (ginkgolide C) and BN 52024 (ginkgolide J) are terpenes isolated from *Ginkgo biloba* L., which are present in the non-flavone fraction of GBE 761. Ginkgolides significantly inhibit both PAF-acether effects and various immune disorders both *in vitro* and *in vivo* in humans and in animals (8-10, 12). BN 52021, the most potent of them, inhibits PAF-binding to rabbit (11) and human (29) washed platelets, PAF-induced aggregation and degranulation of human isolated neutrophils (11), PAF-induced contraction of guinea-pig lung parenchymal strips (45) or IgG-induced hypotension (38), hemoconcentration and extravasation in the rat. BN 52021 also antagonizes edema, cell infiltration, eicosanoid release and lipid peroxidation of intestine (43) and heart ischemia (6).

The absence of posterior communicating arteries is the most often quoted reason for the unique susceptibility of gerbils to carotid ligation (5, 25, 33). Ten minutes of clamping and recirculation produced consequent behavioral disturbances due to brain damage chiefly localized in the cortex and hippocampus (24, 27, 50). Such ischemia has been shown to be accompanied by drastic changes in cerebral metabolism (36) and can probably be linked directly to mitochondrial dysfunction.

Using ginkgolides and other non-chemically related PAF-acether antagonists: kadsurenone (40), a lignan, and brotizolam, a triazolobenzodiazepine (10), we investigated the possible involvement of PAF-acether in cerebral metabolic and behavioral disturbances after bilateral carotid ligation and recirculation in Mongolian gerbils.

MATERIALS AND METHODS

Male gerbils (60-70 g) were anesthetized with ketamine (50 mg.kg^{-1} i.p.). A ventral midline incision was made and the common carotid arteries were exposed. A 3 cm length catheter loop was placed around them and the extremities of the catheter were flame welded. Animals were housed singly after surgery and allowed to recover from anesthesia for one hour.

After that time, removing the catheter, arteries were released from the body and a clamp was placed just behind the catheter, preventing blood flow for 10 minutes. The clamp was then removed, the catheter cut and the necks of the gerbils were sutured. In the control group (sham-operated), surgery was the same except for clamping.

Experiments

Group 1. Ischemia induced after seven days oral pretreatment once a day. Last administration took place one hour before ligature. In this experiment BN 52020 (10 mg.kg^{-1} p.o.), BN 52021 (5 and 10 mg.kg^{-1} p.o.), BN 52022 (10 mg.kg^{-1} p.o.) and BN 52024 (10 mg/kg^{-1} p.o.) were studied.

Group 2. Drugs were administered 10 minutes before recirculation, *i.e.*, at the same time as clamping: BN 52020 (10 mg.kg^{-1} i.p.), BN 52021 (10 mg.kg^{-1} i.p.), BN 52022 (10 mg.kg^{-1} i.p.).

Group 3. Drugs were administered 1 hour after recirculation: BN 52021 (10 mg.kg^{-1} i.p.), kadsurenone (10 mg.kg^{-1} i.p.) and brotizolam (10 mg.kg^{-1} i.p.).

The following parameters effects were studied.

Determination of Stroke Index

The animals were placed in a wooden box (48 x 38 x 19 cm) and scored for 3 minutes. Morbidity was evaluated according to the stroke index chart defined by Mc Graw (34): decrease in alertness and movement, ptosis, cocked head, circling, behavior, hindlimb splaying and rotation, seizure behavior, piloerection, tremor, comatose and death (Table 1).

Each animal was examined one hour after declamping and every hour until the 4th hour (experiment 1) or the 6th hour (experiments 2 and 3).

Isolation of Brain Mitochondria

After the last behavioral observation, animals were killed by decapitation and the brains were quickly removed from the skull. The cortex was not cut off and placed rapidly in the ice-cold isolation medium (mM) [mannitol, 225; sucrose, 75; EDTA, 0.2; Tris-HCl, 5, pH 7.4] and homogenized in a potter fitter with a Teflon pestle. The homogenate was centrifuged for 2 minutes at 1.805 x g. The resulting supernatant was then centrifuged at 17.000 x g for 5 minutes. The resulting pellet was resuspended in 200 μl of isolation medium. The final protein concentration was 20-25 mg.ml^{-1}.

Table 1   Numerical weight of various behavioral impairments following cerebral ischemia in Mongolian gerbils

Symptom	Weight (S_i)
•Hair roughed up or tremor	1
•Obtunded	1
•Paucity of movements	1
•Head cocked	3
•Eyes fixed open	3
•Ptosis	2
•Splayed out hind limb	3
•Extreme rotation of hind limb	3
•Circling behaviour	3
•Seizures	2
•Rolling seizures	3
•Extreme weakness (comatose)	6
•Death	34
Stroke index score	$\dfrac{\Sigma\, Si}{n}$

Mitochondrial Respiratory Activity

Oxygen consumption was studied at 25°C with 1.0-1.5 mg of brain mitochondria using a Gilson oxygraph with a 2.0 ml closed cell and a Clark electrode. NAD-linked respiration was measured by oxidation of the substrate pair: pyruvate and malate (1.0 and 2.5 mM, respectively). For oxygen consumption measurements, the substrate was added first, followed by the brain mitochondria. One minute later, ADP was added. Respiratory rates were determined in the presence of a limited quantity of ADP (300 n mol), defined as state 3 respiration, and after consumption of the added ADP, defined as state 4 respiration. The respiratory control ratio (RCR) is the ratio of state 3 over state 4 respiratory rates (13).

Quantification of Cerebral Edema

After a 10 minute occlusion and 6 hours of reflow, animals (10 sham-operated, 10 ligatured and 10 treated with BN 52021 10 minutes before recirculation) were killed by decapitation. The whole brain was removed from the skull, weighed and then dried (48 hours at 70°C) for water and electrolytes evaluation. Percentage water content was calculated as follows:

$$\text{water (\%)} = \frac{\text{wet weight - dry weight}}{\text{wet weight}} \times 100$$

also improved RCR although its effect was lower than that of BN 52021 (Table 3).

The dehydrated sections were homogenized with 5 ml of 3N nitric acid solution prepared with deionized water. Sodium and potassium concentrations of the supernatant were measured by flame photometry. The value XmEq/l was converted into mEq/kg dry weight of the dehydrated sections according to the following formula:

$$X = \frac{5}{1000} \text{ x } \frac{1}{\text{dry weight}} \text{ x } 1000$$

Additional Method Used

Protein concentration was measured according to the method of Bradford (7).

Statistics

One-way analysis of variance was employed for statistical evaluation using Bartlett's multiple range test to assess differences between experimental groups. Differences with a p value of 0.05 were considered to be statistically significant.

RESULTS

Effects of PAF-Acether Antagonists on Cerebral Ischemia

PREVENTIVE TREATMENT   *Stroke index.* The behavioral pattern at 2, 3 and 4 hours was significantly improved in gerbils pretreated with BN 52021 (10 mg.kg^{-1} p.o.), the stroke index decreasing regularly and being reduced by half at the end of the observation. At 5 mg.kg^{-1} p.o., BN 52021 also showed significant action as early as the first hour although less pronounced than with the highest dose. In contrast, BN 52024 (10 mg.kg^{-1}, p.o.) was devoid of effect. BN 52020 (10 mg.kg^{-1} p.o.) only showed significant action at 4 hours. BN 52022 treatment (10 mg.kg^{-1} p.o.) also improved stroke index but only at 4 hours and this improvement was lower than that obtained with BN 52020 (Table 2).

Mitochondrial respiration. Corroborating the results obtained on behavioral pattern, RCR in gerbils pretreated with BN 52022 (10 mg.kg^{-1} p.o.) and BN 52024 (10 mg.kg^{-1} p.o.) was identical to that in the ligatured controls. In contrast, BN 52021 pretreatment (5 and 10 mg.kg^{-1} p.o.) significantly improved RCR by lowering state 4 and raising state 3. The values obtained with both doses were not significantly different from those in the sham-operated controls. BN 52020 pretreatment (10 mg.kg^{-1} p.o.)

Table 2 Evolution of the stroke index recorded after 10 minutes ischemia and recirculation in conscious Mongolian gerbils. Effect of pretreatment with BN 52021, BN 52022 and BN 52024

Group	Treatment (a) (mg.kg^{-1}, p.o.)	Time after ischemia (h)			
		1	2	3	4
Sham-operated gerbils (b,c)	—	1.3 ±0.58	0.4 ±0.23	0.4 ±0.23	0.3 ±0.19
Ligatured (d)	—	10.6 ±0.16[+++]	11.8 ±0.42[+++]	11.4 ±0.46[+++]	11.6 ±0.41[+++]
Ligatured (d)	BN 52020 10	9.5 ±0.74	9.3 ±0.80*	8.7 ±1.01	6.6 ±1.35**
Ligatured (d)	BN 52021 5	9.4 ±0.45	9.0 ±1.19*	8.9 ±1.55*	6.4 ±1.43**
Ligatured (d)	BN 52021 10	10.1 ±0.30	8.8 ±0.81**	6.8 ±1.26**	5.8 ±1.36***
Ligatured (d)	BN 52022 10	10.4 ±0.31	10.5 ±0.52	8.9 ±1.36	7.1 ±1.22*
Ligatured (d)	BN 52024 10	9.3 ±0.09	7.8 ±2.38	7.3 ±2.59	7.2 ±2.96

(a) The treatments were given once a day for 8 days, the last one took place 1 h before ischemia. (b) Values are mean ±SEM (n=10). (c) Stroke-index score is expressed according to table 1. (d) The Bartlett's multiple range test was used to calculate the significance of the difference between (i) ligatured control group and sham-operated group ([+++]: $p < 0.001$) (ii) ligatured control group and ligatured treated groups (*: $p < 0.05$, **: $p < 0.01$, ***: $p < 0.001$).

Globally the effect of the compounds was as follows: BN 52021 > BN 52020 > BN 52022 > 52024, which reflects the PAF-acether antagonist activity (Fig. 1).

DRUGS ADMINISTERED UPON CLAMPING *Stroke index.* BN 52022 was devoid of effect. BN 52020 caused a regular decrease in the stroke index from the third hour, this effect becoming significant from the fourth hour. BN 52021 was efficient from the first hour and led to a significant decrease in the stroke index from the second hour onwards (Fig. 2).

Mitochondrial respiration. As previously observed, six hours after clamping, uncoupling of the mitochondrial respiration, illustrated by a significant drop in RCR value (3.57±0.18 *vs.* 6.02±0.08), was observed in the ligatured controls (Fig. 3). BN 52022 was inefficient once again. In the animals treated with BN 52020, the RCR was significantly increased (5.24±0.16). When the gerbils were treated with BN 52021, none of the parameters studied were significantly different in comparison with those of sham-operated gerbils (RCR: 5.81±0.23).

Water, sodium and potassium content. Following 10 minutes occlusion and 6 hours of recirculation, water and sodium content increased. In con-

Table 3 Respiratory control ratio (RCR) in gerbil brain mitochondria following 10 minutes carotid ligation and 4 hours recirculation. Effect of pretreatment with BN 52020, BN 52021, BN 52022 and BN 52024

Group	Treatment (a) (mg.kg⁻¹, p.o.)	Respiration (n mole O_2/min/mg)		
		State 3	State 4	R.C.R.
Sham-operated gerbils (b,c)	—	52.7 ±1.79	8.54 ±0.28	6.08 ±0.11
Ligatured (c)	—	38.1 ±2.19**	9.66 ±0.18**	3.94 ±0.23***
Ligatured (c)	BN 52020 10	45.8 ±1.38*	9.18 ±0.32	5.01 ±0.15*
Ligatured (c)	BN 52021 5	50.3 ±1.29**	9.00 ±0.28*	5.61 ±0.12***
Ligatured (c)	BN 52021 10	49.2 ±1.36**	8.90 ±0.33*	5.57 ±0.18***
Ligatured (c)	BN 52022 10	43.5 ±1.54	9.32 ±0.34	4.67 ±0.09
Ligatured (c)	BN 52024 10	38.6 ±4.85	9.32 ±0.59	4.21 ±0.53

(a) The treatments were given once a day for 8 days, the last one took place 1 h before ischemia. (b) Values are mean ±SEM (n = 10). (c) **: $p < 0.01$ and ***: $p < 0.001$ sham-operated *vs.* ligatured; *: $p < 0.05$, **: $p < 0.01$, ***: $p < 0.001$ ligatured *vs.* treated ligatured.

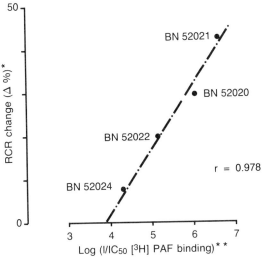

Figure 1 Correlation between PAF-acether antagonistic activity ([³H] binding assay) and the change in respiratory control ratio after cerebral ischemia in Mongolian gerbils.

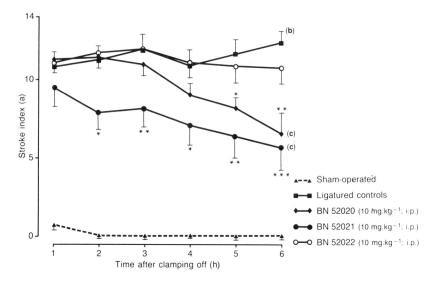

(a) Values are mean ± SEM (n = 10); stroke index score is expressed according to table 1. (b) For all points p < 0.001 vs sham-operated gerbils; (c) * : p < 0.01, ** : p < 0.01, *** : p < 0.001 vs control ligatured gerbils.

Figure 2   Evolution of the stroke index recorded after 10 minutes ischemia and recirculation in conscious Mongolian gerbils. Effect of BN 52020, BN 52021 and BN 52022 given at the time of clamping of carotids.

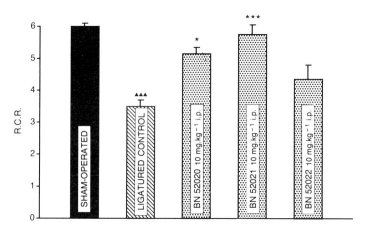

Values are mean ± SEM (n = 10) ; ▲▲▲ : p < 0.001, sham-operated vs control ligatured ; *** : p < 0.001, * : p < 0.05, control ligatured vs treated ligatured.

Figure 3   Respiratory control ratio (RCR) in gerbil brain mitochondria following 10 minutes carotid ligation and 6 hours recirculation. Effect of BN 52020, BN 52021 and BN 52022 given at the time of clamping of carotids.

Table 4 Changes in brain water and electrolyte contents after 10 minutes ischemia and 6 hours recirculation. BN 52021 was administered simultaneously to clamping

	Water content (% of wet weight)	Sodium content (mEq/kg of dry weight)	Potassium content (mEq/kg of dry weight)
Sham-operated	77.97 ±0.71	237 ±6.7	470 ±2.6
Ligatured control (a)	78.87 ±0.40*	272 ±12.6**	450 ±8.1**
BN 52021 (10 mg/kg i.p.) (b)	77.94 ±0.25*	226 ±2.5***	465 ±1.8*

Mean ±SEM (n = 10); (a) *: p<0.05 and **: p<0.01 *vs.* the sham-operated group; (b) *: p<0.05 and ***: p<0.001 *vs.* the control ligatured group.

trast, whereas potassium content decreased as sodium content increased, the degree of change for potassium was less pronounced than that of sodium (Table 4).

In the BN 52021 ischemia group, at 6 hours after restoration of blood flow, water, sodium and potassium content returned to the sham-operated values.

DRUGS ADMINISTERED ONE HOUR AFTER RECIRCULATION *Stroke index.* The decrease in the mean stroke index for animals treated with BN 52021 and kadsurenone was very pronounced between the second and the fifth hour and stabilized at the sixth hour around a value $\cong 4.5$ for both products (Fig. 4). In this experiment, the hypogenic effects of brotizolam did not allow behavioral observations to be made.

Mitochondrial respiration. Six hours after recirculation, for ligatured controls, large reductions were seen in state 3 respiration (-40%) with lesser effects on activity under state 4 conditions. Consequently, the RCR was decreased: 3.6 ± 0.32.

When the gerbils were treated one hour after the clip release with BN 52021 or kadsurenone (10 mg kg^{-1}) no significant decrease in their cerebral mitochondrial ADP-stimulated respiration (state 3) was seen compared with that of sham-operated animals (data not shown).

This is why the RCR values obtained with the sham-operated gerbils were not significantly different from those obtained after treatment with BN 52021, kadsurenone or brotizolam (Fig. 5).

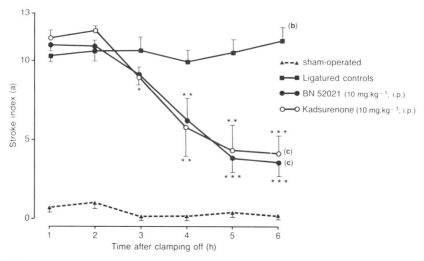

(a) Values are mean ± SEM (n = 10); stroke index score is expressed according to table 1. (b) For all points p < 0.001 *vs* sham-operated gerbils; (c) ★ : p < 0.01, ★★ : p < 0.01, ★★★ : p < 0.001 *vs* control ligatured gerbils.

Figure 4 Evolution of the stroke index recorded after 10 minutes ischemia and recirculation in conscious Mongolian gerbils. Effect of BN 52021 and kadsurenone given 1 hour after clamping off.

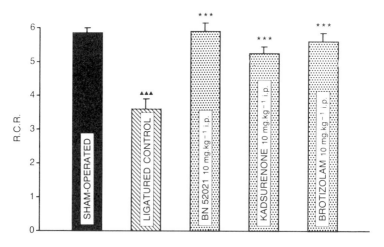

Values are mean ± SEM (n = 10) ; ▲▲▲ : p < 0.001, sham-operated *vs* control ligatured ; ★★★ : p < 0.001, control ligatured *vs* treated ligatured.

Figure 5 Respiratory control ratio (RCR) in gerbil brain mitochondria following 10 minutes carotid ligation and 6 hours recirculation. Effect of BN 52021, kadsurenone and brotizolam given 1 hour after clamping off.

DISCUSSION

In the experiments described in this paper the stroke index values of the ligatured control gerbils reflect a high behavioral disturbance (10.6 *vs*. 1.3 for control group) and a loss of respiratory control (RCR = 3.94 *vs*. 6.08 for control group).

Interestingly, when PAF-acether antagonists were administered preventively, the initial value of the stroke index was identical to that of the controls. In contrast, stroke index evolution over time differed greatly according to the treatment administered: in ligatured control gerbils, this parameter remained high throughout the 4 hours of measurement. Conversely, in animals treated with BN 52021, the most active PAF-antagonist of the ginkgolide series [[^{3}H] PAF-acether binding assay, rabbit platelet membrane: IC_{50} = 10^{-7} M (11)], progressive and significant trend towards normalization was recorded. On the contrary, BN 52024 which is practically devoid of activity on the PAF-acether receptor [IC_{50} = 7.3 x 10^{-5} M], was ineffective and the other antagonists BN 52020 and BN 52022 gave intermediary values which agree totally with their capacity to inhibit PAF-acether binding to its receptor [IC_{50} = 7.3 x 10^{-7} M and 8.1 x 10^{-6} M, respectively (11)]. These data are more than corroborated by the RCR values obtained at the end of the experiment which displays a coefficient correlation equal to 0.978 between RCR values and the capacity to inhibit PAF-acether binding to platelets. These findings clearly show that treatment with PAF-acether antagonists does not modify the initial cerebral impairment but does improve the post-ischemic phase.

When the compounds were administered upon clamping, for the ginkgolide series the same order of beneficial effect was observed: BN 52021 > BN 52020 > BN 52022 > BN 52024 both on the stroke index and the RCR measurements.

Even more interestingly, administered one hour after recirculation, BN 52021 was able to reverse the cerebral impairment trend as assessed by the improved RCR value observed at the end of the experiment.

In order to obtain final proof that this protection was due to a PAF-acether antagonistic effect, we used two other chemically unrelated PAF-acether antagonists: a lignan, kadsurenone [[^{3}H] PAF-acether binding assay rabbit platelet membrane IC_{50} = 1.9 x 10^{-7} M (40)] and a triazolobenzodiapezine, brotizolam (IC_{50} = 3.3 x 10^{-7} M). These two products led to similar recovery. Therefore, PAF-acether appears to play an important role in the post-ischemic phase after bilateral ligation in Mongolian gerbils. These results are in agreement with those of Kochanek (28), who demonstrated the beneficial action of kadsurenone on multifocal ischemia in the dog.

Lipid peroxidation due to free radical formation contributes to brain cell damage in ischemia (15, 18, 19). In addition, upon recirculation there is an enormous accumulation of free fatty acid (FFA) at cerebral level (20) and *in vitro*, the formation of O_2^- (23), as well as the accumulation of FFA, affects mitochondrial metabolism. PAF-acether potently amplifies platelet and leukocyte responses: at very low doses (10^{-16}-10^{-11} M) it dramatically potentiates the release of O_2^- and OH^- from polymorphonuclear cells induced by various stimuli (47). These results may explain why BN 52021 and other PAF-acether antagonists which are not free radical scavengers, inhibit lipid peroxidation in the post-ischemic phase of cerebral ischemia (B. Spinnewyn, unpublished). Such an effect may also be taken into account in explaining the inhibition of unsaturated fatty acid release at cerebral level obtained with BN 52021 in the same gerbil model by Bazan (3).

During ischemia blood flow was drastically reduced. When the carotid blood flow was restored at the termination of ischemia, the CBF (cerebral blood flow) initially overshot the preischemic value (reactive hyperemia). Then the CBF subsequently fell and reached markedly subnormal values (delayed hypoperfusion). When the gerbils were treated with BN 52021 the last phase of hypoperfusion did not occur (3).

Clinical studies have shown that in people having suffered a thromboembolic cerebral infarction, factor IV and β thromboglobulin rates increase greatly (39). In addition, platelet activation can occur in stroke, even though the platelet cyclooxygenase pathway is suppressed. Since PAF-acether releases platelet factor 4 and β thromboglobulin from platelets, the assumption can be made that the production of these mediators in cerebral ischemia may result from PAF-acether production.

Classical features of cerebral edema are an increase in tissue water and sodium contents and a potassium loss. Confirming the protection obtained with the other parameters, BN 52021 antagonized the hydroelectrolytic impairments. This finding is not surprising, since it is well established that PAF-acether increases vascular permeability in various circulatory beds including cerebral arteries, a phenomenon inhibited by PAF-acether antagonists (37).

These results suggest that, in the post-ischemic phase, PAF-acether could play an important role at the cerebral level by favoring the infiltration of blood inflammatory cells, mainly eosinophils, triggering platelets to release a PF4 and β- thromboglobulin and by amplifying the cascade of events due to the reperfusion process. Indeed, clinical studies following cerebral infarction have demonstrated an important eosinophil brain infiltration and the appearance in the cerebrospinal liquid of eosinophilic cationic proteins (21). It has even been postulated that eosinophil cationic proteins may account for the cerebral cell impairments observed after brain ischemia (17).

PAF-acether may account for this phenomenon since: 1) It is one of the most potent chemotactic agents for human eosinophils (48); this effect is also receptor-mediated since specific antagonists inhibit eosinophil locomotion; 2) It induces eosinophil and platelet infiltration in lungs, an effect which is antagonized by BN 52021 and WEB 2086 (31); and 3) Intracutaneous injections of PAF-acether evoke a marked eosinophilic infiltration, a large number of these cells being degranulated (22).

For the first time these results also provide a rationale for the use of PAF-acether antagonists in the treatment of the post-stroke syndrome.

References

1. Baron, J.C. *Phénomènes physiopathologiques au cours de l'ischemie focale aigue du cerveau.* La Revue de Médicine 1983; 38: 1853-1863.
2. Bazan, N.G. *Effects of ischemia and electroconvulsive shock on free fatty acid pool in brain.* Biochem Biophys Acta 1970; 218: 1-10.
3. Beck, T., Abdel-Rahman, M.M., Bielenberg, G.W., Oberpicheler, H., Krieglstein, J. *Comparative study on the effects of two extract fractions of ginkgo biloba on local cerebral blood flow and on brain energy metabolism in the rat under hypoxia.* Pharmacol Cerebral Ischemia; 1986; 345-350.
4. Berry, K., Wisniewski, H.M., Svarzbein, L., Baez, S. *On the relationship of brain vasculature to production of neurological deficit and morphological changes following acute unilateral common carotid artery ligation in gerbils.* J Neurol Sci 1975; 25: 75-92.
5. Berti, F. et al. *PAF, ginkgolides and active anaphylactic shock in lung and heart.* In: Ginkgolides: Chemistry, Biology, Pharmacology and Clinical Perspectives. P. Braquet (Ed.). J.R. Prous Science Publishers: Barcelona 1988; 8: 399-410.
6. Birkle, D.L., Braquet, P., Bazan, N.G. *Inhibition of free polyunsaturated fatty acid accumulation in mouse brain during electroconvulsive shock and ischemia by the specific PAF antagonist, BN 52021.* Symposium of the Society for Neuroscience. 1987; Abstract.
7. Bradford, M. Annal Biochem 1972; 248: 1976.
8. Braquet, P. *Treatment and prevention of PAF-acether disorders provoked by a new series of highly specific inhibitors.* GB Patent 84/18 424 Belg. BE 901. 1984.
9. Braquet, P. *The ginkgolides: Potent platelet-activating factor antagonists isolated from Ginkgo biloba L. Chemistry, pharmacology and clinical applications.* Drugs of the Future 1987; 12: 643-699.
10. Braquet, P., Godfroid, J.J. *PAF-acether specific binding sites: 2. Design of specific antagonists.* TIPS 1986; 7: 387-403.
11. Braquet, P., Spinnewyn, B., Braquet, M., Chabrier, E., Taylor, J.E., Drieu, K. *A new series of highly specific PAF-acether receptor antagonists isolated from Ginkgo biloba.* Proc 4th Cong Hung Pharmacol Soc Budapest 1985; 3: 427-441.
12. Braquet, P., Touqui, L., Shen, T.Y., Vargaftig, B.B. *Perspectives in platelet-activating factor.* Pharmacol Review 1987; 39: 97-145.
13. Chance, B., Williams, G.R. *The respiratory chain and oxidative phosphorylation.* Nature 1955; 175: 1120-1121.
14. Chatterjee, S.S. *Effects of Ginkgo biloba extract on cerebral metabolic processes.* In: Effects of Ginkgo biloba Extract on Organic Cerebral Impairment. A. Agnoli, J.R. Rapin, V. Scapagnini, W.V. Weitbrecht (Eds.). John Wiley: London 1985; 5-15.
15. Demopoulos, H., Flamm, E., Seligman, M., Power, R., Pietronigro, D., Ransohoff, J. *Molecular pathology of lipids in CNS membranes in oxygen and physiological function.* Jöbsis Ed 1977; 491-508.
16. Demopoulos, H., Seligman, M., Schwartz, M., Tomasula, J., Flamm, E. *Molecular pathology of regional cerebral ischemia.* In: Cerebral Ischemia. A. Bes, P. Braquet, R. Paoletti, B.K. Siesjö (Eds.). Excerpta Medica 1984; 259-264.
17. Durack, D.T., Sumi, S.M., Klebanoff, S.J. *Neurotoxicity of human eosinophils.* Proc Natl Acad Sci USA 1979; 76(3): 1443-1447.
18. Flamm, E.S., Demopoulos, H.B., Seligman, M.L. et al. *Possible molecular mechanisms of barbiturate-mediated protection in regional cerebral ischemia.* Acta Neurol Scand 1977; 56(Suppl 64): 7.10-7.11.
19. Flamm, E.S., Demopoulos, H.B., Seligman, M.L., Poser, R.G., Ransohoff, J. *Free radicals in cerebral ischemia.* Stroke 1978;

9(5): 445-447.

20. Gaudet, R.J., Alam, I., Levine, L. *Accumulation of cyclooxygenase products of arachidonic acid metabolism in gerbil brain during reperfusion after bilateral common carotid artery occlusion.* J Neurochem 1980; 35: 653-658.

21. Hällgren, R., Terent, A., Venge, P. *Eosinophil cationic protein (ECP) in the cerebrospinal fluid.* J Neurol Sci 1983; 58: 57-71.

22. Henocq, E., Vargaftig, B.B. *Accumulation of eosinophils in response to intracutaneous PAF-acether and allergens in man.* Lancet 1986; i: 1378-1379.

23. Hillered, L., Ernster, L. *Respiratory activity of isolated rat brain mitochondria following in vitro exposure to oxygen radicals.* J Cereb Blood Flow Metab 1983; 3: 207-214.

24. Ito, U., Spatz, M., Walker, J.T., Jr., Klatzo, I. *Experimental cerebral ischemia in Mongolian gerbils I. Light microscopic observations.* Acta Neuropathol 1975; 32: 209-223.

25. Kahn, K. *The natural course of experimental cerebral infarction in the gerbil.* Neurology 1972; 22: 510-516.

26. Karcher, L., Zagermann, P., Krieglstein, J. *Effect of an extract of Ginkgo biloba on rat brain energy metabolism in hypoxia.* Naunyn-Schmiedeberg's Arch Pharmacol 1984; 327: 31-35.

27. Kirino, T., Tamura, A., Sano, K. *A reversible type of neuronal injury following ischemia in the gerbil hippocampus.* Stroke 1986; 17: 455-459.

28. Kochanek, P., Dutka, A., Kunarii, K., Hallenberk, J. *Platelet-activating factor receptor blockade enhances early neuronal recovery after multifocal brain ischemia in dogs.* Second International Conference on Platelet-Activating Factor. Gatlinburg TN: USA 1986.

29. Küster, L.J., Filep, J., Frölich, J.C. *Mechanism of PAF-acether-inducer platelet aggregation in man.* Thrombosis Research 1986; 43: 425-433.

30. Le Poncin Lafitte, M., Rapin, J.R. *Effects of Ginkgo biloba on changes induced by quantitative cerebral microembolization in rats.* Arch Int Pharmacol Ther 1980; 243: 236-244.

31. Lelouch Tubiana, A., Lefort, J., Pfister, A., Vargaftig, B.B. *Interaction between granulocytes and platelets with the guinea-pigs lungs in passive anaphylactic shock. Correlations with PAF-acether-induced lesions.* Int

Archs Allergy Appl 1987; 83: 198-205.

32. Lepran, I., Lefer, A.M. *Ischemia aggravating effects of platelet-activating factor in acute myocardial ischemia.* Basic Res Cardiol 1985; 80: 135-141.

33. Levine, S., Payan, H. *Effects of ischemia and other procedures on the brain and retina of the gerbil (Meriones unguiculatus).* Exp Neurol 1966; 16: 255-262.

34. McGraw, C.P. *Experimental cerebral infarction effects of pentobarbital in Mongolian gerbils.* Arch Neurol 1977; 34: 334-336.

35. Moskowitz, M.A., Meyer, E., Wurtman, R.J., Lavyne, M.H., Zervas, N.T. Life Sci 1975; 17: 597-602.

36. Nordström, C.H., Rehncrona, S., Siesjö, B.K. *Effects of phenobarbital in cerebral ischemia. Part II: Restitution of cerebral energy state, as well as of glycolytic metabolites, citric acid cycle intermediates and associated amino acids after pronounced incomplete ischemia.* Stroke 1978b; 9: 335-343.

37. Plotkine, M., Massad, L., Allix, M., Capdeville, C., Boulu, R.G. *Cerebral effects of PAF-acether in rats.* 6th Int Conference on Prostaglandins and Related Compounds. Florence: Italy 1986; 300.

38. Sham, A.B., Beamer, N., Coull, B.M. *Enhanced in vivo platelet activation in subtypes of ischemic stroke.* Stroke 1985; 16: 643-647.

39. Shen, T.Y., Hwang, S.B., Chang, M.N., Doebber, T.W., Lam, M.H., Wu, M.S., Wang, X., Hang, C.Q., Li, R.Z. *Characterization of a platelet-activating factor receptor antagonist isolated from haifenteng (Piper futokadsura): Specific inhibition of in vitro and in vivo platelet-activating factor-induced effects.* Proc Natl Acad Sci USA 1985; 82: 672-676.

40. Siesjö, B.K. *Review: Cell damage in the brain; a speculative synthesis.* J Cereb Blood Flow Metab 1981; 1: 155-182.

41. Spinnewyn, B., Blavet, N., Clostre, F. *Effets de l'extrait de Ginkgo biloba sur un modèle d'ischemie cérébrale chez la gerbille.* La Presse Médicale 1986; 1531: 1511-1515.

42. Tagesson, C., Lendahl, M., Otamiri, T. *BN 52021 ameliorates mucosal damage associated with small intestinal ischaemia in rats.* In: Ginkgolides: Chemistry, Biology, Pharmacology and Clinical Perspectives. P. Braquet (Ed.). J.R. Prous Science Publishers: Barcelona 1988; 553-561.

43. Tamura, A., Yamamoto, M., Shimizu, M., Kirino, T., Sano, K. *Behavioral change after focal cerebral ischemia in the rat.* J Cereb Blood Flow Metabol 1985; 5(Suppl. 1): S379-S380.

44. Touvay, C., Vilain, B., Etienne, A., Sirois, P., Borgeat, P., Braquet, P. *Characterization of platelet-activating factor (PAF)-acether-induced contractions of guinea-pig lung strips by selected inhibitors of arachidonic acid metabolism and by PAF-acether antagonists.* Immunopharmacology 1986; 12: 97-104.

45. Vargaftig, B.B., Braquet, P. *PAF-acether today. Relevance for acute experimental anaphylaxis.* Br Med Bull 1987; 43: 312-335.

46. Vercelloti, G.M., Huh, P.W., Yin, H.Q., Nelson, R.D., Jacob, H.S. *Enhancement of PMN-mediated endothelial damage by platelet-activating factor (PAF): PAF primes PMN responses to activating stimuli.* Clin Res 1986; 384: 1-10.

47. Wardlaw, A.J., Moqbel, R., Cromwell, O., Kay, A.B. *PAF-acether is a potent chemotactic factor for human eosinophils.* J Allergy Clin Immunol 1986; 77-236: 917-920.

48. Wieloch, T., Siesjö, B.K. *Ischemic brain injury: The importance of calcium lipolytic activities and free fatty acids.* Path Biol 1982; 305: 269-277.

49. Yamamoto, K., Morimoto, K., Yanagihara, T. *Cerebral ischemia in the gerbil: Transmission electron microscopic and immunoelectron microscopic investigation.* Brain Res 1986; 34: 917-920.

Ginkgolides - Chemistry, Biology, Pharmacology and Clinical Perspectives. P. Braquet (Ed.)
Copyright © 1988, J.R. Prous Science Publishers, S.A.

A PLATELET-ACTIVATING FACTOR ANTAGONIST INHIBITS THE CEREBRAL BLOOD FLOW AND NEUROCHEMICAL CHANGES CAUSED BY CEREBRAL INJURY-REPERFUSION

Nicolas G. Bazan[1], Thomas Panetta[2], Victor L. Marcheselli[1] and Brigitte Spinnewyn[3]

[1]Department of Ophthalmology and [2]Department of Surgery, Louisiana State University, School of Medicine, New Orleans, Louisiana, [3]Institut Henri Beaufour, Le-Plessis Robinson, France

ABSTRACT

The ginkgolide BN 52021, a platelet-activating factor antagonist, protects the gerbil brain after ischemia-reperfusion. Ten minutes after bilateral carotid artery ligation, gerbils were reperfused and injected intraperitoneally with either BN 52021 or vehicle (dimethylsulfoxide). BN 52021 inhibited the development of ischemic injury, as evidenced by an increase in cerebral blood flow after 60 to 90 minutes of reperfusion. There was also a reduction in free fatty acid levels, probably due to inhibition of phospholipase A. Phospholipase C activity may decrease as well, since phosphatidylinositol-4',5'bisphosphate tended to increase and diacylglycerols tended to decrease in BN 52021-treated animals. These findings may reflect protection of cell signal transduction systems by BN 52021.

Address all correspondence to: Dr. Nicolas G. Bazan, LSU Eye Center, 2020 Gravier Street, Suite B, New Orleans, LA 70112, USA.

INTRODUCTION

Cerebral ischemia triggers the activation of phospholipase A_2 and C, resulting in the accumulation of free polyunsaturated fatty acids (1) and diacylglycerols (2). If PAF is generated during ischemia, one consequence may be that it contributes to brain damage through an activation of phospholipases. Alternatively, arachidonic acid may be released during the first step in the synthesis of PAF from 1-alkyl-2-acyl GPC. Arachidonic acid may, in turn, be involved in injury. The PAF antagonist BN 52021 (3), a terpene isolated from *Ginkgo biloba* extract (GBE 761) that inhibits the binding of PAF to platelets and leukocytes (4), decreases PAF-induced calcium mobilization in platelets (5) and inhibits the production of leukotriene C_4 and free radicals in leukocytes (6). BN 52021 also inhibits PAF induced hypotension, prevents electrically-induced PAF-mediated thrombo formation in rat carotid artery (7), and reduces stroke index after unilateral carotid artery ligation in gerbils (4). Moreover, GBE 761 improves cerebral metabolism, protects against hypoxic brain damage, and prolongs survival in rats (8). In the present studies, we have examined the effect of BN 52021 on endogenous brain free fatty acids (FFA), diacylglycerols (DAG) and polyphosphoinositides after ischemia-reperfusion in the gerbil brain. We have also observed the effect of BN 52021on cerebral blood flow (CBF) and systemic blood pressure.

CEREBRAL BLOOD FLOW AND BLOOD PRESSURE

Bilateral artery ligation in the Mongolian gerbil, which has an open circle of Willis, results in cerebral ischemia with reduction of CBF and in a hypertensive response (9). CBF in midbrain decreased by 20-50% after ligation, but was maintained by the hypertensive response in conjunction with an intact posterior circulation. Reactive hyperemia during reperfusion led to increased CBF in forebrain and midbrain, and was accompanied by hypotension resulting in several gerbil deaths. However, five gerbils that were pretreated with BN 52021 prior to bilateral ligation showed no effect on reperfusion hypotension (unpublished data).

Between 60 and 90 minutes of reperfusion, BN 52021 improved CBF in forebrain and midbrain (9). In DMSO-control animals, reactive hyperemia was followed by progressive deterioration of CBF. BN 52021 inhibited ischemia-reperfusion induced injury in the gerbil brain. After 90 minutes of reperfusion, there was complete recovery of CBF in the midbrain. Recovery of CBF in the forebrain was close to baseline levels. Vasospasm, hypotension, hypertensive disruption of the blood brain barrier, and cerebral edema all result in decreased CBF (10).

The FFA pool in DMSO-control animals was 10 times greater in forebrain and 3 times greater in midbrain than sham-controls (Fig. 1). BN 52021 significantly reduced the content of FFA in both brain parts, compared to DMSO-controls. One exception was the content of 16:0 in midbrain, which did not decrease. Diacylglycerol content was consistently lower in BN 52021-treated gerbils than in DMSO-controls (data not shown). However, these differences were consistently, but not significantly, higher than in sham animals. The content of phosphatidylinositol-4-phosphate did not change in any of the conditions studied (9). Phosphatidylinositol-4',5'-biphosphate (PIP_2) levels were consistently higher in forebrain and midbrain of BN 52021-treated animals, with statistically significant increases in the arachidonoyl groups of this phospholipid.

Cerebral ischemia promotes several early events that involve membranes, including activation of phospholipases A and C, which in turn lead to an accumulation of free fatty acids (1) and diacylglycerols (2). Reperfusion leads to activation of the arachidonic acid cascade with increased formation of cyclooxygenase (11) and lipoxygenase (12) reaction products. Free fatty acids decrease during reperfusion (13, 14). Because of the correlation between brain FFA (15) and diacylglycerol (4) accumulation and ischemic brain damage (16), we have studied brain lipid changes at 90 minutes of reperfusion in order to identify neurochemical correlates that improve CBF. The levels of FFA following 90 minutes of reperfusion in gerbils previously reported (13, 14) are comparable to levels found in our BN 52021-treated gerbils. However, the model used in the present studies involves the com-

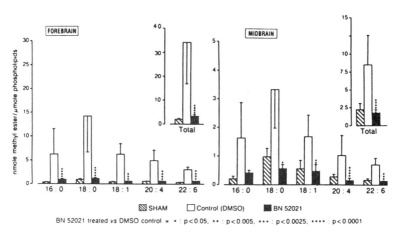

Figure 1 Effects of a PAF antagonist (BN 52021) on endogenous brain free fatty acids after ischemia-reperfusion in gerbils. Values are average ± S.E.M. of seven gerbils killed 90 minutes after reperfusion (9).

bination of ischemia-reperfusion, trauma from burr holes and intracerebral electrodes, polarigraphic measurement of CBF (420 mV polarization current), and intermittent inhalation of hydrogen. These factors prevented survival for more than two to six hours in untreated animals (unpublished data); this phenomenon may provide a lead in explaining the increased FFA content in DMSO-control gerbils. The accumulation of FFA in DMSO animals may also represent a secondary increase in response to deteriorating CBF. The BN 52021-associated reduction in FFA could be the result of decreased phospholipase A activity, increased reacylation, or increased washout into the peripheral circulation or cerebrospinal fluid.

Although decreases in DG and increases in PIP_2 were not statistically significant in BN 52021-treated gerbils, a consistent trend suggesting phospholipase C inhibition was observed (9). This is consistent with the proposed linkage of PAF binding sites to phospholipase C through guanyl nucleotide regulatory proteins (4).

BN 52021 inhibits the deterioration of CBF following ischemia-reperfusion injury in gerbil brain. The role of platelets or endothelial cells in the mechanism of this effect is not known. PAF is associated with endothelial cell injury (17), vasoconstriction, and leukotriene C_4 mediated release of norepinephrine and epinephrine (18). BN 52021 decreases the mobilization and influx of calcium in platelets by interfering with PAF membrane binding, without affecting membrane signal transduction (19). Another PAF antagonist, kadsurenone, has been shown to enhance neuronal recovery without inhibiting platelet accumulation (20). The disruption of the blood brain barrier and the "no-reflow" phenomenon are additional factors contributing to the deterioration of CBF that may be altered by BN 52021 (21). The decreased levels of brain FFA in BN 52021-treated gerbils may be due to a selective inhibition of PAF action or of endogenous generation of this lipid mediator. The resulting decreased activity of phospholipase A, and possibly phospholipase C, may be consequences of reduced PAF cycle turnover or action.

In conclusion, we have shown that a platelet-activating factor antagonist (BN 52021) inhibits the late deterioration of regional cerebral blood flow associated with ischemia-reperfusion injury in the gerbil (9). We hypothesize that this effect is associated with inhibition of phospholipase A activation, resulting in decreased endogenous FFA levels. A slight decrease in DG and a slight increase in PIP_2 suggest the possible coinhibition of phospholipase C activity.

References

1. Bazan, N.G. Biochem Biophys Acta 1970; 218: 1-10.
2. Aveldano, M.I., Bazan, N.G. J Neurochem 1975; 25: 919-920.
3. Spinnewyn, B., Blavet, N., Clostre, F., Bazan, N.G., Braquet, P. Prostaglandins 1987; 34: 237-250.
4. Braquet, P., Shen, T.Y., Touqui, L., Vargaftig, B.B. Pharmacol Rev 1987; 39: 97-145.
5. Baroggi, N., Etienne, A., Braquet, P. Agents Actions 1986; (Suppl) 20: 87-98.
6. Wickham, N.W.R., Vercelotti, G.M., Yin, H.Q., Moldow, C.F., Jacob, H.S. Fed Proc 1987; in press.
7. Braquet, P., Spinnewyn, B., Braquet, M., Bourgain, R.H., Taylor, J.E., Etienne, A., Drieu, K. Blood Vessels 1985; 16: 559-572.
8. Krieglstein, J., Beck, T., Siebert, A. Life Sci 1986; 39: 2237-2334.
9. Panetta, T., Marcheselli, V., Braquet, P., Spinnewyn, B., Bazan, N.G. Biochem Biophys Res Commun 1987; 149: 580-587.
10. Tamaki, K., Sadoshima, S., Baumbach, G.L., Iadecola, C., Reis, D.J., Heistad, D.D. Hypertension 1984; 6 (Suppl 1): 175-181.
11. Gaudet, R.J., Levine, L. Biochem Biophys Res Commun 1979; 86: 893-901.
12. Moskowitz, M.A., Kiwak, K.J., Hekimian, K., Levine, L. Science 1984; 244: 886-889.
13. Yoshida, A., Inoh, S., Asano, I., Sano, K., Kubota, M., Shimazaki, H., Ueta, N. Neurosurg 1980; 53: 323-331.
14. Horrocks, L.A., Dorman, R.V., Porcellati, G. Cerebral Ischemia, Excerpta Medica Congress Series 654. Elsevier Science: Amsterdam 1984; 211-222.
15. Benveniste, J., Chignard, M., LeCouedic, J.P., Vargaftig, B. Thromb Res 1982; 25: 375-385.
16. Bazan, N.G. Adv Exp Med Biol 1976; 72: 317-335.
17. Blank, M.L., Snyder, F., Byers, L.W., Brooks, B., Muirhead, E.E. Biochem Biophys Res Commun 1979; 90: 1194-1200.
18. Kochanek, P., Dutka, A., Kumaroo, K., Hallenbeck. In: Second International Conference on Platelet-Activating Factor and Structurally Related Alkyl Ether Lipids, (Gatlinburg, TN) 1986; 118.
19. Chiang, J., Kowada, M., Ames, A., Wright, R.L., Majno, G. Am J Pathol 1968; 52: 455-476.
20. Hsueh, W., Crussi, F.G., Arroyave, J.L. Am J Pathol 1986; 122: 231-239.
21. Klatzo, I., Ito, U., Go, K.G., Spatz, M. Pathology of Cerebral Microcirculation. Walter de Gruyton: New York/Berlin 1974; 338-341.

Ginkgolides - Chemistry, Biology, Pharmacology and Clinical Perspectives. P. Braquet (Ed.)
Copyright © 1988, J.R. Prous Science Publishers, S.A.

EFFECT OF BN 52041 ON PAF-ACETHER-INDUCED BRAIN EDEMA

Michel Plotkine*, Lena Massad, Monique Allix and Roger Boulu

Laboratoire de Pharmacologie, Université de Paris V, 4, avenue de l'Observatoire, F-75006 Paris, France; *Laboratoire de Pharmacologie II, Université de Lille II, F-59019 Lille, France

INTRODUCTION

Platelet-activating factor (PAF) has been reported to induce vessel hyperpermeability resulting in plasma extravasation. This effect has been described after intradermal and subcutaneous injection of PAF (1,2). To our knowledge, this effect has not been investigated, to date, at the cerebral level. Inasmuch as edema is one of the consequences of various cerebral injuries, this led us to examine the effect of PAF injection on the permeability of brain vessels and the influence of a PAF antagonist BN 52041 (Institut Henri Beaufour, France).

MATERIALS AND METHODS

Fasted Wistar male rats weighing 250-300 g were anesthetized with chloral (300 mg/kg body weight) injected intraperitoneally.

A polyethylene catheter was inserted in the penile vein and the rats were placed on a stereotaxic frame. Colonic temperature was kept at 37°C with a feedback-controlled heating system. One ml of a 1.5% Evans blue solution was then injected into the venous catheter. A burr hole was made over the cortex and a metallic cannula (outer diameter 0.3 mm) was introduced 5 mm deep into the brain parenchyma (A = 1.8 mm; L = 2 mm related to bregma).

Ten microliters containing 2.5 μg of PAF-acether in 1.5% bovine serum albumin (BSA) were injected into the parenchyma over 20 minutes. Control animals received PAF vehicle by the same route.

Address all correspondence to: Prof. R. Boulu, Service de Pharmacodynamie, 4 avenue de l'Observatoire, F-75006 Paris, France.

Another group of rats was treated with the PAF antagonist BN 52041 (20 mg/kg, p.o.), 30 minutes prior to PAF injection. Seventy minutes after parenchymal injection, rats were heparinized (500 IU) and brains were rinsed by intracardiac perfusion with heparinized saline (50 IU/ml).

Brains were removed, frozen and sliced coronally through the plane of the injection. Slices were examined and photographed. The area of Evans blue extravasation was determined using planimetry and expressed as the percentage of total brain slice area. Mann Witney U test was used for the statistical analysis.

RESULTS

No Evans blue extravasation was observed in rats receiving BSA solution. Control rats injected with PAF had extravasation of Evans blue in the area of the injection. This effect was markedly prevented by BN 52041 treatment (Table 1. Fig. 1).

Table 1   Effect of BN 52041 on PAF-acether induced edema

Treatment	Percent area of Evans blue extravasation (mean ± SEM)
Vehicle (n = 5)	0
PAF-acether 2.5 µg (n = 5)	5.24 ± 1.04
BN 52041 20 mg/kg + PAF-acether 2.5 µg (n = 5)	1.14 ± 0.12 P ± 0.01

CONCLUSIONS

Our study clearly demonstrates that PAF-acether injected directly into brain parenchyma increases blood brain barrier permeability and that this effect is prevented by the PAF antagonist BN 52041. This observation indicates that brain vessel permeability is affected similarly to peripheral vessel by PAF-acether.

Therefore, our results suggest that PAF could be one of the factors involved in the pathogenesis of brain edema. Confirmation of such an hypothesis has to be provided by the observation of increased PAF concentration in edematous brain after injury or ischemia.

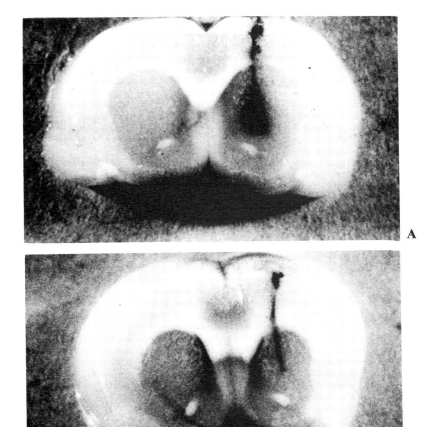

Figure 1 Evans blue extravasation induced by intrastriatal PAF-acether injection in control rat (A) and in BN 52041 (20 mg/kg, oral route) pretreated rat (B).

Furthermore, the marked antagonistic activity of BN-52041 against PAF-acether-induced brain edema suggests that such a mechanism might contribute to the cerebral protective effect of ginkgolides.

References
1. Humphrey, D.M., McManus, L.M., Satouchi, K., Hanahan, D.J., Pinckard, R.N. *Vasoactive properties of acetyl glyceryl ether phosphorylcholine and analogues.* Lab Invest 1982; 46: 422-427.

2. Humphrey, D.M., Hanahan, D.J., Pinckard, R.N. *Induction of leukocytic infiltrates in rabbit skin by acetyl glyceryl ether phosphorylcholine.* Lab Invest 1982; 47: 227-234.

Ginkgolides - Chemistry, Biology, Pharmacology and Clinical Perspectives. P. Braquet (Ed.)
Copyright © 1988, J.R. Prous Science Publishers, S.A.

LYMPHOCYTE FUNCTIONS AS MODULATED BY PLATELET-ACTIVATING FACTOR (PAF-ACETHER) AND ITS RECEPTOR ANTAGONIST BN 52021

Marek Rola-Pleszczynski

Immunology Division, Department of Pediatrics, Faculty of Medecine, University of Sherbrooke, 3001 12th Avenue N., Sherbrooke, QC J1H 5N4, Canada

INTRODUCTION

Cellular immune responses are essentially dependent on various lymphocyte functions generated following activation of a number of lymphocyte subpopulations. Furthermore, accessory cells, usually monocytes or macrophages, are necessary in the initial stages of activation, and often as immunoregulatory cells throughout the process.

When an antigen is presented to the immune system, macrophages will internalize it and process it before presenting it to T-lymphocytes in conjunction with class II major histocompatibility complex molecules. Macrophages will also produce a number of substances capable of affecting lymphocyte functions. Most prominent among those substances is interleukin 1 (IL-1), which is an essential signal for T-cell activation. This process can be mimicked, in the absence of antigen, by mitogens such as phytohemagglutinin (PHA), concanavalin A (ConA) or pokeweed mitogen

691

(PWM). An even more artificial system can bypass monocytes by using phorbol esters (*e.g.*, phorbol myristate acetate (PMA)) in conjunction with a calcium ionophore (*e.g.*, ionomycin or A-23187).

These initial triggers of lymphocyte activation induce very early ionic (Ca^{++}, K^+) fluxes, protein kinase C activation, cyclic nucleotide accumulation, membrane phospholipid metabolism, *etc.* They also lead to synthesis of interleukin 2 (IL-2) by T-cells, a major lymphokine responsible for the subsequent proliferation and clonal expansion of T-cells and activation of later events such as interferon-gamma synthesis, activation of cytotoxic cells, *etc.*

Various lymphocyte subpopulations participate in the above-described events. Helper T-cells, usually identified by their expression of the CD4 membrane antigen, are the main producers of IL-2. They will also support the maturation and differentiation of B-cells into immunoglobulin-producing plasma cells, and help induce the IgM-to-IgG switch. A second major T-cell subset consists of suppressor T-cells, usually identified by their expression of the CD8 membrane antigen. They are also activated during the initial lymphocyte stimulation and serve to down-regulate various stages of T- and B- lymphocyte activities. Furthermore, they serve as the major cytotoxic T-lymphocyte (CTL) effector population. Recent advances have allowed the identification of discreet subpopulations within the CD4 and CD8 populations, with activities such as induction of suppressor cells, or suppressor precursors, or precursors of CTL (or other cytotoxic cells).

Since inflammation usually accompanies or even initiates the more specific immune response, inflammatory cells and their products are being studied to better understand the relationship between the initial nonspecific reactions and the subsequent more specific responses. Polymorphonuclear (PMN) leukocytes, monocytes, endothelial cells, fibroblasts and various other more organ-specific cells participate in inflammatory reactions. Among their products, various proteins, peptides and lipids have been shown to play essential roles and even to interact with immunocompetent cells. Thus, leukotriene B_4, produced by PMN or macrophages, has very powerful immunoregulatory properties (16); histamine can induce suppression via the production of a suppressor-inducing factor (2); prostaglandins have been shown by numerous investigators in many models to markedly affect various stages of lymphocyte functions (9).

Platelet-activating factor (PAF) is also released from various inflammatory cells and has been shown to modulate their functions as well as functions of many other cells and tissues (4). It is in this context that our laboratory embarked on several research projects aimed at elucidating the eventual involvement of PAF as an immunomodulator.

MATERIALS AND METHODS

Chemical Reagents

PAF-acether was obtained from Bachem (Torrance, CA). BN 52021 (9H-1, 7a-(epoxymethano)-1H, 5aH, cyclopenta(c) furo (2-3-6)furo-(3-2:3,4) cyclopenta (1,2-d) furan-5,9,12-(4H)-trione, 3-ter-butyl hexahydro 4,-76,-11 hydroxy-8 methyl) was from the Institut Henri Beaufour (Le Plessis Robinson, France); WEB 2086 was a generous gift from Dr. H. Heuer, Boehringer-Ingelheim and CV-3988 was a generous gift from Dr. M. Nishikawa, Takeda Chemical Ind; indomethacin was from Sigma Chemical Co. (St. Louis, MO); bacto phytohemagglutinin P (PHA) was purchased from Difco Laboratories (Detroit, MI).

Leukocytes

Human peripheral blood mononuclear leukocytes (PBML) were obtained by density centrifugation of heparinized venous blood on a Ficoll-Hypaque gradient. The PBML represented 75 to 85% lymphocytes and 15 to 25% monocytes. In selected experiments, they were passed through a nylon wool column to yield 99% lymphocytes, 95% of which were E-rosetting T-cells. Where indicated, adherent cells were removed after incubation of PBML on microexudate-coated petri dishes for 1 hour at 37°C: this yielded 95-98% lymphocytes with 1-5% monocytes in the non adherent fraction and greater than 95% monocytes in the adherent cell fraction, as assessed by non-specific esterase staining. Viability was greater than 96%.

T-Cell Subset Identification

The following monoclonal antibodies to human lymphocyte membrane antigens were used: OKT4, OKT8 and OKT11 (Ortho Pharmaceutical Corp., Raritan, NJ), which identify CD4, CD8 and CD2 antigens respectively; anti-TAC and anti-HLA-DR, which identify the IL-2 receptor and class II major histocompatibility complex antigens respectively. Fluorescein-conjugated, affinity-purified $F(ab')_2$ goat anti-mouse Ig (FIGAMIg) was purchased from Cappel Laboratories (Cochranville, PA). For identification of lymphocyte subpopulations, 1×10^6 PBML were incubated with 5 μl of antibody for 30 minutes at 4°C; the PBML were then washed and were incubated with FIGAMIg (100 μl of a 1/40 dilution) for an additional 30 minutes. After two washes in PBS, cells were analyzed for fluorescence using a fluorescence-activated cell sorter (FACS 400, Becton Dickinson, Mountain View, CA) with data collected on 5×10^4 viable cells. Although no specific attempt was made to remove dead cells, their different light-scatter characteristics excluded them from the FACS counts. Controls included PBML treated with antibody alone or with FIGAMIg alone.

T-Cell Subset Purification

T-cell subsets bearing either CD4 or CD8 antigens were also sorted into positive and negative fractions by panning T-cells labelled with respective monoclonal antibodies onto goat anti-mouse Ig-precoated Petri dishes. Alternatively, when indicated, antibody-labelled lymphocyte subsets were eliminated by the addition of rabbit complement (C; 1/20 dilution; Cedarlane Laboratories, Hornby, Ontario, Canada), leaving corresponding "negative" subsets for functional studies. In these experiments, lymphocytes were sensitized with the respective monoclonal antibodies at 4°C for 60 minutes followed by the addition of C and incubation at 37°C for 60 minutes. This was effective in removing 95 to 98% of the corresponding "positive" subset.

Proliferation Assay

Mitogen-induced lymphocyte proliferation was assayed by measuring the uptake of [^{3}H]thymidine by PBML during the last 6 hours of a 72 hours culture in the presence of either medium alone (supplemented wih 10% human heat-inactivated AB serum) or phytohemagglutinin (PHA-P, 0.2%; Difco Laboratories). Cultures were performed in 96-well microtiter plates, with 10^5 cells per well. Cells were harvested at 72 hours and total cell-associated radioactivity was measured in dpm.

Suppressor Cell Assay

PBML, nylon-wool-enriched T-cells, adherence-enriched lymphocytes or monocytes or purified T-cell subsets were preincubated for 24 hours with varying concentrations of PAF followed by three washes, mitomycin C treatment (50 μg/ml, 30 minutes), and addition of equal numbers (unless otherwise indicated) of viable preincubated cells to fresh mitogen-stimulated PBML cultures. The results are expressed as percent change in PBML proliferation, using the following formula:

$$\% \text{ change} = \frac{\text{experimental dpm} - \text{control dpm}}{\text{control dpm}} \times 100$$

where experimental consists of co-cultures with cells preincubated with PAF-acether and control consists of co-cultures with cells preincubated with medium alone. Pretreatment of cells with PAF-acether has no effect on their viability.

Il-2 Production and Assay

Twenty-four hour supernatants of mitogen-activated lymphocyte cultures were harvested and assayed for IL-2 activity, using the IL-2-dependent murine CTLL cell line. 5 X 10^3 CTLL cells were plated in microtiter wells and dilutions of experimental supernatants, or human recombinant IL-2 (Amersham), were added and incubated at 37°C for 24 hours. Cultures were harvested using a Skatron cell harvester after a 6-hour pulse with ^{3}H-thymidine (Amersham). Il-2 activity was expressed either as dpm or as units/ml derived from logit analysis of the standard curve with r-IL-2.

Cytotoxic Assay

Cytotoxic activity of PBML was measured by using a ^{51}Cr-release microassay. Target cells were labeled with ^{51}Cr($Na^{51}CrO_4$; New England Nuclear), washed three times, and distributed into microtiter wells at a concentration of 5 X 10^3 cells/well. In most experiments, PBML were then added to half of the wells at a concentration of 2.5 X 10^5 cells/well, giving an effector to target cell (E:T) ratio of 50:1. Alternate wells contained medium alone. Cytotoxicity was assayed by measuring the ^{51}Cr content of 4-hour culture supernatants. Cytotoxic activity was expressed as percent specific ^{51}Cr release by using the following formula:

$$\% \text{ Specific } {}^{51}\text{Cr release } = \frac{RE - RS}{RT - RS} \times 100$$

where RE represents cpm in the presence of PBML; RS, cpm due to spontaneous release; and RT, cpm due to total releasable ^{51}Cr. RT values, obtained by two cycles of freezing and thawing, were in the range of 80% of total cell-associated radioactivity and ranged between 2500 and 4000 cpm. RS values were approximately 15 to 20% of RT. Unless specified otherwise, drugs were added to cultures yielding RE, RS, and RT values. RS and RT were not affected by the drugs used.

Effector-Target Conjugation

Equal numbers of effectors and targets (0.3 ml each of a 2.5 X 10^6 cells/ml concentration in MEM medium) were incubated at 37°C for 30 minutes. PAF and/or other drugs were added in appropriate experiments at the outset of incubation. After incubation, the cell mixtures were centrifuged at 250 X G for 5 minutes at room temperature to promote conjugation. The supernatant was aspirated, and 0.3 ml of MEM medium was added without disruption of the pellet. The pellet was then gently resuspended. The percentage of conjugates was determined as the number of single lymphocytes bound to target cells per 200 total lymphocytes counted.

Statistics

Data were analyzed for statistical significance ($p < 0.05$) using the two-tailed Student's t test.

RESULTS

Lymphocyte Proliferation and IL-2 Production

When monocyte-depleted human lymphocytes were cultured for 72 hours in the presence of PHA, their proliferation was significantly inhibited by the presence of PAF at concentrations of 10^{-10}-10^{-6}M (Fig. 1). Addition of PAF to lymphocyte cultures at initiation (time 0) was ideal for inhibition to be seen, but later addition, at 1 hour or 3 hours was almost as effective. BN 52021 could reverse the suppression caused by PAF by 80-100%, while it had no significant effect by itself.

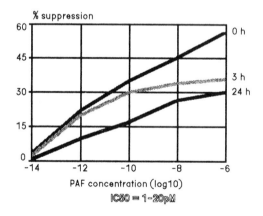

Figure 1   PAF-induced suppression. T cell proliferation. Dose and time dependence.

When IL-2 production by T-cells, instead of proliferation, was measured, PAF was also found to suppress significantly IL-2 production at concentrations of 10^{-12} to 10^{-6}M (Fig. 2). Again addition of PAF early (0 or 1 hours) in the 24-hour culture was optimal. BN 52021 was also capable of reversing most of the PAF-induced inhibition of IL-2 production.

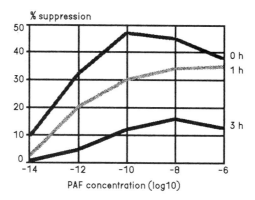

Figure 2   PAF-induced suppression. IL-2 production. Dose and time dependence.

Suppressor Cell Induction

Because these inhibitory effects could not be ascribed to direct toxicity or cell death, the possibility arose that PAF could induce suppressor cells which in turn would inhibit lymphocyte proliferation and/or IL-2 production. Thus we addressed this possibility using a co-culture system as described in Methods. Induction of suppressor leukocytes was indeed found following preincubation of PBML with PAF, at concentrations ranging from 10^{-13} to 10^{-8}M, with maximal effect at 10^{-12}M (Fig. 3).

Separation of PBML into monocytes, T-cells and CD4$^+$ or CD8$^+$ T-cell subsets indicated that both monocytes and CD8$^+$ T-cells could be induced by PAF to actively suppress lymphocyte proliferation. Only monocyte-

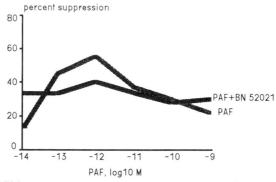

Figure 3   PAF induction of suppressor cells. Effect of PAF receptor antagonist BN 52021.

mediated suppression was indomethacin sensitive, however. On the other hand, PAF-preincubated CD4+ T-cells exerted significant helper effect.

Phenotypic changes in T-cells were also observed following a 24-hour incubation with PAF. While there was a slight decrease in CD4+ cells, there was a significant increase in CD2+, CD8+ and DR+ T-cells.

Induction of Cytotoxic Activity

When monocyte-depleted lymphocytes were cultured with the NK-sensitive K562 target cells, in the presence of graded concentrations of PAF, NK activity was significantly enhanced (Fig. 4). Peak activiy was observed at a concentration of 10^{-13}M. PAF could be added as late as 2 hours into the 4-hour cytotoxicity culture and still enhance NK activity. Lymphocytes could also be preincubated with PAF for 1 to 18 hours, followed by washing, and still retained enhanced NK activity. PAF-induced augmentation of NK activity was not blocked however by the PAF antagonist BN 52021, suggesting that this effect was not mediated through a receptor similar to that found on platelets.

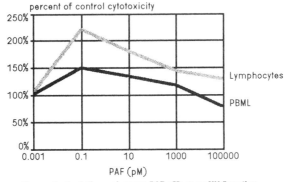

Figure 4   PAF enhances NK activity.

DISCUSSION

Our studies, described in the present chapter, or reported elsewhere (17-19), indicate that PAF, in addition to its many effects on various tissues and cells, has the potential for modulating very strongly several functions of the immune system. When added to a mixed population of lymphocytes and monocytes, it's net effect is that of inhibition of proliferation and IL-2 production, on the one hand, and of augmentation of NK cell activity, on the other. Removal of most monocytes does not modify these effects. While the enhancement of NK cell activity is neither blocked by BN 52021, nor affected by indomethacin, the inhibition of T-cell proliferation and IL-2 production is sensitive to both BN 25021 and indomethacin.

With the use of a co-culture system, in which a cell population is pretreated with PAF, we showed that this mediator can generate active suppressor cells via two pathways: 1) by directly affecting T8+ cells and "activating" them into suppressor effector cells, without the requirement for accessory cells or cyclooxygenase metabolites; and 2) by interacting with monocytes and inducing production of cyclooxygenase metabolites, as indicated by abrogation of suppression in the presence of indomethacin.

We (14, 15) and others (1, 12) have reported similar findings with leukotriene (LT) B_4-induced suppressor cells. Since PAF has been shown to induce LT synthesis in phagocytes (4), it would seem plausible that LTs, and in particular LTB_4 could act as a second messenger in the PAF-induced suppression, when phagocytes were present. This, however, could not be substantiated. Lymphocytes without monocytes do not appear capable of LT synthesis (8) and attempts to detect LT synthesis in our PBML or monocyte cultures following incubation with PAF were unproductive. Furthermore, we could not use 5-lipoxygenase inhibitors because they inhibited lymphocyte proliferation by themselves, making it impossible, at this stage, to resolve the question of LT involvement in PAF-induced suppressor cell function.

Prostaglandins, however, appeared to play a role of second messenger when either PBML or monocytes were preincubated with PAF. This was also suggested by our previous work on LTB_4 (14, 15) and by data from other laboratories using different systems (2, 6, 7, 9, 10, 11). In particular, PGE_2 was shown to induce suppressor cell function when added exogenously to a lymphocyte co-culture (7) of after interaction of monocytes with a histamine-induced suppressor factor (2).

Our findings that PAF receptor antagonists could also induce suppressor cell activity is not readily understood. These compounds usually have no agonist activity on platelets or other tissues which are targets for PAF activity. Further studies are underway to elucidate these observations.

On the other hand, when T-cells were depleted of most monocytes and CD8+ cells, or directly enriched for CD4+ T-cells, interaction of the latter with PAF led to a marked helper effect. It indicated that PAF could directly interact with CD4+ cells in addition to monocytes and CD8+ lymphocytes. It also indicated that, in a mixed population of leukocytes, the net effect induced by PAF would be the algebraic sum of its various and, in some instances, opposite effects on the different cell subpopulations present. It is still unclear, however, given the magnitude of the helper effect on purified $CD4^+$ cells, why the net effect on PBML would still be suppression. At present, cell-cell interactions involved following exposure to PAF are unknown and may account for a net negative effect when PBML are observed. In other environments, such as inflammatory sites, different cell populations may generate different net effects.

Finally, the increased proportions of $CD8^+$ T-cells and decreased proportions of $CD4^+$ cells after 24 hours of incubation with PAF suggest that phenotypic changes may parallel induction of suppressor cells. Similar findings have been reported with suppressor cells induced by concanavalin A (5), adenosine, impromidine (3) and, more recently, LTB_4 (1, 15).

In conclusion, our data suggest that PAF can induce suppressor cells by activating either $CD8^+$ lymphocytes, via a mechanism independent of cyclooxygenase metabolites, or monocytes, via a cyclooxygenase-dependent mechanism. PAF can also induce a helper cell function in $CD4^+$ lymphocytes when they are free of monocytes or $T8^+$ lymphocytes. These findings may help further our understanding of the complex immunoregulatory potential of PAF.

References

1. Atluru, D. et al. *Control of polyclonal immunoglobulin production from human lymphocytes by leukotrienes: Leukotriene B_4 induces an OKT8(+), radiosensitive suppressor cell from resting human OKT8(—) T cells.* J Clin Invest 1984; 74: 1444.

2. Beer, D.J. et al. *Cellular interactions in the generation and expression of histamine-induced suppressor activity.* Cell Immunol 1982; 69: 101.

3. Birch, R.E. et al. *Pharmacologic modification of immunoregulatory T lymphocytes. 11. Modulation of T lymphocyte cell surface characteristics.* Clin Exp Immunol 1982; 48: 231.

4. Chilton, F.H. et al. *Platelet-activating factor. Stimulation of the lipoxygenase pathway in polymorphonuclear leukocytes by 1-0-alkyl-2-0-acetyl-sn-glycero-3-phosphocholine.* J Biol Chem 1982; 257: 5402-5407.

5. Damle, N.K. et al. *Heterogeneity of concanavalin A-induced suppressor T cells in man defined with monoclonal antibodies.* Clin Exp Immunol 1982; 48: 581.

6. Donnelly, R.P. et al. *Inhibitors of prostaglandin synthesis block the induction of staphylococcal enterotoxin A-activated T-*

suppressor cells. Cell Immunol 1983; 81: 61.

7. Fischer, A. et al. *Role of prostaglandin E_2 in the induction of nonspecific T-lymphocyte suppressor activity.* J Immunol 1981; 126: 1452.

8. Goldyne, M.E. et al. *Arachidonic acid metabolism among human mononuclear leukocytes. Lipoxygenase-related pathways.* J Biol Chem 1984, 259: 8815.

9. Goodwin, J.S. et al. *Regulation of the immune response by prostaglandins.* J Clin Immunol 1984; 3: 295-305.

10. Ninneman, J.L. et al. *Induction of prostaglandin synthesis-dependent suppressor cells with enterotoxin: Occurrence in patients with thermal injury.* J Clin Immunol 1983; 3: 142.

11. Orme, I.M. et al. *Inhibitors of prostaglandin synthetase block the generation of suppressor T-cells induced by concanavalin A.* Int J Immunopharmacol 1981; 3: 15.

12. Payan, D.G. et al. *Specific suppression of human lymphocyte function by leukotriene B_4.* J Immunol 1983; 131: 551.

13. Rogers, T.J. et al. *Suppression of B-cell and T-cell responses by the prostaglandin-induced T-cell derived suppressor (PITS).* Cell Immunol 1982; 66: 269.

14. Rola-Pleszczynski, M. et al. *Leukotriene B_4*

induces human suppressor lymphocytes.
Biochem Biophys Res Commun 1982; 108:
1531.

15. Rola-Pleszczynski, M. *Differential effects of leukotriene B₄ on T4⁺and T8⁺ lymphocyte phenotype and immunoregulatory functions.* J Immunol 1985; 135: 1357-1360.

16. Rola-Pleszczynski, M. *Immunoregulation by leukotrienes and other lipoxygenase metabolites.* Immunology Today 1985; 6: 302-307.

17. Rola-Pleszczynski, M. et al. *Inhibition of human lymphocyte proliferation and interleukin-2 production by platelet-activating factor (PAF-acether): Reversal by a specific antagonist, BN 52021.* Biochem Biophys Res Commun 1987; 142: 754-760.

18. Rola-Pleszczynski, M. et al. *Platelet-activating factor induces human suppressor cell activity.* Fed Proc 1987; 46: 444.

19. Rola-Pleszczynski, M. et al. *Enhancement of natural killer (NK) cell activity by platelet-activating factor.* Immunobiol 1987; in press.

Ginkgolides - Chemistry, Biology, Pharmacology
and Clinical Perspectives. P. Braquet (Ed.)
Copyright © 1988, J.R. Prous Science Publishers, S.A.

EFFECT OF PLATELET-ACTIVATING FACTOR AND ITS SPECIFIC RECEPTOR ANTAGONIST, BN 52021 (GINKGOLIDE B), ON INTERLEUKIN 1 (IL1) RELEASE AND SYNTHESIS BY RAT SPLEEN ADHERENT MONOCYTES

Bernadette Pignol, Sylvie Hénane and Jean-Michel Mencia-Huerta

Institut Henri Beaufour, 72 Avenue des Tropiques, F-91952 Les Ulis Cédex, France

INTRODUCTION

Platelet-activating factor (PAF-acether, 1-O-alkyl-2(R)-acetyl-glycero-3-phosphocholine) (2, 15) is a newly generated autacoid produced by several cell types including platelets (12), polymorphonuclear leukocytes (10), mast cells (30), endothelial cells (11) and macrophages (29). PAF-acether appears to play a critical role in anaphylactic shock and inflammatory reactions (8, 33). Indeed, it stimulates various cell types *in vitro* (8, 32), increases vascular permeability (34) and airway resistance (bronchoconstriction) (6), and causes hypotension, thrombocytopenia and neutropenia *in vivo* (16, 42). Recently, several antagonists of PAF-acether

Address all correspondence to: Dr. J.M. Mencia-Huerta, Dept. of Immunology, Institut Henri Beaufour 72, avenue des Tropiques, F-91952 Les Ulis Cédex, France.

became available (4), among which some are extracted from *Ginkgo biloba* leaves (3). These substances, namely BN 52020 (ginkgolide A), BN 52021 (ginkgolide B) and BN 52022 (ginkgolide C) inhibit PAF-acether-induced platelet aggregation, the most potent one being BN 52021 (3, 7). This compound also prevents most of the *in vitro* and *in vivo* effects of PAF-acether, including its binding to platelet and lung membranes (5, 8, and this Telesymposium).

Macrophages play a major role in the development of the inflammatory processes since they are present at the site of such reactions and generate various pro-inflammatory mediators. Upon injection of an inflammatory stimulus, and after the initial recruitment of polymorphonuclear leukocytes, monocytes migrate from the blood to the tissue. Once marginated, they differentiate into macrophages and contribute to local tissue injury.

Besides their classical role in the inflammatory reaction, macrophages are also involved in the regulation of the immune response (18); they process and present the antigen and secrete interleukin 1 (IL1). IL1 increases the production of lymphokines such as IL2 and interferon (24, 41), enhances the activity of cytotoxic T lymphocytes (21) and natural killer cells. IL1 also induces fever (19), proliferation of endothelial cells (9), osteoblasts (23) and B lymphocytes, stimulates chondrocytes to release collagenase (38) and enhances type IV collagen production by epithelial cells (28). IL1 is also chemotactic for polymorphonuclear leukocytes (27, 40) and macrophages. In the latter cell type, IL1 induces prostaglandin production (25). IL1, however, cannot be considered as a marker for macrophages since it is produced by other cell types including endothelial cells, keratinocytes and mesangial cells (32). The capability of IL1 to participate in many aspects of the immune response suggests that this mediator is also an important regulatory molecule of inflammatory reactions (32). Macrophages produce IL1 in response to a variety of stimuli such as lipopolysaccharide (LPS), muramyl dipeptide (MDP) (22) and phorbol myristate acetate (PMA) and these productions are regulated by prostaglandins (25). In addition to producing IL1, macrophages have been shown to generate both lipoxygenase and cyclooxygenase metabolites of arachidonic acid (37) and PAF-acether (29). Although the contribution of macrophage-derived arachidonic acid derivatives in the regulation of the immune response is now established, the possible role of PAF-acether was up to now unknown. In this article we present data supporting the possible role of PAF-acether in the regulation of IL1 release and synthesis from rat monocytes. The interference of the specific PAF-acether antagonist, BN 52021 (ginkgolide B), with the effects of the mediator in such processes, is also analyzed.

MATERIALS AND METHODS

Chemical Reagents

BN 52021 (9H-1, 7a-[epoxymethano]-1H, 6a, 4 cyclopenta [c] furo [2, 3b] furo-[3,2: 3,4]-cyclopenta[1,2-d] furan 5, 9, 12-[4H]-trione, 3-tertbutyl hexahydro-8-methyl (Institut Henri Beaufour, Le Plessis-Robinson, France) was dissolved in dimethylsulfoxide (DMSO) at 60 mM and further diluted in a 10 mM HEPES solution containing NaCl, 137 mM; Na_2HPO_4, 0.4 mM; KCl, 2.7 mM; $MgCl_2$, 1 mM; $CaCl_2$, 1 mM; glucose, 5.6 mM (pH 7.4). Phytohemagglutinin P (PHA) was purchased from Difco Laboratories (Detroit, Michigan, USA). PAF-acether (1-O-hexadecyl- 2(R) -acetyl-glycero-3-phosphocholine) was supplied from Novabiochem (Clery-en-Vexin, France). Lipopolysaccharide (LPS: phenol extract of *E. coli*) and concanavalin A (ConA) were obtained from Sigma (Saint Louis, Missouri, USA).

Monocyte Preparation

Spleen mononuclear cells from Sprague Dawley rats were isolated by centrifugation at 200 x g for 30 minutes on Ficoll- hypaque (Pharmacia, Uppsala, Sweden) gradient. The cells at the interface were collected and washed twice by centrifugation in a phosphate buffered saline solution (PBS) for 10 minutes at 200 x g. The cell suspension was composed of approximatively 85-90% lymphocytes and 10-15% monocytes, as assessed upon observation under a light microscope. Monocytes were separated by adherence on plastic petri dishes for 60 minutes at 37°C under a 5% CO_2/95% air atmosphere. Monolayers were washed with PBS and the cells were detached with a rubber policeman. The cells were transferred into 24 well plates (Corning, Polylabo Block, Strasbourg, France) and cultured in RPMI 1640 supplemented with 5% fetal bovine serum (FBS) (14) at a final concentration of 1x10^6 cells/ml. Since IL1 production is regulated by the self-induced inhibitor PGE_2 (25), dialyzed FBS (FBSd) was used throughout the experiments. The cells were incubated for 24 hours in the presence or absence of 20 µg/ml LPS, PAF-acether (1 fM - 10 µM) or BN 52021 (10 µM), either alone or in combination. In control experiments, appropriate concentrations of the solvent of BN 52021, DMSO, were added. After 24 hour incubation at 37°C the cell suspensions were collected and centrifuged at 200 x g for 10 minutes at room temperature to eliminate possible contaminating cells. One ml of fresh medium was added to the cell monolayers and the samples were frozen. After 3 cycles of freezing/thawing, the supernatants were collected and centrifuged at 200 x g for 10 minutes. The activity in these samples was referred to as the cell-associated IL1 activity. All samples were stored at —70°C prior to measurement of IL1 activity. All experiments were performed in triplicate. In some experiments the possible cytotoxic effect of PAF-acether and BN 52021 on rat monocytes was assessed using the Trypan blue exclusion assay.

IL1 Assay

The IL1 activity in the samples was determined using the mouse thymocyte proliferation assay (31). Briefly, 1.5 x 10^6 C3H/HeJ mouse thymocytes in 100 μl RPMI 1640 medium containing 10% FBSd were cultured in the presence or absence of either PHA (10 μg/ml) or ConA (5 μg/ml) and added with 100 μl of the various samples to be measured. Appropriate controls including medium, PAF-acether or BN 52021, either alone or in combination, were also performed. Cultures were incubated for 72 hours in a humidified 5% CO_2/95% air atmosphere at 37°C, 2 μCi of [^{3}H]thymidine (specific activity; 2 Ci/mmol, Amersham, France) being added for the last 8 hours of the culture period. Cells were harvested after 72 hours with a Skatron cell harvester (Skatron AS, Norway) and filter-associated radioactivity was measured in a Beckman β counter (L.B.K., France) after addition of 5 ml of a toluene solution containing POPOP 0.1 g/l and PPO 5 g/l (Packard, U.S.A.) as scintillation fluid.

RESULTS AND DISCUSSION

In a first set of experiments, PAF-acether was shown to alter markedly and in a dose-dependent fashion the IL1 production by rat monocytes stimulated with LPS. When added at doses ranging from 1 fM to 1 nM to LPS-stimulated rat adherent monocytes, PAF-acether markedly enhanced the release of IL1 (Fig. 1). In contrast, when concentrations of PAF-acether above 10 nM were used, a decrease in LPS-induced IL1 release was observed. Such increases and decreases in IL1 release from monocytes by PAF-acether were noted regardless of the mitogenic agent (either PHA or ConA; data not shown) used in the proliferation assay on thymocytes. In contrast with our work, Salem et al. (39) demonstrated only an increase in IL1 production from human monocytes by PAF-acether. In addition to the species difference, technical variation such as the use of MDP instead of LPS may explain such discrepancy.

To determine whether the observed increases or decreases in LPS-induced IL1 release by PAF-acether were true ones, the cell-associated IL1 activity was also measured in these experiments (Fig. 2). Similar results were obtained since concentrations of PAF-acether below 10 nM markedly increased

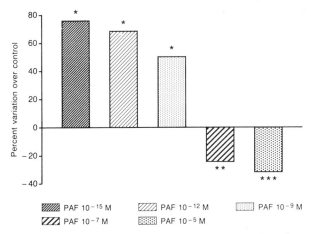

Figure 1 Effects of PAF-acether on the LPS-induced IL1 release from rat spleen adherent monocytes. Purified monocytes were stimulated with 20 μg/ml LPS in the absence or presence of defined concentrations of PAF-acether for 24 hr at 37°C. IL1 activity in the cell-free supernatants was measured in a thymidine incorporation assay using C3H/HeJ thymocytes stimulated with PHA. Similar results were obtained using ConA as the mitogen (data not shown). Results are expressed as percentages of variation in IL1 release calculated over the value obtained in the presence of only LPS. One hundred percent value was 5824 ± 301 cpm (mean ± s.e.m. of 7 experiments). *p<0.05; **p<0.01; ***p<0.005.

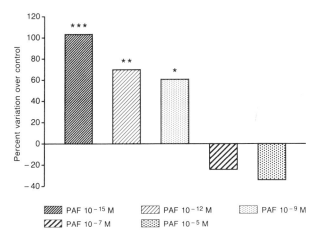

Figure 2 Effects of PAF-acether on the LPS-induced IL1 synthesis by rat spleen adherent monocytes. Purified monocytes were stimulated with 20 μg/ml LPS in the absence or presence of defined concentrations of PAF-acether for 24 hr at 37°C. After 3 cycles of freezing/thawing, cell-associated IL1 activity was measured in a thymidine incorporation assay using C3H/HeJ thymocytes stimulated with PHA. Similar results were obtained using ConA as the mitogen (data not shown). Results are expressed as percentages of variation in IL1 synthesis calculated over the value obtained in the presence of only LPS. One hundred percent value was 6022 ± 232 cpm (mean ± s.e.m. of 6 experiments). *p<0.05; **p<0.01; p<0.005.

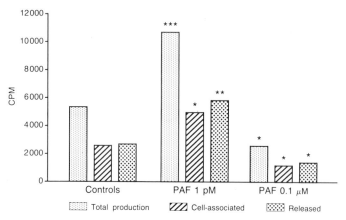

Figure 3 Effects of PAF-acether on the total production, cell-associated and released IL1 activity by rat monocytes stimulated with LPS. Similar experimental protocol as in Fig. 1 and 2. Results are expressed as mean cpm ± s.e.m. of 4-9 experiments. *p<0.05; **p<0.01; ***p<0.005.

cell-associated IL1 activity, whereas concentrations higher than 10 nM markedly decreased it.

As presented in Figure 3 for another set of experiments, the IL1 produced by rat monocytes in the presence of LPS was equally distributed between the extracellular medium and the cells. In the presence of 1 pM or 0.1 μM PAF-acether, respectively, the increase or the decrease were similar in the two compartments. In the absence of LPS-stimulation, PAF-acether at concentrations ranging from 1 pM to 0.1 μM neither induced significant alterations of the released and cell-associated IL1 activity (Table 1) nor affected rat monocyte viability.

Table 1.   Effects of PAF-acether on the released and cell-associated IL1 activity

	Percent variation over control	
PAF-acether	Released	Cell-associated
1 x 10⁻⁷M	36%	33%
1 x 10⁻¹²M	14%	32%

Purified rat spleen adherent monocytes were incubated in the absence or presence of 1 pM or 0.1 μM PAF-acether for 24 hr at 37°C. After 3 cycles of freezing/thawing, cell-associated IL1 activity, as well as that present in the cell-free supernatants was measured in a thymidine incorporation assay using C3H/HeJ thymocytes stimulated with PHA. Similar results were obtained using ConA as the mitogen (data not shown). Results are expressed as percentages of variation in IL1 activity calculated over the value obtained in the absence of LPS. One hundred percent value was 834 ± 227, mean ± s.e.m. of 4-7 experiments.

The present data demonstrate that PAF-acether may play a critical role in the regulation of IL1 production by rat monocytes. The opposite effects of the mediator on the IL1 production suggests that PAF-acether may either act on two different monocyte populations or on two receptor classes present on the same or different cell types. However, stimulation of these receptors by PAF-acether was not sufficient to initiate IL1 synthesis and release since no significant effect of the phospholipid mediator in the absence of LPS was noted. These latter results are in contradiction with those of Barret *et al.* (1), who demonstrated a direct IL1 secretory effect of PAF-acether. Here again, the observed difference may relate to species variation. Also in contradiction with the present data, Barret *et al.* (1) did not observe a actual dose-related increasing effect of PAF-acether on the IL1 production induced by LPS. This discrepancy is presently unexplained.

The PAF-acether antagonist, BN 52021 (10 μM) reversed the increase in LPS-induced IL1 release evoked by 1 pM PAF-acether by an average of 95% (Table 2). In addition, the decrease in IL1 release by 0.1 μM PAF-acether was markedly decreased in the presence of the ginkgolide BN 52021 (10 μM). In these experiments, BN 52021 did not alter cell viability. In addition, BN 52021 (10 μm) reversed by 107% the increase and by 62% the inhibition of LPS-induced cell-associated IL1 activity evoked by 1 pM and 0.1 μM PAF-acether, respectively. Although BN 52021 (10 μM) almost totally reversed the effect of PAF-acether, no direct action of this compound

Table 2   Effects of BN 52021 on the alterations of LPS-induced IL1 release and synthesis from rat spleen adherent monocytes evoked by PAF-acether

PAF-acether	Percent variation over control	
	Released	Cell-associated
1 x 10^{-12} M	120.0 $\pm$ 39.3% *	87.8 $\pm$ 27.3% ***
1 x 10^{-12} M + BN 52021	6.0 $\pm$ 3.0%	−6.1 $\pm$ 4.1%
1 x 10^{-7} M	−52.0 $\pm$ 9.2% *	−46.0 $\pm$ 6.1% *
1 x 10^{-7} M + BN 52021	−13.5 $\pm$ 5.9%	−17.5 $\pm$ 3.2%

Purified monocytes were stimulated with 20 μg/ml LPS in the presence of 1 pM or 0.1 μM PAF-acether, and with or without 10 μM BN 52021, for 24 hr at 37°C. After 3 cycles of freezing/thawing, cell-associated IL1 activity, as well as that present in the cell-free supernatants was measured in a thymidine incorporation assay using C3H/HeJ thymocytes stimulated with PHA. Similar results were obtained using ConA as the mitogen (data not shown). Results are expressed as percentages of variation in IL1 release calculated over the value obtained in the presence of only LPS. One hundred percent value was 5460 $\pm$ 550 cpm (mean $\pm$ s.e.m. of 4-7 experiments). *p < 0.05; ***p < 0.005.

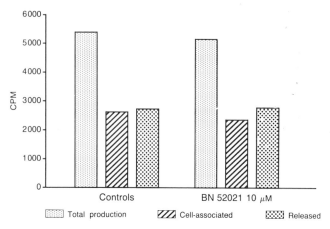

Figure 4 Lack of effect of BN 52021 on the total production, cell-associated and released IL1 activity by rat monocytes stimulated with LPS. Similar experimental protocol as in Fig. 1 and 2. results are expressed in cpm as mean ± s.e.m. of 4-9 experiments.

on the released and cell-associated, LPS-induced IL1 activity by rat monocytes was noted (Fig. 4). In the experiments described above, no effects of PAF-acether (1 pM and 0.1 μM) or BN 52021 (10 μM), either alone or in combination on the IL1-dependent incorporation of ^{3}H-thymidine in C3H/HeJ thymocytes and cell viability were noted.

The ginkgolide BN 52021 has been previously shown to inhibit most, if not all, of the effects of the phospholipid mediator in various *in vitro* and *in vivo* experimental models (7). That PAF-acether acts on rat monocytes at picomolar concentrations and that BN 52021 almost totally abolished the action of low concentrations of PAF-acether is suggestive of the presence of specific high affinity binding sites on the macrophage/monocytes membrane.

The present study does not allow to determine the precise mechanism of action of the phospholipid mediator on rat monocytes. The primary biological signal induced by PAF-acether is the increase in phosphatidyl inositol breakdown, that generates inositol triphosphate and calcium mobilization with subsequent formation of the potent protein kinase C activator, diacylglycerol. The activation of protein kinase C and calcium mobilization will act synergistically to amplify the biological signal induced by PAF-acether. The consequence of such transmembrane signalling will be the activation of phospholipase A_2 and release of arachidonic acid lipoxygenase and cyclooxygenase derivatives regulating cell functions. Therefore, the positive effect of low concentrations of PAF-acether on IL1 production could be explained by the generation of lipoxygenase metabolites by monocytes since PAF-acether activates the 5-lipoxygenase pathway (13, 26) and LTB_4 enhances IL1 production (35). In contrast, the inhibition of IL1 production by 10 μM and 0.1 μM concentrations of PAF-acether suggests that the mediator induced the generation of cyclooxygenase metabolites such as PGE_2 that, in turn, will decrease IL1 production (17, 25). Therefore, the direct measurement of lipoxygenase and cyclooxygenase metabolites in the supernatants of rat monocytes sitmulated with LPS, in the presence and in the absence of PAF-acether, as well as the consequence of the pharmacologic modulation of the arachidonic acid metabolic pathway on the IL1 production (20), might provide information on the mechanism of action of the phospholipid mediator. The present results are in keeping with those previously obtained by Rola- Pleszczynski *et al.* (36), showing that PAF-acether regulates interleukin 2 production and lymphocyte proliferation. Thus, PAF-acether appears to play a major role in the regulation of the immune response and the possibility that PAF-acether antagonists such as the ginkgolide BN 52021 could regulate the immune reactivity *in vivo* remains to be investigated.

References

1. Barret, M.L., et al. *Platelet-activating factor induces interleukin-1 production from adherent macrophages.* Br J Pharmacol 1986; 90: 113p (Abst).

2. Benveniste, J. et al. *Semi-synthèse et structure proposée du facteur activant les plaquettes (P.A.F.): PAF-acéther, un alkyl-ether analogue de la lysophosphatidylcholine.* C R Acad Sci (Paris) 1979; 289D: 1037-1040.

3. Braquet, P. *Treatment or prevention of PAF-acether disorders provoked by a new series of highly specific inhibitors.* GB Patent 84/18 424 (July 19, 1984) Belg.BE901, 915 (see CA 103: 189808d), 1985.

4. Braquet, P. et al. *PAF-acether specific binding sites: 2. Design of specific antagonists.* Trends Pharmacol Sci 1986; 397-403.

5. Braquet, P. In: Advances in Prostaglandin, Thromboxane and Leukotriene Research Vol 16. U. Zor et al. (Eds.). Raven Press: New York 1986; 179-198.

6. Braquet, P. et al. *Platelet-activating factor, a potential mediator of shock.* In: Advances in Prostaglandin, Thromboxane and Leukotriene Research, Vol 17. B. Samuelsson et al. (Eds.). Raven Press: New York 1987; 818-823.

7. Braquet, P. et al. *The promise of PAF-acether antagonists.* In: Adv. Inflammation Research, Vol. 12. Raven Press: New York 1987; in press.

8. Braquet, P. et al. *Perspectives in platelet-activating factor research.* Pharmacol Rev 1987; 39: 97-145.

9. Byars, N. et al. *Interleukin-1-containing conditioned media stimulate the proliferation of capillary endothelial cells.* Fed Proc 1984; 43: 1038 (Abst).

10. Camussi, G. et al. *Mediators of immune-complex-induced aggregation of polymorphonuclear neutrophils. II. Platelet-activating factor as the effector substance of immune-induced aggregation.* Int Arch Allergy Appl Immunol 1981; 64: 25-41.

11. Camussi, G. et al. *The release of platelet-activating factor from human endothelial cells in culture.* J Immunol 1983; 131: 2397-2403.

12. Chignard, M. et al. *The role of platelet-activating factor in platelet aggregation.* Nature (London) 1979; 275: 799-800.

13. Chilton, F.H. et al. *Platelet-activating factor. Stimulation of the lipoxygenase pathway in polymorphonuclear leukocytes by 1-O-alkyl-2-O-acetyl-sn-glycero-3-phosphocholine.* J Biol Chem 1982; 257: 5402-5407.

14. Chu, E., et al. *Role of interleukin 1 in antigen specific T cell proliferation.* J Immunol 1984; 132: 1311-1316.

15. Demopoulos, C.A. et al. *Platelet-activating factor. Evidence for 1-O-alkyl-2-acetyl-sn-glyceryl-3- phosphocholine as the active component (a new class of lipid chemical mediators).* J Biol Chem 1979; 254: 9355-9358.

16. Desquand, S. et al. *Interference of ginkgolide B (BN 52021) with the bronchopulmonary effects of PAF-acether in the guinea-pig.* Eur J Pharmacol 1986; 127: 83-95.

17. Dinarello, C.A. et al. *Role of arachidonate metabolism in the immunoregulatory function of human leukocytic pyrogen/lymphocyte activating factor/interleukine 1.* J Immunol 1983; 130: 890-895.

18. Dinarello, C.A. *Interleukin-1 and the pathogenesis of the acute-phase response.* New Engl J Med 1984; 311: 1413.

19. Dinarello, C.A. et al. *Interleukin 1.* Rev Infect Dis 1984; 6: 51-95.

20. Dinarello, C.A. et al. *The influence of lipoxygenase inhibitors on the in vitro production of human leukocytic pyrogen and lymphocyte activating factor (interleukin 1).* Int J Immunopharmacol 1984; 6: 43-54.

21. Farrar, J.J. et al. *The biochemistry, biology and role of interleukin 2 in the induction of cytotoxic T cell and antibody-forming cell responses.* Immunol Rev 1982; 63: 129.

22. Gery, I. et al. *Potentiation of the T-lymphocyte response to mitogens. I. The responding cell.* J Exp Med 1972; 136: 128-142.

23. Gowen, M. et al. *An interleukin 1-like factor stimulates bone resorption in vitro.* Nature (London) 1983; 306: 378-380.

24. Kasahara, T. et al. *Interleukin 1 (IL1)-dependent lymphokine production by human leukemic T cell line HSB 2 subclones.* J Immunol 1985; 134: 1682-1689.

25. Kunkel, S.L., Chensue, S.W., Phan, S.H. *Prostaglandins as endogenous mediators of interleukin 1 production.* J Immunol 1986; 136: 186.

26. Lin, A.H. et al. *Acetyl-glyceryl- ether-phosphorylcholine stimulates leukotriene B_4 synthesis in human polymorphonuclear leukocytes.* J Clin Invest 1982; 70: 1058-1065.

27. Luger, T.A. et al. *Chemotactic properties of partially purified human epidermal cell-derived thymocyte activating factor (ETAF) for polymorphonuclear and mononuclear cells.* J Immunol 1983; 131: 816-820.

28. Matsushima, K. et al. *Interleukin 1 increases collagen type IV production by murine mammary epithelial cells.* J Immunol 1985; 134: 904-909.

29. Mencia-Huerta, J.M. et al. *Platelet-activating factor and macrophages. I. Evidence for the release from rat and mouse peritoneal macrophages and not from mastocytes.* Eur J Immunol 1979; 9: 409-415.

30. Mencia-Huerta, J.M. et al. *Antigen-initiated release of platelet-activating factor (PAF-acether) from mouse bone marrow-derived mast cells sensitized with monoclonal IgE.* J Immunol 1983; 131: 2958-2964.

31. Mizel, S.B. et al. *Characterization of lymphocyte-activating factor (LAF) produced by a macrophage cell line, P388 D1. II. Biochemical characterization of LAF induced by activated T cells and LPS.* J Immunol 1978; 120: 1504-1511.

32. Oppenheim, J.J., et al. *There is more than one interleukin 1.* Immunol Today 1986; 7: 45-56.

33. Pinckard, R.N. et al. *Physicochemical and functional identity of rabbit platelet-activating factor (PAF) released in vivo during IgE anaphylaxis with PAF released in vitro from IgE sensitized basophils.* J Immunol 1979; 123: 1847-1857.

34. Pirotzky, E. et al. *PAF-acether-induced plasma exudation in rat skin is independent of platelets and neutrophils.* Microcirc Endothelium Lymphatics 1984; 1: 107-122.

35. Rola-Pleszczynski, M. et al. *Leukotrienes augment interleukin 1 production by human monocytes.* J Immunol 1985; 135: 3958-3961.

36. Rola-Pleszczynski, M. et al. *Inhibition of human lymphocyte proliferation and interleukin 2 production by proliferation and interleukin 2 production by platelet-activating factor (PAF-acether): Reversal by a specific antagonist, BN 52021.* Biochem Biophys Res Commun 1987; 142: 3. 654-658.

37. Roubin, R. et al. *Formation of prostaglandins, leukotrienes and PAF-acether by macrophages.* Comp Immunol Microbiol Infect Dis 1985.

38. Saklatvala, J. et al. *Pig catabolin is a form of interleukin 1.* Biochem J 1984; 224: 461-466.

39. Salem, P. et al. *PAF-acether (platelet-activating factor) increases interleukin 1 (IL 1) secretion by human monocytes.* Fed Proc 1987; 46: 3528 (Abst).

40. Sauder, D.N. et al. *Chemotactic cytokines: The role of leukocytic pyrigen and epidermal cell thymocyte-activating factor in neutrophil chemotaxis.* J Immunol 1984; 132: 828-832.

41. Smith, K.A. et al. *The functional relationship of the interleukins.* J Exp Med 1980; 151: 1551-1556.

42. Vargaftig, B.B. et al. *Platelet-activating factor induces a platelet-dependent bronchoconstriction unrelated to the formation of prostaglandin derivatives.* Eur J Pharmacol 1980; 65: 185-192.

Ginkgolides - Chemistry, Biology, Pharmacology and Clinical Perspectives. P. Braquet (Ed.)
Copyright © 1988, J.R. Prous Science Publishers, S.A.

EFFECT OF THE SPECIFIC PLATELET-ACTIVATING FACTOR ANTAGONISTS BN 52020 AND BN 52021 ON INTERLEUKIN-2 PRODUCTION BY HUMAN LYMPHOCYTES

Bernadette Pignol[1], Marek Rola-Plesczynski[2] and Jean-Michel Mencia-Huerta[1]

72 Avenue des Tropiques, Les Ulis, France. [2]Immunology Division, Faculty of Medicine, University of Sherbrooke, Quebec, Canada.

INTRODUCTION

For most cells, the initial trigger for proliferation appears to be the interaction of exogenous growth factors with specific receptors. Activation of these receptors leads to undefined transmembrane signal(s) culminating in cell proliferation. One of the growth factors for lymphocytes is interleukin-2 (IL-2), a glycoprotein of 15,000 Kd produced by T-lymphocytes. IL-2 is secreted by T-cells upon stimulation with the specific antigen when the cells have already been primed, or with a mitogen in the presence of interleukin-1 (IL-1), a product from monocytes/macrophages. Activated T-cells play a critical role in the proliferative response of T-lymphocyte effector cells during the immune response (1).

Address all correspondence to: Dr. Bernadette Pignol, Institut Henri Beaufour, 72, avenue des Tropiques, F-91952 Les Ulis Cédéx, France.

Platelet-activating factor (PAF-acether) is a powerful mediator of inflammatory processes that is produced by platelets, polymorphonuclear leukocytes and macrophages. Until recently, its effect on lymphocyte functions had not been characterized. Several antagonists of PAF-acether have been identified (3). Some of them, BN 52020 and BN 52021, were isolated from *Ginkgo biloba* leaves (4, 5).

The present study was undertaken to determine the effects of PAF-acether, of its isomer [(S)PAF] and of an ethoxylated isostere of PAF-acether in position 2 (ET-PAF) on IL-2 production by human lymphocytes and on lymphocyte proliferation.

MATERIALS AND METHODS

BN 52021 (3-*tert*-Butylhexahydro-4,7b,11-trihydroxy-B-methyl-*9H*-1,7a-(epoxymethano)-1*H*,6a*H*-cyclopenta[*c*]furo-[2,3-*b*]furo[3',2':3,4]cyclopenta [1,2-*d*]furan-5,9,12(4*H*)-trione) was supplied by IHB. BN 52020 (a deoxy-isomer on carbon 1 of BN 52021), synthetic PAF-acether, (S)PAF and ET-PAF were also supplied by IHB.

Preparation of Cell Populations

Peripheral blood mononuclear leukocytes (PBML) were isolated from healthy adult volunteers by centrifugation on Ficoll-Hypaque gradients. These cell preparations were composed of approximately 80-85% lymphocytes and 15-20% monocytes. When indicated, PBML were depleted of monocytes by two adherence steps on plastic Petri dishes for 60 min at 37°C. This resulted in > 98% lymphocytes in the non-adherent fraction. The cells were washed, resuspended and cultured in RPMI-1640 supplemented with 10% fetal bovine serum (FBS). For IL-2 production and assessment of proliferation the cultures were stimulated with phytohemagglutinin (PHA, 10 μg/ml; Burroughs Wellcome, Beckenham, UK). When indicated, defined concentrations of PAF-acether, (S)PAF, ET-PAF or PAF receptor antagonists, BN 52020 or BN 52021, were used either alone or in combination. All cultures were performed in triplicate.

Assay of IL-2

Twenty-four hour supernatants of mitogen-activated lymphocyte cultures were harvested and assayed for IL-2 activity using the IL-2-dependent murine CTLL cell line. CTLL cells (5 x 10³) were transferred in microtiter plates and dilutions of experimental supernatants, or recombinant IL-2 (r-IL-2, Amersham) were added and incubated at 37°C for 24 h. Cultures were harvested using a Skatron cell harvester after a 6 h pulse with [³H]-

thymidine (Amersham). IL-2 activity was expressed as units/ml as calculated from log analysis of a standard curve established with r-IL-2.

Assessment of Proliferation

Lymphocyte proliferation was measured by the uptake of [^{3}H]-thymidine (Amersham) at the end of a 72 h culture period in the presence of PHA. Cells were cultured at 37°C in 96-well microtiter plates at a concentration of 2×10^6 per ml. At 66 h, 50 μl of [^{3}H]-thymidine (1 μCi) was added and the cells harvested after 6 h using Skatron cells harvester. Proliferation was expressed as dpm of radioactivity.

Statistical Analysis

Results were analyzed for statistical significance using the Student's t test or analysis of variance.

RESULTS

As assessed using the IL-2-dependent CTLL cell line, PAF-acether significantly reduced IL-2 production by peripheral blood mononuclear leukocytes (PBML) following PHA stimulation (Table 1). This reduction was about 60-75% at concentrations of 10^{-8} to 10^{-6} M PAF-acether. BN 52021 alone at 10^{-4} M had no effect but reversed the inhibition induced by PAF-acether (Table 1).

Similar results were obtained with human lymphocyte populations almost depleted of monocytes (Table 2), although all values were proportionately lower. PAF-acether decreased IL-2 production by 73 to 86% at concentrations of 10^{-8} M to 10^{-6} M. (S)PAF and ET-PAF were less active than PAF-acether since they reduced, respectively, by 36-40% and 44-52% IL-2 production at concentrations of 10^{-8} to 10^{-6}M.

Table 1 Dose dependent inhibition by PAF-acether of IL-2 production by PBML in response to PHA and reversal by BN 52021 10^{-4}M

		Units of IL-2/ml	
		—	+ BN 52021 (10 μM)
PBML + PHA		5.0 ± 0.5	4.9 ± 0.8
+ PAF-acether	10^{-6} M	2.0 ± 0.3	3.9 ± 0.5
	10^{-7} M	1.5 ± 0.2	3.8 ± 0.4
	10^{-8} M	1.3 ± 0.2	3.3 ± 0.2

Results are expressed as means ± SEM of 3 experiments.

Table 2   Dose-dependent inhibition by PAF-acether, (S)PAF and ET-PAF on IL-2 production by monocyte-depleted human lymphocyte population and reversal by BN 52021 (10^{-4} M)

		Units of IL-2/ml	
		—	+ BN 52021 (10^{-4} M)
Lymphocytes + PHA		2.5 ± 0.2	2.3 ± 0.2
+ PAF-acether	10^{-6} M	0.4 ± 0.1	1.5 ± 0.2
	10^{-7} M	0.6 ± 0.2	1.6 ± 0.2
	10^{-8} M	0.7 ± 0.3	1.8 ± 0.2
+ (S)PAF	10^{-6} M	1.5 ± 0.1	1.7 ± 0.1
	10^{-7} M	1.5 ± 0.1	1.7 ± 0.2
	10^{-8} M	1.6 ± 0.2	1.8 ± 0.1
+ ET-PAF	10^{-6}M	1.2 ± 0.1	1.9 ± 0.2
	10^{-7} M	1.3 ± 0.1	2.0 ± 0.2
	10^{-8} M	1.4 ± 0.2	2.1 ± 0.2

Results are expressed as means ± SEM of 3 experiments.

All of these inhibitions were markedly reversed by BN 52021 (10^{-4} M) with more efficiency when the drug was mixed with PAF-acether > > ET-PAF > (S) PAF. BN 52020 was almost as effective as BN 52021 (data not shown). No direct effect of BN 52020 or BN 52021 alone on PHA-induced lymphocyte proliferation was noted.

Lymphocyte proliferation is dependent on production by helper T-cells of IL-2. Whether or not the PAF-acether-induced impairment in IL-2 production caused an inhibition of lymphocyte proliferation was investigated. The proliferation of PBML in presence of PHA was strongly decreased in presence of PAF-acether by 49 to 60% at concentrations of 10^{-8} to 10^{-6} M. BN 52021 or BN 52020 at 10^{-4}M had no significant effect on lymphocyte proliferation. However, BN 52021 reversed by 80 to 100% the inhibition induced by PAF-acether (Table 3). Similar results were noted with BN 52020 and no effect of BN 52021 or BN 52020 on cell viability was noted (data not shown).

Because several cyclooxygenase metabolites of arachidonic acid and in particular prostaglandins of the E series, can exert a suppressive effect on lymphocyte proliferation, we also attempted to prevent the suppression induced by PAF-acether with indomethacin (10^{-6}M) (Table 4). Indeed, although indomethacin alone had no significant effect on PHA-induced lymphocyte proliferation, it completely suppressed the inhibitory effect of

Table 3 Dose-dependent inhibition by PAF-acether of human PBML proliferation in response to PHA and reversal by BN 52021 (100 μM).

		[^{3}H]-Thymidine incorporation	
			+ BN 52021
PBML + PHA		50,000 ± 5333	51,856 ± 4000
+ PAF-acether	10^{-6} M	20,216 ± 3440	42,461 ± 4680
	10^{-7} M	22,049 ± 5339	44,236 ± 2680
	10^{-8} M	25,935 ± 2666	50,696 ± 4000

Results are expressed as means dpm ± SEM of 3 experiments.

Table 4 Reversal by indomethacin or BN 52021 of the inhibition of PBML proliferation induced by PAF-acether

		[^{3}H]-Thymidine incorporation	
		None	PAF-acether (0.1 μM)
PBML + PHA		40,000 ± 5000	23,000 ± 2941
+ Indomethacin	10^{-6} M	42,500 ± 3823	39,500 ± 4705
+ BN 52021	10^{-4} M	47,000 ± 4704	37,000 ± 5876

Results are expressed as means dpm ± SEM of 3 experiments.

PAF-acether. This result indicates that in this system PAF-acether exerts its effect through cyclooxygenase metabolites, possibly PGE$_2$.

DISCUSSION

From the present results it appears that PAF-acether $>>$ ET-PAF $>$ (S)PAF can play a role in the modulation of the immune response since they decreased both IL-2 production and PBML proliferation. These results are in aggreement with those of Rola-Pleszczynski *et al.* (6), demonstrating that PAF-acether induces T-suppressor cells.

In the present study, the effects of PAF-acether were not due to cell death and were reversed with the concomitant use of an antagonist, either BN 52021 or BN 52020, suggesting that they were mediated through a receptor similar to that present on platelet or leukocyte membranes (2).

The prevention of PAF-acether inhibition by indomethacin suggests that its principal target may be the monocyte, the principal source of PGE$_2$ in the experimental conditions we used. In contrast, when PAF-acether is added to populations depleted in monocytes, higher inhibition is reached. This latter result indicates that lymphocytes also express PAF-acether receptors or binding sites similar to those present on platelet membranes. The possible presence of such receptors on lymphocyte membranes is currently under investigation.

References

1. Smith, K.A. *T cell growth factors.* Immunol Rev 1980; 51: 337-357.
2. Braquet, P. et al. *Perspectives in platelet-activating factor research.* Pharmacol Rev 1987; 39: 97-145.
3. Braquet, P., Godfroid, J.-J. *PAF-acether specific binding sites: 2. Design of specific antagonists.* Trends Pharmacol Sci 1986; 397-403.
4. Braquet, P. *Treatment or prevention of PAF-acether disorders provoked by a new series of highly specific inhibitors.* GB Patent 84/18424 (July 19, 1984). Belg. E 901, 015 (see CA 103: 18980801), 1985.
5. Braquet, P. In: Advances in Prostaglandin, Thromboxane and Leukotrienes Research, Vol. 16. U. Zor et al. (Eds.). Raven Press: New York 1986; 179-198.
6. Rola-Pleszczynski, M. et al. J. Immunol 1988; in press.

Ginkgolides - Chemistry, Biology, Pharmacology and Clinical Perspectives. P. Braquet (Ed.)
Copyright © 1988, J.R. Prous Science Publishers, S.A.

GINKGOLIDE BN 52021 BLOCKS PLATELET-ACTIVATING FACTOR MEDIATED SUPPRESSION OF CELLULAR IMMUNITY

Bryan M. Gebhardt, Haydee E.P. Bazan and Nicolas G. Bazan

Lions Eye Research Laboratories, LSU Eye Center, Louisiana State University Medical Center School of Medicine, New Orleans, LA 70112 U.S.A.

SUMMARY

The purpose of this investigation was to determine the capacity of the ginkgolide, BN 52021, to reverse platelet-activating factor (PAF)-mediated suppression of the mixed lymphocyte reaction (MLR) and the generation of cytotoxic lymphocytes *in vitro*. PAF exerts a dose-dependent suppressive effect on the primary, one-way MLR and has a similar effect on the generation of cytotoxic lymphocytes *in vitro*. BN 52021, a specific platelet-activating factor antagonist, blocks the suppressive effect of PAF on both the primary MLR and the generation of cytotoxic effector cells and, in most experiments, has an overall enhancing effect on these cell-mediated immune responses *in vitro*. Based on these opposing effects of PAF and the antagonist, BN 52021, we decided to focus our attention on the effect of PAF on specific functions of the cells involved in these reactions. We observed that PAF suppresses the expression of class II histocompatibility antigens by adherent, accessory cells in both the primary and secondary mixed lymphocyte cultures. Not suprisingly, the ginkgolide, BN 52021, offsets this

Address all correspondence to: Prof. Bryan M. Gebhardt, Ph. D., LSU Eye Center, 2020 Gravier Street, Suite B, New Orleans, LA 70112, USA.

effect of PAF; under these conditions, the adherent cells, which have important antigen-presenting and monokine-producing functions, were found to express lower than normal amounts of class II histocompatibility antigens. This investigation reveals a specific site of action and a probable explanation for the suppressive action of PAF on cellular immune reactions and an explanation for the antagonistic effect of BN 52021 in preventing PAF from exerting this suppressive effect.

INTRODUCTION

The lipid mediator, platelet-activating factor (PAF), has a dramatic effect on a variety of biological and physiological processes (4, 8). Many of these effects are sufficiently disruptive of homeostatic mechanisms that they cause a disturbance in the normal functioning of the affected system (13, 15, 19, 24).

Close ties between PAF and certain humoral immune reactions have been noted. PAF is present in elevated concentrations at sites of anaphylactic reactions, as well as in kidney allografts undergoing hyperacute (antibody-mediated) rejection (1, 24). However, the participation of PAF in cellular immune reactions has only recently come under scrutiny. It has been reported that PAF modulates cell-mediated rejection of allografts and that it has an effect on mitogen-induced lymphocyte transformation *in vitro* (6, 18). These investigations, which indicate a significant immunomodulatory effect of PAF on cellular immune reactions *in vivo* and *in vitro*, provided the stimulus for the present study. In this paper we report that PAF suppresses alloantigen recognition in mixed lymphocyte culture (MLC) and suppresses the generation of cytotoxic lymphocytes *in vitro*. This suppressive effect of PAF was found to be reversed by the PAF antagonist, BN 52021, and we report for the first time that this PAF antagonist has an immunoenhancing effect on the mixed lymphocyte reaction (MLR). Furthermore, we report that one of the effects of PAF on the cells involved in the MLR is that of suppressing class II histocompatibility expression. It may be that the immunomodulatory effect of PAF on cellular immune reactions is due to its effects on class II-expressing, antigen-presenting cells. This effect on class II antigen expression was also prevented by the PAF antagonist, BN 52021.

MATERIALS AND METHODS

Animals

Rats of the inbred Wistar-Furth (WF) and Fischer 344 (F344) strains were obtained from a commercial supplier (Harlan-Sprague-Dawley, Inc., Indianapolis, IN) as young, adult females weighing approximately 120 grams. For the establishment of MLCs, non-immune rats of each strain were sacrificed by anesthetic overdose and their spleens collected aseptically for the establishment of mixed cultures. For the experiments involving the generation of cytotoxic lymphocytes, rats of each strain were reciprocally immunized with 50 x 10⁶ spleen cells injected intraperitoneally. Ten to 14 days after the intraperitoneal inoculation, the immunized animals were sacrificed and the spleens used as the source of cells for the initiation of mixed cultures for the generation of cytotoxic lymphocytes.

Cell Culture Methods

Primary MLCs were set up in sterile, flat bottomed, 96-well microtiter plates (#3070, Falcon Labware, Becton Dickinson and Co., Lincoln Park, NJ). Non-immune WF and F344 rats were sacrificed by ether euthanasia and the spleens removed aseptically and minced on sterile 80 mesh stainless steel screens moistened with Hanks Balanced Salt Solution (HBSS, Grand Island Biological Co., Grand Island, NY). The resulting spleen cell suspension at a density of 20 x 10⁶ cells/ml from each strain of rat was layered on a 4 ml cushion of Lympho-paque, density 1.086 g/ml (Accurate Chemical and Scientific Corp., Westbury, NY) and centrifuged for 20 minutes at 400 x g. The purified bands of mononuclear cells at the interface of the HBSS and Lympho-paque were collected by aspiration into sterile pipettes and washed at least two times in sterile HBSS. Total cell number and viability were determined by hemocytometer count using the vital dye, trypan blue. The mononuclear spleen cells from each strain of rat were suspended at a concentration of 1 x 10⁶/ml in complete tissue culture medium consisting of RPMI-1640 (Grand Island Biological Co., Grand Island, NY) supplemented with 10% fetal bovine serum (Grand Island Biological Co., Grand Island, NY). Penicillin, 100 U/ml, Fungizone, 0.25 µg/ml, and streptomycin, 100 µg/ml (Grand Island Biological Co., Grand Island, NY) were added to suppress microbial growth. For the establishment of one-way MLCs, portions of each spleen cell suspension were irradiated with 1,500 R using a Gammacell irradiator (AEC of Canada, Ltd., Ottawa, Canada). Control MLCs consisted of purified mononuclear spleen cells from one strain of rat mixed with an equal number of irradiated syngeneic spleen cells. Allogeneic mixed cultures consisted of 0.2 x 10⁶ responder cells in 0.1 ml of culture medium plus 0.2 x 10⁶ irradiated allogeneic stimulator cells in 0.1 ml of culture medium. All cultures were set up in quadruplicate wells of flat bottomed, 96-well microtiter plates. PAF, BN52021, and mixtures of both of these substances at the concentrations indicated in the tables and figures in the Results Section were added to identical sets of quadruplicate wells of the microtiter plates. Solvent controls were included for each experiment.

All primary MLCs were incubated for a total of 96 hours at 37°C in an environment of 5% CO_2 95% air. Eighteen hours before termination of the cultures, one microCurie of tritiated thymidine (^{3}HTdR, specific activity 1.9 Ci/mMole, Schwarz/Mann, Div. of Becton Dickinson and Co., Orangeburg, NY) was added to each well of the culture plates in order to permit the measurement of the proliferative response of responder lymphocytes to the irradiated alloantigenic cells in the presence or absence of PAF and the PAF antagonist. At the end of the incubation period the contents of each culture were harvested using a multiple sample harvester and the cellular DNA collected on glass fiber filter strips. The amount of ^{3}HTdR incorporated into responder cell DNA was determined in a liquid scintillation spectrometer and used as a measure of the recognition of the responder cells to the stimulator alloantigenic signal.

Generation of Cytotoxic Effector Cells and Cell Mediated Cytotoxicity Assay

The generation of cytotoxic effector lymphocytes was carried out in a modified MLC system. Gradient purified WF and F344 splenic mononuclear cells from immune donors were set up in 5:1 ratios of responder to stimulator cells in 16 x 125 mm sterile tissue culture tubes (Falcon Labware, Becton Dickinson and Co., Lincoln Park, NJ) in a total culture volume of 5 ml. Responder cells at a concentration of 5 x 10 cells/ml and irradiated stimulator cells at a concentration of 1 x 10 cells/ml were mixed together in the presence or absence of PAF, BN 52021, or both, in separate tubes and incubated for 5 days at 37°C in the CO_2 incubator. Following incubation, the effector cells from each tube were collected, counted, and incubated in 96-well microtiter plates in several different ratios with ^{51}chromium-labeled allogeneic target cells prepared as follows. Allogeneic (WF and F344) Concanavalin A (ConA)-generated lymphoblasts were used as chromium-labeled target cells in these experiments. The ConA lymphoblasts were obtained by culturing gradient-purified spleen cell suspensions in 5 μg/ml ConA. Purified splenic mononuclear cells were cultured in complete tissue culture medium at a concentration of 5 x 10 cells/ml and a total culture volume of 20 ml in sterile 25 cm² tissue flasks (#25100, Corning Glass Works, Corning, NY). After 48 hours of incubation the lymphoblasts were harvested from culture, washed in HBSS, and suspended in 1 to 2 ml of complete medium containing 100 microCuries of ⁵¹chromium (1.0 milliCuries/ml, ICN Biomedicals, Inc., Costa Mesa, CA). The cells were incubated in the ⁵¹chromium for 1 hour at 37°C, washed three times in complete medium, and reincubated for 30 minutes in complete medium as a means of lowering the amount of spontaneous ⁵¹chromium release. Following this final 30 minute incubation the cells were washed an additional time and resuspended in complete medium at a concentration of 5 x 10⁶ cells/ml. In each experiment the cytotoxic effector cells were incubated with the ⁵¹chromium-labeled target cells at ratios of 10:1, 20:1, 50:1 and 100:1. The mixtures of labeled target cells and cytotoxic effector cells were incubated at 37°C for 5 hours. At the end of the incubation the plates were centrifuged and 50 microliter aliquots of the supernatant collected and tested for released ⁵¹chromium. Total ⁵¹chromium release was determined by adding 50 microliters of a 1% solution of NP40 detergent to control wells containing labeled target cells only. Spontaneous ⁵¹chromium release was determined by incubating labeled target cells alone. The percent cytotoxicity was calculated according to the following formula:

$$\% \text{ Specific Cytotoxicity} = \frac{\text{exp. release CPM-Spont. release CPM}}{\text{total realease CPM-Spont. release CPM}} \times 100$$

ELISA Assay for Quantitation of Class II Histocompatibility Antigen

Primary MLCs were set up in flat bottomed microtiter tissue culture plates as described above. Multiple wells of the microtiter plates were incubated with several molar concentrations of PAF, BN 52021, and combinations of both of these substances. Following a four-day incubation period during which the MLR developed, the microtiter plate wells were emptied of unattached cells and medium by abrupt inversion of the plate on absorbent toweling. All wells of the plates were rinsed two times with HBSS and then allowed to thoroughly air dry to ensure firm binding of the adherent cells to the plate surface. Following drying and gentle rinsing of the microtiter wells with Tris buffer, 0.1 M, pH 7.5, the plates were processed through an ELISA procedure (1), beginning with the incubation of all wells in methyl alcohol containing 1% hydrogen peroxide to inactivate endogenous peroxidase activity. Next, a monoclonal antibody (MCA46, Bioproducts for Science, Inc., Indianapolis, IN) specific for a monomorphic determinant of the rat class II histocompatibility antigen was added to each well. The plates were incubated for 30 minutes at 37°C, washed with Tris buffer, 0.1 M, containing 0.1% Tween 20 detergent (Bio-Rad Laboratories, Richmond, CA). Following this washing step, the quantitation of the monoclonal anti-class II antibody binding to cellular class II antigen was revealed by stepwise incubation of the plate wells in peroxidase-labeled goat anti-rat immunoglobulin (#3213-0081, Organon Teknika-Cappel, Malvern, PA) for 30 minutes, and the demonstration of binding of the peroxidase-labeled antibody using the substrate 3,3', 5,5' tetramethylbenzidine (#98-050, ICN ImmunoBiologicals, Lisle, IL) for 30 minutes. The enzyme substrate reaction was stopped by the addition of 1 N HCl and the optical density in each well at 450 nm was determined spectrophotometrically.

RESULTS

The Effect of PAF and the Ginkgolide Antagonist, BN 52021, on the Primary Mixed Lymphocyte Reaction

PAF consistently suppressed the primary MLR, and the antagonist, BN 52021, was found to prevent PAF-mediated suppression of this reaction (Table 1). BN 52021 alone had an enhancing effect on responder cell reactivity and the presence of both PAF and BN 52021 in the MLCs revealed the dominance of the antagonistic action of BN 52021 over PAF (Table 1). Equimolar amounts of PAF and BN 52021 added to primary MLCs resulted in enhanced reactivity suggesting that BN 52021 can block the action of exogenous PAF and endogenous PAF as well (Table 1).

In other experiments (data not shown), we have observed that for the immunosuppressive effect of PAF and the antagonistic effect of BN 52021 to be seen, these compounds must be present throughout the duration of culture. Both timed removal and timed addition studies indicate that the suppressive effect of PAF is not due to toxicity and that the immunoenhancing effect requires the continuous presence of the ginkgolide for the effect to be most apparent.

The Effect of PAF and BN 52021 on the Generation of Cytotoxic Effector Cells

PAF was found to suppress the maturation of cytotoxic effector cells in secondary MLCs (Fig. 1). In these experiments PAF only, BN 52021 only, or mixtures of both at concentrations ranging from 10^{-7} M to 10^{-11} M were tested for their effect on cytotoxic lymphocyte maturation *in vitro*. The data shown (Fig. 1) were selected to demonstrate the maximum effective concentrations of these compounds. The ginkgolide, BN 52021, has an

Table 1 Effect of PAF and BN 52021 on the Mixed Lymphocyte Reaction[a]

Concentration of PAF/BN 52021 added to cultures	^{3}H-TdR Incorporation (Counts per minute ± standard deviation)	Percent of control[b]
Control	28,641 ± 412	100
10^{-7} PAF	13,422 ± 319	47
10^{-8} PAF	11,949 ± 721	42
10^{-9} PAF	15,140 ± 128	53
10^{-10} PAF	23,277 ± 581	81
10^{-11} PAF	25,995 ± 307	91
10^{-7} BN 52021	33,025 ± 118	115
10^{-8} BN 52021	37,699 ± 514	132
10^{-9} BN 52021	39,628 ± 343	138
10^{-10} BN 52021	35,229 ± 621	123
10^{-11} BN 52021	29,940 ± 377	105
10^{-7} PAF + BN 52021	35,858 ± 412	125
10^{-8} PAF + BN 52021	37,017 ± 901	129
10^{-9} PAF + BN 52021	41,716 ± 452	146
10^{-10} PAF + BN 52021	34,034 ± 511	119
10^{-11} PAF + BN 52021	31,712 ± 540	111

[a]Primary MLCs consisting of W/F strain responder cells and irradiated F344 stimulator cells were incubated for 96 hr in medium containing PAF, BN 52021, or both. ^{3}H-TdR was added during the final 18 hr of incubation and the amount of DNA synthetic activity in the responder cells is expressed as the counts per minute (CPM) of radioactivity of the cellular DNA. The mean CPMs of four identical cultures were determined along with the standard deviation of the mean.
[b]The percent of control was determined by dividing the mean CPMs of the control cultures into the mean CPMs of the PAF/BN 52021-treated cultures.

enhancing effect and blocks the suppressive effect of PAF in this system (Fig. 1). These results support and extend the data obtained in primary MLCs: PAF suppresses the primary MLR and the maturation of cytotoxic effector cells; BN 52021 blocks the suppressive effect of PAF.

The Effect of PAF and BN 52021 on Class II Antigen Expression

Class II histocompatibility antigens are integral parts of the lymphocyte-macrophage antigen presentation network. In the present study we used a quantitative ELISA system for measuring the amount of class II histocompatibility antigen expressed by adherent cells in MLCs and tested the effect

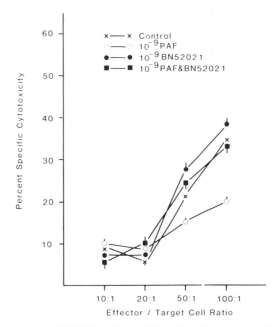

Figure 1 The capacity of BN 52021 to block PAF-mediated suppression of cytotoxic lymphocytes is shown. PAF, BN 52021, or both were added to secondary MLCs and the cytotoxic capacity of the responder cells determined in a 6 hr ^{51}chromium release assay.

of PAF and the ginkgolide antagonist, BN 52021, on class II antigen expression in this system.

The results (Fig. 2) demonstrate that PAF reduces the quantity of class II antigen expressed by adherent cells involved in the MLR, whereas BN 52021, the antagonist, prevents PAF-mediated suppression of class II antigen expression in this system. The ginkgolide antagonist did not enhance the level of class II antigen expression by adherent cells in mixed culture but it was effective in preventing the effect of PAF (Fig. 2). These results provide new insight into the mechanism of action of PAF-mediated suppression of cellular immune reactions.

DISCUSSION

A wealth of information has accumulated indicating the dramatic effects of lipid mediators and products of lipid biosynthesis on immunological reactions, and, in particular, the effect of lipid mediators on immunologically competent lymphocytes (7, 12, 22). The results of this investigation confirm and extend observations regarding the effect of PAF on cell-mediated

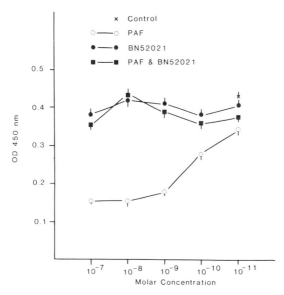

Figure 2 The ginkgolide, BN 52021, blocks PAF-mediated suppression of class II histocompatibility expression by adherent cells. PAF, BN 52021, or both were added to primary MLCs and the density of membrane class II antigen on adherent cells determined in a quantitative ELISA after a 96 hr incubation.

immune reactions such as allograft rejection (6) and mitogen-induced lymphocyte transformation (18). In addition, the results of this investigation indicate a mechanism of action of PAF; the suppression of class II histocompatibility antigen expression can be expected to have a profound influence on the initiation and maintenance of cellular immunological reactions (14, 23). Our finding that the expression of class II histocompatibility antigens is suppressed by PAF and that suppression of class II antigen expression is blocked by the ginkgolide, BN 52021, will provide new insights into the pharmacologic and physiologic effects of lipid mediators as immunomodulators. Snyder *et al.* (20) found that prostaglandins inhibit the expression of class II antigens by macrophages. The results reported here thus confirm and extend previous observations regarding the action of lipid metabolites on immune effector cells such as macrophages.

It is widely recognized that one of the earliest events in lymphocyte activation involves the mobilization of membrane methyltransferases, which catalyze the transfer of methyl groups from S-adenosyl methionine to the membrane phospholipid phosphatidylethanolamine (9, 21). This early change and the subsequent alterations in membrane lipid turnover and alterations in cyclic nucleotide levels, including the production and metabolism of arachidonic acid metabolites such as prostaglandins, have been widely studied in both *in vitro* and *in vivo* immunological systems (2, 7, 10, 12, 16, 22). It has, of course, been known for some time that arachidonic acid metabolites, including prostaglandins, are potent mediators and regulators of inflammatory processes (2); only somewhat more recently has it become apparent that the prostaglandins and leukotrienes also modulate immunological phenomena (5, 17). The results of the present investigation contribute yet another aspect to our knowledge regarding the key role of membrane lipid turnover and metabolism in lymphocyte-mediated immune recognition phenomena.

PAF has been implicated in both cellular and humoral immunological reactions, including anaphylactic shock and inflammatory reactions, immune complex-mediated reactions, hyperacute rejection of organ allografts, and cell-mediated allograft reactions (3, 4). With regard to this latter aspect, *i.e.*, the role of PAF in modulating allograft rejection, considerable further investigation is called for regarding the specific mechanisms of action of PAF; in particular, investigation of the cellular sites of action of this potent lipid mediator must be determined. Do lymphocytes have membrane or cytoplasmic receptors for PAF? Do lymphocytes produce PAF? Do PAF antagonists such as BN 52021 act directly on lymphocytes or through some intermediary cell? These and other questions need to be answered.

The results of this investigation not only support and extend the observations regarding the immunomodulatory action of PAF, but also provide a basis for understanding the effect of this substance on cell-mediated immune reactions. PAF must first act at the level of the cell membrane; exactly how it ultimately affects the membrane expression and density of class II glycoprotein histocompatibility antigens by adherent cells remains to be further investigated. We have demonstrated that the ginkgolide PAF antagonist, BN 52021, prevents this PAF-mediated suppression of class II antigen expression. This finding will no doubt be useful both experimentally and clinically in furthering our understanding of immunological processes and enabling us to regulate deleterious immunological reactions with pharmacologic mediators.

ACKNOWLEDGEMENTS

This work was supported in part by Public Health Service grants EY03150 and EY02377 from the National Eye Institute, National Institutes of Health, Bethesda, Maryland.

References

1. Baumgarten, H. *A cell ELISA for the quantitation of leukocyte antigens.* J Immunol Meth 1986; 94: 91-98.

2. Bourne, H.R., Lichtenstein, L.M., Melmon, K.L., Henney, C.S., Weinstein, Y., Shearer, G.M. *Modulation of inflammation and immunity by cyclic AMP.* Science 1974; 184: 19-28.

3. Braquet, P., Rola-Pleszczynski, M. *The role of PAF in immunological responses.* Immunol Today 1987; 8: 345-352.

4. Braquet, P., Shen, T.Y., Touqui, L., Vargaftig, B.B. *Perspectives in platelet-activating factor research.* Pharmacol Rev 1987; 39: 97-145.

5. Bray, M.A. *Prostaglandins and leukotrienes: Fine tuning the immmune response.* ISI Atlas of Science 1987; 1: 101-106.

6. Foegh, M.L., Khirabadi, B.S., Rowles, J.R., Braquet, P., Ramwell, P.W. *Prolongation of cardiac allograft survival with BN 52021, a specific antagonist of platelet-activating factor.* Transplantation 1986; 42: 86-88.

7. Goodwin, J.S., Ceuppens, J. *Regulation of the immune response by prostaglandins.* J Clin Immunol 1983; 3: 295-315.

8. Hanahan, D., Kumar, R. *Platelet-activating factor; chemical and biochemical characteristics.* Prog Lipid Res 1987; 26: 1-28.

9. Hirata, F., Toyoshima, S., Axelrod, J., Wasdal, M.J. *Phospholipid methylation: A biochemical signal modulating lymphocyte mitogenesis.* Proc Natl Acad Sci USA 1980; 77: 862-865.

10. Horrobin, D.F. *The regulation of prostaglandin biosynthesis: Negative feedback mechanisms and the selective control of formation of 1 and 2 series prostaglandins: Relevance to inflammation and immunity.* Med Hypoth 1980; 6: 687-709.

11. Ito, O., Camussi, G., Tetta, C., Milgrom, F., Andres, G. *Hyperacute renal allograft rejection in the rabbit: The role of platelet-activating factor and of cationic proteins derived from polymorphonuclear leukocytes and from platelets.* Lab Invest 1984; 51: 148-161.

12. Kelly, J.P., Johnson, M.C., Parker, C.W. *Effect of inhibitors of arachidonic acid metabolism on mitogenesis in human leukocytes: Possible role of thromboxanes and products of the lipoxygenase pathway.* J Immunol 1979; 122: 1563-1571.

13. Kornecki, E., Erhlich, Y.H., Lenox, R.H., Hardwick, D.H. *A role for platelet-activating factor (PAF) in neuronal function: Inhibition of platelet activation by triazolobenzodiazepines and interaction of PF with cultured neural cells.* In: Proccedings of the Meeting, "The Promise of PAF", London, Oct. 13-14, 1986; in press.

14. Lafuse, W.P., David, C.S. *Ia antigens.* Transplantation 1984; 38: 443-453.

15. Mallet, A.I., Cunningham, F.M. *Structural identification of platelet-activating factor in psoriatic scale.* Biochem Biophys Res Commun 1985; 126: 192-198.

16. Ninnemann, J.L. *Prostaglandins and immunity.* Immunol Today 1984; 5: 170-172.

17. Parker, C.W. *Lipid mediators produced through the lipoxygenase pathway.* Ann Rev Immunol 1987; 5: 65-84.

18. Rola-Pleszczynski, M., Pignol, B., Pouliot, C., Braquet, P. *Inhibition of human lymphocyte proliferation and interleukin 2 production by platelet-activating factor (PAF-acether): Reversal by a specific antagonist, BN 52021.* Biochem Biophys Res Commun 1987; 142: 754-760.

19. Rosam, A.C., Wallace, J.L., Whittle, B.J. *Potent ulcerogenic actions of platelet-activating factor on the stomach.* Nature 1986; 319: 54-56.

20. Snyder, D.S., Beller, D.I., Unanue, E.R. *Prostaglandins modulate macrophage Ia expression.* Nature 1982; 299: 163-165.

21. Toyoshima, S., Hirata, F., Axelrod, J., Beppu, M., Osawa, T., Waxdal, M.J. *The relationship between phospholipid methylation and calcium influx in murine lymphocytes stimulated with native and modified Con A.* Mol Immunol 1982; 19: 229-234.

22. Traill, K.N., Wick, G. *Lipids and lymphocyte function.* Immunol Today 1984; 5: 1-7.

23. Unanue, E.R., Beller, D., Lu, C.Y., Allen, P.M. *Antigen presentation: Comments on its regulation and mechanism.* J Immunol 1984; 132: 1-6.

24. Vargaftig, B.B., Braquet, P.G. *PAF-acether today - Relevance for acute experimental anaphylaxis.* Br Med Bull 1987; 43: 312-335.

Ginkgolides - Chemistry, Biology, Pharmacology and Clinical Perspectives. P. Braquet (Ed.)
Copyright © 1988, J.R. Prous Science Publishers, S.A.

EFFECT OF GINKGOLIDE B, BN 52021, ON HUMAN NATURAL KILLER CELL CYTOTOXICITY

Yvette Mandi[1], Gyula Farkas[2], Matyas Koltai[3] and Ilona Beladi[1]

[1]Institute of Microbiology, Dept. of Surgery, [2]Institute of Pharmacology, and [3]University Medical School, Szeged, Hungary

INTRODUCTION

Natural killer (NK) cells are a subset of lymphocytes morphologically identified as large granular lymphocytes (LGL) that are cytotoxic to tumor cells, virus-infected cells and hematopoietic cells without prior sensitization. Therefore, NK cells may play a critical role in the initial line of defense against tumor cells and virus infections. In addition, they appear to be involved in bone marrow transplant rejection (1, 2).

Recently, considerable efforts have been devoted to studies of the mechanism(s) by which NK cells recognize and destroy target cells and numerous toxic agents have been suspected to play a key role in the formation of membrane lesions on target cells (3, 4). For instance, phospholipid methylation (5) and phospholipase A_2 activity (6) have been shown to be increased in NK cells following contact with the target cells, suggesting that phospholipid metabolism occurred during this interaction. One of the various products of phospholipid metabolism, platelet-activating factor (PAF-acether) exhibits various potent biological activities and has recently been shown to be generated by LGL (8). Since the contribution of PAF-acether to the cytotoxic process has not been evaluated, the aim of the present study was to investigate its possible role using the PAF-acether antagonist, BN 52021 (ginkgolide B) (9).

Address all correspondence to: Dr. Yvette Mandi, Department of Microbiology, University Medical School, H-6701 Szeged, P.O.B. 464, Hungary.

MATERIALS AND METHODS

Reagents

BN 52021 [9H-1,7a-(epoxymethanol)-1H,6aH-cyclopenta(c) furo (2, 3) furo-(3', 2': 3, 4) cyclopenta (1,2-d) furan-5,9,12-(4H)-trione, 3-tert-butyl-hexahydro-8-methyl] (IHB, Le Plessis Robinson, France) was dissolved in dimethylsulfoxide (DMSO) at a concentration of 100 mM and stored at 4°C until use. The solution was further diluted in the culture medium immediately before the experiments. Human leukocyte interferon (IFN) was obtained from EGIS, (Budapest, Hungary) and exhibited a specific activity of 1 x 10^8 IU/mg.

Cell Preparations

Peripheral blood human lymphocytes from healthy donors were separated on a Ficoll-Uromiro (Pharmacia, Sweden Bracco, Italy) gradient according to a previously published method (10). The cells at the interface were removed and washed three times by centrifugation at 400 g for 10 min in RPMI 1640 (Gibco). The cells were finally resuspended at the appropriate concentration in RPMI 1640 containing 10% fetal calf serum (FCS) (Gibco), supplemented with 100 μg/ml gentamycin and 100 μg/ml penicillin. The cell viability was assessed using the Trypan blue exclusion method. In the experiments where platelets were removed, the mononuclear cells were prepared as follows: the blood was diluted 1/2 in 0.15 M NaCl, layered on the Ficoll-Uromiro gradients and centrifuged for 5 min at 400 g. The plasma layer containing the platelets was removed and replaced by an equivalent volume of 0.15 M NaCl, and the centrifugation continued for 15 min at 800 g. The mononuclear cells at the interface were collected and washed as described above. Henceforth, these samples are referred to as platelet-depleted cell preparations.

NK Assay

K 562 target cells (2-3 x 10^6 cells in RPMI 1640) were labeled with 200 μCi $Na_2{}^{51}CrO_4$ (Amersham) at 37°C for 45 min. The cells were washed 3 times and mixed with effector cells at different effector:target cell ratios, in triplicate cultures in microtitration plates (Greiner). The cell suspensions were incubated for 4 h at 37°C on an atmosphere of 5% CO_2/95% air. Upon the completion of incubation, 0.1 ml of culture supernatant was harvested and counted in a gamma counter. The percentage of cytotoxicity was calculated as follows:

$$\frac{\text{experimental release - spontaneous release}}{\text{total radioactivity incorporated in target cells}} \times 100$$

The variations between triplicates never exceeded 10% of the mean in all sets of experiments.

Treatment of Target Cells with BN 52021

In certain experiments, replicate samples of K 562 target cells ($3\text{-}5 \times 10^6$ cells) were incubated with or without BN 52021 at the dose of 60 μM for 45 min. The cell suspensions were centrifuged at 400 g for 10 min and the supernatants were partially removed except for 200 μl. Two hundred μl of Na_2 $^{51}CrO_4$ (200 μCi) was added to the remaining cell suspension and labeling performed for 45 min at 37°C. The target cells were washed by centrifugation in RPMI 1640 containing 10% FCS and adjusted to the appropriate concentration in the same medium. The total incubation time of the cells with BN 52021 was therefore 90 min. No effect of the drug on Na_2 $^{51}CrO_4$ uptake was noted.

Assay for Lymphocyte/K 562 Adherence

Adherence of NK cells to target cells was assessed by incubating lymphocytes and K 652 in a ratio of 5:1 for 60 min at 37°C. The cell suspension was centrifuged for 3 min at 40 g and the resulting pellet was gently layered on glass coverslips prior to counting under a phase-contrast microscope. The larger K 562 cells could be readily distinguished from the mononuclear cells.

RESULTS AND DISCUSSION

When the PAF-acether antagonist BN 52021 was added during the assay, an inhibition of NK activity was observed (Fig. 1). Such inhibition of cytotoxicity was dose-dependent and occurred at all killer/target ratios. No effect of the solvent of BN 52021 on the cytotoxicity of lymphocytes was noted. Since the inhibition of cytotoxicity by BN 52021 could be due to an alteration of the binding of lymphocytes to K 562 cells, the number of effector cells associated with target cells was determined under the phase-contrast microscope. In 5 control cultures, an average of 15 to 20% of the lymphocytes were shown to be associated with K 562 cells and an identical binding was observed in the presence of BN 52021 (60 μM). However, the number of lysed target cells was 20-30% lower when BN 52021 (60 μM) was present, as compared to control cultures.

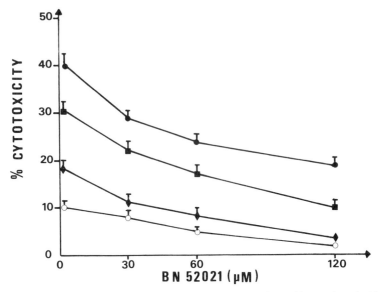

Figure 1 Effect of BN 52021 on NK activity of human lymphocytes. Cytotoxicity was determined in a 4 h ⁵¹Cr release assay using K 562 as target cells at various effector/target cell ratio; (○) 6:1, (   ) 12:1, (■) 25:1 and (●) 50:1. BN 52021 was added at the onset of the assay at the indicated final concentrations. In some experiments, appropriate volume of the solvent alone, DMSO, was added to the culture and no alteration of cytotoxicity was observed.

When lymphocytes were preincubated with BN 52021 (60 μM) for 60 min before the target cells were added, the inhibitory effect of the drug was similar to that observed when it was added immediately at the onset of the reaction (26.3 ± 2.9% *vs.* 30.6 ± 5.2%, respectively). Interestingly, preincubation of lymphocytes with BN 52021 for 18 h did not cause significant inhibition of cytotoxicity (8.3 ± 1.7%). In contrast, the inhibition was more pronounced when the target cells were pretreated for 60 min before the beginning of the assay (48.8 ± 4.1%). When K 562 cells were preincubated for 60 min with BN 52021 and when this drug was also present during the cytotoxicity assay, a slightly higher inhibition (42.5 ± 1.7%) was recorded. This result indicates that BN 52021 acts primarily on the latter cell type rather than on lymphocytes. In addition, these results suggest that for optimal suppression, BN 52021 must be present during the interaction of the effector cells with the targets.

In another series of experiments, the possibility that BN 52021 could inhibit IFN-induced NK cytotoxicity was also investigated. Indeed, this was found to occur since BN 52021 (60 μM) inhibited both the basal (26.6%), as well as the IFN-induced NK (24.2%) activity. Such an inhibition of cytotoxicity was observed at all effector/target cell ratios (data not shown).

Since platelets are extremely sensitive to PAF-acether and usually contaminated lymphocyte preparations, their possible contribution to the cytotoxic process was investigated. Thus, the data obtained from experiments carried out either with or without platelet-depleted lymphocyte cultures were compared. Platelet-depleted lymphocyte preparations exhibited an enhanced cytotoxic activity as compared to that of control populations (81.3 ± 5.0% vs. 35.0 ± 6.9% cytotoxicity, respectively). In addition, a higher suppressive effect of BN 52021 on NK activity was noted when the cell preparations were depleted in platelets (55.4% inhibition of cytotoxicity) as compared to that observed when the whole population was used (20-30% inhibition, see above).

This difference might be due to the fact that PAF-acether possibly released during the triggering of lymphocytes by the target cells is adsorbed, at least in part, on platelets which exhibit high affinity specific binding sites (11). The capability of BN 52021 to suppress the cytotoxicity of platelet-depleted cell populations also indicates that PAF-acether released from the effector lymphocytes could itself participate directly in the NK cytotoxicity, and not via the release or generation of factor(s) originating from platelets.

From the present data it seems reasonable to speculate that activated NK cells release PAF-acether, and/or its metabolic product(s), which ultimately are involved in the injury of the target cells. It is also possible that the release of PAF-acether affects the target cells, making then more sensitive to lysis. As NK cells are involved in the rejection (2) of bone marrow transplants, investigation of the protective effect of BN 52021 on hematopoietic cells might be important in the future. In addition, it is possible that PAF-acether receptors are present on K 562 cells. Activation of such receptors would thus enhance the sensitivity of the target cells to NK-dependent killing. Therefore, the involvement of a pathway(s) other than those implicating PAF-acether in the ultimate NK lytic mechanism(s) is not excluded.

References

1. Lotzova, E. et al. *Direct evidence for the involvement of natural killer cells in bone marrow transplantation.* In: Cells and other Effector Cells. R.B. Herbermann (Ed.). Academic Press: New York 1982; 1535-1540.

2. Herberman, R.B. *Natural killer cells and their possible role with relevance to transplantation.* Transplantation 1982; 34: 1-7.

3. Herberman, R.B. *Overview on NK cells and possible mechanisms for their cytotoxic activity.* In: Mechanisms of Cell-Mediated Cytotoxicity. Eds. W.R. Clarck, P. Golstein (Eds.). Plenum Press: New York 1982; 337-388.

4. Young, J.D. et al. *Purification and characterisation of a cytolytic pore forming protein from granules of cloned lymphocytes with natural killer activity.* Cell 1986; 44: 849-859.

5. Targan, S. et al. *NK-target cell interactions in binding, triggering, programming, and lethal hit stages of NK cytotoxicity.* In: Mechanisms of Cytotoxicity by NK Cells. R.B. Herberman, D. Callewaert (Eds.). Academic Press: New York 1985; 155-172.

6. Hoffman, T. et al. *Phospholipid methylation and phospholipase A$_2$ activation in cytotox-*

icity by human natural killer cells. Proc Natl Acad Sci USA 1981; 78: 3839-3843.

7. Braquet, P. et al. *Perspectives in platelet-activating factor research.* Pharmacol Review 1987; 39: 97-145.

8. Malavasi, F. et al. *Fc receptor triggering induces expression of surface activation antigens and releases platelet-activating factor in large granular lymphocytes.* Proc Natl Acad Sci USA 1986; 83: 2443-2447.

9. Braquet, P. et al. *BN 52021 and related com-* *pounds: A new series of highly specific PAF-acether receptor antagonists isolated from Ginkgo biloba L.* Blood Vessels 1985; 16: 558-572.

10. Böyum, A. *Separation of leukocytes from blood and bone marrow.* Scand J Clin Lab Invest 1968; 21 (Suppl 97): 77-83.

11. Valone, F.H. et al. *Specific binding of phospholipid platelet-activating factor by human platelets.* J Immunol 1982; 129: 1637-1641.

Ginkgolides - Chemistry, Biology, Pharmacology and Clinical Perspectives. P. Braquet (Ed.)
Copyright © 1988, J.R. Prous Science Publishers, S.A.

GRAFT PROTECTIVE EFFECT OF BN 52021, A SPECIFIC PAF-ACETHER ANTAGONIST IN AN IN VITRO LANGERHANS ISLET-SPLENIC LYMPHOCYTE MODEL

Gyula Farkas[1], Yvette Mándi[2], Matyas Koltai[3] and Pierre Braquet[4]

Medical School, Szeged, Hungary; [4]Institut Henri Beaufour, Le Plessis Robinson, France

ABSTRACT

An *in vitro* model for cellular cytotoxicity against rat Langerhans islets was elaborated. The optimal cytotoxicity was observed at both 200:1 and 400:1 effector-target ratio. The protective effect of BN 52021, a specific PAF-acether antagonist, at a concentration of 30 μmol/ml was examined in this cellular rejection model. When Langerhans islets were treated with BN 52021, the inhibition of the cellular reaction was the most expressed. Using BN 52021 pretreated splenic lymphocytes in this model, the inhibition was sightly lower. In the present study, BN 52021 was found to have a significant protective effect on the target cells in this rejection model based on cell-to-cell interaction.

INTRODUCTION

Platelet-activating factor (PAF-acether) is regarded as a potent mediator of inflammatory and acute allergic reactions (1) and as a participant in the

Address all correspondence to: Dr. Gyula Farkas, Department of Surgery, University Medical School, H-6701 Szeged, P.O.B. 464, Hungary.

pathogenesis of antibody and complement-mediated hyperacute allograft rejection (3, 6). PAF-acether may also play a role in the cell-to-cell interaction within the graft. Recently, it has also been shown that BN 52021 significantly prolonged the survival of rat cardiac allograft (5).

An *in vitro* model for cellular cytotoxicity against Langerhans islets was elaborated in our laboratory some years ago (4). This reaction can be regarded as a "clear" model for cellular rejection based on cell-to-cell interaction.

The aim of our work was to study the effect of BN 52021, in our *in vitro* cellular rejection model.

Materials and Methods

Adult male inbred RA (RT 1nd) and LE (RT 1^a) rats were used during these experiments. Pancreatic Langerhans islets were isolated with a modified collagenase digestion technique. Rat pancreas was minced with scissors and then subjected to collagenase (Sigma) digestion for 10 minutes at 37°C. The tissue was then reduced to smaller pieces with a mechanical tissue chopper and was digested for another 10 minutes. Using this method, approximately 800 islets could be received from each pancreas. Then 200 islets were placed in a 35 mm plastic Petri dish containing 2 ml of Eagle's medium, pH 7.4, supplemented with 20% fetal calf serum (GIBCO) and antibiotics. Islets were incubated at 37°C in an atmosphere of air containing 5% CO_2. Media were renewed first on the third day, and then every second day. The amount of insulin released into the medium during incubation was measured by insulin radioimmunoassay kits (Hungarian Academy of Sciences, Isotope Institute).

Rat splenic lymphocytes were prepared by the following method: splenic parenchyma was minced into 2-3 mm pieces in RPMI 1640 medium. These were homogenized in a glass homogenizer and then filtered through a double-layered nylon filter to obtain a suspension of single cells. The cell suspension was diluted in RPMI 1640 medium and layered onto a Ficoll (Pharmacia)-Uromiro (Bracco) gradient at a specific gravity of 1085. The viability of the separated lymphocytes was assayed by trypan blue exclusion. The cell number was adjusted to the appropriate effector to target ratio.

The *in vitro* model for cellular rejection was elaborated. 4×10^4 and 8×10^4 RA viable splenic lymphocytes were added to 200 LE Langerhans islets on the third day of incubation. The damage to the Langerhans islets was monitored by insulin radioimmunoassay.

The PAF-acether, BN 52021 (Institut Henri Beaufour, Paris, France) was dissolved in dimethylsulfoxide (DMSO). The protective effect of BN 52021 at a concentration of 30 $\mu mol/ml$ was examined in our elaborated cellular reaction model. On the third day of incubation of Langerhans islets six groups were formed: group 1 (n = 6) control Langerhans islets, group 2 (n = 6) Langerhans islets mixed with splenic lymphocytes, control for rejection, group 3 (n = 6) Langerhans islets treated with BN 52021 but after 24 hours the medium was changed and splenic lymphocytes were added to the pretreated islets, group 4 (n = 6) Langerhans islets mixed with splenic lymphocytes and BN 52021 at the same time, group 5 (n = 6) same as group 3 but after 24 hours splenic lymphocytes and BN 52021 were added together. Finally, group 6 (n = 6) Langerhans islets treated with DMSO without splenic lymphocytes. During 10 days of incubation the amount of insulin released into the medium was measured by insulin radioimmunoassay.

The results were statistically evaluated by the unpaired Student's t test.

RESULTS

In our *in vitro* model for cellular rejection the cytotoxic reaction was observed at both 200:1 and 400:1 effector-target ratio (Table 1). After five days of incubation the insulin release markedly decreased and finally its production was significantly lower in the mixed lymphocyte Langerhans islets cultures than in the pure Langerhans islets cultures ($p < 0.001$).

Table 1 Effect of splenic lymphocytes on allogeneic Langerhans islets (Insulin conc. μU/ml)

Effector: Target Ratio	3 Days	5 Days	7 Days	9 Days	11 Days
200:1	300 ± 7.1	199 ± 8.2	89 ± 6.1	60 ± 2.3*	58 ± 7.3*
400:1	302 ± 6.5	201 ± 7.2	92 ± 2.6	59 ± 4.1*	57 ± 5.2*
Control Langerhans Islets	301 ± 5.4	202 ± 5.8	201 ± 6.2	196 ± 4.2	192 ± 5.2

*$p < 0.001$

In further experiments, 200:1 effector-target ratio was used.

The results of the protective effect of BN 52021 at a concentration of 30 μmol/ml are shown in Figure 1. During the incubation of mixed cell cultures with BN 52021, the insulin release was significantly higher than in mixed cell cultures without BN 52021 ($p < 0.001$). The insulin production was almost the same in group 3 (Langerhans islets pretreated with BN 52021) and group 1 (control Langerhans islets). In group 4 (splenic lymphocytes treated with BN 52021) and group 5 (both Langerhans islets and splenic lymphocytes were treated with BN 52021) the insulin release was slightly lower than in group 3. Finally, DMSO treated Langerhans islets produced almost the same insulin concentrations as group 1 (control Langerhans islets).

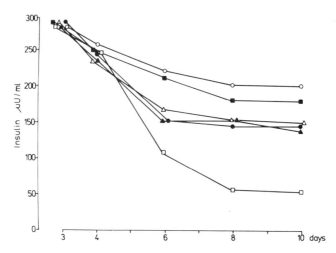

Figure 1 Protective effect of BN 52021 (30 μmol/ml) on rat Langerhans islets exposed to splenic lymphocytes. Langerhans islets (200) were incubated without lymphocytes as a control (○). Langerhans islets were incubated with 4x10⁴ allogenic lymphocytes as a control for rejection (□) BN 52021 was added at a concentration of 30 μmol/ml to Langerhans islets and 24 hours later splenic lymphocytes were added (■). Langerhans islets were incubated with splenic lymphocytes, pretreated with BN 52021 (△). Langerhans islets and splenic lymphocytes were treated with BN 52021 before mixed culture (▲). DMSO was added to Langerhans islets (●). Each point on the curves represents the mean of six separate experiments. SD never exceeded ±6.5 (not shown).

DISCUSSION

In the present study, BN 52021 was shown to be responsible for the prevention of cytotoxicity in our test system. No PAF-acether release during acute allograft rejection has been reported yet, but it is supposed that PAF-acether might be involved in cell mediated graft rejection. This hypothesis is confirmed by our results. The mechanism through which BN 52021 inhibits cellular rejection may be an effect on calcium flux (5). It may be assumed that the PAF-acether antagonist exerts a direct effect on lymphocytes, as well.

We used two approaches for studying the effect of BN 52021. When the Langerhans islets were treated with BN 52021, inhibition of the cellular reaction was the most expressed. It can be regarded as a direct effect on the target cells (5). Using pretreated splenic lymphocytes in this model, inhibition was significant in regard to control cytotoxicity but was sightly lower than in the above circumstances. In this case it can be supposed that BN 52021 may affect lymphocyte proliferation (2).

Experiments are in progress to determine the *in vitro* effects of different doses of BN 52021 in our model and to investigate *in vivo* allogen transplantation of Langerhans islets pretreated with BN 52021.

In conclusion, BN 52021, a specific PAF-acether antagonist, was studied in our *in vitro* model for cellular cytotoxicity against Langerhans islets. BN 52021 was found to have a significant protective effect on the target cells in this rejection model based on cell-to-cell interaction.

References

1. Braquet, P., Vargaftig, B.B. *Pharmacology of platelet activating factor.* Transpl Proc 1986; 18 (Suppl 4): 10-19.

2. Braquet, P., Touqui, L., Shen, T.Y., Vargaftig, B.B. *Perspectives in platelet activating factor research.* Pharmacol Review 1987; 39: 97-145.

3. Camussi, G. *Platelet activating factor and allograft rejection.* Transpl Proc 1986; 18 (Suppl 4): 91-93.

4. Farkas, G., Pusztai, R., Mándi, Y., Béládi, I. *In vitro model for cellular cytotoxicity against rat Langerhans islets.* Transplantation 1983; 36: 583-584.

5. Foegh, M.L., Khirabadi, B.S., Rowles, J.R., Braquet, P., Ramwell, P.W. *Prolongation of cardiac allograft survival with BN 52021, a specific antagonist of platelet-activating factor.* Transplantation 1986; 42: 86-88.

6. Ito, O., Camussi, G.; Tetta, C., Milgrom, F., Andres, G. *Hyperacute renal allograft rejection in rabbit: The role of platelet-activating factor and of cationic proteins derived from polymorphonuclear leukocytes and from platelets.* Lab Invest 1984; 51: 148-161.

Ginkgolides - Chemistry, Biology, Pharmacology and Clinical Perspectives. P. Braquet (Ed.)
Copyright © 1988, J.R. Prous Science Publishers, S.A.

PAF AND BN 52021 IN ORGAN TRANSPLANT REJECTION

Marie L. Foegh[1] and Peter W. Ramwell[2]

Georgetown University Medical Center, [1]Department of Surgery, Division of Transplantation, [2]Department of Physiology and Biophysics, Reservoir Road, N.W., Washington D.C. 20007, USA

INTRODUCTION

The implication of platelet-activating factor (PAF) in transplant rejection is a recent discovery (1, 7, 9). The first association was found in hyperacute rejection in rabbits (7); the investigators preimmunized rabbits by skin transplantation, the kidney transplantation was performed causing hyperacute rejection with release of PAF in the blood effluent from the transplant. This observation was followed by the finding that the ginkgolide, BN 52021, acted synergistically with cyclosporin A and azathioprine in prolonging cardiac allograft survival in a rat transplant model of acute rejection (1, 9).

Hyperacute rejection is a humoral-mediated event caused by preformed antibodies and involves complement activation. The main changes are destruction of peritubular capillaries and fibrinoid necrosis of the walls of small arteries and arterioles. Platelet aggregates and polymorphonuclear-cytes are found intravascularly. An additional feature is extensive deposition of fibrin within the vessel walls. This type of rejection is seen experimentally when the recipient is presensitized towards the donor or when transplantation is performed crossing species (xenografts). In patients receiving organ transplants, hyperacute rejection is rarely seen because of tissue matching. In contrast, most patients experience acute cell-mediated rejection in which lymphocytes first accumulate in the graft. These lymphocytes undergo blastogenesis and proliferation. In the transplanted organ white cells recirculate continuously through the parenchyma. The point of entry is most likely the capillary endothelium and the point of exit is primarily the graft

Address all correspondence to: Dr. Marie L. Foegh, Dept. of Surgery, Division of Transplantation, Georgetown University Medical Center, Reservoir Road, N.W., Washington D.C. 20007, USA.

lymphatics. This recirculation pattern provides a natural route whereby the host recognizes the graft whereby antigen-recognizing immunocompetent lymphocytes are triggered. Monocytes appear in the graft in increasing numbers. If the rejection is not reversed the monocytes will mature into macrophages.

The immunosuppressants currently used in organ transplant patients are cyclosporin A (CsA) or azathioprine combined with prednisone. More recently a combination of all three drugs (triple therapy) has been used in high doses during the immediate post-transplant period. These drugs possess serious side effects; CsA induces nephrotoxicity and hypertension, azathioprine causes bone marrow suppression and corticosteroids promote aseptic bone necrosis, cataract and diabetes. The side effects are generally dose-related and therefore new treatment modalities are important to reduce the dose of CsA or azathioprine or which will replace corticosteroids.

CsA inhibits interleukin 2 (IL2) formation from lymphocytes and azthioprine inhibits cell replication including lymphocyte proliferation. Corticosteroids inhibit interleukin 1 (IL1) and IL2 formation; the effect on IL2 may be indirect through inhibition of IL1. In cell-mediated rejection the T lymphocytes require two signals from the macrophages in order to proliferate. The signals are IL1 and foreign antigen presentation (Fig. 1). In addition, the lymphocyte must recognize class II (DR) antigen on the

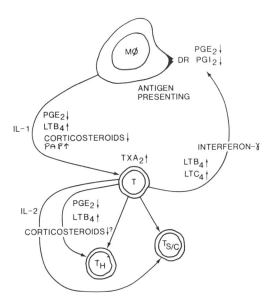

Figure 1   Modulation of macrophage-lymphocyte interaction by PAF and eicosanoids.

macrophage (or other antigen presenting cells). Once stimulated, the lymphocytes produce IL2 which is needed for the clonal proliferation of T-helper cells (CD_4) and cytotoxic T-cells (CD_8). T-cells and macrophages release several substances which act as local immunomodulators. PAF and arachidonate products are produced during the macrophage-lymphocyte interaction and depending on the relative amounts of the lipid mediators PAF, prostaglandins, thromboxane and leukotrienes, the final result will either be enhancement or attenuation of the lymphocyte response. PAF, thromboxane and the leukotrienes will enhance lymphocyte proliferation, while PGE_2, PGD_2 and prostacyclin (PGI_2) will attenuate (2). In addition to their immunomodulatory role the vascular effects of PAF and the eicosanoids may also be important during transplant rejection when perfusion is compromised.

As illustrated in Figure 1, the anti-rejection eicosanoids like PGE_2 interfere with the macrophage-lymphocyte interaction by decreasing IL1 and IL2 production as well as decreasing the class II antigen expression on the macrophage. The pro-rejection eicosanoids, leukotrienes and thromboxane, will promote T-cell clonal expansion. The direct effect of TXA_2 has not been studied since it is not practical due to the short biological half life. Goodwin and collaborators have shown that LTB_4 enhance both IL1 production and IL2 receptor expression, and further that inhibition of IL2 by corticosteroids can be overcome by adding LTB_4 (5). Most recently PAF has been added to the list of factors stimulating interleukin 1 formation (10). γ-Interferon is another lymphokine released during T-cell proliferation. The formation of γ-interferon is enhanced by LTC_4 and LTD_4 (2), and γ-interferon will increase class II antigen expression on macrophages (2). Thus, the eicosanoids and PAF modulate the macrophage-lymphocyte interaction through the same monokines and lymphokines that CsA and corticosteroids exert their inhibitory effect. We have explored, therefore, in an animal transplant model the possibility of replacing corticosteroids with the PAF antagonist BN 52021.

PROLONGATION OF RAT CARDIAC SURVIVAL WITH BN 52021

The rat heterotopic cardiac transplant model is convenient for pharmacological studies. Lewis x Brown-Norway F_1 hybrid rats serve as donors and Lewis rats are the recipient. The donor heart is placed intraabdominally and the aorta and the pulmonary artery are anastomosed end-to-side to the abdominal aorta and vena cava, respectively. This is a perfused beating heart. The transplanted heart is monitored daily by abdominal palpation. Graft rejection is defined as the day of cessation of heart beats. Histological-

ly the usual pathology of rejection is seen, namely, mononuclear cell infiltration, myocytolysis and hemorrhage (8). The rat strain combination
used in this study resulted in the rejection of the cardiac allograft at post-
transplant day 9.0 ± 0.2 days when untreated, day 10.7 ± 0.6 when treated
with azathioprine (5 mg/kg/day i.p.), and day 10.3 ± 0.4 when treated
with CsA (0.5 mg/kg/day). There were no significant differences in graft
survival between the three groups. The combination of BN 52021 (20
mg/kg/day i.m.) with either azathioprine or cyclosporin A increased
significantly graft survival to the same extent as prednisone in combination with azathioprine and CsA (1, 3). The likelihood that BN 52021 is exerting its effect by blocking PAF is strengthened by similar experiments
with other PAF antagonists. In the same model we have used L 652731
(Merck, Sharp & Dohme, USA) and RP 48740 (Rhône-Poulenc, France)
in combination with azathioprine and cyclosporin A. In combination with
cyclosporin A all the PAF antagonists prolonged cardiac graft survival.

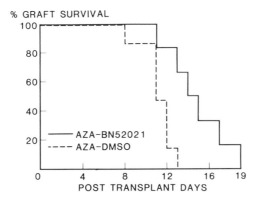

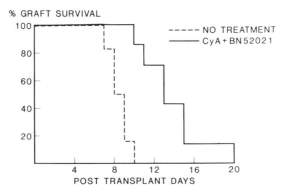

Figure 2   Rat cardiac allograft survival in rats receiving azathioprine + BN 52021 20 mg/kg/day i.m. (upper panel) and CsA + BN 52021 20 mg/kg/day i.m. (lower panel).

However, BN 52021 had an additional property since it is the only PAF antagonist tested so far which prolongs graft survival when combined only with azathioprine. Cyclosporin A and azathioprine exert their immunosuppression through different mechanisms. Cyclosporin A inhibits interleukin 2 formation, whereas azathioprine (the imidazol derivative of 6-mercaptopurin) interferes with DNA synthesis. Thus, BN 52021 may have qualitatively different effects compared to the other two PAF antagonists or may be more potent.

The mechanism by which BN 52021 exerts its effect on cardiac allograft survival is not known. Two possibilities were explored in our laboratory using 111-Indium labelling of syngeneic lymphocytes and platelets. An initial step in cell-mediated rejection is accumulation of lymphocytes within the graft due to an increase in lymphocyte influx. This is followed by increased proliferation *in situ*. By labelling syngeneic lymphocytes obtained by thoracic duct drainage we studied the effect of BN 52021 on lymphocyte accumulation. 111-Indium labelled synegenic lymphocytes were injected on post-transplant day 5 and the animals sacrificed 24 hours later. Lymphocyte accumulation in the cardiac graft was determined by counting the organs in a scintillation counter. The data were expressed as accumulation in the graft as compared to the native heart. The ratio was 2.52 ± 0.21 for the group receiving azathioprine + BN 52021 and 2.31 ± 0.44 for the group receiving azathioprine only (9). Thus, BN 52021 did not affect lymphocyte accumulation in the cardiac graft. It is interesting that similar experiments with prednisolone did not affect lymphocyte accumulation either (9). The possibility that the graft prolonging effect of BN 52021 may be through attenuation of the *in situ* lymphocyte blastogenic response and proliferation needs to be explored *in vivo*. Recent *in vitro* data support the idea that interleukin 1 release is enhanced by PAF and BN 52021 prevented this action of PAF (10).

Platelets are an important element in rejection; this has been demonstrated by 111-Indium labelling of platelets and by fine needle aspiration cytology. In the latter, platelets are visualized as loose intravascular aggregates. These loose aggregates dissolve upon successful reversal of rejection. In prolonged rejection and irreversible rejection an increasing number of platelets agglutinate onto the graft endothelial cells (6). Platelet deposition on the vasculature of the rat heterotopic cardiac allograft model used by us occurs on days eight to nine. The same experiment was done with 111-Indium labelling of syngeneic platelets obtained from the same strain as the recipient (Lewis). The labelled platelets were injected on day 8 to 9 and the recipients were sacrificed 24 hours later. Again no effect of BN 52021 was observed on platelet accumulation in the cardiac allograft. The ratio of graft/native heart was 4.02 ± 0.60 in the rats treated with BN 52021 and azathioprine, whereas the ratio was $3.48 + 0.42$ in the azathioprine treated group. This graft is responsive to treatment of the recipient since the thromboxane antagonist, L 640035, significantly decreased platelet deposition (10). Rat platelets, at least *in vitro*, are insensitive to PAF, thus the lack of effect on platelet deposition is not unexpected. Therefore the beneficial effect of BN 52021 and other PAF antagonists in prolonging graft survival in rats is unlikely to be mediated by an effect on platelets. It is important to investigate this role of platelets in recipients with platelets responsive to PAF.

CONCLUSIONS

The involvement of PAF in cell-mediated rejection is suggested from our findings that BN 52021 and other PAF antagonists act synergistically with cyclosporin A in prolonging rat cardiac allograft survival. The ginkgolide BN 52021 also acts synergistically with azathioprine, unlike the other PAF antagonists, and therefore may possess other properties.

The mechanism of action of the PAF antagonists is not clear but is likely to be an attenuation of lymphocyte proliferation through an inhibition of interleukin 1 and interleukin 2 release.

References

1. Foegh, M.L., Khirabadi, B.S., Rowles, J.R., Braquet, P., Ramwell, P.W. *Prolongation of cardiac allograft survival with BN 52021, a specific antagonist of platelet-activating factor.* Transplantation 1986; 42: 86.

2. Foegh, M.L., Alijani, M.R., Helfrich, G.B., Khirabadi, B.S., Lim, K., Ramwell, P.W. *Lipid mediators in organ transplantation.* Transpl Proc 1986; 18 (Suppl 5): 20.

3. Foegh, M.L., Khirabadi, B.S., Rowles, J.R., Braquet, P., Ramwell, P.W. *Inhibition of PAF and leukotriene expression in acute cardiac allograft rejection in rats.* Pharmacol Res Commun 1986; 18: 127.

4. Foegh, M.L., Khirabadi, B.S., Ramwell, P.W. *Platelet deposition in rat cardiac allografts and the effect of a thromboxane antagonist.* J Heart Transpl 1986; 5: 338.

5. Goodwin, J.S. *Role of leukotriene B_4 in T cell activation.* Transpl Proc 1986; 18 (Suppl 5): 49.

6. Hayry, P., Ferry, B., Leszczynski, D., Manca, F., Jaakola, M., Halttunen, J., von Willebrand, E., Schellenkens, H. vs. Meide,

P. *Generation and breakdown of a vicious cycle in context of acute allograft rejection.* Transpl Proc 1986; 18 (Suppl 5): 52.

7. Ito, S., Camussi, G., Tetta, C., Milgrom, F., Andres, G. *Hyperacute allograft rejection in the rabbit.* Lab Invest 1984; 51: 148.

8. Kawagushi, A., Goldman, M.H., Shapiro, R., Foegh, M.L., Ramwell, P.W., Lower, R.R. *Urinary thromboxane excretion in cardiac allograft rejection in immunsuppressed rats.* Transplantation 1987; 43: 346.

9. Khirabadi, B.S., Foegh, M.L., Ramwell, P.W. *The effect of prednisolone, thromboxane and platelet-activating factor receptor antagonists on lymphocyte and platelet migration in experimental cardiac transplantation.* Transplantation 1987; 43: 626.

10. Pignol, B., Henane, S., Mencia-Huerta, J.M., Rola-Pleszczynski, M., Braquet, P. *Effect of platelet-activating factor (PAF-acether) and its specific receptor antagonist, BN 52021, on interleukin 1 (IL1) release and synthesis by rat adherent spleen monocytes.* Prostaglandins 1987; 33: 931-939.

Ginkgolides - Chemistry, Biology, Pharmacology and Clinical Perspectives. P. Braquet (Ed.)
Copyright © 1988, J.R. Prous Science Publishers, S.A.

INTERFERENCE OF A GINKGOLIDE WITH MODELS OF CORNEAL DISEASES

Nicolas L.J. Verbeij and Nicolas J. van Haeringen

The Netherlands Ophthalmic Research Institute, Amsterdam, The Netherlands

INTRODUCTION

Platelet-activating factor (1-O-alkyl-2-acetyl-glycero-3-phosphocholine, PAF-acether) is one of the most potent inducers of platelet aggregation and has a wide spectrum of biological activities as a very potent mediator of inflammation, increasing vascular permeability.

A specific PAF-acether antagonist BN 52021, a ginkgolide isolated from *Ginkgo biloba* extract which interferes with receptors for PAF-acether (3), is now available.

Various cell types are potential sources for the formation of PAF-acether in pathophysiological conditions; PAF-acether is released during chemical or immune stimulation of neutrophils, vascular endothelium, thrombocytes and macrophages (2, 12).

In the eye, PAF-acether decrease the biwave response of the rat electroretinogram *in vitro* (6), and when systemically administered PAF-acether gives rise to edema of the rabbit retina *in vivo* (4). Treatment with the *Ginkgo biloba* extract resulted in protection of the retinal tissue against argon laser damage (5).

Address all correspondence to: N.L.J. Verbeij, The Netherlands Ophthalmic Research Institute, P.O. Box 12141, NL-1100 AC Amsterdam, The Netherlands.

In the cornea, implantation of polymere pellets impregnated with PAF-acether causes formation of newly formed vessels in this normally non-vascular tissue (9).

Immune keratitis can be used as a model to evaluate the effect of drugs on leukocyte infiltration, neovascularization and edema in corneal tissue.

The participation of mediators in this pathology is beginning to be demonstrated but the results obtained on animal models with specific inhibitors of cyclooxygenase are contradictory. Corticosteroids prevent the occurrence of keratitis completely and nonsteroid antiinflammatory drugs such as indomethacin demonstrated inhibition of leukocyte infiltration at high concentrations (1). However, at lower concentrations an increase of leukocyte infiltration was observed (11), indicating that inhibition of the formation of prostaglandins in the cyclooxygenase pathway may facilitate the generation of leukotrienes in the lipoxygenase pathway and that at high concentrations inhibition of both pathways takes place.

In order to clarify the possible role for PAF-acether in the model of corneal inflammation and in corneal wound healing we investigated the effect of topical application with the PAF-acether receptor antagonist BN 52021.

MATERIALS AND METHODS

Animals

Male pigmented Chinchilla rabbits (2-2.5 kg) were sedated with Hypnorm (fluanison 10 mg/ml and phentanyl citrate 0.2 mg/ml) 0.75 ml/kg body weight and oxybuprocain (novesin) was applied on the cornea for topical anesthesia.

Corneal Denudation

The entire corneal epithelium was removed from both eyes by scraping with a perpendicular blade from limbus to limbus. The removal of the corneal epithelium was performed carefully in order to preserve as far as possible the integrity of the basement membrane (Fig. 1).

Immune Keratitis

Immunization was performed by injection of 20 μl of pyrogen-free human serum albumin (20% solution) using a 27 gauge needle in the corneal stroma of both eyes according to Morawiecki (8) (Fig. 2).

Wound Healing

Wounds after corneal scraping were stained with fluorescein (0.25% solution of fluorescein sodium), the eye was washed with NaCl 0.9% in order

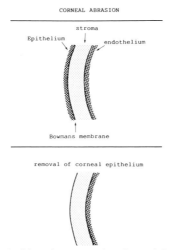

Figure 1   Schematic representation of corneal denudation.

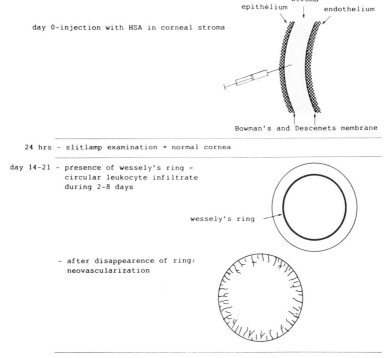

Figure 2   Schematic representation of the model of immunogenic keratitis.

to remove excess fluorescein and photographed at regular time intervals until healed. Photographs were projected and wounded areas were determined by planimetry. Results were calculated in percent re-epithealization of the cornea.

Corneal Thickness

Corneal thickness was measured with a Haag-Streit slit lamp and pachometer, fitted with central fixation lights according to Mishima and Hedbys (7). The use of the fixation lights is essential in order to obtain consistent measurements of central corneal thickness. From each eye the mean of three measurements was taken. The difference between the corneal thickness after and before abrasion or immunization is presented as corneal thickness.

In the immune keratitis experiment for each animal the values of both eyes were averaged.

The observations were organized in a masked fashion, where the observer was not aware of the schedule of drug treatment.

Corneal Aspect

The number of days was recorded during which a white ring or a diffuse, completely opaque cornea was present and during which neovascularization was visible.

Drug Treatment

BN 52021 was freshly prepared every day as a 1% suspension in viscous ophthalmic solvent containing 0.5% hydroxypropylmethylcellulose and 0.9% NaCl without addition of preservatives.

In the corneal abrasion experiment in eight rabbits at random one eye was treated with 30 μl of a 1% suspension of BN 52021 and the other eye with the vehicle, three times daily by instillation into the conjunctival sac. Treatment started one day before abrasion and continued for the duration of the experiment.

In the immune keratitis experiment in eight rabbits both eyes were treated with 30 μl of BN 52021 and in eight rabbits both eyes received the vehicle three times daily by instillation into the conjunctival sac. Treatment started eight days after immunization and continued for the duration of the experiments.

RESULTS

Immune Keratitis

Seven to ten days after intracorneal injection of HSA the appearance of keratitis in the eyes of the vehicle-treated rabbits started with clouding of the cornea at the limbus and between day 14 and 17 an opaque ring was formed, known as Wessely's ring (13), remaining for one to eight days. Sometimes the whole cornea became completely opaque in this period. Two to four days after the appearance of the white ring vascularization of the cornea started from the limbus and progressed until about day 24 and then regressed quickly, resulting in all cases in a clear cornea 30 days after immunization. Swelling of the cornea as recorded by pachometry started at about eight days after immunization and lasted until about day 30.

All animals injected with HSA responded with white ring formation and neovascularization. Control rabbits with normal cornea treated with BN 52021 showed no changes in the aspect of the cornea.

In rabbits treated with BN 52021 the period of corneal opacification was significantly shorter but not the period of neovascularization, as compared to that in non-treated animals (Table 1). The extent of swelling, determined as mean area under the curve (Fig. 3), was significantly different from that in untreated controls.

Table 1 Immunogenic keratitis in rabbits treated with topical BN 52021

	Period of corneal opacity (days)	Period of corneal neovascularization (days)	Pachometry AUC (% of control)
Controls (n = 8)	5.5 + 0.7	6.8 + 1.6	100 + 23
BN 52021 1% (n = 8)	2.5$^+$ + 1.6	7.0 + 1.6	59* + 21

AUC: area under the curve.
All values are mean + SEM.
$^+$Mann-Whitney U test (P < 0.05 for BN 52021 *vs.* control).
*Wilcoxon's signed rank test (P < 0.01 for BN 52021 *vs.* control).

Corneal Abrasion

In the vehicle-treated eyes complete restoration of the corneal surface was observed by 168 hours after scraping of the epithelium.

In all animals improvement was observed in the treated eye at 6 hours with complete restoration at 96 hours (Fig. 4).

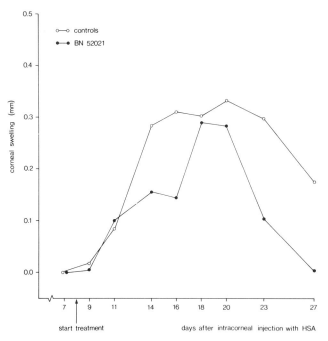

Figure 3 Effect of treatment with eye drops containing 1% BN 52021 (●) on corneal thickness as compared to vehicle-treated controls (○) in rabbits during immune keratitis provoked by injection with human serum albumin (HSA).

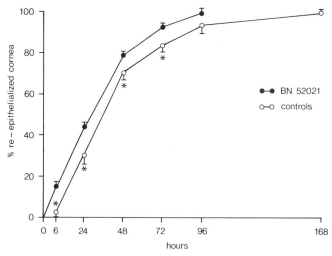

Figure 4 Effect of treatment with eye drops containing 1% BN 52021 (●) on corneal re-epithelialization as compared to vehicle-treated controls (○) in rabbits after corneal denudation.

Corneal swelling in vehicle-treated eyes was observed until 168 hours after scraping of the epithelium. In the eyes treated with BN 52021, after 6 hours less swelling was recorded as compared to the vehicle-treated contralateral eye. This difference in swelling persisted until at 168 hours after scraping the corneal swelling in the treated eyes had disappeared and the corneal thickness was the same as before the experiment (Fig. 5).

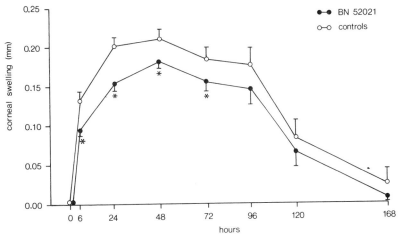

Figure 5 Effect of treatment with eye drops containing 1% BN 52021 (●) on corneal swelling as compared to vehicle-treated controls (○) in rabbits after corneal denudation.

DISCUSSION

From a therapeutic point of view topical treatment of affections of the eye has the advantage of a direct accessibility to the surface of the eye with medications and the possibility of rapid resorption through the cornea into the inner eye. In our experiments a viscous solvent was used, giving a longer cornea-contact time, in order to promote local drug resorption into the cornea.

In preliminary experiments with the model of immune keratitis we tried to ameliorate drug resorption in the cornea by removal of the corneal epithelium, which might be a barrier against drug penetration. There was no difference in the observed effect of BN 52021 on immune keratitis; however, it was striking that the epithelial defect healed earlier in the eye treated with BN 52021 as compared to the vehicle-treated contralateral eye. This prompted us to investigate in a separate experiment the effect of BN 52021 after corneal denudation in a normal eye.

The effect of the specific PAF-acether antagonist BN 52021 on leukocyte infiltration and corneal swelling in immune keratitis and on wound healing and corneal swelling after corneal denudation reveal a role for PAF-acether in these signs of ocular inflammation. Rochels (9) proved that PAF-acether, implanted in polymere pellets in the rabbit cornea, gives rise to neovascularization. This process of PAF-acether-induced corneal neovascularization can be fully inhibited by topical treatment with indomethacin, suggesting the formation of prostaglandins as a necessary step in the growth of new vessels. If there exists a positive feedback system between PAF and prostaglandins in the inflamed cornea this system is not inhibited efficiently enough by BN 52021 to prevent to some extent neovascularization.

In both models BN 52021 was given prophylactically before signs of inflammation started to occur. Corneal thickness in immune keratitis was only influenced before and after maximal swelling in contrast to the swelling after denudation, which was directly less intensive from the beginning and throughout the experiment.

From studies with nonsteroidal antiinflammatory compounds such as indomethacin and flurbiprofen it is known that prostaglandins probably do not play a role in conjunctival epithelial cell migration after corneal denudation (10). The time-related effect of BN 52021 on corneal swelling and re-epithelialization already within six hours after corneal denudation and the parallel in the course of these parameters until complete healing of the cornea suggest a common cause mediated by PAF-acether. From the experiments it cannot be determined if improved healing of corneal wounds is the cause or the effect of decreased corneal swelling.

References

1. Belford Jr., R., Smolin, G., Hall, J.M., Okumoto, M. *Indomethacin and the corneal immune response.* Am J Ophthal 1976; 81: 650-655.

2. Benveniste, J. *PAF-acether (platelet-activating factor).* Adv Prost Thromb Leuk Res 1985; 13: 11-18.

3. Braquet, P., Etienne, A., Touvay, C., Bourgain, R.H., Lefort, J., Vargaftig, B.B. *Involvement of platelet-activating factor in respiratory anaphylaxis, demonstrated by PAF-acether inhibitor BN 52021.* Lancet 1985; 1: 1501.

4. Braquet, P., Vidal, R.F., Braquet, M., Hamard, H., Vargaftig, B.B. *Involvement of leukotrienes and PAF-acether in the increased microvascular permeability of the rabbit*
retina. Agents and Actions 1984; 15: 82-85.

5. Clairambault, P., Magnier, B., Droy-Lefaix, M.T., Magnier, M., Pairault, C. *Effet de l'extrait de Ginkgo biloba sur les lesions induites par une photocoagulation au laser a l'argon sur la retine de lapin.* Sem Hop Paris 1986; 62: 57-59.

6. Doly, M., Droy, M.T., Bonhomme, B., Ruchoux, M.M., Braquet, P., Meyniel, .G. *Alyeration of electrophysiological function of alloxan induced diabetic rats isolated retina. Effects of Ginkgo biloba extract treatment.* Curr Eye Res 1987; in press.

7. Mishima, S., Hedbys, B.O. *Measurement of corneal thickness with the Haag-Streit pachometer.* Arch Ophthal 1968; 80: 710-713.

8. Morawiecki, J. *Prazipitationserscheinungen in*

der lebenden Hornhaut bei Antigen-Antikorperreaktionen. Ophthalmologica 1956; 132: 236-243.

9. Rochels, R. *Tierexperimentelle Untersuchungen zue Rolle von Enzundungsmediatoren bei der Hornhautneovaskularisation.* Doc Ophthal 1984; 57: 215-262.

10. Srinivasan, B.D., Kulkarni, P.S. *The effect of steroidal and anti-inflammatory agents on corneal re-epithelialization.* Invest Ophthal Vis Sci 1981; 20: 688-691.

11. Van Haeringen, N.J., Van Delft, J.L., Barthen, E.R., De Wolff-Rouendaal, D.,

Oosterhuis, J.A. *Effect of indomethacin on immunogenic keratitis.* Curr Eye Res 1986; 5: 307-311.

12. Vargaftig, B.B., Chignard, M., Benveniste, J., Lefort, J., Wal, F. *Background and present status of research on platelet-activating factor (PAF-acether).* Ann NY Acad Sci 1981; 370: 119-137.

13. Wessely, K. *Ueber anaphylaktischen Erscheinungen an der Hornhaut (Experimentelle Erzeugung einer parachymatosen Keratitis durch artfremdes Serum).* Munch Med Wschr 1911; 58: 1713-1714.

Ginkgolides - Chemistry, Biology, Pharmacology and Clinical Perspectives. P. Braquet (Ed.)
Copyright © 1988, J.R. Prous Science Publishers, S.A.

PLATELET-ACTIVATING FACTOR, ELECTRORETINOGRAM AND GINKGOLIDE B—THERAPEUTICAL PROSPECTS

Michel Doly, Brigitte Bonhomme and Gaston Meyniel

Laboratoire de Biophysique, INSERM Unit U. 71, F-63001 Clermont-Ferrand Cédéx, France

INTRODUCTION

PAF (platelet-activating factor)-acether is a phospholipidic type mediator of inflammation, belonging to the class of «autacoids», identified as 1-O-alkyl-2-lyso-*sn*-glycero-3-phosphorylcholine (3). This molecule was described for the first time in 1972 by Benveniste *et al.* (2) as being released by rabbit basophils sensitized by IgE and able to induce platelet aggregation. Since then, PAF-acether has been shown to exist in many inflammation cells such as neutrophils, monocytes, macrophages and endothelial cells (30). Among its numerous, varied effects, PAF-acether can modify membranous ionic permeabilities as shown by (i) inhibition of potassium transport in human red cells and mice macrophages (21); (ii) induction of smooth muscle contraction; and (iii) modifications of cardiac contractility and vascular permeability (10, 29).

Prior works had allowed us to establish that other mediators of inflammation such as the hydroxyl radical (OH·) (15, 16) or leukotrienes (17) were able to modify membranous permeability to sodium in the outer segment of the photoreceptor cell. These works were performed on albino rat isolated retinas. The results which we now present relate to the effects of PAF-acether on the retinal function, as assessed by the electroretinogram (ERG) of the rat isolated retina kept surviving by perfusion. In this experimental pro-

Address all correspondence to: Prof. Michel Doly, Laboratoire de Biophysique, Facultés de Médecine et de Pharmacie, B.P. 38, 28 place Henri-Dunant, F-63001 Clermont-Ferrand Cédex, France.

tocol (14), the electroretinogram records the effect of retina stimulation by light for several hours. This electrophysiological signal involves a succession of variations in membranous ionic permeabilities and thus allows quantifying the retinal function of which it reflects the integrity. In addition, by its embryologic origins, the retina constitutes an excellent brain model and the results obtained with PAF-acether on the retina should allow hypotheses to be made concerning the effects of PAF-acether in the brain.

In order to define more precisely the specificity of the results observed, our study was performed not only with PAF-acether but also with lyso-PAF and with a specific PAF antagonist: ginkgolide B, or BN 52021 (8). Indeed, analysis of the results obtained in the presence of PAF-acether and a specific antagonist could suggest the presence of specific PAF-acether receptors in the retina.

MATERIALS AND METHODS

The experimental technique to keep isolated retinas surviving which we have developed is directly inspired by that of Arden *et al.* (1). We chose to experiment with albino rat retinas since this animal has an almost exclusively scotopic vision (27). The animals were adapted to the dark for at least two hours and then sacrificed. One of the eyes was removed and incised along the equator. The retina was progressively detached from the pigmentary epithelium, then released by incision at the point of insertion of the optical nerve. The dissection was made in the perfusion liquid with the following composition: NaCl, 121.5 mM; KCl, 3.1 mM; $CaCl_2$, 0.4 mM; $MgSO_4$, 0.6 mM; $NaHCO_3$, 24.4 mM; NaH_2PO_4, 0.5 mM; sodium glutamate, 0.5 mM; glucose, 28 mM; freshly reconstituted human plasma, 3%. Once dissected, the retina was mounted like a membrane in a cell perfused by the nutritive liquid, maintained at 37°C and permanently bubbled by a mixture of 95% O_2 and 5% CO_2.

The light stimulation was executed using a photostimulator emitting flashes of white light to the retina (300 lux; 1 ms). The electroretinogram was obtained using two electrodes located on both sides of the retina, in the perfusion cell, and connected to an amplifier-recorder joined to a signal processing system.

PAF-acether (1-O-hexadecyl-2-(R)-acetyl-glycero-3-phosphorylcholine) and lyso-PAF-acether were supplied by Bachem Feinchemikalien AG (Switzerland). After having been dissolved in the nutritive solution, they were added to the perfusion liquid in an approximate volume of 1 ml for 1 litre of solution. We experimented with the following concentrations: PAF-acether: 2.10^{-11} M, 2.10^{-9} M and 2.10^{-7} M. Ginkgolide B, BN 52021: 9H-1, 7a-(epoxymethano)-1H,5aH, cyclopenta c furo 2-3-b furo-3'-2': 3,4

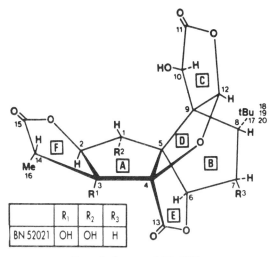

Figure 1   Structure of BN 52021.

	R₁	R₂	R₃
BN 52021	OH	OH	H

cyclopenta 1,2-d furan-5,9,12- 44-trione,3-tert-butyl hexahydro-4, 7b, -11 hydroxy-8 methyl was supplied by Institut Henri Beaufour (I.H.B. Le Plessis Robinson, France) (Fig. 1). It was also solubilized in the nutritive liquid and added, for the experimentation, in the perfusion solution in an approximate volume of 1 ml per litre solution. The results we now present were obtained with a single concentration of BN 52021: 2.10^{-5} M in the presence of 2.10^{-7} M PAF-acether.

RESULTS

The electroretinogram or variation in transretinal potential obtained with the isolated retina can be divided into three waves (Fig. 2): a precocious and negative a-wave, then a positive b-wave followed by a slow and negative variation in potential which corresponds to the end of PIII process. We chose to quantify the ERG by measuring the b-wave amplitude. Indeed, with respect to the a-wave or PIII which are mainly generated by the photoreceptor cell, the b-wave arises in the Müller cells (13), *i.e.,* in the internal layers of the retina. Thus, its genesis implies integrity of the intra-retinal nervous connections, and its amplitude seems to be the best reflection of the quality of retinal metabolism. B-wave amplitude in response to a standard stimulus is not constant throughout all the survival. The average evolution curve of the b-wave amplitude over time (which we will call the survival curve) is shown in Figure 3.

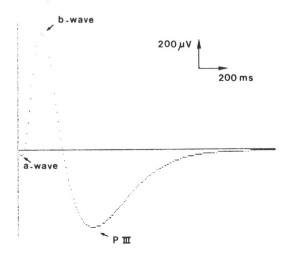

Figure 2 An example of electroretinogram recorded on rat isolated retina in response to white light stimulation (300 lux; 1 ms).

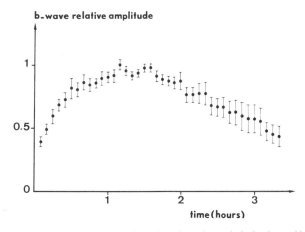

Figure 3 Normal evolution of b-wave amplitude throughout the survival of retinas; white light stimulation: 300 lux; 1 ms (mean ± s.e.m.).

The curve shows an ascending adaptation phase, then a stationary phase when the amplitude varies only slightly, and then a regular decline phase until the end of survival. All our experiments were performed when the amplitude of the b-wave had a practically constant value which we take as the reference value (100%).

When PAF-acether (2.10^{-7} M) is added to the perfusion solution, the ERG b-wave amplitude decreases rapidly and irreversibly (Fig. 4). Thus, approx-

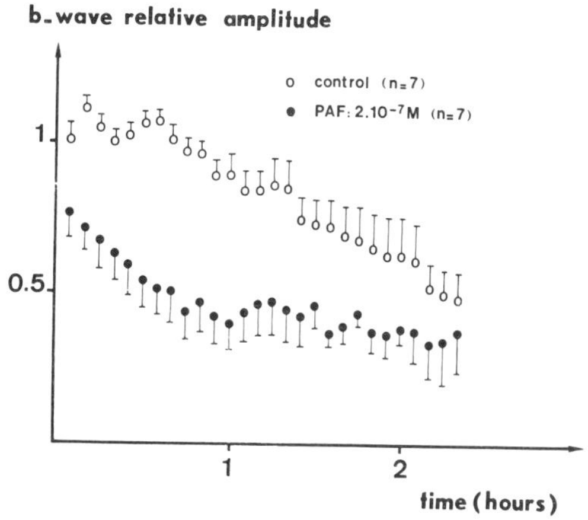

Figure 4 Effects of 2.10⁻⁷ M PAF-acether on the b-wave amplitude of ERG (white light, 300 lux; 1 ms) (mean ± s.e.m.).

imately 40 minutes after the addition of PAF-acether, the b-wave reaches 50% of its reference value, whereas in the normal survival conditions, this level is reached only approximately 2 hours and 30 minutes later. It is remarkable to note, however, that after a rapid fall in amplitude of around 1 hour, the b-wave seems to stabilize, the survival curve slope being quite comparable in the presence or absence of PAF-acether. In accordance with the same protocol, we experimented with three different concentrations of PAF-acether: 2.10^{-11} M; 2.10^{-9} M and 2.10^{-7} M. Our results show that the extent to which the b-wave is affected is all the more pronounced as the PAF-acether concentration is higher: thus, 40 minutes after the addition of PAF-acether, the amplitude of the b-wave reaches 74% of its reference value with 2.10^{-11} M, 48% with 2.10^{-9} M and 43% with 2.10^{-7} M (Fig. 5). Once again, it can be observed that the decrease in amplitude of the b-wave is not regular: it is far more rapid in the first hour following the addition of PAF-acether. Furthermore, it can also be noted that no matter what the concentration of PAF-acether is, after the first hour of perfusion, the survival curves have a practically normal slope. When lyso-PAF (2.10^{-7} M) is added to the perfusion liquid, the average survival curve obtained is quite normal and totally different from that obtained with PAF-acether at an identical concentration (Fig. 6); thus, one hour after addition, the b-wave amplitude is equal to its reference value with lyso-PAF and is at 43% of this value with PAF-acether.

The results obtained in our experimental model are radically different if PAF-acether (2.10^{-7} M) is added alone or in the presence of BN 52021 (2.10^{-5} M). It can be observed (Fig. 7) that the survival curve obtained is

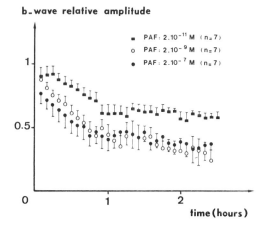

Figure 5 Dose-dependent effects of PAF-acether on ERG recorded on isolated rat retina (white light, 300 lux; 1 ms) (mean ± s.e.m.).

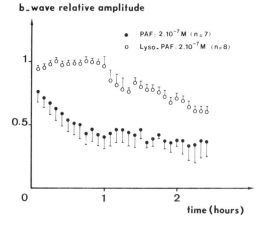

Figure 6 Comparison of PAF-acether and lyso-PAF on the isolated retina (white light, 300 lux; 1 ms) (mean ± s.e.m.).

practically normal in the presence of BN 52021: thus, one hour after perfusion, the amplitude of the b-wave is around 90% of its reference value. Subsequently, the survival curve evolves quite normally; an even longer stabilization of the b-wave can be noted in the presence of BN 52021 than in normal perfusion conditions.

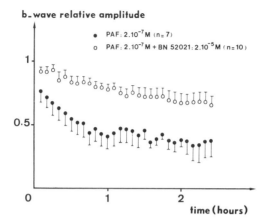

Figure 7   Total inhibition of PAF-acether induced decrease of b-wave amplitude by BN 52021 (white light, 300 lux; 1 ms) (mean $\pm$ s.e.m.).

DISCUSSION

An electroretinogram is the specific electrophysiological response of the retina to light stimulation. The response arises in the photoreceptor cells but involves all the retina. The initial stage of the visual process is the absorption of photons by the retinal photopigment, rhodopsin. This photopigment is localized in the rod outer segments and is an intrinsic protein which is part of membrane of the disks regularly stacked within the outer segment. The molecule rhodopsin includes two associated parts: one proteinic part, opsin and a chromophoric group: retinal cis-11. It is the latter which is responsible for absorbing light photons-with maximum efficiency at 500 nm-this absorption causing photoisomerization of the molecule. Following this purely photochemical initial stage there is an electrophysiological stage. The isomerization of rhodopsin leads to hyperpolarization of the membrane of the rod outer segment caused by a decrease in the membranous permeability to Na^+ ions (22). Thus, the flux Na^+ entering in darkness is stopped by light, the ions accumulating in the extracellular medium, along the membrane, causing its hyperpolarisation. This variation in potential of the membrane is the first electric signal of visual perception and thus the origin of the electroretinogram. Interestingly, in the rods of vertebrates, the saccular membrane and the rod outer segment membrane are totally independent. Thus, since it is photoisomerization of rhodopsin which leads to the membranous hyperpolarization of the photoreceptor cell, it is necessary to make a «messenger» intervene between these two membranes.

Ca^{2+} ions have been widely proposed as holding this role (25, 34): indeed an increase in the concentration of Ca^{2+} has been able to be measured, within the rod, in response to light stimulation and it can be believed that, by binding to the intracellular membranous site, Ca^{2+} ions can oppose the penetration of Na^+ ions. However, this first hypothesis has not been entirely accepted since it does not explain the amplification phenomenon occurring between the isomerization of rhodopsin and the variation in permeability to Na^+ of the outer segment membrane. This is why an enzymatic process was sought in direct relation with the variations in cGMP concentration observed upon light stimulation (7, 24). Thus, cyclic cGMP has been proposed as a messenger; indeed, light leads to activation of a phosphodiesterase responsible for cGMP hydrolysis and thus the decrease in its intracellular concentration (31, 33). However, according to the recent works by Fesenko et al. (20), rod outer segment membrane conductance of Na^+ ions is indeed controlled by cGMP. Thus the precise role of Ca^{2+} ions in visual transduction is still to be elucidated.

At cellular level, the way PAF-acether acts is now understood quite well. Most often, PAF-acether binds to the specific membranous receptors and activates the phosphatidylinositol cycle (PI), controlled by a phospholipase C (5, 10, 23). The main consequence of the binding of PAF-acether to its receptor is the formation of diacylglycerol and inositol 1,4,5-triphosphate (IP3): the first compound stimulates proteinic phosphorylation, whereas the role of the second one is to mobilize intracellular calcium. Thus PAF acether can be compared with a mediator using Ca^{2+} ions as the messsenger and the transduction mechanism of this mediator could be summarized as hydrolysis of phosphoinositides modulated by receptors (4). The formation of IP3 triggered by the binding of PAF-acether to its specific membranous receptor could be the explanation for the effects of PAF-acether on the retinal function. Indeed several recent works (6, 11, 19) clearly establish that IP3 could participate in the visual transduction mechanism which, from the photoisomerization of rhodopsin, leads to hyperpolarization of the rod outer segment membrane. Thus, after intracellular injection of IP3, Waloga et al. (32) observed a reversible hyperpolarization of the photoreceptor cell comparable to that induced by light. Furthermore this hyperpolarization caused by IP3 inhibits the subsequent electrophysiologic response of the cell to light stimulation. Similarly the rod response to the injection of IP3 is practically suppressed when the cell is adapted to light but is reestablished in adaptation to darkness. Thus, it appears that in the rod outer segment membrane, IP3 and visible light could have quite comparable electrophysiological consequences. In these conditions, it appears logical to propose the following sequence to interpret the functional repercussions of PAF-acether on the retina: (i) PAF-acether binds to membranous receptors which could be localized in the photoreceptor cell; (11) this specific binding leads to the release of IP3 in the intracellular medium; (iii) membranous hyperpolarization of the rod outer segment follows, which in practice makes subsequent light stimulation inefficient, and this would correspond to the irreversible fall in the ERG amplitude. This hypothesis concerning the action of PAF-acether on the retina is to be compared with the fact that in certain experimental conditions, the retina of the vertebrate can synthesize and release PAF-acether (12) and that IP3 can release calcium from rod outer segments (26). In these conditions it could be supposed that PAF-acether could play the role of a real intra-retinal mediator modulating the response to light. Moreover we were able to demonstrate the specific PAF-acether binding sites in the rat retina (18).

The study we have made clearly shows that ginkgolide B is a powerful PAF-acether antagonist (8). Indeed, when BN 52021 is added simultaneously with PAF-acether in the liquid perfusing the retina, the effects of the latter on the ERG are totally suppressed. In other experimental models (9, 28), BN 52021 opposes the effects of PAF-acether by inhibiting its binding to its specific receptors. Along with those we obtained on the isolated retina, these results constitute an additional argument for the presence of specific and functional receptors of PAF-acether in the retina. Thus, if PAF-acether, as we suppose, modulates the retinal function, BN 52021 could play a first ranking role in the treatment of retinal functional impairments linked with the increased release of PAF-acether.

Finally, it appears important to us to observe that the retina constitutes an irreplaceable model of cerebral tissue and that our results are in favor of the existence of PAF-acether specific cerebral receptors on which BN 52021 could also play an important role.

ACKNOWLEDGEMENTS

This experimental work was conducted thanks entirely to financial support from Institut Henri Beaufour. We would like to pay special thanks to Madame Gisèle Thiers and Madame Jacqueline Viallefont for their technical cooperation.

References

1. Arden, G.B. et al. *The effect of ions on the photoresponses of pigeon cones*. J Physiol (Lond) 1970; 211: 331.

2. Benveniste, J. et al. *Leukocyte-dependent histamine release from rabbit platelets: The role of IgE, basophils and a platelet-activating factor*. J Exp Med 1972; 136: 1356.

3. Benveniste, J. et al. *Structural analysis of purified platelet-activating factor by lipases*. Nature 1977; 269: 170.

4. Berridge, M.J. *Inositol triphosphate and diacylglycerol as second messengers*. Biochem J 1984; 220: 345.

5. Billah, M.M. et al. *Platelet-activating factor*

stimulates metabolism of phosphoinositides in horse platelets: Possible relationship to Ca^{2+} mobilization during stimulation. Proc Natl Acad Sci USA 1983; 80: 965.

6. Birkle, D.L. et al. The arachidonic acid cascade and phospholipid and docosahexaenoic acid metabolism in the retina. Retinal Res 1986; 5: 309.

7. Bitensky, M.W. et al. Adenyl cyclase as a link between photon capture and changes in membranes permeability of frog photoreceptors. Proc Natl Acad Sci USA 1971; 68: 561.

8. Braquet, P. et al. Treatment or prevention of PAF-acether disorders provoked by a new series of highly specific inhibitors. GB Patent 84/18,424 (19 July 1984) Belg. BE 901.915 (see CA 103: 189 808 d, 1985).

9. Braquet, P. et al. BN 52021 and related compounds: A new series of highly specific PAF-acether receptor antagonists isolated from Ginkgo biloba. Blood Vessels 1985; 16: 559.

10. Braquet, P., Godfroid, J.J. Conformational properties of the PAF-acether receptors in platelets based on structure-activity studies. In: PAF. F. Snyder (Ed.). Plenum Press: New York 1987; 191.

11. Brown, J.E. et al. Myo-inositol polyphosphate may be a messenger for visual excitation in Limulus photoreceptors. Nature 1984; 311: 160.

12. Bussolino, F. et al. Production of platelet-activating factor by chick retina. J Biol Chem 1986; 261: 16502.

13. Dick, J. et al. Extracellular K^+ activity changes related to electroretinogram components. II. Rabbit (E-type) retina. J Gen Physiol 1985; 85: 911.

14. Doly, M. et al. Mechanism of the formation of X-ray-induced phosphenes. I. Electrophysiological investigations. Rad Res 1980; 82: 93.

15. Doly, M. et al. Effects of lipid peroxidation on the isolated rat retina. Ophthal Res 1984; 16: 292.

16. Doly, M. et al. Effets des radicaux libres oxygénés sur láctivité électrophysiologique de la rétine isolée de rat. J Ophthalmol 1985; 8: 273.

17. Doly, M. et al. Electrophysiological consequences of leukotrienes applied on isolated rat retina. Prostaglandins 1985; 30: 457.

18. Doly, M. et al. Presence of specific PAF-acether binding sites in the retinal. Eur J Pharmacol; in press.

19. Fein, A. et al. Photoreceptor excitation and adaptation by inositol 1,4,5-triphosphate.

Nature 1984; 311: 157.

20. Fesenko, E.E. et al. Induction by cyclic GMP of cationic conductance in plasma membrane of retinal rod outer segment. Nature 1985; 313: 310.

21. Garay, R. et al. Involvement of K^+ movements in the membrane signal induced by PAF-acether. Biochem Pharmacol 1986; 35: 2811.

22. Hagins, W.A. et al. The visual process: Excitatory mechanisms in the primary receptor cells. Ann Rev Bioph Bioeng 1972; 1: 131.

23. Lapetina, E.G. Platelet-activating factor stimulates the phosphatidylinositol cycle. J Biol Chem 1982; 257: 7314.

24. Miller, J.A. et al. Phosphorylation and dephosphorylation of frog outer segment membranes as part of the visual process. J Biol Chem 1975; 250: 4427.

25. Oakley, B. et al. [Ca^{2+}] in modulation of membrane sodium conductance in rod outer segments. In: W.H. Miller (Ed.). Academic Press: New York 1981; 405: 416.

26. Parker, K.R. et al. Inositol triphosphate stimulates Ca^{2+} release from toad retinal rod outer segment preparations. Biophys J 1986; 49: 31a.

27. Rodieck, R.W. The Vertebrate Retina. W.H. Freeman and Company: San Francisco 1973.

28. Sánchez-Crespo, M. et al. Inhibition of the vascular actions of IgG aggregates by BN 52021 a highly specific antagonist of PAF-acether. Immunopharmacology 1985; 10: 69.

29. Shen, T.Y. et al. Characterization of a platelet-activating factor receptor antagonist isolated from haifenteng (Piper-futokadsura): Specific inhibition of in vitro and in vivo platelet-activating factor effects. Proc Natl Acad Sci USA 1985; 82: 672.

30. Snyder, F. Chemical and biochemical aspects of platelet-activating factor: A novel class of acetylated ether-linked choline - phospholipids. Med Res Rev 1986; 5: 107.

31. Stein, P.J. et al. Biochemistry of the cyclic nucleotide-related enzymes in rod photoreceptors. Retinal Res 1982; 1: 227.

32. Waloga, G. et al. Effects of inositol 1,4,5-triphosphate injections into salamander rods. Biochem Biophys Res Commun 1985; 126: 59.

33. Yee, R. et al. Light-activated phosphodiesterase of the rod outer segment. J Biol Chem 1978; 253: 8902.

34. Yoshikami, S. et al. Light, calcium and the photocurrent of rods and cones. Biophys J 1971; 11: 47a.

Ginkgolides - Chemistry, Biology, Pharmacology and Clinical Perspectives. P. Braquet (Ed.)
Copyright © 1988, J.R. Prous Science Publishers, S.A.

EFFECT OF BN 52021 ON THE ARACHIDONIC ACID CASCADE IN THE INFLAMED CORNEA

Haydee E.P. Bazan and Nicolas G. Bazan

LSU Eye Center, Department of Ophthalmology, LSU Medical School, New Orleans 70112, LA, USA

INTRODUCTION

The cornea is the transparent tissue on the front of the eye. It consists of three major layers: the epithelium, the stroma and the endothelium. The epithelium is the outermost layer of tissue and constitutes 10-15% of the total thickness. It consists of six layers of cells, and its primary function is to provide a very smooth refractory surface on the front of the eye. The stroma accounts for about 90% of the thickness of the tissue, and is composed mainly of collagen fibers attached to proteoglycans in which keratocytes occupy only 3% of the volume. The main function of the stroma is to provide the mechanical strength required for changes that occur during intraocular pressure and external trauma. The stroma has a tendency to swell due to the water-binding capacity of the proteoglycan that composes the tissue; this produces edema, resulting in discomfort and reduction of vision. This swelling tendency is counteracted by the functions of two living cell layers: the above-mentioned epithelium, which forms a semipermeable membrane, and the endothelium, which comprises a single layer of cells on the posterior surface of the cornea adjacent to the aqueous humor. The cells of the endothelium form a hexagonal pattern and are responsible for the active dehydration of the cornea (1). Although mitosis of the endothelial cells can occur as a result of injury (2), their capacity to regenerate is very limited in humans.

The cornea is one of the parts of the eye most exposed to injury and infection, and the cells that compose this tissue respond rapidly to injury.

Address all correspondence to: Haydee E.P. Bazan, LSU Eye Center, 2020 Gravier Street, New Orleans, LA 70112, USA.

Studies on rabbit cornea have shown an active increase in the capacity to synthesize prostaglandins in the epithelium and stroma, but not in the endothelium, 2 h after cryogenic lesion (3). In the same studies, mono- and dihydroxy eicosatetraenoic acids (HETEs) increased in epithelium, while 12-HETE increased in the stroma and in the endothelium (3). After *in vivo* labeling with arachidonic acid, cryogenic lesion of the cornea produced an increase in arachidonic acid metabolites released to the aqueous humor (4).

Another lipid, 1-0-alkyl-2 acyl-*sn* glycero 3-phosphocholine (PAF), is also involved in inflammatory reactions (5), and different types of mammalian cells have been reported to release PAF upon stimulation (6, 7). PAF stimulates arachidonic acid release (8) and the production of labeled HETEs and leukotriene B_4 (9). Here we report that ginkgolide BN 52021 specifically inhibits the lipoxygenase-mediated reactions in the tissue when topically applied to the inflamed cornea.

EFFECT OF PROLONGED BN 52021 TREATMENT ON THE ARACHIDONIC ACID CASCADE IN INFLAMED CORNEA

Rabbits were injected intracamerally with $(1-^{14}C)$-arachidonic acid (Spec act 60 mmol/μCi). An outline of the experiment is given in Figure 1. An alkali burn was made in the anesthetized cornea with a 6 mm diameter filter paper soaked in 2 N NaOH and applied for 1 minute. Corneas were then extensively washed with a 0.9% NaCl solution. Two drops of a 1% suspension

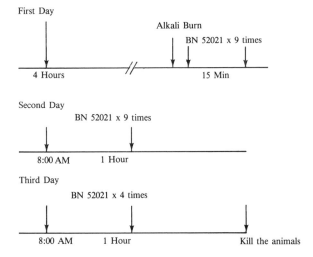

Figure 1   Scheme of cornea alkali burn model with prolonged BN 52021 treatment.

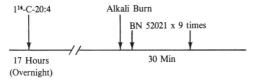

Figure 2   Experimental design of cornea alkali burn model with short BN 52021 treatment.

of BN 52021 were applied topically every 15 minutes the first day, and every hour the second and third day after the burn.

Two days after injury, there was slight inhibition in the synthesis of labeled HETE lipoxygenase products in the cornea and of prostaglandin 6K-F$_{1\alpha}$ (a stable metabolite of PGI$_2$), concomitant with an increase in the synthesis of PGE$_2$ (Table 1). Labeled prostaglandins and HETEs were detected in the aqueous humor after alkali burn (Table 2). The only noticeable change was a decrease in labeled 12-HETE production after treatment with the ginkgolide.

Table 1   Effect of BN 52021 on PG and HETE products in alkali burned corneas

	—	+ BN 52021
5-HETE	0.19	0.16
12-HETE	0.67	0.52
PGE$_2$	0.16	0.23
PGF$_2{}^\alpha$	0.02	0.02
6K-F$_{1\alpha}$	0.10	0.04

Corneal lipids were extracted with hexane: isopropanol (3:2 v/v) and the (1-^{14}C) arachidonic acid metabolites isolated by thin layer chromatography (4). Two corneas were used per sample. Values are expressed as percentage of the total arachidonic acid incorporated in the tissue lipids and correspond to the mean of two samples.

Table 2   Effect of prolonged treatment with BN 52021 on the release of arachidonic acid metabolized in the aqueous humor

	cpm/ml	
	—	+
5-HETE	210	300
12-HETE	663	446
Total PGs	228	270

Aqueous humor was sampled from the eye with a tuberculine syringe using a 27-gauge needle and the lipids extracted with hexane-isopropanol (3:2 v/v).

EFFECT OF SHORT-TERM BN 52021 TREATMENT ON ARACHIDONIC ACID METABOLITES

Rabbits were labeled with $(1\text{-}^{14}C)$-arachidonic acid 17 hours before alkali burn, and the drug was applied every 30 minutes for a period of 2.5 hours. This model allows a longer period for equilibration between the exogenous fatty acids and the membrane lipids. In fact, almost 90% of the total labeled arachidonic acid remained in the cornea and was esterified in the phospholipids.

A significant and selective decrease in 5-and 12-HETEs was found with the PAF antagonist (Table 3). It is interesting that BN 52021 did not interfere with the synthesis of prostaglandins. Moreover, there was a slight increase in the labeling of PGE_2. It has been suggested that prostaglandins play a role in the control of intraocular pressure (10), while LTB_4 (a metabolite of 5-lipoxygenase) has been demonstrated to be chemotactic in the eye (11). Moreover, in this last experimental condition, the PAF antagonist completely inhibited the formation of labeled HETEs in the aqueous humor (12), while it did not affect the synthesis of prostaglandins.

Table 3 Effect of short treatment with BN 52021 on the formation of labeled prostaglandins and HETEs in alkali burned cornea

	—	+
5-HETE	0.40 ± 0.01	0.08 ± 0.01
12-HETE	0.47 ± 0.01	0.04 ± 0.01
PGE_2	0.14 ± 0.02	0.18 ± 0.03
PGF_2^{α}	0.06 ± 0.01	0.09 ± 0.03
$6K\text{-}PGF_{1_{\alpha}}$	0.03 ± 0.01	0.03 ± 0.01

Values are percentage of total $1\text{-}^{14}C$ arachidonic acid uptake in the cornea and represent mean (± SEM) of three values.

The role of PAF in the inflammatory response in the cornea is not known, but the experiments described here suggest a possible selective role in modulating the formation of metabolites of the arachidonic acid cascade after corneal inflammation. In recent studies, PAF has been isolated from alkali burned corneas 3 h after injury, and its bioactivity has been demonstrated by platelet activation (13) and ATP release (unpublished). Moreover, the PAF-induced aggregation was blocked by 9×10^{-6} M BN 52021. These studies clearly show that PAF is involved in the inflammatory response of the anterior segment of the eye, and that ginkgolide BN 52021 exerts an inhibitory effect on this response.

ACKNOWLEDGEMENTS

This work was supported by NIH grant EY04928.

References

1. Maurice, D.M. *The permeability to sodium ions of the living rabbit cornea.* J Physiol 1951; 112: 367.

2. Van Horn, D.L., Sendele, D.D., Seidemann, S., Buco, P.Y. *Regenerative capacity of the corneal endothelium in rabbit and cat.* Invest Ophthalmol Vis Sci 1977; 16: 597.

3. Bazan, H.E.P., Birkle, D.L., Beuerman, R., Bazan, N.G. *Cryogenic lesion alters the metabolism of arachidonic acid in rabbit cornea layers.* Invest Ophthalmol Vis Sci 1985; 26: 474.

4. Bazan, H.E.P. *Corneal injury alters eicosanoid formation in the rabbit anterior segment in vivo.* Invest Ophthalmol Vis Sci 1987; 28: 314.

5. Benveniste, J. *Platelet-activating factor, a new mediator of anaphylaxis and immune complex deposition from rabbit and human basophils.* Nature 1974; 249: 581.

6. Lynch, J.M., Lotner, G.Z., Betz, S.J., Henson, P.M. *The release of a platelet-activating factor by stimulated rabbit neutrophils.* J Immunol 1979; 123: 1219.

7. Camussi, G., Tetta, C., Codar, R., Benveniste, J. *Release of platelet-activating factor in human pathology. I. Evidence for the occurrence of basophile degranulation and release of platelet-activating factor in systemic lupus erythematosus.* Lab Invest 1981; 44: 241.

8. Shaw, Y.O., Kensick, S.J., Kanahan, D.J. *Activation of rabbit platelet phospholipase and thromboxane synthesis by 1-0-hexadecyl/octadecyl-2-acetyl-sn-glycerol-3-phosphorylcholine (platelet-activating factor).* Biochim Biophys Acta 1981; 663: 222.

9. Chilton, F.H., O'Flaherty, T.O., Walsh, C.E., Thomas, M.J., Wykle, R.L, DeChatelet, L.R., Waite, B.M. *Platelet-activating factor. Stimulation of the lipoxygenase pathway in polymorphonuclear leukocytes by 1-0-alkyl-2-acetyl-sn-glycero-3 phosphocholine.* J Biol Chem 1982; 257: 5402.

10. Camras, C.B., Bito, L.Z. *The pathophysiological effects of nitrogen mustard on the rabbit eye. I. The biphasic intraocular pressure response and the role of prostaglandins.* Exp Eye Res 1980; 30: 41.

11. Bhattacherjee, P., Hammond, B., Salmon, Y.A., Stepney, R., Eakins, K.E. *Chemotatic response to some arachidonic acid lipoxygenase products in the rabbit eye.* Eur J Pharmacol 1981; 73: 21.

12. Bazan, H.E.P., Braquet, P., Reddy, S.T.K., Bazan, N.G. *Inhibition of the alkali burn-induced lipoxygenation of arachidonic acid in the rabbit cornea in vivo by a platelet-activating factor antagonist.* J Ocular Pharmacology 1987; 3: 359.

13. Bazan, H.E.P., Reddy, S.T.K., Woodland, J.M., Bazan, N.G. *The accumulation of platelet-activating factor in the injured cornea may be interrelated with the synthesis of lipoxygenase products.* Biochem Biophys Res Commun 1987; 149: 915.

Ginkgolides - Chemistry, Biology, Pharmacology and Clinical Perspectives. P. Braquet (Ed.)
Copyright © 1988, J.R. Prous Science Publishers, S.A.

REGULATION OF CANDIDA ALBICANS KILLING ACTIVITY OF HUMAN EPIDERMAL CELLS

Attila Dobozy, János Hunyadi, Miklos Csató and [1]Pierre Braquet

Department of Dermatology, University Medical School, Szeged, Hungary. [1]Institut Henri Beaufour, F-92350 Le Plessis-Robinson, France

ABSTRACT

Human keratinocytes are able to express cell surface antigens characteristic of cells of macrophage origin. Furthermore, there is an increasing amount of evidence proving that keratinocytes in certain circumstances possess a phagocytic function and show *Candida albicans* killing activity. In the present study, the regulating effects of lipid mediators with regard to the UV-B irradiation-induced elevated *Candida albicans* killing activity of human keratinocytes were investigated.

The results indicate that UVL irradiation of freshly separated human keratinocytes in doses without influence on the viability results in a pronounced and significant enhancement of the Candida killing activity of these cells *in vitro*. The increase was dose-dependent. Pretreatment of the keratinocytes with indomethacin or dexamethasone abolished the UVL-induced stimulation. Similarly, the potent platelet-activating factor antagonist ginkgolide B (BN 52021) caused an inhibition of the increasing effect, which proved to be dose-dependent. These results indicate that the lipid mediators play an important role in the enhancement of the killing activity of the irradiated-keratinocytes.

Address all correspondence to: Prof. Attila Dobozy, Department of Dermatology, University Medical School, H-6701 Szeged, Hungary.

INTRODUCTION

Ultraviolet light (UVL) exposure has been shown to be capable of causing demonstrable changes in certain immune responses. Experimental data from several laboratories have indicated that the exposure of lymphoid cell populations to large doses of UVL effectively ablates their ability to act as stimulator cells in allogenic mixed lymphocyte reactions (13, 14). The activity of antigen specific T-cells is reduced by UV-B light (5) and a similar dose-dependent abrogation of the antigen presenting function of macrophages and Langerhans cells has also been reported (15). Analyses of animal experiments indicated that UVL exposure results in a long-lasting change of immunoreactivity, which is apparently mediated by the emergence of a population of T-suppressor lymphocytes (4, 10). On the other hand, UVL irradiation enhances the generation of epidermal cell-derived thymocyte activating factor (ETAF, similar in function and physicochemical characteristics to interleukin-1), which results in neutrophilia through the release of polymorphonuclear leukocytes (PMNs) into the blood from the bone marrow stores (6, 9, 15).

In preliminary experiments we have observed that whole body UV-B irradiation results in stimulation of the *Candida albicans* killing activity of human peripheral blood PMNs (7). Furthermore, UVL irradiation enhances the *Candida albicans* killing activity of freshly separated epidermal cells (ECs) *in vitro* (1). Newly synthetized mediators such as platelet-activating factor (PAF), slow-reacting substance of anaphylaxis, different kinds of interleukins, *etc.*, are presumed to be involved in these phenomena. In the present study, a potent PAF-acether antagonist (ginkgolide B), indomethacin and dexamethasone were used to investigate the regulating effects of lipid mediators with regard to the UV-B irradiation-induced elevated *Candida albicans* killing activity of human keratinocytes.

MATERIALS AND METHODS

Volunteers

ECs were prepared from fresh surgical skin specimens of healthy volunteers who underwent plastic surgery.

All experiments were carried out with the informed consent of the patients. The study was approved by the Human Investigation Committee in Szeged.

Preparation of Epidermal Cells

An EC suspension was made by the method described previously (1). Briefly, after removal of subcutaneous tissue and as much reticular dermis as possible, tissues were cut into small strips and incubated with 0.25% trypsin (Gibco, Grand Island, NY) overnight at 4°C. The epidermis was then peeled off the dermis and a single cell suspension (10^6 cells/ml) was prepared in Dulbecco's modified Eagle medium (MEM) (Gibco, Grand Island, NY) supplemented with 20% fetal bovine serum and 20 mM Hepes buffer. The viability of the cells was always higher than 85%, as determined by trypan blue exclusion.

Candida Killing Assay

Candida killing assay was carried out with a modification of the method of Lehrer and Cline (12). The method was described in detail earlier (2).

UVL Irradiation

EC suspensions were exposed to UVL irradiation (light source: Saalmann-SUP lamp, Germany; radiation spectrum: 290-370 nm) up to 220 mJ/cm². UV irradiation had practically no influence on the cell viability in this dose. The cell suspension was washed three times and used immediately in the Candida killing assay.

Investigations of Mechanisms Involved in UVL-Induced Augmentation of Candida albicans Killing Activity of Keratinocytes

In order to clarify the possible mechanisms involved in the augmentation of the killing activity by UVL irradiation, ECs were pre-incubated with 100 μg/ml indomethacin, 1 μg/ml dexamethasone or the different concentrations of ginkgolide B. None of the drugs influenced the cell viability at the concentrations employed.

Each experiment was carried out in duplicate. Student's paired t test was used for statistical analysis.

RESULTS

UVL irradiation of freshly separated human ECs in doses without influence on the viability resulted in a pronounced and significant enhancement of the Candida killing activity of these cells *in vitro*. The increase was dose-dependent (Fig. 1).

% of killed Candida cells

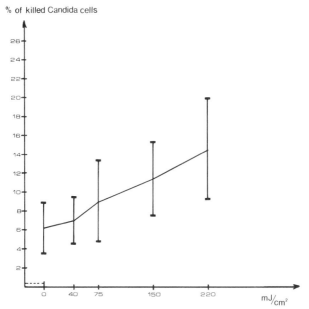

Figure 1 Effect of UVL irradiation on *Candida albicans* killing activity of human epidermal cells *in vitro*. Candida killing activity is expressed as the percentage of nonviable, killed yeast cells. Data indicate the mean ± S.D. values. The difference between the activities of non-irradiated cells and of those treated by UVL in a dose of 220 mJ/cm² is statistically significant (p < 0.0001). (n = 30).

Pretreatment of the ECs with indomethacin or dexamethasone abolished the UVL-induced stimulation (Table 1). Similarly, ginkgolide B caused an inhibition of the increasing effect, which proved to be dose-dependent (Table 1).

Table 1 Effect of pretreatment of epidermal cells (EC) with indomethacin, dexamethasone and ginkgolide B on the UVL (220 mJ/cm²) induced enhancement of Candida killing activity. Candida killing activity is expressed as the percentage of nonviable, killed yeast cells. Data represent the ± S.D. values

		Candida killing activity of UVL irradiated EC	
Pretreated with	n	(mean ± S.D.)	P
None	8	16.77 ± 6.55	
Indomethacin	8	6.34 ± 3.53	< 0.005
Dexamethasone	9	6.49 ± 2.51	< 0.005
Ginkgolide B			
10 μmol/ml	8	11.0 ± 5.5	N.S.
30 μmol/ml	8	7.87 ± 3.13	< 0.05
100 μmol/ml	9	7.55 ± 3.2	< 0.01
300 μmol/ml	9	5.66 ± 4.03	< 0.005

DISCUSSION

It is well known that human keratinocytes are able to express cell surface antigens characteristic of cells of macrophage origin, such as OKM5 and HLA DR (8, 11). Furthermore, there is an increasing amount of evidence proving that keratinocytes in certain circumstances possess a phagocytic function (3, 16) and show *Candida albicans* killing activity (1). Our present experimental data indicate that UV-B irradiation increases the killing activity of these cells.

The investigations reported here demonstrate that indomethacin, dexamethasone and the PAF-acether antagonist ginkgolide B inhibit the UVL-induced enhanced keratinocyte Candida killing activity. These results indicate that the lipid mediators play an important role in the enhancement of the killing activity of the irradiated keratinocytes.

References

1. Csato, M., Dobozy, A. *Enhancement of Candida albicans killing activity of separated human epidermal cells by ultraviolet radiation.* Br J Derm 1987; 116: 469.

2. Csato, M., Dobozy, A. *A study on the Candida killing activity of polymorphonuclear leucocytes in patients with psoriasis vulgaris.* Arch Dermatol Res 1981; 271: 229.

3. Csato, M., Bozoky, B., Hunyadi, J., Dobozy, A. *Candida albicans phagocytosis by separated human epidermal cells.* Arch Derm Res 1986; 279: 136.

4. Daynes, R.A., Spellman, C.W. *Evidence for the generation of suppressor cells by ultraviolet radiation.* Cell Immunol 1977; 31: 182.

5. Fox, I.J., Perry, L.L., Sy, M.-S., Benacerraf, B., Greene, M.J. *The influence of ultraviolet light irradiation on the immune system.* J Clin Immunol Immunopathol 1980; 117: 141.

6. Gahring, L., Baltz, M., Pepys, M.B., Daynes, R. *Effect of ultraviolet radiation on production of epidermal cell thymocyte-activating factor/interleukin-1 in vivo and in vitro (acute phase reaction desensitization).* Proc Natl Acad Sci 1984; 81: 1198.

7. Hunyadi, J., Csato, M., Kenderessy, A.Sz. *Untersuchung der Candida albicans-Abtötungsaktivität von PMN-Granulocyten bei Akne-Patienten unter SUP-Therapie. 3.* Herforder SUP-Symposium, Bad Oenhaussen, 30 May-1 June 1986.

8. Hunyadi, J., Simon, M., Jr. *Expression of OKM5 antigen on human keratinocytes in*

vitro upon stimulation with gamma-interferon. Acta Derm Venereol (Stockh) 1986; 66: 527.

9. Kampschmidt, R.F., Long, R.D., Upchurch, H.F. *Neutrophil releasing activity in rats injected with endogeneous pyrogen.* Proc Soc Exp Biol Med 1972; 139: 1224.

10. Kripke, M.L. *Immunologic mechanisms in UV radiation carcinogenesis.* Adv Cancer Res 1981; 34: 69.

11. Lampert, I.A. *Expression of HLA-DR (Ia like) antigen on epidermal keratinocytes in human dermatoses.* Clin Exp Immunol 1984; 57: 93.

12. Lehrer, R.I., Cline, M.J. *Interaction of Candida albicans with human leukocytes and serum.* J Bacteriol 1969; 98: 996.

13. Levis, W.R., Lincoln, P.M., Dattner, A.M. *Effect of ultraviolet light on dinitrochlorobenzene-specific antigen presentation function.* J Immunol 1978; 121: 1496.

14. Lindahl-Kiessling, K., Safwenberg, J. *Inability of UV-irradiated lymphocytes to stimulate allogenic cells in mixed lymphocyte culture.* Int Arch Allergy Appl Immunol 1971; 41: 670.

15. Luger, T.A., Stadler, B.M., Luger, B.M. *Epidermal cell derived thymocyte activating factor (ETAF).* J Immunol 1981; 127: 1493.

16. Mottaz, J.H., Zelickson, A.S. *The phagocytic nature of the keratinocyte in human epidermis after the stripping.* J Invest Dermatol 1970; 54: 272.

Ginkgolides - Chemistry, Biology, Pharmacology and Clinical Perspectives. P. Braquet (Ed.)
Copyright © 1988, J.R. Prous Science Publishers, S.A.

STUDIES ON THE REGULATION OF MURINE CONTACT DERMATITIS BY SYSTEMIC TREATMENT WITH A PAF ANTAGONIST, BN 52021

Miklos Csato*, Andrea Fuchs and Beate M. Czarnetzki

Department of Dermatology, University of Münster, Von-Esmarch-Str. 56, D-4400 Münster, Federal Republic of Germany

ABSTRACT

In order to investigate the potential role of platelet -activating factor (PAF) in allergic and irritant contact dermatitis, mice were fed with a specific PAF receptor antagonist. Sensitization was done on two consecutive days with 0.5% DNFB and three days later, a contact dermatitis was elicited by painting the ears with an 0.3% solution of DNFB. An irritant dermatitis was elicited by painting the ears once with 0.5% croton oil. BN 52021 had no effect on the sensitization phase of allergic contact dermatitis. It caused, however, a statistically significant suppression of the allergic dermatitis when given during its elicitation phase and also reduced the croton oil-induced irritant dermatitis. These data suggest that PAF plays a role in the elicitation of edema and cellular infiltration of contact dermatitis.

INTRODUCTION

In recent years, several lipid mediators have been discovered with edema-producing and chemotactic properties. One of them is PAF, an ether phospholipid that in addition to the above properties, induces platelet ag-

Address all correspondence to Prof. Beate M. Czarnetzki, Dept. of Dermatology, University of Münster, Von-Esmarch-Strassc 56, D-4400 Münster, FRG.
*Dr. Csato is recipient of a Humboldt fellowship and member of the Department of Dermatology, University of Szeged, Hungary.

gregation and secretory activities of inflammatory cells (4, 8). PAF has been shown to induce wheal and flare reactions after intradermal injection (1, 2), and PAF-like substances have been isolated from cutaneous inflammatory tissues (6, 7). The contribution of PAF to the induction and maintenance of such processes is, however, unclear.

BN 52021 is a specific PAF receptor antagonist that has been shown to suppress the *in vitro* and *in vivo* PAF activities (3). In the present investigation we have studied the effect of BN 52021 on the immunological sensitization of mice and on the elicitation of allergic and irritant contact dermatitis in the same animals.

MATERIALS AND METHODS

The methods for sensitization and elicitation of allergic contact dermatitis have been described before in detail (9). Briefly, sensitization was induced by painting the razor shaved abdomen of female Balb/c mice with 15 μl of 0.5% dinitrofluorobenzene (DNFB) (Sigma, Munich, FRG) in acetone/olive oil (4:1) on two successive days. Elicitation was done by painting 20 μl of a 0.3% solution on the ears of the same animals three days later. Irritant dermatitis was induced by a single application of a 0.5% solution of croton oil in acetone/olive oil (4:1) to the ears of unprimed mice.

BN 52021 (a generous gift of Prof. P. Braquet, Institut Henri Beaufour, Le Plessis-Robinson, France) was suspended in a 1.25% solution of arabic gum and water (1:10). One group of animals was fed a dose of 50 mg/kg/day via a gastric tube one day before and during the two days of sensitization. Another group was treated 2 hours before elicitation of allergic and irritant contact dermatitis and at 24 hour intervals for the following five days. In each experimental set-up, animals without BN 52021 treatment served as controls.

Modulation of allergic sensitization or of irritant dermatitis was evaluated by measuring ear thickness of treated ears of animals at 24 hour intervals for up to five days. Each experiment was done with groups of 10-15 animals, and experiments were repeated twice. Results were expressed in means $\pm$ 1 SD, and statistical significance of the data was analyzed with the unpaired Student's *t* test, comparing treated and control animals' ear thickness at each day separately.

RESULTS

As can be seen in Table 1, BN 52021 suppressed DNFB-induced allergic dermatitis during the entire time of treatment. It also diminished the croton oil-induced irritant dermatitis (Table 2). The reducing effect proved to be

Table 1   Effect of systemic treatment with BN 52021 on DNFB-induced ear thickness in the mouse. Tabulated data represent the ear thickness of the animals (x 10⁻² mm) and are the means ± 1 SD.

Days	Control (n = 58)	BN 52021 (n = 52)	p <
1	29.22 ± 5.32	26.79 ± 4.13	0.01
2	39.59 ± 4.08	34.11 ± 4.49	0.00001
3	45.03 ± 4.97	39.00 ± 3.93	0.00001
4	47.96 ± 6.11	39.50 ± 5.80	0.00001
5	46.08 ± 6.71	36.69 ± 6.15	0.00001

Table 2   Effect of systemic treatment with BN 52021 on croton oil-induced ear thickness in the mouse. Tabulated data represent the ear thickness of the animals (x 10⁻² mm) and are the means ± 1 SD. n.s. = not significant.

Days	Control (n = 20)	BN 52021 (n = 20)	p <
1	24.65 ± 1.46	23.65 ± 2.25	n.s.
2	31.50 ± 2.96	29.20 ± 3.33	0.05
3	30.25 ± 2.46	27.45 ± 2.25	0.001
4	28.80 ± 1.73	26.15 ± 1.98	0.001
5	28.35 ± 1.84	25.70 ± 2.34	0.001

significant with the exception of day 1. In contrast, BN 52021 did not decrease the ear thickness to DNFB when fed to animals during sensitization (not shown).

DISCUSSION

The present data show that inhibition of PAF activities through systemic treatment with the specific receptor antagonist, BN 52021, reduces markedly the swelling of cutaneous tissue during contact dermatitis. PAF-induced swelling of the skin has been shown to be due to both an increase of intradermal fluid and an influx of inflammatory cells (8), as would be expected from the *in vivo* activities of the mediator (4, 5). Inhibition of both of these aspects of inflammatory reaction explains probably the marked and extended suppressive properties of BN 52021 on contact dermatitis.

The efficacy of BN 52021 appeared to be weaker in irritant than in allergic dermatitis. Since this process cannot be differentiated from allergic contact dermatitis by gross inspection of the skin or by histopathology, one must postulate that mediators other than PAF are also involved in the induction of edema and inflammatory cell infiltration in irritant dermatitis. This might be due to the requirement of intact cells or enzyme systems for the production of PAF *in vivo*, conditions that might not prevail when a toxic stimulus is set. In previous studies, it has been shown that activation of the 5-lipoxygenase and involvement of the leukotrienes C_4/D_4 is less prominent in irritant compared to allergic contact dermatitis (9, 10).

BN 52021 failed to inhibit the induction phase of allergic contact dermatitis. On the other hand, PAF has been shown to affect antigen-presenting immune cells *in vitro* (4). Possible reasons for this discrepancy are that PAF concentrations in the tissue during *in vivo* sensitization are too low to have an effect on the induction of specific immunity or that the inhibitor is not effective enough to interfere with this process. A more likely reason might be, however, that the *in vitro* experiments are done with PAF concentrations that are too high and irrelevant to be operative *in vivo*. The variability of the data in the literature on the *in vitro* effects would also favor the latter explanation (4).

The present data are as yet preliminary and leave several questions open regarding the development of a therapeutic agent in contact eczema. Thus, it is unclear whether the PAF inhibitor will be effective in humans who have an established, chronic dermatitis, or whether additional inhibitors are necessary to induce healing of the reaction. Nevertheless, the present data point the way to a potentially useful new therapeutic approach in allergic contact dermatitis.

References

1. Archer, C.B., Page., C.P., Paul, W., Morley, J., MacDonald, D.M. *Early and late inflammatory effects of PAF-acether in the skin of experimental animals and man.* J Invest Dermatol 1983; 80: 346.
2. Archer, C.B., Page, C.P., Paul, W., Morley, J., MacDonald, D.M. *Inflammatory cell accumulation in response to intracutaneous PAF-acether: A mediator for acute and persistent inflammation?* Br J Dermatol 1985; 113 (Suppl. 28): 133-135.
3. Braquet, P., Drieu, K., Etienne, A. *Le ginkgolide B (BN 52021): Un puissant inhibiteur du PAF-acether isolé du Ginkgo biloba L.* Actual Chim Ther (Paris) 1986; 13: 237.
4. Braquet, P., Touqui, L., Shen, T.Y., Vargaftig, B.B. *Perspectives in platelet activating factor research.* Pharmacol Rev 1987; 39: 97-145.
5. Czarnetzki, B.M., Benveniste, J. *Effect of 1-0-octadecyl-2-0-acetyl-sn-glycero-3-phosporylcholine (PAF-acether) on leukocytes. I. Analysis of the in vitro migration of human* neutrophils. Chem Phys Lipids 1981; 29: 317-326.
6. Grandel, K.E., Farr, R.S., Wanderer, A.A., Eisenstadt, T.C., Wasserman, I.S. *Association of platelet-activating factor with primary acquired cold urticaria.* N Engl J Med 1985; 313: 405-409.
7. Mallet, A.I., Cunningham, F.M. *Structural identification of platelet-activating factor in psoriatic scales.* Biochem Biophys Res Commun 1985; 126: 192-198.
8. Pirotzky, E., Pfister, A., Benveniste, J. *A role of PAF-acether (platelet-activating factor) in acute skin inflammation?* Br J Dermatol 1985; 113 (Suppl 28): 91-94.
9. Rosenbach, T., Csato, M., Czarnetzki, B.M. *Studies on the role of leukotrienes in murine allergic and irritant contact dermatitis.* J Invest Dermatol, in press.
10. Ruzicka, T., Printz, M.P. *Arachidonic acid metabolism in skin: Experimental contact dermatitis in guinea pigs.* Int Arch Allergy Appl Immunol 1982; 69: 347-353.

INDEX

A

B

C

788

H

790

L

M